A Brief Guide to Getting the Most from This Book

① Read the Book

Feature	Description	B...
Section-Opening Scenarios	Every section opens with a scenario presenting a unique application of mathematics in your life outside the classroom.	Re... ...os is everywhere will help motivate your learning.
Detailed Worked-Out Examples	Examples are clearly written and provide step-by-step solutions. No steps are omitted, and each step is thoroughly explained to the right of the mathematics.	The blue annotations will help you understand the solutions by providing the reason why every mathematics step is true.
Applications Using Real-World Data	Interesting applications from nearly every discipline, supported by up-to-date real-world data, are included in every section.	Ever wondered how you'll use mathematics? This feature will show you how mathematics can solve real problems.
Study Tips	The book's study tip boxes offer suggestions for problem solving, point out common errors to avoid, and provide informal hints and suggestions.	By seeing common mistakes, you'll be able to avoid them.
Explanatory Voice Balloons	Voice balloons help to demystify mathematics. They translate mathematical language into plain English, clarify problem-solving procedures, and present alternative ways of understanding.	Does math ever look foreign to you? This feature often translates math into everyday English.

② Work the Problems

Feature	Description	Benefit
Check Point Examples	Each example is followed by a similar matched problem, called a Check Point, that offers you the opportunity to work a similar exercise. The answers to the Check Points are provided in the answer section.	You learn best by doing. You'll solidify your understanding of worked examples if you try a similar problem right away to be sure you understand what you've just read.
Extensive and Varied Exercise Sets	An abundant collection of exercises is included in an exercise set at the end of each section. Exercises are organized within categories. Your instructor will usually provide guidance on which exercises to work. The exercises in the first category, Practice Exercises, follow the same order as the section's worked examples.	The parallel order of the Practice Exercises lets you refer to the worked examples and use them as models for solving these problems.

D1450062

Review for Quizzes and Tests

Feature	Description	Benefit
Chapter Review Grids	Each chapter contains a review chart that summarizes the definitions and concepts in every section of the chapter. Examples that illustrate these key concepts are also included in the chart.	Review this chart and you'll know the most important material in the chapter!
Chapter Review Exercises	A comprehensive collection of review exercises for each of the chapter's sections follows the review grid.	Practice makes perfect. These exercises contain the most significant problems for each of the chapter's sections.
Chapter Tests	Each chapter contains a practice test with approximately 25 problems that cover the important concepts in the chapter.	You can use the chapter test to determine whether you have mastered the material covered in the chapter.

CENTRAL TEXAS COLLEGE EDITION
THINKING MATHEMATICALLY
BLITZER

Taken from:

Thinking Mathematically, Fourth Edition
by Robert Blitzer

CENTRAL TEXAS COLLEGE

PEARSON CUSTOM PUBLISHING
75 Arlington Street, Suite 300, Boston, MA 02116
A Pearson Education Company

The Pathway to Success in Your College Courses

Your journey through college can be winding, filled with detours and potholes, or it can be relatively straight and smooth. The information below will help you have a pleasant experience along the way.

Time Management

> *I am definitely going to take a course on time management . . . just as soon as I can work it into my schedule.*
> — Louis E. Boone

The time you spend preparing to study relates directly to a successful outcome. But time, or lack thereof, is a common complaint. How often do you comment that you don't have enough time to accomplish everything you wish to do?

How Do You Spend Your Time?

The first step in time management is to see how you currently spend your time. Have you ever taken the time to add up all of the hours you spend on your regular activities? Take a moment to write down everything you do during a seven-day period. These questions will help you consider all of the activities you do.

- You may spend 40 hours a week on your job, but what about commute time?
- You have to fuel your body. How many hours a week do you spend eating?
- Good grooming is essential. How many hours a week do you spend bathing and dressing?
- How much time do you give to your friends and family?

Remember, there are only 168 hours in a week. Is there any time left to sleep?

How Can I Make More Time?

You can't add hours to the day or days to the week, but if you learn to plan your time wisely, you should be able to make better use of the time you have. As an added bonus, you should feel less stress. Scheduling your time is a step in the right direction.

Develop schedules:

Long term
- Include fixed commitments only
- Include weekly obligations-job, classes, church, meetings, etc.
- Plan enough time for study-as a minimum, use two hours for every one hour in the classroom.
- Plan for weekly reviews-at least one hour each week for each class.

Intermediate

- One per week
- List major events and amount of work to be accomplished in each subject.
- Try to study at the same time every day.
- Make use of free hours between classes.
- Include non-study activities.

Short term

- Daily
- Use small note card you can carry with you.
- Write specifically what you need to accomplish that day.
- Mark out each item as it is completed.

Study Environment

Where you study and how you study is as important as how often you study.

- Identify a quiet place with a desk or table, a chair, and good lighting.
- Your bed might be inviting, but remember your goal is to stay awake and concentrate.
- Although music or some type of background noise might be ok, avoid the TV.
- It's too easy to get engrossed in a show rather than your course work.
- Watching CSI can be interesting, but it probably won't help you with your Introduction to Criminal Justice final exam.
- Make sure you have everything you need: your textbooks, notes, paper and pencil, and a clock.
- Why a clock? To help you manage your time.
- And, don't forget to take regular breaks.

Learning Styles

- If you are assembling a toy or using a new computer program, do you put instructions aside and refer to them only when you run into trouble?
- Do you have to see a name or address in writing in order to remember it?
- Do you enjoy audio books, or do you find your mind wandering as you listen?

Your answers to these questions relate to your preferred learning style, and like clothing, one learning style doesn't fit all. If you have access to the Internet, you can take a learning style inventory at *http://www.vark-learn.com/english/index.asp* and then view helpsheets at *http://www.vark-learn.com/english/page.asp?p=helpsheets* related to your preferred learning style.

Visual Learners

- learn through seeing
- need to see the teacher's body language and facial expression to fully understand the content of a lesson.
- tend to prefer sitting at the front of the classroom to avoid visual obstructions (e.g. people's heads).
- may think in pictures and learn best from visual displays including: diagrams, illustrated text books, overhead transparencies, videos, flip charts and hand-outs.
- During a lecture or classroom discussion, visual learners often prefer to take detailed notes to absorb the information.

If you are a visual learner, here are some suggestions just for you:
- use visual materials such as pictures, charts, maps, graphs, etc.
- have a clear view of your teachers when they are speaking so you can see their body language and facial expression
- use color to highlight important points in text
- take notes or ask your teacher to provide handouts
- illustrate your ideas as a picture or brainstorming bubble before writing them down
- write a story and illustrate it
- use multi-media (e.g. computers, videos, and filmstrips)
- study in a quiet place away from verbal disturbances
- read illustrated books
- visualize information as a picture to aid memorization

Aural Learners

- learn through listening
- learn best through verbal lectures, discussions, talking things through and listening to what others have to say.
- interpret the underlying meanings of speech through listening to tone of voice, pitch, speed and other nuances. Written information may have little meaning until it is heard.
- often benefit from reading text aloud and using a tape recorder.

If you are an aural learner, here are some suggestions just for you:
- participate in class discussions/debates
- make speeches and presentations
- use a tape recorder during lectures instead of taking notes
- read text out aloud
- create musical jingles to aid memorization
- create mnemonics to aid memorization
- discuss your ideas verbally
- dictate to someone while they write down your thoughts
- use verbal analogies, and story telling to demonstrate your point

Read/Write Learners

- learn through reading and writing
- learn best by reading and re-reading the textbook and their notes, writing and rewriting their notes, and in general, organizing items into lists.

Kinesthetic Learners

- learn through moving, doing, and touching
- learn best through a hands-on approach, actively exploring the physical world around them.
- may find it hard to sit still for long periods and may become distracted by their need for activity and exploration.

If you are a tactile/kinesthetic learner, here are some suggestions just for you:
- take frequent study breaks

- move around to learn new things (e.g. read while on an exercise bike, mold a piece of clay to learn a new concept)
- work at a standing position
- chew gum while studying
- use bright colors to highlight reading material
- dress up your work space with posters
- if you wish, listen to music while you study
- skim through reading material to get a rough idea what it is about before settling down to read it in detail.

Multimodal Learners

- don't have a single preferred learning style.
- learn best through combinations.

If you have multiple preferences, you are in the majority as somewhere between fifty and seventy percent of any population seems to fit into that group.

Reading Skills and Strategies

Good reading skills are essential to your success in your college-level classes. Here are a couple of reasons why:

- In high school, you may have been able to get good grades without reading much of the text. Now that you're in college, professors will expect you to read the textbook and they may test you on information not discussed in class but covered in the reading. In fact, many professors test on assigned readings as a check to make sure students are using their texts.
- The average freshman is assigned over 250 pages of reading each week, so clearly you're going to need to keep up with your reading assignments. If you do not read during week one, that means that you will need to read 500 pages the next week-just to stay caught up! If you choose not to read during the second week either . . . well, you can see how the work can just snowball.

Improving Your Reading Skills and Applying Reading Strategies

A good reader:

- seizes the main ideas.
- thinks about what the author is saying
- is active, not passive.
- concentrates on what is being read.
- remembers as much as possible.
- applies what is being read to personal experience.

Go to *http://www.how-to-study.com/pqr.htm* for more on reading skills.

SQ3R is one recommended method for improving your reading comprehension. The letters in the name stand for these five steps:

Survey: Before you read, scan the titles, headings, pictures, and summaries. Consider using the heading and subheadings as an outline for notes as you read.

Question: Ask yourself questions based on Step 1 and look for answers as you complete Step 3. For example, if a subheading is entitled "Basic Concepts of Reading," change it to read, "What are the Basic Concepts of Reading?"

Read: Read and take notes.

Recall: Without referring to the book or your notes, think about what you have read. See if your questions were answered. Could you explain the content to someone else? Try putting major concepts in your own words.

Review: Look at your questions, answers, notes and book to see how well you did recall. Observe carefully the points stated incorrectly or omitted. Fix carefully in mind the logical sequence of the entire idea, concepts, or problem. Finish up with a mental picture of the WHOLE.

Another method is **PQR3**, which stands for

Preview: Preview what you are going to read.

Question: Question what you are going to learn after the preview.

Read: Read the assignment.

Recite: Stop every once in a while, look up from the book, and put in your own words what you have just read.

Review: After you have finished, review the main points.

(Sounds similar to SQ3R, doesn't it?) Go to *http://www.how-to-study.com/pqr.htm* to learn more about this method.

There is even a related study method known as **M.U.R.D.E.R.**

Mood: Set a positive mood for yourself to study in.

Understand: Mark any information you don't understand in a particular unit and keep a focus on one unit or a manageable group of exercise.

Recall: After studying the unit, stop and put what you have learned into your own words.

Digest: Go back to what you did not understand and reconsider the information. Contact external expert sources (e.g., other books or an instructor) if you still cannot understand it.

Expand: ask three kinds of questions concerning the studied material:

- If I could speak to the author, what questions would I ask or what criticism would I offer?
- How could I apply this material to what I am interested in?
- How could I make this information interesting and understandable to other students?

Review: Go over the material you've covered. Review what strategies helped you understand and/or retain information in the past and apply these to your current studies.

Check this system out at *http://www.studygs.net/murder.htm*.

Notetaking

Why take notes?

- It triggers basic lecturing processes and helps you to remember information.
- It helps you to concentrate in class.
- It helps you prepare for tests.
- Your notes are often a source of valuable clues for what information the instructor thinks most important (i.e., what will show up on the next test).
- Your notes often contain information that cannot be found elsewhere (i.e., in your textbook).

Evaluate your present notetaking system. Ask yourself:

- Did I use complete phrases or sentences that mean something to me later?
- Did I use any form at all?
- Are my notes clear or confusing?
- Did I capture main points and all subpoints?
- Did I streamline using abbreviations and shortcuts?

If you answered "no" to any of these questions, you may need to develop some new notetaking skills!

Guidelines for Taking Notes

- Concentrate on the lecture or on the reading material.
- Take notes consistently.
- Take notes selectively.
  –Do NOT try to write down every word.
  –Remember that the average lecturer speaks approximately 125-140 words per minute, and the average note-taker writes at a rate of about 25 words per minute.
- Translate ideas into your own words.
- Organize notes into some sort of logical form.
- Be brief. Write down only the major points and important information.
- Write legibly. Notes are useless if you cannot read them later!
- Don't be concerned with spelling and grammar.

There are many reasons for taking lecture notes.

- Making yourself take notes forces you to listen carefully and test your understanding of the material.
- When you are reviewing, notes provide a gauge to what is important in the text.
- Personal notes are usually easier to remember than the text.
- The writing down of important points helps you to remember then even before you have studied the material formally.

Instructors usually give clues to what is important to take down. Some of the more common clues are:

- Material written on the blackboard.
- Repetition
- Emphasis
  –Emphasis can be judged by tone of voice and gesture.
  –Emphasis can be judged by the amount of time the instructor spends on points and the number of examples he or she uses.
- Word signals (e.g. "There are **two points of view** on . . . " "The **third** reason is . . . " " In **conclusion** . . . ")
- Summaries given at the end of class.
- Reviews given at the beginning of class.

Each student should develop his or her own method of taking notes, but most students find the following suggestions helpful:

- Make your notes brief.
  –Never use a sentence where you can use a phrase. Never use a phrase where you can use a word.

- –Use abbreviations and symbols, but be consistent.
- Put most notes in your own words. However, the following should be noted exactly:
  - –Formulas
  - –Definitions
  - – Specific facts
- Use outline form and/or a numbering system. Indention helps you distinguish major from minor points.
- Date your notes. Perhaps number the pages.
- If you miss a statement, write key words, skip a few spaces, and get the information later.
- Don't try to use every space on the page. Leave room for coordinating your notes with the text after the lecture. (You may want to list key terms in the margin or make a summary of the contents of the page.)

Here are some hints ("Do not's") regarding taking notes on classroom lectures that can save time for almost any student.

Do not plan to rewrite or type your notes later. To do so is to use a double amount of time; once to take the original notes a second to rewrite them. The advice is simple: DO IT RIGHT THE FIRST TIME!

Do not take notes in shorthand. Though shorthand is a valuable tool for a secretary, it is almost worthless for a student doing academic work. Here's why. Notes in shorthand cannot be studied in that form. They must first be transcribed. The act of transcribing notes takes an inordinate amount of time and energy but does not significantly contribute to their mastery. It is far better to have taken the notes originally in regular writing and then spend the time after that in direct study and **recitation** of the notes.

Do not record the lesson on a cassette tape or any other tape. The lecture on tape precludes flexibility. This statement can be better understood when seen in the light of a person who has taken his/her notes in regular writing. Immediately after taking the notes this person can study them in five minutes before the next class as s/he walks toward the next building, as s/he drinks his/her coffee, or whatever. Furthermore, this student, in looking over his/her notes, may decide that the notes contain only four worthwhile ideas which s/he can highlight, relegating the rest of the lecture to obscurity. Whereas the lecture on tape has to be listened to in its entirety including the worthwhile points as well as the "garbage," handwritten notes may be studied selectively. A student who takes the easy way out - recording the lecture on tape as he or she sits back doing nothing—will box him or herself into inflexibility.

Learning to make notes effectively will help you to improve your study and work habits and to remember important information. Often, students are deceived into thinking that because they **understand** everything that is said in class they will therefore remember it. This is dead wrong! Write it down.

As you make notes, you will develop skill in selecting important material and in discarding unimportant material. The secret to developing this skill is practice. Check your results constantly. Strive to improve. Notes enable you to retain important facts and data and to develop an accurate means of arranging necessary information.

Hints on Note Making

- Don't write down everything that you read or hear.
  - –Be alert and attentive to the main points.
  - –Concentrate on the "meat" of the subject and forget the trimmings.
- Notes should consist of key words or very short sentences. If a speaker gets sidetracked it

is often possible to go back and add further information.

- Take accurate notes.
  - You should usually use your own words, but try not to change the meaning.
  - If you quote **directly** from an author, quote **correctly**.
- Think a minute about your material before you start making notes.
  - Don't take notes just to be taking notes!
  - Take notes that will be of real value to you when you look over them at a later date.
- Have a uniform system of punctuation and abbreviation that will make sense to you.
  - Use a skeleton outline and show importance by indenting.
  - Leave lots of white space for later additions.
- Omit descriptions and full explanations.
  - Keep your notes short and to the point.
  - Condense your material so you can grasp it rapidly.
- Don't worry about missing a point.
- Don't keep notes on oddly shaped pieces of paper.
  - Keep notes in order and in one place.
- Shortly after making your notes, go back and rework (not redo) your notes by adding extra points and spelling out unclear items.
  - Remember, we forget rapidly. Budget time for this vital step just as you do for the class itself.
- Review your notes regularly. This is the only way to achieve lasting memory.

These are only a few of the many methods for taking notes.

- the Cornell Method
- the Outline Method
- the Mapping Method (or Mindmapping)
- the Charting Method
- the Sentence Method

For details on these methods, go to *http://www.sas.calpoly.edu/asc/ssl/notetaking.systems.html*. Also check out this resource about note taking: *http://www.how-to-study.com/Taking%20Notes%20in%20Class.htm*

Memory Techniques

We hope that the information on preparing to study has been helpful, but do you feel that your real problem is remembering? Don't worry. There are ways to help you build your memory skills too.

Acronym

- An *acronym* is defined as "a word formed from the initial letters of a name," such as PCS for permanent change of station or SOC for Servicemembers Opportunity Colleges, "or by combining initial letters or parts of a series of words," as radar for radio detecting and ranging.
- Can you think of other acronyms?

Mnemonic

- A *mnemonic* is defined as "a device, such as a formula or rhyme, used as an aid in remembering."

Examples

As a child, you might have determined the number of days in a given month

- by reciting the rhyme "Thirty days hath September, April, June, and November . . . ." or
- by using your knuckles ("peaks" have 31 days and "valleys" have 30, except February, of course).

If you have studied music, you might have used these techniques for remembering the names of the notes:

- FACE represents the names of the notes in the spaces on the staff.
- The first letters of the words in sentence "Every good boy does fine" represent the names of the notes on the lines on the staff.

A mnemonic used to recall the steps for simplifying algebraic expressions is "Please excuse my dear Aunt Sally."

- Perform operations within the innermost parentheses and work outward.
- Evaluate all exponential expressions.
- Perform multiplications and divisions as they occur, working from left to right.
- Perform additions and subtractions as they occur, working from left to right.

Use the sentence "My Very Educated Mother Just Served Us Nine Pizzas" to recall the order of the planets from the sun

- Mercury
- Venus
- Earth
- Mars
- Jupiter
- Saturn
- Uranus
- Neptune
- Pluto

Big Brown Rabbits Often Yield Great Big Vocal Groans When Gingerly Slapped for the color codes for resistors

- Black
- Brown
- Red
- Orange
- Yellow
- Green
- Blue
- Violet
- Gray
- White
- Gold
- Silver

Preparing For and Taking Tests

If you have practiced the strategies we have outlined in this orientation, you should be reviewing on a regular basis as you study rather than waiting to cram right before a test.

- Try to anticipate what is important and will be on the test, and use any review materials that are available, such as practice tests or review sheets.
- This doesn't mean that you don't need to study right before a test, but you shouldn't have to stay up all night to prepare for it, and you should feel more confident when you take the test.

Do You Suffer From Test Anxiety?

- Do you do great on homework assignments, but you dread test days?
- Do you forget everything you know when you sit down to take a test?
- Does it seem like what you studied has nothing to do with the test you are taking?

Once you are sitting in the hot spot with your pencil in hand, use the DETER strategy for taking tests as described at *http://www.how-to-study.com/A%20Strategy%20for%20Taking%20Tests.htm*.

Directions: Read and understand the test directions.
Examine: Examine the entire test to see what is required.
Time: Determine how much time to allow for each item.
Easiest: Answer the easiest items first.
Review: Allow time to review the test to check your answers for accuracy and completeness.

Again, practice makes perfect. There are several web sites for taking practice tests. Here are a few:

- *http://www.actstudent.org/testprep/index.html*
- *http://4tests.com/*
- *http://www.collegeboard.com/*
- *http://www.ets.org/*

Computer Basics

For many classes, you need to know the basics about using a computer and possibly even surfing the Internet in order to complete certain assignments. If you are taking a distance learning class, you MUST have some basic knowledge of computers and the Internet.

You must be able to

- prepare, save, and retrieve files
- send and receive emails with attachments
- deposit files in an electronic drop box
- locate and navigate web sites
- download software and plug ins
- participate in discussion boards.

A good resource for learning about these items is *http://www.learnthenet.com/english/index.html*.

- Once you have reached this site, note the "How To" list at the left side of the screen.
- If you are a novice, you might want to start with "How to Use this Site."
- Otherwise, start with "Master the Basics" and then work your way down the list.

You will find information ranging from making the connection to the Internet to building your own web site.

- Click on each underlined word or title to access the information.
- This information is also available as the "Animated Internet."

Jan's Illustrated Computer Literacy 101 at *http://www.jegsworks.com/Lessons/index.html* includes lessons on the topics listed on the next screens, and the approach is very detailed yet easy to understand. Even if you have never touched a mouse before, you should be able to follow along.

Do you want to learn about specific items; i.e., WindowsXP or MSWord2003?

- These are Microsoft products.
- You can go to *http://www.microsoft.com/* and find training on just about every product produced by Microsoft—even older versions.

The information above is just a teaser. We have included only a few websites because websites come and go. To learn more, check out the Internet and use a search engine, such as GOOGLE (*www.google.com*), to find sites on the topics we have referenced.

Contents •••••••

1

Problem Solving and Critical Thinking   1

2

Set Theory   45

3

Logic 107

4

Number Representation and Calculation 195

5

Number Theory and the Real Number System 227

6

Algebra: Equations and Inequalities   303

7

Algebra: Graphs, Functions, and Linear Systems   367

8

Consumer Mathematics and Financial Management   443

12

Statistics 679

13

Mathematical Systems 747

14

Voting and Apportionment 771

15

Graph Theory 823

About the Author ●●●●●●

Bob and his horse Jerid

Bob Blitzer is a native of Manhattan and received a Bachelor of Arts degree with dual majors in mathematics and psychology (minor: English Literature) from the City College of New York. His unusual combination of academic interests led him toward a Master of Arts in mathematics from the University of Miami and a doctorate in behavioral sciences from Nova University. Bob is most energized by teaching mathematics and has taught a variety of mathematics courses at Miami Dade College for nearly 30 years. He has received numerous teaching awards, including Innovator of the Year from the League for Innovations in the Community College, and was among the first group of recipients at Miami Dade College for an endowed chair based on excellence in the classroom. In addition to *Thinking Mathematically*, Bob has written textbooks covering introductory algebra, intermediate algebra, algebra and trigonometry, and precalculus, all published by Prentice Hall.

Preface ● ● ● ● ● ●

Thinking Mathematically, **Fourth Edition** provides a general survey of mathematical topics that are useful in our contemporary world. My primary purpose in writing the book was to show students how mathematics can be applied to their lives in interesting, enjoyable, and meaningful ways. The book's variety of topics and flexibility of sequence make it appropriate for a one- or two-term course in liberal arts mathematics, quantitative reasoning, finite mathematics, mathematics for education majors, as well as for courses specifically designed to meet state-mandated requirements in mathematics.

I wrote the book to help diverse students, with different backgrounds and career plans, to succeed. **Thinking Mathematically**, **Fourth Edition**, has four major goals:

1. To help students acquire knowledge of fundamental mathematics.
2. To show students how mathematics can solve authentic problems that apply to their lives.
3. To enable students to understand and reason with quantitative issues and mathematical ideas they are likely to encounter in college, career, and life.
4. To enable students to develop problem-solving skills, while fostering critical thinking, within an interesting setting.

One major obstacle in the way of achieving these goals is the fact that very few students actually read their textbook. This been a regular source of frustration for me and my colleagues in the classroom. Anecdotal evidence gathered over years highlights two basic reasons why students do not take advantage of their textbook:

"I'll never use this information."

"I can't follow the explanations."

I've written every page of the Fourth Edition with the intent of eliminating these two objections. The ideas and tools I've used to do so are described for the student in "A Brief Guide to Getting the Most from This Book," which appears inside the front cover.

What's New in the Fourth Edition?

- **Practice Plus Exercises.** More challenging practice exercises that often require students to combine several skills or concepts have been added to the exercise sets. The 442 Practice Plus Exercises in the Fourth Edition provide instructors with the option of creating assignments that take practice exercises to a more challenging level than in the previous edition.
- **New Applications and Real-World Data.** I researched hundreds of books, magazines, almanacs, and online data sites to prepare the Fourth Edition. The Fourth Edition contains more new, innovative, applications, supported by data that extend as far up to the present as possible, than any previous revisions of this book. There are 453 new exercises in the application category of the exercise sets, as well as 54 titled, worked-out examples that are based on new applications.
- **More Than 1400 New Examples and Exercises.** In addition to the 442 Practice Plus Exercises and the 507 new application examples and exercises, the Fourth Edition contains more than 500 new exercises that appear in the practice category of the exercise sets.

- **Integration of Graphs and Mathematical Models.** Mathematical modeling is introduced in Chapter 1. The integrated use of graphs and models is provided so that students can interpret and reason with information involving numbers and mathematical ideas.
- **Increased Study Tip Boxes.** The book's Study Tip boxes offer suggestions for problem solving, point out common errors to avoid, and provide informal hints and suggestions. These invaluable hints appear in greater abundance in the Fourth Edition.
- **New Enrichment Essays ("Blitzer Bonuses").** The Fourth Edition contains a variety of new, but optional, enrichment essays.
- **Chapter Test Prep Video CD.** Found within MyMathLab, these videos provide students with step-by-step solutions for each of the exercises in the book's chapter tests.

What Content and Organizational Changes Have Been Made to the Fourth Edition?

- Section 1.1 (Inductive and Deductive Reasoning) contains a greater variety of examples and exercises that require students to identify patterns and engage in inductive reasoning.
- Section 1.2 (Estimation, Graphs, and Mathematical Models) includes a new discussion on rounding the decimal part of a decimal number. Also included is an early discussion of mathematical modeling and mathematical models. Students are shown how to reason with quantitative information presented graphically by developing linear models that estimate relationships between variables.
- Section 2.1 (Basic Set Concepts) reviews inequality notation and uses this notation to represent various sets containing natural numbers. Following the discussion of one-to-one correspondences and equivalent sets, the section concludes with a new, but brief, introduction to infinite sets. This "tease" on infinite sets is developed in more detail at the conclusion of Section 2.2 and in the Blitzer Bonus at the end of that section.
- Section 2.2 (Subsets) is now devoted exclusively to ideas about subsets. Venn diagrams are no longer introduced in this section.
- Section 2.3 (Venn Diagrams and Set Operations) contains a new discussion on sets and precise use of everyday English. The words *or* and *and* are related to set operations through practical contexts involving graphs and real-world data. The formula for the cardinal number of the union of two finite sets was moved from the section on surveys to this section.
- Section 2.4 (Set Operations and Venn Diagrams with Three Sets) contains a new example explaining how to determine a Venn diagram from three sets and a universal set. Graphics with clarifying voice balloons illustrate the process in a step-by-step manner.
- Section 2.5 (Survey Problems) uses new graphics with clarifying voice balloons to illustrate how to determine a Venn diagram for a survey. A new follow-up example involving the use of a survey's Venn diagram places English words and phrases such as *neither, none, exactly one, at least two, and, or,* and *but* into the context of mathematical ideas about sets.
- Section 3.2 (Compound Statements and Connectives) now contains translations of $p \rightarrow q$ and $p \leftrightarrow q$ that involve the words *necessary* and *sufficient*. The section concludes with a new discussion on dominance of connectives.
- Section 3.3 (Truth Tables for Negation, Conjunction, and Disjunction) emphasizes truth tables that require four cases, but now includes tables with two cases, as well as those with eight cases. There is a new example on

determining the truth value of a compound statement for a specific case within the context of graphical data.

- Section 3.6 (Arguments and Truth Tables) contains new applications that span the gamut from the Menendez brothers' criminal case to Nixon's resignation. The exercise set contains a brief discussion, with exercises, of common fallacies in everyday reasoning.

- Chapter 4 (Number Representation and Calculation) contains new discussions of digital technology, including a Blitzer Bonus that relates base two and truth tables to computers. There are new application exercises in Exercise Set 4.3 based on these ideas.

- Chapter 6 (Algebra: Equations and Inequalities) now opens with a discussion of mathematical modeling and mathematical models, repeated from Chapter 1 for those who did not cover that chapter. The mathematical models that appear throughout Chapter 6 range from how responses to negative life events vary with sense of humor to how blood pressure varies with age.

- Chapter 7 (Algebra: Graphs, Functions, and Linear Systems) has been reorganized. After functions are introduced in the first section, the next four sections are devoted to linear models, including linear functions and their graphs, systems of linear equations in two variables, linear inequalities in two variables, and linear programming. The last section of the chapter focuses on approximating reality with nonlinear models.

- Section 7.1 (Graphing and Functions) contains new examples involving data presented graphically and functions that model the data.

- Section 7.3 (Systems of Linear Equations in Two Variables) contains new applications involving revenue functions, cost functions, break-even points, and profit functions.

- Section 7.6 (Approximating Reality with Nonlinear Models) is a new section in which the shape of data presented in scatter plots suggests modeling with exponential functions, logarithmic functions, and quadratic functions.

- Section 8.1 (Percent, Sales Tax, and Income Tax) contains a new objective on computing income tax.

- Section 8.3 (Compound Interest) now discusses formulas for compound interest subject to n compoundings per year, as well as to continuous compounding.

- Section 8.4 (Annuities, Stocks, and Bonds) is a new section on determining the value of an annuity, as well as determining regular annuity payments needed to achieve a financial goal. Stocks and bonds, presented as a separate section in the previous edition, have been moved to this section following the discussion of annuities.

- Section 8.6 (Amortization and the Cost of Home Ownership) now develops the loan payment formula for installment loans using formulas for compound interest and the value of an annuity. As in the previous edition, the loan payment formula is used to compute the monthly payment and interest costs for a mortgage. However, the Fourth Edition also applies the formula to determine payments and interest for other kinds of installment loans, including car loans and student loans.

- Section 10.3 (Polygons, Perimeter, and Tessellations) relates geometric ideas to the visual arts with a new discussion of tessellations and their angle requirements.

- Section 11.4 (Fundamentals of Probability) contains an early introduction to contingency tables, or two-way tables that relate two categories of data using row variables and column variables. New contingency tables with real-world data are used in Section 11.4, Section 11.6 (Events Involving *Not* and *Or*; Odds), and Section 11.7 (Events Involving *And*; Conditional Probability).

- Section 12.1 (Sampling, Frequency Distributions, and Graphs) has new and more current examples illustrating misleading visual displays.
- Section 12.4 (The Normal Distribution) contains new applications that can be modeled by the normal distribution. There is also a new, but brief, discussion of quartiles as commonly encountered percentiles.

I hope that my love for learning, as well as my respect for the diversity of students I have taught and learned from over the years, is apparent throughout this new edition. By connecting mathematics to the whole spectrum of learning, it is my intent to show students that their world is profoundly mathematical, and indeed, π is in the sky.

Robert Blitzer

To the Student ●●●●●●

I have written this book to give you control over the part of your life that involves numbers and mathematical ideas. Gaining an understanding and appreciation of mathematics will help you participate fully in the twenty-first century. In some ways, you cannot get along in life without the mathematics in this book. For example, if you do not understand the basic ideas of investment, you may find it impossible to achieve your financial goals. If you do not have at least a rudimentary understanding of logic, you may not be able to analyze information objectively, possibly arriving at conclusions hastily without a method for considering all the evidence.

This book has been written so that you can learn about the power of mathematics directly from its pages. All concepts are carefully explained, important definitions and procedures are set off in boxes, and worked-out examples that present solutions in a step-by-step manner appear in every section. Each example is followed by a similar matched problem, called a Check Point, for you to try so that you can actively participate in the learning process as you read the book. (Answers to all Check Points appear in the back of the book.) Study Tip boxes offer hints and suggestions and often point out common errors to avoid. A great deal of attention has been given to applying mathematics to your life to make your learning experience both interesting and relevant.

As you begin your studies, I would like to offer some specific suggestions for using this book and for being successful in this course:

1. **Read the book.** Read each section with pen (or pencil) in hand. Move through the worked-out examples with great care. These examples provide a model for doing exercises in the exercise sets. As you proceed through the reading, do not give up if you do not understand every single word. Things will become clearer as you read on and see how various procedures are applied to specific worked-out examples.

2. **Work problems every day and check your answers.** The way to learn mathematics is by doing mathematics, which means working the Check Points and assigned exercises in the exercise sets. The more exercises you work, the better you will understand the material.

3. **Review for quizzes and tests.** After completing a chapter, study the two-column review chart, work the exercises in the Chapter Review, and work the exercises in the Chapter Test. Answers to all these exercises are given in the back of the book.

> The methods that I've used to help you read the book, work the problems, and review for tests are described in "A Brief Guide to Getting the Most from This Book," which appears inside the front cover. Spend a few minutes reviewing the guide to familiarize yourself with the book's features and their benefits.

4. **Use the resources available with this book.** Additional resources to aid your study are described on page xvi. These resources include a Solutions Manual, a Chapter Test Prep Video CD, MyMathLab, an online version of the book with links to multimedia resources, MathXL®, an online homework, tutorial, and assessment system of the text, and tutorial support at the PH Tutor Center.

5. **Attend all lectures.** No book is intended to be a substitute for valuable insights and interactions that occur in the classroom. In addition to arriving for lecture on time and being prepared, you will find it useful to read a section before it is covered in lecture. This will give you a clear idea of the new material that will be discussed.

I wrote this book in Point Reyes National Seashore, 40 miles north of San Francisco. The park consists of 75,000 acres with miles of pristine surf-washed beaches, forested ridges, and bays bordered by white cliffs. It was my hope to convey the beauty and excitement of mathematics using nature's unspoiled beauty as a source of inspiration and creativity. Enjoy the pages that follow as you empower yourself with the mathematics needed to succeed in college, your career, and in your life.

Regards,

Bob

Robert Blitzer

Acknowledgments ●●●●●●

I wish to express my appreciation to all the reviewers for their helpful feedback, frequently transmitted with wit, humor, and intelligence. Every change to this edition is the result of their thoughtful comments and suggestions. In particular, I would like to thank:

Laurel Berry, *Bryant and Stratton College*
Kris Bowers, *Florida State University*
Gerard Buskes, *University of Mississippi*
Fred Butler, *West Virginia University*
Jimmy Chang, *St. Petersburg College*
Jerry Chen, *Suffolk County Community College*
Ivette Chuca, *El Paso Community College*
David Cochener, *Austin Peay State University*
Elizabeth T. Dameron, *Tallahassee Community College*
Tristen Denley, *University of Mississippi*
Suzanne Feldberg, *Nassau Community College*
Margaret Finster, *Erie Community College*
Lyn Geisler III, *Randolph-Macon College*
Dale Grussing, *Miami Dade College*
Cindy Gubitose, *Southern Connecticut State University*
Virginia Harder, *College at Oneonta*
Joseph Lloyd Harris, *Gulf Coast Community College*
Julia Hassett, *Oakton Community College*
Sonja Hensler, *St. Petersburg College*
Larry Hoehn, *Austin Peay State University*
Alec Ingraham, *New Hampshire College*
Linda Kuroski, *Erie Community College—City Campus*
Jamie Langille, *University of Nevada, Las Vegas*
Veronique Lanuqueitte, *St. Petersburg College*
Mitzi Logan, *Pitt Community College*
Linda Lohman, *Jefferson Community College*
Mike Marcozzi, *University of Nevada, Las Vegas*
Diana Martelly, *Miami Dade College*
Jim Matovina, *Community College of Southern Nevada*
Erik Matsuoka, *Leeward Community College*
Marcel Maupin, *Oklahoma State University*
Diana McCammon, *Delgado Community College*
Mex McKinley, *Florida Keys Community College*
Paul Mosbos, *State University of New York—Cortland*
Tammy Muhs, *University of Central Florida*
Cornelius Nelan, *Quinnipiac University*
Lawrence S. Orilia, *Nassau Community College*
Richard F. Patterson, *University of North Florida*
Frank Pecchioni, *Jefferson Community College*
Stan Perrine, *Charleston Southern University*

Anthony Pettofrezzo, *University of Central Florida*
Val Pinciu, *Southern Connecticut State University*
Evelyn Popplo-Cody, *Marshall University*
Virginia S. Powell, *University of Louisiana at Monroe*
Kim Query, *Lindenwood College*
Anne Quinn, *Edinboro University of Pennsylvania*
Bill Quinn, *Frederick Community College*
Sharonda Ragland, *ECPI College of Technology*
Shawn Robinson, *Valencia Community College*
Gary Russell, *Brevard Community College*
Mary Lee Seitz, *Erie Community College*
Laurie A. Stahl, *State University of New York—Fredonia*
Abolhassan Taghavy, *Richard J. Daley College & Chicago State University*
Ann Thrower, *Kilgore College*
Mike Tomme, *Community College of Southern Nevada*
Sherry Tornwall, *University of Florida*
Christopher Scott Vaughen, *Miami Dade College*
Bill Vaughters, *Valencia Community College*
Karen Villareal, *University of New Orleans*
Don Warren, *Edison Community College*
Shirley Wilson, *North Central College*
James Wooland, *Florida State University*
Cindy Zarske, *Fullerton College*
Marilyn Zopp, *McHenry County College*

Additional acknowledgments are extended to Dan Miller, for preparing the solutions manuals, Brad Davis, for preparing the answer section and serving as accuracy checker, the Preparè, Inc. formatting team, for the book's brilliant paging, Aaron Darnall at Scientific Illustrators, for superbly illustrating the book, Rachel Lucas, photo researcher, for obtaining the book's new photographs, Rebecca Muller, for preparing the CD Lecture series, including the Chapter Test Prep Video CDs, Liz Dameron, for preparing the *CLAST Manual*, and Barbara Mack, whose talents as production editor kept every aspect of this complex project moving through its many stages.

I would like to thank my editors at Prentice Hall, Sally Yagan and Chuck Synovec, and Project Manager, Michael Bell, who guided and coordinated the book from manuscript through production. Thanks to John Christiana, for the beautiful cover and interior design, Wayne Parkins and Patrice Jones, for their innovative marketing efforts, and to the entire Prentice Hall sales force, for their confidence and enthusiasm about the book.

Resources to Help You Study ●●●●●●

Student Resources

Student Study Pack
Everything a student needs to succeed in one place. Packaged with the book or available for purchase stand-alone, the Study Pack contains:

Student Solutions Manual
Fully worked solutions to odd-numbered exercises and all check points.

Pearson Tutor Center
Tutors provide one-on-one tutoring for any problem with an answer at the back of the book. Students access the Tutor Center via toll-free phone, fax, or e-mail.

CD Lecture Series
A comprehensive set of CD-ROMs tied to the textbook, containing short video clips of an instructor working key book examples.

CLAST Manual
The *CLAST Manual* helps build students' proficiency in 55 mathematical skills in the fields of Arithmetic, Geometry, Algebra, Statistics, and Logic. Written as an additional supplement for students who are required to take the CLAST (students in the State of Florida), the first part of the *CLAST Manual* focuses on the skill-by-skill description of each of the 55 skills required in the exam, including worked out examples. The second part of this manual is a collection of CLAST-style homework exercises linked to various sections of *Thinking Mathematically 4e*.

Instructor Resources

Instructor Resource Distribution
All instructor resources can be downloaded from the Web site, *www.prenhall.com*. Select "Browse our catalog," then, click on "Mathematics;" select your course and choose your text. Under "Resources," on the left side, select "instructor" and choose the supplement you need to download. You will be required to run through a one time registration before you can complete this process.

Instructor Solutions Manual
Fully worked solutions to all textbook exercises and chapter projects.

TestGen
Easily create tests from textbook section objectives. Questions are algorithmically generated allowing for unlimited versions. Edit problems or create your own.

Test Item File
A printed test bank derived from TestGen.

PowerPoint Lecture Slides
Fully editable slides that follow the textbook. Project in class or post to a Web site in an online course.

Mini-Lectures
Mini-Lectures are provided for the Teaching Assistant, adjunct, part-time instructor, or even full-time instructor for lecture preparation by providing learning objectives, examples not found in the text, teaching notes, and the answers to said examples. Mini-Lectures are available from the Instructor's Resource Center and MyMathLab.

Instructor's Edition
Provides answers to all exercises in the back of the text.

MathXL®
MathXL® is a powerful online homework, tutorial, and assessment system that accompanies your textbook. Instructors can create, edit, and assign online homework and tests using algorithmically generated exercises correlated at the objective level to the textbook. Student work is tracked in an online gradebook. Students can take chapter tests and receive personalized study plans based on their results. The study plan diagnoses weaknesses and links students to tutorial exercises for objectives they need to study. Students can also access video clips from selected exercises. MathXL® is available to qualified adopters. For more information, visit our Web site at *www.mathxl.com*, or contact your Prentice Hall sales representative for a demonstration.

MyMathLab
MyMathLab is a text-specific, customizable online course for your textbooks. MyMathLab is powered by CourseCompass™—Pearson Education's online teaching and learning environment—and by MathXL®—our online homework, tutorial, and assessment system. MyMathLab gives you the tools you need to deliver all or a portion of your course online, whether your students are in a lab setting or working from home.

MyMathLab provides a rich and flexible set of course materials, featuring free-response exercises that are algorithmically generated for unlimited practice. Students can use online tools such as video lectures and a multimedia textbook to improve their performance. Instructors can use MyMathLab's homework and test managers to select and assign online exercises correlated to the textbook, and can import TestGen tests for added flexibility. The online gradebook—designed specifically for mathematics—automatically tracks students' homework and test results and gives the instructor control over how to calculate final grades. MyMathLab is available to qualified adopters. For more information, visit our Web site at *www.mymathlab.com* or contact your Prentice Hall sales representative for a product demonstration.

1

Problem Solving and Critical Thinking

T he cost of a college education is skyrocketing.

TUITION AND FEES AT FOUR-YEAR COLLEGES

	School Year Ending 1998	School Year Ending 2005
Public	$3111	$5132
Private	$13,785	$20,082

Source: The College Board

If these trends continue, what can we expect by the 2010s and beyond? We can answer this question by using estimation techniques that allow us to represent the data mathematically. With such representations, called *mathematical models*, we can gain insights and predict what might occur in the future on a variety of issues, ranging from college costs to an aging America, and even the amount that lobbyists spend on Congressional lawmakers.

A mathematical model for our aging country is developed in Example 8 of Section 1.2. Problems involving college costs appear as Exercises 51–52 in Exercise Set 1.2. Conniving Washington lobbyists lurk in Exercise 30 in the Review Exercises.

SECTION 1.1 • INDUCTIVE AND DEDUCTIVE REASONING

Calvin and Hobbes   by Bill Watterson

Many people associate mathematics with tedious computation, meaningless algebraic procedures, and intimidating sets of equations. The truth is that mathematics is the most powerful means we have of exploring our world and describing how it works. The word *mathematics* comes from the Greek word *mathematikos*, which means "inclined to learn." To be mathematical literally means to be inquisitive, open-minded, and interested in a lifetime of pursuing knowledge!

Mathematics and Your Life

A major goal of this book is to show you how mathematics can be applied to your life in interesting, enjoyable, and meaningful ways. Here is a brief, although far from complete, preview of what you can expect.

An understanding of logic will help you to determine what is meant and what is not necessarily meant in spoken and written language. It will give you special tools to analyze information objectively, and to avoid arriving at conclusions hastily without considering all the evidence.

Literacy in numbers will provide you with an understanding of what numbers really mean. For example, the national debt of the United States is about $8.6 trillion. What exactly does this huge number mean? How much would each citizen have to pay the government to retire the debt? In Chapter 5, you will be given a technique that will provide a surprising answer to this question.

An understanding of probability theory will enable you to study outcomes of events to determine what to expect in the long run. Basic ideas of probability will give you a tool for peering into the future and seeing aspects of the universe that would otherwise be invisible.

Managing your personal finances is not an easy task. Achieving your financial goals depends on understanding basic ideas about savings, loans, and investments. Knowledge of consumer mathematics can pay, literally, by making your financial goals a reality.

You can hardly pick up a newspaper without being bombarded with numbers and graphs that describe how we live, what we want, and even how we are likely to die. These numbers influence which products are sold in stores, which movies are shown in theaters, which treatments are available for disease, and which policies are likely to be supported by politicians. An understanding of statistics will help you comprehend where these numbers come from and how they are used to make decisions.

Mathematics and Your Career

Generally speaking, the income of an occupation is related to the amount of education required. This, in turn, is usually related to the skill level required in language and mathematics. With our increasing reliance on technology, the more mathematics you know, the more career choices you will have.

"It is better to take what may seem to be too much math rather than too little. Career plans change, and one of the biggest roadblocks in undertaking new educational or training goals is poor preparation in mathematics. Furthermore, not only do people qualify for more jobs with more math, they are also better able to perform their jobs."

OCCUPATIONAL OUTLOOK
QUARTERLY

Mathematics and Your World

Mathematics is a science that helps us recognize, classify, and explore the hidden patterns of our universe. Focusing on areas as different as planetary motion, animal markings, shapes of viruses, aerodynamics of figure skaters, and the very origin of the universe, mathematics is the most powerful tool available for revealing the underlying structure of our world. Within the last 30 years, mathematicians have even found order in chaotic events such as the uncontrolled storm of noise in the nerve cells of the brain during an epileptic seizure.

1 Understand and use inductive reasoning.

Inductive Reasoning

Mathematics involves the study of patterns. In everyday life, we frequently rely on patterns and routines to draw conclusions. Here is an example:

> The last six times I went to the beach, the traffic was light on Wednesdays and heavy on Sundays. My conclusion is that weekdays have lighter traffic than weekends.

This type of reasoning process is referred to as *inductive reasoning*, or *induction*.

INDUCTIVE REASONING

Inductive reasoning is the process of arriving at a general conclusion based on observations of specific examples.

Although inductive reasoning is a powerful method of drawing conclusions, we can never be absolutely certain that these conclusions are true. For this reason, the conclusions are called **conjectures**, **hypotheses**, or educated guesses. A strong inductive argument does not guarantee the truth of the conclusion, but rather provides strong support for the conclusion. If there is just one case for which the conjecture does not hold, then the conjecture is false. Such a case is called a **counterexample**.

Here are two examples of inductive reasoning:

- **Strong Inductive Argument**
  In a random sample of 1172 U.S. children ages 6 through 14, 17% said getting bossed around is a bad thing about being a kid. We can conclude that there is a 95% probability that between 14.1% and 19.9% of all U.S. children ages 6 through 14 feel that getting bossed around is a bad thing about being a kid.

  > In Chapter 12, you will learn how observations from a randomly selected group, one in which each member of the population has an equal chance of being selected, can provide probabilities of what is true about an entire population.

- **Weak Inductive Argument**
  Men have difficulty expressing their feelings. Neither my dad nor my boyfriend has ever cried in front of me.

  > When generalizing from observations about your own circumstances and experiences, avoid jumping to hasty conclusions based on a few observations. Psychologists theorize that we do this - that is, place everyone in a neat category - to feel more secure about ourselves and our relationships to others.

Inductive reasoning is extremely important to mathematicians. Discovery in mathematics often begins with an examination of individual cases to reveal patterns about numbers.

EXAMPLE 1   USING INDUCTIVE REASONING

Identify a pattern in each list of numbers. Then use this pattern to find the next number.

a. 3, 12, 21, 30, 39, __48__   **b.** 3, 12, 48, 192, 768, __3072__

c. 3, 4, 6, 9, 13, 18, __24__   **d.** 3, 6, 18, 36, 108, 216, __324__

SOLUTION

a. Because 3, 12, 21, 30, 39, _____ is increasing relatively slowly, let's use addition as the basis for our individual observations.

$$3, \quad 12, \quad 21, \quad 30, \quad 39, \quad \underline{\quad}$$
$$3 + 9 = 12 \quad 12 + 9 = 21 \quad 21 + 9 = 30 \quad 30 + 9 = 39$$

Generalizing from these observations, we conclude that each number after the first is obtained by adding 9 to the previous number. Using this pattern, the next number is $39 + 9$, or 48.

b. Because 3, 12, 48, 192, 768, _____ is increasing relatively rapidly, let's use multiplication as the basis for our individual observations.

$$3, \quad 12, \quad 48, \quad 192, \quad 768, \quad \underline{\quad}$$
$$3 \times 4 = 12 \quad 12 \times 4 = 48 \quad 48 \times 4 = 192 \quad 192 \times 4 = 768$$

Generalizing from these observations, we conclude that each number after the first is obtained by multiplying the previous number by 4. Using this pattern, the next number is 768×4, or 3072.

c. Because 3, 4, 6, 9, 13, 18, _____ is increasing relatively slowly, let's use addition as the basis for our individual observations.

$$3, \quad 4, \quad 6, \quad 9, \quad 13, \quad 18, \quad \underline{\quad}$$
$$3 + 1 = 4 \quad 4 + 2 = 6 \quad 6 + 3 = 9 \quad 9 + 4 = 13 \quad 13 + 5 = 18$$

Generalizing from these observations, we conclude that each number after the first is obtained by adding a counting number to the previous number. The additions begin with 1 and continue through each successive counting number. Using this pattern, the next number is $18 + 6$, or 24.

d. Because 3, 6, 18, 36, 108, 216, _____ is increasing relatively rapidly, let's use multiplication as the basis for our individual observations.

$$3, \quad 6, \quad 18, \quad 36, \quad 108, \quad 216, \quad \underline{\quad}$$
$$3 \times 2 = 6 \quad 6 \times 3 = 18 \quad 18 \times 2 = 36 \quad 36 \times 3 = 108 \quad 108 \times 2 = 216$$

Generalizing from these observations, we conclude that each number after the first is obtained by multiplying the previous number by 2 or by 3. The multiplications begin with 2 and then alternate, multiplying by 2, then 3, then 2, then 3, and so on. Using this pattern, the next number is 216×3, or 648.

○

 Identify a pattern in each list of numbers. Then use this pattern to find the next number.

a. 3, 9, 15, 21, 27, __33__

b. 2, 10, 50, 250, __1250__

c. 3, 6, 18, 72, 144, 432, 1728, __3456__

d. 1, 9, 17, 3, 11, 19, 5, 13, 21, __7, 15, 23__

STUDY TIP

The illusion in Figure 1.1 is an ambiguous figure containing two patterns, where it is not clear which pattern should predominate. Do you see a wine goblet or two faces looking at each other? Like this ambiguous figure, some lists of numbers can display more than one pattern, particularly if only a few numbers are given. Inductive reasoning can result in more than one probable next number in a list.

Example: $1, 2, 4, \underline{}$

Pattern: Each number after the first is obtained by multiplying the previous number by 2. The missing number is 4×2, or 8.

Pattern: Each number after the first is obtained by adding successive counting numbers, starting with 1, to the previous number. The second number is $1 + 1$, or 2. The third number is $2 + 2$, or 4. The missing number is $4 + 3$, or 7.

Inductive reasoning can also result in different patterns that produce the same probable next number in a list.

Example: $1, 4, 9, 16, 25, \underline{}$

Pattern: Start by adding 3 to the first number. Then add successive odd numbers, 5, 7, 9, and so on. The missing number is $25 + 11$, or 36.

Pattern: Each number is obtained by squaring its position in the list: The first number is $1^2 = 1 \times 1 = 1$, the second number is $2^2 = 2 \times 2 = 4$, the third number is $3^2 = 3 \times 3 = 9$, and so on. The missing sixth number is $6^2 = 6 \times 6$, or 36.

The numbers that we found in Example 1 are probable numbers. Perhaps you found patterns other than the ones we pointed out that might have resulted in different answers.

FIGURE 1.1

In our next example, the patterns are a bit more complex than the additions and multiplications we encountered in Example 1.

EXAMPLE 2 USING INDUCTIVE REASONING

Identify a pattern in each list of numbers. Then use this pattern to find the next number.

a. $1, 1, 2, 3, 5, 8, 13, 21, \underline{}$ **b.** $23, 54, 95, 146, 117, 98, \underline{}$

SOLUTION

a. Starting with the third number in the list, let's form our observations by comparing each number with the two numbers that immediately precede it.

$$1, \quad 1, \quad 2, \quad 3, \quad 5, \quad 8, \quad 13, \quad 21, \quad \underline{}$$

| preceded by 1 and 1: $1 + 1 = 2$ | preceded by 1 and 2: $1 + 2 = 3$ | preceded by 2 and 3: $2 + 3 = 5$ | preceded by 3 and 5: $3 + 5 = 8$ | preceded by 5 and 8: $5 + 8 = 13$ | preceded by 8 and 13: $8 + 13 = 21$ |

Generalizing from these observations, we conclude that the first two numbers are 1. Each number thereafter is the sum of the two preceding numbers. Using this pattern, the next number is $13 + 21$, or 34. (The numbers 1, 1, 2, 3, 5, 8, 13, 21, and 34 are the first nine terms of the *Fibonacci sequence*, discussed in Chapter 5, Section 5.7.)

b. Let's use the digits that form each number as the basis for our individual observations. Focus on the sum of the digits, as well as the final digit increased by 1.

$2 + 3 = 5$ $5 + 4 = 9$ $9 + 5 = 14$ $1 + 4 + 6 = 11$ $1 + 1 + 7 = 9$

$$23, \quad 54, \quad 95, \quad 146, \quad 117, \quad 98, \quad \underline{}$$

$3 + 1 = 4$ $4 + 1 = 5$ $5 + 1 = 6$ $6 + 1 = 7$ $7 + 1 = 8$

Generalizing from these observations, we conclude that for each number after the first, we obtain the first digit or the first two digits by adding the digits of the previous number. We obtain the last digit by adding 1 to the final digit of the preceding number. Applying this pattern to the number that follows 98, the first two digits are $9 + 8$, or 17. The last digit is $8 + 1$, or 9. Thus, the next number in the list is 179.

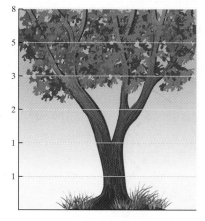

As this tree branches, the number of branches forms the Fibonacci sequence.

The Patterns of Fibonacci

When expressed in decimal form, the fraction $\dfrac{1}{998,999}$ contains a portion of the Fibonacci sequence.

$$\frac{1}{998,999} = 0.000001001002003005008013021034055089\ldots$$

The first eleven numbers of the Fibonacci sequence are 1, 1, 2, 3, 5, 8, 13, 21, 34, 55, and 89. Starting with 2, each successive number is the sum of the two previous numbers.

CHECK POINT 2 Identify a pattern in each list of numbers. Then use this pattern to find the next number.

  a. 1, 3, 4, 7, 11, 18, 29, 47, ___76___

  b. 2, 3, 5, 9, 17, 33, 65, 129, _____ .

This electron microscope photograph shows the knotty shape of the Ebola virus.

Mathematics is more than recognizing number patterns. It is about the patterns that arise in the world around us. For example, by describing patterns formed by various kinds of knots, mathematicians are helping scientists investigate the knotty shapes and patterns of viruses. One of the weapons used against viruses is based on recognizing visual patterns in the possible ways that knots can be tied.

Our next example deals with recognizing visual patterns.

EXAMPLE 3 FINDING THE NEXT FIGURE IN A VISUAL SEQUENCE

Describe two patterns in this sequence of figures. Use the patterns to draw the next figure in the sequence.

 , , , , _____

SOLUTION The more obvious pattern is that the figures alternate between circles and squares. We conclude that the next figure will be a circle. We can identify the second pattern in the four regions containing no dots, one dot, two dots, and three dots. The dots are placed in order (no dots, one dot, two dots, three dots) in a clockwise direction. However, the entire pattern of the dots rotates counterclockwise as we follow the figures from left to right.

This means that the next figure should be a circle with a single dot in the right-hand region, two dots in the bottom region, three dots in the left-hand region, and no dots in the top region. This figure is drawn in Figure 1.2.

FIGURE 1.2

3 Describe two patterns in this sequence of figures. Use the patterns to draw the next figure in the sequence.

Deductive Reasoning

2 | Understand and use deductive reasoning.

We use inductive reasoning in everyday life. Many of the conjectures that come from this kind of thinking seem highly likely, although we can never be absolutely certain that they are true. Another method of reasoning, called *deductive reasoning*, or *deduction*, can be used to prove that some conjectures are true.

> **DEDUCTIVE REASONING**
> **Deductive reasoning** is the process of proving a specific conclusion from one or more general statements. A conclusion that is proved true by deductive reasoning is called a **theorem**.

Deductive reasoning allows us to draw a specific conclusion from one or more general statements. Here are two examples of deductive reasoning. Notice that in both everyday situations, the general statement from which the conclusion is drawn is implied rather than directly stated.

Everyday Situation	Deductive Reasoning
One player to another in a Scrabble game: "You have to remove those five letters. You can't use TEXAS as a word."	• All proper names are pro- *general statement* hibited in Scrabble. TEXAS is a proper name. Therefore, TEXAS is pro- *conclusion* hibited in Scrabble.
Advice to college freshmen on choosing classes: "Never sign up for a 7 A.M. class. Yes, you did it in high school, but Mom was always there to keep waking you up, and if by some miracle you do make it to an early class, you will sleep through the lecture when you get there." (*Source: How to Survive Your Freshman Year*, Hundreds of Heads Books, 2004)	• All people need to sleep at 7 A.M. *general statement* You sign up for a class at 7 A.M. Therefore, you'll sleep through the lecture or not even make *conclusion* it to class. In Chapter 3, you'll learn how to prove this conclusion from the general statement in the first line. But is the general statement really true? Can we make assumptions about the sleeping patterns of all people, or are we using deductive reasoning to reinforce an untrue reality assumption?

Our next example illustrates the difference between inductive and deductive reasoning. The first part of the example involves reasoning that moves from specific examples to a general statement, illustrating inductive reasoning. The second part of the example begins with the general case rather than specific examples, and illustrates deductive reasoning. To begin with the general case, we use a letter to represent any one of various numbers. A letter used to represent any number in a collection of numbers is called a **variable**.

EXAMPLE 4   USING INDUCTIVE AND DEDUCTIVE REASONING

Consider the following procedure:

> Select a number. Multiply the number by 6. Add 8 to the product. Divide this sum by 2. Subtract 4 from the quotient.

a. Repeat this procedure for at least four different numbers. Write a conjecture that relates the result of this process to the original number selected.

b. Represent the original number by the variable n and use deductive reasoning to prove the conjecture in part (a).

SOLUTION

a. First, let us pick our starting numbers. We will use 4, 7, 11, and 100, but we could pick any four numbers. Next we will apply the procedure given in this example to 4, 7, 11, and 100, four individual cases, in Table 1.1.

TABLE 1.1 APPLYING A PROCEDURE TO FOUR INDIVIDUAL CASES

Select a number.	4	7	11	100
Multiply the number by 6.	$4 \times 6 = 24$	$7 \times 6 = 42$	$11 \times 6 = 66$	$100 \times 6 = 600$
Add 8 to the product.	$24 + 8 = 32$	$42 + 8 = 50$	$66 + 8 = 74$	$600 + 8 = 608$
Divide this sum by 2.	$\dfrac{32}{2} = 16$	$\dfrac{50}{2} = 25$	$\dfrac{74}{2} = 37$	$\dfrac{608}{2} = 304$
Subtract 4 from the quotient.	$16 - 4 = 12$	$25 - 4 = 21$	$37 - 4 = 33$	$304 - 4 = 300$

Because we are asked to write a conjecture that relates the result of this process to the original number selected, let us focus on the result of each case.

Original number selected	4	7	11	100
Result of the process	12	21	33	300

Do you see a pattern? Our conjecture is that the result of the process is three times the original number selected. We have used inductive reasoning.

b. Now we begin with the general case rather than specific examples. We use the variable n to represent any number.

Select a number.	n
Multiply the number by 6.	$6n$ (This means 6 times n.)
Add 8 to the product.	$6n + 8$
Divide this sum by 2.	$\dfrac{6n + 8}{2} = \dfrac{6n}{2} + \dfrac{8}{2} = 3n + 4$
Subtract 4 from the quotient.	$3n + 4 - 4 = 3n$

Using the variable n to represent any number, the result is $3n$, or three times the number n. This proves that the result of the procedure is three times the original number selected for any number. We have used deductive reasoning.

CHECK POINT 4 Consider the following procedure:

> Select a number. Multiply the number by 4. Add 6 to the product. Divide this sum by 2. Subtract 3 from the quotient.

a. Repeat this procedure for at least four different numbers. Write a conjecture that relates the result of this process to the original number selected.

b. Represent the original number by the variable n and use deductive reasoning to prove the conjecture in part (a).

BLITZER BONUS

The Patterns of Chaos

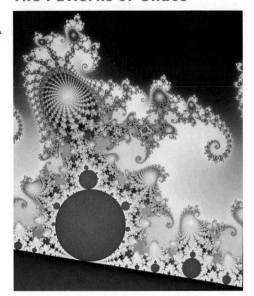

A magnification of the Mandelbrot set. R. F. Voss, "29-Fold M-set Seahorse" computer-generated image.
© 1990 R. F. Voss/IBM Research.

"The single most compelling reason to explore the world of mathematics is that it is beautiful, and pondering its intriguing ideas is great fun. I'm constantly perplexed by how many people do not believe this, yet over 50,000 professional mathematicians in America practice their trade with enthusiasm and fervor."

Calvin Clawson, *Mathematical Mysteries*,
Plenum Press, 1996

One of the new frontiers of mathematics suggests that there is an underlying order in things that appear to be random, such as the hiss and crackle of background noises as you tune a radio. Irregularities in the heartbeat, some of them severe enough to cause a heart attack, or irregularities in our sleeping patterns, such as insomnia, are examples of chaotic behavior. Chaos in the mathematical sense does not mean a complete lack of form or arrangement. In mathematics, chaos is used to describe something that appears to be random but is not actually random. The patterns of chaos appear in images like the one shown on the left, called the Mandelbrot set. Magnified portions of this image yield repetitions of the original structure, as well as new and unexpected patterns. The Mandelbrot set transforms the hidden structure of chaotic events into a source of wonder and inspiration.

EXERCISE SET 1.1 ●●●●●●

• Practice Exercises

In Exercises 1–30, identify a pattern in each list of numbers. Then use this pattern to find the next number. (More than one pattern might exist, so it is possible that there is more than one correct answer.)

1. 8, 12, 16, 20, 24, _____

2. 19, 24, 29, 34, 39, _____

3. 37, 32, 27, 22, 17, _____

4. 33, 29, 25, 21, 17, _____

5. 3, 9, 27, 81, 243, _____

6. 2, 8, 32, 128, 512, _____

7. 1, 2, 4, 8, 16, _____

8. 1, 5, 25, 125, _____

9. 1, 4, 1, 8, 1, 16, 1, _____

10. 1, 4, 1, 7, 1, 10, 1, _____

11. 4, 2, 0, −2, −4, _____

12. 6, 3, 0, −3, −6, _____

13. $\frac{1}{2}, \frac{1}{6}, \frac{1}{10}, \frac{1}{14}, \frac{1}{18},$ _____

14. $1, \frac{1}{2}, \frac{1}{3}, \frac{1}{4}, \frac{1}{5},$ _____

15. $1, \frac{1}{3}, \frac{1}{9}, \frac{1}{27},$ _____

16. $1, \frac{1}{2}, \frac{1}{4}, \frac{1}{8},$ _____

17. 3, 7, 12, 18, 25, 33, _____

18. 2, 5, 9, 14, 20, 27, _____

19. 3, 6, 11, 18, 27, 38, _____

20. 2, 5, 10, 17, 26, 37, _____

21. 3, 7, 10, 17, 27, 44, _____

22. 2, 5, 7, 12, 19, 31, _____

23. 2, 7, 12, 5, 10, 15, 8, 13, _____

24. 3, 9, 15, 5, 11, 17, 7, 13, _____

25. 3, 6, 5, 10, 9, 18, 17, 34, _____

26. 2, 6, 5, 15, 14, 42, 41, 123, _____

27. 64, −16, 4, −1, _____

28. 125, −25, 5, −1, _____

29. $(6, 2), (0, -4), \left(7\frac{1}{2}, 3\frac{1}{2}\right), (2, -2), (3, \underline{\quad})$

30. $\left(\frac{2}{3}, \frac{4}{9}\right), \left(\frac{1}{5}, \frac{1}{25}\right), (7, 49), \left(-\frac{5}{6}, \frac{25}{36}\right), \left(-\frac{4}{7}, \underline{\quad}\right)$

In Exercises 31–34, identify a pattern in each sequence of figures. Then use the pattern to find the next figure in the sequence.

31. ☐ , △ , ○ , ☐ , △ , _____

32. ◹ , ◿ , ◺ , ◹ , ◺ , _____

33. , , , _____

34. , , _____

Exercises 35–38 describe procedures that are to be applied to numbers. In each exercise,

    a. *Repeat the procedure for four numbers of your choice. Write a conjecture that relates the result of the process to the original number selected.*

    b. *Represent the original number by the variable n and use deductive reasoning to prove the conjecture in part (a).*

35. Select a number. Multiply the number by 4. Add 8 to the product. Divide this sum by 2. Subtract 4 from the quotient.

36. Select a number. Multiply the number by 3. Add 6 to the product. Divide this sum by 3. Subtract the original selected number from the quotient.

37. Select a number. Add 5. Double the result. Subtract 4. Divide by 2. Subtract the original selected number.

38. Select a number. Add 3. Double the result. Add 4. Divide by 2. Subtract the original selected number.

In Exercises 39–44, use inductive reasoning to predict the next line in each sequence of computations. Then use a calculator or perform the arithmetic by hand to determine whether your conjecture is correct.

39.
$$1 + 2 = \frac{2 \times 3}{2}$$
$$1 + 2 + 3 = \frac{3 \times 4}{2}$$
$$1 + 2 + 3 + 4 = \frac{4 \times 5}{2}$$
$$1 + 2 + 3 + 4 + 5 = \frac{5 \times 6}{2}$$

40.
$$3 + 6 = \frac{6 \times 3}{2}$$
$$3 + 6 + 9 = \frac{9 \times 4}{2}$$
$$3 + 6 + 9 + 12 = \frac{12 \times 5}{2}$$
$$3 + 6 + 9 + 12 + 15 = \frac{15 \times 6}{2}$$

41.
$$1 + 3 = 2 \times 2$$
$$1 + 3 + 5 = 3 \times 3$$
$$1 + 3 + 5 + 7 = 4 \times 4$$
$$1 + 3 + 5 + 7 + 9 = 5 \times 5$$

42.
$$\frac{1}{1 \times 2} + \frac{1}{2 \times 3} = \frac{2}{3}$$
$$\frac{1}{1 \times 2} + \frac{1}{2 \times 3} + \frac{1}{3 \times 4} = \frac{3}{4}$$
$$\frac{1}{1 \times 2} + \frac{1}{2 \times 3} + \frac{1}{3 \times 4} + \frac{1}{4 \times 5} = \frac{4}{5}$$

43.
$$9 \times 9 + 7 = 88$$
$$98 \times 9 + 6 = 888$$
$$987 \times 9 + 5 = 8888$$
$$9876 \times 9 + 4 = 88{,}888$$

44.
$$1 \times 9 - 1 = 8$$
$$21 \times 9 - 1 = 188$$
$$321 \times 9 - 1 = 2888$$
$$4321 \times 9 - 1 = 38{,}888$$

• Practice Plus

In Exercises 45–46, use inductive reasoning to predict the next line in each sequence of computations. Then use a calculator or perform the arithmetic by hand to determine whether your conjecture is correct.

45.
$$33 \times 3367 = 111{,}111$$
$$66 \times 3367 = 222{,}222$$
$$99 \times 3367 = 333{,}333$$
$$132 \times 3367 = 444{,}444$$

46.
$$1 \times 8 + 1 = 9$$
$$12 \times 8 + 2 = 98$$
$$123 \times 8 + 3 = 987$$
$$1234 \times 8 + 4 = 9876$$
$$12{,}345 \times 8 + 5 = 98{,}765$$

47. Study the pattern in these examples:
$$a^2 \,\#\, a^4 = a^{10} \quad a^3 \,\#\, a^2 = a^7 \quad a^5 \,\#\, a^3 = a^{11}.$$

Select the equation that describes the pattern.

    a. $a^x \,\#\, a^y = a^{2x+y}$

    b. $a^x \,\#\, a^y = a^{x+2y}$

    c. $a^x \,\#\, a^y = a^{x+y+4}$

    d. $a^x \,\#\, a^y = a^{xy+2}$

48. Study the pattern in these examples:
$$a^5 * a^3 * a^2 = a^5 \quad a^3 * a^7 * a^2 = a^6 \quad a^2 * a^4 * a^8 = a^7.$$

Select the equation that describes the pattern.

    a. $a^x * a^y * a^z = a^{x+y+z}$

    b. $a^x * a^y * a^z = a^{\frac{xyz}{2}}$

    c. $a^x * a^y * a^z = a^{\frac{x+y+z}{2}}$

    d. $a^x * a^y * a^z = a^{\frac{xy}{2}+z}$

49. The trend in the data displayed by the graph leaves little for Hollywood executives (or even King Kong) to beat their chests about. Study the pattern, or trend, shown by the data. Then select the expression that *best* describes the number of movie tickets sold, in billions, *n* years after 2002.

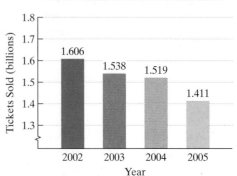

Theater Attendance: Number of Movie Tickets Sold in the United States

Source: Entertainment Weekly

    a. $1.6 + 0.06n$

    b. $1.6 + 1.06n$

    c. $1.6 - 0.06n$

    d. $1.6 - 1.06n$

50. The data displayed by the graph indicate that watching movies at home is becoming more popular. Study the pattern, or trend, shown by the data. Then select the expression that *best* describes the number of hours Americans watched prerecorded movies at home n years after 2004.

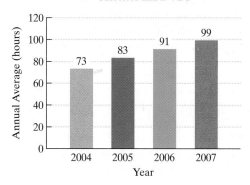

Number of Hours Americans Age 12 and Older Watch Prerecorded Video Cassettes and DVDs

Source: U.S. Census Bureau

a. $73.6 + 12.5n$
b. $73.6 + 8.6n$
c. $73.6 - 12.5n$
d. $73.6 - 8.6n$

• Application Exercises

In Exercises 51–54, identify the reasoning process, induction or deduction, in each example. Explain your answer.

51. It can be shown that
$$1 + 2 + 3 + \cdots + n = \frac{n(n + 1)}{2}.$$
I can use this formula to conclude that the sum of the first one hundred counting numbers, $1 + 2 + 3 + \cdots + 100$, is
$$\frac{100(100 + 1)}{2} = \frac{100(101)}{2} = 50(101), \text{ or } 5050.$$

52. An HMO does a follow-up study on 200 randomly selected patients given a flu shot. None of these people became seriously ill with the flu. The study concludes that all HMO patients be urged to get a flu shot in order to prevent a serious flu.

53. The data in the graph are from a random sample of 1200 full-time four-year undergraduate college students on 100 U.S. campuses.

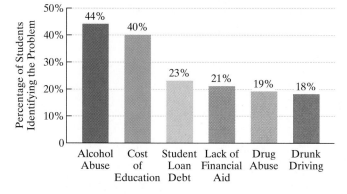

The Greatest Problems on Campus

Source: Student Monitor LLC

We can conclude that there is a high probability that approximately 44% of all full-time four-year college students in the United States believe that alcohol abuse is the greatest problem on campus.

54. The course policy states that work turned in late will be marked down a grade. I turned in my report a day late, so it was marked down from B to C.

55. The ancient Greeks studied **figurate numbers**, so named because of their representations as geometric arrangements of points.

Triangular Numbers

1   3   6   10   15   21

Square Numbers

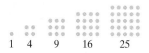

1   4   9   16   25

Pentagonal Numbers

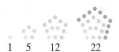

1   5   12   22

a. Use inductive reasoning to write the five triangular numbers that follow 21.

b. Use inductive reasoning to write the five square numbers that follow 25.

c. Use inductive reasoning to write the five pentagonal numbers that follow 22.

d. Use inductive reasoning to complete this statement: If a triangular number is multiplied by 8 and then 1 is added to the product, a _____ number is obtained.

56. The triangular arrangement of numbers shown below is known as **Pascal's triangle**, credited to French mathematician Blaise Pascal (1623–1662). Use inductive reasoning to find the six numbers designated by question marks.

$$
\begin{array}{ccccccccccc}
 & & & & & 1 & & & & & \\
 & & & & 1 & & 1 & & & & \\
 & & & 1 & & 2 & & 1 & & & \\
 & & 1 & & 3 & & 3 & & 1 & & \\
 & 1 & & 4 & & 6 & & 4 & & 1 & \\
? & & ? & & ? & & ? & & ? & & ? \\
\end{array}
$$

• Writing in Mathematics

Writing about mathematics will help you to learn mathematics. For all writing exercises in this book, use complete sentences to respond to the questions. Some writing exercises can be answered in a sentence; others require a paragraph or two. You can decide how much you need to write as long as your writing clearly and directly answers the question in the exercise. Standard references such as a dictionary and a thesaurus may be helpful.

57. The word *induce* comes from a Latin term meaning to lead. Explain what leading has to do with inductive reasoning.

58. Describe what is meant by deductive reasoning. Give an example.

59. Give an example of a decision that you made recently in which the method of reasoning you used to reach the decision was induction. Describe your reasoning process.

60. The April 26, 2004 issue of *Time* magazine is a special issue on the lives and ideas of the world's most influential people. Consult this issue of *Time* and select one of the people who used inductive or deductive reasoning in his or her work.

   a. Explain how the person you selected used one of these types of reasoning.

   b. Explain why you selected this particular person.

• **Critical Thinking Exercises**

61. If $(6 - 2)^2 = 36 - 24 + 4$ and $(8 - 5)^2 = 64 - 80 + 25$, use inductive reasoning to write a compatible expression for $(11 - 7)^2$.

62. Study the first three figures. Then use inductive reasoning to determine the area of the same type of figure with a radius of 9 and a height of 10.

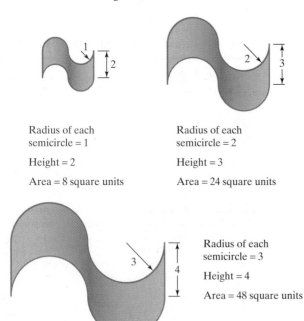

Radius of each
semicircle = 1

Height = 2

Area = 8 square units

Radius of each
semicircle = 2

Height = 3

Area = 24 square units

Radius of each
semicircle = 3

Height = 4

Area = 48 square units

63. Write a list of numbers that has two patterns so that the next number in the list can be 15 or 20.

64. a. Repeat the following procedure with at least five people. Write a conjecture that relates the result of the procedure to each person's birthday.

   Take the number of the month of your birthday (January = 1, February = 2, ..., December = 12), multiply by 5, add 6, multiply this sum by 4, add 9, multiply this new sum by 5, and add the number of the day on which you were born. Finally, subtract 165.

   b. Let *M* represent the month number and let *D* represent the day number of any person's birthday. Use deductive reasoning to prove your conjecture in part (a).

• **Technology Exercises**

65. a. Use a calculator to find 6×6, 66×66, 666×666, and 6666×6666.

   b. Describe a pattern in the numbers being multiplied and the resulting products.

   c. Use the pattern to write the next two multiplications and their products. Then use your calculator to verify these results.

   d. Is this process an example of inductive or deductive reasoning? Explain your answer.

66. a. Use a calculator to find 3367×3, 3367×6, 3367×9, and 3367×12.

   b. Describe a pattern in the numbers being multiplied and the resulting products.

   c. Use the pattern to write the next two multiplications and their products. Then use your calculator to verify these results.

   d. Is this process an example of inductive or deductive reasoning? Explain your answer.

• **Group Exercise**

67. Stereotyping refers to classifying people, places, or things according to common traits. Prejudices and stereotypes can function as assumptions in our thinking, appearing in inductive and deductive reasoning. For example, it is not difficult to find inductive reasoning that results in generalizations such as these, as well as deductive reasoning in which these stereotypes serve as assumptions:

   School has nothing to do with life.

   Intellectuals are nerds.

   People on welfare are lazy.

Each group member should find one example of inductive reasoning and one example of deductive reasoning in which stereotyping occurs. Upon returning to the group, present each example and then describe how the stereotyping results in faulty conjectures or prejudging situations and people.

SECTION 1.2 • ESTIMATION, GRAPHS, AND MATHEMATICAL MODELS

OBJECTIVES

1. Use estimation techniques to arrive at an approximate answer to a problem.

2. Apply estimation techniques to information given by graphs.

3. Develop mathematical models that estimate relationships between variables.

If present trends continue, is it possible that our descendants could live to be 200 years of age? To answer this question, we need to examine data for life expectancy and develop estimation techniques for representing the data mathematically. In this section, you will learn estimation methods that will enable you to obtain mathematical representations of data displayed by graphs, using these representations to predict what might occur in the future.

---

1 Use estimation techniques to arrive at an approximate answer to a problem.

Estimation

Estimation is the process of arriving at an approximate answer to a question. For example, companies estimate the amount of their products consumers are likely to use, and economists estimate financial trends. If you are about to cross a street, you may estimate the speed of oncoming cars so that you know whether or not to wait before crossing. Rounding numbers is also an estimation method. You might round a number without even being aware that you are doing so. You may say that you are 20 years old, rather than 20 years 5 months, or that you will be home in about a half-hour, rather than 25 minutes.

You will find estimation to be equally valuable in your work for this class. Making mistakes with a calculator or a computer is easy. Estimation can tell us whether the answer displayed for a computation makes sense.

In this section, we demonstrate several estimation methods. In the second part of the section, we apply these techniques to information given by graphs.

Performing computations using rounded numbers is one way to check whether an answer displayed by a calculator or a computer is reasonable. Rounding whole numbers depends on knowing the place values of the digits. (The digits that we use in base ten are 0, 1, 2, 3, 4, 5, 6, 7, 8, and 9. In Chapter 4, we'll explore other ways of representing numbers, including bases other than ten.) The place that a digit occupies in a number tells us its value in that number. Here is an example using the population of the United States at 5:35 A.M. on January 26, 2006.

Place values

hundred million | ten million | million | hundred thousand | ten thousand | thousand | hundred | ten | one

2 9 5 , 7 3 4 , 1 3 4

This number is read "two hundred ninety-five million, seven hundred thirty-four thousand, one hundred thirty four."

> **ROUNDING WHOLE NUMBERS**
>
> **1.** Look at the digit to the right of the digit where rounding is to occur.
> **2. a.** If the digit to the right is 5 or greater, add 1 to the digit to be rounded. Replace all digits to the right with zeros.
>   **b.** If the digit to the right is less than 5, do not change the digit to be rounded. Replace all digits to the right with zeros.

The symbol ≈ means *is approximately equal to*. We will use this symbol when rounding numbers.

EXAMPLE 1   ROUNDING A WHOLE NUMBER

Round the U.S. population (295,734,134) as follows:

a. to the nearest million

b. to the nearest thousand.

SOLUTION

a.   295,734,134   ≈   296,000,000

| Millions digit, where rounding is to occur | Digit to the right is greater than 5. | Add 1 to the digit to be rounded. | Replace all digits to the right with zeros. |

The U.S. population to the nearest million is two hundred ninety-six million.

b.   295,734,134   ≈   295,734,000

| Thousands digit, where rounding is to occur | Digit to the right is less than 5. | Do not change the digit to be rounded. | Replace all digits to the right with zeros. |

The U.S. population to the nearest thousand is two hundred ninety-five million seven hundred thirty-four thousand.   ○

 Round the U.S. population (295,734,134) as follows:

a. to the nearest hundred million

b. to the nearest hundred thousand.

Rounding can also be applied to decimal notation, used to denote a part of a whole. Once again, the place that a digit occupies tells us its value. Here's an example using the first seven digits of the number π (pi). (We'll have more to say about π, whose digits extend endlessly with no repeating pattern, in Chapter 5.)

$$\pi \approx 3 . 1 \ 4 \ 1 \ 5 \ 9 \ 2$$

Decimal point

We round the decimal part of a decimal number in nearly the same way that we round whole numbers. The only difference is that we drop the digits to the right of the rounding place, rather than replacing these digits with zeros.

EXAMPLE 2   ROUNDING THE DECIMAL PART OF A NUMBER

Round 3.141592, the first seven digits of π, as follows:

a. to the nearest hundredth

b. to the nearest thousandth.

SOLUTION

a.   3.141592 $\approx$ 3.14

| Hundredths digit, where rounding is to occur | Digit to the right is less than 5. | Do not change the digit to be rounded. | Drop all digits to the right. |

The number π to the nearest hundredth is three and fourteen hundredths.

b.   3.141592 $\approx$ 3.142

| Thousandths digit, where rounding is to occur | Digit to the right is 5. | Add 1 to the digit to be rounded. | Drop all digits to the right. |

The number π to the nearest thousandth is three and one hundred forty-two thousandths.

 Round 3.141592, the first seven digits of π, as follows:

a. to the nearest tenth

b. to the nearest ten-thousandth.

EXAMPLE 3   ESTIMATION BY ROUNDING

You purchased bread for $2.59, detergent for $2.17, a sandwich for $3.65, an apple for $0.47, and coffee for $5.79. The total bill was $18.67. Is this amount reasonable?

SOLUTION If you are in the habit of carrying a calculator to the store, you can answer the question by finding the exact cost of the purchase. However, estimation can be used to determine if the bill is reasonable even if you do not have a calculator. We will round the cost of each item to the nearest dollar.

| Round to the nearest dollar. | Use digits in the tenths place to do the rounding. |

Bread	$2.59	$\approx$ $3.00
Detergent	$2.17	$\approx$ $2.00
Sandwich	$3.65	$\approx$ $4.00
Apple	$0.47	$\approx$ $0.00
Coffee	$5.79	$\approx$ $6.00
		$15.00

The total bill, $18.67, seems a bit high compared to the $15.00 estimate. You should check the bill before paying it.

CHECK POINT 3 You and a friend ate lunch at Ye Olde Cafe. The check for the meal showed soup for $2.40, tomato juice for $1.25, a roast beef sandwich for $4.60, a chicken salad sandwich for $4.40, two coffees totaling $1.40, apple pie for $1.85, and chocolate cake for $2.95.

a. Round the cost of each item to the nearest dollar and obtain an estimate for the food bill.

b. The total bill before tax was $21.85. Is this amount reasonable?

EXAMPLE 4   ESTIMATION BY ROUNDING

A carpenter who works full time earns $28 per hour.

a. Estimate the carpenter's weekly salary.

b. Estimate the carpenter's annual salary.

SOLUTION

a. In order to simplify the calculation, we can round the hourly rate of $28 to $30. Be sure to write out the units for each number in the calculation. The work week is 40 hours per week and the rounded salary is $30 per hour. We express this as

$$\frac{40 \text{ hours}}{\text{week}} \quad \text{and} \quad \frac{\$30}{\text{hour}}.$$

The word *per* is represented by the division bar. We multiply these two numbers to estimate the carpenter's weekly salary. We cancel out units that are identical if they are above and below the division bar.

$$\frac{40 \ \cancel{\text{hours}}}{\text{week}} \times \frac{\$30}{\cancel{\text{hour}}} = \frac{\$1200}{\text{week}}$$

Thus, the carpenter earns approximately $1200 per week, written $\approx \$1200$.

b. For the estimate of annual salary, we may round 52 weeks to 50 weeks. The annual salary is approximately the product of $1200 per week and 50 weeks per year:

$$\frac{\$1200}{\cancel{\text{week}}} \times \frac{50 \ \cancel{\text{weeks}}}{\text{year}} = \frac{\$60,000}{\text{year}}.$$

Thus, the carpenter earns approximately $60,000 per year, or $60,000 annually, written $\approx \$60,000$. ○

 4 A landscape architect who works full time earns $52 per hour.

a. Estimate the landscape architect's weekly salary.

b. Estimate the landscape architect's annual salary.

2 | Apply estimation techniques to information given by graphs.

Estimation with Graphs

Magazines and newspapers often display information using circle, bar, and line graphs. The following examples illustrate how rounding and other estimation techniques can be applied to each of these graphs.

Circle graphs, also called **pie charts**, show how a whole quantity is divided into parts. Circle graphs are divided into pieces, called **sectors**. Figure 1.3 shows two circle graphs that indicate most Americans think dogs count as company.

Dogs Count as Company
If you are at home with your dog and no other people are there, are you alone?

Responses by Dog Owners in the United States

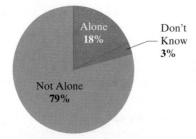

Responses by Nonowners in the United States

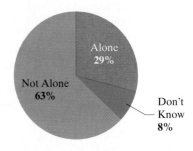

FIGURE 1.3
Source: The American Kennel Club

In our next example, we will use the circle graph for dog owners to estimate a calculation. Although different rounding results in different estimates, the whole idea behind the rounding process is to make calculations simple.

> **EXAMPLE 5** APPLYING ESTIMATION TECHNIQUES TO A CIRCLE GRAPH

According to the American Pet Association, there are 43,143,849 dog owners in the United States.

a. Use the appropriate information in Figure 1.3 to determine a calculation that shows the number of dog owners who think dogs count as company.

b. Use rounding to find a reasonable estimate for this calculation.

STUDY TIP

To convert a number from percent form to decimal form, move the decimal point two places to the left and drop the percent sign. Example:

$$79\% = 79.\% = 0.79\%$$

A review of percents can be found in Section 8.1.

SOLUTION

a. The circle graph on the left in Figure 1.3 indicates that 79% of dog owners think dogs count as company. With a total of 43,143,849 dog owners, the number who believe this is determined by finding 79% of 43,143,849.

| The number of dog owners who think dogs count as company | is | 79% | of | the total number of dog owners. |

$$= 0.79 \times 43{,}143{,}849$$

b. We can use rounding to obtain a reasonable estimate of $0.79 \times 43{,}143{,}849$.

Round to the nearest ten million.

$$0.79 \times 43{,}143{,}849 \approx 0.8 \times 40{,}000{,}000 = 32{,}000{,}000$$

Round to the nearest tenth.

```
  40,000,000
×        0.8
32,000,000.0
```

Our answer indicates that approximately 32,000,000 (32 million) dog owners in the United States think dogs count as company.

CHECK POINT 5 There are 178,586,613 adults in the United States ages 18 and older who are not dog owners.

a. Use the appropriate information in Figure 1.3 to determine a calculation that shows the number of nonowners who think dogs count as company.

b. Use rounding to find a reasonable estimate for this calculation.

Bar graphs are convenient for showing comparisons among items. The bars may be either horizontal or vertical, and their heights or lengths are used to show the amounts of different items. Figure 1.4 on the next page is an example of a typical bar graph. The graph shows life expectancy for American men and American women born in various years from 1950 through 2002.

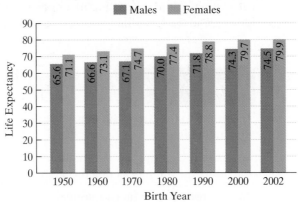

FIGURE 1.4
Source: National Center for Health Statistics

EXAMPLE 6   APPLYING ESTIMATION AND INDUCTIVE REASONING TO DATA IN A BAR GRAPH

Use the data for the men in Figure 1.4 to estimate each of the following:

a. a man's increased life expectancy, rounded to the nearest hundredth of a year, for each subsequent birth year

b. the life expectancy, to the nearest tenth of a year, of a man born in 2020.

SOLUTION

a. One way to estimate increased life expectancy for each subsequent birth year is to generalize from observations in 1950 (male life expectancy: 65.6 years) and in 2002 (male life expectancy: 74.5 years). The yearly increase in life expectancy is the change in life expectancy from 1950 to 2002 divided by the change in time from 1950 to 2002.

Yearly increase in life expectancy **is approximately** $\dfrac{\text{change in life expectancy from 1950 to 2002}}{\text{change in time from 1950 to 2002}}$

$$\approx \frac{74.5 - 65.6}{2002 - 1950}$$

life expectancy in 2002 minus life expectancy in 1950

Change in time is 2002 − 1950, or 52 years.

TECHNOLOGY

Here is the calculator keystroke sequence needed to perform this computation.

(74.5 − 65.6) ÷ (2002 − 1950) .

Press = on a scientific calculator or ENTER on a graphing calculator to display the answer. As specified, we round to the nearest hundredth.

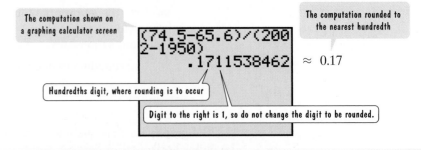

The computation shown on a graphing calculator screen

(74.5-65.6)/(2002-1950)
.1711538462 ≈ 0.17

The computation rounded to the nearest hundredth

Hundredths digit, where rounding is to occur

Digit to the right is 1, so do not change the digit to be rounded.

For each subsequent birth year, a man's life expectancy is increasing by approximately 0.17 year.

b. We can use our computation in part (a) to estimate the life expectancy of an American man born in 2020. The bar graph indicates that men born in 1950 had a life expectancy of 65.6 years. The year 2020 is 70 years after 1950 and life expectancy is increasing by approximately 0.17 year for each subsequent birth year.

Life expectancy for a man born in 2020	is approximately	life expectancy for a man born in 1950	plus	yearly increase in life expectancy	times	the number of years from 1950 to 2020.
	≈ 65.6		+	0.17	×	70

$$= 65.6 + 11.9$$

$$= 77.5$$

Because the directions specified that we round to the nearest tenth, further rounding is not necessary. An American man born in 2020 will have a life expectancy of approximately 77.5 years.

○

 Use the data for the women in Figure 1.4 to estimate each of the following:

a. a woman's increased life expectancy, rounded to the nearest hundredth of a year, for each subsequent birth year

b. the life expectancy, to the nearest tenth of a year, of a woman born in 2050.

· ●

Line graphs are often used to illustrate trends over time. Some measure of time, such as months or years, frequently appears on the horizontal axis. Amounts are generally listed on the vertical axis. Points are drawn to represent the given information. The graph is formed by connecting the points with line segments.

Figure 1.5 is an example of a typical line graph. The graph shows the average age at which women in the United States married for the first time from 1890 through 2003. The years are listed on the horizontal axis and the ages are listed on the vertical axis. The symbol ⌇ on the vertical axis shows that there is a break in values between 0 and 20. Thus, the first tick mark on the vertical axis represents an average age of 20.

Figure 1.5 shows how to find the average age at which women married for the first time in 1980.

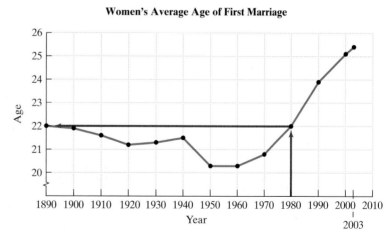

FIGURE 1.5
Source: U.S. Census Bureau

Step 1. Locate 1980 on the horizontal axis.

Step 2. Locate the point on the line graph above 1980.

Step 3. Read across to the corresponding age on the vertical axis.

The age is 22. Thus, in 1980, women in the United States married for the first time at an average age of 22.

EXAMPLE 7   USING A LINE GRAPH

We live in an era of democratic aspirations. The number of democracies worldwide is on the rise. The line graph in Figure 1.6 shows the number of democracies worldwide, in four-year periods, from 1973 through 2001, including 2002.

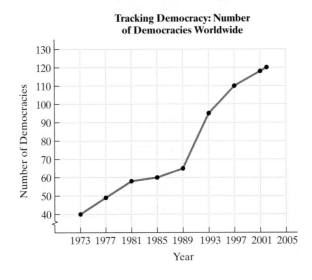

FIGURE 1.6

Source: The Freedom House

a. Find an estimate for the number of democracies in 1989.

b. In which four-year period did the number of democracies increase at the greatest rate?

c. In which year were there 110 democracies?

SOLUTION

a. Estimating Democracies in 1989   b. Identifying the Period of the Greatest Rate of Increase   c. Identifying the Year when There Were 110 Democracies

Use the graph in Figure 1.6 to solve this exercise.

a. Find an estimate for the number of democracies in 2001.

b. In which four-year period did the number of democracies increase at the slowest rate?

c. In which year were there 49 democracies?

3 Develop mathematical models that estimate relationships between variables.

Mathematical Models

We have seen that American men born in 1950 have a life expectancy of 65.6 years, increasing by approximately 0.17 year for each subsequent birth year. We can use variables to express the life expectancy, E, for American men born x years after 1950.

Life expectancy for American men	is	life expectancy for a man born in 1950	plus	yearly increase in life expectancy	times the number of birth years after 1950.
E	$=$	65.6	$+$	$0.17x$	

A **formula** is a statement of equality that uses letters to express a relationship between two or more variables. Thus, $E = 65.6 + 0.17x$ is a formula describing life expectancy, E, for American men born x years after 1950. Be aware that this formula provides *estimates* of life expectancy, as shown in Table 1.2.

TABLE 1.2 COMPARING ACTUAL DATA WITH ESTIMATES GIVEN BY A FORMULA

Birth Year	Life Expectancy: Actual Data	Life Expectancy: Formula Estimate $E = 65.6 + 0.17x$
1950	65.6	$E = 65.6 + 0.17(0) = 65.6 + 0 = 65.6$
1960	66.6	$E = 65.6 + 0.17(10) = 65.6 + 1.7 = 67.3$
1970	67.1	$E = 65.6 + 0.17(20) = 65.6 + 3.4 = 69.0$
1980	70.0	$E = 65.6 + 0.17(30) = 65.6 + 5.1 = 70.7$
1990	71.8	$E = 65.6 + 0.17(40) = 65.6 + 6.8 = 72.4$
2000	74.3	$E = 65.6 + 0.17(50) = 65.6 + 8.5 = 74.1$
2002	74.5	$E = 65.6 + 0.17(52) = 65.6 + 8.84 = 74.44$

In each row, we substitute the number of years after 1950 for x. The best estimates occur in 1950, 1990, 2000, and 2002.

The process of finding formulas to describe real-world phenomena is called **mathematical modeling**. Such formulas, together with the meaning assigned to the variables, are called **mathematical models**. We often say that these formulas model, or describe, the relationships among the variables.

EXAMPLE 8   MODELING THE GRAYING OF AMERICA

The bar graph in Figure 1.7 gives the median age of the U.S. population in the indicated year. (The median age is the age in the middle when all the ages of the U.S. population are arranged from youngest to oldest. We'll have lots to say about the median in Chapter 12.)

a. Estimate the yearly increase in the median age of the U.S. population.

b. Write a mathematical model that estimates the median age, M, of the U.S. population x years after 1970.

c. Use the mathematical model from part (b) to predict the median age of the U.S. population in 2050.

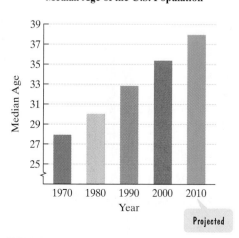

The Graying of America:
Median Age of the U.S. Population

FIGURE 1.7
Source: U.S. Census Bureau

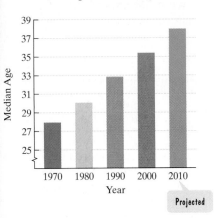

The Graying of America:
Median Age of the U.S. Population

FIGURE 1.7 (repeated)

SOLUTION

a. We can use the data from 1970 and 2010 to estimate the yearly increase in the median age. The blue bar representing 1970 extends approximately midway between 27 and 29, so the median age in 1970 was approximately 28. The green bar representing 2010 extends approximately midway between 37 and 39, so the median age in 2010 will be approximately 38.

$$\underbrace{\text{Yearly increase in the median age}}\ \underbrace{\text{is approximately}}\ \underbrace{\frac{\text{change in the median age from 1970 to 2010}}{\text{change in time from 1970 to 2010}}}.$$

$$\approx \frac{38 - 28}{2010 - 1970}$$

$$= \frac{10}{40} = \frac{1}{4} = 0.25$$

Each year the median age of the U.S. population is increasing by approximately 0.25 year.

b. Now we use variables to obtain a mathematical model that estimates the median age, M, x years after 1970.

$$\underbrace{\text{The median age of the U.S. population}}_{M}\ \underbrace{\text{is}}_{=}\ \underbrace{\text{the median age in 1970}}_{28}\ \underbrace{\text{plus}}_{+}\ \underbrace{\text{yearly increase in median age}}\ \underbrace{\text{times the number of years after 1970.}}_{0.25x}$$

The mathematical model $M = 28 + 0.25x$ estimates the median age, M, of the U.S. population x years after 1970.

c. Now let's use this mathematical model to predict the median age in 2050. Because 2050 is 80 years after 1970 ($2050 - 1970 = 80$), we substitute 80 for x.

$M = 28 + 0.25x$ This is the mathematical model from part (b).

$M = 28 + 0.25(80)$ Substitute 80 for x.

$\quad = 28 + 20$ Multiply: 0.25(80) = 20.

$\quad = 48$ Add. On a calculator, enter 28 $\boxed{+}$ .25 $\boxed{\times}$ 80 and press $\boxed{=}$ or $\boxed{\text{ENTER}}$.

Our model predicts that the median age of the U.S. population in 2050 will be 48.

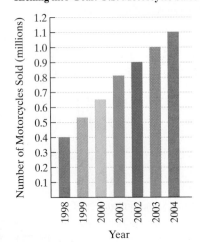

Kicking into Gear: U.S. Motorcycle Sales

FIGURE 1.8
Source: Motorcycle Industry Council

CHECK POINT 8 Talk about a booming business cycle: TV's *American Chopper* is the hottest thing since *Easy Rider* and motorcycles are selling faster than they have in a generation. The bar graph in Figure 1.8 shows the number of motorcycles sold in the United States, in millions, from 1998 through 2004.

a. Estimate the yearly increase, in millions, in the number of motorcycles sold. Round to the nearest hundredth of a million.

b. Write a mathematical model that estimates the number of motorcycles sold in the United States, M, in millions, x years after 1998.

c. Use the mathematical model from part (b) to predict motorcycle sales, to the nearest tenth of a million, in 2013.

Sometimes a mathematical model gives an estimate that is not a good approximation or is extended to include values of the variable that do not make sense. In these cases, we say that **model breakdown** has occurred.

EXERCISE SET 1.2 ●●●●●●

• Practice Exercises

1. According to the U.S. Census Bureau, 47,451,875 Americans speak a language other than English at home. Round this number to the nearest, **a.** hundred, **b.** thousand, **c.** ten thousand, **d.** hundred thousand, **e.** million, **f.** ten million.

2. According to the U.S. Bureau of Justice, there were 2,161,580 prisoners in the United States in 2004. Round this number to the nearest **a.** hundred, **b.** thousand, **c.** ten thousand, **d.** hundred thousand, **e.** million.

> *Pi goes on and on and on …*
> *And e is just as cursed.*
> *I wonder: Which is larger*
> *When their digits are reversed?*
>
> *Martin Gardner*

Although most people are familiar with π, the number e is more significant in mathematics, showing up in problems involving population growth and compound interest, and at the heart of the statistical bell curve. One way to think of e is the dollar amount you would have in a savings account at the end of the year if you invested $1 at the beginning of the year and the bank paid an annual interest rate of 100% compounded continuously (compounding interest every trillionth of a second, every quadrillionth of a second, etc.). Although continuous compounding sounds terrific, at the end of the year your $1 would have grown to a mere $e, or $2.72, rounded to the nearest cent. Here is a better approximation for e.

$$e \approx 2.718281828459045$$

In Exercises 3–8, use this approximation to round e as specified.

3. to the nearest thousandth
4. to the nearest ten-thousandth
5. to the nearest hundred-thousandth
6. to the nearest millionth
7. to nine decimal places
8. to ten decimal places

In Exercises 9–34, because different rounding results in different estimates, there is not one single, correct answer to each exercise.

In Exercises 9–22, obtain an estimate for each computation by rounding the numbers so that the resulting arithmetic can easily be performed by hand or in your head. Then use a calculator to perform the computation. How reasonable is your estimate when compared to the actual answer?

9. $359 + 596$
10. $248 + 797$
11. $8.93 + 1.04 + 19.26$
12. $7.92 + 3.06 + 24.36$
13. $32.15 - 11.239$
14. $46.13 - 15.237$
15. 39.67×5.5
16. 78.92×6.5
17. 0.79×414
18. 0.67×211
19. $47.83 \div 2.9$
20. $54.63 \div 4.7$
21. 32% of 187,253
22. 42% of 291,506

In Exercises 23–34, determine each estimate without using a calculator. Then use a calculator to perform the computation necessary to obtain an exact answer. How reasonable is your estimate when compared to the actual answer?

23. Estimate the total cost of six grocery items if their prices are $3.47, $5.89, $19.98, $2.03, $11.85, and $0.23.

24. Estimate the total cost of six grocery items if their prices are $4.23, $7.79, $28.97, $4.06, $13.43, and $0.74.

25. A full-time employee who works 40 hours per week earns $19.50 per hour. Estimate that person's annual income.

26. A full-time employee who works 40 hours per week earns $29.85 per hour. Estimate that person's annual income.

27. You lease a car at $605 per month for 3 years. Estimate the total cost of the lease.

28. You lease a car at $415 per month for 4 years. Estimate the total cost of the lease.

29. A raise of $310,000 is evenly distributed among 294 professors. Estimate the amount each professor receives.

30. A raise of $310,000 is evenly distributed among 196 professors. Estimate the amount each professor receives.

31. If a person who works 40 hours per week earns $61,500 per year, estimate that person's hourly wage.

32. If a person who works 40 hours per week earns $38,950 per year, estimate that person's hourly wage.

33. The average life expectancy in Canada is 80.1 years. Estimate the country's life expectancy in hours.

34. The average life expectancy in Mozambique is 40.3 years. Estimate the country's life expectancy in hours.

• Practice Plus

In Exercises 35–36, obtain an estimate for each computation without using a calculator. Then use a calculator to perform the computation. How reasonable is your estimate when compared to the actual answer?

35. $\dfrac{0.19996 \times 107}{0.509}$

36. $\dfrac{0.47996 \times 88}{0.249}$

37. Ten people ordered calculators. The least expensive was $19.95 and the most expensive was $39.95. Half ordered a $29.95 calculator. Select the best estimate of the amount spent on calculators.

 a. $240 **b.** $310 **c.** $345 **d.** $355

38. Ten people ordered calculators. The least expensive was $4.95 and the most expensive was $12.95. Half ordered a $6.95 calculator. Select the best estimate of the amount spent on calculators.

 a. $160 **b.** $105 **c.** $75 **d.** $55

39. Traveling at an average rate of between 60 and 70 miles per hour for 3 to 4 hours, select the best estimate for the distance traveled.

 a. 90 miles **b.** 190 miles
 c. 225 miles **d.** 275 miles

40. Traveling at an average rate of between 40 and 50 miles per hour for 3 to 4 hours, select the best estimate for the distance traveled.

 a. 120 miles **b.** 160 miles
 c. 195 miles **d.** 210 miles

41. Imagine that you counted 60 numbers per minute and continued to count nonstop until you reached 10,000. Determine a reasonable estimate of the number of hours it would take you to complete the counting.

42. Imagine that you counted 60 numbers per minute and continued to count nonstop until you reached one million. Determine a reasonable estimate of the number of days it would take you to complete the counting.

• Application Exercises

The circle graph shows the percentage of the 221,730,462 American adults who drink caffeinated beverages on a daily basis and the number of cups consumed per day. Use this information to solve Exercises 43–44.

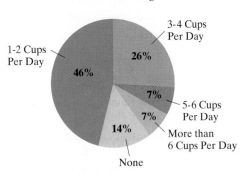

A Wired Nation: Percentage of American Adults Drinking Caffeinated Beverages

Source: Harris Interactive

43. Without using a calculator, estimate the number of American adults who drink from one to two cups of caffeinated beverages per day.

44. Without using a calculator, estimate the number of American adults who drink from three to four cups of caffeinated beverages per day.

An online test of English spelling looked at how well people spelled difficult words. The bar graph shows how many people per 100 spelled each word correctly. Use this information to solve Exercises 45–46.

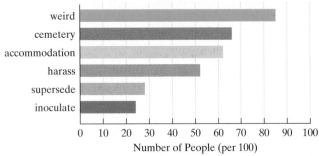

Number of People per 100 Spelling Various Words Correctly

Source: Vivian Cook, *Accomodating Brocolli in the Cemetary or Why Can't Anybody Spell?*, Simon and Schuster, 2004

45. a. Estimate the number of people per 100 who spelled *weird* correctly.

  b. In a group consisting of 8729 randomly selected people, estimate how many more people can correctly spell *weird* than *inoculate*.

46. a. Estimate the number of people per 100 who spelled *cemetery* correctly.

  b. In a group consisting of 7219 randomly selected people, estimate how many more people can correctly spell *cemetery* than *supersede*.

The bar graph shows the average amount that U.S. consumers spent on four pieces of the entertainment pie from 2002 through 2004. Use this information to solve Exercises 47–48.

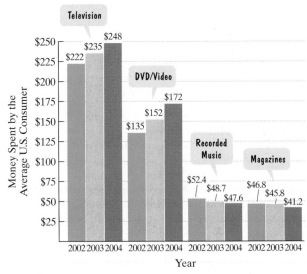

Average Amount U.S. Consumers Spent on Entertainment

Source: Veronis, Suhler, Stevenson, *Communications Industry Forecast and Report*

47. Use the data shown for television (broadcast, cable, and satellite) to estimate each of the following:

  a. the average yearly increase in the amount U.S. consumers spent on television

  b. the amount U.S. consumers will spend on television in 2010.

48. Use the data shown for DVDs and videos to estimate each of the following:

  a. the average yearly increase in the amount U.S. consumers spent on DVDs and videos

  b. the amount U.S. consumers will spend on DVDs and videos in 2010.

The line graph shows cigarette consumption per U.S. adult from 1910 through 2004. Use this information to solve Exercises 49–50.

Cigarette Consumption per U.S. Adult

Source: U.S. Department of Health and Human Services

49. a. For the period shown, in which year was cigarette consumption at a maximum? Find a reasonable estimate of consumption for that year.

   b. In which ten-year period did cigarette consumption increase at the greatest rate?

   c. In which year was cigarette consumption approximately 1500 cigarettes per adult?

50. a. For the period shown, in which year was cigarette consumption at a minimum? Find a reasonable estimate of consumption for that year.

   b. In which ten-year period did cigarette consumption decrease at the greatest rate?

   c. In which year was cigarette consumption approximately 700 cigarettes per adult?

51. The bar graph shows the average cost of tuition and fees at private four-year U.S. colleges.

Average Cost of Tuition and Fees at Private Four-Year U.S. Colleges

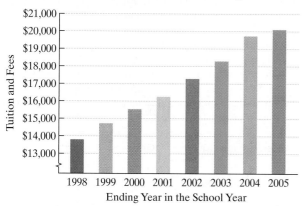

Source: The College Board

   a. Estimate the yearly increase in tuition and fees.

   b. Write a mathematical model that estimates the average cost, C, of tuition and fees at private four-year U.S. colleges for the school year ending x years after 1998.

   c. Use the mathematical model from part (b) to predict the average cost of tuition and fees in 2012.

52. The bar graph shows the average cost of tuition and fees at public four-year U.S. colleges.

Average Cost of Tuition and Fees at Public Four-Year U.S. Colleges

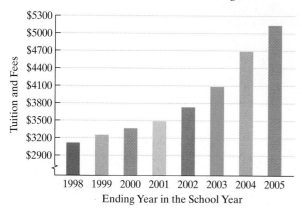

Source: The College Board

   a. Estimate the yearly increase in tuition and fees.

   b. Write a mathematical model that estimates the average cost, C, of tuition and fees at public four-year U.S. colleges for the school year ending x years after 1998.

   c. Use the mathematical model from part (b) to predict the average cost of tuition and fees in 2012.

• Writing in Mathematics

53. What is estimation? When is it helpful to use estimation?

54. Explain how to round 218,543 to the nearest thousand and to the nearest hundred thousand.

55. Explain how to round 14.26841 to the nearest hundredth and to the nearest thousandth.

56. What does the $\approx$ symbol mean?

57. In this era of calculators and computers, why is there a need to develop estimation skills?

58. Describe a circle graph.

59. Describe a bar graph.

60. Describe a line graph.

61. What does it mean when we say that a formula models real-world phenomena?

62. In 2000, there were 39.8 million Americans without health insurance. This number has increased by approximately 1.7 million people per year. Describe how to use this information to write a mathematical model that describes the number of Americans without health insurance, N, in millions, x years after 2000.

63. Explain how to use the mathematical model from Exercise 62 to predict how many Americans will not have health insurance in 2010. Describe one event that could occur in the future that would make this prediction highly inaccurate.

64. Describe one way in which you use estimation in a nonacademic area of your life.

65. A forecaster at the National Hurricane Center needs to estimate the time until a hurricane with high probability of striking South Florida will hit Miami. Is it better to overestimate or underestimate? Explain your answer.

• Critical Thinking Exercises

66. Take a moment to read the verse preceding Exercises 3–8 that mentions the numbers π and e, whose decimal representations continue infinitely with no repeating patterns. The verse was written by the American mathematician (and accomplished amateur magician!) Martin Gardner (1914–), author of more than 60 books, and best known for his "Mathematical Games" column, which ran in *Scientific American* for 25 years. Explain the humor in Gardner's question.

In Exercises 67–70, match the story with the correct graph. The graphs are labeled (a), (b), (c), and (d).

67. As the blizzard got worse, the snow fell harder and harder.

68. The snow fell more and more softly.

69. It snowed hard, but then it stopped. After a short time, the snow started falling softly.

70. It snowed softly, and then it stopped. After a short time, the snow started falling hard.

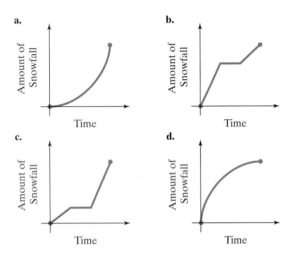

a.

b.

c.

d.

71. American children ages 2 to 17 spend 19 hours 40 minutes per week watching television.

(*Source:* TV-Turnoff Network)

From ages 2 through 17, inclusive, estimate the number of days an American child spends watching television. How many years, to the nearest tenth of a year, is that?

72. If you spend $1000 each day, estimate how long it will take to spend a billion dollars.

• Group Exercises

73. Group members should devise an estimation process that can be used to answer each of the following questions. Use input from all group members to describe the best estimation process possible.

  a. Is it possible to walk from San Francisco to New York in a year?

  b. How much money is spent on ice cream in the United States each year?

74. Group members should begin by consulting an almanac, newspaper, magazine, or the Internet to find two graphs that show "intriguing" data changing from year to year. In one graph, the data values should be increasing relatively steadily. In the second graph, the data values should be decreasing relatively steadily. For each graph selected, write a mathematical model that estimates the changing variable x years after the graph's starting date. Then use each mathematical model to make predictions about what might occur in the future. Are there circumstances that might affect the accuracy of the prediction? List some of these circumstances.

SECTION 1.3 • PROBLEM SOLVING

OBJECTIVE

1. Solve problems using the organization of the four-step problem-solving process.

1 Solve problems using the organization of the four-step problem-solving process.

Critical thinking and problem solving are essential skills in both school and work. A model for problem solving was established by the charismatic teacher and mathematician George Polya (1887–1985) in *How to Solve It* (Princeton University Press, Princeton, N.J., 1957). This book, first published in 1945, has sold more than 1 million copies and is available in 17 languages. Using a four-step procedure for problem solving, Polya's book demonstrates how to think clearly in any field.

Problem solving can be thought of in terms of Polya's four steps. Think of these steps as guidelines that will help you organize the process of problem solving, rather than a list of rigid rules that need to be memorized. You may be able to solve certain problems without thinking about or using every step in the four-step process.

POLYA'S FOUR STEPS IN PROBLEM SOLVING

Step 1. Understand the problem. Read the problem several times. The first reading can serve as an overview. In the second reading, write down what information is given and determine exactly what it is that the problem requires you to find.

Step 2. Devise a plan. The plan for solving the problem might involve one or more of these suggested problem-solving strategies:

- Use inductive reasoning to look for a pattern.
- Make a systematic list or a table.
- Use estimation to make an educated guess at the solution. Check the guess against the problem's conditions and work backward to eventually determine the solution.
- Try expressing the problem more simply and solve a similar simpler problem.
- Use trial and error.
- List the given information in a chart or table.
- Try making a sketch or a diagram to illustrate the problem.
- Relate the problem to a similar problem that you have seen before. Try applying the procedures used to solve the similar problem to the new one.
- Look for a "catch" if the answer seems too obvious. Perhaps the problem involves some sort of trick question deliberately intended to lead the problem solver in the wrong direction.
- Use the given information to eliminate possibilities.
- Use common sense.

Step 3. Carry out the plan and solve the problem.

Step 4. Look back and check the answer. The answer should satisfy the conditions of the problem. The answer should make sense and be reasonable. If this is not the case, recheck the method and any calculations. Perhaps there is an alternate way to arrive at a correct solution.

The very first step in problem solving involves evaluating the given information in a deliberate manner. Is there enough given to solve the problem? Is the information relevant to the problem's solution or are some facts not necessary to arrive at a solution?

"If you don't know where you're going, you'll probably end up some place else."

YOGI BERRA

EXAMPLE 1   FINDING WHAT IS MISSING

Which necessary piece of information is missing and prevents you from solving the following problem?

> A man purchased five shirts, each at the same discount price. How much did he pay for them?

SOLUTION

Step 1. Understand the problem. Here's what is given:

> Number of shirts purchased: 5.

We must find how much the man paid for the five shirts.

Step 2. Devise a plan. The amount that the man paid for the five shirts is the number of shirts, 5, times the cost of each shirt. The discount price of each shirt is not given. This missing piece of information makes it impossible to solve the problem.

 Which necessary piece of information is missing and prevents you from solving the following problem?

> The bill for your meal totaled $20.36, including the tax. How much change should you receive from the cashier?

EXAMPLE 2   FINDING WHAT IS UNNECESSARY

In the following problem, one more piece of information is given than is necessary for solving the problem. Identify this unnecessary piece of information. Then solve the problem.

> A roll of E-Z Wipe paper towels contains 100 sheets and costs $1.38. A comparable brand, Kwik-Clean, contains five dozen sheets per roll and costs $1.23. If you need three rolls of paper towels, which brand is the better value?

SOLUTION

Step 1. Understand the problem. Here's what is given:

E-Z Wipe: 100 sheets per roll; $1.38

Kwik-Clean: 5 dozen sheets per roll; $1.23

Needed: 3 rolls.

We must determine which brand offers the better value.

Step 2. Devise a plan. The brand with the better value is the one that has the lower price per sheet. Thus, we can compare the two brands by finding the cost for one sheet of E-Z Wipe and one sheet of Kwik-Clean. The price per sheet, or the *unit price*, is the price of a roll divided by the number of sheets in the roll. The fact that three rolls are required is not relevant to the problem. This unnecessary piece of information is not needed to find which brand is the better value.

Step 3. Carry out the plan and solve the problem.

E-Z Wipe:
$$\text{price per sheet} = \frac{\text{price of a roll}}{\text{number of sheets per roll}}$$
$$= \frac{\$1.38}{100 \text{ sheets}} = \$0.0138 \approx \$0.01$$

Kwik-Clean:
$$\text{price per sheet} = \frac{\text{price of a roll}}{\text{number of sheets per roll}}$$
$$= \frac{\$1.23}{60 \text{ sheets}} = \$0.0205 \approx \$0.02$$

> 5 dozen = 5 × 12, or 60 sheets

By comparing unit prices, we see that E-Z Wipe, at approximately $0.01 per sheet, is the better value.

Step 4. Look back and check the answer. We can double-check the arithmetic in each of our unit-price computations. We can also see if these unit prices satisfy the problem's conditions. The product of each brand's price per sheet and the number of sheets per roll should result in the given price for a roll.

E-Z Wipe: Check $0.0138   Kwik-Clean: Check $0.0205

$0.0138 × 100 = $1.38 $0.0205 × 60 = $1.23

> These are the given prices for a roll of each respective brand.

The unit prices satisfy the problem's conditions.

Unit Prices and Sneaky Pricejacks

In *200% of Nothing* (John Wiley & Sons, 1993), author A. K. Dewdney writes, "It must be something of a corporate dream come true when a company charges more for a product and no one notices." He gives two examples of "sneaky price-jacks," both easily detected using unit prices. The manufacturers of Mennen Speed Stick deodorant increased the size of the package that held the stick, left the price the same, and reduced the amount of actual deodorant in the stick from 2.5 ounces to 2.25. Fabergé's Brut left the price and size of its cologne jar the same, but reduced its contents from 5 ounces to 4. Surprisingly, the new jar read, "Now, more Brut!" *Consumer Reports* contacted Fabergé to see how this could be possible. Their response: The new jar contained "more fragrance." *Consumer Reports* moaned, "Et tu Brut?"

A generalization of our work in Example 2 allows you to compare different brands and make a choice between various products of different sizes. When shopping at the supermarket, a useful number to keep in mind is a product's *unit price*. The **unit price** is the total price divided by the total units. Among comparable brands, the best value is the product with the lowest unit price, assuming that the units are kept uniform.

The word *per* is used to state unit prices. For example, if a 12-ounce box of cereal sells for $3.00, its unit price is determined as follows:

$$\text{Unit price} = \frac{\text{total price}}{\text{total units}} = \frac{\$3.00}{12 \text{ ounces}} = \$0.25 \text{ per ounce}.$$

 Solve the following problem. If the problem contains information that is not relevant to its solution, identify this unnecessary piece of information.

> A manufacturer packages its apple juice in bottles and boxes. A 128-ounce bottle costs $5.39 and a 9-pack of 6.75-ounce boxes costs $3.15. Which packaging option is the better value?

EXAMPLE 3   APPLYING THE FOUR-STEP PROCEDURE

By paying $100 cash up front and the balance at $20 a week, how long will it take to pay for a bicycle costing $680?

SOLUTION

Step 1. Understand the problem. Here's what is given:

Cost of the bicycle: $680

Amount paid in cash: $100

Weekly payments: $20.

If necessary, consult a dictionary to look up any unfamiliar words. The word *balance* means the amount still to be paid. We must find the balance to determine the number of weeks required to pay off the bicycle.

Step 2. Devise a plan. Subtract the amount paid in cash from the cost of the bicycle. This results in the amount still to be paid. Because weekly payments are $20, divide the amount still to be paid by 20. This will give the number of weeks required to pay for the bicycle.

Step 3. Carry out the plan and solve the problem. Begin by finding the balance, the amount still to be paid for the bicycle.

$$
\begin{array}{rl}
\$680 & \text{\textit{cost of the bicycle}} \\
-\$100 & \text{\textit{amount paid in cash}} \\
\hline
\$580 & \text{\textit{amount still to be paid}}
\end{array}
$$

Now divide the $580 balance by $20, the payment per week. The result of the division is the number of weeks needed to pay off the bicycle.

$$\frac{\dfrac{\$580}{\$20}}{\text{week}} = \$580 \times \frac{\text{week}}{\$20} = \frac{580 \text{ weeks}}{20} = 29 \text{ weeks}$$

It will take 29 weeks to pay for the bicycle.

STUDY TIP

An effective way to see if you understand a problem is to restate the problem in your own words.

Step 4. Look back and check the answer. We can certainly double-check the arithmetic either by hand or with a calculator. We can also see if the answer, 29 weeks to pay for the bicycle, satisfies the condition that the bicycle costs $680.

This is the answer we are checking.		
$20	weekly payment	$580	total of weekly payments
× 29	number of weeks	+$100	amount paid in cash
$580	total of weekly payments	$680	cost of bicycle

The answer of 29 weeks satisfies the condition that the cost of the bicycle is $680.

 By paying $350 cash up front and the balance at $45 per month, how long will it take to pay for a computer costing $980?

Making lists is a useful strategy in problem solving.

EXAMPLE 4   SOLVING A PROBLEM BY MAKING A LIST

Suppose you are an engineer programming the automatic gate for a 50-cent toll. The gate should accept exact change only. It should not accept pennies. How many coin combinations must you program the gate to accept?

SOLUTION

Step 1. Understand the problem. The total change must always be 50 cents. One possible coin combination is two quarters. Another is five dimes. We need to count all such combinations.

Step 2. Devise a plan. Make a list of all possible coin combinations. Begin with the coins of larger value and work toward the coins of smaller value.

Step 3. Carry out the plan and solve the problem. First we must find all of the coins that are not pennies but can combine to form 50 cents. This includes half-dollars, quarters, dimes, and nickels. Now we can set up a table. We will use these coins as table headings.

Half-Dollars	Quarters	Dimes	Nickels

Each row in the table will represent one possible combination for exact change. We start with the largest coin, the half-dollar. Only one half-dollar is needed to make exact change. No other coins are needed. Thus, we put a 1 in the half-dollars column and 0 in the other columns to represent the first possible combination.

Half-Dollars	Quarters	Dimes	Nickels
1	0	0	0

Likewise, two quarters are also exact change for 50 cents. We put a 0 in the half-dollars column, a 2 in the quarters column, and 0s in the columns for dimes and nickels.

Half-Dollars	Quarters	Dimes	Nickels
1	0	0	0
0	2	0	0

In this manner, we can find all possible combinations for exact change for the 50-cent toll. These combinations are shown in Table 1.3.

TABLE 1.3 EXACT CHANGE FOR 50 CENTS: NO PENNIES			
Half-Dollars	**Quarters**	**Dimes**	**Nickels**
1	0	0	0
0	2	0	0
0	1	2	1
0	1	1	3
0	1	0	5
0	0	5	0
0	0	4	2
0	0	3	4
0	0	2	6
0	0	1	8
0	0	0	10

Count the coin combinations shown in Table 1.3. How many coin combinations must the gate accept? You must program the gate to accept 11 coin combinations.

Step 4. Look back and check the answer. Double-check Table 1.3 to make sure that no possible combinations have been omitted and that the total in each row is 50 cents. Double-check your count of the number of combinations.

CHECK POINT

4 Suppose you are an engineer programming the automatic gate for a 30-cent toll. The gate should accept exact change only. It should not accept pennies. How many coin combinations must you program the gate to accept?

Sketches and diagrams are sometimes useful in problem solving.

EXAMPLE 5   SOLVING A PROBLEM BY USING A DIAGRAM

Four runners are in a one-mile race: Maria, Aretha, Thelma, and Debbie. Points are awarded only to the women finishing first or second. The first-place winner gets more points than the second-place winner. How many different arrangements of first- and second-place winners are possible?

SOLUTION

Step 1. Understand the problem. Three possibilities for first and second position are

Maria-Aretha

Maria-Thelma

Aretha-Maria.

Notice that Maria finishing first and Aretha finishing second is a different outcome than Aretha finishing first and Maria finishing second. Order makes a difference because the first-place winner gets more points than the second-place winner. We must count all possibilities for first and second position.

Step 2. Devise a plan. If Maria finishes first, then each of the other three runners could finish second:

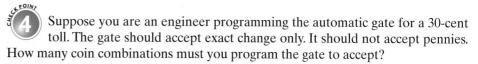

First place	**Second place**	**Possibilities for first and second place**
Maria	Aretha	Maria-Aretha
	Thelma	Maria-Thelma
	Debbie	Maria-Debbie

Similarly, we can list each woman as the possible first-place runner. Then we will list the other three women as possible second-place runners. Next we will determine the possibilities for first and second place. This diagram will show how the runners can finish first or second.

Step 3. Carry out the plan and solve the problem. Now we complete the diagram started in step 2. The diagram is shown in Figure 1.9.

First place	Second place	Possibilities for first and second place
Maria	Aretha Thelma Debbie	Maria-Aretha Maria-Thelma Maria-Debbie
Aretha	Maria Thelma Debbie	Aretha-Maria Aretha-Thelma Aretha-Debbie
Thelma	Maria Aretha Debbie	Thelma-Maria Thelma-Aretha Thelma-Debbie
Debbie	Maria Aretha Thelma	Debbie-Maria Debbie-Aretha Debbie-Thelma

> Because of the way Figure 1.9 branches from first to second place, it is called a **tree diagram**. We will be using tree diagrams in Chapter 11 as a problem-solving tool in the study of uncertainty and probability.

FIGURE 1.9 Possible ways for four runners to finish first and second

Count the number of possibilities shown under the third column, "Possibilities for first and second place." Can you see that there are 12 possibilities? Therefore, 12 different arrangements of first- and second-place winners are possible.

Step 4. Look back and check the answer. Check the diagram in Figure 1.9 to make sure that no possible first- and second-place outcomes have been left out. Double-check your count for the winning pairs of runners.

CHECK POINT 5 Your "lecture wardrobe" is rather limited—just two pairs of jeans to choose from (one blue, one black) and three T-shirts to choose from (one beige, one yellow, and one blue). How many different outfits can you form?

In Chapter 15, we will be studying diagrams, called *graphs*, that provide structures for describing relationships. In Example 6, we use such a diagram to illustrate the relationship between cities and their one-way airfares.

EXAMPLE 6 USING A REASONABLE OPTION TO SOLVE A PROBLEM WITH MORE THAN ONE SOLUTION

A sales director who lives in city A is required to fly to regional offices in cities B, C, D, and E. Other than starting and ending the trip in city A, there are no restrictions as to the order in which the other three cities are visited.

The one-way fares between each of the four cities are given in Table 1.4. A diagram that illustrates this information is shown in Figure 1.10.

TABLE 1.4 ONE-WAY AIRFARES

	A	B	C	D	E
A	*	$180	$114	$147	$128
B	$180	*	$116	$145	$195
C	$114	$116	*	$169	$115
D	$147	$145	$169	*	$194
E	$128	$195	$115	$194	*

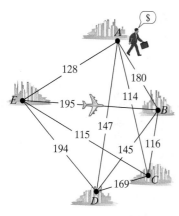

FIGURE 1.10

Give the sales director an order for visiting cities B, C, D, and E once, returning home to city A, for less than $750.

SOLUTION

Step 1. Understand the problem. There are many ways to visit cities B, C, D, and E once, and return home to A. One route is

$$A, E, D, C, B, A.$$ \[Fly from A to E to D to C to B and then back to A.\]

The cost of this trip involves the sum of five costs, shown in both Table 1.4 and Figure 1.10:

$$\$128 + \$194 + \$169 + \$116 + \$180 = \$787.$$

We must find a route that costs less than $750.

Step 2. Devise a plan. The sales director starts at city A. From there, fly to the city to which the airfare is cheapest. Then from there fly to the next city to which the airfare is cheapest, and so on. From the last of the cities, fly home to city A. Compute the cost of this trip to see if it is less than $750. If it is not, use trial and error to find other possible routes and select an order (if there is one) whose cost is less than $750.

Step 3. Carry out the plan and solve the problem. See Figure 1.11. The route is indicated using red lines with arrows.

- Start at A.
- Choose the line segment with the smallest number: 114. Fly from A to C. (cost: $114)
- From C, choose the line segment with the smallest number that does not lead to A: 115. Fly from C to E. (cost: $115)
- From E, choose the line segment with the smallest number that does not lead to a city already visited: 194. Fly from E to D. (cost: $194)
- From D, there is little choice but to fly to B, the only city not yet visited. (cost: $145)
- From B, return home to A. (cost: $180)

The route that we are considering is

$$A, C, E, D, B, A.$$

Let's see if the cost is less than $750. The cost is

$$\$114 + \$115 + \$194 + \$145 + \$180 = \$748.$$

Because the cost is less than $750, the sales director can follow the order A, C, E, D, B, A.

Step 4. Look back and check the answer. Use Table 1.4 or Figure 1.11 to verify that the five numbers used in the sum shown above are correct. Use estimation to verify that $748 is a reasonable cost for the trip.

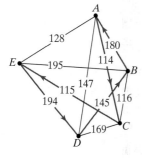

FIGURE 1.11

CHECK POINT 6 As in Example 6, a sales director who lives in city A is required to fly to regional offices in cities B, C, D, and E. The diagram in Figure 1.12 shows the one-way airfares between any two cities. Give the sales director an order for visiting cities B, C, D, and E once, returning home to city A, for less than $1460.

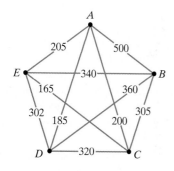

FIGURE 1.12

BLITZER BONUS

Trick Questions: Thinking Outside the Box

Problem: Use line four segments to connect all nine dots, touching each dot exactly once with your pencil point, without lifting the pencil from the paper.

Incorrect Attempts

A Correct Solution

End

Start

When people attempt to solve this problem, a mental set causes them to think of the dots as representing a box. As shown by the correct solution, it's necessary to draw the lines to extend out of the box of dots—literally "thinking outside the box."
(*Source*: Saundra K. Ciccarelli and Glenn E. Meyer, *Psychology*, Prentice Hall, 2006)

Trick questions require you to think carefully before answering. Unless you think outside the box, you'll be duped by some sort of trick or catch.

Sample: Do they have a fourth of July in England?
Answer: Of course they do. However, there is no national holiday on that date!

See if you can answer the questions that follow without developing mental whiplash. The answers appear in the answer section.

1. A farmer had 17 sheep. All but 12 died. How many sheep does the farmer have left?

2. Some months have 30 days. Some have 31. How many months have 28 days?

3. A doctor had a brother, but this brother had no brothers. What was the relationship between doctor and brother?

4. If you had only one match and entered a log cabin in which there was a candle, a fireplace, and a woodburning stove, which should you light first?

EXERCISE SET 1.3 ●●●●●●

Everyone can become a better, more confident problem solver. As in learning any other skill, learning problem solving requires hard work and patience. Work as many problems as possible in this exercise set. You may feel confused once in a while, but do not be discouraged. Thinking about a particular problem and trying different methods can eventually lead to new insights. Be sure to check over each answer carefully!

• Practice and Application Exercises

In Exercises 1–4, what necessary piece of information is missing that prevents solving the problem?

1. If a student saves $35 per week, how long will it take to save enough money to buy a computer?

2. If a steak sells for $8.15, what is the cost per pound?

3. If it takes you four minutes to read a page in a book, how many words can you read in one minute?

4. By paying $1500 cash and the balance in equal monthly payments, how many months would it take to pay for a car costing $12,495?

In Exercises 5–8, one more piece of information is given than is necessary for solving the problem. Identify this unnecessary piece of information. Then solve the problem.

5. A salesperson receives a weekly salary of $350. In addition, $15 is paid for every item sold in excess of 200 items. How much extra is received from the sale of 212 items?

6. You have $250 to spend and you need to purchase four new tires. If each tire weighs 21 pounds and costs $42 plus $2.50 tax, how much money will you have left after buying the tires?

7. A parking garage charges $2.50 for the first hour and $0.50 for each additional hour. If a customer gave the parking attendant $20.00 for parking from 10 A.M. to 3 P.M., how much did the garage charge?

8. An architect is designing a house. The scale on the plan is 1 inch = 6 feet. If the house is to have a length of 90 feet and a width of 30 feet, how long will the line representing the house's length be on the blueprint?

Use Polya's four-step method in problem solving to solve Exercises 9–40.

9. **a.** Which is the better value: a 15.3-ounce box of cereal for $3.37 or a 24-ounce box of cereal for $4.59?

   b. The supermarket displays the unit price for the 15.3-ounce box in terms of cost per ounce, but displays the unit price for the 24-ounce box in terms of cost per pound. What are the unit prices, to the nearest cent, given by the supermarket?

   c. Based on your work in parts (a) and (b), does the better value always have the lower displayed unit price? Explain your answer.

10. a. Which is the better value: a 12-ounce jar of honey for $2.25 or an 18-ounce jar of honey for $3.24?

    b. The supermarket displays the unit price for the 12-ounce jar in terms of cost per ounce, but displays the unit price for the 18-ounce jar in terms of cost per quart. Assuming 32 ounces in a quart, what are the unit prices, to the nearest cent, given by the supermarket?

    c. Based on your work in parts (a) and (b), does the better value always have the lower displayed unit price? Explain your answer.

11. One person earns $48,000 per year. Another earns $3750 per month. How much more does the first person earn in a year than the second?

12. At the beginning of a year, the odometer on a car read 25,124 miles. At the end of the year, it read 37,364 miles. If the car averaged 24 miles per gallon, how many gallons of gasoline did it use during the year?

13. A television sells for $750. Instead of paying the total amount at the time of the purchase, the same television can be bought by paying $100 down and $50 a month for 14 months. How much is saved by paying the total amount at the time of the purchase?

14. In a basketball game, the Bulldogs scored 34 field goals, each counting 2 points, and 13 foul goals, each counting 1 point. The Panthers scored 38 field goals and 8 foul goals. Which team won? By how many points did it win?

15. Calculators were purchased at $65 per dozen and sold at $20 for three calculators. Find the profit on six dozen calculators.

16. Pens are bought at 95¢ per dozen and sold in groups of four for $2.25. Find the profit on 15 dozen pens.

17. Each day a small business owner sells 200 pizza slices at $1.50 per slice and 85 sandwiches at $2.50 each. If business expenses come to $60 per day, what is the owner's profit for a ten-day period?

18. A college tutoring center pays math tutors $5.15 per hour. Tutors earn an additional $1.20 per hour for each hour over 40 hours per week. A math tutor worked 42 hours one week and 45 hours the second week. How much did the tutor earn in this two-week period?

19. A car rents for $220 per week plus $0.25 per mile. Find the rental cost for a two-week trip of 500 miles for a group of three people.

20. A college graduate receives a salary of $2750 a month for her first job. During the year she plans to spend $4800 for rent, $8200 for food, $3750 for clothing, $4250 for household expenses, and $3000 for other expenses. With the money that is left, she expects to buy as many shares of stock at $375 per share as possible. How many shares will she be able to buy?

21. Charlene decided to ride her bike from her home to visit her friend Danny. Three miles away from home, her bike got a flat tire and she had to walk the remaining two miles to Danny's home. She could not repair the tire and had to walk all the way back home. How many more miles did Charlene walk than she rode?

22. A store received 200 containers of juice to be sold by April 1. Each container cost the store $0.75 and sold for $1.25. The store signed a contract with the manufacturer in which the manufacturer agreed to a $0.50 refund for every container not sold by April 1. If 150 containers were sold by April 1, how much profit did the store make?

23. A storeowner ordered 25 calculators that cost $30 each. The storeowner can sell each calculator for $35. The storeowner sold 22 calculators to customers. He had to return 3 calculators and pay a $2 charge for each returned calculator. Find the storeowner's profit.

24. New York City and Washington, D.C. are about 240 miles apart. A car leaves New York City at noon traveling directly south toward Washington, D.C. at 55 miles per hour. At the same time and along the same route, a second car leaves Washington, D.C. bound for New York City traveling directly north at 45 miles per hour. How far has each car traveled when the drivers meet for lunch at 2:24 P.M.?

25. An automobile purchased for $23,000 is worth $2700 after 7 years. Assuming that the car's value depreciated steadily from year to year, what was it worth at the end of the third year?

26. An automobile purchased for $34,800 is worth $8550 after 7 years. Assuming that the car's value depreciated steadily from year to year, what was it worth at the end of the third year?

27. A vending machine accepts nickels, dimes, and quarters. Exact change is needed to make a purchase. How many ways can a person with five nickels, three dimes, and two quarters make a 45-cent purchase from the machine?

28. How many ways can you make change for a quarter using only pennies, nickels, and dimes?

29. The members of the Student Activity Council on your campus are meeting to select two speakers for a month-long event celebrating artists and entertainers. The choices are Johnny Depp, Jamie Foxx, Jon Stewart, and Hilary Swank. How many different ways can the two speakers be selected?

30. The members of the Student Activity Council on your campus are meeting to select two speakers for a month-long event exploring why some people are most likely to succeed. The choices are Bill Clinton, Sean Combs, Donald Trump, Oprah Winfrey, and Tiger Woods. How many different ways can the two speakers be selected?

31. If you spend $4.79, in how many ways can you receive change from a five-dollar bill?

32. If you spend $9.74, in how many ways can you receive change from a ten-dollar bill?

33. You throw three darts at the board shown. Each dart hits the board and scores a 1, 5, or 10. How many different total scores can you make?

34. Suppose that you throw four darts at the board shown. With these four darts, there are 16 ways to hit four different numbers whose sum is 100. Describe one way you can hit four different numbers on the board that total 100.

35. Five housemates (A, B, C, D, and E) agreed to share the expenses of a party equally. If A spent $42, B spent $10, C spent $26, D spent $32, and E spent $30, who owes money after the party and how much do they owe? To whom is money owed and how much should they receive? In order to resolve these discrepancies, who should pay how much to whom?

36. Six houses are spaced equally around a circular road. If it takes 10 minutes to walk from the first house to the third house, how long would it take to walk all the way around the road?

37. If a test has four true/false questions, in how many ways can there be three answers that are false and one answer that is true?

38. There are five people in a room. Each person shakes the hand of every other person exactly once. How many handshakes are exchanged?

39. Five runners, Andy, Beth, Caleb, Darnell, and Ella, are in a one-mile race. Andy finished the race seven seconds before Caleb. Caleb finished the race two seconds before Beth. Beth finished the race six seconds after Darnell. Ella finished the race eight seconds after Darnell. In which order did the runners finish the race?

40. Eight teams are competing in a vollyball tournament. Any team that loses a game is eliminated from the tournament. How many games must be played to determine the tournament winner?

In Exercises 41–42, you have three errands to run around town, although in no particular order. You plan to start and end at home. You must go to the bank, the post office, and the dry cleaners. Distances, in miles, between any two of these locations are given in the diagram.

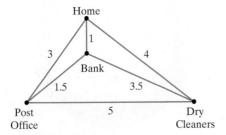

41. Determine a route whose distance is less than 12 miles for running the errands and returning home.

42. Determine a route whose distance exceeds 12 miles for running the errands and returning home.

43. The map shows five western states. Trace a route on the map that crosses each common state border exactly once.

44. The layout of a city with land masses and bridges is shown. Trace a route that shows people how to walk through the city so as to cross each bridge exactly once.

45. Jose, Bob, and Tony are college students living in adjacent dorm rooms. Bob lives in the middle dorm room. Their majors are business, psychology, and biology, although not necessarily in that order. The business major frequently uses the new computer in Bob's dorm room when Bob is in class. The psychology major and Jose both have 8 A.M. classes, and the psychology major knocks on Jose's wall to make sure he is awake. Determine Bob's major.

46. The figure represents a map of 13 countries. If countries that share a common border cannot be the same color, what is the minimum number of colors needed to color the map?

The sudoku (pronounced: sue-DOE-koo) craze, a number puzzle popular in Japan, hit the United States in 2005. A sudoku ("single number") puzzle consists of a 9-by-9 grid of 81 boxes subdivided into nine 3-by-3 squares. Some of the square boxes contain numbers. Here is an example:

2					6	7		
4	5							1
	9		7					
			3					
		4				2	8	
	1			2	4			
	8	3	9		7			
6	2			5		4	1	
							9	

The objective is to fill in the remaining squares so that every row, every column, and every 3-by-3 square contains each of the digits from 1 through 9 exactly once. (You can work this puzzle in Exercise 62, perhaps consulting one of the dozens of sudoku books in which the numerals 1 through 9 have created a cottage industry for publishers. There's even a Sudoku for Dummies.*)*

   Trying to slot numbers into small checkerboard grids is not unique to sudoku. In Exercises 47–50, we explore some of the intricate patterns in other arrays of numbers, including magic squares. *A* **magic square** *is a square array of numbers arranged so that the numbers in all rows, all columns, and the two diagonals have the same sum. Here is an example of a magic square in which the sum of the numbers in each row, each column, and each diagonal is 15:*

Column 1:	Column 2:	Column 3:
8 + 3 + 4 = 15	1 + 5 + 9 = 15	6 + 7 + 2 = 15

8	1	6	Row 1: 8 + 1 + 6 = 15
3	5	7	Row 2: 3 + 5 + 7 = 15
4	9	2	Row 3: 4 + 9 + 2 = 15

Diagonal:	Diagonal:
6 + 5 + 4 = 15	8 + 5 + 2 = 15

Exercises 47–48 are based on magic squares.

47. a. Use the properties of a magic square to fill in the missing numbers.

5		18
	15	
		25

b. Show that the number of letters in the word for each number in the square in part (a) generates another magic square.

48. a. Use the properties of a magic square to fill in the missing numbers.

96		37	45
	43		
		25	57
23		82	78

b. Show that if you reverse the digits for each number in the square in part (a), another magic square is generated.

(*Source* for the *alphamagic square* in Exercise 47 and the *mirrormagic square* in Exercise 48: Clifford A. Pickover, *A Passion for Mathematics,* John Wiley & Sons, Inc., 2005)

49. As in sudoku, fill in the missing numbers in the 3-by-3 square so that it contains each of the digits from 1 through 9 exactly once. Furthermore, in this *antimagic square,* the rows, the columns, and the two diagonals must have *different* sums.

9		7
	1	
3		5

50. The missing numbers in the 4-by-4 array are one-digit numbers. The sums for each row, each column, and one diagonal are listed in the voice balloons outside the array. Find the missing numbers.

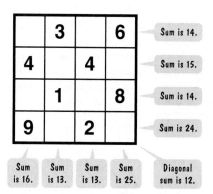

	3		6	Sum is 14.
4		4		Sum is 15.
		1		8	Sum is 14.
9		2		Sum is 24.

| Sum is 16. | Sum is 13. | Sum is 13. | Sum is 25. | Diagonal sum is 12. |

51. Some numbers in the printing of a division problem have become illegible. They are designated below by *. Fill in the blanks.

```
         1**
    **)4***
        28
        *56
        ***
         ***
         ***
           0
```

Writing in Mathematics

In Exercises 52–54, explain the plan needed to solve the problem.

52. If you know how much was paid for several pounds of steak, find the cost of one pound.

53. If you know a person's age, find the year in which that person was born.

54. If you know how much you earn each hour, find your yearly income.

55. Write your own problem that can be solved using the four-step procedure. Then use the four steps to solve the problem.

• Critical Thinking Exercises

56. Gym lockers are to be numbered from 1 through 99 using metal numbers to be nailed onto each locker. How many 7s are needed?

57. You are on vacation in an isolated town. Everyone in the town was born there and has never left. You develop a toothache and check out the two dentists in town. One dentist has gorgeous teeth and one has teeth that show the effects of poor dental work. Which dentist should you choose and why?

58. India Jones is standing on a large rock in the middle of a square pool filled with hungry, man-eating piranhas. The edge of the pool is 20 feet away from the rock. India's mom wants to rescue her son, but she is standing on the edge of the pool with only two planks, each $19\frac{1}{2}$ feet long. How can India be rescued using the two planks?

59. One person tells the truth on Monday, Tuesday, Wednesday, and Thursday, but lies on all other days. A second person lies on Tuesday, Wednesday, and Thursday, but tells the truth on all other days. If both people state "I lied yesterday," then what day of the week is it today?

60. (This logic problem dates back to the eighth century.) A farmer needs to take his goat, wolf, and cabbage across a stream. His boat can hold him and one other passenger (the goat, wolf, or cabbage). If he takes the wolf with him, the goat will eat the cabbage. If he takes the cabbage, the wolf will eat the goat. Only when the farmer is present are the cabbage and goat safe from their respective predators. How does the farmer get everything across the stream?

61. As in sudoku, fill in the missing numbers along the sides of the triangle so that it contains each of the digits from 1 through 9 exactly once. Furthermore, each side of the triangle should contain four digits whose sum is 17.

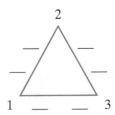

62. Solve the sudoku puzzle at the top of the left column on page 37.

63. A version of this problem, called the *missing dollar problem*, first appeared in 1933. Three people eat at a restaurant and receive a total bill for $30. They divide the amount equally and pay $10 each. The waiter gives the bill and the $30 to the manager, who realizes there is an error: The correct charge should be only $25. The manager gives the waiter five $1 bills to return to the customers, with the restaurant's apologies. However, the waiter is dishonest, keeping $2 and giving back only $3 to the customers. In conclusion, each of the three customers has paid $9 and the waiter has stolen $2, giving a total of $29. However, the original bill was $30. Where has the missing dollar gone?

64. A firefighter spraying water on a fire stood on the middle rung of a ladder. When the smoke became less thick, the firefighter moved up 4 rungs. However it got too hot, so the firefighter backed down 6 rungs. Later, the firefighter went up 7 rungs and stayed until the fire was out. Then, the firefighter climbed the remaining 4 rungs and entered the building. How many rungs does the ladder have?

65. The Republic of Margaritaville is composed of four states, A, B, C, and D. According to the country's constitution, the congress will have 30 seats, divided among the four states according to their respective populations. The table shows each state's population.

POPULATION OF MARGARITAVILLE BY STATE

State	A	B	C	D	Total
Population (in thousands)	275	383	465	767	1890

Allocate the 30 congressional seats among the four states in a fair manner.

• Group Exercises

Exercises 66–70 describe problems that have many plans for finding an answer. Group members should describe how the four steps in problem solving can be applied to find a solution. It is not necessary to actually solve each problem. Your professor will let the group know if the four steps should be described verbally by a group spokesperson or in essay form.

66. How much will it cost to install bicycle racks on campus to encourage students to use bikes, rather than cars, to get to campus?

67. How many new counselors are needed on campus to prevent students from waiting in long lines for academic advising?

68. By how much would taxes in your state have to be increased to cut tuition at community colleges and state universities in half?

69. Is your local electric company overcharging its customers?

70. Should solar heating be required for all new construction in your community?

71. Group members should describe a problem in need of a solution. Then, as in Exercises 66–70, describe how the four steps in problem solving can be applied to find a solution.

●●●●●● CHAPTER SUMMARY, REVIEW, AND TEST

● S U M M A R Y　DEFINITIONS AND CONCEPTS　　　　　EXAMPLES

1.1　Inductive and Deductive Reasoning

a. Inductive reasoning is the process of arriving at a general conclusion based on observations of specific examples. The conclusion is called a conjecture or a hypothesis. A case for which a conjecture is false is called a counterexample.

Ex. 1, p. 3;
Ex. 2, p. 5;
Ex. 3, p. 6

b. Deductive reasoning is the process of proving a specific conclusion from one or more general statements. The statement that is proved is called a theorem.

Ex. 4, p. 8

1.2　Estimation, Graphs, and Mathematical Models

a. The procedure for rounding whole numbers is given in the box on page 14. The symbol $\approx$ means *is approximately equal to*.

Ex. 1, p. 14

b. Decimal parts of numbers are rounded in nearly the same way as whole numbers. However, digits to the right of the rounding place are dropped.

Ex. 2, p. 15

c. Estimation is the process of arriving at an approximate answer to a question. Computations can be estimated by using rounding that results in simplified arithmetic.

Ex. 3, p. 15;
Ex. 4, p. 16

d. Estimation is useful when interpreting information given by circle, bar, or line graphs.

Ex. 5, p. 17;
Ex. 6, p. 18;
Ex. 7, p. 20

e. The process of finding formulas to describe real-world phenomena is called mathematical modeling. Such formulas, together with the meaning assigned to the variables, are called mathematical models.

Ex. 8, p. 21

1.3　Problem Solving

1. Understand the problem.
2. Devise a plan.
3. Carry out the plan and solve the problem.
4. Look back and check the answer.

Ex. 1, p. 27;
Ex. 2, p. 28;
Ex. 3, p. 29;
Ex. 4, p. 30;
Ex. 5, p. 31;
Ex. 6, p. 32

R E V I E W　E X E R C I S E S

1.1

1. Which reasoning process is shown in the following example? Explain your answer.

All books by Stephen King have made the best-seller list. *Carrie* is a novel by Stephen King. Therefore, *Carrie* was on the best-seller list.

2. Which reasoning process is shown in the following example? Explain your answer.

All books by Stephen King have made the best-seller list. Therefore, it is highly probable that the novel King is currently working on will make the best-seller list.

In Exercises 3–10, identify a pattern in each list of numbers. Then use this pattern to find the next number.

3. 4, 9, 14, 19, _____

4. 7, 14, 28, 56, _____

5. 1, 3, 6, 10, 15, _____

6. $\dfrac{3}{4}, \dfrac{3}{5}, \dfrac{1}{2}, \dfrac{3}{7},$ _____

7. 40, −20, 10, −5, _____

8. 40, −20, −80, −140, _____

9. 2, 2, 4, 6, 10, 16, 26, _____

10. 2, 6, 12, 36, 72, 216, _____

11. Identify a pattern in the following sequence of figures. Then use the pattern to find the next figure in the sequence.

 , , , , _____

In Exercises 12–13, use inductive reasoning to predict the next line in each sequence of computations. Then perform the arithmetic to determine whether your conjecture is correct.

12.
$$2 = 4 - 2$$
$$2 + 4 = 8 - 2$$
$$2 + 4 + 8 = 16 - 2$$
$$2 + 4 + 8 + 16 = 32 - 2$$
_____

13.
$$111 \div 3 = 37$$
$$222 \div 6 = 37$$
$$333 \div 9 = 37$$
_____

14. Consider the following procedure:

Select a number. Double the number. Add 4 to the product. Divide the sum by 2. Subtract 2 from the quotient.

a. Repeat the procedure for four numbers of your choice. Write a conjecture that relates the result of the process to the original number selected.

b. Represent the original number by the variable n and use deductive reasoning to prove the conjecture in part (a).

1.2

15. In 2004, there were 4,115,590 live births in the United States, the most since 1990.

(*Source*: National Center for Health Statistics)
Round the number of live births to the nearest

a. hundred.

b. thousand.

c. hundred thousand.

d. million.

16. A magnified view of the boundary of this black "buglike" shape, called the Mandelbrot set, was illustrated in the Blitzer Bonus on page 9.

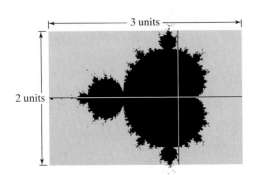

The area of the yellow rectangular region is the product of its length, 3 units, and its width, 2 units, or 6 square units. It is conjectured that the area of the black buglike region representing the Mandelbrot set is

$$\sqrt{6\pi - 11} - e \approx 1.5065916514855 \text{ square units.}$$

(*Source*: Robert P. Munafo, *Mandelbrot Set Glossary and Encyclopedia*)
Round the area of the Mandelbrot set to

a. the nearest tenth.

b. the nearest hundredth.

c. the nearest thousandth.

d. seven decimal places.

In Exercises 17–20, obtain an estimate for each computation by rounding the numbers so that the resulting arithmetic can easily be performed by hand or in your head. Then use a calculator to perform the computation. How reasonable is your estimate when compared to the actual answer?

17. $1.57 + 4.36 + 9.78$

18. 8.83×49

19. $19.894 \div 4.179$

20. 62.3% of 3847.6

In Exercises 21–24, determine each estimate without using a calculator. Then use a calculator to perform the computation necessary to obtain an exact answer. How reasonable is your estimate when compared to the actual answer?

21. Estimate the total cost of six grocery items if their prices are $8.47, $0.89, $2.79, $0.14, $1.19, and $4.76.

22. Estimate the salary of a worker who works for 78 hours at $6.85 per hour.

23. At a yard sale, a person bought 21 books at $0.85 each, two chairs for $11.95 each, and a ceramic plate for $14.65. Estimate the total amount spent.

24. The circle graph shows the political ideology of the approximately 4,177,000 U.S. college freshmen in 2004. Estimate the number of liberals.

Political Ideology of U.S. College Freshmen

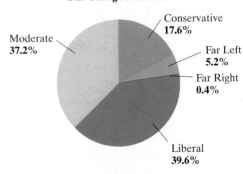

Source: The Chronicle of Higher Education

25. A small private school employs ten teachers with salaries ranging from $817 to $992 per week. Which of the following is the best estimate of the monthly payroll for the teachers?

   a. $30,000

   b. $36,000

   c. $42,000

   d. $50,000

26. Select the best estimate for the number of seconds in a day.

   a. 1500

   b. 15,000

   c. 86,000

   d. 100,000

27. In 2005, an online survey of 2036 U.S. college students ages 18 to 24 found that 62% of female students and 61% of male students said they had been sexually harassed while in college. Furthermore, another student or group of students usually was the perpetrator. Some of the survey results are shown by the bar graph.

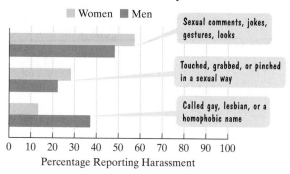

Percentage of U.S. College Students Reporting Sexual Harassment on Campus

Source: American Association of University Women Educational Foundation

   a. Which of the incidents shown was reported by a greater percentage of men than women? Estimate the percentage of women and the percentage of men reporting this incident.

   b. In 2004, there were approximately 6,245,000 women ages 18 to 24 enrolled in U.S. colleges. Estimate the number of women who were harassed on campus by sexual comments, jokes, gestures, or looks.

28. The bar graph shows the number of Americans without health insurance from 2000 through 2004.

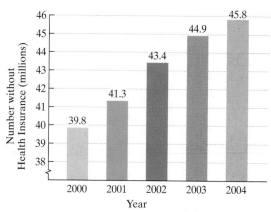

Number of Americans without Health Insurance

Source: U.S. Census Bureau

   a. Estimate the average yearly increase in the number of Americans without health insurance.

   b. If the trend shown by the graph continues, estimate the number of Americans who will not have health insurance in 2012.

29. The line graph shows the number of high-school dropouts in the United States, in thousands, for selected years from 1980 through 2004.

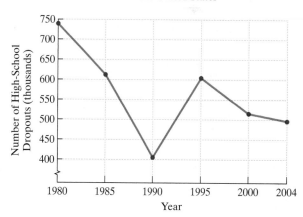

Number of High-School Dropouts in the United States

Source: National Center for Education Statistics

   a. For the period shown, in which year did the number of high-school dropouts reach a minimum? Find a reasonable estimate, to the nearest ten thousand, for the number of dropouts in that year.

   b. In which five-year period did the number of dropouts decrease at the greatest rate?

   c. In which year were there approximately 610,000 dropouts?

30. In 2006, conniving lobbyists buying lawmakers and the ease with which some lawmakers allowed themselves to be bought put pressure on Congress to mend a broken system. The bar graph shows the amount spent on Washington lobbying, in billions of dollars, each year from 1999 through 2004.

Amount Spent on Washington Lobbying

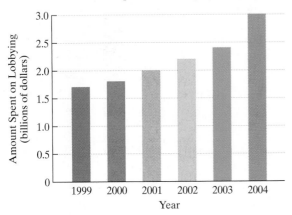

Source: Center for Public Integrity

a. Estimate the yearly increase, in billions of dollars, in the amount spent on Washington lobbying.

b. Write a mathematical model that estimates the amount spent on Washington lobbying, L, in billions of dollars, x years after 1999.

c. If the trend shown by the data does not change and Congress does not mend the system, use your mathematical model from part (b) to predict the amount spent on Washington lobbying in 2013.

1.3

31. What necessary piece of information is missing that prevents solving the following problem?

If 3 milligrams of a medicine is given for every 20 pounds of body weight, how many milligrams should be given to a six-year-old child?

32. In the following problem, there is one more piece of information given than is necessary for solving the problem. Identify this unnecessary piece of information. Then solve the problem.

A taxicab charges $3.00 for the first mile and 50 cents for each additional half-mile. After a six-mile trip, a customer handed the taxi driver a $20 bill. Find the cost of the trip.

Use the four-step method in problem solving to solve Exercises 33–38.

33. If there are seven frankfurters in one pound, how many pounds would you buy for a picnic to supply 28 people with two frankfurters each?

34. A car rents for $175 per week plus $0.30 per mile. Find the rental cost for a three-week trip of 1200 miles.

35. You are choosing between two plans at a discount warehouse. Plan A offers an annual membership fee of $100 and you pay 80% of the manufacturer's recommended list price. Plan B offers an annual membership fee of $40 and you pay 90% of the manufacturer's recommended list price. If you anticipate purchasing $1500 of merchandise in a year, which plan offers the better deal? By how much?

36. Miami is on Eastern Standard Time and San Francisco is on Pacific Standard Time, three hours earlier than Eastern Standard Time. A flight leaves Miami at 10 A.M. Eastern Standard Time, stops for 45 minutes in Houston, Texas, and arrives in San Francisco at 1:30 P.M. Pacific time. What is the actual flying time from Miami to San Francisco?

37. An automobile purchased for $37,000 is worth $2600 after eight years. Assuming that the value decreased steadily each year, what was the car worth at the end of the fifth year?

38. Suppose you are an engineer programming the automatic gate for a 35-cent toll. The gate is programmed for exact change only and will not accept pennies. How many coin combinations must you program the gate to accept?

●●●●●● CHAPTER 1 TEST

1. Which reasoning process is shown in the following example?

The course policy states that if you turn in at least 80% of the homework, your lowest exam grade will be dropped. I turned in 90% of the homework, so my lowest grade will be dropped.

2. Which reasoning process is shown in the following example?

We examine the fingerprints of 1000 people. No two individuals in this group of people have identical fingerprints. We conclude that for all people, no two people have identical fingerprints.

In Exercises 3–6, find the next number, line, or figure, as appropriate.

3. 0, 5, 10, 15, _____

4. $\frac{1}{6}, \frac{1}{12}, \frac{1}{24}, \frac{1}{48}$, _____

5.
$$3367 \times 3 = 10,101$$
$$3367 \times 6 = 20,202$$
$$3367 \times 9 = 30,303$$
$$3367 \times 12 = 40,404$$
_____

6.
, , , , , _____

7. Consider the following procedure:

Select a number. Multiply the number by 4. Add 8 to the product. Divide the sum by 2. Subtract 4 from the quotient.

a. Repeat this procedure for three numbers of your choice. Write a conjecture that relates the result of the process to the original number selected.

b. Represent the original number by the variable n and use deductive reasoning to prove the conjecture in part (a).

8. Round 3,279,425 to the nearest hundred thousand.

9. Round 706.3849 to the nearest hundredth.

In Exercises 10–13, determine each estimate without using a calculator. Different rounding results in different estimates, so there is not one single correct answer to each exercise. Use rounding to make the resulting calculations simple.

10. For a spring break vacation, a student needs to spend $47.00 for gas, $311.00 for food, and $405.00 for a hotel room. If the student takes $681.79 from savings, estimate how much more money is needed for the vacation.

11. The cost for opening a restaurant is $485,000. If 19 people decide to share equally in the business, estimate the amount each must contribute.

12. Find an estimate of 0.48992×121.976.

13. The circle graph shows the breakdown, by continent or region, of the approximately 39,285,000 world AIDS cases. Estimate the number of AIDS cases in Africa.

World AIDS Cases, by Continent or Region

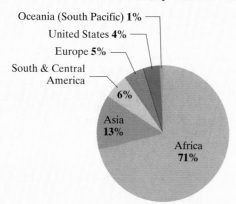

Source: World Health Organization

14. If the odometer of a car reads 71,911.5 miles and it averaged 28.9 miles per gallon, select the best estimate for the number of gallons of gasoline used.

a. 2400   **b.** 3200   **c.** 4000

d. 4800   **e.** 5600

15. The stated intent of the 1994 "don't ask, don't tell" policy was to reduce the number of discharges of gay men and lesbians from the military. The line graph shows the number of active-duty gay servicemembers discharged from the military for homosexuality under the policy.

Number of Active-Duty Gay Servicemembers Discharged from the Military for Homosexuality

Source: General Accountability Office

a. For the period shown, in which year did the number of discharges reach a maximum? Find a reasonable estimate of the number of discharges for that year.

b. In which year were approximately 850 gay servicemembers discharged under the "don't ask, don't tell" policy?

c. Find a reasonable estimate of the total number of military discharges under "don't ask, don't tell" from 1994 through 2003.

16. The bar graph shows the percentage of cigarette smokers among U.S. adults from 1970 through 2004.

Butt Out: Percentage of Cigarette Smokers Among U.S. Adults

Source: Centers for Disease Control and Prevention

(Be sure to refer to the bar graph at the bottom of page 43.)

a. Estimate the yearly decrease, to the nearest tenth of a percent, in the percentage of cigarette smokers among U.S. adults.

b. Write a mathematical model that estimates the percentage of smokers, S, among U.S. adults x years after 1970.

c. If the trend shown by the data continues, use your mathematical model from part (b) to predict the percentage of cigarette smokers among U.S. adults in 2010.

17. The cost of renting a boat from Estes Rental is $9 per 15 minutes. The cost from Ship and Shore Rental is $20 per half-hour. If you plan to rent the boat for three hours, which business offers the better deal and by how much?

18. A bus operates between Miami International Airport and Miami Beach, 10 miles away. It makes 20 round trips per day carrying 32 passengers per trip. If the fare each way is $11.00, how much money is taken in from one day's operation?

19. By paying $50 cash up front and the balance at $35 a week, how long will it take to pay for a computer costing $960?

20. In 2000, the population of Greece was 10,600,000, with projections of a population decrease of 28,000 people per year. In the same year, the population of Belgium was 10,200,000, with projections of a population decrease of 12,000 people per year.

(*Source:* United Nations)

According to these projections, which country will have the greater population in 2035 and by how many more people?

CHAPTER

2

Set Theory

You want to organize a blood drive on campus with the local Red Cross. The Red Cross asked you whether the number of potential donors warrants a commitment to provide medical staff for the blood drive. So you took a survey to obtain information. Your survey asked students two questions:

1. Would you be willing to donate blood?
2. Would you be willing to help serve a free breakfast to blood donors?

Now the survey results are in. How will you organize and present the results to the Red Cross in an efficient manner?

The need to sort and organize information obtained through surveys is related to our need to find order and meaning by classifying things into collections, called *sets*. In this chapter, we analyze a variety of collections, ranging from sets of television's most popular shows to sets of places with the greatest number of shark attacks, and even collections of famous people on whom the FBI kept files.

The problem of organizing and presenting the results of the blood drive survey appears as Example 1 in Section 2.5. In Exercise Set 2.4, you'll find TV's most popular shows (Exercises 93–98) and Jaws on the attack (Exercise 105). The set of famous Americans watched by the FBI is divided into smaller collections, called *subsets*, in Exercise 21 of the Chapter 2 Test.

45

SECTION 2.1 • BASIC SET CONCEPTS

We tend to place things in categories, allowing us to order and structure the world. For example, you can categorize yourself by your age, your ethnicity, your academic major, or your gender. Our minds cannot find order and meaning without creating collections. Mathematicians call such collections *sets*. A **set** is a collection of objects whose contents can be clearly determined. The objects in a set are called the **elements**, or **members**, of the set.

A set must be **well defined**, meaning that its contents can be clearly determined. Using this criterion, the collection of actors who have won Academy Awards is a set. We can always determine whether or not a particular actor is an element of this collection. By contrast, consider the collection of great actors. Whether or not a person belongs to this collection is a matter of how we interpret the word *great*. In this text, we will only consider collections that form well-defined sets.

Methods for Representing Sets

An example of a set is the set of the days of the week, whose elements are Monday, Tuesday, Wednesday, Thursday, Friday, Saturday, and Sunday.

Capital letters are generally used to name sets. Let's use W to represent the set of the days of the week.

Three methods are commonly used to designate a set. One method is a **word description**. We can describe set W as the set of the days of the week. A second method is the **roster method**. This involves listing the elements of a set inside a pair of braces, { }. The braces at the beginning and end indicate that we are representing a set. The roster form uses commas to separate the elements of the set. Thus, we can designate the set W by listing its elements:

$W = \{$Monday, Tuesday, Wednesday, Thursday, Friday, Saturday, Sunday$\}$.

Grouping symbols such as parentheses, ( ), and square brackets, [ ], are not used to represent sets. Only commas are used to separate the elements of a set. Separators such as colons or semicolons are not used. Finally, the order in which the elements are listed in a set is not important. Thus, another way of expressing the set of the days of the week is

$W = \{$Saturday, Sunday, Monday, Tuesday, Wednesday, Thursday, Friday$\}$.

1 | Use three methods to represent sets.

EXAMPLE 1   REPRESENTING A SET USING A DESCRIPTION

Write a word description of the set

$P = \{$Washington, Adams, Jefferson, Madison, Monroe$\}$.

SOLUTION Set P is the set of the first five presidents of the United States.

Write a word description of the set

$$L = \{a, b, c, d, e, f\}.$$

EXAMPLE 2	REPRESENTING A SET USING THE ROSTER METHOD

Set C is the set of U.S. coins with a value of less than a dollar. Express this set using the roster method.

SOLUTION $C = \{$penny, nickel, dime, quarter, half-dollar$\}$

 Set M is the set of months beginning with the letter A. Express this set using the roster method.

The third method for representing a set is with **set-builder notation**. Using this method, the set of the days of the week can be expressed as

$$W = \{x \mid x \text{ is a day of the week}\}.$$

Set W	is	the set of	all elements x	such that

We read this notation as "Set W is the set of all elements x such that x is a day of the week." Before the vertical line is the variable x, which represents an element in general. After the vertical line is the condition x must meet in order to be an element of the set.

STUDY TIP

Any letter can be used to represent the variable in set-builder notation. Thus, $\{x \mid x$ is a day of the week$\}$, $\{y \mid y$ is a day of the week$\}$, and $\{z \mid z$ is a day of the week$\}$ all represent the same set.

Table 2.1 contains two examples of sets, each represented with a word description, the roster method, and set-builder notation.

TABLE 2.1 SETS USING THREE DESIGNATIONS

Word Description	Roster Method	Set-Builder Notation
B is the set of members of the Beatles in 1963.	$B = \{$George Harrison, John Lennon, Paul McCartney, Ringo Starr$\}$	$B = \{x \mid x$ was a member of the Beatles in 1963$\}$
S is the set of states whose names begin with the letter A.	$S = \{$Alabama, Alaska, Arizona, Arkansas$\}$	$S = \{x \mid x$ is a U.S. state whose name begins with the letter A$\}$

EXAMPLE 3	CONVERTING FROM SET-BUILDER TO ROSTER NOTATION

Express set

$$A = \{x \mid x \text{ is a month that begins with the letter M}\}$$

using the roster method.

SOLUTION Set A is the set of all elements x such that x is a month beginning with the letter M. There are two such months, namely March and May. Thus,

$$A = \{\text{March, May}\}.$$

The Beatles climbed to the top of the British music charts in 1963, conquering the United States a year later.

Express the set

$$O = \{x \mid x \text{ is a positive odd number less than } 10\}$$

using the roster method.

The representation of some sets by the roster method can be rather long, or even impossible, if we attempt to list every element. For example, consider the set of all lowercase letters of the English alphabet. If L is chosen as a name for this set, we can use set-builder notation to represent L as follows:

$$L = \{x \mid x \text{ is a lowercase letter of the English alphabet}\}.$$

A complete listing using the roster method is rather tedious:

$$L = \{a, b, c, d, e, f, g, h, i, j, k, l, m, n, o, p, q, r, s, t, u, v, w, x, y, z\}.$$

We can shorten the listing in set L by writing

$$L = \{a, b, c, d, \ldots, z\}.$$

The three dots after the element d, called an *ellipsis*, indicate that the elements in the set continue in the same manner up to and including the last element z.

2 | Define and recognize the empty set.

The Empty Set

Consider the following sets:

$$\{x \mid x \text{ is a fawn that speaks}\}$$
$$\{x \mid x \text{ is a number greater than } 10 \text{ and less than } 4\}.$$

Can you see what these sets have in common? They both contain no elements. There are no fawns that speak. There are no numbers that are both greater than 10 and also less than 4. Sets such as these that contain no elements are called the *empty set*, or the *null set*.

> **THE EMPTY SET**
> The **empty set**, also called the **null set**, is the set that contains no elements. The empty set is represented by { } or ∅.

Notice that { } and Ø have the same meaning. However, the empty set is not represented by {Ø}. This notation represents a set containing the element Ø.

EXAMPLE 4   RECOGNIZING THE EMPTY SET

Which one of the following is the empty set?

a. {0}   **b.** 0

c. {x|x is a number less than 4 or greater than 10}

d. {x|x is a square with exactly three sides}

SOLUTION

a. {0} is a set containing one element, 0. Because this set contains an element, it is not the empty set.

b. 0 is a number, not a set, so it cannot possibly be the empty set. It does, however, represent the number of members of the empty set.

c. {x|x is a number less than 4 or greater than 10} contains all numbers that are either less than 4, such as 3, or greater than 10, such as 11. Because some elements belong to this set, it cannot be the empty set.

d. {x|x is a square with exactly three sides} contains no elements. There are no squares with exactly three sides. This set is the empty set.

 Which one of the following is the empty set?

a. {x|x is a number less than 3 or greater than 5}

b. {x|x is a number less than 3 and greater than 5}

c. nothing   **d.** {Ø}

BLITZER BONUS

The Musical Sounds of the Empty Set

John Cage (1912–1992), the American avant-garde composer, translated the empty set into the quietest piece of music ever written. His piano composition *4′33″* requires the musician to sit frozen in silence at a piano stool for 4 minutes, 33 seconds, or 273 seconds. (The significance of 273 is that at approximately −273°C, all molecular motion stops.) The set

{x|x is a musical sound from *4′33″*}

is the empty set. There are no musical sounds in the composition. Mathematician Martin Gardner wrote, "I have not heard *4′33″* performed, but friends who have tell me it is Cage's finest composition."

3 Use the symbols ∈ and ∉.

Notations for Set Membership

We now consider two special notations that indicate whether or not a given object belongs to a set.

> **THE NOTATIONS ∈ AND ∉**
>
> The symbol ∈ is used to indicate that an object is an element of a set. The symbol ∈ is used to replace the words "is an element of."
>
> The symbol ∉ is used to indicate that an object is *not* an element of a set. The symbol ∉ is used to replace the words "is not an element of."

EXAMPLE 5   USING THE SYMBOLS $\in$ AND $\notin$

Determine whether each statement is true or false:

a. $r \in \{a, b, c, \ldots, z\}$ **b.** $7 \notin \{1, 2, 3, 4, 5\}$ **c.** $\{a\} \in \{a, b\}$.

SOLUTION

a. Because r is an element of the set $\{a, b, c, \ldots, z\}$, the statement

$$r \in \{a, b, c, \ldots, z\}$$

is true.

Observe that an element can belong to a set in roster notation when three dots appear even though the element is not listed.

b. Because 7 is not an element of the set $\{1, 2, 3, 4, 5\}$, the statement

$$7 \notin \{1, 2, 3, 4, 5\}$$

is true.

c. Because $\{a\}$ is a set and the set $\{a\}$ is not an element of the set $\{a, b\}$, the statement

$$\{a\} \in \{a, b\}$$

is false.

 Determine whether each statement is true or false:

a. $8 \in \{1, 2, 3, \ldots, 10\}$

b. $r \notin \{a, b, c, z\}$

c. $\{\text{Monday}\} \in \{x \mid x \text{ is a day of the week}\}$.

4 | Apply set notation to sets of natural numbers.

Sets of Natural Numbers

For the remainder of this section, we will focus on the set of numbers used for counting:

$$\{1, 2, 3, 4, 5, 6, 7, 8, 9, 10, 11, \ldots\}.$$

The set of counting numbers is also called the set of **natural numbers**. We represent this set by the bold face letter **N**.

> ### THE SET OF NATURAL NUMBERS
> $$\mathbf{N} = \{1, 2, 3, 4, 5, \ldots\}$$

The three dots, or ellipsis, after the 5 indicate that there is no final element and that the listing goes on forever.

EXAMPLE 6   REPRESENTING SETS OF NATURAL NUMBERS

Express each of the following sets using the roster method:

a. Set A is the set of natural numbers less than 5.

b. Set B is the set of natural numbers greater than or equal to 25.

c. $E = \{x \mid x \in \mathbf{N} \text{ and } x \text{ is even}\}$.

SOLUTION

a. The natural numbers less than 5 are 1, 2, 3, and 4. Thus, set A can be expressed using the roster method as

$$A = \{1, 2, 3, 4\}.$$

b. The natural numbers greater than or equal to 25 are 25, 26, 27, 28, and so on. Set B in roster form is

$$B = \{25, 26, 27, 28, \ldots\}.$$

The three dots show that the listing goes on forever.

c. The set-builder notation

$$E = \{x \mid x \in \mathbf{N} \text{ and } x \text{ is even}\}$$

indicates that we want to list the set of all x such that x is an element of the set of natural numbers and x is even. The set of numbers that meet both conditions is the set of even natural numbers. The set in roster form is

$$E = \{2, 4, 6, 8, \dots\}.$$

Express each of the following sets using the roster method:

a. Set A is the set of natural numbers less than or equal to 3.

b. Set B is the set of natural numbers greater than 14.

c. $O = \{x \mid x \in \mathbf{N} \text{ and } x \text{ is odd}\}$.

Inequality symbols are frequently used to describe sets of natural numbers. Table 2.2 reviews basic inequality notation.

TABLE 2.2 INEQUALITY NOTATION AND SETS

Inequality Symbol and Meaning		Example Set-Builder Notation	Roster Method
$x < a$	x is less than a.	$\{x \mid x \in \mathbf{N} \text{ and } x < 4\}$ — x is a natural number less than 4.	$\{1, 2, 3\}$
$x \leq a$	x is less than or equal to a.	$\{x \mid x \in \mathbf{N} \text{ and } x \leq 4\}$ — x is a natural number less than or equal to 4.	$\{1, 2, 3, 4\}$
$x > a$	x is greater than a.	$\{x \mid x \in \mathbf{N} \text{ and } x > 4\}$ — x is a natural number greater than 4.	$\{5, 6, 7, 8, \dots\}$
$x \geq a$	x is greater than or equal to a.	$\{x \mid x \in \mathbf{N} \text{ and } x \geq 4\}$ — x is a natural number greater than or equal to 4.	$\{4, 5, 6, 7, \dots\}$
$a < x < b$	x is greater than a and less than b.	$\{x \mid x \in \mathbf{N} \text{ and } 4 < x < 8\}$ — x is a natural number greater than 4 and less than 8.	$\{5, 6, 7\}$
$a \leq x \leq b$	x is greater than or equal to a and less than or equal to b.	$\{x \mid x \in \mathbf{N} \text{ and } 4 \leq x \leq 8\}$ — x is a natural number greater than or equal to 4 and less than or equal to 8.	$\{4, 5, 6, 7, 8\}$
$a \leq x < b$	x is greater than or equal to a and less than b.	$\{x \mid x \in \mathbf{N} \text{ and } 4 \leq x < 8\}$ — x is a natural number greater than or equal to 4 and less than 8.	$\{4, 5, 6, 7\}$
$a < x \leq b$	x is greater than a and less than or equal to b.	$\{x \mid x \in \mathbf{N} \text{ and } 4 < x \leq 8\}$ — x is a natural number greater than 4 and less than or equal to 8.	$\{5, 6, 7, 8\}$

STUDY TIP

A page of sheet music, filled with symbols and notations, *represents* a piece of music. Similarly, the symbols and notations throughout this book are representations of mathematical ideas. Mathematical notation no more *is* mathematics than musical notation *is* music. As you become familiar with various mathematical notations, the ideas represented by the symbols can then live and breathe in your mind.

EXAMPLE 7   REPRESENTING SETS OF NATURAL NUMBERS

Express each of the following sets using the roster method:

a. $\{x \mid x \in \mathbf{N} \text{ and } x \leq 100\}$ **b.** $\{x \mid x \in \mathbf{N} \text{ and } 70 \leq x < 100\}$.

SOLUTION

a. $\{x \mid x \in \mathbf{N} \text{ and } x \leq 100\}$ represents the set of natural numbers less than or equal to 100. This set can be expressed using the roster method as

$$\{1, 2, 3, 4, \ldots, 100\}.$$

b. $\{x \mid x \in \mathbf{N} \text{ and } 70 \leq x < 100\}$ represents the set of natural numbers greater than or equal to 70 and less than 100. This set in roster form is $\{70, 71, 72, 73, \ldots, 99\}$.

○

 Express each of the following sets using the roster method:

a. $\{x \mid x \in \mathbf{N} \text{ and } x < 200\}$ **b.** $\{x \mid x \in \mathbf{N} \text{ and } 50 < x \leq 200\}$.

5 | Determine a set's cardinal number.

Cardinality and Equivalent Sets

The number of elements in a set is called the **cardinal number**, or **cardinality**, of the set. For example, the set {a, e, i, o, u} contains five elements and therefore has the cardinal number 5. We can also say that the set has a cardinality of 5.

> **DEFINITION OF A SET'S CARDINAL NUMBER**
> The **cardinal number** of set A, represented by $n(A)$, is the number of distinct elements in set A. The symbol $n(A)$ is read "n of A."

Notice that the cardinal number of a set refers to the number of *distinct*, or different, elements in the set. **Repeating elements in a set neither adds new elements to the set nor changes its cardinality**. For example, $A = \{3, 5, 7\}$ and $B = \{3, 5, 5, 7, 7, 7\}$ represent the same set with three distinct elements, 3, 5, and 7. Thus, $n(A) = 3$ and $n(B) = 3$.

EXAMPLE 8   DETERMINING A SET'S CARDINAL NUMBER

Find the cardinal number of each of the following sets:

a. $A = \{7, 9, 11, 13\}$ **b.** $B = \{0\}$
c. $C = \{13, 14, 15, \ldots, 22, 23\}$ **d.** $\varnothing$.

SOLUTION The cardinal number for each set is found by determining the number of elements in the set.

a. $A = \{7, 9, 11, 13\}$ contains four distinct elements. Thus, the cardinal number of set A is 4. We also say that set A has a cardinality of 4, or $n(A) = 4$.

b. $B = \{0\}$ contains one element, namely 0. The cardinal number of set B is 1. Therefore, $n(B) = 1$.

c. Set $C = \{13, 14, 15, \ldots, 22, 23\}$ lists only five elements. However, the three dots indicate that the natural numbers from 16 through 21 are also in the set. Counting the elements in the set, we find that there are 11 natural numbers in set C. The cardinality of set C is 11, and $n(C) = 11$.

d. The empty set, $\varnothing$, contains no elements. Thus, $n(\varnothing) = 0$.

○

 Find the cardinal number of each of the following sets:

a. $A = \{6, 10, 14, 15, 16\}$ **b.** $B = \{872\}$
c. $C = \{9, 10, 11, \ldots, 15, 16\}$ **d.** $D = \{\ \}$.

6 | Recognize equivalent sets.

Sets that contain the same number of elements are said to be *equivalent*.

> **DEFINITION OF EQUIVALENT SETS**
>
> Set A is **equivalent** to set B means that set A and set B contain the same number of elements. For equivalent sets, $n(A) = n(B)$.

Here is an example of two equivalent sets:

$n(A) = n(B) = 5$

$$A = \{x \mid x \text{ is a vowel}\} = \{a, e, i, o, u\}$$
$$B = \{x \mid x \in \mathbf{N} \text{ and } 3 \le x \le 7\} = \{3, 4, 5, 6, 7\}.$$

It is not necessary to count elements and arrive at 5 to determine that these sets are equivalent. The lines with arrowheads, $\updownarrow$, indicate that each element of set A can be paired with exactly one element of set B and each element of set B can be paired with exactly one element of set A. We say that the sets can be placed in a **one-to-one correspondence**.

> **ONE-TO-ONE CORRESPONDENCES AND EQUIVALENT SETS**
>
> **1.** If set A and set B can be placed in a one-to-one correspondence, then A is equivalent to B: $n(A) = n(B)$.
>
> **2.** If set A and set B cannot be placed in a one-to-one correspondence, then A is not equivalent to B: $n(A) \ne n(B)$.

EXAMPLE 9 DETERMINING IF SETS ARE EQUIVALENT

Table 2.3 shows the celebrities who hosted NBC's *Saturday Night Live* most frequently and the number of times each starred on the show. Let

A = the set of the five most frequent hosts on *Saturday Night Live*

B = the set of the number of times each of the five
most frequent *Saturday Night Live* hosts starred on the show.

Are these sets equivalent? Explain.

SOLUTION Let's begin by expressing each set in roster form.

$$A = \{\text{Martin, Baldwin, Goodman, Henry, Chase}\}$$
$$B = \{\ 14, \quad 12, \quad 10, \quad 9\}$$

Do not write the 12 twice. We are interested in each set's _distinct_ elements.

TABLE 2.3 MOST FREQUENT HOSTS OF *SATURDAY NIGHT LIVE*

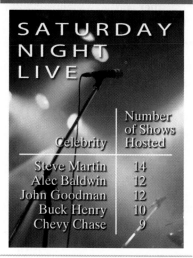

Celebrity	Number of Shows Hosted
Steve Martin	14
Alec Baldwin	12
John Goodman	12
Buck Henry	10
Chevy Chase	9

Source: NBC Universal

There are two ways to determine that these sets are not equivalent.

Method 1. Trying to Set Up a One-to-One Correspondence

The lines with arrowheads indicate that the correspondence between the sets is not one-to-one. The elements Baldwin and Goodman from set A are both paired with the element 12 from set B. These sets are not equivalent.

Method 2. Counting Elements

Set A contains five distinct elements: $n(A) = 5$. Set B contains four distinct elements: $n(B) = 4$. Because the sets do not contain the same number of elements, they are not equivalent.

TABLE 2.4 TOP FIVE LANGUAGES SPOKEN BY THE YOUTH OF 2050

Language	Estimated Number (in millions) of 15–24-Year-Old Speakers
Chinese	166
Hindu/Urdu	74
Arabic	72
English	65
Spanish	63

Source: David Graddol, *The Future of English?*, British Council

7 | Distinguish between finite and infinite sets.

Table 2.4 shows the top five languages that will be spoken by the youth of 2050 and the number, in millions, of 15–24-year-old speakers. Let

A = the set of the five languages spoken by the greatest number of 15–24-year-olds in 2050

B = the set of the number of 15–24-year-old speakers, in millions, of each of the top five languages spoken by the youth of 2050.

Are these sets equivalent? Without counting elements in the sets, explain your answer.

Finite and Infinite Sets

Example 9 illustrated that to compare the cardinalities of two sets, pair off their elements. If there is not a one-to-one correspondence, the sets have different cardinalities and are not equivalent. Although this idea is obvious in the case of *finite sets*, some unusual conclusions emerge when dealing with *infinite sets*.

> **FINITE SETS AND INFINITE SETS**
> Set A is a **finite set** if $n(A) = 0$ (that is, A is the empty set) or $n(A)$ is a natural number. A set whose cardinality is not 0 or a natural number is called an **infinite set**.

An example of an infinite set is the set of natural numbers, $\mathbf{N} = \{1, 2, 3, 4, 5, 6, \ldots\}$, where the ellipsis indicates that there is no last, or final, element. Does this set have a cardinality? The answer is yes, albeit one of the strangest numbers you've ever seen. The set of natural numbers is assigned the infinite cardinal number $\aleph_0$ (read: "aleph-null," aleph being the first letter of the Hebrew alphabet). What follows is a succession of mind-boggling results, including a hierarchy of different infinite numbers in which $\aleph_0$ is the smallest infinity:

$$\aleph_0 < \aleph_1 < \aleph_2 < \aleph_3 < \aleph_4 < \aleph_5 \ldots.$$

These ideas, which are impossible for our imaginations to grasp, are developed in Section 2.2 and the Blitzer Bonus at the end of that section.

8 | Recognize equal sets.

Equal Sets

We conclude this section with another important concept of set theory, equality of sets.

> **DEFINITION OF EQUALITY OF SETS**
> Set A is **equal** to set B means that set A and set B contain exactly the same elements, regardless of order or possible repetition of elements. We symbolize the equality of sets A and B using the statement $A = B$.

For example, if $A = \{w, x, y, z\}$ and $B = \{z, y, w, x\}$, then $A = B$ because the two sets contain exactly the same elements.

Because equal sets contain the same elements, they also have the same cardinal number. For example, the equal sets $A = \{w, x, y, z\}$ and $B = \{z, y, w, x\}$ have four elements each. Thus, both sets have the same cardinal number: 4. Notice that a possible one-to-one correspondence between the equal sets A and B can be obtained by pairing each element with itself:

$$A = \{w, \quad x, \quad y, \quad z\}$$

$$B = \{z, \quad y, \quad w, \quad x\}$$

This illustrates an important point: **If two sets are equal, then they must be equivalent.**

EXAMPLE 10   DETERMINING WHETHER SETS ARE EQUAL

Determine whether each statement is true or false:

    a. $\{4, 8, 9\} = \{8, 9, 4\}$ **b.** $\{1, 3, 5\} = \{0, 1, 3, 5\}$.

SOLUTION

    a. The sets $\{4, 8, 9\}$ and $\{8, 9, 4\}$ contain exactly the same elements. Therefore, the statement

$$\{4, 8, 9\} = \{8, 9, 4\}$$

    is true.

    b. As we look at the given sets, $\{1, 3, 5\}$ and $\{0, 1, 3, 5\}$, we see that 0 is an element of the second set, but not the first. The sets do not contain exactly the same elements. Therefore, the sets are not equal. This means that the statement

$$\{1, 3, 5\} = \{0, 1, 3, 5\}$$

    is false.

 Determine whether each statement is true or false:

    a. $\{O, L, D\} = \{D, O, L\}$ **b.** $\{4, 5\} = \{5, 4, \varnothing\}$.

STUDY TIP

In English, the words *equal* and *equivalent* often mean the same thing. This is not the case in set theory. **Equal sets** contain the **same elements**. **Equivalent sets** contain the **same number of elements**. If two sets are equal, then they must be equivalent. However, if two sets are equivalent, they are not necessarily equal.

EXERCISE SET 2.1 ●●●●●●

• Practice Exercises

In Exercises 1–6, determine which collections are not well defined and therefore not sets.

1. The collection of U.S. presidents

2. The collection of part-time and full-time students currently enrolled at your college

3. The collection of the five worst U.S. presidents

4. The collection of elderly full-time students currently enrolled at your college

5. The collection of natural numbers greater than one million

6. The collection of even natural numbers greater than 100

In Exercises 7–14, write a description of each set. (More than one correct description may be possible.)

7. {Mercury, Venus, Earth, Mars, Jupiter, Saturn, Uranus, Neptune}

8. {Saturday, Sunday}

9. {January, June, July}

10. {April, August}

11. $\{6, 7, 8, 9, \ldots\}$

12. $\{9, 10, 11, 12, \ldots\}$

13. $\{6, 7, 8, 9, \ldots, 20\}$

14. $\{9, 10, 11, 12, \ldots, 25\}$

In Exercises 15–32, express each set using the roster method.

15. The set of the four seasons in a year

16. The set of months of the year that have exactly 30 days

17. $\{x \mid x$ is a month that ends with the letters b-e-r$\}$

18. $\{x \mid x$ is a letter of the alphabet that follows d and comes before j$\}$

19. The set of natural numbers less than 4

20. The set of natural numbers less than or equal to 6

21. The set of odd natural numbers less than 13

22. The set of even natural numbers less than 10

23. $\{x \mid x \in \mathbf{N}$ and $x \leq 5\}$

24. $\{x \mid x \in \mathbf{N}$ and $x \leq 4\}$

25. $\{x \mid x \in \mathbf{N}$ and $x > 5\}$

26. $\{x \mid x \in \mathbf{N}$ and $x > 4\}$

27. $\{x \mid x \in \mathbf{N}$ and $6 < x \leq 10\}$

28. $\{x \mid x \in \mathbf{N}$ and $7 < x \leq 11\}$

29. $\{x \mid x \in \mathbf{N}$ and $10 \leq x < 80\}$

30. $\{x \mid x \in \mathbf{N}$ and $15 \leq x < 60\}$

31. $\{x|x + 5 = 7\}$ **32.** $\{x|x + 3 = 9\}$

In Exercises 33–46, determine which sets are the empty set.

33. $\{\varnothing, 0\}$ **34.** $\{0, \varnothing\}$

35. $\{x|x$ is a woman who served as U.S. president before 2000$\}$

36. $\{x|x$ is a living U.S. president born before 1700$\}$

37. $\{x|x$ is the number of women who served as U.S. president before 2000$\}$

38. $\{x|x$ is the number of living U.S. presidents born before 1700$\}$

39. $\{x|x$ is a U.S. state whose name begins with the letter X$\}$

40. $\{x|x$ is a month of the year whose name begins with the letter X$\}$

41. $\{x|x < 2$ and $x > 5\}$

42. $\{x|x < 3$ and $x > 7\}$

43. $\{x|x \in \mathbf{N}$ and $2 < x < 5\}$

44. $\{x|x \in \mathbf{N}$ and $3 < x < 7\}$

45. $\{x|x$ is a number less than 2 or greater than 5$\}$

46. $\{x|x$ is a number less than 3 or greater than 7$\}$

In Exercises 47–66, determine whether each statement is true or false.

47. $3 \in \{1, 3, 5, 7\}$ **48.** $6 \in \{2, 4, 6, 8, 10\}$

49. $12 \in \{1, 2, 3, \ldots, 14\}$ **50.** $10 \in \{1, 2, 3, \ldots, 16\}$

51. $5 \in \{2, 4, 6, \ldots, 20\}$ **52.** $8 \in \{1, 3, 5, \ldots 19\}$

53. $11 \notin \{1, 2, 3, \ldots, 9\}$ **54.** $17 \notin \{1, 2, 3, \ldots, 16\}$

55. $37 \notin \{1, 2, 3, \ldots, 40\}$ **56.** $26 \notin \{1, 2, 3, \ldots, 50\}$

57. $4 \notin \{x|x \in \mathbf{N}$ and x is even$\}$

58. $2 \in \{x|x \in \mathbf{N}$ and x is odd$\}$

59. $13 \notin \{x|x \in \mathbf{N}$ and $x < 13\}$

60. $20 \notin \{x|x \in \mathbf{N}$ and $x < 20\}$

61. $16 \notin \{x|x \in \mathbf{N}$ and $15 \le x < 20\}$

62. $19 \notin \{x|x \in \mathbf{N}$ and $16 \le x < 21\}$

63. $\{3\} \in \{3, 4\}$ **64.** $\{7\} \in \{7, 8\}$

65. $-1 \notin \mathbf{N}$ **66.** $-2 \notin \mathbf{N}$

In Exercises 67–80, find the cardinal number for each set.

67. $A = \{17, 19, 21, 23, 25\}$

68. $A = \{16, 18, 20, 22, 24, 26\}$

69. $B = \{2, 4, 6, \ldots, 30\}$

70. $B = \{1, 3, 5, \ldots, 21\}$

71. $C = \{x|x$ is a day of the week that begins with the letter A$\}$

72. $C = \{x|x$ is a month of the year that begins with the letter W$\}$

73. $D = \{$five$\}$

74. $D = \{$six$\}$

75. $A = \{x|x$ is a letter in the word *five*$\}$

76. $A = \{x|x$ is a letter in the word *six*$\}$

77. $B = \{x|x \in \mathbf{N}$ and $2 \le x < 7\}$

78. $B = \{x|x \in \mathbf{N}$ and $3 \le x < 10\}$

79. $C = \{x|x < 4$ and $x \ge 12\}$

80. $C = \{x|x < 5$ and $x \ge 15\}$

In Exercises 81–90,

     a. *Are the sets equivalent? Explain.*

     b. *Are the sets equal? Explain.*

81. A is the set of students at your college. B is the set of students majoring in business at your college.

82. A is the set of states in the United States. B is the set of people who are now governors of the states in the United States.

83. $A = \{1, 2, 3, 4, 5\}$
$B = \{0, 1, 2, 3, 4\}$

84. $A = \{1, 3, 5, 7, 9\}$
$B = \{2, 4, 6, 8, 10\}$

85. $A = \{1, 1, 1, 2, 2, 3, 4\}$
$B = \{4, 3, 2, 1\}$

86. $A = \{0, 1, 1, 2, 2, 2, 3, 3, 3, 3\}$
$B = \{3, 2, 1, 0\}$

87. $A = \{x|x \in \mathbf{N}$ and $6 \le x < 10\}$
$B = \{x|x \in \mathbf{N}$ and $9 < x \le 13\}$

88. $A = \{x|x \in \mathbf{N}$ and $12 < x \le 17\}$
$B = \{x|x \in \mathbf{N}$ and $20 \le x < 25\}$

89. $A = \{x|x \in \mathbf{N}$ and $100 \le x \le 105\}$
$B = \{x|x \in \mathbf{N}$ and $99 < x < 106\}$

90. $A = \{x|x \in \mathbf{N}$ and $200 \le x \le 206\}$
$B = \{x|x \in \mathbf{N}$ and $199 < x < 207\}$

In Exercises 91–96, determine whether each set is finite or infinite.

91. $\{x|x \in \mathbf{N}$ and $x \ge 100\}$

92. $\{x|x \in \mathbf{N}$ and $x \ge 50\}$

93. $\{x|x \in \mathbf{N}$ and $x \le 1{,}000{,}000\}$

94. $\{x|x \in \mathbf{N}$ and $x \le 2{,}000{,}000\}$

95. The set of natural numbers less than 1

96. The set of natural numbers less than 0

• Practice Plus

In Exercises 97–100, express each set using set-builder notation. Use inequality notation to express the condition x must meet in order to be a member of the set. (More than one correct inequality may be possible.)

97. $\{61, 62, 63, 64, \ldots\}$

98. $\{36, 37, 38, 39, \ldots\}$

99. $\{61, 62, 63, 64, \ldots, 89\}$

100. $\{36, 37, 38, 39, \ldots, 59\}$

In Exercises 101–104, give examples of two sets that meet the given conditions. If the conditions are impossible to satisfy, explain why.

101. The two sets are equivalent but not equal.

102. The two sets are equivalent and equal.

103. The two sets are equal but not equivalent.

104. The two sets are neither equivalent nor equal.

• Application Exercises

The bar graph shows the countries with the greatest percentage of their population having used marijuana. In Exercises 105–112, use the information given by the graph to represent each set by the roster method, or use the appropriate notation to indicate that the set is the empty set.

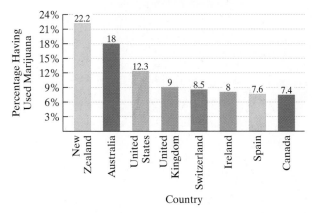

Reefer Madness: Countries with the Greatest Marijuana Use

Source: Organization for Economic Cooperation and Development

105. The set of countries in which the percentage using marijuana exceeds 12%

106. The set of countries in which the percentage using marijuana exceeds 9%

107. The set of countries in which the percentage using marijuana is at least 8% and at most 18%

108. The set of countries in which the percentage using marijuana is at least 8.5% and at most 20%

109. $\{x \,|\, x$ is a country in which $8\% \leq$ percentage using marijuana $< 12.3\%\}$

110. $\{x \,|\, x$ is a country in which $7.6\% \leq$ percentage using marijuana $< 9\%\}$

111. $\{x \,|\, x$ is a country in which percentage using marijuana $> 22.2\%\}$

112. $\{x \,|\, x$ is a country in which percentage using marijuana $\geq 22.2\%\}$

A study of 900 working women in Texas showed that their feelings changed throughout the day. The line graph shows 15 different times in a day and the average level of happiness for the women at each time. Based on the information given by the graph, represent each of the sets in Exercises 113–116 using the roster method.

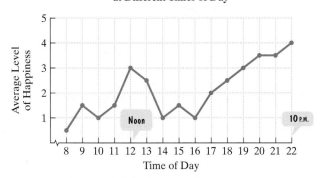

Average Level of Happiness at Different Times of Day

Time of Day

Source: D. Kahneman et al. "A Survey Method for Characterizing Daily Life Experience," *Science*.

113. $\{x \,|\, x$ is a time of the day when the average level of happiness is 3$\}$

114. $\{x \,|\, x$ is a time of the day when the average level of happiness is 1$\}$

115. $\{x \,|\, x$ is a time of the day when 3 $<$ average level of happiness $< 4\}$

116. $\{x \,|\, x$ is a time of the day when 3 $<$ average level of happiness $\leq 4\}$

117. Do the results of Exercise 113 or 114 indicate a one-to-one correspondence between the set representing the time of day and the set representing average level of happiness? Are these sets equivalent?

• Writing in Mathematics

118. What is a set?

119. Describe the three methods used to represent a set. Give an example of a set represented by each method.

120. What is the empty set?

121. Explain what is meant by *equivalent sets*.

122. Explain what is meant by *equal sets*.

123. Use cardinality to describe the difference between a finite set and an infinite set.

• Critical Thinking Exercises

124. Which one of the following is true?

   a. Two sets can be equal but not equivalent.

   b. Any set in roster notation that contains three dots must be an infinite set.

   c. $n(\varnothing) = 1$

   d. Some sets that can be written in set-builder notation cannot be written in roster form.

125. Which one of the following is true?

   a. The set of fractions between 0 and 1 is an infinite set.

   b. The set of multiples of 4 between 0 and 4,000,000,000 is an infinite set.

   c. If the elements in a set cannot be counted in a trillion years, the set is an infinite set.

   d. Because 0 is not a natural number, it can be deleted from any set without changing the set's cardinality.

126. In a certain town, a barber shaves all those men and only those men who do not shave themselves. Consider each of the following sets:

   $A = \{x \,|\, x$ is a man of the town who shaves himself$\}$

   $B = \{x \,|\, x$ is a man of the town who does not shave himself$\}$.

   The one and only barber in the town is Sweeney Todd. If s represents Sweeney Todd,

   a. is $s \in A$?

   b. is $s \in B$?

SECTION 2.2 • SUBSETS

OBJECTIVES

1. Recognize subsets and use the notation ⊆.
2. Recognize proper subsets and use the notation ⊂.
3. Determine the number of subsets of a set.
4. Apply concepts of subsets and equivalent sets to infinite sets.

TABLE 2.5 PERCENTAGE OF TATTOOED AMERICANS, BY AGE GROUP

Age Group	Percent Tattooed
18–24	13%
25–29	36%
30–39	28%
40–49	14%
50–64	10%
65+	7%

Source: Harris Interactive

1 | Recognize subsets and use the notation ⊆.

Emerging from their often unsavory reputation of the recent past, tattoos have gained increasing prominence as a form of body art and self-expression. A Harris poll conducted in 2003 estimated that 30 million Americans, or 16% of the adult population, have at least one tattoo.

Table 2.5 shows the percentage of Americans, by age group, with tattoos. The categories in the table divide the set of tattooed Americans into smaller sets, called *subsets*, based on age. The age subsets can be broken into still-smaller subsets. For example, tattooed Americans ages 25–29 can be categorized by gender, political party affiliation, race/ethnicity, or any other area of interest. This suggests numerous possible subsets of the set of Americans with tattoos. Every American in each of these subsets is also a member of the set of tattooed Americans.

Subsets

Situations in which all the elements of one set are also elements of another set are described by the following definition:

DEFINITION OF A SUBSET OF A SET
Set A is a **subset** of set B, expressed as

$$A \subseteq B,$$

if every element in set A is also an element in set B.

Let's apply this definition to the set of people ages 25–29 in Table 2.5.

The set of tattooed Americans in the 25-29 age group — is a subset of — the set of all tattooed Americans.

$\{x \mid x$ is a tattooed American and $25 \leq x$'s age $\leq 29\}$ $\subseteq$ $\{x \mid x$ is a tattooed American$\}$

Every person in this set, to the left of the subset symbol, — is also a member of this set, to the right of the subset symbol.

The notation $A \not\subseteq B$ means that A **is not a subset** of B. Set A is not a subset of set B if there is at least one element of set A that is not an element of set B. For example, consider the following sets:

$$A = \{1, 2, 3\} \quad \text{and} \quad B = \{1, 2\}.$$

Can you see that 3 is an element of set A that is not in set B? Thus, set A is not a subset of set B: $A \not\subseteq B$.

We can show that $A \subseteq B$ by showing that every element of set A also occurs as an element of set B. We can show that $A \not\subseteq B$ by finding one element of set A that is not in set B.

EXAMPLE 1   USING THE SYMBOLS $\subseteq$ AND $\not\subseteq$

Write $\subseteq$ or $\not\subseteq$ in each blank to form a true statement:

a. $A = \{1, 3, 5, 7\}$
$B = \{1, 3, 5, 7, 9, 11\}$
A____B

b. $A = \{x \mid x \text{ is a letter in the word } proof\}$
$B = \{y \mid y \text{ is a letter in the word } roof\}$
A____B

c. $A = \{x \mid x \text{ is a planet of Earth's solar system}\}$
$B = \{\text{Mercury, Venus, Earth, Mars, Jupiter, Saturn, Uranus, Neptune}\}$
A____B.

SOLUTION

a. All the elements of $A = \{1, 3, 5, 7\}$ are also contained in $B = \{1, 3, 5, 7, 9, 11\}$. Therefore, set A is a subset of set B:

$$A \subseteq B.$$

b. Let's write the set of letters in the word *proof* and the set of letters in the word *roof* in roster form. In each case, we consider only the distinct elements, so there is no need to repeat the o.

$$A = \{p, r, o, f\} \qquad B = \{r, o, f\}$$

> The element p is in set A but not in set B.

Because there is an element in set A that is not in set B, set A is not a subset of set B:

$$A \not\subseteq B.$$

c. All the elements of

$$A = \{x \mid x \text{ is a planet of the Earth's solar system}\}$$

are contained in

$$B = \{\text{Mercury, Venus, Earth, Mars, Jupiter, Saturn, Uranus, Neptune}\}.$$

Furthermore, the sets are equal ($A = B$). Because all elements in set A are also in set B, set A is a subset of set B:

$$A \subseteq B.$$

Write $\subseteq$ or $\not\subseteq$ in each blank to form a true statement:

a. $A = \{1, 3, 5, 6, 9, 11\}$
$B = \{1, 3, 5, 7\}$
A____B

b. $A = \{x \mid x \text{ is a letter in the word } roof\}$
$B = \{y \mid y \text{ is a letter in the word } proof\}$
A____B

c. $A = \{x \mid x \text{ is a day of the week}\}$
$B = \{\text{Monday, Tuesday, Wednesday, Thursday, Friday, Saturday, Sunday}\}$
A____B.

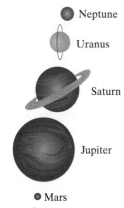

Neptune

Uranus

Saturn

Jupiter

Mars
Earth
Venus
Mercury

The eight planets in Earth's solar system

No, we did not forget Pluto. In 2006, based on the requirement that a planet must dominate its own orbit (Pluto is slave to Neptune's orbit), the International Astronomical Union removed Pluto from the list of planets and decreed that it belonged to a new category of heavenly body, a "dwarf planet."

Proper Subsets

In Example 1(c) and Check Point 1(c), the given equal sets illustrate that **every set is a subset of itself**. If A is any set, then $A \subseteq A$ because it is obvious that each element of A is a member of A.

If we know that set A is a subset of set B and we exclude the possibility of equal sets, then set A is called a *proper subset* of set B, written $A \subset B$.

> **DEFINITION OF A PROPER SUBSET OF A SET**
> Set A is a **proper subset** of set B, expressed as $A \subset B$, if set A is a subset of set B and sets A and B are not equal $(A \neq B)$.

Try not to confuse the symbols for subset, $\subseteq$, and proper subset, $\subset$. Because the lower half of the subset symbol in $A \subseteq B$ suggests an equal sign, it is *possible* that sets A and B are equal, although they do not have to be. By contrast, the missing lower line for the proper subset symbol in $A \subset B$ indicates that sets A and B *cannot* be equal.

STUDY TIP

- The notation for "is a subset of," $\subseteq$, is similar to the notation for "is less than or equal to," $\leq$. Because the notations share similar ideas, $A \subseteq B$ applies to finite sets only if set A is smaller than or equal to set B.

- The notation for "is a proper subset of," $\subset$, is similar to the notation for "is less than," $<$. Because the notations share similar ideas, $A \subset B$ applies to finite sets only if set A is smaller than set B.

EXAMPLE 2   USING THE SYMBOLS $\subseteq$ AND $\subset$

Write $\subseteq$, $\subset$, or both in each blank to form a true statement:

a. $A = \{x \mid x \text{ is a person and } x \text{ lives in San Francisco}\}$
$B = \{x \mid x \text{ is a person and } x \text{ lives in California}\}$
A____B

b. $A = \{2, 4, 6, 8\}$
$B = \{2, 8, 4, 6\}$
A____B.

SOLUTION

a. Every person living in San Francisco is also a person living in California. Because each person in set A is contained in set B, set A is a subset of set B:

$$A \subseteq B.$$

Can you see that the two sets do not contain the same elements and, consequently, are not equal? A person living in California outside San Francisco is in set B, but not in set A. Because the sets are not equal, set A is a proper subset of set B:

$$A \subset B.$$

The symbols $\subseteq$ and $\subset$ can both be placed in the blank to form a true statement.

b. Every number in $A = \{2, 4, 6, 8\}$ is contained in $B = \{2, 8, 4, 6\}$, so set A is a subset of set B:

$$A \subseteq B.$$

Because the sets contain the same elements and are equal, set A is *not* a proper subset of set B. The symbol $\subset$ cannot be placed in the blank if we want to form a true statement. (Because set A is not a proper subset of set B, it is correct to write $A \not\subset B$.)

○

2 Write ⊆, ⊂, or both in each blank to form a true statement:

 a. $A = \{2, 4, 6, 8\}$

   $B = \{2, 8, 4, 6, 10\}$

   A_____B

 b. $A = \{x \mid x \text{ is a person and } x \text{ lives in Atlanta}\}$

   $B = \{x \mid x \text{ is a person and } x \text{ lives in Georgia}\}$

   A_____B.

STUDY TIP

Do not confuse the symbols ∈ and ⊆. The symbol ∈ means "is an element of" and the symbol ⊆ means "is a subset of." Notice the difference between the following true statements:

$$4 \in \{4, 8\} \qquad\qquad \{4\} \subseteq \{4, 8\}.$$

> 4 is an element of the set {4, 8}.

> The **set** containing 4 is a subset of the set {4, 8}.

Subsets and the Empty Set

The meaning of $A \subseteq B$ leads to some interesting properties of the empty set.

EXAMPLE 3   THE EMPTY SET AS A SUBSET

Let $A = \{\ \}$ and $B = \{1, 2, 3, 4, 5\}$. Is $A \subseteq B$?

SOLUTION A is not a subset of B ($A \nsubseteq B$) if there is at least one element of set A that is not an element of set B. Because A represents the empty set, there are no elements in set A, period, much less elements in A that do not belong to B. Because we cannot find an element in $A = \{\ \}$ that is not contained in $B = \{1, 2, 3, 4, 5\}$, this means that $A \subseteq B$. Equivalently, $\emptyset \subseteq B$.

 3 Let $A = \{\ \}$ and $B = \{6, 7, 8\}$. Is $A \subseteq B$?

 Example 3 illustrates the principle that **the empty set is a subset of every set.** Furthermore, the empty set is a proper subset of every set except itself.

> **THE EMPTY SET AS A SUBSET**
>
> **1.** For any set B, $\emptyset \subseteq B$.
> **2.** For any set B other than the empty set, $\emptyset \subset B$.

The Number of Subsets of a Given Set

3   Determine the number of subsets of a set.

If a set contains n elements, how many subsets can be formed? Let's observe some special cases, namely sets with $0, 1, 2,$ and 3 elements. We can use inductive reasoning to arrive at a general conclusion. We begin by listing subsets and counting the number of subsets in our list. This is shown in Table 2.6 on the next page.

TABLE 2.6 THE NUMBER OF SUBSETS: SOME SPECIAL CASES

Set	Number of Elements	List of All Subsets	Number of Subsets
{ }	0	{ }	1
{a}	1	{a}, { }	2
{a, b}	2	{a, b}, {a}, {b}, { }	4
{a, b, c}	3	{a, b, c}, {a, b}, {a, c}, {b, c}, {a}, {b}, {c}, { }	8

Table 2.6 suggests that when we increase the number of elements in the set by one, the number of subsets doubles. The number of subsets appears to be a power of 2.

Number of elements	0	1	2	3
Number of subsets	$1 = 2^0$	$2 = 2^1$	$4 = 2 \times 2 = 2^2$	$8 = 2 \times 2 \times 2 = 2^3$

The power of 2 is the same as the number of elements in the set. Using inductive reasoning, if the set contains n elements, then the number of subsets that can be formed is 2^n.

NUMBER OF SUBSETS

The number of subsets of a set with n elements is 2^n.

For a given set, we know that every subset except the set itself is a proper subset. In Table 2.6, we included the set itself when counting the number of subsets. If we want to find the number of proper subsets, we must exclude counting the given set, thereby decreasing the number by 1.

NUMBER OF PROPER SUBSETS

The number of proper subsets of a set with n elements is $2^n - 1$.

EXAMPLE 4 FINDING THE NUMBER OF SUBSETS AND PROPER SUBSETS

Find the number of subsets and the number of proper subsets for each set:

a. {a, b, c, d, e}

b. $\{x \mid x \in \mathbf{N}$ and $9 \le x \le 15\}$.

SOLUTION

a. A set with n elements has 2^n subsets. Because the set {a, b, c, d, e} contains 5 elements, there are $2^5 = 2 \times 2 \times 2 \times 2 \times 2 = 32$ subsets. Of these, we must exclude counting the given set as a proper subset, so there are $2^5 - 1 = 32 - 1 = 31$ proper subsets.

b. We can write $\{x \mid x \in \mathbf{N}$ and $9 \le x \le 15\}$ in roster form as {9, 10, 11, 12, 13, 14, 15}. Because this set contains 7 elements, there are $2^7 = 2 \times 2 \times 2 \times 2 \times 2 \times 2 \times 2 = 128$ subsets. Of these, there are $2^7 - 1 = 128 - 1 = 127$ proper subsets. ○

4 Find the number of subsets and the number of proper subsets for each set:

a. {a, b, c, d}   **b.** $\{x \mid x \in \mathbf{N}$ and $3 \le x \le 8\}$.

**Smartest Dogs
Rank/Breed**

1. Border collie

2. Poodle

3. German shepherd

4. Golden retriever
Source: The Intelligence of Dogs

EXAMPLE 5 FINDING THE NUMBER OF SUBSETS AND PROPER SUBSETS

According to *The Intelligence of Dogs* by Stanley Coren, the four smartest breeds of dogs are

1. Border collie
2. Poodle
3. German shepherd
4. Golden retriever.

A man is trying to decide whether to buy a dog. He can afford up to four dogs, but may buy fewer or none at all. However, if the man makes a purchase, he will buy one or more of the four smartest breeds. The kennel has only one dog from each breed—that is, one border collie, one poodle, one German shepherd, and one golden retriever.

a. Consider the set that represents these breeds:

{border collie, poodle, German shepherd, golden retriever}.

Find the number of subsets of this set. What does this number represent in practical terms?

b. List all the subsets and describe what they represent for the prospective dog owner.

c. How many of the subsets are proper subsets?

SOLUTION

a. A set with n elements has 2^n subsets. Because the set of breeds contains four elements, the number of subsets is $2^4 = 2 \times 2 \times 2 \times 2 = 16$. In practical terms, there are 16 different ways to make a selection.

b. Purchase no dogs: $\varnothing$

Purchase one dog: {border collie}, {poodle}, {German shepherd}, {golden retriever}

Purchase two dogs: {border collie, poodle},

{border collie, German shepherd},

{border collie, golden retriever},

{poodle, German shepherd},

{poodle, golden retriever},

{German shepherd, golden retriever}

Purchase three dogs: {border collie, poodle, German shepherd},

{border collie, poodle, golden retriever},

{border collie, German shepherd, golden retriever},

{poodle, German shepherd, golden retriever}

Purchase four dogs: {border collie, poodle, German shepherd, golden retriever}

As predicted in part(a), 16 different selections are possible.

c. Every set except

{border collie, poodle, German shepherd, golden retriever}

is a proper subset of the given set. There are $16 - 1$, or 15, proper subsets. Although we obtained this number by counting, we can also use the fact that the number of proper subsets of a set with n elements is $2^n - 1$. Because the set of breeds contains four elements, there are $2^4 - 1$ proper subsets:

$$2^4 - 1 = (2 \times 2 \times 2 \times 2) - 1 = 16 - 1 = 15 \text{ proper subsets.}$$

5 You recently purchased three books, shown by the set

{*The Da Vinci Code*, *The Lord of the Rings*, *America* (*The Book*)}.

Now you are deciding which books, if any, to take on vacation. You have enough room to pack up to three books, but may take fewer or none at all.

a. Find the number of subsets of the given set. What does this number represent in practical terms?

b. List all the subsets and describe what they represent in terms of vacation reading.

c. How many of the subsets are proper subsets?

---

4 | Apply concepts of subsets and equivalent sets to infinite sets.

"Infinity is where things happen that don't."

W. W. Sawyer, *Prelude to Mathematics*, Penguin Books, 1960

The Number of Subsets of Infinite Sets

In Section 2.1, we mentioned that the infinite set of natural numbers, $\{1, 2, 3, 4, 5, 6, \dots\}$, is assigned the transfinite cardinal number $\aleph_0$ (read "aleph-null"). Equivalently, there are $\aleph_0$ natural numbers.

Once we accept the cardinality of sets with infinitely many elements, a surreal world emerges in which there is no end to an ascending hierarchy of infinities. Because the set of natural numbers contains $\aleph_0$ elements, it has $2^{\aleph_0}$ subsets, where $2^{\aleph_0} > \aleph_0$. Denoting $2^{\aleph_0}$ by $\aleph_1$, we have $\aleph_1 > \aleph_0$. Because the set of subsets of the natural numbers contains $\aleph_1$ elements, it has $2^{\aleph_1}$ subsets, where $2^{\aleph_1} > \aleph_1$. Denoting $2^{\aleph_1}$ by $\aleph_2$, we now have $\aleph_2 > \aleph_1 > \aleph_0$. Continuing in this manner, $\aleph_0$ is the "smallest" transfinite cardinal number in an infinite hierarchy of different infinities!

BLITZER BONUS

Cardinal Numbers of Infinite Sets

P. J. Crook, *Time and Time Again* 1981. Courtesy Barry Friedman Limited, New York.

The mirrors in the painting *Time and Time Again* have the effect of repeating the image infinitely many times, creating an endless tunnel of mirror images. There is something quite fascinating about the idea of endless infinity. Did you know that for thousands of years religious leaders warned that human beings should not examine the nature of the infinite? Religious teaching often equated infinity with the concept of a Supreme Being. One of the last victims of the Inquisition, Giordano Bruno, was burned at the stake for his explorations into the characteristics of infinity. It was not until the 1870s that the German mathematician Georg Cantor (1845–1918) began a careful analysis of the mathematics of infinity.

It was Cantor who assigned the transfinite cardinal number $\aleph_0$ to the set of natural numbers. He used one-to-one correspondences to establish some surprising equivalences between the set of natural numbers and its proper subsets. Here are two examples:

Natural Numbers: $\{1, 2, 3, 4, \ 5, \ 6, \ ..., \ n, ...\}$

Even Natural Numbers: $\{2, 4, 6, 8, 10, 12, ..., 2n, ...\}$

Each natural number, n, is paired with its double, $2n$, in the set of even natural numbers.

Natural Numbers: $\{1, 2, 3, 4, 5, 6, ..., n, ...\}$

Odd Natural Numbers: $\{1, 3, 5, 7, 9, 11, ..., 2n - 1, ...\}$

Each natural number, n, is paired with 1 less than its double, $2n$ - 1, in the set of odd natural numbers.

These one-to-one correspondences indicate that the set of even natural numbers and the set of odd natural numbers are equivalent to the set of all natural numbers. In fact, an infinite set, such as the natural numbers, can be *defined* as any set that can be placed in a one-to-one correspondence with a proper subset of itself. This definition boggles the mind because it implies that part of a set has the same number of objects as the entire set. There are $\aleph_0$ even natural numbers, $\aleph_0$ odd natural numbers, and $\aleph_0$ natural numbers. Because the even and odd natural numbers combined make up the entire set of natural numbers, we are confronted with an unusual statement of transfinite arithmetic:

$$\aleph_0 + \aleph_0 = \aleph_0.$$

As Cantor continued studying infinite sets, his observations grew stranger and stranger. It was Cantor who showed that some infinite sets contain more elements than others. This was too much for his colleagues, who considered this work ridiculous. Cantor's mentor, Leopold Kronecker, told him, "Look at the crazy ideas that are now surfacing with your work with infinite sets. How can one infinity be greater than another? Best to ignore such inconsistencies. By considering these monsters and infinite numbers mathematics, I will make sure that you never gain a faculty position at the University of Berlin." Although Cantor was not burned at the stake, universal condemnation of his work resulted in numerous nervous breakdowns. His final days, sadly, were spent in a psychiatric hospital. However, Cantor's work later regained the respect of mathematicians. Today, he is seen as a great mathematician who demystified infinity.

EXERCISE SET 2.2 ●●●●●○

• Practice Exercises

In Exercises 1–12, write $\subseteq$ or $\nsubseteq$ in each blank so that the resulting statement is true.

1. $\{1, 2, 5\}$ _____ $\{1, 2, 3, 4, 5, 6, 7\}$

2. $\{2, 3, 7\}$ _____ $\{1, 2, 3, 4, 5, 6, 7\}$

3. $\{-3, 0, 3\}$ _____ $\{-3, -1, 1, 3\}$

4. $\{-4, 0, 4\}$ _____ $\{-4, -3, -1, 1, 3, 4\}$

5. $\{\text{Monday, Friday}\}$ _____
$\{\text{Saturday, Sunday, Monday, Tuesday, Wednesday}\}$

6. $\{\text{Mercury, Venus, Earth}\}$ _____
$\{\text{Venus, Earth, Mars, Jupiter}\}$

7. $\{x | x$ is a key on a piano$\}$ _____
$\{x | x$ is a black key on a piano$\}$

8. $\{x | x$ is a dog$\}$ _____ $\{x | x$ is a pure-bred dog$\}$

9. $\{c, o, n, v, e, r, s, a, t, i, o, n\}$ _____
$\{v, o, i, c, e, s, r, a, n, t, o, n\}$

10. $\{r, e, v, o, l, u, t, i, o, n\}$ _____ $\{t, o, l, o, v, e, r, u, i, n\}$

11. $\left\{\frac{4}{7}, \frac{9}{13}\right\}$ _____ $\left\{\frac{7}{4}, \frac{13}{9}\right\}$

12. $\left\{\frac{1}{2}, \frac{1}{3}\right\}$ _____ $\{2, 3, 5\}$

In Exercises 13–22, determine whether $\subseteq$, $\subset$, both, or neither can be placed in each blank to form a true statement.

13. $\{\text{V, C, R}\}$ _____ $\{\text{V, C, R, S}\}$

14. $\{\text{F, I, N}\}$ _____ $\{\text{F, I, N, K}\}$

15. $\{0, 2, 4, 6, 8\}$ _____ $\{8, 0, 6, 2, 4\}$

16. $\{9, 1, 7, 3, 4\}$ _____ $\{1, 3, 4, 7, 9\}$

17. $\{x | x$ is a person living in Alabama$\}$ _____
$\{y | y$ is a person living in the American South$\}$

18. $\{x | x$ is a person living in Massachusetts$\}$ _____
$\{y | y$ is a person living in a New England state$\}$

19. $\{x | x$ is a person living in Washington, D.C.$\}$ _____
$\{y | y$ is a person living in the U.S. capital$\}$

20. $\{x | x$ is a person living in London$\}$ _____
$\{y | y$ is a person living in the capital of England$\}$

21. $\{x | x$ is a person living in Alabama$\}$ _____
$\{y | y$ is a person living in Birmingham$\}$

22. $\{x | x$ is a person living in Massachusetts$\}$ _____
$\{y | y$ is a person living in Boston$\}$

In Exercises 23–36, determine whether each statement is true or false. If the statement is false, explain why.

23. Ralph $\in \{\text{Ralph, Alice, Trixie, Norton}\}$

24. Canada $\in \{\text{Mexico, United States, Canada}\}$

25. Ralph $\subseteq \{\text{Ralph, Alice, Trixie, Norton}\}$

26. Canada $\subseteq \{\text{Mexico, United States, Canada}\}$

27. $\{\text{Ralph}\} \subseteq \{\text{Ralph, Alice, Trixie, Norton}\}$

28. $\{\text{Canada}\} \subseteq \{\text{Mexico, United States, Canada}\}$

29. $\varnothing \in \{\text{Archie, Edith, Mike, Gloria}\}$

30. $\varnothing \subseteq \{\text{Charlie Chaplin, Groucho Marx, Woody Allen}\}$

31. $\{4\} \in \{\{4\}, \{8\}\}$ **32.** $\{1\} \in \{\{1\}, \{3\}\}$

33. $\{1, 4\} \nsubseteq \{4, 1\}$ **34.** $\{1, 4\} \not\subset \{4, 1\}$

35. $0 \notin \varnothing$ **36.** $0 \nsubseteq \varnothing$

In Exercises 37–42, list all the subsets of the given set.

37. {border collie, poodle} **38.** {Romeo, Juliet}

39. {t, a, b} **40.** {I, II, III}

41. {0} **42.** ∅

In Exercises 43–50, calculate the number of subsets and the number of proper subsets for each set.

43. {2, 4, 6, 8} **44.** $\left\{\frac{1}{2}, \frac{1}{3}, \frac{1}{4}, \frac{1}{5}\right\}$

45. {2, 4, 6, 8, 10, 12} **46.** {a, b, c, d, e, f}

47. {x | x is a day of the week}

48. {x | x is a U.S. coin worth less than a dollar}

49. {x | x ∈ **N** and 2 < x < 6}

50. {x | x ∈ **N** and 2 ≤ x ≤ 6}

• Practice Plus

In Exercises 51–64, determine whether each statement is true or false. If the statement is false, make the necessary change(s) to produce a true statement.

51. The set {1, 2, 3, ..., 1000} has 2^{1000} proper subsets.

52. The set {1, 2, 3, ..., 10,000} has $2^{10,000}$ proper subsets.

53. {x | x ∈ **N** and 30 < x < 50} ⊆ {x | x ∈ **N** and 30 ≤ x ≤ 50}

54. {x | x ∈ **N** and 20 ≤ x ≤ 60} ⊄ {x | x ∈ **N** and 20 < x < 60}

55. ∅ ⊄ {∅, {∅}} **56.** {∅} ⊄ {∅, {∅}}

57. ∅ ∈ {∅, {∅}} **58.** {∅} ∈ {∅, {∅}}

59. If A ⊆ B and d ∈ A, then d ∈ B.

60. If A ⊆ B and B ⊆ C, then A ⊆ C.

61. If set A is equivalent to the set of natural numbers, then $n(A) = \aleph_0$.

62. If set A is equivalent to the set of even natural numbers, then $n(A) = \aleph_0$.

63. The set of subsets of {a, e, i, o, u} contains 64 elements.

64. The set of subsets of {a, b, c, d, e, f} contains 128 elements.

• Application Exercises

Sets and subsets allow us to order and structure data. In the data shown below, the set of tattooed Americans is divided into subsets categorized by party affiliation. These subsets are further broken down into subsets categorized by gender. All numbers in the branching tree diagram are based on the number of people per 10,000 American adults.

Breakdown of Tattooed Americans by Party Affiliation and Gender

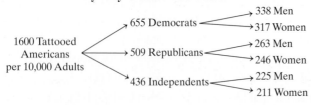

Source: Harris Interactive

Let

T = the set of tattooed Americans

R = the set of tattooed Republicans

D = the set of tattooed Democrats

M = the set of tattooed Democratic men

W = the set of tattooed Democratic women.

In Exercises 65–74, determine whether each statement is true or false. If the statement is false, make the necessary change(s) to produce a true statement.

65. D ∈ T **66.** R ∈ T

67. M ⊂ T **68.** W ⊂ T

69. If x ∈ D, then x ∈ W. **70.** If x ∈ D, then x ∈ M.

71. If x ∈ R, then x ∉ D. **72.** If x ∈ D, then x ∉ R.

73. The set of elements in M and W combined is equal to set D.

74. The set of elements in M and W combined is equivalent to set D.

Use the formula for the number of subsets of a set with n elements to solve Exercises 75–80.

75. Houses in Euclid Estates are all identical. However, a person can purchase a new house with some, all, or none of a set of options. This set includes {pool, screened-in balcony, lake view, alarm system, upgraded landscaping}. How many options are there for purchasing a house in this community?

76. A cheese pizza can be ordered with some, all, or none of the following set of toppings: {beef, ham, mushrooms, sausage, peppers, pepperoni, olives, prosciutto, onion}. How many different variations are available for ordering a pizza?

77. Based on more than 1500 ballots sent to film notables, the American Film Institute rated the top U.S. movies. The Institute selected *Citizen Kane* (1941), *Casablanca* (1942), *The Godfather* (1972), *Gone With the Wind* (1939), *Lawrence of Arabia* (1962), and *The Wizard of Oz* (1939) as the top six films. Suppose that you have all six films on video and decide to view some, all, or none of these films. How many viewing options do you have?

78. A small town has four police cars. If a radio dispatcher receives a call, depending on the nature of the situation, no cars, one car, two cars, three cars, or all four cars can be sent. How many options does the dispatcher have for sending the police cars to the scene of the caller?

79. According to the U.S. Census Bureau, the most ethnically diverse U.S. cities are New York City, Los Angeles, Miami, Chicago, Washington, D.C., Houston, San Diego, and Seattle. If you decide to visit some, all, or none of these cities, how many travel options do you have?

80. Some of the movies with all-time box office grosses include

Titanic ($601 million), *Star Wars: Episode IV—A New Hope* ($461 million), *Shrek 2* ($441 million),

E. T. the Extra-Terrestrial ($435 million),

Star Wars: Episode I—The Phantom Menace ($431 million),

Spider-Man ($404 million), and

The Lord of the Rings: The Return of the King ($377 million).

Suppose that you have all seven films on video and decide, over the course of a week, to view some, all, or none of these films. How many viewing options do you have?

• Writing in Mathematics

81. Explain what is meant by a subset.

82. What is the difference between a subset and a proper subset?

83. Explain why the empty set is a subset of every set.

84. Describe the difference between the symbols $\in$ and $\subseteq$. Explain how each symbol is used.

85. Describe the formula for finding the number of subsets for a given set. Give an example.

86. Describe how to find the number of proper subsets for a given set. Give an example.

• Critical Thinking Exercises

87. Which one of the following is true?

   a. The set $\{3\}$ has 2^3, or eight, subsets.

   b. All sets have subsets.

   c. Every set has a proper subset.

   d. The set $\{3, \{1, 4\}\}$ has eight subsets.

88. Suppose that a nickel, a dime, and a quarter are on a table. You may select some, all, or none of the coins. Specify all of the different amounts of money that can be selected.

89. If a set has 127 proper subsets, how many elements are there in the set?

• Group Exercises

90. This activity is a group research project and should result in a presentation made by group members to the entire class. Georg Cantor was certainly not the only genius in history who faced criticism during his lifetime, only to have his work acclaimed as a masterpiece after his death. Describe the life and work of three other people, including at least one mathematician, who faced similar circumstances.

91. Research useful Web sites and present a report on infinite sets and their cardinalities. Explain why the sets of whole numbers, integers, and rational numbers each have cardinal number $\aleph_0$. Be sure to define these sets and show the one-to-one correspondences between each set and the set of natural numbers. Then explain why the set of real numbers does not have cardinal number $\aleph_0$ by describing how a real number can always be left out in a pairing with the natural numbers. Spice up the more technical aspects of your report with ideas you discovered about infinity that you find particularly intriguing.

SECTION 2.3 • VENN DIAGRAMS AND SET OPERATIONS

OBJECTIVES

1. Understand the meaning of a universal set.

2. Understand the basic ideas of a Venn diagram.

3. Use Venn diagrams to visualize relationships between two sets.

4. Find the complement of a set.

5. Find the intersection of two sets.

6. Find the union of two sets.

7. Perform operations with sets.

8. Determine sets involving set operations from a Venn diagram.

9. Understand the meaning of *and* and *or*.

10. Use the formula for $n(A \cup B)$.

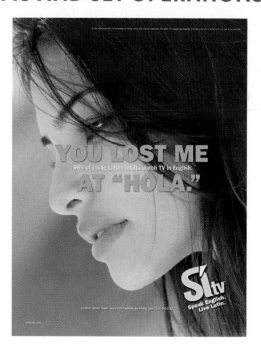

Sí TV, a 24-hour cable channel targeted to young U.S. Latinos, was launched in 2004 and is now in more than 15 million households. Its motto: "Speak English. Live Latin." As Latino spending power steadily rises, corporate America has discovered that Hispanic Americans, particularly young spenders between the ages of 14 and 34, want to be spoken to in English, even as they stay true to their Latino identity.

What is the primary language spoken at home by U.S. Hispanics? In this section, we use sets to analyze the answer to this question. By doing so, you will see how sets and their visual representations provide precise ways of organizing, classifying, and describing a wide variety of data.

1 Understand the meaning of a universal set.

Languages Spoken at Home by U.S. Hispanics

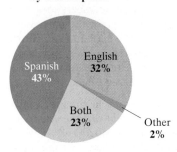

FIGURE 2.1
Source: Time, August 22, 2005

2 Understand the basic ideas of a Venn diagram.

STUDY TIP

The size of the circle representing set A in a Venn diagram has nothing to do with the number of elements in set A.

FIGURE 2.3

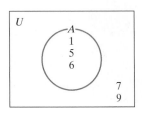

FIGURE 2.4

3 Use Venn diagrams to visualize relationships between two sets.

Universal Sets and Venn Diagrams

The circle graph in Figure 2.1 categorizes America's 40 million Hispanics by the primary language spoken at home. The graph's sectors define four sets:

- the set of U.S. Hispanics who speak Spanish at home
- the set of U.S. Hispanics who speak English at home
- the set of U.S. Hispanics who speak both Spanish and English at home
- the set of U.S. Hispanics who speak neither Spanish nor English at home.

In discussing sets, it is convenient to refer to a general set that contains all elements under discussion. This general set is called the *universal set*. A **universal set**, symbolized by U, is a set that contains all the elements being considered in a given discussion or problem. Thus, a convenient universal set for the sets described above is

$$U = \text{the set of U.S. Hispanics.}$$

Notice how this universal set restricts our attention so that we can divide it into the four subsets shown by the circle graph in Figure 2.1.

We can obtain a more thorough understanding of sets and their relationship to a universal set by considering diagrams that allow visual analysis. **Venn diagrams**, named for the British logician John Venn (1834–1923), are used to show the visual relationship among sets.

Figure 2.2 is a Venn diagram. The universal set is represented by a region inside a rectangle. Subsets within the universal set are depicted by circles, or sometimes by ovals or other shapes. In this Venn diagram, set A is represented by the light blue region inside the circle.

The dark blue region in Figure 2.2 represents the set of elements in the universal set U that are not in set A. By combining the regions shown by the light blue shading and the dark blue shading, we obtain the universal set, U.

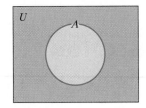

FIGURE 2.2

EXAMPLE 1 DETERMINING SETS FROM A VENN DIAGRAM

Use the Venn diagram in Figure 2.3 to determine each of the following sets:

a. U **b.** A **c.** the set of elements in U that are not in A.

SOLUTION

a. Set U, the universal set, consists of all the elements within the rectangle. Thus, $U = \{\square, \triangle, \$, M, 5\}$.

b. Set A consists of all the elements within the circle. Thus, $A = \{\square, \triangle\}$.

c. The set of elements in U that are not in A, shown by the set of all the elements outside the circle, is $\{\$, M, 5\}$.

 Use the Venn diagram in Figure 2.4 to determine each of the following sets:

a. U

b. A

c. the set of elements in U that are not in A.

Representing Two Sets in a Venn Diagram

There are a number of different ways to represent two subsets of a universal set in a Venn diagram. To help understand these representations, let's revisit the scenario that opened the chapter.

You need to determine whether there is sufficient support on campus to have a blood drive. You take a survey to obtain information, asking students

Would you be willing to donate blood?

Would you be willing to help serve a free breakfast to blood donors?

Set *A* represents the set of students willing to donate blood. Set *B* represents the set of students willing to help serve breakfast to donors. Possible survey results include the following:

- No students willing to donate blood are willing to serve breakfast, and vice versa.

- All students willing to donate blood are willing to serve breakfast.

- The same students who are willing to donate blood are willing to serve breakfast.

- Some of the students willing to donate blood are willing to serve breakfast.

We begin by using Venn diagrams to visualize these results. To do so, we consider four basic relationships and their visualizations.

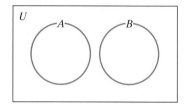

FIGURE 2.5

Relationship 1: Disjoint Sets Two sets that have no elements in common are called **disjoint sets**. Two disjoint sets, *A* and *B*, are shown in the Venn diagram in Figure 2.5. Disjoint sets are represented as circles that do not overlap. No elements of set *A* are elements of set *B*, and vice versa.

If set *A* represents the set of students willing to donate blood and set *B* represents the set of students willing to serve breakfast to donors, the set diagram illustrates

> No students willing to donate blood are willing to serve breakfast, and vice versa.

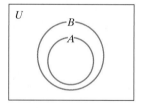

FIGURE 2.6

Relationship 2: Proper Subsets If set *A* is a proper subset of set *B* $(A \subset B)$, the relationship is shown in the Venn diagram in Figure 2.6. All elements of set *A* are elements of set *B*. If an *x* representing an element is placed inside circle *A*, it automatically falls inside circle *B*.

If set *A* represents the set of students willing to donate blood and set *B* represents the set of students willing to serve breakfast to donors, the set diagram illustrates

> All students willing to donate blood are willing to serve breakfast.

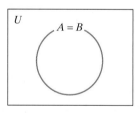

FIGURE 2.7

Relationship 3: Equal Sets If $A = B$, then set *A* contains exactly the same elements as set *B*. This relationship is shown in the Venn diagram in Figure 2.7. Because all elements in set *A* are in set *B*, and vice versa, this diagram illustrates that when $A = B$, then $A \subseteq B$ and $B \subseteq A$.

If set *A* represents the set of students willing to donate blood and set *B* represents the set of students willing to serve breakfast to donors, the set diagram illustrates

> The same students who are willing to donate blood are willing to serve breakfast.

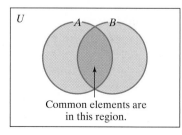

FIGURE 2.8

Relationship 4: Sets with Some Common Elements In mathematics, the word *some* means *there exists at least one*. If set *A* and set *B* have at least one element in common, then the circles representing the sets must overlap. This is illustrated in the Venn diagram in Figure 2.8.

If set *A* represents the set of students willing to donate blood and set *B* represents the set of students willing to serve breakfast to donors, the presence of at least one student in the dark blue region in Figure 2.8 illustrates

> Some students willing to donate blood are willing to serve breakfast.

In Figure 2.9 on the next page, we've numbered each of the regions in the Venn diagram in Figure 2.8. Let's make sure we understand what these regions represent in terms of the campus blood drive scenario. Remember that *A* is the set of blood donors and *B* is the set of breakfast servers.

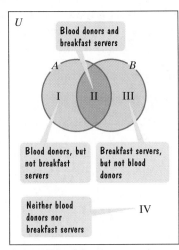

A: Set of blood donors
B: Set of breakfast servers

FIGURE 2.9

In Figure 2.9, we'll start with the innermost region, region II, and work outward to region IV.

Region II	This region represents the set of students willing to donate blood and serve breakfast. The elements that belong to both set A and set B are in this region.
Region I	This region represents the set of students willing to donate blood, but not serve breakfast. The elements that belong to set A but not to set B are in this region.
Region III	This region represents the set of students willing to serve breakfast, but not donate blood. The elements that belong to set B but not to set A are in this region.
Region IV	This region represents the set of students surveyed who are not willing to donate blood and are not willing to serve breakfast. The elements that belong to the universal set U that are not in sets A or B are in this region.

EXAMPLE 2   DETERMINING SETS FROM A VENN DIAGRAM

Use the Venn diagram in Figure 2.10 to determine each of the following sets:

a. U **b.** B

c. the set of elements in A but not B

d. the set of elements in U that are not in B

e. the set of elements in both A and B.

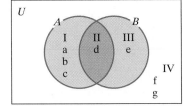

FIGURE 2.10

SOLUTION

a. Set U, the universal set, consists of all elements within the rectangle. Taking the elements in regions I, II, III, and IV, we obtain $U = \{a, b, c, d, e, f, g\}$.

b. Set B consists of the elements in regions II and III. Thus, $B = \{d, e\}$.

c. The set of elements in A but not B, found in region I, is $\{a, b, c\}$.

d. The set of elements in U that are not in B, found in regions I and IV, is $\{a, b, c, f, g\}$.

e. The set of elements in both A and B, found in region II, is $\{d\}$.

 Use the Venn diagram in Figure 2.10 to determine each of the following sets:

a. A; **b.** the set of elements in B but not A; **c.** the set of elements in U that are not in A; **d.** the set of elements in U that are not in A or B.

The Complement of a Set

4 | Find the complement of a set.

In arithmetic, we use operations such as addition and multiplication to combine numbers. We now turn to three set operations, called *complement, intersection,* and *union.* We begin by defining a set's complement.

DEFINITION OF THE COMPLEMENT OF A SET

The **complement** of set A, symbolized by A', is the set of all elements in the universal set that are *not* in A. This idea can be expressed in set-builder notation as follows:

$$A' = \{x | x \in U \text{ and } x \notin A\}.$$

[image: shaded region representing A' with U and A labeled]

FIGURE 2.11

The shaded region in Figure 2.11 represents the complement of set A, or A'. This region lies outside circle A, but within the rectangular universal set.

In order to find A', a universal set U must be given. A fast way to find A' is to cross out the elements in U that are given to be in set A. A' is the set that remains.

EXAMPLE 3   FINDING A SET'S COMPLEMENT

Let $U = \{1, 2, 3, 4, 5, 6, 7, 8, 9\}$ and $A = \{1, 3, 4, 7\}$. Find A'.

SOLUTION Set A' contains all the elements of set U that are not in set A. Because set A contains the elements 1, 3, 4, and 7, these elements cannot be members of set A':

$$\{\cancel{1}, 2, \cancel{3}, \cancel{4}, 5, 6, \cancel{7}, 8, 9\}.$$

Thus, set A' contains 2, 5, 6, 8, and 9:

$$A' = \{2, 5, 6, 8, 9\}.$$

A Venn diagram illustrating A and A' is shown in Figure 2.12.

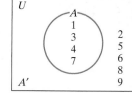

FIGURE 2.12

CHECK POINT 3 Let $U = \{a, b, c, d, e\}$ and $A = \{a, d\}$. Find A'.

5 Find the intersection of two sets.

The Intersection of Sets

If A and B are sets, we can form a new set consisting of all elements that are in both A and B. This set is called the *intersection* of the two sets.

> **DEFINITION OF THE INTERSECTION OF SETS**
> The **intersection** of sets A and B, written $A \cap B$, is the set of elements common to both set A and set B. This definition can be expressed in set-builder notation as follows:
> $$A \cap B = \{x \mid x \in A \quad \text{and} \quad x \in B\}.$$

In Example 4, we are asked to find the intersection of two sets. This is done by listing the common elements of both sets. Because the intersection of two sets is also a set, we enclose these elements with braces.

EXAMPLE 4   FINDING THE INTERSECTION OF TWO SETS

Find each of the following intersections:

a. $\{7, 8, 9, 10, 11\} \cap \{6, 8, 10, 12\}$
b. $\{1, 3, 5, 7, 9\} \cap \{2, 4, 6, 8\}$
c. $\{1, 3, 5, 7, 9\} \cap \emptyset$.

SOLUTION

a. The elements common to $\{7, 8, 9, 10, 11\}$ and $\{6, 8, 10, 12\}$ are 8 and 10. Thus,

$$\{7, 8, 9, 10, 11\} \cap \{6, 8, 10, 12\} = \{8, 10\}.$$

The Venn diagram in Figure 2.13 illustrates this situation.

b. The sets $\{1, 3, 5, 7, 9\}$ and $\{2, 4, 6, 8\}$ have no elements in common. Thus,

$$\{1, 3, 5, 7, 9\} \cap \{2, 4, 6, 8\} = \emptyset.$$

The Venn diagram in Figure 2.14 illustrates this situation. The sets are disjoint.

c. There are no elements in $\emptyset$, the empty set. This means that there can be no elements belonging to both $\{1, 3, 5, 7, 9\}$ and $\emptyset$. Therefore,

$$\{1, 3, 5, 7, 9\} \cap \emptyset = \emptyset.$$

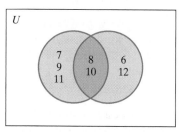

FIGURE 2.13 The numbers 8 and 10 belong to both sets.

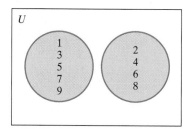

FIGURE 2.14 These disjoint sets have no common elements.

CHECK POINT 4 Find each of the following intersections:

  a. $\{1, 3, 5, 7, 10\} \cap \{6, 7, 10, 11\}$
  b. $\{1, 2, 3\} \cap \{4, 5, 6, 7\}$
  c. $\{1, 2, 3\} \cap \emptyset$.

The Union of Sets

6 Find the union of two sets.

Another set that we can form from sets A and B consists of elements that are in A or B or in both sets. This set is called the *union* of the two sets.

> ### DEFINITION OF THE UNION OF SETS
> The **union** of sets A and B, written $A \cup B$, is the set of elements that are members of set A or of set B or of both sets. This definition can be expressed in set-builder notation as follows:
> $$A \cup B = \{x \mid x \in A \quad \text{or} \quad x \in B\}.$$

We can find the union of set A and set B by listing the elements of set A. Then, we include any elements of set B that have not already been listed. Enclose all elements that are listed with braces. This shows that the union of two sets is also a set.

EXAMPLE 5   FINDING THE UNION OF TWO SETS

Find each of the following unions:

  a. $\{7, 8, 9, 10, 11\} \cup \{6, 8, 10, 12\}$
  b. $\{1, 3, 5, 7, 9\} \cup \{2, 4, 6, 8\}$
  c. $\{1, 3, 5, 7, 9\} \cup \emptyset$.

STUDY TIP

When finding the union of two sets, some elements may appear in both sets. List these common elements only once, *not twice*, in the union of the sets.

SOLUTION This example uses the same sets as in Example 4. However, this time we are finding the unions of the sets, rather than their intersections.

  a. To find $\{7, 8, 9, 10, 11\} \cup \{6, 8, 10, 12\}$, start by listing all the elements from the first set, namely 7, 8, 9, 10, and 11. Now list all the elements from the second set that are not in the first set, namely 6 and 12. The union is the set consisting of all these elements. Thus,
  $$\{7, 8, 9, 10, 11\} \cup \{6, 8, 10, 12\} = \{6, 7, 8, 9, 10, 11, 12\}.$$

  b. To find $\{1, 3, 5, 7, 9\} \cup \{2, 4, 6, 8\}$, list the elements from the first set, namely 1, 3, 5, 7, and 9. Now add to the list the elements in the second set that are not in the first set. This includes every element in the second set, namely 2, 4, 6, and 8. The union is the set consisting of all these elements, so
  $$\{1, 3, 5, 7, 9\} \cup \{2, 4, 6, 8\} = \{1, 2, 3, 4, 5, 6, 7, 8, 9\}.$$

  c. To find $\{1, 3, 5, 7, 9\} \cup \emptyset$, list the elements from the first set, namely 1, 3, 5, 7, and 9. Because there are no elements in $\emptyset$, the empty set, there are no additional elements to add to the list. Thus,
  $$\{1, 3, 5, 7, 9\} \cup \emptyset = \{1, 3, 5, 7, 9\}.$$

Examples 4 and 5 illustrate the role that the empty set plays in intersection and union.

> ### THE EMPTY SET IN INTERSECTION AND UNION
> For any set A,
> **1.** $A \cap \emptyset = \emptyset$
> **2.** $A \cup \emptyset = A$.

CHECK POINT 5 Find each of the following unions:

    a. $\{1, 3, 5, 7, 10\} \cup \{6, 7, 10, 11\}$

    b. $\{1, 2, 3\} \cup \{4, 5, 6, 7\}$

    c. $\{1, 2, 3\} \cup \varnothing$.

---

7 | Perform operations with sets.

Performing Set Operations

Some problems involve more than one set operation. The set notation specifies the order in which we perform these operations. **Always begin by performing any operations inside parentheses.** Here are two examples involving sets we will find in Example 6.

STUDY TIP

The words *union* and *intersection* are helpful in distinguishing these two operations. Union, as in a marriage union, suggests joining things, or uniting them. Intersection, as in the intersection of two crossing streets, brings to mind the area common to both, suggesting things that overlap.

- Finding $(A \cup B)'$

  Step 1. Parentheses indicate to first find the union of A and B.

  Step 2. Find the complement of $A \cup B$.

- Finding $A' \cap B'$

  Step 1. Find the complement of A.

  Step 2. Find the complement of B.

  Step 3. Find the intersection of A' and B'.

EXAMPLE 6   PERFORMING SET OPERATIONS

Given

$$U = \{1, 2, 3, 4, 5, 6, 7, 8, 9, 10\}$$
$$A = \{1, 3, 7, 9\}$$
$$B = \{3, 7, 8, 10\},$$

find each of the following sets:

    a. $(A \cup B)'$ **b.** $A' \cap B'$.

SOLUTION

a. To find $(A \cup B)'$ we will first work inside the parentheses and determine $A \cup B$. Then we'll find the complement of $A \cup B$, namely $(A \cup B)'$.

$$A \cup B = \{1, 3, 7, 9\} \cup \{3, 7, 8, 10\} \quad \text{These are the given sets.}$$
$$= \{1, 3, 7, 8, 9, 10\} \quad \text{Join (unite) the elements, listing the common elements (3 and 7) only once.}$$

Now find $(A \cup B)'$, the complement of $A \cup B$.

$$(A \cup B)' = \{1, 3, 7, 8, 9, 10\}'$$
$$= \{2, 4, 5, 6\} \quad \text{List the elements in the universal set that are not listed in } \{1, 3, 7, 8, 9, 10\}: \{\cancel{1}, 2, \cancel{3}, 4, 5, 6, \cancel{7}, \cancel{8}, \cancel{9}, \cancel{10}\}.$$

b. To find $A' \cap B'$, we must first identify the elements in A' and B'. Set A' is the set of elements of U that are not in set A:

$$A' = \{2, 4, 5, 6, 8, 10\}. \quad \text{List the elements in the universal set that are not listed in } A = \{1, 3, 7, 9\}: \{\cancel{1}, 2, \cancel{3}, 4, 5, 6, \cancel{7}, 8, \cancel{9}, 10\}.$$

Set B' is the set of elements of U that are not in set B:

$$B' = \{1, 2, 4, 5, 6, 9\}. \quad \text{List the elements in the universal set that are not listed in } B = \{3, 7, 8, 10\}: \{1, 2, \cancel{3}, 4, 5, 6, \cancel{7}, \cancel{8}, 9, \cancel{10}\}.$$

Now we can find $A' \cap B'$, the set of elements belonging to both A' and to B':

$$A' \cap B' = \{2, 4, 5, 6, 8, 10\} \cap \{1, 2, 4, 5, 6, 9\}$$

$$= \{2, 4, 5, 6\}.$$

The numbers 2, 4, 5, and 6 are common to both sets.

 Given $U = \{a, b, c, d, e\}$, $A = \{b, c\}$, and $B = \{b, c, e\}$, find each of the following sets:

a. $(A \cup B)'$ b. $A' \cap B'$.

EXAMPLE 7   DETERMINING SETS FROM A VENN DIAGRAM

8 Determine sets involving set operations from a Venn diagram.

The Venn diagram in Figure 2.15 percolates with interesting numbers. Use the diagram to determine each of the following sets:

a. $A \cup B$ b. $(A \cup B)'$ c. $A \cap B$

d. $(A \cap B)'$ e. $A' \cap B$ f. $A \cup B'$.

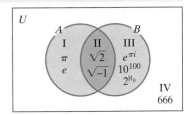

FIGURE 2.15

SOLUTION

Set to Determine	Description of Set	Regions in Venn Diagram	Set in Roster Form
a. $A \cup B$	set of elements in A or B or both	I, II, III	$\{\pi, e, \sqrt{2}, \sqrt{-1}, e^{\pi i}, 10^{100}, 2^{\aleph_0}\}$
b. $(A \cup B)'$	set of elements in U that are not in $A \cup B$	IV	$\{666\}$
c. $A \cap B$	set of elements in both A and B	II	$\{\sqrt{2}, \sqrt{-1}\}$
d. $(A \cap B)'$	set of elements in U that are not in $A \cap B$	I, III, IV	$\{\pi, e, e^{\pi i}, 10^{100}, 2^{\aleph_0}, 666\}$
e. $A' \cap B$	set of elements that are not in A and are in B	III	$\{e^{\pi i}, 10^{100}, 2^{\aleph_0}\}$
f. $A \cup B'$	set of elements that are in A or not in B or both	I, II, IV	$\{\pi, e, \sqrt{2}, \sqrt{-1}, 666\}$

FIGURE 2.16

 Use the Venn diagram in Figure 2.16 to determine each of the following sets:

a. $A \cap B$ b. $(A \cap B)'$ c. $A \cup B$

d. $(A \cup B)'$ e. $A' \cup B$ f. $A \cap B'$.

9 Understand the meaning of *and* and *or*.

Sets and Precise Use of Everyday English

Set operations and Venn diagrams provide precise ways of organizing, classifying, and describing the vast array of sets and subsets we encounter every day. Let's see how this applies to the sets from the beginning of this section:

U = the set of U.S. Hispanics

S = the set of U.S. Hispanics who speak Spanish at home

E = the set of U.S. Hispanics who speak English at home.

When describing collections in everyday English, the word **or** refers to the **union** of sets. Thus, U.S. Hispanics who speak Spanish or English at home means those who speak Spanish or English or both. The word **and** refers to the **intersection** of sets. Thus, U.S. Hispanics who speak Spanish and English at home means those who speak both languages.

In Figure 2.17, we revisit the circle graph showing languages spoken at home by U.S. Hispanics. To the right of the circle graph, we've organized the data using a Venn diagram. The voice balloons indicate how the Venn diagram provides a more accurate understanding of the subsets and their data.

Languages Spoken at Home by U.S. Hispanics

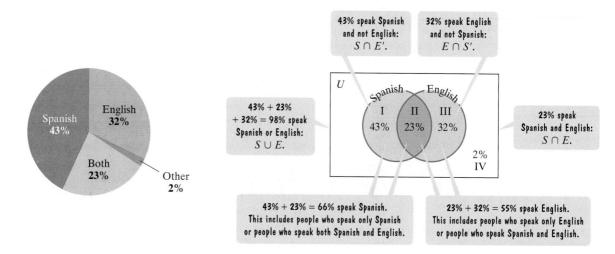

FIGURE 2.17 Comparing a circle graph and a Venn diagram
Source: Time, August 22, 2005

10 | Use the formula for $n(A \cup B)$.

The Cardinal Number of the Union of Two Finite Sets

Can the number of elements in A or B, $n(A \cup B)$, be determined by adding the number of elements in A and the number of elements in B, $n(A) + n(B)$? The answer is no. Figure 2.18 illustrates that by doing this, we are counting elements in both sets, $A \cap B$, or region II, twice.

To find the number of elements in the union of finite sets A and B, add the number of elements in A and the number of elements in B. Then subtract the number of elements common to both sets. We perform this subtraction so that we do not count the number of elements in the intersection twice, once for $n(A)$, and again for $n(B)$.

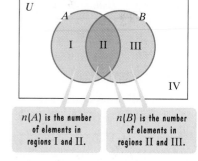

$n(A)$ is the number of elements in regions I and II.

$n(B)$ is the number of elements in regions II and III.

FIGURE 2.18

FORMULA FOR THE CARDINAL NUMBER OF THE UNION OF TWO FINITE SETS

$$n(A \cup B) = n(A) + n(B) - n(A \cap B)$$

The number of elements in A or B is   the number of elements in A plus the number of elements in B minus the number of elements in A and B.

EXAMPLE 8   USING THE FORMULA FOR $n(A \cup B)$

Some of the results of the campus blood drive survey indicated that 490 students were willing to donate blood, 340 students were willing to help serve a free breakfast to blood donors, and 120 students were willing to donate blood and serve breakfast. How many students were willing to donate blood or serve breakfast?

SOLUTION Let A = the set of students willing to donate blood and B = the set of students willing to serve breakfast. We are interested in how many students were willing to donate blood or serve breakfast. Thus, we need to determine $n(A \cup B)$.

number of blood donors or breakfast servers	number of blood donors	number of breakfast servers	number of blood donors and breakfast servers

$$n(A \cup B) = n(A) + n(B) - n(A \cap B)$$

$$= 490 + 340 - 120$$

$$= 830 - 120$$

$$= 710$$

We see that 710 students were willing to donate blood or serve a free breakfast.

CHECK POINT 8 The admissions department at a college looked at the registration of 500 of its students and found the following results: 244 students were registered in a mathematics class, 230 students were registered in an English class, and 89 students were registered in a math class and an English class. How many students were registered in a math class or an English class?

EXERCISE SET 2.3 ●●●●●●

• Practice Exercises

In Exercises 1–4, describe a universal set U that includes all elements in the given sets. Answers may vary.

1. A = {Bach, Mozart, Beethoven}
   B = {Brahms, Schubert}

2. A = {William Shakespeare, Charles Dickens}
   B = {Mark Twain, Robert Louis Stevenson}

3. A = {Pepsi, Sprite}
   B = {Coca Cola, Seven-Up}

4. A = {Acura RSX, Toyota Camry, Mitsubishi Lancer}
   B = {Dodge Ram, Chevrolet Impala}

In Exercises 5–8, let U = {a, b, c, d, e, f, g}, *A* = {a, b, f, g}, *B* = {c, d, e}, *C* = {a, g}, *and D* = {a, b, c, d, e, f}. *Use the roster method to write each of the following sets.*

5. A' 6. B' 7. C' 8. D'

In Exercises 9–12, let U = {1, 2, 3, 4, ..., 20}, *A* = {1, 2, 3, 4, 5}, *B* = {6, 7, 8, 9}, *C* = {1, 3, 5, 7, ..., 19}, *and D* = {2, 4, 6, 8, ..., 20}. *Use the roster method to write each of the following sets.*

9. A' 10. B' 11. C' 12. D'

In Exercises 13–16, let U = {1, 2, 3, 4, ...}, *A* = {1, 2, 3, 4, ..., 20}, *B* = {1, 2, 3, 4, ..., 50}, *C* = {2, 4, 6, 8, ...}, *and D* = {1, 3, 5, 7, ...}. *Use the roster method to write each of the following sets.*

13. A' 14. B' 15. C' 16. D'

In Exercises 17–40, let

$$U = \{1, 2, 3, 4, 5, 6, 7\}$$
$$A = \{1, 3, 5, 7\}$$
$$B = \{1, 2, 3\}$$
$$C = \{2, 3, 4, 5, 6\}.$$

Find each of the following sets.

17. $A \cap B$	18. $B \cap C$	19. $A \cup B$	20. $B \cup C$
21. A'	22. B'	23. $A' \cap B'$	24. $B' \cap C$
25. $A \cup C'$	26. $B \cup C'$	27. $(A \cap C)'$	28. $(A \cap B)'$
29. $A' \cup C'$	30. $A' \cup B'$	31. $(A \cup B)'$	32. $(A \cup C)'$
33. $A \cup \varnothing$	34. $C \cup \varnothing$	35. $A \cap \varnothing$	36. $C \cap \varnothing$
37. $A \cup U$	38. $B \cup U$	39. $A \cap U$	40. $B \cap U$

In Exercises 41–66, let

$$U = \{a, b, c, d, e, f, g, h\}$$
$$A = \{a, g, h\}$$
$$B = \{b, g, h\}$$
$$C = \{b, c, d, e, f\}.$$

Find each of the following sets.

41. $A \cap B$	42. $B \cap C$	43. $A \cup B$	44. $B \cup C$
45. A'	46. B'	47. $A' \cap B'$	48. $B' \cap C$
49. $A \cup C'$	50. $B \cup C'$	51. $(A \cap C)'$	52. $(A \cap B)'$
53. $A' \cup C'$	54. $A' \cup B'$	55. $(A \cup B)'$	56. $(A \cup C)'$
57. $A \cup \varnothing$	58. $C \cup \varnothing$	59. $A \cap \varnothing$	60. $C \cap \varnothing$
61. $A \cup U$	62. $B \cup U$	63. $A \cap U$	64. $B \cap U$
65. $(A \cap B) \cup B'$		66. $(A \cup B) \cap B'$	

In Exercises 67–78, use the Venn diagram to represent each set in roster form.

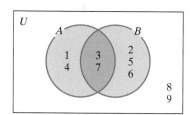

67. A **68.** B **69.** U **70.** $A \cup B$

71. $A \cap B$ **72.** A' **73.** B' **74.** $(A \cap B)'$

75. $(A \cup B)'$ **76.** $A' \cap B$ **77.** $A \cap B'$ **78.** $A \cup B'$

In Exercises 79–92, use the Venn diagram to determine each set or cardinality.

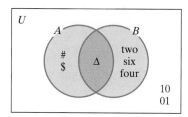

79. B **80.** A **81.** $A \cup B$

82. $A \cap B$ **83.** $n(A \cup B)$ **84.** $n(A \cap B)$

85. $n(A')$ **86.** $n(B')$ **87.** $(A \cap B)'$

88. $(A \cup B)'$ **89.** $A' \cap B$ **90.** $A \cap B'$

91. $n(U) - n(B)$ **92.** $n(U) - n(A)$

Use the formula for the cardinal number of the union of two sets to solve Exercise 93–96.

93. Set A contains 17 elements, set B contains 20 elements, and 6 elements are common to sets A and B. How many elements are in $A \cup B$?

94. Set A contains 30 elements, set B contains 18 elements, and 5 elements are common to sets A and B. How many elements are in $A \cup B$?

95. Set A contains 8 letters and 9 numbers. Set B contains 7 letters and 10 numbers. Four letters and 3 numbers are common to both sets A and B. Find the number of elements in set A or set B.

96. Set A contains 12 numbers and 18 letters. Set B contains 14 numbers and 10 letters. One number and 6 letters are common to both sets A and B. Find the number of elements in set A or set B.

• Practice Plus

In Exercises 97–104, let

$$U = \{x \mid x \in \mathbf{N} \text{ and } x < 9\}$$
$$A = \{x \mid x \text{ is an odd natural number and } x < 9\}$$
$$B = \{x \mid x \text{ is an even natural number and } x < 9\}$$
$$C = \{x \mid x \in \mathbf{N} \text{ and } 1 < x < 6\}.$$

Find each of the following sets.

97. $A \cup B$ **98.** $B \cup C$ **99.** $A \cap U$ **100.** $A \cup U$

101. $A \cap C'$ **102.** $A \cap B'$ **103.** $(B \cap C)'$ **104.** $(A \cap C)'$

In Exercises 105–108, use the Venn diagram to determine each set or cardinality.

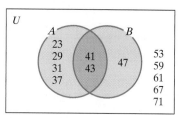

105. $A \cup (A \cup B)'$
106. $(A' \cap B) \cup (A \cap B)$
107. $n(U)[n(A \cup B) - n(A \cap B)]$
108. $n(A \cap B)[n(A \cup B) - n(A')]$

• Application Exercises

A math tutor working with a small group of students asked each student when he or she had studied for class the previous weekend. Their responses are shown in the Venn diagram.

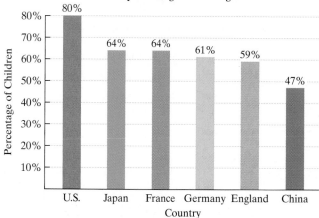

In Exercises 109–116, use the Venn diagram to list the elements of each set in roster form.

109. The set of students who studied Saturday

110. The set of students who studied Sunday

111. The set of students who studied Saturday or Sunday

112. The set of students who studied Saturday and Sunday

113. The set of students who studied Saturday and not Sunday

114. The set of students who studied Sunday and not Saturday

115. The set of students who studied neither Saturday nor Sunday

116. The set of students surveyed by the math tutor

The bar graph shows the percentage of children in the world's leading industrial countries who daydream about being rich.

Percentage of Children Ages 7–12 Daydreaming about Being Rich

Source: Roper Starch Worldwide for A.B.C. Research

In Exercises 117–122, use the information in the graph on the previous page to place the indicated country in the correct region of the following Venn diagram.

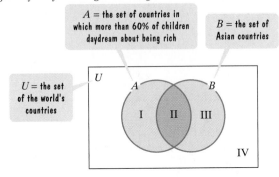

117. U.S. **118.** Japan **119.** France **120.** Germany
121. England **122.** China

A **palindromic number** is a natural number whose value does not change if its digits are reversed. Examples of palindromic numbers are 11, 454, and 261,162. In Exercises 123–132, use this definition to place the indicated natural number in the correct region of the following Venn diagram.

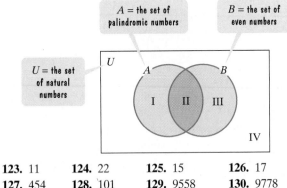

123. 11 **124.** 22 **125.** 15 **126.** 17
127. 454 **128.** 101 **129.** 9558 **130.** 9778
131. 9559 **132.** 9779

As a result of cultural expectations about what is appropriate behavior for each gender, boys and girls differ substantially in their toy preferences. The graph shows the percentage of boys and girls asking for various types of toys in letters to Santa Claus. Use the information in the graph to write each set in Exercises 133–138 in roster form or express the set as ∅.

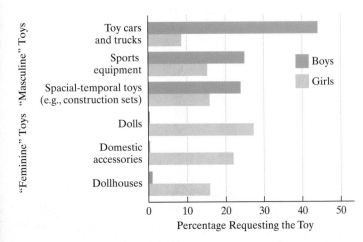

Toys Requested by Children

Source: Richard, J.G., & Simpson, C.H. (1982). Children, gender and social structure: An analysis of the contents of letters to Santa Claus. *Child Development*, 53, 429–436.

133. $\{x \mid x$ is a toy requested by more than 10% of the boys$\} \cap \{x \mid x$ is a toy requested by less than 20% of the girls$\}$

134. $\{x \mid x$ is a toy requested by fewer than 5% of the boys$\} \cap \{x \mid x$ is a toy requested by fewer than 20% of the girls$\}$

135. $\{x \mid x$ is a toy requested by more than 10% of the boys$\} \cup \{x \mid x$ is a toy requested by less than 20% of the girls$\}$

136. $\{x \mid x$ is a toy requested by fewer than 5% of the boys$\} \cup \{x \mid x$ is a toy requested by fewer than 20% of the girls$\}$

137. The set of toys requested by more than 40% of the boys and more than 10% of the girls

138. The set of toys requested by more than 40% of the boys or more than 10% of the girls

139. A winter resort took a poll of its 350 visitors to see which winter activities people enjoyed. The results were as follows: 178 people liked to ski, 154 people liked to snowboard, and 49 people liked to ski and snowboard. How many people in the poll liked to ski or snowboard?

140. A pet store surveyed 200 pet owners and obtained the following results: 96 people owned cats, 97 people owned dogs, and 29 people owned cats and dogs. How many people in the survey owned cats or dogs?

• Writing in Mathematics

141. Describe what is meant by a universal set. Provide an example.

142. What is a Venn diagram and how is it used?

143. Describe the Venn diagram for two disjoint sets. How does this diagram illustrate that the sets have no common elements?

144. Describe the Venn diagram for proper subsets. How does this diagram illustrate that the elements of one set are also in the second set?

145. Describe the Venn diagram for two equal sets. How does this diagram illustrate that the sets are equal?

146. Describe the Venn diagram for two sets with common elements. How does the diagram illustrate this relationship?

147. Describe what is meant by the complement of a set.

148. Is it possible to find a set's complement if a universal set is not given? Explain your answer.

149. Describe what is meant by the intersection of sets. Give an example.

150. Describe what is meant by the union of sets. Give an example.

151. Describe how to find the cardinal number of the union of two finite sets.

• Critical Thinking Exercises

152. Which one of the following is true?
    a. $n(A \cup B) = n(A) + n(B)$
    b. $A \cap A' = \varnothing$
    c. $(A \cup B) \subseteq A$
    d. If $A \subseteq B$, then $A \cap B = B$.

153. Which one of the following is true?

   a. $A \cap U = U$

   b. $A \cup \varnothing = \varnothing$

   c. If $A \subseteq B$, then $A \cap B = \varnothing$.

   d. If $B \subseteq A$, then $A \cap B = B$.

In Exercises 154–157, if $A \neq B$, draw a Venn diagram that correctly illustrates the relationship between the sets.

154. $A \cap B = A$ **155.** $A \cap B = B$

156. $A \cup B = A$ **157.** $A \cup B = B$

SECTION 2.4 • SET OPERATIONS AND VENN DIAGRAMS WITH THREE SETS

OBJECTIVES

1. Perform set operations with three sets.

2. Use Venn diagrams with three sets.

3. Use Venn diagrams to prove equality of sets.

Our bodies are fragile and complex, vulnerable to disease, and easily damaged. The imminent mapping of the human genome—all 140,000 genes—could lead to rapid advances in treating heart disease, cancer, Alzheimer's, and AIDS. Neural stem cell research could make it possible to repair brain damage and even re-create whole parts of the brain. There appears to be no limit to the parts of our bodies that can be replaced. By contrast, at the start of the twentieth century, we lacked a basic understanding of the different types of human blood. The discovery of blood types, which can be illustrated by a Venn diagram with three sets, rescued surgery patients from random, often lethal, transfusions. In this sense, the Venn diagram that you encounter in this section reinforces our optimism that life does improve, and that we are better off today than we were one hundred years ago.

Set Operations with Three Sets

We now know how to find the union and intersection of two sets. We also know how to find a set's complement. In Example 1, we apply set operations to situations containing three sets.

1   Perform set operations with three sets.

| **EXAMPLE 1** | SET OPERATIONS WITH THREE SETS |

Given

$$U = \{1, 2, 3, 4, 5, 6, 7, 8, 9\}$$
$$A = \{1, 2, 3, 4, 5\}$$
$$B = \{1, 2, 3, 6, 8\}$$
$$C = \{2, 3, 4, 6, 7\},$$

find each of the following sets:

a. $A \cup (B \cap C)$

b. $(A \cup B) \cap (A \cup C)$

c. $A \cap (B \cup C')$.

SOLUTION Before determining each set, let's be sure we perform the operations in the correct order. Remember that we begin by performing any set operations inside parentheses.

- Finding $A \cup (B \cap C)$

  Step 1. Find the intersection of B and C.

  Step 2. Find the union of A and $(B \cap C)$.

- Finding $(A \cup B) \cap (A \cup C)$

  Step 1. Find the union of A and B.

  Step 2. Find the union of A and C.

  Step 3. Find the intersection of $(A \cup B)$ and $(A \cup C)$.

- Finding $A \cap (B \cup C')$

  Step 1. Find the complement of C.

  Step 2. Find the union of B and C'.

  Step 3. Find the intersection of A and $(B \cup C')$.

$U = \{1, 2, 3, 4, 5, 6, 7, 8, 9\}$

$A = \{1, 2, 3, 4, 5\}$

$B = \{1, 2, 3, 6, 8\}$

$C = \{2, 3, 4, 6, 7\}$

The given sets (repeated)

a. To find $A \cup (B \cap C)$, first find the set within the parentheses, $B \cap C$:

$$B \cap C = \{1, 2, 3, 6, 8\} \cap \{2, 3, 4, 6, 7\} = \{2, 3, 6\}.$$

Common elements are 2, 3, and 6.

Now finish the problem by finding $A \cup (B \cap C)$:

$$A \cup (B \cap C) = \{1, 2, 3, 4, 5\} \cup \{2, 3, 6\} = \{1, 2, 3, 4, 5, 6\}.$$

List all elements in A and then add the only unlisted element in $B \cap C$, namely 6.

b. To find $(A \cup B) \cap (A \cup C)$, first find the sets within parentheses. Start with $A \cup B$:

$$A \cup B = \{1, 2, 3, 4, 5\} \cup \{1, 2, 3, 6, 8\} = \{1, 2, 3, 4, 5, 6, 8\}.$$

List all elements in A and then add the unlisted elements in B, namely 6 and 8.

Now find $A \cup C$:

$$A \cup C = \{1, 2, 3, 4, 5\} \cup \{2, 3, 4, 6, 7\} = \{1, 2, 3, 4, 5, 6, 7\}.$$

List all elements in A and then add the unlisted elements in C, namely 6 and 7.

Now finish the problem by finding $(A \cup B) \cap (A \cup C)$:

$$(A \cup B) \cap (A \cup C) = \{1, 2, 3, 4, 5, 6, 8\} \cap \{1, 2, 3, 4, 5, 6, 7\} = \{1, 2, 3, 4, 5, 6\}.$$

Common elements are 1, 2, 3, 4, 5, and 6.

c. As in parts (a) and (b), to find $A \cap (B \cup C')$, begin with the set in parentheses. First we must find C', elements in U that are not in C:

$$C' = \{1, 5, 8, 9\}.$$ List the elements in U that are not in $C = \{2, 3, 4, 6, 7\}$: $\{1, \not2, \not3, \not4, 5, \not6, \not7, 8, 9\}$.

Now we can identify elements of $B \cup C'$:

$$B \cup C' = \{1, 2, 3, 6, 8\} \cup \{1, 5, 8, 9\} = \{1, 2, 3, 5, 6, 8, 9\}.$$

> List all elements in B and then add the unlisted elements in C', namely 5 and 9.

Now finish the problem by finding $A \cap (B \cup C')$:

$$A \cap (B \cup C') = \{1, 2, 3, 4, 5\} \cap \{1, 2, 3, 5, 6, 8, 9\} = \{1, 2, 3, 5\}.$$

> Common elements are 1, 2, 3, and 5.

CHECK POINT **1** Given $U = \{a, b, c, d, e, f\}$, $A = \{a, b, c, d\}$, $B = \{a, b, d, f\}$, and $C = \{b, c, f\}$, find each of the following sets:

    a. $A \cup (B \cap C)$

    b. $(A \cup B) \cap (A \cup C)$

    c. $A \cap (B \cup C')$.

2 | Use Venn diagrams with three sets.

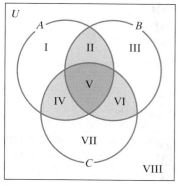

FIGURE 2.19 Three intersecting sets separate the universal set into eight regions.

Venn Diagrams with Three Sets

Venn diagrams can contain three or more sets, such as the diagram in Figure 2.19. The three sets in the figure separate the universal set, U, into eight regions. The numbering of these regions is arbitrary—that is, we can number any region as I, any region as II, and so on. Here is a description of each region, starting with the innermost region, region V, and working outward to region VIII.

The Region Shown in Dark Blue

Region V	This region represents elements that are common to sets A, B, and C: $A \cap B \cap C$.

The Regions Shown in Light Blue

Region II	This region represents elements in both sets A and B that are not in set C: $(A \cap B) \cap C'$.
Region IV	This region represents elements in both sets A and C that are not in set B: $(A \cap C) \cap B'$.
Region VI	This region represents elements in both sets B and C that are not in set A: $(B \cap C) \cap A'$.

The Regions Shown in White

Region I	This region represents elements in set A that are in neither sets B nor C: $A \cap (B' \cap C')$.
Region III	This region represents elements in set B that are in neither sets A nor C: $B \cap (A' \cap C')$.
Region VII	This region represents elements in set C that are in neither sets A nor B: $C \cap (A' \cap B')$.
Region VIII	This region represents elements in the universal set U that are not in sets A, B, or C: $A' \cap B' \cap C'$.

EXAMPLE 2	DETERMINING SETS FROM A VENN DIAGRAM WITH THREE INTERSECTING SETS

Use the Venn diagram in Figure 2.20 to determine each of the following sets:

a. A **b.** $A \cup B$ **c.** $B \cap C$

d. C' **e.** $A \cap B \cap C$.

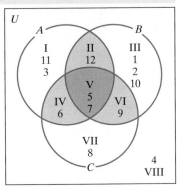

FIGURE 2.20

SOLUTION

Set to Determine	Description of Set	Regions in Venn Diagram	Set in Roster Form
a. A	set of elements in A	I, II, IV, V	$\{11, 3, 12, 6, 5, 7\}$
b. $A \cup B$	set of elements in A or B or both	I, II, III, IV, V, VI	$\{11, 3, 12, 1, 2, 10, 6, 5, 7, 9\}$
c. $B \cap C$	set of elements in both B and C	V, VI	$\{5, 7, 9\}$
d. C'	set of elements in U that are not in C	I, II, III, VIII	$\{11, 3, 12, 1, 2, 10, 4\}$
e. $A \cap B \cap C$	set of elements in A and B and C	V	$\{5, 7\}$

○

 Use the Venn diagram in Figure 2.20 to determine each of the following sets:

a. C **b.** $B \cup C$ **c.** $A \cap C$

d. B' **e.** $A \cup B \cup C$.

In Example 2, we used a Venn diagram showing elements in the regions to determine various sets. Now we are going to reverse directions. We'll use sets $A, B, C,$ and U to determine the elements in each region of a Venn diagram.

To construct a Venn diagram illustrating the elements in $A, B, C,$ and $U,$ **start by placing elements into the innermost region and work outward.** Because the four inner regions represent various intersections, find $A \cap B, A \cap C, B \cap C,$ and $A \cap B \cap C.$ Then use these intersections, and the given sets to place the various elements into regions. This procedure is illustrated in Example 3.

DETERMINING A VENN DIAGRAM FROM SETS

Construct a Venn diagram illustrating the following sets:

$$A = \{a, d, e, g, h, i, j\}$$
$$B = \{b, e, g, h, l\}$$
$$C = \{a, c, e, h\}$$
$$U = \{a, b, c, d, e, f, g, h, i, j, k, l\}.$$

SOLUTION We begin by finding four intersections. In each case, common elements are shown in red.

- $A \cap B = \{a, d, e, g, h, i, j\} \cap \{b, e, g, h, l\} = \{e, g, h\}$
- $A \cap C = \{a, d, e, g, h, i, j\} \cap \{a, c, e, h\} = \{a, e, h\}$

- $B \cap C = \{b, e, g, h, l\} \cap \{a, c, e, h\} = \{e, h\}$
- $A \cap B \cap C = \{e, g, h\} \cap \{a, c, e, h\} = \{e, h\}$

This is $A \cap B$ from above.

Now we can place elements into regions, starting with the innermost region, region V, and working outward.

STEP 1

$A \cap B \cap C$:
Region V

$A \cap B \cap C = \{e, h\}$
Place e and h into V.

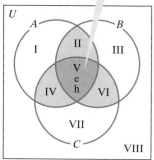

STEP 2

$A \cap B$:
Regions II and V

$A \cap B = \{e, g, h\}$
With e and h in V,
place g into II.

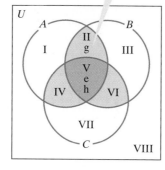

STEP 3

$A \cap C$:
Regions IV and V

$A \cap C = \{a, e, h\}$
With e and h in V,
place a into IV.

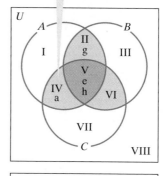

STEP 4

$B \cap C$:
Regions V and VI

$B \cap C = \{e, h\}$
With e and h in V,
place no letters into VI.

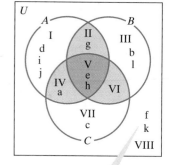

A:
Regions I, II, IV, V

$A = \{a, d, e, g, h, i, j\}$
With a, e, g, and h already placed
in A, place d, i, and j into I.

STEP 5

B:
Regions II, III, V, VI

$B = \{b, e, g, h, l\}$
With e, g, and h already placed
in B, place b and l into III.

STEP 6

C:
Regions IV, V, VI, VII

$C = \{a, c, e, h\}$
With a, e, and h already
placed in C, place c into VII.

STEP 7

U:
Regions I–VIII

$U = \{a, b, c, d, e, f, g, h, i, j, k, l\}$
With all letters, except f and k, already
placed in U, place f and k into VIII.

STEP 8

The completed Venn diagram in step 8 illustrates the given sets.

CHECK POINT 3 Construct a Venn diagram illustrating the following sets:

$$A = \{1, 3, 6, 10\}$$
$$B = \{4, 7, 9, 10\}$$
$$C = \{3, 4, 5, 8, 9, 10\}$$
$$U = \{1, 2, 3, 4, 5, 6, 7, 8, 9, 10\}.$$

3 Use Venn diagrams to prove equality of sets.

STUDY TIP

In summary, here are the two forms of reasoning discussed in Chapter 1.

- **Inductive Reasoning:** Starts with individual observations and works to a general conjecture (or educated guess)
- **Deductive Reasoning:** Starts with general cases and works to the proof of a specific statement (or theorem)

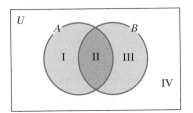

FIGURE 2.21

Proving the Equality of Sets

In Section 2.3, you were given two sets and asked to find $(A \cap B)'$ and $A' \cup B'$. In the example, $(A \cap B)'$ and $A' \cup B'$ resulted in the same set. This occurs regardless of which sets we choose for A and B. Examining these individual cases and applying inductive reasoning, a conjecture (or educated guess) is that $(A \cap B)' = A' \cup B'$.

We can apply deductive reasoning to *prove* the statement $(A \cap B)' = A' \cup B'$ for *all* sets A and B. To prove that $(A \cap B)'$ and $A' \cup B'$ are equal, we use a Venn diagram. If both sets represent the same regions in this general diagram, then this proves that they are equal. Example 4 shows how this is done.

EXAMPLE 4   PROVING THE EQUALITY OF SETS

Use the Venn diagram in Figure 2.21 to prove that

$$(A \cap B)' = A' \cup B'.$$

SOLUTION Begin with the regions represented by $(A \cap B)'$.

Set	Regions in the Venn Diagram
A	I, II
B	II, III
$A \cap B$	II (This is the region common to A and B.)
$(A \cap B)'$	I, III, IV (These are the regions in U that are not in $A \cap B$.)

Next, find the regions represented by $A' \cup B'$.

Set	Regions in the Venn Diagram
A'	III, IV (These are the regions not in A.)
B'	I, IV (These are the regions not in B.)
$A' \cup B'$	I, III, IV (These are the regions obtained by uniting the regions representing A' and B'.)

Both $(A \cap B)'$ and $A' \cup B'$ are represented by the same regions, I, III, and IV, of the Venn diagram. This result proves that

$$(A \cap B)' = A' \cup B'$$

for all sets A and B.   ○

Can you see how we applied deductive reasoning in Example 4? We started with the two general sets in the Venn diagram in Figure 2.21 and worked to the specific conclusion that $(A \cap B)'$ and $A' \cup B'$ represent the same regions in the diagram. Thus, the statement $(A \cap B)' = A' \cup B'$ is a theorem.

 Use the Venn diagram in Figure 2.21 to solve this exercise.

   a. Which region is represented by $(A \cup B)'$?

   b. Which region is represented by $A' \cap B'$?

   c. Based on parts (a) and (b), what can you conclude?

The statements proved in Example 4 and Check Point 4 are known as *De Morgan's laws*, named for the British logician Augustus De Morgan (1806–1871).

> **DE MORGAN'S LAWS**
>
> $(A \cap B)' = A' \cup B'$: The complement of the intersection of two sets is the union of the complements of those sets.
>
> $(A \cup B)' = A' \cap B'$: The complement of the union of two sets is the intersection of the complements of those sets.

EXAMPLE 5   PROVING THE EQUALITY OF SETS

Use a Venn diagram to prove that

$$A \cup (B \cap C) = (A \cup B) \cap (A \cup C).$$

SOLUTION Use a Venn diagram with three sets A, B, and C, drawn in Figure 2.22. Begin with the regions represented by $A \cup (B \cap C)$.

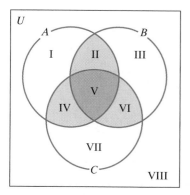

U

FIGURE 2.22

Set	Regions in the Venn Diagram
A	I, II, IV, V
$B \cap C$	V, VI (These are the regions common to B and C.)
$A \cup (B \cap C)$	I, II, IV, V, VI (These are the regions obtained by uniting the regions representing A and $B \cap C$.)

Next, find the regions represented by $(A \cup B) \cap (A \cup C)$.

Set	Regions in the Venn Diagram
A	I, II, IV, V
B	II, III, V, VI
C	IV, V, VI, VII
$A \cup B$	I, II, III, IV, V, VI (Unite the regions representing A and B.)
$A \cup C$	I, II, IV, V, VI, VII (Unite the regions representing A and C.)
$(A \cup B) \cap (A \cup C)$	I, II, IV, V, VI (These are the regions common to $A \cup B$ and $A \cup C$.)

Both $A \cup (B \cap C)$ and $(A \cup B) \cap (A \cup C)$ are represented by the same regions, I, II, IV, V, and VI, of the Venn diagram. This result proves that

$$A \cup (B \cap C) = (A \cup B) \cap (A \cup C)$$

for all sets A, B, and C. Thus, the statement is a theorem. ○

  Use the Venn diagram in Figure 2.22 to solve this exercise.

a. Which regions are represented by $A \cap (B \cup C)$?

b. Which regions are represented by $(A \cap B) \cup (A \cap C)$?

c. Based on parts (a) and (b), what can you conclude?

BLITZER BONUS

Blood Types and Venn Diagrams

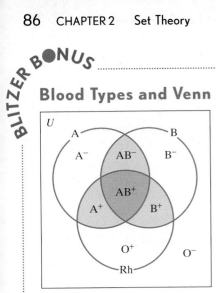

FIGURE 2.23 Human blood types

In the early 1900s, the Austrian immunologist Karl Landsteiner discovered that all blood is not the same. Blood serum drawn from one person often clumped when mixed with the blood cells of another. The clumping was caused by different antigens, proteins, and carbohydrates that trigger antibodies and fight infection. Landsteiner classified blood types based on the presence or absence of the antigens A, B, and Rh in red blood cells. The Venn diagram in Figure 2.23 contains eight regions representing the eight common blood groups.

In the Venn diagram, blood with the Rh antigen is labeled positive and blood lacking the Rh antigen is labeled negative. The region where the three circles intersect represents type AB⁺, indicating that a person with this blood type has the antigens A, B, and Rh. Observe that type O blood (both positive and negative) lacks A and B antigens. Type O⁻ lacks all three antigens, A, B, and Rh.

In blood transfusions, the recipient must have all or more of the antigens present in the donor's blood. This discovery rescued surgery patients from random, often lethal, transfusions. This knowledge made the massive blood drives during World War I possible. Eventually, it made the modern blood bank possible as well.

EXERCISE SET 2.4 ●●●●●●

• Practice Exercises

In Exercises 1–12, let

$$U = \{1, 2, 3, 4, 5, 6, 7\}$$
$$A = \{1, 3, 5, 7\}$$
$$B = \{1, 2, 3\}$$
$$C = \{2, 3, 4, 5, 6\}.$$

Find each of the following sets.

1. $A \cup (B \cap C)$
2. $A \cap (B \cup C)$
3. $(A \cup B) \cap (A \cup C)$
4. $(A \cap B) \cup (A \cap C)$
5. $A' \cap (B \cup C')$
6. $C' \cap (A \cup B')$
7. $(A' \cap B) \cup (A' \cap C')$
8. $(C' \cap A) \cup (C' \cap B')$
9. $(A \cup B \cup C)'$
10. $(A \cap B \cap C)'$
11. $(A \cup B)' \cap C$
12. $(B \cup C)' \cap A$

In Exercises 13–24, let

$$U = \{a, b, c, d, e, f, g, h\}$$
$$A = \{a, g, h\}$$
$$B = \{b, g, h\}$$
$$C = \{b, c, d, e, f\}.$$

Find each of the following sets.

13. $A \cup (B \cap C)$
14. $A \cap (B \cup C)$
15. $(A \cup B) \cap (A \cup C)$
16. $(A \cap B) \cup (A \cap C)$
17. $A' \cap (B \cup C')$
18. $C' \cap (A \cup B')$

19. $(A' \cap B) \cup (A' \cap C')$
20. $(C' \cap A) \cup (C' \cap B')$
21. $(A \cup B \cup C)'$
22. $(A \cap B \cap C)'$
23. $(A \cup B)' \cap C$
24. $(B \cup C)' \cap A$

In Exercises 25–32, use the Venn diagram shown to answer each question.

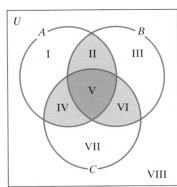

25. Which regions represent set B?
26. Which regions represent set C?
27. Which regions represent $A \cup C$?
28. Which regions represent $B \cup C$?
29. Which regions represent $A \cap B$?
30. Which regions represent $A \cap C$?
31. Which regions represent B'?
32. Which regions represent C'?

In Exercises 33–44, use the Venn diagram to represent each set in roster form.

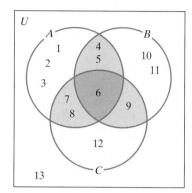

33. A **34.** B **35.** $A \cup B$

36. $B \cup C$ **37.** $(A \cup B)'$ **38.** $(B \cup C)'$

39. $A \cap B$ **40.** $A \cap C$ **41.** $A \cap B \cap C$

42. $A \cup B \cup C$ **43.** $(A \cap B \cap C)'$ **44.** $(A \cup B \cup C)'$

In Exercises 45–48, construct a Venn diagram illustrating the given sets.

45. $A = \{4, 5, 6, 8\}, B = \{1, 2, 4, 5, 6, 7\},$
$C = \{3, 4, 7\}, U = \{1, 2, 3, 4, 5, 6, 7, 8, 9\}$

46. $A = \{a, e, h, i\}, B = \{b, c, e, f, h, i\},$
$C = \{e, f, g\}, U = \{a, b, c, d, e, f, g, h, i\}$

47. $A = \{+, -, \times, \div, \rightarrow, \leftrightarrow\}$
$B = \{\times, \div, \rightarrow\}$
$C = \{\wedge, \vee, \rightarrow, \leftrightarrow\}$
$U = \{+, -, \times, \div, \wedge, \vee, \rightarrow, \leftrightarrow, \sim\}$

48. $A = \{x_3, x_9\}$
$B = \{x_1, x_2, x_3, x_5, x_6\}$
$C = \{x_3, x_4, x_5, x_6, x_9\}$
$U = \{x_1, x_2, x_3, x_4, x_5, x_6, x_7, x_8, x_9\}$

Use the Venn diagram shown to solve Exercises 49–52.

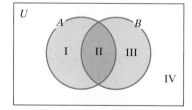

49. a. Which region is represented by $A \cap B$?
b. Which region is represented by $B \cap A$?
c. Based on parts (a) and (b), what can you conclude?

50. a. Which regions are represented by $A \cup B$?
b. Which regions are represented by $B \cup A$?
c. Based on parts (a) and (b), what can you conclude?

51. a. Which region(s) is/are represented by $(A \cap B)'$?
b. Which region(s) is/are represented by $A' \cap B'$?
c. Based on parts (a) and (b), are $(A \cap B)'$ and $A' \cap B'$ equal for all sets A and B? Explain your answer.

52. a. Which region(s) is/are represented by $(A \cup B)'$?
b. Which region(s) is/are represented by $A' \cup B'$?
c. Based on parts (a) and (b), are $(A \cup B)'$ and $A' \cup B'$ equal for all sets A and B? Explain your answer.

In Exercises 53–58, use the Venn diagram for Exercises 49–52 in the previous column to determine whether the given sets are equal for all sets A and B.

53. $A' \cup B$, $A \cap B'$ **54.** $A' \cap B$, $A \cup B'$
55. $(A \cup B)'$, $(A \cap B)'$ **56.** $(A \cup B)'$, $A' \cap B$
57. $(A' \cap B)'$, $A \cup B'$ **58.** $(A \cup B')'$, $A' \cap B$

Use the Venn diagram shown to solve Exercises 59–62.

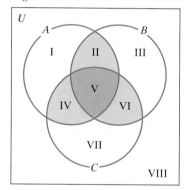

59. a. Which regions are represented by $(A \cap B) \cup C$?
b. Which regions are represented by $(A \cup C) \cap (B \cup C)$?
c. Based on parts (a) and (b), what can you conclude?

60. a. Which regions are represented by $(A \cup B) \cap C$?
b. Which regions are represented by $(A \cap C) \cup (B \cap C)$?
c. Based on parts (a) and (b), what can you conclude?

61. a. Which regions are represented by $A \cap (B \cup C)$?
b. Which regions are represented by $A \cup (B \cap C)$?
c. Based on parts (a) and (b), are $A \cap (B \cup C)$ and $A \cup (B \cap C)$ equal for all sets A, B, and C? Explain your answer.

62. a. Which regions are represented by $C \cup (B \cap A)$?
b. Which regions are represented by $C \cap (B \cup A)$?
c. Based on parts (a) and (b), are $C \cup (B \cap A)$ and $C \cap (B \cup A)$ equal for all sets A, B, and C? Explain your answer.

In Exercises 63–68, use the Venn diagram shown above to determine which statements are true for all sets A, B, and C, and, consequently, are theorems.

63. $A \cap (B \cup C) = (A \cap B) \cup C$
64. $A \cup (B \cap C) = (A \cup B) \cap C$
65. $B \cup (A \cap C) = (A \cup B) \cap (B \cup C)$
66. $B \cap (A \cup C) = (A \cap B) \cup (B \cap C)$
67. $A \cap (B \cup C)' = A \cap (B' \cap C')$
68. $A \cup (B \cap C)' = A \cup (B' \cup C')$

• Practice Plus

69. a. Let $A = \{c\}, B = \{a, b\}, C = \{b, d\}$, and $U = \{a, b, c, d, e, f\}$. Find $A \cup (B' \cap C')$ and $(A \cup B') \cap (A \cup C')$.
b. Let $A = \{1, 3, 7, 8\}, B = \{2, 3, 6, 7\}, C = \{4, 6, 7, 8\}$, and $U = \{1, 2, 3, \ldots, 8\}$. Find $A \cup (B' \cap C')$ and $(A \cup B') \cap (A \cup C')$.

c. Based on your results in parts (a) and (b), use inductive reasoning to write a conjecture that relates $A \cup (B' \cap C')$ and $(A \cup B') \cap (A \cup C')$.

d. Use deductive reasoning to determine whether your conjecture in part (c) is a theorem.

70. a. Let $A = \{3\}, B = \{1, 2\}, C = \{2, 4\}$, and $U = \{1, 2, 3, 4, 5, 6\}$. Find $(A \cup B)' \cap C$ and $A' \cap (B' \cap C)$.

b. Let $A = \{d, f, g, h\}, B = \{a, c, f, h\}, C = \{c, e, g, h\}$, and $U = \{a, b, c, \ldots, h\}$. Find $(A \cup B)' \cap C$ and $A' \cap (B' \cap C)$.

c. Based on your results in parts (a) and (b), use inductive reasoning to write a conjecture that relates $(A \cup B)' \cap C$ and $A' \cap (B' \cap C)$.

d. Use deductive reasoning to determine whether your conjecture in part (c) is a theorem.

In Exercises 71–78, use the symbols $A, B, C, \cap, \cup,$ and $',$ as necessary, to describe each shaded region. More than one correct symbolic description may be possible.

71.

72.

73.

74.

75.

76.

77.

78.

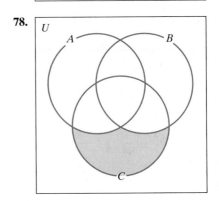

• Application Exercises

A math tutor working with a small study group has classified students in the group by whether or not they scored 90% or above on each of three tests. The results are shown in the Venn diagram.

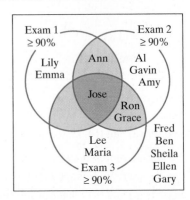

In Exercises 79–90, use the Venn diagram to represent each set in roster form.

79. The set of students who scored 90% or above on exam 2

80. The set of students who scored 90% or above on exam 3

81. The set of students who scored 90% or above on exam 1 and exam 3

82. The set of students who scored 90% or above on exam 1 and exam 2

83. The set of students who scored 90% or above on exam 1 and not on exam 2

84. The set of students who scored 90% or above on exam 3 and not on exam 1

85. The set of students who scored 90% or above on exam 1 or not on exam 2

86. The set of students who scored 90% or above on exam 3 or not on exam 1

87. The set of students who scored 90% or above on *exactly one* test

88. The set of students who scored 90% or above on *at least two* tests

89. The set of students who scored 90% or above on exam 2 and not on exam 1 and exam 3

90. The set of students who scored 90% or above on exam 1 and not on exam 2 and exam 3

91. Use the Venn diagram shown at the bottom of the previous page to describe a set of students that is the empty set.

92. Use the Venn diagram shown at the bottom of the previous page to describe the set {Fred, Ben, Sheila, Ellen, Gary}.

The chart shows the most popular shows on television in 2003, 2004, and 2005.

MOST POPULAR TELEVISION SHOWS

2003	2004	2005
1. *Friends*	1. *Friends*	1. *CSI*
2. *CSI*	2. *CSI*	2. *American Idol*
3. *E.R.*	3. *American Idol*	3. *Desperate Housewives*
4. *Everybody Loves Raymond*	4. *Apprentice*	4. *Without a Trace*
5. *Law and Order*	5. *Desperate Housewives*	5. *Survivor*
6. *Survivor*	6. *E.R.*	6. *Grey's Anatomy*

Source: Nielsen Media Research

In Exercises 93–98, use the Venn diagram to indicate in which region, I through VIII, each television show should be placed.

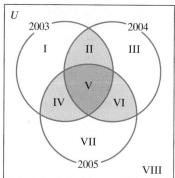

93. *Friends*

94. *Desperate Housewives*

95. *CSI*

96. *60 Minutes*

97. *Everybody Loves Raymond*

98. *Grey's Anatomy*

The chart shows the top single recordings of all time.

TOP SINGLE RECORDINGS

Title	Artist or Group	Sales	Year Released
"Candle in the Wind"	Elton John	37 million	1997
"White Christmas"	Bing Crosby	30 million	1942
"Rock Around the Clock"	Bill Haley and His Comets	17 million	1954
"I Want to Hold Your Hand"	The Beatles	12 million	1963
"It's Now or Never"	Elvis Presley	10 million	1960
"Hey Jude"	The Beatles	10 million	1968
"I Will Always Love You"	Whitney Houston	10 million	1992
"Hound Dog"	Elvis Presley	9 million	1956
"Diana"	Paul Anka	9 million	1957
"I'm a Believer"	The Monkees	8 million	1966

Source: RIAA

In Exercises 99–104, use the Venn diagram to indicate in which region, I through VIII, each recording should be placed.

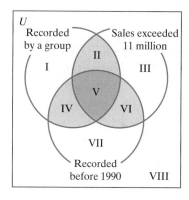

99. "Candle in the Wind"

100. "White Christmas"

101. "I Want to Hold Your Hand"

102. "Hey Jude"

103. "Diana"

104. "I'm a Believer"

105. The chart shows the ten places where the greatest number of people have been attacked by sharks.

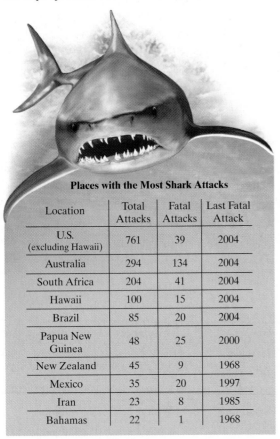

Places with the Most Shark Attacks

Location	Total Attacks	Fatal Attacks	Last Fatal Attack
U.S. (excluding Hawaii)	761	39	2004
Australia	294	134	2004
South Africa	204	41	2004
Hawaii	100	15	2004
Brazil	85	20	2004
Papua New Guinea	48	25	2000
New Zealand	45	9	1968
Mexico	35	20	1997
Iran	23	8	1985
Bahamas	22	1	1968

Source: International Shark Attack File

Let U = the set of locations shown in the chart, A = the set of locations with at least 100 total attacks, B = the set of locations with no more than 40 fatal attacks, and C = the set of locations where the last fatal attack occurred in 2004. Use the information in the chart to construct a Venn diagram that illustrates these sets.

106. The chart shows the ten films nominated for the most Oscars.

FILMS WITH THE MOST OSCAR NOMINATIONS

Film	Nominations	Awards	Year
All About Eve	14	6	1950
Titanic	14	11	1997
Gone with the Wind	13	8	1939
From Here to Eternity	13	8	1953
Shakespeare in Love	13	7	1998
Mary Poppins	13	5	1964
Who's Afraid of Virginia Woolf?	13	5	1966
Forrest Gump	13	6	1994
The Lord of the Rings: The Fellowship of the Ring	13	4	2001
Chicago	13	6	2004

Source: Academy of Motion Picture Arts and Sciences

Using abbreviated film titles, let U = { *Eve, Titanic, Wind, Eternity, Love, Poppins, Woolf, Gump, Ring, Chicago*}, A = the set of films nominated for 14 Oscars, B = the set of films that won at least 7 Oscars, and C = the set of films that won Oscars after 1965. Use the information in the chart to construct a Venn diagram that illustrates these sets.

• Writing in Mathematics

107. If you are given four sets, A, B, C, and U, describe what is involved in determining $(A \cup B)' \cap C$. Be as specific as possible in your description.

108. Describe how a Venn diagram can be used to prove that $(A \cup B)'$ and $A' \cap B'$ are equal sets.

• Critical Thinking Exercises

The eight blood types discussed in the Blitzer Bonus on page 86 are shown once again in the Venn diagram. In blood transfusions, the set of antigens in a donor's blood must be a subset of the set of antigens in a recipient's blood. Thus, the recipient must have all or more of the antigens present in the donor's blood. Use this information to solve Exercises 109–112.

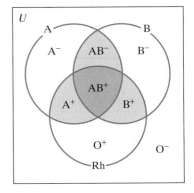

Human blood types

109. What is the blood type of a universal recipient?

110. What is the blood type of a universal donor?

111. Can an A^+ person donate blood to an A^- person?

112. Can an A^- person donate blood to an A^+ person?

• Group Exercises

113. Each group member should find out his or her blood type. (If you cannot obtain this information, select a blood type that you find appealing!) Read the introduction to Exercises 109–112. Referring to the Venn diagram for these exercises, each group member should determine all other group members to whom blood can be donated and from whom it can be received.

114. The group should define three sets, each of which categorizes U, the set of students in the group, in different ways. Examples include the set of students with blonde hair, the set of students no more than 23 years old, and the set of students whose major is undecided. Once you have defined the sets, construct a Venn diagram with three intersecting sets and eight regions. Each student should determine which region he or she belongs to. Illustrate the sets by writing each first name in the appropriate region.

SECTION 2.5 • SURVEY PROBLEMS

O B J E C T I V E S

1. Use Venn diagrams to visualize a survey's results.

2. Use survey results to complete Venn diagrams and answer questions about the survey.

Mexico's 2006 election, its closest-ever race for president, exposed an emerging trend in Latin America: a sharpening divide between the rich and the poor. Although Mexico's economy expanded by 4.4% in 2004 and 3% in 2005, at the end of 2005, almost half of the country's 107 million people still lived in poverty. (*Source*: *Newsweek*, July 17, 2006) Figure 2.24 shows that Mexicans tend to see societal injustice, rather than personal laziness, as the primary cause of poverty.

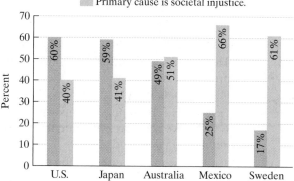

FIGURE 2.24 Percentages for each country may not add to 100% because less frequently identified primary causes of poverty were omitted from the graph.
Source: Ronald Inglehart et al., *World Values Surveys and European Values Surveys*

Suppose a survey is taken that asks randomly selected adults in the United States and Mexico the following question:

Do you agree or disagree that the primary cause of poverty is societal injustice?

In this section, you will see how sets and Venn diagrams are used to tabulate information collected in such a survey. In survey problems, it is helpful to remember that **and** means **intersection**, **or** means **union**, and **not** means **complement**. Furthermore, *but* means the same thing as *and*. Thus, **but** means **intersection**.

1 | Use Venn diagrams to visualize a survey's results.

Visualizing the Results of a Survey

In Section 2.1, we defined the cardinal number of set A, denoted by $n(A)$, as the number of elements in set A. Venn diagrams are helpful in determining a set's cardinality.

| **EXAMPLE 1** | USING A VENN DIAGRAM TO VISUALIZE THE RESULTS OF A SURVEY |

We return to the campus survey in which students were asked two questions:

Would you be willing to donate blood?
Would you be willing to help serve a free breakfast to blood donors?

Set A represents the set of students willing to donate blood. Set B represents the set of students willing to help serve breakfast to donors. The survey

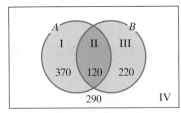

A: Set of students willing to donate blood
B: Set of students willing to serve breakfast to donors

FIGURE 2.25 Results of a survey

results are summarized in Figure 2.25. Use the diagram to answer the following questions:

a. How many students are willing to donate blood?
b. How many students are willing to help serve a free breakfast to blood donors?
c. How many students are willing to donate blood and serve breakfast?
d. How many students are willing to donate blood or serve breakfast?
e. How many students are willing to donate blood but not serve breakfast?
f. How many students are willing to serve breakfast but not donate blood?
g. How many students are neither willing to donate blood nor serve breakfast?
h. How many students were surveyed?

SOLUTION

a. The number of students willing to donate blood can be determined by adding the numbers in regions I and II. Thus, $n(A) = 370 + 120 = 490$. There are 490 students willing to donate blood.

b. The number of students willing to help serve a free breakfast to blood donors can be determined by adding the numbers in regions II and III. Thus, $n(B) = 120 + 220 = 340$. There are 340 students willing to help serve breakfast.

c. The number of students willing to donate blood and serve breakfast appears in region II, the region representing the intersection of the two sets. Thus, $n(A \cap B) = 120$. There are 120 students willing to donate blood and serve breakfast.

d. The number of students willing to donate blood or serve breakfast is found by adding the numbers in regions I, II, and III, representing the union of the two sets. We see that $n(A \cup B) = 370 + 120 + 220 = 710$. Therefore, 710 students in the survey are willing to donate blood or serve breakfast.

e. The region representing students who are willing to donate blood but not serve breakfast, $A \cap B'$, is region I. We see that 370 of the students surveyed are willing to donate blood but not serve breakfast.

f. Region III represents students willing to serve breakfast but not donate blood: $B \cap A'$. We see that 220 students surveyed are willing to help serve breakfast but not donate blood.

g. Students who are neither willing to donate blood nor serve breakfast, $A' \cap B'$, fall within the universal set, but outside circles A and B. These students fall in region IV, where the Venn diagram indicates that there are 290 elements. There are 290 students in the survey who are neither willing to donate blood nor serve breakfast.

h. We can find the number of students surveyed by adding the numbers in regions I, II, III, and IV. Thus, $n(U) = 370 + 120 + 220 + 290 = 1000$. There were 1000 students surveyed.

CHECK POINT 1 In a survey on musical tastes, respondents were asked: Do you listen to classical music? Do you listen to jazz? The survey results are summarized in Figure 2.26. Use the diagram to answer the following questions.

a. How many respondents listened to classical music?
b. How many respondents listened to jazz?
c. How many respondents listened to both classical music and jazz?
d. How many respondents listened to classical music or jazz?
e. How many respondents listened to classical music but not jazz?
f. How many respondents listened to jazz but not classical music?
g. How many respondents listened to neither classical music nor jazz?
h. How many people were surveyed?

FIGURE 2.26

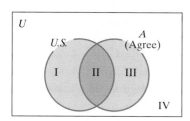

2 | Use survey results to complete Venn diagrams and answer questions about the survey.

Solving Survey Problems

Venn diagrams are used to solve problems involving surveys. Here are the steps needed to solve survey problems:

> ### SOLVING SURVEY PROBLEMS
> 1. Use the survey's description to define sets and draw a Venn diagram.
> 2. Use the survey's results to determine the cardinality for each region in the Venn diagram. **Start with the intersection of the sets, the innermost region, and work outward.**
> 3. Use the completed Venn diagram to answer the problem's questions.

EXAMPLE 2   SURVEYING PEOPLE'S ATTITUDES

A survey is taken that asks 2000 randomly selected U.S. and Mexican adults the following question:

> Do you agree or disagree that the primary cause of poverty is societal injustice?

The results of the survey showed that

> 1060 people agreed with the statement.
> 400 Americans agreed with the statement.
>
> *Source*: World Values Surveys

If half the adults surveyed were Americans,
  a. How many Mexicans agreed with the statement?
  b. How many Mexicans disagreed with the statement?

SOLUTION

Step 1. Define sets and draw a Venn diagram. The Venn diagram in Figure 2.27 shows two sets. Set *U.S.* is the set of Americans surveyed. Set A (labeled "Agree") is the set of people surveyed who agreed with the statement. By representing the Americans surveyed with circle *U.S.*, we do not need a separate circle for the Mexicans. The group of people outside circle *U.S.* must be the set of Mexicans. Similarly, by visualizing the set of people who agreed with the statement as circle A, we do not need a separate circle for those who disagreed. The group of people outside the A (Agree) circle must be the set of people disagreeing with the statement.

FIGURE 2.27

Step 2. Determine the cardinality for each region in the Venn diagram, starting with the innermost region and working outward. We are given the following cardinalities:

> There were 2000 people surveyed: $n(U) = 2000$.
> Half the people surveyed were Americans: $n(U.S.) = 1000$.
> The number of people who agreed with the statement was 1060: $n(A) = 1060$.
> There were 400 Americans who agreed with the statement: $n(U.S. \cap A) = 400$.

Now let's use these numbers to determine the cardinality of each region, starting with region II, moving outward to regions I and III, and ending with region IV.

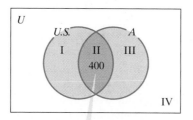

II represents the set of Americans who agreed with the statement. We are given that $n(U.S. \cap A) = 400$.

We are given that set *U.S.*, regions I and II, contains 1000 people: $n(U.S.) = 1000$. With 400 elements in II, this leaves $1000 - 400 = 600$ people in I.

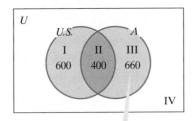

Move out to region III.

We are given that set A, regions II and III, contains 1060 people: $n(A) = 1060$. With 400 elements in II, this leaves $1060 - 400 = 660$ people in III.

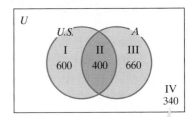

End with IV, the outer region.

We are given that set U, regions I, II, III, and IV, contains 2000 people: $n(U) = 2000$. With $600 + 400 + 660 = 1660$ elements in I, II, and III, this leaves $2000 - 1660 = 340$ people in IV.

Is the Primary Cause of Poverty Societal Injustice?

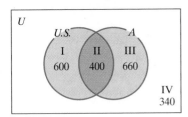

FIGURE 2.28

Step 3. Use the completed Venn diagram to answer the problem's questions. The completed Venn diagram that illustrates the survey's results is shown in Figure 2.28.

a. The Mexicans who agreed with the statement are those members of the set of people who agreed who are not Americans, shown in region III. This means that 660 Mexicans agreed that societal injustice is the primary cause of poverty.

b. The Mexicans who disagreed with the statement can be found outside the circles of people who agreed and people who are Americans. This corresponds to region IV, whose cardinality is 340. Thus, 340 Mexicans disagreed that societal injustice is the primary cause of poverty.

CHECK POINT 2 In a Gallup poll, 2000 U.S. adults were selected at random and asked to agree or disagree with the following statement:

Job opportunities for women are not equal to those for men.

The results of the survey showed that

1190 people agreed with the statement.

700 women agreed with the statement.

Source: The People's Almanac

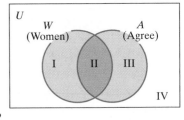

If half the people surveyed were women,

a. How many men agreed with the statement?

b. How many men disagreed with the statement?

When tabulating survey results, more than two circles within a Venn diagram are often needed. For example, consider a *Time*/CNN poll that sought to determine how Americans felt about reserving a certain number of college scholarships exclusively for minorities and women. Respondents were asked the following question:

Do you agree or disagree with the following statement: Colleges should reserve a certain number of scholarships exclusively for minorities and women?

Source: Time Almanac

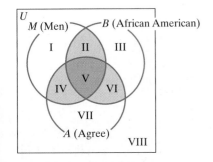

FIGURE 2.29

Suppose that we want the respondents to the poll to be identified by gender (man or woman), ethnicity (African American or other), and whether or not they agreed with the statement. A Venn diagram into which the results of the survey can be tabulated is shown in Figure 2.29.

Based on our work in Example 2, we only used one circle in the Venn diagram to indicate the gender of the respondent. We used M for men, so the set of women respondents, M', consists of the regions outside circle M. Similarly, we used B for the set of African-American respondents, so the regions outside circle B account for all other ethnicities. Finally, we used A for the set of respondents who agreed with the statement. Those who disagreed lie outside circle A.

In the next example, we create a Venn diagram with three intersecting sets to illustrate a survey's results. In our final example, we use this Venn diagram to answer questions about the survey.

> **EXAMPLE 3** **CONSTRUCTING A VENN DIAGRAM FOR A SURVEY**

Sixty people were contacted and responded to a movie survey. The following information was obtained:

a. 6 people liked comedies, dramas, and science fiction.
b. 13 people liked comedies and dramas.
c. 10 people liked comedies and science fiction.
d. 11 people liked dramas and science fiction.
e. 26 people liked comedies.
f. 21 people liked dramas.
g. 25 people liked science fiction.

Use a Venn diagram to illustrate the survey's results.

SOLUTION The set of people surveyed is a universal set with 60 elements containing three subsets:

$$C = \text{the set of those who like comedies}$$
$$D = \text{the set of those who like dramas}$$
$$S = \text{the set of those who like science fiction.}$$

We draw these sets in Figure 2.30. Now let's use the numbers in (a) through (g), as well as the fact that 60 people were surveyed, which we call condition (h), to determine the cardinality of each region in the Venn diagram.

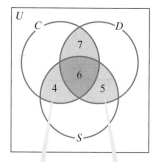

(a) **6 people liked comedies, drama, and science fiction:** $n(C \cap D \cap S) = 6$.

(b) **13 people liked comedies and drama:** $n(C \cap D) = 13$. With 6 counted, there are $13 - 6 = 7$ people in this region.

(c) **10 people liked comedies and science fiction:** $n(C \cap S) = 10$. With 6 counted, there are $10 - 6 = 4$ people in this region.

(d) **11 people liked drama and science fiction:** $n(D \cap S) = 11$. With 6 counted, there are $11 - 6 = 5$ people in this region.

(e) **26 people liked comedies:** $n(C) = 26$. With $7 + 6 + 4 = 17$ counted, there are $26 - 17 = 9$ people in this region.

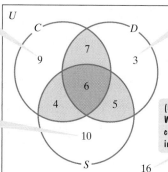

(f) **21 people liked dramas:** $n(D) = 21$. With $7 + 6 + 5 = 18$ counted, there are $21 - 18 = 3$ people in this region.

(g) **25 people liked science fiction:** $n(S) = 25$. With $4 + 6 + 5 = 15$ counted, there are $25 - 15 = 10$ people in this region.

(h) **60 people were surveyed:** $n(U) = 60$. With $9 + 7 + 3 + 4 + 6 + 5 + 10 = 44$ counted, there are $60 - 44 = 16$ people in this region.

With a cardinality in each region, we have completed the Venn diagram that illustrates the survey's results.

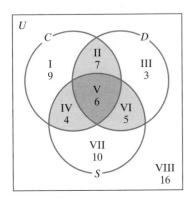

FIGURE 2.31

CHECK POINT 3 A survey of 250 memorabilia collectors showed the following results: 108 collected baseball cards. 92 collected comic books. 62 collected stamps. 29 collected baseball cards and comic books. 5 collected baseball cards and stamps. 2 collected comic books and stamps. 2 collected all three types of memorabilia. Use a Venn diagram to illustrate the survey's results.

EXAMPLE 4   USING A SURVEY'S VENN DIAGRAM

The Venn diagram in Figure 2.31 shows the results of the movie survey in Example 3. How many of those surveyed liked

a. comedies, but neither dramas nor science fiction?
b. dramas and science fiction, but not comedies?
c. dramas or science fiction, but not comedies?
d. exactly one movie style?
e. at least two movie styles?
f. none of the movie styles?

SOLUTION

$C \cap (D' \cap S')$

a. Those surveyed who liked comedies, but neither dramas nor science fiction, are represented in region I. There are 9 people in this category.

$(D \cap S) \cap C'$

b. Those surveyed who liked dramas and science fiction, but not comedies, are represented in region VI. There are 5 people in this category.

c. We are interested in those surveyed who liked dramas or science fiction, but not comedies:

Dramas or science fiction,   but   not comedies

$$(D \cup S) \cap C'.$$

Regions II, III, IV, V, VI, VII   Regions III, VI, VII, VIII

The intersection of the regions in the voice balloons consists of the common regions shown in red, III, VI, and VII. There are $3 + 5 + 10 = 18$ elements in these regions. There are 18 people who liked dramas or science fiction, but not comedies.

d. Those surveyed who liked exactly one movie style are represented in regions I, III, and VII. There are $9 + 3 + 10 = 22$ elements in these regions. Thus, 22 people liked exactly one movie style.

e. Those surveyed who liked at least two movie styles are people who liked two or more types of movies. People who liked two movie styles are represented in regions II, IV, and VI. Those who liked three movie styles are represented in region V. Thus, we add the number of elements in regions II, IV, V, and VI: $7 + 4 + 6 + 5 = 22$. Thus, 22 people liked at least two movie styles.

f. Those surveyed who liked none of the movie styles are represented in region VIII. There are 16 people in this category.

CHECK POINT 4 Use the Venn diagram you constructed in Check Point 3 to determine how many of those surveyed collected

a. comic books, but neither baseball cards nor stamps.
b. baseball cards and stamps, but not comic books.
c. baseball cards or stamps, but not comic books.
d. exactly two types of memorabilia.
e. at least one type of memorabilia.
f. none of the types of memorabilia.

E X E R C I S E   S E T   2 . 5   ●●●●●●

• Practice Exercises

Use the accompanying Venn diagram, which shows the number of elements in regions I through IV, to answer the questions in Exercises 1–8.

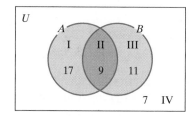

1. How many elements belong to set A?
2. How many elements belong to set B?
3. How many elements belong to set A but not set B?
4. How many elements belong to set B but not set A?
5. How many elements belong to set A or set B?
6. How many elements belong to set A and set B?
7. How many elements belong to neither set A nor set B?
8. How many elements are there in the universal set?

Use the accompanying Venn diagram, which shows the number of elements in region II, to answer Exercises 9–10.

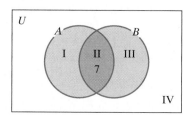

9. If $n(A) = 21, n(B) = 29$, and $n(U) = 48$, find the number of elements in each of regions I, III, and IV.
10. If $n(A) = 23, n(B) = 27$, and $n(U) = 53$, find the number of elements in each of regions I, III, and IV.

Use the accompanying Venn diagram, which shows the cardinality of each region, to answer Exercises 11–26.

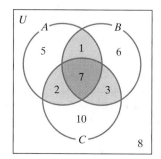

11. How many elements belong to set B?
12. How many elements belong to set A?
13. How many elements belong to set A but not set C?
14. How many elements belong to set B but not set A?
15. How many elements belong to set A or set C?
16. How many elements belong to set A or set B?
17. How many elements belong to set A and set C?
18. How many elements belong to set A and set B?

19. How many elements belong to set B and set C, but not to set A?
20. How many elements belong to set A and set C, but not to set B?
21. How many elements belong to set B or set C, but not to set A?
22. How many elements belong to set A or set C, but not to set B?
23. Considering sets A, B, and C, how many elements belong to exactly one of these sets?
24. Considering sets A, B, and C, how many elements belong to exactly two of these sets?
25. Considering sets A, B, and C, how many elements belong to at least one of these sets?
26. Considering sets A, B, and C, how many elements belong to at least two of these sets?

The accompanying Venn diagram shows the number of elements in region V. In Exercises 27–28, use the given cardinalities to determine the number of elements in each of the other seven regions.

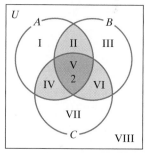

27. $n(U) = 30, n(A) = 11, n(B) = 8, n(C) = 14,$
    $n(A \cap B) = 3, n(A \cap C) = 5, n(B \cap C) = 3$
28. $n(U) = 32, n(A) = 21, n(B) = 15, n(C) = 14,$
    $n(A \cap B) = 6, n(A \cap C) = 7, n(B \cap C) = 8$

• Practice Plus

In Exercises 29–32, use the Venn diagram and the given conditions to determine the number of elements in each region, or explain why the conditions are impossible to meet.

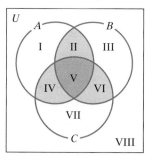

29. $n(U) = 38, n(A) = 26, n(B) = 21, n(C) = 18,$
    $n(A \cap B) = 17, n(A \cap C) = 11, n(B \cap C) = 8,$
    $n(A \cap B \cap C) = 7$
30. $n(U) = 42, n(A) = 26, n(B) = 22, n(C) = 25,$
    $n(A \cap B) = 17, n(A \cap C) = 11, n(B \cap C) = 9,$
    $n(A \cap B \cap C) = 5$

(In Exercises 31–32, continue to refer to the Venn diagram at the bottom of the previous page.)

31. $n(U) = 40, n(A) = 10, n(B) = 11, n(C) = 12,$
$n(A \cap B) = 6, n(A \cap C) = 9, n(B \cap C) = 7,$
$n(A \cap B \cap C) = 2$

32. $n(U) = 25, n(A) = 8, n(B) = 9, n(C) = 10,$
$n(A \cap B) = 6, n(A \cap C) = 9, n(B \cap C) = 8,$
$n(A \cap B \cap C) = 5$

• Application Exercises

As discussed in the text on page 94, a poll asked respondents if they agreed with the statement

> Colleges should reserve a certain number of scholarships exclusively for minorities and women.

Hypothetical results of the poll are tabulated in the Venn diagram. Use these cardinalities to solve Exercises 33–38.

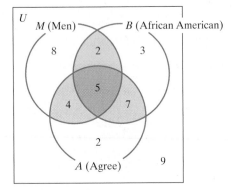

33. How many respondents agreed with the statement?

34. How many respondents disagreed with the statement?

35. How many women agreed with the statement?

36. How many people who are not African American agreed with the statement?

37. How many women who are not African American disagreed with the statement?

38. How many men who are not African American disagreed with the statement?

39. A pollster conducting a telephone poll of a city's residents asked two questions:

   1. Do you currently smoke cigarettes?

   2. Regardless of your answer to question 1, would you support a ban on smoking in all city parks?

  a. Construct a Venn diagram that allows the respondents to the poll to be identified by whether or not they smoke cigarettes and whether or not they support the ban.

  b. Write the letter b in every region of the diagram that represents smokers polled who support the ban.

  c. Write the letter c in every region of the diagram that represents nonsmokers polled who support the ban.

  d. Write the letter d in every region of the diagram that represents nonsmokers polled who do not support the ban.

40. A pollster conducting a telephone poll at a college campus asked students two questions:

   1. Do you binge drink three or more times per month?

   2. Regardless of your answer to question 1, are you frequently behind in your school work?

a. Construct a Venn diagram that allows the respondents to the poll to be identified by whether or not they binge drink and whether or not they frequently fall behind in school work.

b. Write the letter b in every region of the diagram that represents binge drinkers who are frequently behind in school work.

c. Write the letter c in every region of the diagram that represents students polled who do not binge drink but who are frequently behind in school work.

d. Write the letter d in every region of the diagram that represents students polled who do not binge drink and who do not frequently fall behind in their school work.

41. A pollster conducting a telephone poll asked three questions:

   1. Are you religious?

   2. Have you spent time with a person during his or her last days of a terminal illness?

   3. Should assisted suicide be an option for terminally ill people?

a. Construct a Venn diagram with three circles that can assist the pollster in tabulating the responses to the three questions.

b. Write the letter b in every region of the diagram that represents all religious persons polled who are not in favor of assisted suicide for the terminally ill.

c. Write the letter c in every region of the diagram that represents the people polled who do not consider themselves religious, who have not spent time with a terminally ill person during his or her last days, and who are in favor of assisted suicide for the terminally ill.

d. Write the letter d in every region of the diagram that represents the people polled who consider themselves religious, who have not spent time with a terminally ill person during his or her last days, and who are not in favor of assisted suicide for the terminally ill.

e. Write the letter e in a region of the Venn diagram other than those in parts (b)–(d) and then describe who in the poll is represented by this region.

42. A poll asks respondents the following question:

Do you agree or disagree with this statement: In order to address the trend in diminishing male enrollment, colleges should begin special efforts to recruit men?

a. Construct a Venn diagram with three circles that allows the respondents to be identified by gender (man or woman), education level (college or no college), and whether or not they agreed with the statement.

b. Write the letter b in every region of the diagram that represents men with a college education who agreed with the statement.

c. Write the letter c in every region of the diagram that represents women who disagreed with the statement.

d. Write the letter d in every region of the diagram that represents women without a college education who agreed with the statement.

e. Write the letter e in a region of the Venn diagram other than those in parts (b)–(d) and then describe who in the poll is represented by this region.

In Exercises 43–48, construct a Venn diagram and determine the cardinality for each region. Use the completed Venn diagram to answer the questions.

43. A survey of 75 college students was taken to determine where they got the news about what's going on in the world. Of those surveyed, 29 students got the news from newspapers, 43 from television, and 7 from both newspapers and television.

Of those surveyed,

a. How many got the news from only newspapers?

b. How many got the news from only television?

c. How many got the news from newspapers or television?

d. How many did not get the news from either newspapers or television?

44. A survey of 120 college students was taken at registration. Of those surveyed, 75 students registered for a math course, 65 for an English course, and 40 for both math and English.

Of those surveyed,

a. How many registered only for a math course?

b. How many registered only for an English course?

c. How many registered for a math course or an English course?

d. How many did not register for either a math course or an English course?

45. A survey of 80 college students was taken to determine the musical styles they listened to. Forty-two students listened to rock, 34 to classical, and 27 to jazz. Twelve students listened to rock and jazz, 14 to rock and classical, and 10 to classical and jazz. Seven students listened to all three musical styles.

Of those surveyed,

a. How many listened to only rock music?

b. How many listened to classical and jazz, but not rock?

c. How many listened to classical or jazz, but not rock?

d. How many listened to music in exactly one of the musical styles?

e. How many listened to music in at least two of the musical styles?

f. How many did not listen to any of the musical styles?

46. A survey of 180 college men was taken to determine participation in various campus activities. Forty-three students were in fraternities, 52 participated in campus sports, and 35 participated in various campus tutorial programs. Thirteen students participated in fraternities and sports, 14 in sports and tutorial programs, and 12 in fraternities and tutorial programs. Five students participated in all three activities.

Of those surveyed,

a. How many participated in only campus sports?

b. How many participated in fraternities and sports, but not tutorial programs?

c. How many participated in fraternities or sports, but not tutorial programs?

d. How many participated in exactly one of these activities?

e. How many participated in at least two of these activities?

f. How many did not participate in any of the three activities?

47. An anonymous survey of college students was taken to determine behaviors regarding alcohol, cigarettes, and illegal drugs. The results were as follows: 894 drank alcohol regularly, 665 smoked cigarettes, 192 used illegal drugs, 424 drank alcohol regularly and smoked cigarettes, 114 drank alcohol regularly and used illegal drugs, 119 smoked cigarettes and used illegal drugs, 97 engaged in all three behaviors, and 309 engaged in none of these behaviors.

(*Source:* Jamie Langille, University of Nevada Las Vegas)

a. How many students were surveyed?

Of those surveyed,

b. How many drank alcohol regularly or smoked cigarettes?

c. How many used illegal drugs only?

d. How many drank alcohol regularly and smoked cigarettes, but did not use illegal drugs?

e. How many drank alcohol regularly or used illegal drugs, but did not smoke cigarettes?

f. How many engaged in exactly two of these behaviors?

g. How many engaged in at least one of these behaviors?

48. In the August 2005 issue of *Consumer Reports*, readers suffering from depression reported that alternative treatments were less effective than prescription drugs. Suppose that 550 readers felt better taking prescription drugs, 220 felt better through meditation, and 45 felt better taking St. John's wort. Furthermore, 95 felt better using prescription drugs and meditation, 17 felt better using prescription drugs and St. John's wort, 35 felt better using meditation and St. John's wort, 15 improved using all three treatments, and 150 improved using none of these treatments. (Hypothetical results are partly based on percentages given in *Consumer Reports*.)

a. How many readers suffering from depression were included in the report?

Of those included in the report,

b. How many felt better using prescription drugs or meditation?

c. How many felt better using St. John's wort only?

d. How many improved using prescription drugs and meditation, but not St. John's wort?

e. How many improved using prescription drugs or St. John's wort, but not meditation?

f. How many improved using exactly two of these treatments?

g. How many improved using at least one of these treatments?

• Writing in Mathematics

49. Suppose that you are drawing a Venn diagram to sort and tabulate the results of a survey. If results are being tabulated along gender lines, explain why only a circle representing women is needed, rather than two separate circles representing the women surveyed and the men surveyed.

50. Suppose that you decide to use two sets, *M* and *W*, to sort and tabulate the responses for men and women in a survey. Describe the set of people represented by regions II and IV in the Venn diagram shown. What conclusion can you draw?

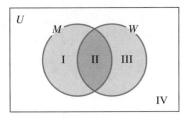

Critical Thinking Exercises

51. Which one of the following is true?

a. In a survey, 110 students were taking mathematics, 90 were taking psychology, and 20 were taking neither. Thus, 220 students were surveyed.

b. If $A \cap B = \emptyset$, then $n(A \cup B) = n(A) + n(B)$.

c. When filling in cardinalities for regions in a two-set Venn diagram, the innermost region, the intersection of the two sets, should be the last region to be filled in.

d. $n(A')$ cannot be obtained by subtracting $n(A)$ from $n(U)$.

52. In a survey of 150 students, 90 were taking mathematics and 30 were taking psychology.

a. What is the least number of students who could have been taking both courses?

b. What is the greatest number of students who could have been taking both courses?

c. What is the greatest number of students who could have been taking neither course?

53. A person applying for the position of college registrar submitted the following report to the college president on 90 students: 31 take math; 28 take chemistry; 42 take psychology; 9 take math and chemistry; 10 take chemistry and psychology; 6 take math and psychology; 4 take all three subjects; and 20 take none of these courses. The applicant was not hired. Explain why.

Group Exercise

54. This group activity is intended to provide practice in the use of Venn diagrams to sort responses to a survey. The group will determine the topic of the survey. Although you will not actually conduct the survey, it might be helpful to imagine carrying out the survey using the students on your campus.

a. In your group, decide on a topic for the survey.

b. Devise three questions that the pollster will ask to the people who are interviewed.

c. Construct a Venn diagram that will assist the pollster in sorting the answers to the three questions. The Venn diagram should contain three intersecting circles within a universal set and eight regions.

d. Describe what each of the regions in the Venn diagram represents in terms of the questions in your poll.

●●●●●● CHAPTER SUMMARY, REVIEW, AND TEST

● SUMMARY DEFINITIONS AND CONCEPTS	EXAMPLES
2.1 Basic Set Concepts	
a. A set is a collection of objects whose contents can be clearly determined. The objects in a set are called the elements, or members, of the set.	
b. Sets can be designated by word descriptions, the roster method (a listing within braces, separating elements with commas), or set-builder notation: $\{$ x $\|$ condition (s) $\}$. The set of / all elements x / such that / x meets these conditions	Ex. 1, p. 46; Ex. 2, p. 47; Ex. 3, p. 47
c. The empty set, or the null set, represented by $\{\ \}$ or $\emptyset$, is a set that contains no elements.	Ex. 4, p. 49
d. The symbol $\in$ means that an object is an element of a set. The symbol $\notin$ means that an object is not an element of a set.	Ex. 5, p. 50
e. The set of natural numbers is $\mathbf{N} = \{1, 2, 3, 4, 5, \ldots\}$. Inequality symbols, summarized in Table 2.2 on page 51, are frequently used to describe sets of natural numbers.	Ex. 6, p. 50; Ex. 7, p. 52
f. The cardinal number of a set A, $n(A)$, is the number of distinct elements in set A. Repeating elements in a set neither adds new elements to the set nor changes its cardinality.	Ex. 8, p. 52
g. Equivalent sets have the same number of elements, or the same cardinality. A one-to-one correspondence between sets A and B means that each element in A can be paired with exactly one element in B, and vice versa. If two sets can be placed in a one-to-one correspondence, then they are equivalent.	Ex. 9, p. 53
h. Set A is a finite set if $n(A) = 0$ or if $n(A)$ is a natural number. A set that is not finite is an infinite set.	

i. Equal sets have exactly the same elements, regardless of order or possible repetition of elements. If two sets are equal, then they must be equivalent.   Ex. 10, p. 55

2.2   Subsets

a. Set A is a subset of set B, expressed as $A \subseteq B$, if every element in set A is also in set B. The notation $A \nsubseteq B$ means that set A is not a subset of set B, so there is at least one element of set A that is not an element of set B.   Ex. 1, p. 59

b. Set A is a proper subset of set B, expressed as $A \subset B$, if A is a subset of B and $A \neq B$.   Ex. 2, p. 60

c. The empty set is a subset of every set.   Ex. 3, p. 61

d. A set with n elements has 2^n subsets and $2^n - 1$ proper subsets.   Ex. 4, p. 62;
Ex. 5, p. 63

2.3   Venn Diagrams and Set Operations

a. A universal set, symbolized by U, is a set that contains all the elements being considered in a given discussion or problem.   Ex. 1, p. 68

b. Venn Diagrams: Representing Two Subsets of a Universal Set   Ex. 2, p. 70

No A are B.
A and B are disjoint.

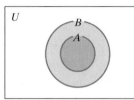

All A are B.
$A \subset B$

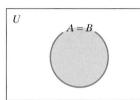

A and B are
equal sets.

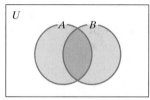

Some (at least
one) A are B.

c. A' (the complement of set A), which can be read A prime or **not** A, is the set of all elements in the universal set that are not in A.   Ex. 3, p. 71

d. $A \cap B$ (A intersection B), which can be read set A **and** set B, is the set of elements common to both set A and set B.   Ex. 4, p. 71

e. $A \cup B$ (A union B), which can be read set A **or** set B, is the set of elements that are members of set A or of set B or of both sets.   Ex. 5, p. 72

f. Some problems involve more than one set operation. Begin by performing any operations inside parentheses.   Ex. 6, p. 73

g. Elements of sets involving a variety of set operations can be determined from Venn diagrams.   Ex. 7, p. 74

h. Cardinal Number of the Union of Two Sets   Ex. 8, p. 75

$$n(A \cup B) = n(A) + n(B) - n(A \cap B)$$

2.4   Set Operations and Venn Diagrams with Three Sets

a. When using set operations involving three sets, begin by performing operations within parentheses.   Ex. 1, p. 79

b. The figure below shows a Venn diagram with three intersecting sets that separate the universal set, U, into eight regions. Elements of sets involving a variety of set operations can be determined from this Venn diagram.   Ex. 2, p. 82

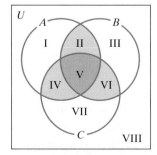

c. To construct a Venn diagram illustrating the elements in $A, B, C,$ and $U,$ first find $A \cap B,$ $A \cap C,$ $B \cap C,$ and $A \cap B \cap C.$ Then place elements into the eight regions shown at the bottom of the previous page, starting with the innermost region, region V, and working outward to region VIII.

Ex. 3, p. 82

d. If two specific sets represent the same regions of a general Venn diagram, then this deductively proves that the two sets are equal.

Ex. 4, p. 84
Ex. 5, p. 85

2.5 Survey Problems

a. Venn diagrams can be used to organize information collected in surveys. When interpreting cardinalities in such diagrams, *and* and *but* mean intersection, *or* means union, and *not* means complement.

Ex. 1, p. 91

b. To solve a survey problem,

1. Define sets and draw a Venn diagram.

2. Fill in the cardinality of each region, starting with the innermost region and working outward.

3. Use the completed diagram to answer the problem's questions.

Ex. 2, p. 93;
Ex. 3, p. 95;
Ex. 4, p. 96

REVIEW EXERCISES

2.1

In Exercises 1–2, write a description of each set. (More than one correct description may be possible.)

1. {Tuesday, Thursday}

2. {1, 2, 3, . . . , 10}

In Exercises 3–5, express each set using the roster method.

3. $\{x | x$ is a letter in the word *miss*$\}$

4. $\{x | x \in \mathbf{N}$ and $8 \leq x < 13\}$

5. $\{x | x \in \mathbf{N}$ and $x \leq 30\}$

In Exercises 6–7, determine which sets are the empty set.

6. {∅}

7. $\{x | x < 4$ and $x \geq 6\}$

In Exercises 8–9, fill in the blank with either $\in$ or $\notin$ to make each statement true.

8. 93 _____ {1, 2, 3, 4, . . . , 99, 100}

9. {d} _____ {a, b, c, d, e}

In Exercises 10–11, find the cardinal number for each set.

10. $A = \{x | x$ is a month of the year$\}$

11. $B = \{18, 19, 20, . . . , 31, 32\}$

In Exercises 12–13, fill in the blank with either $=$ or $\neq$ to make each statement true.

12. {0, 2, 4, 6, 8} _____ {8, 2, 6, 4}

13. $\{x | x \in \mathbf{N}$ and $x > 7\}$ _____ {8, 9, 10, . . . , 100}

In Exercises 14–15, determine if the pairs of sets are equivalent, equal, both, or neither.

14. $A = \{x | x$ is a lowercase letter that comes before f in the English alphabet$\}$

  $B = \{2, 4, 6, 8, 10\}$

15. $A = \{x | x \in \mathbf{N}$ and $3 < x < 7\}$

  $B = \{4, 5, 6\}$

In Exercises 16–17, determine whether each set is finite or infinite.

16. $\{x | x \in \mathbf{N}$ and $x < 50,000\}$

17. $\{x | x \in \mathbf{N}$ and x is even$\}$

2.2

In Exercises 18–20, write $\subseteq$ or $\nsubseteq$ in each blank so that the resulting statement is true.

18. {penny, nickel, dime}

  _____ {half-dollar, quarter, dime, nickel, penny}

19. $\{-1, 0, 1\}$ _____ $\{-3, -2, -1, 1, 2, 3\}$

20. ∅ _____ $\{x | x$ is an odd natural number$\}$

In Exercises 21–22, determine whether $\subseteq$, $\subset$, both, or neither can be placed in each blank to form a true statement.

21. $\{1, 2\}$ _____ $\{1, 1, 2, 2\}$

22. $\{x | x$ is a person living in the United States$\}$

  _____ $\{y | y$ is a person living on planet Earth$\}$

In Exercises 23–29, determine whether each statement is true or false. If the statement is false, explain why.

23. Texas $\in$ {Oklahoma, Louisiana, Georgia, South Carolina}

24. $4 \subseteq \{2, 4, 6, 8, 10, 12\}$

25. $\{e, f, g\} \subset \{d, e, f, g, h, i\}$

26. $\{\ominus, \varnothing\} \subset \{\varnothing, \ominus\}$

27. $\{3, 7, 9\} \subseteq \{9, 7, 3, 1\}$

28. {six} has 2^6 subsets.

29. $\varnothing \subseteq \{\ \}$

30. List all subsets for the set $\{1, 5\}$. Which one of these subsets is not a proper subset?

In Exercises 31–32, find the number of subsets and the number of proper subsets for each set.

31. $\{2, 4, 6, 8, 10\}$

32. $\{x | x$ is a month that begins with the letter J$\}$

2.3

In Exercises 33–37, let $U = \{1, 2, 3, 4, 5, 6, 7, 8\}$, $A = \{1, 2, 3, 4\}$, and $B = \{1, 2, 4, 5\}$. Find each of the following sets.

33. $A \cap B$ **34.** $A \cup B'$ **35.** $A' \cap B$

36. $(A \cup B)'$ **37.** $A' \cap B'$

In Exercises 38–45, use the Venn diagram to represent each set in roster form.

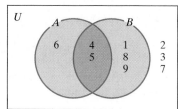

38. A **39.** B' **40.** $A \cup B$

41. $A \cap B$ **42.** $(A \cap B)'$ **43.** $(A \cup B)'$

44. $A \cap B'$ **45.** U

46. Set A contains 25 elements, set B contains 17 elements, and 9 elements are common to sets A and B. How many elements are in $A \cup B$?

2.4

In Exercises 47–48, let

$$U = \{1, 2, 3, 4, 5, 6, 7, 8\}$$
$$A = \{1, 2, 3, 4\}$$
$$B = \{1, 2, 4, 5\}$$
$$C = \{1, 5\}.$$

Find each of the following sets.

47. $A \cup (B \cap C)$ **48.** $(A \cap C)' \cup B$

In Exercises 49–54, use the Venn diagram to represent each set in roster form.

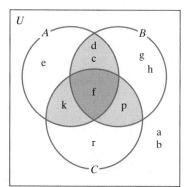

49. $A \cup C$ **50.** $B \cap C$ **51.** $(A \cap B) \cup C$

52. $A \cap C'$ **53.** $(A \cap C)'$ **54.** $A \cap B \cap C$

55. Construct a Venn diagram illustrating the following sets: $A = \{q, r, s, t, u\}$, $B = \{p, q, r\}$, $C = \{r, u, w, y\}$, and $U = \{p, q, r, s, t, u, v, w, x, y\}$.

56. Use a Venn diagram with two intersecting circles to prove that $(A \cup B)' = A' \cap B'$.

57. Use a Venn diagram with three intersecting circles to determine whether the following statement is a theorem:

$$A \cap (B \cup C) = A \cup (B \cap C).$$

58. The U.S. Committee for Refugees and Immigrants issues grades for treatment of refugees. Here are its grades for selected countries, as well as for the European Union:

	Detaining Refugees	Allowing Refugees to Work	Allowing Refugees to Move Freely
United States	D	A	A
European Union	D	B	A
Saudi Arabia	B	D	C
South Africa	F	C	B
Chad	B	B	C
Iran	F	F	C
Russia	F	F	F

Source: U.S. Committee for Refugees and Immigrants

Considering D or F a failing grade, the data can be organized in the following Venn diagram:

Failing in the Treatment of Refugees

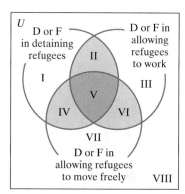

Use the data to determine the region in the Venn diagram into which each of the following countries should be placed.

a. United States

b. Saudi Arabia

c. Chad

d. Iran

e. Russia

2.5

59. A pollster conducting a telephone survey of college students asked two questions:

    1. Are you a registered Republican?

    2. Are you in favor of the death penalty?

a. Construct a Venn diagram with two circles that can assist the pollster in tabulating the responses to the two questions.

b. Write the letter b in every region of the diagram that represents students polled who are registered Republicans who are not in favor of the death penalty.

c. Write the letter c in every region of the diagram that represents students polled who are not registered Republicans and who are in favor of the death penalty.

In Exercises 60–61, construct a Venn diagram and determine the cardinality for each region. Use the completed Venn diagram to answer the questions.

60. A survey of 1000 American adults was taken to analyze their investments. Of those surveyed, 650 had invested in stocks, 550 in bonds, and 400 in both stocks and bonds. Of those surveyed,

  a. How many invested in only stocks?

  b. How many invested in stocks or bonds?

  c. How many did not invest in either stocks or bonds?

61. A survey of 200 students at a nonresidential college was taken to determine how they got to campus during the fall term. Of those surveyed, 118 used cars, 102 used public transportation, and 70 used bikes. Forty-eight students used cars and public transportation, 38 used cars and bikes, and 26 used public transportation and bikes. Twenty-two students used all three modes of transportation. Of those surveyed,

  a. How many used only public transportation?

  b. How many used cars and public transportation, but not bikes?

  c. How many used cars or public transportation, but not bikes?

  d. How many used exactly two of these modes of transportation?

  e. How many did not use any of the three modes of transportation to get to campus?

●●●●●● CHAPTER 2 TEST

1. Express the following set using the roster method:

$$\{x \mid x \in \mathbf{N} \quad \text{and} \quad 17 < x \le 24\}.$$

In Exercises 2–9, determine whether each statement is true or false. If the statement is false, explain why.

2. $\{6\} \in \{1, 2, 3, 4, 5, 6, 7\}$

3. If $A = \{x \mid x$ is a day of the week$\}$ and $B = \{2, 4, 6, \ldots, 14\}$, then sets A and B are equivalent.

4. $\{2, 4, 6, 8\} = \{8, 8, 6, 6, 4, 4, 2\}$

5. $\{d, e, f, g\} \subseteq \{a, b, c, d, e, f\}$

6. $\{3, 4, 5\} \subset \{x \mid x \in \mathbf{N} \quad \text{and} \quad x < 6\}$

7. $14 \notin \{1, 2, 3, 4, \ldots, 39, 40\}$

8. $\{a, b, c, d, e\}$ has 25 subsets.

9. The empty set is a proper subset of any set, including itself.

10. List all subsets for the set $\{6, 9\}$. Which of these subsets is not a proper subset?

In Exercises 11–15, let

$$U = \{a, b, c, d, e, f, g\}$$
$$A = \{a, b, c, d\}$$
$$B = \{c, d, e, f\}$$
$$C = \{a, e, g\}.$$

Find each of the following sets or cardinalities.

11. $A \cup B$

12. $(B \cap C)'$

13. $A \cap C'$

14. $(A \cup B) \cap C$

15. $n(A \cup B')$

In Exercises 16–18, use the Venn diagram to represent each set in roster form.

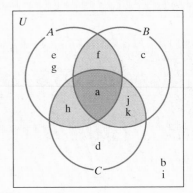

16. A'

17. $A \cap B \cap C$

18. $(A \cap B) \cup (A \cap C)$

19. Construct a Venn diagram illustrating the following sets: $A = \{1, 4, 5\}$, $B = \{1, 5, 6, 7\}$, and $U = \{1, 2, 3, 4, 5, 6, 7\}$.

20. Use the Venn diagram shown to determine whether the following statement is a theorem:

$$A' \cap (B \cup C) = (A' \cap B) \cup (A' \cap C).$$

Show work clearly as you develop the regions represented by each side of the statement.

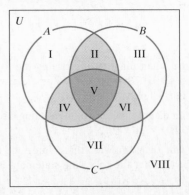

21. Here is a list of some famous people on whom the FBI kept files:

Famous Person	Length of FBI File
Bud Abbott (entertainer)	14 pages
Charlie Chaplin (entertainer)	2063 pages
Albert Einstein (scientist)	1800 pages
Martin Luther King, Jr. (civil rights leader)	17,000 pages
Elvis Presley (entertainer)	663 pages
Jackie Robinson (athlete)	131 pages
Eleanor Roosevelt (first lady; U.N. representative)	3000 pages
Frank Sinatra (entertainer)	1275 pages

Source: Paul Grobman, *Vital Statistics*, Plume, 2005

The data can be organized in the following Venn diagram:

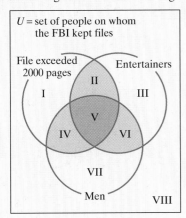

Use the data to determine the region in the Venn diagram into which each of the following people should be placed.

a. Chaplin

b. Einstein

c. King

d. Roosevelt

e. Sinatra

22. A winter resort took a poll of its 350 visitors to see which winter activities people enjoyed. The results were as follows: 178 liked to ski, 154 liked to snowboard, 57 liked to ice skate, 49 liked to ski and snowboard, 15 liked to ski and ice skate, 2 liked to snowboard and ice skate, and 2 liked all three activities.

a. Use a Venn diagram to illustrate the survey's results.

Use the Venn diagram to determine how many of those surveyed enjoyed

b. exactly one of these activities.

c. none of these activities.

d. at least two of these activities.

e. snowboarding and ice skating, but not skiing.

f. snowboarding or ice skating, but not skiing.

g. only skiing.

3
Logic

We are inundated with arguments that attempt to convince us of a variety of claims. P. T. Barnum (1810–1881), cofounder of the circus called "the Greatest Show on Earth," shamelessly engaged in the art of ballyhoo and humbug. His philosophy:

There is a sucker born every minute.
Each time the second hand sweeps to the top,
Like dandelions up they pop,
Their ears so big, their eyes so wide.
And though I feed 'em bonafide baloney,
With no truth in it,
Why you can bet I'll find some rube to buy my corn.
'Cause there's a sure-as-shootin' sucker born a minute,
And I'm referrin' to the minute you was born.

"There Is a Sucker Born Every Minute" from the Broadway musical *Barnum*. ©1980 Notable Music Co., Inc. Music: Cy Coleman; Lyrics: Michael Stewart. All rights reserved.

Logic is a kind of self-defense to avoid being suckered in by the Barnums of the world. It will enable you to apply deductive reasoning to arrive at valid conclusions in complicated situations and to avoid being fooled into believing things for which insufficient reasons are available. The rules of logic will help you to evaluate the vast array of claims facing you as a consumer, a citizen, a student, and a human being. Understanding logic will also allow you to construct better and more convincing arguments of your own, thereby becoming a more effective advocate for your beliefs.

SECTION 3.1 • STATEMENTS, NEGATIONS, AND QUANTIFIED STATEMENTS

History is filled with bad predictions. Here are examples of statements that turned out to be notoriously false:

> *"The actual building of roads devoted to motor cars will not occur in the future."*
>
> *Harper's Weekly*, August 2, 1902

> *"As far as sinking a ship with a bomb is conceived, you just can't do it."*
>
> REAR ADMIRAL CLARK WOODWARD, U.S. Navy, 1939

> *"A Japanese attack on Pearl Harbor is a strategic impossibility."*
>
> GEORGE FIELDING ELIOT, "The Impossible War with Japan,"
> *American Mercury*, September 1938

> *"Television won't be able to hold onto any market. People will soon get tired of staring at a plywood box every night."*
>
> DARRYL F. ZANUCK, 1949

> *"Whatever happens in Vietnam, I can conceive of nothing except military victory."*
>
> LYNDON B. JOHNSON, in a speech at West Point, 1967

> *"When the President does it, that means that it is not illegal."*
>
> RICHARD M. NIXON, TV interview with David Frost, May 20, 1977

Understanding that these statements are false enables us to mentally negate each statement and, with the assistance of historical perspective, obtain a true statement. We begin our study of logic by looking at statements and their negations.

Statements and Using Symbols to Represent Statements

1 | Identify English sentences that are statements.

In everyday English, we use many different kinds of sentences. Some of these sentences are clearly true or false. Others are opinions, questions, and exclamations such as *Help*! or *Fire*! However, in logic we are concerned solely with statements, and not all English sentences are statements.

> **DEFINITION OF A STATEMENT**
> A **statement** is a sentence that is either true or false, but not both simultaneously.

Here are two examples of statements:

1. London is the capital of England.
2. William Shakespeare wrote the last episode of *The Sopranos*.

Statement 1 is true and statement 2 is false. Shakespeare had nothing to do with *The Sopranos* (perhaps writer's block after *Macbeth*).

As long as a sentence is either true or false, *even if we do not know which it is,* then that sentence is a statement. For example, the sentence

The United States has the world's highest divorce rate

is a statement. It's clearly either true or false, and it's not necessary to know which it is.

Some sentences, such as commands, questions, and opinions, are not statements because they are not either true or false. The following sentences are not statements:

1. Read pages 23–57.   (This is an order or command.)
2. If I start losing my memory, how will I know?   (This is a question.)
3. *Titanic* is the greatest movie of all time.   (This is an opinion.)

2 | Express statements using symbols.

In symbolic logic, we use lowercase letters such as *p, q, r,* and *s* to represent statements. Here are two examples:

p: London is the capital of England.

q: William Shakespeare wrote the last episode of *The Sopranos*.

The letter *p* represents the first statement.
The letter *q* represents the second statement.

3 | Form the negation of a statement.

Negating Statements

The sentence "London is the capital of England" is a true statement. The *negation* of this statement, "London is not the capital of England," is a false statement. The **negation** of a statement has a meaning that is opposite that of the original meaning. Thus, the negation of a true statement is a false statement and the negation of a false statement is a true statement.

EXAMPLE 1   FORMING NEGATIONS

Form the negation of each statement:

a. Shakespeare wrote the last episode of *The Sopranos*.
b. Today is not Monday.

SOLUTION

a. The most common way to negate this statement is to introduce *not* into the sentence. The negation is

Shakespeare did not write the last episode of *The Sopranos*.

The English language provides many ways of expressing a statement's meaning. Here is another way to express the negation:

It is not true that Shakespeare wrote the last episode of *The Sopranos*.

b. The negation of "Today is not Monday" is

It is not true that today is not Monday.

The negation is more naturally expressed in English as

Today is Monday.

Form the negation of each statement:

   a. Paris is the capital of Spain.

   b. July is not a month.

---

4 | Express negations using symbols.

The negation of statement p is expressed by writing $\sim p$. We read this as "not p" or "It is not true that p."

EXAMPLE 2   EXPRESSING NEGATIONS SYMBOLICALLY

Let p and q represent the following statements:

   p: Shakespeare wrote the last episode of *The Sopranos*.
   q: Today is not Monday.

Express each of the following statements symbolically:

   a. Shakespeare did not write the last episode of *The Sopranos*.
   b. Today is Monday.

SOLUTION

a. Shakespeare did not write the last episode of *The Sopranos* is the negation of statement p. Therefore, it is expressed symbolically as $\sim p$.

b. Today is Monday is the negation of statement q. Therefore, it is expressed symbolically as $\sim q$.

STUDY TIP

Letters such as p, q, or r can represent any statement, including English statements containing the word *not*. When choosing letters to represent statements, you may prefer to use the symbol $\sim$ with negated English statements. However, it is not wrong to let p, q, or r represent such statements.

 Let p and q represent the following statements:

   p: Paris is the capital of Spain.

   q: July is not a month.

Express each of the following statements symbolically:

   a. Paris is not the capital of Spain.
   b. July is a month.

---

5 | Translate a negation represented by symbols into English.

In Example 2, we translated English statements into symbolic statements. In Example 3, we reverse the direction of our translation.

EXAMPLE 3   TRANSLATING A SYMBOLIC STATEMENT INTO WORDS

Let p represent the following statement:

   p: The United States has the world's highest divorce rate.

Express the symbolic statement $\sim p$ in words.

SOLUTION The symbol $\sim$ is translated as "not." Therefore, $\sim p$ represents

   The United States does not have the world's highest divorce rate.

This can also be expressed as

   It is not true that the United States has the world's highest divorce rate.

Let q represent the following statement:

   q: Chicago O'Hare is the world's busiest airport.

Express the symbolic statement $\sim q$ in words.

6   Express quantified statements in two ways.

Quantified Statements

In English, we frequently encounter statements containing the words **all**, **some**, and **no** (or **none**). These words are called **quantifiers**. A statement that contains one of these words is a **quantified statement**. Here are some examples:

> All poets are writers.
>
> Some people are bigots.
>
> No math books have pictures.
>
> Some students do not work hard.

Using our knowledge of the English language, we can express each of these quantified statements in two equivalent ways, that is, in two ways that have exactly the same meaning. These equivalent statements are shown in Table 3.1.

TABLE 3.1 EQUIVALENT WAYS OF EXPRESSING QUANTIFIED STATEMENTS		
Statement	**An Equivalent Way to Express the Statement**	**Example (Two Equivalent Quantified Statements)**
All *A* are *B*.	There are no *A* that are not *B*.	All poets are writers. There are no poets that are not writers.
Some *A* are *B*.	There exists at least one *A* that is a *B*.	Some people are bigots. At least one person is a bigot.
No *A* are *B*.	All *A* are not *B*.	No math books have pictures. All math books do not have pictures.
Some *A* are not *B*.	Not all *A* are *B*.	Some students do not work hard. Not all students work hard.

7   Write negations of quantified statements.

Forming the negation of a quantified statement can be a bit tricky. Suppose we want to negate the statement "All writers are poets." Because this statement is false, its negation must be true. The negation is "Not all writers are poets." This means the same thing as "Some writers are not poets." Notice that the negation is a true statement.

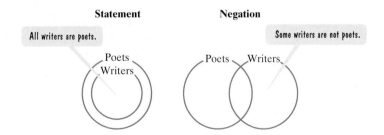

In general, the negation of "All *A* are *B*" is "Some *A* are not *B*." Likewise, the negation of "Some *A* are not *B*" is "All *A* are *B*."

Now let's investigate how to negate a statement with the word *some*. Consider the statement "Some canaries weigh 50 pounds." Because *some* means "there exists at least one," the negation is "It is not true that there is at least one canary that weighs 50 pounds." Because it is not true that there is even one such critter, we can express the negation as "No canary weighs 50 pounds."

Statement	Negation

Some canaries weigh 50 pounds.

Canaries   50-pound objects

No canary weighs 50 pounds.

Canaries   50-pound objects

In general, the negation of "Some *A* are *B*" is "No *A* are *B*." Likewise, the negation of "No *A* are *B*" is "Some *A* are *B*."

Negations of quantified statements are summarized in Table 3.2.

TABLE 3.2 NEGATIONS OF QUANTIFIED STATEMENTS		
Statement	**Negation**	**Example (A Quantified Statement and Its Negation)**
All *A* are *B*.	Some *A* are not *B*.	All people take exams honestly. The negation is Some people do not take exams honestly.
Some *A* are *B*.	No *A* are *B*.	Some roads are open. The negation is No roads are open.

(The negations of the statements in the second column are the statements in the first column.)

STUDY TIP

This diagram should help you remember the negations for quantified statements. The statements diagonally opposite each other are negations.

All *A* are *B*.   No *A* are *B*.

Some *A* are *B*.   Some *A* are not *B*.

EXAMPLE 4   NEGATING A QUANTIFIED STATEMENT

The mechanic told me, "All piston rings were replaced." I later learned that the mechanic never tells the truth. What can I conclude?

SOLUTION Let's begin with the mechanic's statement:

All piston rings were replaced.

Because the mechanic never tells the truth, I can conclude that the truth is the negation of what I was told. The negation of "All *A* are *B*" is "Some *A* are not *B*." Thus, I can conclude that

Some piston rings were not replaced.

Because *some* means *at least one*, I can also correctly conclude that

At least one piston ring was not replaced.

○

CHECK POINT 4 The board of supervisors told us, "All new tax dollars will be used to improve education." I later learned that the board of supervisors never tells the truth. What can I conclude? Express the conclusion in two equivalent ways.

E X E R C I S E   S E T   3 . 1 ●●●●●●

• Practice Exercises

In Exercises 1–14, determine whether or not each sentence is a statement.

1. The musical *Rent* is based on Puccini's opera *La Bohème*.
2. All female Shakespearean roles were played by men in sixteenth-century England.
3. George W. Bush was the Democratic candidate for president in 2004.
4. John Kerry was the Republican candidate for president in 2004.
5. Take the most interesting classes you can find.
6. Don't try to study on a Friday night in the dorms.
7. The average human brain contains 100 billion neurons.
8. There are 2,500,000 rivets in the Eiffel Tower.
9. Is the unexamined life worth living?
10. Is this the best of all possible worlds?
11. Some Catholic countries have legalized same-sex marriage.
12. Some U.S. presidents were assassinated.
13. $9 + 6 = 16$ 14. $9 \times 6 = 64$

In Exercises 15–20, form the negation of each statement.

15. It is raining.
16. It is snowing.
17. The Dallas Cowboys are not the team with the most Super Bowl wins.
18. The New York Yankees are not the team with the most World Series wins.
19. It is not true that chocolate in moderation is good for the heart.
20. It is not true that Albert Einstein was offered the presidency of Israel.

In Exercises 21–24, let p, q, r, and s represent the following statements:

> *p: One works hard.*
> *q: One succeeds.*
> *r: The temperature outside is not freezing.*
> *s: It is not true that the heater is working.*

Express each of the following statements symbolically.

21. One does not work hard.
22. One does not succeed.
23. The temperature outside is freezing.
24. The heater is working.

According to Condensed Knowledge: A Deliciously Irreverent Guide to Feeling Smart Again *(Harper Collins, 2004), each statement listed below is false. (Who knew?)*

> *p: Listening to classical music makes infants smarter.*
> *q: Subliminal advertising makes you buy things.*
> *r: Sigmund Freud's father was not 20 years older than his mother.*
> *s: Humans and bananas do not share approximately 60% of the same DNA structure.*

In Exercises 25–28, use the representations shown to express each symbolic statement in words. What can you conclude about the resulting verbal statement?

25. ~*p*   26. ~*q*   27. ~*r*   28. ~*s*

Exercises 29–36 contain quantified statements. For each exercise,

   a. *Express the quantified statement in an equivalent way, that is, in a way that has exactly the same meaning.*

   b. *Write the negation of the quantified statement. (The negation should begin with "all," "some," or "no.")*

29. All whales are mammals.
30. All journalists are writers.
31. Some students are business majors.
32. Some movies are comedies.
33. Some thieves are not criminals.
34. Some pianists are not keyboard players.
35. No Democratic presidents have been impeached.
36. No women have served as Supreme Court justices.

Here's another list of false statements from Condensed Knowledge.

> *p: No Africans have Jewish ancestry.*
> *q: No religious traditions recognize sexuality as central to their understanding of the sacred.*
> *r: All rap is hip-hop.*
> *s: Some hip-hop is not rap.*

In Exercises 37–40, use the representations shown to express each symbolic statement in words. Verbal statements should begin with "all," "some," or "no." What can you conclude about each resulting verbal statement?

37. ~*p*   38. ~*q*   39. ~*r*   40. ~*s*

• Practice Plus

Exercises 41–44 contain diagrams that show relationships between two sets. (These diagrams are just like the Venn diagrams studied in Chapter 2. However, the circles are not enclosed in a rectangle representing a universal set.)

   a. *Use each diagram to write a statement beginning with the word "all," "some," or "no" that illustrates the relationship between the sets.*

   b. *Determine if the statement in part (a) is true or false. If it is false, write its negation.*

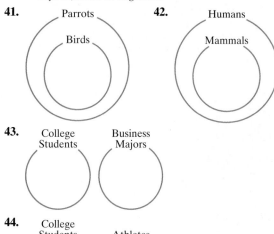

41. Parrots / Birds   42. Humans / Mammals

43. College Students   Business Majors

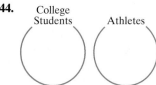

44. College Students   Athletes

In Exercises 45–50,

   a. *Express each statement in an equivalent way that begins with "all," "some," or "no."*

   b. *Write the negation of the statement in part (a).*

45. Nobody doesn't like Sara Lee.

46. A problem well stated is a problem half solved.

47. Nothing is both safe and exciting.

48. Many a person has lived to regret a misspent youth.

49. Not every great actor is a Tom Hanks.

50. Not every generous philanthropist is a Bill Gates.

• Application Exercises

In Exercises 51 and 52, choose the correct statement.

51. The City Council of a large northern metropolis promised its citizens that in the event of snow, all major roads connecting the city to its airport would remain open. The City Council did not keep its promise during the first blizzard of the season. Therefore, during the first blizzard:

   a. No major roads connecting the city to the airport were open.

   b. At least one major road connecting the city to the airport was not open.

   c. At least one major road connecting the city to the airport was open.

   d. The airport was forced to close.

52. During the Watergate scandal in 1974, President Richard Nixon assured the American people that "In all my years of public service, I have never obstructed justice." Later, events indicated that the president was not telling the truth. Therefore, in his years of public service:

   a. Nixon always obstructed justice.

   b. Nixon sometimes did not obstruct justice.

   c. Nixon sometimes obstructed justice.

   d. Nixon never obstructed justice.

Our culture celebrates romantic love—affection and sexual passion for another person—as the basis for marriage. However, the bar graph illustrates that in some countries, romantic love plays a less important role in marriage.

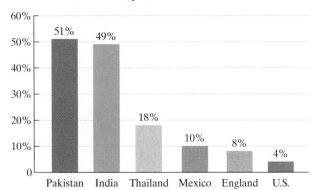

Percentage of College Students Willing to Marry without Romantic Love

Source: Robert Levine, "Is Love a Luxury?" *American Demographics*

In Exercises 53–60, use the graph where necessary to determine whether each statement is true or false. If the statement is false, write its negation.

53. A majority of college students in Pakistan are willing to marry without romantic love.

54. Nearly half of India's college students are willing to marry without romantic love.

55. No college students in the United States are willing to marry without romantic love.

56. All college students in Pakistan are willing to marry without romantic love.

57. Not all college students in Mexico are willing to marry without romantic love.

58. Not all college students in England are willing to marry without romantic love.

59. The sentence "5% of college students in Australia are willing to marry without romantic love" is not a statement.

60. The sentence "12% of college students in the Philippines are willing to marry without romantic love" is not a statement.

• Writing in Mathematics

61. What is a statement? Explain why commands, questions, and opinions are not statements.

62. Explain how to form the negation of a given English statement. Give an example.

63. Describe how the negation of statement *p* is expressed using symbols.

64. List the words identified as quantifiers. Give an example of a statement that uses each of these quantifiers.

65. Explain how to write the negation of a quantified statement in the form "All *A* are *B*." Give an example.

66. Explain how to write the negation of a quantified statement in the form "Some *A* are *B*." Give an example.

67. If the ancient Greek god Zeus could do anything, could he create a rock so huge that he could not move it? Explain your answer.

• Critical Thinking Exercises

68. Give an example of a sentence that is not a statement because it is true and false simultaneously.

69. Give an example in which the statement "Some *A* are not *B*" is true, but the statement "Some *B* are not *A*" is false.

70. The statement

   She isn't dating him because he is muscular

is confusing because it can mean two different things. Describe the two different meanings that make this statement ambiguous.

SECTION 3.2 • COMPOUND STATEMENTS AND CONNECTIVES

O B J E C T I V E S

1. **Express compound statements in symbolic form.**

2. **Express symbolic statements with parentheses in English.**

3. **Use the dominance of connectives.**

What conditions enable us to flourish and our hearts to sing? Researchers in the new science of happiness have learned some surprising things about what it doesn't take to ring our inner chimes. Neither wealth nor a good education are sufficient for happiness. Put in another way, we should not rely on the following statement:

If you're wealthy or well educated, then you'll be happy.

We can break this statement down into three basic sentences:

You're wealthy. You're well educated. You'll be happy.

These sentences are called **simple statements** because each one conveys one idea with no connecting words. Statements formed by combining two or more simple statements are called **compound statements**. Words called **connectives** are used to join simple statements to form a compound statement. Connectives include words such as **and, or, if . . . then**, and **if and only if**.

Compound statements appear throughout written and spoken language. We need to be able to understand the logic of such statements to analyze information objectively. In this section, we analyze four kinds of compound statements.

1 | Express compound statements in symbolic form.

And Statements

If p and q represent two simple statements, then **the compound statement "p and q" is symbolized by $p \wedge q$**. The compound statement formed by connecting statements with the word **and** is called a **conjunction**. The symbol for *and* is $\wedge$.

EXAMPLE 1	TRANSLATING FROM ENGLISH TO SYMBOLIC FORM

Let p and q represent the following simple statements:

  p: It is after 5 P.M.
  q: They are working.

Write each compound statement below in symbolic form:

  a. It is after 5 P.M. and they are working.
  b. It is after 5 P.M. and they are not working.

SOLUTION

a.   It is after 5 P.M.   and   they are working.

              p $\wedge$ q

The symbolic form is $p \wedge q$.

b.   It is after 5 P.M.   and   they are not working.

              p $\wedge$ $\sim q$

The symbolic form is $p \wedge \sim q$.

Use the representations in Example 1 to write each compound statement below in symbolic form:

a. They are working and it is after 5 P.M.

b. It is not after 5 P.M. and they are working.

The English language has a variety of ways to express the connectives that appear in compound statements. Table 3.3 shows a number of ways to translate $p \wedge q$ into English.

TABLE 3.3 COMMON ENGLISH EXPRESSIONS FOR $p \wedge q$		
Symbolic Statement	**English Statement**	**Example** p: It is after 5 P.M. q: They are working.
$p \wedge q$	p and q.	It is after 5 P.M. and they are working.
$p \wedge q$	p but q.	It is after 5 P.M., but they are working.
$p \wedge q$	p yet q.	It is after 5 P.M., yet they are working.
$p \wedge q$	p nevertheless q.	It is after 5 P.M.; nevertheless, they are working.

STUDY TIP

Not every English statement with the word *and* is a conjunction.

- Not a conjunction:

  "Nonviolence and truth are inseparable."

  —GANDHI

  This statement cannot be broken down into two simple statements. It is itself a simple statement.

- Conjunction:

  Pizza and beer are not recommended for people with ulcers.

  Can be broken down as follows: Pizza is not recommended for people with ulcers and beer is not recommended for people with ulcers.

Or Statements

The connective *or* can mean two different things. For example, consider this statement:

I visited London or Paris.

The statement can mean

I visited London or Paris, but not both.

This is an example of the **exclusive or**, which means "one or the other, but not both." By contrast, the statement can mean

I visited London or Paris or both.

This is an example of the **inclusive or**, which means "either or both."

In this chapter and in mathematics in general, when the connective *or* appears, it means the *inclusive or*. If p and q represent two simple statements, then the compound statement "p or q" means p or q or both. The compound statement formed by connecting statements with the word *or* is called a **disjunction. The symbol for *or* is** $\vee$**. Thus, we can symbolize the compound statement "p or q or both" by** $p \vee q$**.**

EXAMPLE 2	TRANSLATING FROM ENGLISH TO SYMBOLIC FORM

Let *p* and *q* represent the following simple statements:

    p: The bill receives majority approval.

    q: The bill becomes a law.

Write each compound statement below in symbolic form:

a. The bill receives majority approval or the bill becomes a law.

b. The bill receives majority approval or the bill does not become a law.

SOLUTION

a.

         p   ∨   *q*

The symbolic form is $p \vee q$.

b.

         p   ∨   ~*q*

The symbolic form is $p \vee \sim q$.

 2 Let *p* and *q* represent the following simple statements:

    p: You graduate.

    q: You satisfy the math requirement.

Write each compound statement below in symbolic form:

a. You graduate or you satisfy the math requirement.

b. You satisfy the math requirement or you do not graduate.

If-Then Statements

The diagram in Figure 3.1 shows that

    All poets are writers.   *The set of poets is a subset of the set of writers.*

In Section 3.1, we saw that this can be expressed as

    There are no poets that are not writers.

Another way of expressing this statement is

    If a person is a poet, then that person is a writer.

The form of this statement is "If *p*, then *q*." **The compound statement "If *p*, then *q*" is symbolized by $p \rightarrow q$.** The compound statement formed by connecting statements with "if–then" is called a **conditional statement**. The symbol for "if–then" is $\rightarrow$.

    In a conditional statement, the statement before the $\rightarrow$ connective is called the **antecedent**. The statement after the $\rightarrow$ connective is called the **consequent**:

$$\text{antecedent} \rightarrow \text{consequent}.$$

All poets are writers. If a person is a poet, then that person is a writer.

FIGURE 3.1

EXAMPLE 3	TRANSLATING FROM ENGLISH TO SYMBOLIC FORM

Let *p* and *q* represent the following simple statements:

    p: A person is a father.

    q: A person is a male.

p: A person is a father.

q: A person is a male.

The given representations (repeated)

Write each compound statement below in symbolic form:

a. If a person is a father, then that person is a male.

b. If a person is a male, then that person is a father.

c. If a person is not a male, then that person is not a father.

SOLUTION

a.

$$p \quad \rightarrow \quad q$$

The symbolic form is $p \rightarrow q$.

b.

$$q \quad \rightarrow \quad p$$

The symbolic form is $q \rightarrow p$.

c.

$$\sim q \quad \rightarrow \quad \sim p$$

The symbolic form is $\sim q \rightarrow \sim p$.

○

  Use the representations in Example 3 to write each compound statement below in symbolic form:

a. If a person is not a father, then that person is not a male.

b. If a person is a male, then that person is not a father.

Conditional statements in English often omit the word *then* and simply use a comma. When *then* is included, the comma can be included or omitted. Here are some examples:

If a person is a father, then that person is a male.

If a person is a father then that person is a male.

If a person is a father, that person is a male.

Table 3.4 shows some of the common ways to translate $p \rightarrow q$ into English.

TABLE 3.4 COMMON ENGLISH EXPRESSIONS FOR $p \rightarrow q$		
Symbolic Statement	**English Statement**	**Example** *p:* A person is a father. *q:* A person is a male.
$p \rightarrow q$	If p then q.	If a person is a father, then that person is a male.
$p \rightarrow q$	q if p.	A person is a male if that person is a father.
$p \rightarrow q$	p is sufficient for q.	Being a father is sufficient for being a male.
$p \rightarrow q$	q is necessary for p.	Being a male is necessary for being a father.
$p \rightarrow q$	p only if q.	A person is a father only if that person is a male.
$p \rightarrow q$	Only if q, p.	Only if a person is a male is that person a father.

The sufficient condition of a conditional statement is the part that precedes →, or the antecedent. The necessary condition of a conditional statement is the part that follows →, or the consequent.

The *if* part or the *sufficient* part   The *only if* part or the *necessary* part

---

EXAMPLE 4   TRANSLATING FROM ENGLISH TO SYMBOLIC FORM

Let p and q represent the following simple statements:

   p: We suffer huge budget deficits.

   q: We control military spending.

Write the following compound statement in symbolic form:

   Controlling military spending is necessary for not suffering huge budget deficits.

SOLUTION   The necessary part of a conditional statement follows the *if–then* connective. Because "controlling military spending" is the necessary part, we can rewrite the compound statement as follows:

If   we do not suffer huge budget deficits,   then   we control military spending.

$$\sim p \quad\quad \rightarrow \quad\quad q$$

The symbolic form is $\sim p \rightarrow q$.

 Use the representations in Example 4 to write the following compound statement in symbolic form.

   Suffering huge budget deficits is necessary for not controlling military spending.

If and Only If Statements

If a conditional statement is true, reversing the antecedent and consequent may result in a statement that is not necessarily true:

- If a person is a father, then that person is a male.

   true

- If a person is a male, then that person is a father.

   not necessarily true

However, some true conditional statements are still true when the antecedent and consequent are reversed:

- If a person is an unmarried male, then that person is a bachelor.

   true

- If a person is a bachelor, then that person is an unmarried male.

   also true

Rather than deal with two separate conditionals, we can combine them into one *biconditional statement:*

   A person is an unmarried male if and only if that person is a bachelor.

   If p and q represent two simple statements, then **the compound statement "p if and only if q" is symbolized by $p \leftrightarrow q$.** The compound statement formed by connecting statements with *if and only if* is called a **biconditional**. The symbol for *if and only if* is ↔. The phrase *if and only if* can be abbreviated as *iff*.

TABLE 3.5 WORDS WITH THE MOST MEANINGS IN THE *OXFORD ENGLISH DICTIONARY*

Word	Meanings
Set	464
Run	396
Go	368
Take	343
Stand	334

EXAMPLE 5 — TRANSLATING FROM ENGLISH TO SYMBOLIC FORM

Table 3.5 shows that the word *set* has 464 meanings, making it the word with the most meanings in the English language. Let p and q represent the following simple statements:

p: The word is *set*.

q: The word has 464 meanings.

Write each of the compound statements below in its symbolic form:

a. The word is *set* if and only if the word has 464 meanings.

b. The word does not have 464 meanings if and only if the word is not *set*.

SOLUTION

a.

The word is *set* → p | if and only if → $\leftrightarrow$ | the word has 464 meanings. → q

The symbolic form is $p \leftrightarrow q$. Observe that each of the following statements is true:

If the word is *set*, then it has 464 meanings.

If the word has 464 meanings, then it is *set*.

b.

The word does not have 464 meanings → $\sim q$ | if and only if → $\leftrightarrow$ | the word is not *set*. → $\sim p$

The symbolic form is $\sim q \leftrightarrow \sim p$.

 CHECK POINT 5 Let p and q represent the following simple statements:

p: The word is *run*.

q: The word has 396 meanings.

Write each of the compound statements below in its symbolic form:

a. The word has 396 meanings if and only if the word is *run*.

b. The word is not *run* if and only if the word does not have 396 meanings.

Table 3.6 shows some of the common ways to translate $p \leftrightarrow q$ into English.

TABLE 3.6 COMMON ENGLISH EXPRESSIONS FOR $p \leftrightarrow q$

Symbolic Statement	English Statement	Example p: A person is an unmarried male. q: A person is a bachelor.
$p \leftrightarrow q$	p if and only if q.	A person is an unmarried male if and only if that person is a bachelor.
$p \leftrightarrow q$	q if and only if p.	A person is a bachelor if and only if that person is an unmarried male.
$p \leftrightarrow q$	If p then q, and if q then p.	If a person is an unmarried male then that person is a bachelor, and if a person is a bachelor then that person is an unmarried male.
$p \leftrightarrow q$	p is necessary and sufficient for q.	Being an unmarried male is necessary and sufficient for being a bachelor.
$p \leftrightarrow q$	q is necessary and sufficient for p.	Being a bachelor is necessary and sufficient for being an unmarried male.

Table 3.7 summarizes the statements discussed in the first two sections of this chapter.

TABLE 3.7 STATEMENTS OF SYMBOLIC LOGIC

Name	Symbolic Form	Common English Translations
Negation	$\sim p$	Not p. It is not true that p.
Conjunction	$p \wedge q$	p and q. p but q.
Disjunction	$p \vee q$	p or q.
Conditional	$p \rightarrow q$	If p, then q. p is sufficient for q. q is necessary for p.
Biconditional	$p \leftrightarrow q$	p if and only if q. p is necessary and sufficient for q.

2 | Express symbolic statements with parentheses in English.

Symbolic Statements with Parentheses

Parentheses in symbolic statements indicate which statements are to be grouped together. For example, $\sim(p \wedge q)$ means the negation of the entire statement $p \wedge q$. By contrast, $\sim p \wedge q$ means that only statement p is negated. We read $\sim(p \wedge q)$ as "it is not true that p and q." We read $\sim p \wedge q$ as "not p and q." Unless parentheses appear in a symbolic statement, the symbol $\sim$ negates only the statement that immediately follows it.

EXAMPLE 6   EXPRESSING SYMBOLIC STATEMENTS WITH AND WITHOUT PARENTHESES IN ENGLISH

Let p and q represent the following simple statements:

p: She is wealthy.

q: She is happy.

Write each of the following symbolic statements in words:

a. $\sim(p \wedge q)$ **b.** $\sim p \wedge q$ **c.** $\sim(p \vee q)$.

SOLUTION The voice balloons illustrate the differences among the three statements.

- $\sim(p \wedge q)$ • $\sim p \wedge q$ • $\sim(p \vee q)$

| It is not true that | she is wealthy and she is happy. | | She is not wealthy | and | she is happy. | | It is not true that | she is wealthy or she is happy. |

STUDY TIP

It is not always necessary to use p and q to represent two simple statements. You can select letters that help you remember what the statements represent. For example, in Example 6, you may prefer using w and h rather than p and q:

w: She is wealthy.

h: She is happy.

a. The symbolic statement $\sim(p \wedge q)$ means the negation of the entire statement $p \wedge q$. A translation of $\sim(p \wedge q)$ is

It is not true that she is wealthy and happy.

We can also express this statement as

It is not true that she is both wealthy and happy.

b. A translation of $\sim p \wedge q$ is

She is not wealthy and she is happy.

c. The symbolic statement $\sim(p \vee q)$ means the negation of the entire statement $p \vee q$. A translation of $\sim(p \vee q)$ is

It is not true that she is wealthy or happy.

We can express this statement as

She is neither wealthy nor happy.

The Data for the Statements in Example 6

Despite the array of delightful toys that money can buy, current research by University of Illinois psychologist Edward Diener (a.k.a Dr. Happiness) indicates that once your basic needs are met, additional income does little to raise your satisfaction with life. The graph in Figure 3.2 shows that having a high annual income is not necessary for being happy:

You are happy → You have a high annual income.

> If you are happy, you have a high annual income.
> This statement is not true for the 68% of Americans earning less than $35,000 per year who are happy most of the time.

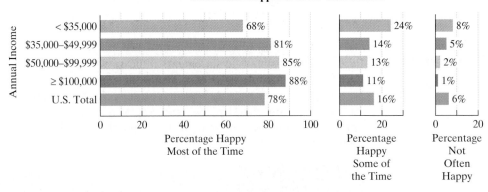

Income and Happiness in the United States

FIGURE 3.2
Source: Time poll conducted December 2004

Let *p* and *q* represent the following simple statements:

p: He earns $105,000 yearly.

q: He is often happy.

Write each of the following symbolic statements in words:

a. $\sim(p \wedge q)$ **b.** $\sim q \wedge p$ **c.** $\sim(q \rightarrow p)$.

Many compound statements contain more than one connective. When expressed symbolically, parentheses are used to indicate which simple statements are grouped together. When expressed in English, commas are used to indicate the groupings. Here is a table that illustrates groupings using parentheses in symbolic statements and commas in English statements:

Symbolic Statement	Statements to Group Together	English Translation
$(q \wedge \sim p) \rightarrow \sim r$	$q \wedge \sim p$	If q and not p, then not r.
$q \wedge (\sim p \rightarrow \sim r)$	$\sim p \rightarrow \sim r$	q, and if not p then not r.

The statement in the first row is an *if–then* conditional statement. Notice that the symbol → is outside the parentheses. By contrast, the statement in the second row is an *and* conjunction. In this case, the symbol $\wedge$ is outside the parentheses. Notice that when we translate the symbolic statement into English, **the simple statements in parentheses appear on the same side of the comma.**

| EXAMPLE 7 | EXPRESSING SYMBOLIC STATEMENTS WITH PARENTHESES IN ENGLISH |

Let p, q, and r represent the following simple statements:

p: A student misses lecture.
q: A student studies.
r: A student fails.

Write each of the symbolic statements below in words:

a. $(q \wedge \sim p) \to \sim r$ **b.** $q \wedge (\sim p \to \sim r)$.

SOLUTION

a. $(q \quad \wedge \quad \sim p) \quad \to \quad \sim r$

If | A student studies | and | A student does not miss lecture | , then | A student does not fail.

One possible English translation for the symbolic statement is

> If a student studies and does not miss lecture, then the student does not fail.

Observe how the symbolic statements in parentheses appear on the same side of the comma in the English translation.

b. $q \quad \wedge \quad (\sim p \quad \to \quad \sim r)$

A student studies | , and if | A student does not miss lecture | then | A student does not fail.

One possible English translation for the symbolic statement is

> A student studies, and if a student does not miss lecture then the student does not fail.

Once again, the symbolic statements in parentheses appear on the same side of the comma in the English statement.

 Let p, q, and r represent the following simple statements:

> p: The plant is fertilized.
> q: The plant is not watered.
> r: The plant wilts.

Write each of the symbolic statements in words:

a. $(p \wedge \sim q) \to \sim r$ **b.** $p \wedge (\sim q \to \sim r)$.

3 | Use the dominance of connectives.

Dominance of Connectives

In Example 7, the statements $(q \wedge \sim p) \to \sim r$ and $q \wedge (\sim p \to \sim r)$ had different meanings. If we are given $q \wedge \sim p \to \sim r$ without parentheses, how do we know which statements to group together?

If a symbolic statement appears without parentheses, statements before and after the most _dominant connective_ should be grouped. Symbolic connectives are categorized from the least dominant, negation, to the most dominant, the biconditional.

DOMINANCE OF CONNECTIVES

The **dominance of connectives** used in symbolic logic is defined in the following order:

1. Negation, $\sim$ 2. Conjunction, $\wedge$ 3. Conditional, $\to$ 4. Biconditional, $\leftrightarrow$
                          Disjunction, $\vee$

Least dominant   Same level of dominance   Most dominant

Table 3.8 shows a number of symbolic statements without parentheses. The meaning of each statement is then clarified by placing grouping symbols (parentheses), as needed, before and after the most dominant connective used.

TABLE 3.8 USING THE DOMINANCE OF CONNECTIVES

Statement	Most Dominant Connective Highlighted in Red	Statement's Meaning Clarified with Grouping Symbols	Type of Statement
$p \rightarrow q \wedge \sim r$	$p \rightarrow q \wedge \sim r$	$p \rightarrow (q \wedge \sim r)$	Conditional
$p \wedge q \rightarrow \sim r$	$p \wedge q \rightarrow \sim r$	$(p \wedge q) \rightarrow \sim r$	Conditional
$p \leftrightarrow q \rightarrow r$	$p \leftrightarrow q \rightarrow r$	$p \leftrightarrow (q \rightarrow r)$	Biconditional
$p \rightarrow q \leftrightarrow r$	$p \rightarrow q \leftrightarrow r$	$(p \rightarrow q) \leftrightarrow r$	Biconditional
$p \wedge \sim q \rightarrow r \vee s$	$p \wedge \sim q \rightarrow r \vee s$	$(p \wedge \sim q) \rightarrow (r \vee s)$	Conditional
$p \wedge q \vee r$	$\wedge$ and $\vee$ have the same level of dominance.	The meaning is ambiguous.	?

Grouping symbols must be given with this statement to determine whether it means $(p \wedge q) \vee r$, a disjunction, or $p \wedge (q \vee r)$, a conjunction.

EXAMPLE 8 USING THE DOMINANCE OF CONNECTIVES

Write each compound statement below in symbolic form:

a. I do not fail the course if and only if I study hard and I pass the final.

b. I do not fail the course if and only if I study hard, and I pass the final.

SOLUTION We begin by assigning letters to the simple statements. Let each letter represent an English statement that is not negated. We can then represent any negated simple statement with the negation symbol, $\sim$. Use the following representations:

p: I fail the course.

q: I study hard.

r: I pass the final.

a.

I do not fail the course	iff	I study hard	and	I pass the final.
$\sim p$	$\leftrightarrow$	q	$\wedge$	r

Because the most dominant connective that appears is $\leftrightarrow$, the symbolic form with parentheses is $\sim p \leftrightarrow (q \wedge r)$.

b.

I do not fail the course	iff	I study hard	,	and	I pass the final.

$(\sim p \quad \leftrightarrow \quad q) \quad \wedge \quad r$

In this statement, the comma indicates the grouping, so it is not necessary to apply the dominance of connectives. The symbolic form of the statement is $(\sim p \leftrightarrow q) \wedge r$.

STUDY TIP

Only apply the dominance of connectives if grouping symbols (parentheses) are not given in compound symbolic statements or commas do not appear in compound English statements.

CHECK POINT 8 Write each compound statement below in symbolic form:

a. If there is too much homework or a teacher is boring then I do not take that class.

b. There is too much homework, or if a teacher is boring then I do not take that class.

EXERCISE SET 3.2 ●●●●●●

• Practice Exercises

In Exercises 1–6, let p and q represent the following simple statements:

> *p: I'm leaving*
> *q: You're staying.*

Write each compound statement in symbolic form.

 1. I'm leaving and you're staying.

 2. You're staying and I'm leaving.

 3. You're staying and I'm not leaving.

 4. I'm leaving and you're not staying.

 5. You're not staying, but I'm leaving.

 6. I'm not leaving, but you're staying.

In Exercises 7–10, let p and q represent the following simple statements:

> *p: I study.*
> *q: I pass the course.*

Write each compound statement in symbolic form.

 7. I study or I pass the course.

 8. I pass the course or I study.

 9. I study or I do not pass the course.

10. I do not study or I do not pass the course.

In Exercises 11–18, let p and q represent the following simple statements:

> *p: This is an alligator.*
> *q: This is a reptile.*

Write each compound statement in symbolic form.

11. If this is an alligator, then this is a reptile.

12. If this is a reptile, then this is an alligator.

13. If this is not an alligator, then this is not a reptile.

14. If this is not a reptile, then this is not an alligator.

15. This is not an alligator if it's not a reptile.

16. This is a reptile if it's an alligator.

17. Being a reptile is necessary for being an alligator.

18. Being an alligator is sufficient for being a reptile.

In Exercises 19–26, let p and q represent the following simple statements:

> *p: You are human.*
> *q: You have feathers.*

Write each compound statement in symbolic form.

19. You do not have feathers if you are human.

20. You are not human if you have feathers.

21. Not being human is necessary for having feathers.

22. Not having feathers is necessary for being human.

23. Being human is sufficient for not having feathers.

24. Having feathers is sufficient for not being human.

25. You have feathers only if you're not human.

26. You're human only if you do not have feathers.

In Exercises 27–32, let p and q represent the following simple statements:

> *p: The campus is closed.*
> *q: It is Sunday.*

Write each compound statement in symbolic form.

27. The campus is closed if and only if it is Sunday.

28. It is Sunday if and only if the campus is closed.

29. It is not Sunday if and only if the campus is not closed.

30. The campus is not closed if and only if it is not Sunday.

31. Being Sunday is necessary and sufficient for the campus being closed.

32. The campus being closed is necessary and sufficient for being Sunday.

In Exercises 33–40, let p and q represent the following simple statements:

> *p: The heater is working.*
> *q: The house is cold.*

Write each symbolic statement in words.

33. $\sim p \wedge q$ **34.** $p \wedge \sim q$ **35.** $p \vee \sim q$

36. $\sim p \vee q$ **37.** $p \rightarrow \sim q$ **38.** $q \rightarrow \sim p$

39. $p \leftrightarrow \sim q$ **40.** $\sim p \leftrightarrow q$

In Exercises 41–48, let q and r represent the following simple statements:

> *q: It is July 4th.*
> *r: We are having a barbecue.*

Write each symbolic statement in words.

41. $q \wedge \sim r$ **42.** $\sim q \wedge r$ **43.** $\sim q \vee r$

44. $q \vee \sim r$ **45.** $r \rightarrow \sim q$ **46.** $q \rightarrow \sim r$

47. $\sim q \leftrightarrow r$ **48.** $q \leftrightarrow \sim r$

In Exercises 49–58, let p and q represent the following simple statements:

> *p: Romeo loves Juliet.*
> *q: Juliet loves Romeo.*

Write each symbolic statement in words.

49. $\sim (p \wedge q)$ **50.** $\sim (q \wedge p)$ **51.** $\sim p \wedge q$

52. $\sim q \wedge p$ **53.** $\sim (q \vee p)$ **54.** $\sim (p \vee q)$

55. $\sim q \vee p$ **56.** $\sim p \vee q$ **57.** $\sim p \wedge \sim q$

58. $\sim q \wedge \sim p$

In Exercises 59–66, let p, q, and r represent the following simple statements:

> *p: The temperature outside is freezing.*
> *q: The heater is working.*
> *r: The house is cold.*

Write each compound statement in symbolic form.

59. The temperature outside is freezing and the heater is working, or the house is cold.

60. If the temperature outside is freezing, then the heater is working or the house is not cold.

61. If the temperature outside is freezing or the heater is not working, then the house is cold.

62. It is not the case that if the house is cold then the heater is not working.

63. The house is cold, if and only if the temperature outside is freezing and the heater isn't working.

64. If the heater is working, then the temperature outside is freezing if and only if the house is cold.

65. Sufficient conditions for the house being cold are freezing outside temperatures and a heater not working.

66. A freezing outside temperature is both necessary and sufficient for a cold house if the heater is not working.

In Exercises 67–80, let p, q, and r represent the following simple statements:

p: The temperature is above 85°.
q: We finished studying.
r: We go to the beach.

Write each symbolic statement in words. If a symbolic statement is given without parentheses, place them, as needed, before and after the most dominant connective and then translate into English.

67. $(p \wedge q) \rightarrow r$ **68.** $(q \wedge r) \rightarrow p$ **69.** $p \wedge (q \rightarrow r)$

70. $p \wedge (r \rightarrow q)$ **71.** $\sim r \rightarrow \sim p \vee \sim q$ **72.** $\sim p \rightarrow q \vee r$

73. $(\sim r \rightarrow \sim q) \vee p$ **74.** $(\sim p \rightarrow \sim r) \vee q$ **75.** $r \leftrightarrow p \wedge q$

76. $r \leftrightarrow q \wedge p$ **77.** $(p \leftrightarrow q) \wedge r$ **78.** $q \rightarrow (r \leftrightarrow p)$

79. $\sim r \rightarrow \sim (p \wedge q)$ **80.** $\sim (p \wedge q) \rightarrow \sim r$

In Exercises 81–90, write each compound statement in symbolic form. Let letters assigned to the simple statements represent English sentences that are not negated. If commas do not appear in compound English statements, use the dominance of connectives to show grouping symbols (parentheses) in symbolic statements.

81. If I like the teacher or the course is interesting then I do not miss class.

82. If the lines go down or the transformer blows then we do not have power.

83. I like the teacher, or if the course is interesting then I do not miss class.

84. The lines go down, or if the transformer blows then we do not have power.

85. I miss class if and only if it's not true that both I like the teacher and the course is interesting.

86. We have power if and only if it's not true that both the lines go down and the transformer blows.

87. If I like the teacher I do not miss class if and only if the course is interesting.

88. If the lines go down we do not have power if and only if the transformer blows.

89. If I do not like the teacher and I miss class then the course is not interesting or I spend extra time reading the textbook.

90. If the lines do not go down and we have power then the transformer does not blow or there is an increase in the cost of electricity.

• Practice Plus

In Exercises 91–96, write each compound statement in symbolic form. Assign letters to simple statements that are not negated and show grouping symbols in symbolic statements.

91. If it's not true that being French is necessary for being a Parisian then it's not true that being German is necessary for being a Berliner.

92. If it's not true that being English is necessary for being a Londoner then it's not true that being American is necessary for being a New Yorker.

93. Filing an income tax report and a complete statement of earnings is necessary for each taxpayer or an authorized tax preparer.

94. Falling in love with someone in your class or picking someone to hate are sufficient conditions for showing up to vent your emotions and not skipping.
(Paraphrased from a student at the University of Georgia)

95. It is not true that being wealthy is a sufficient condition for being happy and living contentedly.

96. It is not true that being happy and living contentedly are necessary conditions for being wealthy.

In Exercises 97–100, use grouping symbols to clarify the meaning of each symbolic statement.

97. $p \rightarrow q \vee r \leftrightarrow p \wedge r$ **98.** $p \wedge q \rightarrow r \leftrightarrow p \vee r$

99. $p \rightarrow p \leftrightarrow p \wedge p \rightarrow \sim p$ **100.** $p \rightarrow p \leftrightarrow p \vee p \rightarrow \sim p$

• Application Exercises

Exercises 101–106 contain statements made by well-known people. Use letters to represent each non-negated simple statement and rewrite the given compound statement in symbolic form.

101. "If you cannot get rid of the family skeleton, you may as well make it dance." (George Bernard Shaw)

102. "I wouldn't turn out the way I did if I didn't have all the old-fashioned values to rebel against." (Madonna)

103. "If you know what you believe then it makes it a lot easier to answer questions, and I can't answer your question." (George W. Bush)

104. "If you don't like what you're doing, you can always pick up your needle and move to another groove." (Timothy Leary)

105. "If I were an intellectual, I would be pessimistic about America, but since I'm not an intellectual, I am optimistic about America." (General Lewis B. Hershey, Director of the Selective Service during the Vietnam war) (For simplicity, regard "optimistic" as "not pessimistic.")

106. "You cannot be both a good socializer and a good writer." (Erskine Caldwell)

• Writing in Mathematics

107. Describe what is meant by a compound statement.

108. What is a conjunction? Describe the symbol that forms a conjunction.

109. What is a disjunction? Describe the symbol that forms a disjunction.

110. What is a conditional statement? Describe the symbol that forms a conditional statement.

111. What is a biconditional statement? Describe the symbol that forms a biconditional statement.

112. Discuss the difference between the symbolic statements $\sim(p \wedge q)$ and $\sim p \wedge q$.

113. If a symbolic statement does not contain parentheses, how are the grouping symbols determined?

114. Suppose that a friend tells you, "This summer I plan to visit Paris or London." Under what condition can you conclude that if your friend visits Paris, London will not be visited? Under what condition can you conclude that if your friend visits Paris, London might be visited? Assuming your friend has told you the truth, what can you conclude if you know that Paris will not be visited? Explain each of your answers.

• Critical Thinking Exercises

115. Use letters to represent each simple statement in the compound statement that follows. Then express the compound statement in symbolic form.

Shooting unarmed civilians is morally justifiable if and only if bombing them is morally justifiable, and as the former is not morally justifiable, neither is the latter.

116. Using a topic on which you have strong opinions, write a compound statement that contains at least two different connectives. Then express the statement in symbolic form.

• Group Exercise

117. Each group member should find a legal document that contains at least six connectives in one paragraph. The connectives should include at least three different kinds of connectives, such as *and, or, if–then,* and *if and only if.* Share your example with other members of the group and see if the group can explain what some of the more complicated statements actually mean.

SECTION 3.3 • TRUTH TABLES FOR NEGATION, CONJUNCTION, AND DISJUNCTION

OBJECTIVES

1. Use the definitions of negation, conjunction, and disjunction.

2. Construct truth tables.

3. Determine the truth value of a compound statement for a specific case.

In 2006, *USA Today* analyzed patterns in the deaths of four-year college students since January 2000. Their most dominant finding was that freshmen emerged as the class most likely to make a fatal mistake. Freshmen accounted for more than one-third of all undergraduate deaths, even though they made up only 24% of the population enrolled in four-year institutions.

In this section, you will work with two circle graphs based on data from the *USA Today* study. By determining when statements involving negation, $\sim$ (not), conjunction, $\wedge$ (and), and disjunction, $\vee$ (or), are true and when they are false, you will be able to draw conclusions from the data. Classifying a statement as true or false is called **assigning a truth value to the statement**.

1 | Use the definitions of negation, conjunction, and disjunction.

Negation, $\sim$

The negation of a true statement is a false statement. We can express this in a table in which T represents true and F represents false.

p	$\sim p$
T	F

The negation of a false statement is a true statement. This, too, can be shown in table form.

p	$\sim p$
F	T

Combining the two tables results in Table 3.9, called the **truth table for negation**. This truth table expresses the idea that $\sim p$ has the opposite truth value from p.

TABLE 3.9 NEGATION	
p	$\sim p$
T	F
F	T

$\sim p$ has the opposite truth value from p.

Conjunction, $\wedge$

A friend tells you, "I visited London and I visited Paris." In order to understand the truth values for this statement, let's break it down into its two simple statements:

> p: I visited London.
> q: I visited Paris.

There are four possible cases to consider.

Case 1   Your friend actually visited both cities, so p is true and q is true. The conjunction "I visited London and I visited Paris" is true because your friend did both things. If both p and q are true, the conjunction $p \wedge q$ is true. We can show this in truth table form:

p	q	$p \wedge q$
T	T	T

Case 2   Your friend actually visited London, but did not tell the truth about visiting Paris. In this case, p is true and q is false. Your friend didn't do what was stated, namely visit both cities, so $p \wedge q$ is false. If p is true and q is false, the conjunction $p \wedge q$ is false.

p	q	$p \wedge q$
T	F	F

Case 3   This time, London was not visited, but Paris was. This makes p false and q true. As in case 2, your friend didn't do what was stated, namely visit both cities, so $p \wedge q$ is false. If p is false and q is true, the conjunction $p \wedge q$ is false.

p	q	$p \wedge q$
F	T	F

Case 4   This time your friend visited neither city, so p is false and q is false. The statement that both were visited, $p \wedge q$, is false.

p	q	$p \wedge q$
F	F	F

I visited London and I visited Paris.

Let's use a truth table to summarize all four cases. Only in the case that your friend visited London and visited Paris is the conjunction true. Each of the four cases appears in Table 3.10, the truth table for conjunction, $\wedge$. The definition of conjunction is given in words to the right of the table.

THE DEFINITION OF CONJUNCTION

TABLE 3.10 CONJUNCTION

p	q	$p \wedge q$
T	T	T
T	F	F
F	T	F
F	F	F

A conjunction is true only when both simple statements are true.

Table 3.11 contains an example of each of the four cases in the conjunction truth table.

TABLE 3.11 STATEMENTS OF CONJUNCTION AND THEIR TRUTH VALUES

Statement	Truth Value	Reason
$3 + 2 = 5$ and London is in England.	T	Both simple statements are true.
$3 + 2 = 5$ and London is in France.	F	The second simple statement is false.
$3 + 2 = 6$ and London is in England.	F	The first simple statement is false.
$3 + 2 = 6$ and London is in France.	F	Both simple statements are false.

STUDY TIP

As soon as you find one simple statement in a conjunction that is false, you know that the conjunction is false.

The statements that come before and after the main connective in a compound statement do not have to be simple statements. Consider, for example, the compound statement

$$(\sim p \vee q) \wedge \sim q.$$

The statements that make up this conjunction are $\sim p \vee q$ and $\sim q$. The conjunction is true only when both $\sim p \vee q$ and $\sim q$ are true. Notice that $\sim p \vee q$ is not a simple statement. We call $\sim p \vee q$ and $\sim q$ the *component statements* of the conjunction. The statements making up a compound statement are called **component statements**.

Disjunction, $\vee$

Now your friend states, "I will visit London or I will visit Paris." Because we assume that this is the inclusive "or," if your friend visits either or both of these cities, the truth has been told. The disjunction is false only in the event that neither city is visited. An *or* statement is true in every case, except when both component statements are false.

The truth table for disjunction, $\vee$, is shown in Table 3.12. The definition of disjunction is given in words to the right of the table.

THE DEFINITION OF DISJUNCTION

TABLE 3.12 DISJUNCTION

p	q	$p \vee q$
T	T	T
T	F	T
F	T	T
F	F	F

A disjunction is false only when both component statements are false.

Table 3.13 contains an example of each of the four cases in the disjunction truth table.

TABLE 3.13 STATEMENTS OF DISJUNCTION AND THEIR TRUTH VALUES

Statement	Truth Value	Reason
3 + 2 = 5 or London is in England.	T	Both component statements are true.
3 + 2 = 5 or London is in France.	T	The first component statement is true.
3 + 2 = 6 or London is in England.	T	The second component statement is true.
3 + 2 = 6 or London is in France.	F	Both component statements are false.

STUDY TIP

As soon as you find one component statement in a disjunction that is true, you know that the disjunction is true.

EXAMPLE 1 USING THE DEFINITIONS OF NEGATION, CONJUNCTION, AND DISJUNCTION

Let p and q represent the following statements:

p: $10 > 4$

q: $3 < 5$.

Determine the truth value for each statement:

a. $p \wedge q$ **b.** $\sim p \wedge q$ **c.** $p \vee \sim q$ **d.** $\sim p \vee \sim q$.

SOLUTION

a. $p \wedge q$ translates as

$$10 > 4 \quad \text{and} \quad 3 < 5.$$

10 is greater than 4 is true. 3 is less than 5 is true.

By definition, a conjunction, $\wedge$, is true only when both component statements are true. Thus, $p \wedge q$ is a true statement.

b. $\sim p \wedge q$ translates as

$$10 \not> 4 \quad \text{and} \quad 3 < 5.$$

10 is not greater than 4 is false. 3 is less than 5 is true.

By definition, a conjunction, $\wedge$, is true only when both component statements are true. In this conjunction, only one of the two component statements is true. Thus, $\sim p \wedge q$ is a false statement.

c. $p \vee \sim q$ translates as

$$10 > 4 \quad \text{or} \quad 3 \not< 5.$$

10 is greater than 4 is true. 3 is not less than 5 is false.

By definition, a disjunction, $\vee$, is false only when both component statements are false. In this disjunction, only one of the two component statements is false. Thus, $p \vee \sim q$ is a true statement.

d. $\sim p \vee \sim q$ translates as

$$10 \not> 4 \quad \text{or} \quad 3 \not< 5.$$

10 is not greater than 4 is false. 3 is not less than 5 is false.

By definition, a disjunction, $\vee$, is false only when both component statements are false. Thus, $\sim p \vee \sim q$ is a false statement.

Let *p* and *q* represent the following statements:

$$p: 3 + 5 = 8$$

$$q: 2 \times 7 = 20.$$

Determine the truth value for each statement:

a. $p \wedge q$ **b.** $p \wedge \sim q$ **c.** $\sim p \vee q$ **d.** $\sim p \vee \sim q$.

Constructing Truth Tables

2 Construct truth tables.

Truth tables can be used to gain a better understanding of English statements. The truth tables in this section are based on the definitions of negation, $\sim$, conjunction, $\wedge$, and disjunction, $\vee$. It is helpful to remember these definitions in words.

> **DEFINITIONS OF NEGATION, CONJUNCTION, AND DISJUNCTION**
>
> **1.** Negation $\sim$: not
>   The negation of a statement has the opposite truth value from the statement.
> **2.** Conjunction $\wedge$: and
>   The only case in which a conjunction is true is when both component statements are true.
> **3.** Disjunction $\vee$: or
>   The only case in which a disjunction is false is when both component statements are false.

We will begin by constructing truth tables for compound statements that contain the simple statements *p* and *q*. In cases like this, there are four possible combinations of truth values for *p* and *q*. We will always list the combinations of truth values for *p* and *q* in the following order. This order is not necessary, but it is a standard and makes for a consistent presentation.

p	*q*	
T	T	
T	F	
F	T	
F	F	

The final column heading in a truth table should be the given compound statement. Each column heading will tell you exactly how to fill in the four truth values for the statement at the top of the column. If a column heading involves negation, $\sim$ (not), fill in the column by looking back at the column that contains the statement that must be negated. Take the opposite of the truth values in this column.

If a column heading involves the symbol for conjunction, $\wedge$ (and), fill in the truth values in the column by looking back at two columns—the column for the statement before the $\wedge$ connective and the column for the statement after the $\wedge$ connective. Fill in the column by applying the definition of conjunction, writing T only when both component statements are true.

If a column heading involves the symbol for disjunction, $\vee$ (or), fill in the truth values in the column by looking back at two columns—the column for the statement before the $\vee$ connective and the column for the statement after the $\vee$ connective. Fill in the column by applying the definition of disjunction, writing F only when both component statements are false.

Let's unravel all this by looking at specific examples.

EXAMPLE 2   CONSTRUCTING A TRUTH TABLE

Construct a truth table for

$$\sim(p \wedge q)$$

to determine when the statement is true and when the statement is false.

SOLUTION The parentheses indicate that we must first determine the truth values for the conjunction $p \wedge q$. After this, we determine the truth values for the negation $\sim(p \wedge q)$ by taking the opposite of the truth values for $p \wedge q$.

Step 1. As with all truth tables, first list the simple statements on top. Then show all the possible truth values for these statements. In this case there are two simple statements and four possible combinations, or cases.

p	q	
T	T	
T	F	
F	T	
F	F	

Step 2. Make a column for $p \wedge q$, the statement within the parentheses in $\sim(p \wedge q)$. Use $p \wedge q$ as the heading for the column, and then fill in the truth values for the conjunction by looking back at the p and q columns. A conjunction is true only when both component statements are true.

p	q	$p \wedge q$	
T	T	T	p and q are true, so $p \wedge q$ is true.
T	F	F	
F	T	F	
F	F	F	

Step 3. Construct one more column for $\sim(p \wedge q)$. Fill in this column by negating the values in the $p \wedge q$ column. Using the negation definition, take the opposite of the truth values in the third column. This completes the truth table for $\sim(p \wedge q)$.

p	q	$p \wedge q$	$\sim(p \wedge q)$
T	T	T	F
T	F	F	T
F	T	F	T
F	F	F	T

The final column in the truth table for $\sim(p \wedge q)$ tells us that the statement is false only when both p and q are true. For example, using

    p: Harvard is a college (true)

    q: Yale is a college (true),

the statement $\sim(p \wedge q)$ translates as

    It is not true that Harvard and Yale are colleges.

This compound statement is false. It *is* true that Harvard and Yale are colleges.

 Construct a truth table for $\sim(p \vee q)$ to determine when the statement is true and when the statement is false.

EXAMPLE 3   CONSTRUCTING A TRUTH TABLE

Construct a truth table for

$$\sim p \lor \sim q$$

to determine when the statement is true and when the statement is false.

SOLUTION Without parentheses, the negation symbol, $\sim$, negates only the statement that immediately follows it. Therefore, we first determine the truth values for $\sim p$ and for $\sim q$. Then we determine the truth values for the *or* disjunction, $\sim p \lor \sim q$.

Step 1. List the simple statements on top and show the four possible cases for the truth values.

p	*q*	
T	T	
T	F	
F	T	
F	F	

Step 2. Make columns for $\sim p$ and for $\sim q$. Fill in the $\sim p$ column by looking back at the *p* column, the first column, and taking the opposite of the truth values in that column. Fill in the $\sim q$ column by taking the opposite of the truth values in the second column, the *q* column.

p	*q*	$\sim p$	$\sim q$
T	T	F	F
T	F	F	T
F	T	T	F
F	F	T	T

Step 3. Construct one more column for $\sim p \lor \sim q$. To determine the truth values of $\sim p \lor \sim q$, look back at the $\sim p$ column, labeled column 3 below, and the $\sim q$ column, labeled column 4 below. Now use the disjunction definition on the entries in columns 3 and 4. Disjunction definition: An *or* statement is false only when both component statements are false. This occurs only in the first row.

p	*q*	$\sim p$	$\sim q$	$\sim p \lor \sim q$	
T	T	F	F	F	$\sim p$ is false and $\sim q$ is false, so $\sim p \lor \sim q$ is false.
T	F	F	T	T	
F	T	T	F	T	
F	F	T	T	T	
		column 3	column 4		

CHECK POINT 3 Construct a truth table for $\sim p \land \sim q$ to determine when the statement is true and when the statement is false.

EXAMPLE 4   CONSTRUCTING A TRUTH TABLE

Construct a truth table for

$$(\sim p \lor q) \land \sim q$$

to determine when the statement is true and when the statement is false.

SOLUTION The statement is an *and* conjunction because the conjunction symbol, $\land$, is outside the parentheses. We cannot determine the truth values for the statement until we first determine the truth values for $\sim p \lor q$ and for $\sim q$, the component statements before and after the $\land$ connective:

$$\boxed{(\sim p \lor q)} \land \boxed{\sim q}.$$

We'll need a column with truth values for this component statement.

We'll need a column with truth values for this component statement.

Step 1. The compound statement involves two simple statements and four possible cases.

p	q	
T	T	
T	F	
F	T	
F	F	

$\boxed{(\sim p \lor q)} \land \boxed{\sim q}$

Column needed

Column needed

Step 2. Because we need a column with truth values for $\sim p \lor q$, begin with $\sim p$. Use $\sim p$ as the heading. Fill in the column by looking back at the p column, labeled column 1 below, and take the opposite of the truth values in that column.

p	q	$\sim p$
T	T	F
T	F	F
F	T	T
F	F	T
column 1		

Step 3. Now add a $\sim p \lor q$ column. To determine the truth values of $\sim p \lor q$, look back at the $\sim p$ column, labeled column 3 below, and the q column, labeled column 2 below. Now use the disjunction definition on the entries in columns 3 and 2. Disjunction definition: An *or* statement is false only when both component statements are false. This occurs only in the second row.

p	q	$\sim p$	$\sim p \lor q$
T	T	F	T
T	F	F	F
F	T	T	T
F	F	T	T
	column 2	column 3	

$\sim p$ is false and q is false, so $\sim p \lor q$ is false.

Step 4. The statement following the ∧ connective is ~q, so add a ~q column. Fill in the column by looking back at the q column, column 2, and take the opposite of the truth values in that column.

p	q	~p	~p ∨ q	~q
T	T	F	T	F
T	F	F	F	T
F	T	T	T	F
F	F	T	T	T
column 2				

Step 5. The final column heading is

$$(\sim p \lor q) \land \sim q,$$

which is our given statement. To determine its truth values, look back at the $\sim p \lor q$ column, labeled column 4 below, and the $\sim q$ column, labeled column 5 below. Now use the conjunction definition on the entries in columns 4 and 5. Conjunction definition: An *and* statement is true only when both component statements are true. This occurs only in the last row.

p	q	~p	~p ∨ q	~q	(~p ∨ q) ∧ ~q
T	T	F	T	F	F
T	F	F	F	T	F
F	T	T	T	F	F
F	F	T	T	T	T
			column 4	column 5	

> ~p ∨ q is true and ~q is true, so (~p ∨ q) ∧ ~q is true.

The truth table is now complete. By looking at the truth values in the last column, we can see that the compound statement

$$(\sim p \lor q) \land \sim q$$

is true only in the fourth row, that is, when p is false and q is false.

 CHECK POINT 4 Construct a truth table for $(p \land \sim q) \lor \sim p$ to determine when the statement is true and when the statement is false.

Some compound statements, such as $p \lor \sim p$, consist of only one simple statement. In cases like this, there are only two true–false possibilities: p can be true or p can be false.

EXAMPLE 5   CONSTRUCTING A TRUTH TABLE

Construct a truth table for

$$p \lor \sim p$$

to determine when the statement is true and when the statement is false.

SOLUTION We first determine the truth values for $\sim p$. Then we determine the truth values for the *or* disjunction, $p \lor \sim p$.

Step 1. The compound statement involves one simple statement and two possible cases.

p	
T	
F	

Step 2. Add a column for ~p.

p	~p
T	F
F	T

Take the opposite of the truth values in the first column.

Step 3. Construct one more column for p ∨ ~p.

p	~p	p ∨ ~p
T	F	T
F	T	T

Look back at columns 1 and 2 and apply the disjunction definition: An *or* statement is false only when both component statements are false. This does not occur in either row.

The truth table is now complete. By looking at the truth values in the last column, we can see that the compound statement p ∨ ~p is true in all cases.

A compound statement that is always true is called a **tautology**. Example 5 proves that p ∨ ~p is a tautology.

 Construct a truth table for

$$p \wedge \sim p$$

to determine when the statement is true and when the statement is false.

Blitzer Bonus

Tautologies and Commercials

Think about the logic in the following statement from a commercial for a high-fiber cereal:

> Some studies suggest a high-fiber, low-fat diet may reduce the risk of some kinds of cancer.

From a strictly logical point of view, "may reduce" means "It may reduce the risk of cancer or it may not." The symbolic translation of this sentence, p ∨ ~p, is a tautology. The claim made in the cereal commercial can be made about any substance that is not known to actually cause cancer and, like p ∨ ~p, will always be true.

TABLE 3.14

	p	q	r
Case 1	T	T	T
Case 2	T	T	F
Case 3	T	F	T
Case 4	T	F	F
Case 5	F	T	T
Case 6	F	T	F
Case 7	F	F	T
Case 8	F	F	F

There are eight different true–false combinations for compound statements consisting of three simple statements.

Some compound statements involve three simple statements, usually represented by p, q, and r. In this situation, there are eight different true-false combinations, shown in Table 3.14. The first column has four Ts followed by four Fs. The second column has two Ts, two Fs, two Ts, and two Fs. Under the third statement, r, T alternates with F. It is not necessary to list the eight cases in this order, but this systematic method ensures that no case is repeated and that all cases are included.

EXAMPLE 6   CONSTRUCTING A TRUTH TABLE WITH EIGHT CASES

a. Construct a truth table for the following statement:
I study hard and ace the final, or I fail the course.

b. Suppose that you study hard, you do not ace the final, and you fail the course. Under these conditions, is the compound statement in part (a) true or false?

SOLUTION

a. We begin by assigning letters to the simple statements. Use the following representations:
   p: I study hard.
   q: I ace the final.
   r: I fail the course.

Now we can write the given statement in symbolic form.

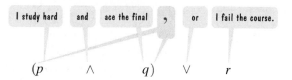

| I study hard | and | ace the final | , | or | I fail the course. |

$$(p \qquad \wedge \qquad q) \qquad \vee \qquad r$$

The statement $(p \wedge q) \vee r$ is a disjunction because the *or* symbol, $\vee$, is outside the parentheses. We cannot determine the truth values for this disjunction until we have determined the truth values for $p \wedge q$ and for r, the statements before and after the $\vee$ connective. The completed truth table appears as follows:

> The conjunction is true only when p, the first column, is true and q, the second column, is true.

> The disjunction is false only when $p \wedge q$, column 4, is false and r, column 3, is false.

> Show eight possible cases.

> These are the conditions in part (b).

p	q	r	$p \wedge q$	$(p \wedge q) \vee r$
T	T	T	T	T
T	T	F	T	T
T	F	T	F	T
T	F	F	F	F
F	T	T	F	T
F	T	F	F	F
F	F	T	F	T
F	F	F	F	F

b. We are given the following:

p: I study hard.   — This is true. We are told you study hard.

q: I ace the final.   — This is false. We are told you do not ace the final.

r: I fail the course.   — This is true. We are told you fail the course.

The given conditions, T F T, correspond to case 3 of the truth table, indicated by the voice balloon on the far left. Under these conditions, the original compound statement is true, shown by the red T in the truth table.

CHECK POINT 6

a. Construct a truth table for the following statement:

I study hard, and I ace the final or fail the course.

b. Suppose that you do not study hard, you ace the final, and you fail the course. Under these conditions, is the compound statement in part (a) true or false?

3 | Determine the truth value of a compound statement for a specific case.

Determining Truth Values for Specific Cases

A truth table shows the truth values of a compound statement for every possible case. In our next example, we will determine the truth value of a compound statement for a specific case in which the truth values of the simple statements are known. This does not require constructing an entire truth table. By substituting the truth values of the simple statements into the symbolic form of the compound statement and using the appropriate definitions, we can determine the truth value of the compound statement.

EXAMPLE 7   DETERMINING THE TRUTH VALUE OF A COMPOUND STATEMENT

College administrators, public health officials, and parents increasingly have become concerned about the safety of college students after highly publicized deaths on campus from alcohol abuse and other causes. The data in Figure 3.3 indicate that freshmen are uniquely vulnerable.

Undergraduate Enrollment and Deaths in the United States

Percentage of Undergraduate Students

Percentage of Undergraduate Deaths

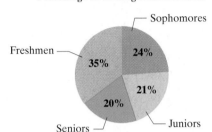

FIGURE 3.3
Source: USA Today

Use the information in the circle graphs to determine the truth value of the following statement:

> It is not true that freshmen make up 24% of the undergraduate college population and account for more than one-third of the undergraduate deaths, or seniors do not account for 30% of the undergraduate deaths.

SOLUTION We begin by assigning letters to the simple statements, using the graphs to determine whether each simple statement is true or false. As always, we let these letters represent statements that are not negated.

p: Freshmen make up 24% of the undergraduate college population. | This statement is true.

q: Freshmen account for more than one-third of the undergraduate deaths. | This statement is true. They account for 35% of the deaths, which is greater than $\frac{1}{3}$: $\frac{1}{3} = 33\frac{1}{3}\%$.

r: Seniors account for 30% of the undergraduate deaths. | This statement is false. They account for 20% of the deaths.

Using these representations, the given compound statement can be expressed in symbolic form as

$$\sim(p \land q) \lor \sim r.$$

Now we substitute the truth values for p, q, and r that we obtained from the circle graphs to determine the truth value for the given compound statement.

$\sim(p \land q) \lor \sim r$ This is the given compound statement in symbolic form.

$\sim(T \land T) \lor \sim F$ Substitute the truth values obtained from the graph.

$\quad\quad \sim T \lor \sim F$ Replace $T \land T$ with T. Conjunction is true when both parts are true.

$\quad\quad\quad F \lor T$ Replace $\sim T$ with F and $\sim F$ with T. Negation gives the opposite truth value.

$\quad\quad\quad\quad T$ Replace $F \lor T$ with T. Disjunction is true when at least one part is true.

We conclude that the given statement is true.   ○

 7 Use the information in the circle graphs in Figure 3.3 to determine the truth value for the following statement:

> Freshmen and juniors make up the same percentage of the undergraduate college population or seniors make up 35% of the population, and freshmen and juniors do not account for the same percentage of the undergraduate deaths.

EXERCISE SET 3.3 ●●●●●●

• Practice Exercises

In Exercises 1–16, let p and q represent the following statements:

   $p: 4 + 6 = 10$
   $q: 5 \times 8 = 80$

Determine the truth value for each statement.

1. $\sim q$	**2.** $\sim p$	**3.** $p \wedge q$	**4.** $q \wedge p$
5. $\sim p \wedge q$	**6.** $p \wedge \sim q$	**7.** $\sim p \wedge \sim q$	**8.** $q \wedge \sim q$
9. $q \vee p$	**10.** $p \vee q$	**11.** $p \vee \sim q$	**12.** $\sim p \vee q$
13. $p \vee \sim p$	**14.** $q \vee \sim q$	**15.** $\sim p \vee \sim q$	**16.** $\sim q \vee \sim p$

In Exercises 17–24, complete the truth table for the given statement by filling in the required columns.

17. $\sim p \wedge p$

p	$\sim p$	$\sim p \wedge p$
T		
F		

18. $\sim(\sim p)$

p	$\sim p$	$\sim(\sim p)$
T		
F		

19. $\sim p \wedge q$

p	q	$\sim p$	$\sim p \wedge q$
T	T		
T	F		
F	T		
F	F		

20. $\sim p \vee q$

p	q	$\sim p$	$\sim p \vee q$
T	T		
T	F		
F	T		
F	F		

21. $\sim(p \vee q)$

p	q	$p \vee q$	$\sim(p \vee q)$
T	T		
T	F		
F	T		
F	F		

22. $\sim(p \vee \sim q)$

p	q	$\sim q$	$p \vee \sim q$	$\sim(p \vee \sim q)$
T	T			
T	F			
F	T			
F	F			

23. $\sim p \wedge \sim q$

p	q	$\sim p$	$\sim q$	$\sim p \wedge \sim q$
T	T			
T	F			
F	T			
F	F			

24. $p \wedge \sim q$

p	q	$\sim q$	$p \wedge \sim q$
T	T		
T	F		
F	T		
F	F		

In Exercises 25–42, construct a truth table for the given statement.

25. $p \vee \sim q$	**26.** $\sim q \wedge p$
27. $\sim(\sim p \vee q)$	**28.** $\sim(p \wedge \sim q)$
29. $(p \vee q) \wedge \sim p$	**30.** $(p \wedge q) \vee \sim p$
31. $\sim p \vee (p \wedge \sim q)$	**32.** $\sim p \wedge (p \vee \sim q)$
33. $(p \vee q) \wedge (\sim p \vee \sim q)$	**34.** $(p \wedge \sim q) \vee (\sim p \wedge q)$
35. $(p \wedge \sim q) \vee (p \wedge q)$	**36.** $(p \vee \sim q) \wedge (p \vee q)$
37. $p \wedge (\sim q \vee r)$	**38.** $p \vee (\sim q \wedge r)$
39. $(r \wedge \sim p) \vee \sim q$	**40.** $(r \vee \sim p) \wedge \sim q$
41. $\sim(p \vee q) \wedge \sim r$	**42.** $\sim(p \wedge q) \vee \sim r$

In Exercises 43–52,

   a. Write each statement in symbolic form. Assign letters to simple statements that are not negated.

   b. Construct a truth table for the symbolic statement in part (a).

   c. Use the truth table to indicate one set of conditions that make the compound statement true, or state that no such conditions exist.

43. You did not do the dishes and you left the room a mess.

44. You did not do the dishes, but you did not leave the room a mess.

45. It is not true that I bought a meal ticket and did not use it.

46. It is not true that I ordered pizza while watching late-night TV and did not gain weight.

47. The student is intelligent or an overachiever, and not an overachiever.

48. You're blushing or sunburned, and you're not sunburned.

49. Married people are healthier than single people and more economically stable than single people, and children of married people do better on a variety of indicators.

50. You walk or jog, or engage in something physical.

51. I go to office hours and ask questions, or my professor does not remember me.

52. You marry the person you love, but you do not always love that person or do not always have a successful marriage.

In Exercises 53–62, determine the truth value for each statement when p is false, q is true, and r is false.

53. $p \wedge (q \vee r)$

54. $p \vee (q \wedge r)$

55. $\sim p \vee (q \wedge \sim r)$

56. $\sim p \wedge (\sim q \wedge r)$

57. $\sim (p \wedge q) \vee r$

58. $\sim (p \vee q) \wedge r$

59. $\sim (p \vee q) \wedge \sim (p \wedge r)$

60. $\sim (p \wedge q) \vee \sim (p \vee r)$

61. $(\sim p \wedge q) \vee (\sim r \wedge p)$

62. $(\sim p \vee q) \wedge (\sim r \vee p)$

• Practice Plus

In Exercises 63–66, construct a truth table for each statement.

63. $\sim [\sim (p \wedge \sim q) \vee \sim (\sim p \vee q)]$

64. $\sim [\sim (p \vee \sim q) \wedge \sim (\sim p \wedge q)]$

65. $[(p \wedge \sim r) \vee (q \wedge \sim r)] \wedge \sim (\sim p \vee r)$

66. $[(p \vee \sim r) \wedge (q \vee \sim r)] \vee \sim (\sim p \vee r)$

In Exercises 67–70, write each statement in symbolic form and construct a truth table. Then indicate under what conditions, if any, the compound statement is true.

67. You notice this notice or you do not, and you notice this notice is not worth noticing.

68. You notice this notice and you notice this notice is not worth noticing, or you do not notice this notice.

69. It is not true that $x \leq 3$ or $x \geq 7$, but $x > 3$ and $x < 7$.

70. It is not true that $x < 5$ or $x > 8$, but $x \geq 5$ and $x \leq 8$.

• Application Exercises

The graph shows the percent distribution of divorces in the United States by number of years of marriage.

Percent Distribution of Divorces by Number of Years of Marriage

Source: Divorce Center

In Exercises 71–80, let p, q, and r represent the following simple statements:

> *p: The chance of divorce peaks during the fourth year of marriage.*
> *q: The chance of divorce decreases after four years of marriage.*
> *r: More than 2% of all divorces occur during the 25th year of marriage.*

Write each symbolic statement in words. Then use the information given by the graph to determine the truth value of the statement.

71. $p \wedge \sim q$ **72.** $p \wedge \sim r$ **73.** $\sim p \wedge r$ **74.** $q \wedge \sim p$

75. $p \vee \sim q$ **76.** $p \vee \sim r$ **77.** $\sim p \vee r$ **78.** $q \vee \sim p$

79. $(p \wedge q) \vee r$ **80.** $p \wedge (q \vee r)$

The circle graphs show the changing ideological spectrum for U.S. college freshmen.

How U.S. College Freshmen Characterize Their Political Views

  ■ Liberal   ■ Middle of the Road   ■ Conservative

| 1984 | 1994 | 2004 |

Source: UCLA Higher Education Research Institute

In Exercises 81–84, write each statement in symbolic form. Then use the information in the graphs to determine the truth value of the compound statement.

81. It is not true that in 2004, 29.5% of college freshmen were liberal and 25.1% were conservative.

82. It is not true that in 1994, 28.7% of college freshmen were liberal or 23.9% were conservative.

83. From 1984 through 2004, the percentage of liberal college freshmen increased or the percentage of conservative college freshmen decreased, and the percentage of moderates did not increase.

84. From 1984 through 2004, the percentage of conservative college freshmen increased, but the percentage of liberals did not increase or the percentage of moderates increased.

85. To qualify for the position of music professor, an applicant must have a master's degree in music, and be able to play at least three musical instruments or have at least five years' experience playing with a symphony orchestra.

There are three applicants for the position:

- *Bolero Mozart* has a master's degree in journalism and plays the piano, tuba, and violin.

- *Cha-Cha Bach* has a master's degree in music, plays the piano and the harp, and has two years' experience with a symphony orchestra.

- *Hora Gershwin* has a master's degree in music, plays 14 instruments, and has two years' experience in a symphony orchestra.

  a. Which of the applicants qualifies for the position?

  b. Explain why each of the other applicants does not qualify for the position.

86. To qualify for the position of art professor, an applicant must have a master's degree in art, and a body of work judged as excellent by at least two working artists or at least two works on public display in the United States.

There are three applicants for the position:

- *Adagio Picasso* needs two more courses to complete a master's degree in art, has a body of work judged as excellent by ten working artists, and has over 50 works on public display in a number of different American cities.

- *Rondo Seurat* has a master's degree in art, a body of work judged as excellent by a well-known working artist, and two works on public display in New York City.

- *Yodel Van Gogh* has a master's degree in art, is about to complete a doctorate in art history, has 20 works on public display in Paris, France, and has a body of work judged as excellent by a working artist.

a. Which of the applicants qualifies for the position?

b. Explain why each of the other applicants does not qualify for the position.

• Writing in Mathematics

87. Under which conditions is a conjunction true?

88. Under which conditions is a conjunction false?

89. Under which conditions is a disjunction true?

90. Under which conditions is a disjunction false?

91. Describe how to construct a truth table for a compound statement.

92. Describe the information given by the truth values in the final column of a truth table.

93. Describe how to set up the eight different true-false combinations for a compound statement consisting of three simple statements.

94. The circle graphs in Figure 3.3 on page 138 indicate that college freshmen account for more than one-third of undergraduate deaths, although they comprise only 24% of the undergraduate population. What explanations can you offer for these grim statistics?

• Critical Thinking Exercises

95. Use the circle graphs in Exercises 81–84 to write a true compound statement with each of the following characteristics. Do not use any of the simple statements that appear in Exercises 81–84.

a. The statement contains three different simple statements.

b. The statement contains two different connectives.

c. The statement contains one simple statement with the word *not*.

96. If $\sim(p \vee q)$ is true, determine the truth values for p and q.

97. The truth table that defines $\vee$, the *inclusive or*, indicates that the compound statement is true if one or both of its component statements are true. The symbol for the *exclusive or* is $\veebar$. The *exclusive or* means *either p or q*, but *not both*. Use this meaning to construct the truth table that defines $p \veebar q$.

• Group Exercise

98. Each member of the group should find a graph that is of particular interest to that person. Share the graphs. The group should select the three graphs that it finds most intriguing. For the graphs selected, group members should write four compound statements. Two of the statements should be true and two should be false. One of the statements should contain three different simple statements and two different connectives.

SECTION 3.4 • TRUTH TABLES FOR THE CONDITIONAL AND THE BICONDITIONAL

OBJECTIVES

1. Understand the logic behind the definition of the conditional.

2. Construct truth tables for conditional statements.

3. Understand the definition of the biconditional.

4. Construct truth tables for biconditional statements.

5. Determine the truth value of a compound statement for a specific case.

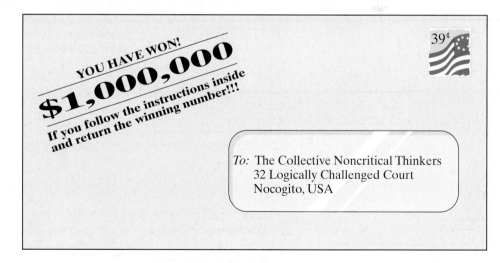

Your author received junk mail with this claim:

> If your Super Million Dollar Prize Entry Number matches the winning preselected number and you return the number before the deadline stated below, you will win $1,000,000.00.

Should he obediently return the number before the deadline or trash the whole thing?

In this section, we will use logic to analyze the claim in the junk mail. By understanding when statements involving the conditional, $\rightarrow$ (if–then), and the biconditional, $\leftrightarrow$ (if and only if), are true and when they are false, you will be able to determine the truth value of the claim.

1 | Understand the logic behind the definition of the conditional.

Conditional Statements, →

We begin by looking at the truth table for conditional statements. Suppose that your professor promises you the following:

If you pass the final, then you pass the course.

Break the statement down into its two component statements:

p: You pass the final.

q: You pass the course.

Translated into symbolic form, your professor's statement is $p \rightarrow q$. We now look at the four cases shown in Table 3.15, the truth table for the conditional.

TABLE 3.15
CONDITIONAL

	p	*q*	$p \rightarrow q$
Case 1	T	T	T
Case 2	T	F	F
Case 3	F	T	T
Case 4	F	F	T

Case 1   (T, T) You do pass the final and you do pass the course. Your professor did what was promised, so the conditional statement is true.

Case 2   (T, F) You pass the final, but you do not pass the course. Your professor did not do what was promised, so the conditional statement is false.

Case 3   (F, T) You do not pass the final, but you do pass the course. Your professor's original statement talks about only what would happen if you passed the final. It says nothing about what would happen if you did not pass the final. Your professor did not break the promise of the original statement, so the conditional statement is true.

Case 4   (F, F) You do not pass the final and you do not pass the course. As with case 3, your professor's original statement talks about only what would happen if you passed the final. The promise of the original statement has not been broken. Therefore, the conditional statement is true.

Table 3.15 illustrates that a conditional statement is false only when the antecedent, the statement before the → connective, is true and the consequent, the statement after the → connective, is false. A conditional statement is true in all other cases.

THE DEFINITION OF THE CONDITIONAL

p	*q*	$p \rightarrow q$
T	T	T
T	F	F
F	T	T
F	F	T

A conditional is false only when the antecedent is true and the consequent is false.

2 | Construct truth tables for conditional statements.

Constructing Truth Tables

Our first example shows how truth tables can be used to gain a better understanding of conditional statements.

EXAMPLE 1   CONSTRUCTING A TRUTH TABLE

Construct a truth table for

$$\sim q \rightarrow \sim p$$

to determine when the statement is true and when the statement is false.

SOLUTION   Remember that without parentheses, the symbol $\sim$ negates only the statement that immediately follows it. Therefore, we cannot determine the truth values for this conditional statement until we first determine the truth values for $\sim q$ and for $\sim p$, the statements before and after the → connective.

Step 1. List the simple statements on top and show the four possible cases for the truth values.

p	q	
T	T	
T	F	
F	T	
F	F	

Step 2. Make columns for ~q and for ~p. Fill in the ~q column by looking back at the q column, the second column, and taking the opposite of the truth values in this column. Fill in the ~p column by taking the opposite of the truth values in the first column, the p column.

p	q	~q	~p
T	T	F	F
T	F	T	F
F	T	F	T
F	F	T	T

Step 3. Construct one more column for $\sim q \rightarrow \sim p$. Look back at the ~q column, labeled column 3 below, and the ~p column, labeled column 4 below. Now use the conditional definition to determine the truth values for $\sim q \rightarrow \sim p$ based on columns 3 and 4. Conditional definition: An *if–then* statement is false only when the antecedent is true and the consequent is false. This occurs only in the second row.

p	q	~q	~p	$\sim q \rightarrow \sim p$
T	T	F	F	T
T	F	T	F	F
F	T	F	T	T
F	F	T	T	T
		column 3	column 4	

> ~q is true and ~p is false, so $\sim q \rightarrow \sim p$ is false.

Construct a truth table for $\sim p \rightarrow \sim q$ to determine when the statement is true and when the statement is false.

The truth values for $p \rightarrow q$, as well as those for $\sim q \rightarrow \sim p$ from Example 1, are shown in Table 3.16. Notice that $p \rightarrow q$ and $\sim q \rightarrow \sim p$ have the same truth value in each of the four cases. What does this mean? **Every time you hear or utter a conditional statement, you can reverse and negate the antecedent and consequent, and the statement's truth value will not change.** Here's an example from a student providing advice on campus fashion:

- If you're cool, you won't wear clothing with your school name on it.
- If you wear clothing with your school name on it, you're not cool.

TABLE 3.16

p	q	$p \rightarrow q$	$\sim q \rightarrow \sim p$
T	T	T	T
T	F	F	F
F	T	T	T
F	F	T	T

> $p \rightarrow q$ and $\sim q \rightarrow \sim p$ have the same truth values.

> If the fashion tip above is true then so is this, and if it's false then this is false as well.

We'll have lots more to say about this (that is, variations of conditional statements, not tips on dressing up and down around campus) in the next section.

EXAMPLE 2   CONSTRUCTING A TRUTH TABLE

Construct a truth table for

$$[(p \lor q) \land \sim p] \rightarrow q$$

to determine when the statement is true and when the statement is false.

SOLUTION The statement is a conditional statement because the *if–then* symbol, $\rightarrow$, is outside the grouping symbols. We cannot determine the truth values for this conditional until we first determine the truth values for the statements before and after the $\rightarrow$ connective.

We'll need a column with truth values for this statement. Prior to this column, we'll need columns for $p \lor q$ and for $\sim p$.

We'll need a column with truth values for this statement. This will be the second column of the truth table.

The disjunction, $\lor$, is false only when both component statements are false.

The truth value of $\sim p$ is opposite that of p.

The conjunction, $\land$, is true only when both $p \lor q$ and $\sim p$ are true.

The conditional, $\rightarrow$, is false only when $(p \lor q) \land \sim p$ is true and q is false.

Show four possible cases.

p	q	$p \lor q$	$\sim p$	$(p \lor q) \land \sim p$	$[(p \lor q) \land \sim p] \rightarrow q$
T	T	T	F	F	T
T	F	T	F	F	T
F	T	T	T	T	T
F	F	F	T	F	T

The completed truth table shows that the conditional statement in the last column, $[(p \lor q) \land \sim p] \rightarrow q$, is true in all cases.

In Section 3.3, we defined a **tautology** as a compound statement that is always true. Example 2 proves that the conditional statement $[(p \lor q) \land \sim p] \rightarrow q$ is a tautology.

Conditional statements that are tautologies are called **implications**. For the conditional statement

$$[(p \lor q) \land \sim p] \rightarrow q$$

we can say that

$$(p \lor q) \land \sim p \text{ implies } q.$$

Using *p:* I am visiting London and *q:* I am visiting Paris, we can say that

I am visiting London or Paris, and I am not visiting London, implies that I am visiting Paris.

Construct a truth table for $[(p \rightarrow q) \land \sim q] \rightarrow \sim p$ and show that the compound statement is a tautology.

Some compound statements are false in all possible cases. Such statements are called **self-contradictions**. An example of a self-contradiction is the statement $p \land \sim p$:

p	$\sim p$	$p \land \sim p$
T	F	F
F	T	F

$p \land \sim p$ is always false.

If p represents "I am going," then $p \land \sim p$ translates as "I am going and I am not going." Such a translation sounds like a contradiction.

BLITZER BONUS

VP Speak and Self-Contradictions

Apparently born with both feet and hands in his mouth, Dan Quayle, 44th vice president under the first president Bush, offered a seemingly endless supply of convoluted compound statements, embarrassing himself with entertaining regularity. Two samples of his peculiar wit and wisdom:

- "The Holocaust was an obscene period in our nation's history. I mean in this century's history. But we all lived in this century. I didn't live in this century."
- "We are on an irreversible trend, towards more freedom and democracy—but that can change."

Both examples contain self-contradictions.

p $\land$ $\sim p$

We all lived in this century	and	I didn't.
It's irreversible	but	that can change.

EXAMPLE 3   CONSTRUCTING A TRUTH TABLE WITH EIGHT CASES

The following is from an editorial that appeared in *The New York Times*:

> Our entire tax system depends upon the vast majority of taxpayers who attempt to pay the taxes they owe having confidence that they're being treated fairly and that their competitors and neighbors are also paying what is due. <u>If the public concludes that the IRS cannot meet these basic expectations, the risk to the tax system will become very high and the effects very difficult to reverse.</u>

The New York Times, February 13, 2000

a. Construct a truth table for the underlined statement.

b. Suppose that the public concludes that the IRS cannot meet basic expectations, the risk to the tax system becomes very high, but the effects are not very difficult to reverse. Under these conditions, is the underlined statement true or false?

SOLUTION

a. We begin by assigning letters to the simple statements. Use the following representations:

   p: The public concludes that the IRS *can* meet basic expectations (of fair treatment and others paying what is due).

   q: The risk to the tax system will become very high.

   r: The effects will be very difficult to reverse.

The underlined statement in symbolic form is

$$\sim p \quad \rightarrow \quad (q \quad \land \quad r).$$

... cannot meet basic expectations   ... high risk   ... difficult to reverse effects

The statement $\sim p \to (q \wedge r)$ is a conditional statement because the *if–then* symbol, $\to$, is outside the parentheses. We cannot determine the truth values for this conditional until we have determined the truth values for $\sim p$ and for $q \wedge r$, the statements before and after the $\to$ connective. Because the compound statement consists of three simple statements, represented by p, q, and r, the truth table must contain eight cases. The completed truth table appears as follows:

> The conjunction is true only when q, column 2, is true and r, column 3, is true.

> Take the opposite of the truth values in column 1.

> The conditional is false only when the $\sim p$ column is true and the $q \wedge r$ column is false.

> Show eight possible cases.

> These are the conditions in part (b).

p	q	r	$\sim p$	$q \wedge r$	$\sim p \to (q \wedge r)$
T	T	T	F	T	T
T	T	F	F	F	T
T	F	T	F	F	T
T	F	F	F	F	T
F	T	T	T	T	T
F	T	F	T	F	F
F	F	T	T	F	F
F	F	F	T	F	F

b. We are given that p (... can meet basic expectations) is false, q (... high risk) is true, and r (... difficult to reverse effects) is false. The given conditions, F T F, correspond to case 6 of the truth table, indicated by the voice balloon on the far left. Under these conditions, the original compound statement is false, shown by the red F in the truth table. ○

CHECK POINT 3 An advertisement makes the following claim:

> If you use Hair Grow and apply it daily, then you will not go bald.

    a. Construct a truth table for the claim.

    b. Suppose you use Hair Grow, forget to apply it every day, and you go bald. Under these conditions, is the claim in the advertisement false?

3 Understand the definition of the biconditional.

Biconditional Statements

In Section 3.2, we introduced the biconditional connective, $\leftrightarrow$, translated as "if and only if." The biconditional statement $p \leftrightarrow q$ means that $p \to q$ and $q \to p$. We write this symbolically as

$$(p \to q) \wedge (q \to p).$$

To create the truth table for $p \leftrightarrow q$, we will first make a truth table for the conjunction of the two conditionals $p \to q$ and $q \to p$. The truth table for $(p \to q) \wedge (q \to p)$ is shown as follows:

> The conditional is false only when p is true and q is false.

> The conditional is false only when q is true and p is false.

> The conjunction is true only when both $p \to q$ and $q \to p$ are true.

> Show four possible cases.

p	q	$p \to q$	$q \to p$	$(p \to q) \wedge (q \to p)$
T	T	T	T	T
T	F	F	T	F
F	T	T	F	F
F	F	T	T	T

The truth values in the column for $(p \rightarrow q) \wedge (q \rightarrow p)$ show the truth values for the biconditional statement $p \leftrightarrow q$.

THE DEFINITION OF THE BICONDITIONAL

p	q	$p \leftrightarrow q$
T	T	T
T	F	F
F	T	F
F	F	T

A biconditional is true only when the component statements have the same truth value.

Before we continue our work with truth tables, let's take a moment to summarize the basic definitions of symbolic logic.

THE DEFINITIONS OF SYMBOLIC LOGIC

1. Negation ~: not
   The negation of a statement has the opposite meaning, as well as the opposite truth value, from the statement.

2. Conjunction ∧: and
   The only case in which a conjunction is true is when both component statements are true.

3. Disjunction ∨: or
   The only case in which a disjunction is false is when both component statements are false.

4. Conditional →: if–then
   The only case in which a conditional is false is when the first component statement, the antecedent, is true and the second component statement, the consequent, is false.

5. Biconditional ↔: if and only if
   The only cases in which a biconditional is true are when the component statements have the same truth value.

---

4 | Construct truth tables for biconditional statements.

EXAMPLE 4   CONSTRUCTING A TRUTH TABLE

Construct a truth table for

$$(p \vee q) \leftrightarrow (\sim q \rightarrow p)$$

to determine whether the statement is a tautology.

SOLUTION   The statement is a biconditional because the biconditional symbol, ↔, is outside the parentheses. We cannot determine the truth values for this biconditional until we determine the truth values for the statements in parentheses.

$$\boxed{(p \vee q)} \leftrightarrow \boxed{(\sim q \rightarrow p)}$$

We need a column with truth values for this statement.   We need a column with truth values for this statement.

The completed truth table for $(p \lor q) \leftrightarrow (\sim q \to p)$ appears as follows:

p	q	$p \lor q$	$\sim q$	$\sim q \to p$	$(p \lor q) \leftrightarrow (\sim q \to p)$
T	T	T	F	T	T
T	F	T	T	T	T
F	T	T	F	T	T
F	F	F	T	F	T

We applied the definition of the biconditional to fill in the last column. In each case, the truth values of $p \lor q$ and $\sim q \to p$ are the same. Therefore, the biconditional $(p \lor q) \leftrightarrow (\sim q \to p)$ is true in each case. Because all cases are true, the biconditional is a tautology.

○

 CHECK POINT 4 Construct a truth table for $(p \lor q) \leftrightarrow (\sim p \to q)$ to determine whether the statement is a tautology.

---

5 Determine the truth value of a compound statement for a specific case.

EXAMPLE 5   DETERMINING THE TRUTH VALUE OF A COMPOUND STATEMENT

Your author recently received a letter from his credit card company that began as follows:

Dear Mr. Bob Blitzer,

I am pleased to inform you that a personal Super Million Dollar Prize Entry Number—665567010—has been assigned in your name as indicated above. <u>If your Super Million Dollar Prize Entry Number matches the winning preselected number and you return the number before the deadline stated below, you will win $1,000,000.00.</u> It's as simple as that.

Consider the claim in the underlined conditional statement. Suppose that your Super Million Dollar Prize Entry Number does not match the winning preselected number (those dirty rotten scoundrels!), you obediently return the number before the deadline, and you win only a free issue of a magazine (with the remaining 11 issues billed to your credit card). Under these conditions, can you sue the credit card company for making a false claim?

SOLUTION   Let's begin by assigning letters to the simple statements in the claim. We'll also indicate the truth value of each simple statement.

p: Your Super Million Dollar Prize Entry Number matches the winning preselected number.   *false*

q: You return the number before the stated deadline.   *true*

r: You win $1,000,000.00.   *false; To make matters worse, you were duped into buying a magazine subscription.*

Now we can write the underlined claim in the letter to Bob in symbolic form.

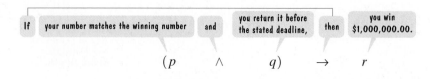

We substitute the truth values for p, q, and r to determine the truth value for the credit card company's claim.

$(p \wedge q) \rightarrow r$ This is the claim in symbolic form.

$(F \wedge T) \rightarrow F$ Substitute the truth values for the simple statements.

$F \rightarrow F$ Replace $F \wedge T$ with F. Conjunction is false when one part is false.

T Replace $F \rightarrow F$ with T. The conditional is true with a false antecedent and a false consequent.

Our truth-value analysis indicates that you cannot sue the credit card company for making a false claim. Call it conditional trickery, but the company's claim is true.

CHECK POINT 5 Consider the underlined claim in the letter in Example 5. Suppose that your number actually matches the winning preselected number, you do not return the number, and you win nothing. Under these conditions, determine the claim's truth value.

BLITZER BONUS

Conditional Wishful Thinking

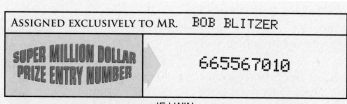

ASSIGNED EXCLUSIVELY TO MR.	BOB BLITZER
SUPER MILLION DOLLAR PRIZE ENTRY NUMBER ▶	665567010

IF I WIN,
I PREFER MY $1,000,000 PRIZE:
☐ in installments of $33,333.34 annually until the entire $1,000,000.00 is paid out
☐ lump-sum settlement of $546,783.00

Bob's credit card company is too kind. It even offers options as to how he wants to receive his million-dollar winnings. With this lure, people who do not think carefully might interpret the conditional claim in the letter to read as follows:

If you return your winning number and do so before the stated deadline, you win $1,000,000.00.

This misreading is wishful thinking. There is no winning number to return. What there is, of course, is a deceptive attempt to sell magazines.

EXERCISE SET 3.4 ●●●●●●

• Practice Exercises

In Exercises 1–16, construct a truth table for the given statement.

1. $p \rightarrow \sim q$ **2.** $\sim p \rightarrow q$

3. $\sim (q \rightarrow p)$ **4.** $\sim (p \rightarrow q)$

5. $(p \wedge q) \rightarrow (p \vee q)$ **6.** $(p \vee q) \rightarrow (p \wedge q)$

7. $(p \rightarrow q) \wedge \sim q$ **8.** $(p \rightarrow q) \wedge \sim p$

9. $(p \vee q) \rightarrow r$ **10.** $p \rightarrow (q \vee r)$

11. $r \rightarrow (p \wedge q)$ **12.** $r \rightarrow (p \vee q)$

13. $\sim r \wedge (\sim q \rightarrow p)$ **14.** $\sim r \wedge (q \rightarrow \sim p)$

15. $\sim (p \wedge r) \rightarrow (\sim q \vee r)$ **16.** $\sim (p \vee r) \rightarrow (\sim q \wedge r)$

In Exercises 17–32, construct a truth table for the given statement.

17. $p \leftrightarrow \sim q$ **18.** $\sim p \leftrightarrow q$

19. $\sim (p \leftrightarrow q)$ **20.** $\sim (q \leftrightarrow p)$

21. $(p \leftrightarrow q) \rightarrow p$ **22.** $(p \leftrightarrow q) \rightarrow q$

23. $(\sim p \leftrightarrow q) \rightarrow (\sim p \rightarrow q)$ **24.** $(p \leftrightarrow \sim q) \rightarrow (q \rightarrow \sim p)$

25. $[(p \wedge q) \wedge (q \rightarrow p)] \leftrightarrow (p \wedge q)$

26. $[(p \rightarrow q) \vee (p \wedge \sim p)] \leftrightarrow (\sim q \rightarrow \sim p)$

27. $(p \leftrightarrow q) \rightarrow \sim r$ **28.** $(p \rightarrow q) \leftrightarrow \sim r$

29. $(p \wedge r) \leftrightarrow \sim (q \vee r)$ **30.** $(p \vee r) \leftrightarrow \sim (q \wedge r)$

31. $[r \vee (\sim q \wedge p)] \leftrightarrow \sim p$ **32.** $[r \wedge (q \vee \sim p)] \leftrightarrow \sim q$

In Exercises 33–56, use a truth table to determine whether each statement is a tautology, a self-contradiction, or neither.

33. $[(p \to q) \wedge q] \to p$
34. $[(p \to q) \wedge p] \to q$
35. $[(p \to q) \wedge \sim q] \to \sim p$
36. $[(p \to q) \wedge \sim p] \to \sim q$
37. $[(p \vee q) \wedge p] \to \sim q$
38. $[(p \vee q) \wedge \sim q] \to p$
39. $(p \to q) \to (\sim p \vee q)$
40. $(q \to p) \to (p \vee \sim q)$
41. $(p \wedge q) \wedge (\sim p \vee \sim q)$
42. $(p \vee q) \wedge (\sim p \wedge \sim q)$
43. $\sim(p \wedge q) \leftrightarrow (\sim p \wedge \sim q)$
44. $\sim(p \vee q) \leftrightarrow (\sim p \wedge \sim q)$
45. $(p \to q) \leftrightarrow (q \to p)$
46. $(p \to q) \leftrightarrow (\sim p \to \sim q)$
47. $(p \to q) \leftrightarrow (\sim p \vee q)$
48. $(p \to q) \leftrightarrow (p \vee \sim q)$
49. $(p \leftrightarrow q) \leftrightarrow [(q \to p) \wedge (p \to q)]$
50. $(q \leftrightarrow p) \leftrightarrow [(p \to q) \wedge (q \to p)]$
51. $(p \wedge q) \leftrightarrow (\sim p \vee r)$
52. $(p \wedge q) \to (\sim q \vee r)$
53. $[(p \to q) \wedge (q \to r)] \to (p \to r)$
54. $[(p \to q) \wedge (q \to r)] \to (\sim r \to \sim p)$
55. $[(q \to r) \wedge (r \to \sim p)] \leftrightarrow (q \wedge p)$
56. $[(q \to \sim r) \wedge (\sim r \to p)] \leftrightarrow (q \wedge \sim p)$

In Exercises 57–64,

    a. Write each statement in symbolic form. Assign letters to simple statements that are not negated.

    b. Construct a truth table for the symbolic statement in part (a).

    c. Use the truth table to indicate one set of conditions that make the compound statement false, or state that no such conditions exist.

57. If you do homework right after class then you will not fall behind, and if you do not do homework right after class then you will.

58. If you do a little bit each day then you'll get by, and if you do not do a little bit each day then you won't.

59. If you "cut-and-paste" from the Internet and do not cite the source, then you will be charged with plagiarism.

60. If you take more than one class with a lot of reading, then you will not have free time and you'll be in the library until 1 A.M.

61. You'll be comfortable in your room if and only if you're honest with your roommate, or you won't enjoy the college experience.

62. I fail the course if and only if I rely on a used book with highlightings by an idiot, or I do not buy a used book.

63. I enjoy the course if and only if I choose the class based on the professor and not the course description.

64. I do not miss class if and only if they take attendance or there are pop quizzes.

In Exercises 65–74, determine the truth value for each statement when p is false, q is true, and r is false.

65. $\sim(p \to q)$
66. $\sim(p \leftrightarrow q)$
67. $\sim p \leftrightarrow q$
68. $\sim p \to q$
69. $q \to (p \wedge r)$
70. $(p \wedge r) \to q$
71. $(\sim p \wedge q) \leftrightarrow \sim r$
72. $\sim p \leftrightarrow (\sim q \wedge r)$
73. $\sim[(p \to \sim r) \leftrightarrow (r \wedge \sim p)]$
74. $\sim[(\sim p \to r) \leftrightarrow (p \vee \sim q)]$

• Practice Plus

In Exercises 75–78, use grouping symbols to clarify the meaning of each statement. Then construct a truth table for the statement.

75. $p \to q \leftrightarrow p \wedge q \to \sim p$
76. $q \to p \leftrightarrow p \vee q \to \sim p$
77. $p \to \sim q \vee r \leftrightarrow p \wedge r$
78. $\sim p \to q \wedge r \leftrightarrow p \vee r$

In Exercises 79–82, construct a truth table for each statement. Then use the table to indicate one set of conditions that make the compound statement false, or state that no such conditions exist.

79. Loving a person is necessary for marrying that person, but not loving someone is sufficient for not marrying that person.

80. Studying hard is necessary for getting an A, but not studying hard is sufficient for not getting an A.

81. It is not true that being happy and living contentedly are necessary conditions for being wealthy.

82. It is not true that being wealthy is a sufficient condition for being happy and living contentedly.

• Application Exercises

The bar graph shows the average number of hours per month that American women and men talked on their cellphones from 2001 through 2005.

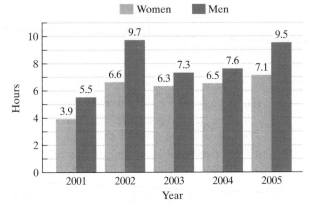

Average Number of Hours per Month Americans Talk on Cellphones

Source: Cingular Wireless

In Exercises 83–86, write each statement in symbolic form. (Average hours in each simple statement refer to the average number of hours per month talking on cellphones.) Then use the information in the graph to determine the truth value of the compound statement.

83. If for every year shown men did not average more hours than women and men averaged more hours than women in 2002 through 2005, then women averaged more hours than men in 2001.

84. If for every year shown men averaged more hours than women, then it is not the case that women averaged more hours than men in 2001 or in 2002.

85. Men averaged 2.4 hours more than women in 2005 if and only if they averaged 1.2 hours more than women in 2004, or men averaged fewer hours in 2005 than in 2002.

86. Men averaged 2.4 hours more than women in 2005 if and only if they averaged 1.6 hours more than women in 2001, and women averaged fewer hours in 2003 than in 2002.

The circle graph shows the results of a survey in which American adults were asked the following question:

> If you got conflicting or different reports of the same news story from television, newspapers, radio, or magazines, which would you be most inclined to believe?

The circle graph shows the percentage of American adults finding each medium the most believable.

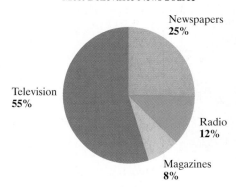

Most Believable News Source

Source: Thomas R. Dye, *Who's Running America? Seventh Edition,* Prentice Hall, 2002

In Exercises 87–90, write each statement in symbolic form. Then use the information given by the graph to determine the truth value of each compound statement.

87. Thirty-five percent find newspapers the most believable news source or 45% do not find television the most believable news source, if and only if more people believe a news story in a magazine than on radio.

88. Thirty-five percent find newspapers the most believable news source and 45% do not find television the most believable news source, if and only if more people believe a news story in a magazine than on radio.

89. If more people believe newspapers than radio and magazines combined, then 22% find radio the most believable news source and 8% find magazines the most believable news source.

90. If fewer people believe newspapers than radio and magazines combined, then 22% find radio the most believable news source or 8% find magazines the most believable news source.

• Writing in Mathematics

91. Explain when conditional statements are true and when they are false.

92. Explain when biconditional statements are true and when they are false.

93. What is the difference between a tautology and a self-contradiction?

94. Based on the meaning of the inclusive or, explain why it is reasonable that if $p \vee q$ is true, then $\sim p \rightarrow q$ must also be true.

95. Based on the meaning of the inclusive or, explain why if $p \vee q$ is true, then $p \rightarrow \sim q$ is not necessarily true.

• Critical Thinking Exercises

96. Which one of the following is true?

    a. A conditional statement is false only when the consequent is true and the antecedent is false.

    b. Some implications are not tautologies.

    c. An equivalent form for a conditional statement is obtained by reversing the antecedent and consequent, and then negating the resulting statement.

    d. A compound statement consisting of two simple statements that are both false can be true.

97. Consider the statement "If you get an A in the course, I'll take you out to eat." If you complete the course and I do take you out to eat, can you conclude that you got an A? Explain your answer.

In Exercises 98–99, the headings for the columns in the truth tables are missing. Fill in the statements to replace the missing headings. (More than one correct statement may be possible.)

98.

> Do not repeat the statement from the third column.

p	q				
T	T	T	F	T	T
T	F	F	F	F	T
F	T	T	T	T	T
F	F	T	T	T	T

99.

> Do not repeat the previous statement.

p	q				
T	T	T	T	F	F
T	F	T	F	T	T
F	T	T	F	T	T
F	F	F	F	T	T

100. A compound statement involving two simple statements has 4 different true-false possibilities. A compound statement involving three simple statements has 8 different true-false possibilities, and one with four simple statements has 16 different true-false possibilities. How many true-false possibilities are there for a compound statement involving n simple statements?

SECTION 3.5 • EQUIVALENT STATEMENTS, VARIATIONS OF CONDITIONAL STATEMENTS, AND DE MORGAN'S LAWS

OBJECTIVES

1. Use a truth table to show that statements are equivalent.

2. Write the contrapositive for a conditional statement.

3. Write the converse and inverse of a conditional statement.

4. Write the negation of a conditional statement.

5. Use De Morgan's laws.

Actors Tommy Lee Jones and Will Smith

TOP U.S. LAST NAMES

Name	% of All Names
Smith	1.006%
Johnson	0.810%
Williams	0.699%
Brown	0.621%
Jones	0.621%
Davis	0.480%
Miller	0.424%
Wilson	0.339%
Moore	0.312%
Anderson	0.311%
Taylor	0.311%
Thomas	0.311%

Source: Russell Ash, *The Top 10 of Everything 2006*

The top U.S. last names shown above make up more than 6% of the entire population. One American in every 16 bears one of the names in the table. The list indicates that the following statement is true:

> If your last name is Brown, your name is shared by 0.621% of the population.

Does this mean that if your name is shared by 0.621% of the population, then it's Brown? If your last name isn't Brown, can we conclude that it's not shared by 0.621% of the population? Furthermore, if your name is not shared by 0.621% of the population, can we conclude that it's not Brown? In this section, we will use truth tables and logic to unravel this verbal morass of conditional statements.

1 | Use a truth table to show that statements are equivalent.

Equivalent Statements

Equivalent compound statements are made up of the same simple statements and have the same corresponding truth values for all true-false combinations of these simple statements. If a compound statement is true, then its equivalent statement must also be true. Likewise, if a compound statement is false, its equivalent statement must also be false.

Truth tables are used to show that two statements are equivalent. When translated into English, equivalencies can be used to gain a better understanding of English statements.

EXAMPLE 1 | SHOWING THAT STATEMENTS ARE EQUIVALENT

a. Show that $p \vee \sim q$ and $\sim p \rightarrow \sim q$ are equivalent.

b. Use the result from part (a) to write a statement that is equivalent to

> The bill receives majority approval or the bill does not become law.

SOLUTION

a. Construct a truth table that shows the truth values for $p \vee \sim q$ and $\sim p \rightarrow \sim q$. The truth values for each statement are shown below.

p	q	$\sim q$	$p \vee \sim q$	$\sim p$	$\sim p \rightarrow \sim q$
T	T	F	T	F	T
T	F	T	T	F	T
F	T	F	F	T	F
F	F	T	T	T	T

Corresponding truth values are the same.

The table shows that the truth values for $p \vee \sim q$ and $\sim p \rightarrow \sim q$ are the same. Therefore, the statements are equivalent.

b. The statement

The bill receives majority approval or the bill does not become law

can be expressed in symbolic form using the following representations:

p: The bill receives majority approval.

q: The bill becomes law.

In symbolic form, the statement is $p \vee \sim q$. Based on the truth table in part (a), we know that an equivalent statement is $\sim p \rightarrow \sim q$. The equivalent statement can be expressed in words as

If the bill does not receive majority approval, then the bill does not become law.

Notice that the given statement and its equivalent are both true.

CHECK POINT 1

a. Show that $p \vee q$ and $\sim q \rightarrow p$ are equivalent.

b. Use the result from part (a) to write a statement that is equivalent to

I attend classes or I lose my scholarship.

A special symbol, $\equiv$, is used to show that two statements are equivalent. Because $p \vee \sim q$ and $\sim p \rightarrow \sim q$ are equivalent, we can write

$$p \vee \sim q \equiv \sim p \rightarrow \sim q \quad \text{or} \quad \sim p \rightarrow \sim q \equiv p \vee \sim q.$$

EXAMPLE 2   SHOWING THAT STATEMENTS ARE EQUIVALENT

Show that $\sim(\sim p) \equiv p$.

SOLUTION Determine the truth values for $\sim(\sim p)$ and p. These are shown in the truth table at the left.

The truth values for $\sim(\sim p)$ were obtained by taking the opposite of each truth value for $\sim p$. The table shows that the truth values for $\sim(\sim p)$ and p are the same. Therefore, the statements are equivalent:

$$\sim(\sim p) \equiv p.$$

p	$\sim p$	$\sim(\sim p)$
T	F	T
F	T	F

Corresponding truth values are the same.

The equivalence in Example 2 illustrates that **the double negation of a statement is equivalent to the statement.** For example, the statement "It is not true that Ernest Hemingway was not a writer" means the same thing as "Ernest Hemingway was a writer."

CHECK POINT 2 Show that $\sim[\sim(\sim p)] \equiv \sim p$.

EXAMPLE 3 EQUIVALENCIES AND TRUTH TABLES

Select the statement that is not equivalent to

Miguel is blushing or sunburned.

a. If Miguel is blushing, then he is not sunburned.
b. Miguel is sunburned or blushing.
c. If Miguel is not blushing, then he is sunburned.
d. If Miguel is not sunburned, then he is blushing.

SOLUTION To determine which of the choices is not equivalent to the given statement, begin by writing the given statement and the choices in symbolic form. Then construct a truth table and compare each statement's truth values to those of the given statement. The nonequivalent statement is the one that does not have exactly the same truth values as the given statement.

The simple statements that make up "Miguel is blushing or sunburned" can be represented as follows:

p: Miguel is blushing.
q: Miguel is sunburned.

Here are the symbolic representations for the given statement and the four choices:

Miguel is blushing or sunburned: $p \vee q$.

a. If Miguel is blushing, then he is not sunburned: $p \rightarrow \sim q$.
b. Miguel is sunburned or blushing: $q \vee p$.
c. If Miguel is not blushing, then he is sunburned: $\sim p \rightarrow q$.
d. If Miguel is not sunburned, then he is blushing: $\sim q \rightarrow p$.

Next, construct a truth table that contains the truth values for the given statement, $p \vee q$, as well as those for the four options. The truth table is shown as follows:

Equivalent

		Given		(a)	(b)		(c)	(d)
p	*q*	$p \vee q$	$\sim q$	$p \rightarrow \sim q$	$q \vee p$	$\sim p$	$\sim p \rightarrow q$	$\sim q \rightarrow p$
T	T	T	F	F	T	F	T	T
T	F	T	T	T	T	F	T	T
F	T	T	F	T	T	T	T	T
F	F	F	T	T	F	T	F	F

Not equivalent

The statement in option (a) does not have the same corresponding truth values as those for $p \vee q$. Therefore, this statement is not equivalent to the given statement.

We can use our understanding of the inclusive *or* to see why the following statements are not equivalent:

Miguel is blushing or sunburned.
If Miguel is blushing, then he is not sunburned.

Let us assume that the first statement is true. The inclusive *or* tells us that Miguel might be both blushing and sunburned. This means that the second statement might not be true. The fact that Miguel is blushing does not indicate that he is not sunburned; he might be both.

Select the statement that is not equivalent to

> If it's raining, then I need a jacket.
> **a.** It's not raining or I need a jacket.
> **b.** I need a jacket or it's not raining.
> **c.** If I need a jacket, then it's raining.
> **d.** If I do not need a jacket, then it's not raining.

2 | Write the contrapositive for a conditional statement.

Variations of the Conditional Statement $p \rightarrow q$

In Section 3.4, we learned that $p \rightarrow q$ is equivalent to $\sim q \rightarrow \sim p$. The truth value of a conditional statement does not change if the antecedent and the consequent are reversed and then both of them are negated. The **contrapositive** is a statement obtained by reversing and negating the antecedent and the consequent.

p	q	$p \rightarrow q$	$\sim q \rightarrow \sim p$
T	T	T	T
T	F	F	F
F	T	T	T
F	F	T	T

$p \rightarrow q$ and $\sim q \rightarrow \sim p$ are equivalent.

> **A CONDITIONAL STATEMENT AND ITS EQUIVALENT CONTRAPOSITIVE**
>
> $$p \rightarrow q \equiv \sim q \rightarrow \sim p$$
>
> The truth value of a conditional statement does not change if the antecedent and consequent are reversed and both are negated. The statement $\sim q \rightarrow \sim p$ is called the **contrapositive** of the conditional $p \rightarrow q$.

EXAMPLE 4   WRITING EQUIVALENT CONTRAPOSITIVES

Write the contrapositive for each of the following statements:

a. If you live in Los Angeles, then you live in California.

b. If the patient is not breathing, then the patient is dead.

c. If all people obey the law, then prisons are not needed.

d. $\sim(p \wedge q) \rightarrow r$

SOLUTION In parts (a)–(c), we write each statement in symbolic form. Then we form the contrapositive by reversing and negating the antecedent and the consequent. Finally, we translate the symbolic form of the contrapositive back into English.

a. Use the following representations:

p: You live in Los Angeles.

q: You live in California.

> If you live in Los Angeles, then you live in California.
>
> p $\rightarrow$ q
>
> $p \rightarrow q$ This is the statement's symbolic form.
>
> $\sim q \rightarrow \sim p$ Form the contrapositive: Reverse and negate the components.

Translating $\sim q \rightarrow \sim p$ into English, the contrapositive is

> If you do not live in California, then you do not live in Los Angeles.

Notice that the given conditional statement and its contrapositive are both true.

b. Use the following representations:

p: The patient is breathing.

q: The patient is dead.

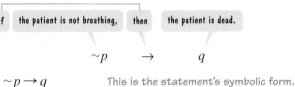

$$\sim p \qquad \rightarrow \qquad q$$

$\sim p \rightarrow q$	This is the statement's symbolic form.
$\sim q \rightarrow \sim(\sim p)$	Form the contrapositive: Reverse and negate components.
$\sim q \rightarrow p$	Simplify. The double negation of a statement is equivalent to the statement.

Translating $\sim q \rightarrow p$ into English, the contrapositive is

If the patient is not dead, then the patient is breathing.

c. Use the following representations:

p: All people obey the law.

q: Prisons are needed.

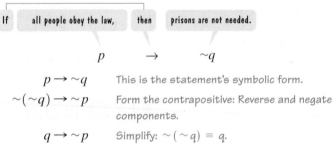

$$p \qquad \rightarrow \qquad \sim q$$

$p \rightarrow \sim q$	This is the statement's symbolic form.
$\sim(\sim q) \rightarrow \sim p$	Form the contrapositive: Reverse and negate components.
$q \rightarrow \sim p$	Simplify: $\sim(\sim q) \equiv q$.

Recall, as shown in the margin, that the negation of *all* is *some … not*. Using this negation and translating $q \rightarrow \sim p$ into English, the contrapositive is

If prisons are needed, then some people do not obey the law.

d.

$\sim(p \wedge q) \rightarrow r$	This is the given symbolic statement.
$\sim r \rightarrow \sim[\sim(p \wedge q)]$	Form the contrapositive: Reverse and negate the components.
$\sim r \rightarrow (p \wedge q)$	Simplify: $\sim[\sim(p \wedge q)] \equiv p \wedge q$.

The contrapositive of $\sim(p \wedge q) \rightarrow r$ is $\sim r \rightarrow (p \wedge q)$. Using the dominance of connectives, the contrapositive can be expressed as $\sim r \rightarrow p \wedge q$.

Write the contrapositive for each of the following statements:

a. If you can read this, then you're driving too closely.

b. If you do not have clean underwear, it's time to do the laundry.

c. If all students are honest, then supervision during exams is not required.

d. $\sim(p \vee r) \rightarrow \sim q$

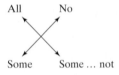

Negations of
Quantified Statements

All   No

Some   Some … not

3 Write the converse and inverse of a conditional statement.

The truth value of a conditional statement does not change if the antecedent and the consequent are reversed and then both of them are negated. But what happens to the conditional's truth values if just one, but not both, of these changes is made? If the antecedent and the consequent are reversed but not negated, the resulting statement is called the **converse** of the conditional statement. By negating both the antecedent and the consequent but not reversing them, we obtain the **inverse** of the conditional statement.

VARIATIONS OF THE CONDITIONAL STATEMENT

Name	Symbolic Form	English Translation
Conditional	$p \rightarrow q$	If p, then q.
Converse	$q \rightarrow p$	If q, then p.
Inverse	$\sim p \rightarrow \sim q$	If not p, then not q.
Contrapositive	$\sim q \rightarrow \sim p$	If not q, then not p.

Let's see what happens to the truth value of a true conditional statement when we form its converse and its inverse.

Conditional statement   If it's a BMW, it's a car.   true

Converse: Reverse components.   If it's a car, it's a BMW.   Not necessarily true

Inverse: Negate components   If it's not a BMW, it's not a car.   Not necessarily true

These statements illustrate that if a conditional statement is true, its converse and inverse are not necessarily true. Because the equivalent of a true statement must be true, we see that a conditional statement is not equivalent to its converse or its inverse.

The relationships among the truth values for a conditional statement, its converse, its inverse, and its contrapositive are shown in the truth table that follows:

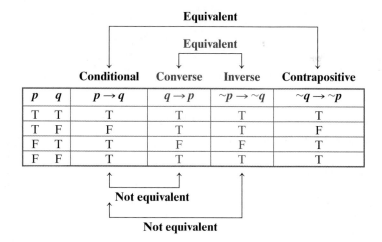

		Conditional	Converse	Inverse	Contrapositive
p	q	$p \rightarrow q$	$q \rightarrow p$	$\sim p \rightarrow \sim q$	$\sim q \rightarrow \sim p$
T	T	T	T	T	T
T	F	F	T	T	F
F	T	T	F	F	T
F	F	T	T	T	T

Equivalent — Equivalent — Not equivalent — Not equivalent

The truth table confirms that a conditional statement is equivalent to its contrapositive. The table also shows that a conditional statement is not equivalent to its converse; in some cases they have the same truth value, but in other cases they have opposite truth values. Also, a conditional statement is not equivalent to its inverse. By contrast, the converse and the inverse are equivalent to each other.

EXAMPLE 5   WRITING VARIATIONS OF A CONDITIONAL STATEMENT

The following conditional statement is surprisingly true:

If it's a lead pencil, then it does not contain lead.

(The so-called lead is actually a mixture of graphite and clay.) Write the statement's converse, inverse, and contrapositive.

SOLUTION Use the following representations:

p: It's a lead pencil.

q: It contains lead.

$$p \qquad \rightarrow \qquad \sim q$$

We now work with $p \rightarrow \sim q$ to form the converse, inverse, and contrapositive. We then translate the symbolic form of each statement back into English.

	Symbolic Statement	English Translation
Given Conditional Statement	$p \rightarrow \sim q$	If it's a lead pencil, then it does not contain lead. *true*
Converse: Reverse the components of $p \rightarrow \sim q$.	$\sim q \rightarrow p$	If it does not contain lead, then it's a lead pencil. *not necessarily true*
Inverse: Negate the components of $p \rightarrow \sim q$.	$\sim p \rightarrow \sim(\sim q)$ simplifies to $\sim p \rightarrow q$	If it is not a lead pencil, then it contains lead. *not necessarily true*
Contrapositive: Reverse and negate the components of $p \rightarrow \sim q$.	$\sim(\sim q) \rightarrow \sim p$ simplifies to $q \rightarrow \sim p$	If it contains lead, then it's not a lead pencil. *true*

 Write the converse, inverse, and contrapositive of the following statement:

If you are in Iran, then you don't see a Club Med.

4 | Write the negation of a conditional statement.

The Negation of the Conditional Statement $p \rightarrow q$

Suppose that your accountant makes the following statement:

If you itemize deductions, then you pay less in taxes.

When will your accountant have told you a lie? The only case in which you have been lied to is when you itemize deductions and you do *not* pay less in taxes. We can analyze this situation symbolically with the following representations:

p: You itemize deductions.

q: You pay less in taxes.

We represent each compound statement in symbolic form.

$p \rightarrow q$: If you itemize deductions, then you pay less in taxes.

$p \wedge \sim q$: You itemize deductions and you do not pay less in taxes.

The truth table that follows shows that the negation of $p \rightarrow q$ is $p \wedge \sim q$.

p	q	$p \rightarrow q$	$\sim q$	$p \wedge \sim q$
T	T	T	F	F
T	F	F	T	T
F	T	T	F	F
F	F	T	T	F

These columns have opposite truth values, so $p \wedge \sim q$ negates $p \rightarrow q$.

THE NEGATION OF A CONDITIONAL STATEMENT
The negation of $p \rightarrow q$ is $p \wedge \sim q$. This can be expressed as

$$\sim (p \rightarrow q) \equiv p \wedge \sim q.$$

To form the negation of a conditional statement, leave the antecedent (the first part) unchanged, change the *if–then* connective to *and*, and negate the consequent (the second part).

EXAMPLE 6   WRITING THE NEGATION OF A CONDITIONAL STATEMENT

Write the negation of

If too much homework is given, a class should not be taken.

SOLUTION   Use the following representations:

p: Too much homework is given.

q: A class should be taken.

The symbolic form of the conditional statement is $p \rightarrow \sim q$.

$p \rightarrow \sim q$	This is the given statement in symbolic form.
$p \wedge \sim (\sim q)$	Form the negation: Copy the antecedent, change $\rightarrow$ to $\wedge$, and negate the consequent.
$p \wedge q$	Simplify: $\sim (\sim q) \equiv q$.

Translating $p \wedge q$ into English, the negation of the given statement is

Too much homework is given and the class should be taken.

CHECK POINT

6 Write the negation of

If you do not have a fever, you do not have the flu.

The box that follows summarizes what we have learned about conditional statements:

STUDY TIP

Don't confuse the inverse of $p \rightarrow q$ with the negation of $p \rightarrow q$. You obtain the inverse, $\sim p \rightarrow \sim q$, which is an *if–then* statement, by negating the two component statements. However, this process does not make the inverse the negation. The negation of $p \rightarrow q$ is $p \wedge \sim q$, which is an *and* statement.

THE CONDITIONAL STATEMENT $p \rightarrow q$

CONTRAPOSITIVE

$p \rightarrow q$ is equivalent to $\sim q \rightarrow \sim p$ (the contrapositive).

CONVERSE AND INVERSE

1. $p \rightarrow q$ is not equivalent to $q \rightarrow p$ (the converse).
2. $p \rightarrow q$ is not equivalent to $\sim p \rightarrow \sim q$ (the inverse).

NEGATION

The negation of $p \rightarrow q$ is $p \wedge \sim q$.

---

5 Use De Morgan's laws.

De Morgan's Laws

De Morgan's laws, named after the English mathematician Augustus De Morgan (1806–1871), were introduced in Chapter 2, where they applied to sets:

$$(A \cap B)' = A' \cup B'$$
$$(A \cup B)' = A' \cap B'.$$

Similar relationships apply to the statements of symbolic logic:

$$\sim(p \wedge q) \equiv \sim p \vee \sim q$$
$$\sim(p \vee q) \equiv \sim p \wedge \sim q.$$

Here is a truth table that serves as a deductive proof for the first of these two equivalences:

p	q	$p \wedge q$	$\sim(p \wedge q)$	$\sim p$	$\sim q$	$\sim p \vee \sim q$
T	T	T	F	F	F	F
T	F	F	T	F	T	T
F	T	F	T	T	F	T
F	F	F	T	T	T	T

Truth values are the same, proving that $\sim(p \wedge q) \equiv \sim p \vee \sim q$.

We can prove that $\sim(p \vee q) \equiv \sim p \wedge \sim q$ in a similar manner. Do this now by constructing a truth table and showing that $\sim(p \vee q)$ and $\sim p \wedge \sim q$ have the same corresponding truth values.

DE MORGAN'S LAWS

1. $\sim(p \wedge q) \equiv \sim p \vee \sim q$
2. $\sim(p \vee q) \equiv \sim p \wedge \sim q$

EXAMPLE 7 USING A DE MORGAN LAW

Write a statement that is equivalent to

It is not true that Atlanta and California are cities.

SOLUTION Let p and q represent the following statements:

p: Atlanta is a city.

q: California is a city.

The statement is of the form $\sim(p \wedge q)$. An equivalent statement is $\sim p \vee \sim q$. We can translate this as

Atlanta is not a city or California is not a city.

 Write a statement that is equivalent to

It is not true that Bart Simpson and Tony Soprano are cartoon characters.

EXAMPLE 8 USING A DE MORGAN LAW

The underlined portion of the following quote is an equivalent paraphrase of the famous "I have a dream speech" given by Martin Luther King, Jr. in 1963 during the March on Washington for civil rights:

"I have a dream that my four little children will one day live in a nation where <u>it is not true that they will be judged by the color of their skin or not by the content of their character</u>. I have a dream today."

Write a statement that is equivalent to the underlined passage.

SOLUTION Let p and q represent the following statements:

p: My children will be judged by the color of their skin.

q: My children will be judged by the content of their character.

$\sim(p \vee \sim q)$ This is the underlined passage in symbolic form.

$\sim p \wedge \sim(\sim q)$ Use a De Morgan law to write an equivalent statement.

$\sim p \wedge q$ Simplify: $\sim(\sim q) \equiv q$.

Translating $\sim p \wedge q$ into English, a statement that is equivalent to the underlined passage is

My children will not be judged by the color of their skin but by the content of their character.

 Write a statement that is equivalent to

It is not true that you leave by 5 P.M. or you do not arrive home on time.

De Morgan's laws can be used to write the negation of a compound statement that is a conjunction ($\wedge$, *and*) or a disjunction ($\vee$, *or*).

DE MORGAN'S LAWS AND NEGATIONS

1. $\sim(p \wedge q) \equiv \sim p \vee \sim q$

   The negation of $p \wedge q$ is $\sim p \vee \sim q$. To negate a conjunction, negate each component statement and change *and* to *or*.

2. $\sim(p \vee q) \equiv \sim p \wedge \sim q$

   The negation of $p \vee q$ is $\sim p \wedge \sim q$. To negate a disjunction, negate each component statement and change *or* to *and*.

We can apply these rules to English conjunctions or disjunctions and immediately obtain their negations without having to introduce symbolic representations.

EXAMPLE 9   NEGATING CONJUNCTIONS AND DISJUNCTIONS

Write the negation for each of the following statements:

a. All students do laundry on weekends and I do not.

b. Some college professors are entertaining lecturers or I'm bored.

SOLUTION To negate some of the simple statements, we use the negations of quantified statements shown in the margin.

Negations of Quantified Statements

a. Conjunction:

b. Disjunction:

 Write the negation for each of the following statements:

   a. All horror movies are scary and some are funny.

   b. Your workouts are strenuous or you do not get stronger.

EXAMPLE 10   USING A DE MORGAN LAW TO FORMULATE A CONTRAPOSITIVE

Write a statement that is equivalent to

   If it rains, I do not go outdoors and I study.

SOLUTION We begin by writing the conditional statement in symbolic form. Let p, q, and r represent the following simple statements:

p: It rains.   *q:* I go outdoors.   *r:* I study.

Using these representations, the given conditional statement can be expressed in symbolic form as

$$p \to (\sim q \wedge r). \qquad \text{If it rains, I do not go outdoors and I study.}$$

An equivalent statement is the contrapositive.

$\sim(\sim q \wedge r) \rightarrow \sim p$ Form the contrapositive: Reverse and negate the components.

$[\sim(\sim q) \vee \sim r] \rightarrow \sim p$ Use a De Morgan law to negate the conjunction: Negate each component and change $\wedge$ to $\vee$.

$(q \vee \sim r) \rightarrow \sim p$ Simplify: $\sim(\sim q) \equiv q$.

Thus,

$$p \rightarrow (\sim q \wedge r) \equiv (q \vee \sim r) \rightarrow \sim p.$$

Using the representations for p, q, and r, a statement that is equivalent to "If it rains, I do not go outdoors and I study" is

If I go outdoors or I do not study, it is not raining.

 Write a statement that is equivalent to

If it is not windy, we can swim and we cannot sail.

A Gödelian Universe

At the age of 10, Czech mathematician Kurt Gödel (1906–1978) was studying mathematics, religion, and several languages. By age 25 he had produced what many mathematicians consider the most important result of twentieth-century mathematics: Gödel proved that all deductive systems eventually give rise to statements that cannot be proved to be either true or false within that system. Take someone who says "I am lying." If he is then he isn't, and if he isn't then he is. There is no way to determine whether the statement is true or false. There are similar undecidable statements in every branch of mathematics, from number theory to algebra.

Gödel's Theorem suggests infinitely many layers, none of which are capable of capturing all truth in one logical system. Gödel showed that statements arise in a system that cannot be proved or disproved within that system. To prove them, one must ascend to a "richer" system in which the previous undecidable statement can now be proved, but this richer system will in turn lead to new statements that cannot be proved, and so on. The process goes on forever.

Is the universe Gödelian in the sense there is no end to the discovery of its mathematical laws and in which the ultimate reality is always out of reach? The situation is echoed in the painting *The Two Mysteries* by René Magritte. A small picture of a pipe is shown with a caption that asserts (to translate from the French) "This is not a pipe." Above the fake pipe is a presumably genuine larger pipe, but it too is painted on the canvas. In Magritte's Gödelian universe, reality is infinitely layered, and it is impossible to say what reality really is.

René Magritte (1898–1967) *Les Deux Mysteres* (*The Two Mysteries*), 1966, oil on canvas, 65 × 80 cm. Private Collection. Phototheque R. Magritte—ADAGP/Art Resource, NY. © 2008 C. Herscovici, Brussels/Artists Rights Society (ARS), New York.

EXERCISE SET 3.5 ●●●●●●

• Practice Exercises

1. a. Use a truth table to show that $\sim p \rightarrow q$ and $p \vee q$ are equivalent.

   b. Use the result from part (a) to write a statement that is equivalent to

      If the United States does not energetically support the development of solar-powered cars, then it will suffer increasing atmospheric pollution.

2. a. Use a truth table to show that $p \rightarrow q$ and $\sim p \vee q$ are equivalent.

   b. Use the result from part (a) to write a statement that is equivalent to

      If a number is even, then it is divisible by 2.

In Exercises 3–14, use a truth table to determine whether the two statements are equivalent.

   3. $\sim p \rightarrow q, q \rightarrow \sim p$ **4.** $\sim p \rightarrow q, p \rightarrow \sim q$

5. $(p \to \sim q) \land (\sim q \to p), p \leftrightarrow \sim q$

6. $(\sim p \to q) \land (q \to \sim p), \sim p \leftrightarrow q$

7. $(p \land q) \land r, p \land (q \land r)$

8. $(p \lor q) \lor r, p \lor (q \lor r)$

9. $(p \land q) \lor r, p \land (q \lor r)$

10. $(p \lor q) \land r, p \lor (q \land r)$

11. $(p \lor r) \to \sim q, (\sim p \land \sim r) \to q$

12. $(p \land \sim r) \to q, (\sim p \lor r) \to \sim q$

13. $\sim p \to (q \lor \sim r), (r \land \sim q) \to p$

14. $\sim p \to (\sim q \land r), (\sim r \lor q) \to p$

15. Select the statement that is equivalent to

I saw the original *King Kong* or the 2005 version.

   a. If I did not see the original *King Kong*, I saw the 2005 version.

   b. I saw both the original *King Kong* and the 2005 version.

   c. If I saw the original *King Kong*, I did not see the 2005 version.

   d. If I saw the 2005 version, I did not see the original *King Kong*.

16. Select the statement that is equivalent to

Citizen Kane or *Howard the Duck* appears in a list of greatest U.S. movies.

   a. If *Citizen Kane* appears in the list of greatest U.S. movies, *Howard the Duck* does not.

   b. If *Howard the Duck* does not appear in the list of greatest U.S. movies, then *Citizen Kane* does.

   c. Both *Citizen Kane* and *Howard the Duck* appear in a list of greatest U.S. movies.

   d. If *Howard the Duck* appears in the list of greatest U.S. movies, *Citizen Kane* does not.

17. Select the statement that is *not* equivalent to

It is not true that Sondheim and Picasso are both musicians.

   a. Sondheim is not a musician or Picasso is not a musician.

   b. If Sondheim is a musician, then Picasso is not a musician.

   c. Sondheim is not a musician and Picasso is not a musician.

   d. If Picasso is a musician, then Sondheim is not a musician.

18. Select the statement that is *not* equivalent to

It is not true that England and Africa are both countries.

   a. If England is a country, then Africa is not a country.

   b. England is not a country and Africa is not a country.

   c. England is not a country or Africa is not a country.

   d. If Africa is a country, then England is not a country.

In Exercises 19–30, write the converse, inverse, and contrapositive of each statement.

19. If I am in Chicago, then I am in Illinois.

20. If I am in Birmingham, then I am in the South.

21. If the stereo is playing, then I cannot hear you.

22. If it is blue, then it is not an apple.

23. "If you don't laugh, you die." (humorist Alan King)

24. "If it doesn't fit, you must acquit." (lawyer Johnnie Cochran)

25. If the president is telling the truth, then all troops were withdrawn.

26. If the review session is successful, then no students fail the test.

27. If all institutions place profit above human need, then some people suffer.

28. If all hard workers are successful, then some people are not hard workers.

29. $\sim q \to \sim r$ 30. $\sim p \to r$

In Exercises 31–40, write the negation of each conditional statement.

31. If I am in Los Angeles, then I am in California.

32. If I am in Houston, then I am in Texas.

33. If it is purple, then it is not a carrot.

34. If the TV is playing, then I cannot concentrate.

35. If he doesn't, I will.

36. If she says yes, he says no.

37. If there is a blizzard, then all schools are closed.

38. If there is a tax cut, then all people have extra spending money.

39. $\sim q \to \sim r$ 40. $\sim p \to r$

In Exercises 41–56, use De Morgan's laws to write a statement that is equivalent to the given statement.

41. It is not true that Australia and China are both islands.

42. It is not true that Florida and California are both peninsulas.

43. It is not the case that my high school encouraged creativity and diversity.

44. It is not the case that the course covers logic and dream analysis.

45. It is not the case that Jewish scripture gives a clear indication of a heaven or an afterlife.

46. It is not true that Martin Luther King, Jr. supported violent protest or the Vietnam war.

47. It is not the case that the United States has eradicated poverty or racism.

48. It is not the case that the movie is interesting or entertaining.

49. $\sim(\sim p \land q)$ 50. $\sim(p \lor \sim q)$

51. If you attend lecture and study, you succeed.

52. If you suffer from synesthesia, you can literally taste music and smell colors.

53. If he does not cook, his wife or child does.

54. If it is Saturday or Sunday, I do not work.

55. $p \to (q \lor \sim r)$ 56. $p \to (\sim q \land \sim r)$

In Exercises 57–68, write the negation of each statement.

57. I'm going to Seattle or San Francisco.

58. This course covers logic or statistics.

59. I study or I do not pass.

60. I give up tobacco or I am not healthy.

61. I am not going and he is going.

62. I do not apply myself and I succeed.

63. A bill becomes law and it does not receive majority approval.

64. They see the show and they do not have tickets.

65. $p \lor \sim q$ 66. $\sim p \lor q$ 67. $p \land (q \lor r)$ 68. $p \lor (q \land r)$

In Exercises 69–76, determine which, if any, of the three given statements are equivalent. You may use information about a conditional statement's converse, inverse, or contrapositive, De Morgan's laws, or truth tables.

69. a. If he is guilty, then he does not take a lie-detector test.
   b. He is not guilty or he takes a lie-detector test.
   c. If he is not guilty, then he takes a lie-detector test.

70. a. If the train is late, then I am not in class on time.
   b. The train is late or I am in class on time.
   c. If I am in class on time, then the train is not late.

71. a. It is not true that I have a ticket and cannot go.
   b. I do not have a ticket and can go.
   c. I have a ticket or I cannot go.

72. a. I work hard or I do not succeed.
   b. It is not true that I do not work hard and succeed.
   c. I do not work hard and I do succeed.

73. a. If the grass turns yellow, you did not use fertilizer or water.
   b. If you use fertilizer and water, the grass will not turn yellow.
   c. If the grass does not turn yellow, you used fertilizer and water.

74. a. If you do not file or provide fraudulent information, you will be prosecuted.
   b. If you file and do not provide fraudulent information, you will not be prosecuted.
   c. If you are not prosecuted, you filed or did not provide fraudulent information.

75. a. I'm leaving, and Tom is relieved or Sue is relieved.
   b. I'm leaving, and it is false that Tom and Sue are not relieved.
   c. If I'm leaving, then Tom is relieved or Sue is relieved.

76. a. You play at least three instruments, and if you have a master's degree in music then you are eligible.
   b. You are eligible, if and only if you have a master's degree in music and play at least three instruments.
   c. You play at least three instruments, and if you are not eligible then you do not have a master's degree in music.

• Practice Plus

In Exercises 77–80, express each statement in "if … then" form. (More than one correct wording in "if … then" form is possible.) Then write the statement's converse, inverse, contrapositive, and negation.

77. No pain is sufficient for no gain.

78. Not observing the speed limit is necessary for getting a speeding ticket.

79. Being neither hedonistic nor ascetic are necessary for following Buddha's "Middle Way."

80. Going into heat and not finding a mate are sufficient for a female ferrat's death.

In Exercises 81–84, write the negation of each statement. Express each negation in a form such that the symbol ~ negates only simple statements.

81. $p \rightarrow (r \wedge \sim s)$ **82.** $p \rightarrow (\sim r \vee s)$

83. $p \wedge (r \rightarrow \sim s)$ **84.** $p \vee (\sim r \rightarrow s)$

• Application Exercises

In the United States, 28 different last names comprise 10% of the entire population. The bar graph shows the top five last names and the percentage of the U.S. population that has each of these names.

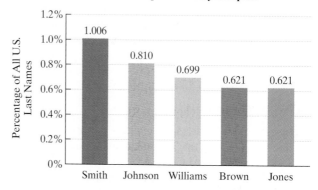

Top Five Last Names and the Percentage of the U.S. Population They Comprise

Source: Russell Ash, The Top 10 of Everything 2006

In Exercises 85–92,
   a. Use the information given by the graph to determine the truth value of the compound statement.
   b. Write the compound statement's negation.
   c. Use the information given by the graph to determine the truth value of the negation in part (b).

85. Smith comprises 1.006% and Johnson comprises 0.699%.

86. Smith comprises 1.006% and Williams comprises 0.810%.

87. Brown comprises 0.699% or Williams does not comprise 0.621%.

88. Jones comprises 0.699% or Johnson does not comprise 1.006%.

89. If Brown does not comprise 0.621%, then Jones does not comprise 0.621%.

90. If Jones does not comprise 0.621%, then Brown does not comprise 0.621%.

91. Smith is the top name and comprises 1.006%, or Johnson does not comprise 0.810%.

92. Johnson is the top name or comprises 0.810%, and Smith does not comprise 1.6%.

• Writing in Mathematics

93. What are equivalent statements?

94. Describe how to determine if two statements are equivalent.

95. Describe how to obtain the contrapositive of a conditional statement.

96. Describe how to obtain the converse and the inverse of a conditional statement.

97. Give an example of a conditional statement that is true, but whose converse and inverse are not necessarily true. Try to make the statement somewhat different from the conditional statements that you have encountered throughout this section. Explain why the converse and the inverse that you wrote are not necessarily true.

98. Explain how to write the negation of a conditional statement.

99. Explain how to write the negation of a conjunction.

100. Give an example of a disjunction that is true, even though one of its component statements is false. Then write the negation of the disjunction and explain why the negation is false.

101. Read the Blitzer Bonus on page 158. The Dormouse's last statement is the setup for a joke. The punchline, delivered by the Hatter to the Dormouse, is, "For you, it's the same thing." Explain the joke. What does this punchline have to do with the difference between a conditional and a biconditional statement?

• Critical Thinking Exercises

102. Which one of the following is true?

a. $\sim q \to (p \land r)$ is equivalent to $\sim(p \lor r) \to q$.

b. The inverse of a statement's converse is the statement's contrapositive.

c. A conditional statement can sometimes be true if its contrapositive is false.

d. A conditional statement can never be false if its converse is true.

103. Write the negation for the following conjunction:

We will neither replace nor repair the roof, and we will sell the house.

104. Write the contrapositive and the negation for the following statement:

Some people eating Turkey is necessary for it to be Thanksgiving.

• Group Exercise

105. Can you think of an advertisement in which the person using a product is extremely attractive or famous? It is true that if you are this attractive or famous person, then you use the product. (Or at least pretend, for monetary gain, that you use the product!) In order to get you to buy the product, here is what the advertisers would *like* you to believe: If I use this product, then I will be just like this attractive or famous person. This, the converse, is not necessarily true and, for most of us, is unfortunately false. Each group member should find an example of this kind of deceptive advertising to share with the other group members.

SECTION 3.6 • ARGUMENTS AND TRUTH TABLES

O B J E C T I V E S

1. Use truth tables to determine validity.

2. Recognize and use forms of valid and invalid arguments.

A noted criminal case in 1995 involved Lyle and Erik Menendez, who shot and killed their parents. Although everyone agreed that the brothers committed the crime, it took two trials before they were convicted. The *arguments* in the trial centered around the boys' motivation: Was the killing a premeditated act by two children hoping to receive an inheritance, or was it an act motivated by years of abuse and a desperate sense of helplessness and rage?

> 1 | Use truth tables to determine validity.

An **argument** consists of two parts: the given statements, called the **premises**, and a **conclusion**. Here's the prosecutor's argument from the Menendez brothers' criminal case:

Premise 1: If children murder their parents in cold blood, they deserve to be punished to the full extent of the law.

Premise 2: These children murdered their parents in cold blood.

Conclusion: Therefore, these children deserve to be punished to the full extent of the law.

(*Source:* Sherry Diestler, *Becoming a Critical Thinker, Fourth Edition,* Prentice Hall, 2005)

It appears that if the premises are true, then the jurors must decide to punish the brothers to the full extent of the law. The true premises force the conclusion to be true, making this an example of a *valid argument*.

> ### DEFINITION OF A VALID ARGUMENT
> An argument is **valid** if the conclusion is true whenever the premises are assumed to be true. An argument that is not valid is said to be an **invalid argument**, also called a **fallacy**.

Truth tables can be used to test validity. We begin by writing the argument in symbolic form. Let's do this for the prosecutor's argument in the Menendez case. Represent each simple statement with a letter:

p: Children murder their parents in cold blood.

q: They deserve to be punished to the full extent of the law.

Now we write the two premises and the conclusion in symbolic form:

Premise 1: $p \rightarrow q$ If children murder their parents in cold blood, they deserve to be punished to the full extent of the law.

Premise 2: p <u>These children murdered their parents in cold blood.</u>

Conclusion: $\therefore q$ Therefore, these children need to be punished to the full extent of the law.

(The three-dot triangle, $\therefore$, is read "therefore.")

To decide whether this argument is valid, we rewrite it as a conditional statement that has the following form:

$$[(p \rightarrow q) \land p] \rightarrow q.$$

If premise 1 and premise 2,   then   conclusion.

At this point, we can determine whether the conjunction of the premises implies that the conclusion is true for all possible truth values for *p* and *q*. We construct a truth table for the statement

$$[(p \rightarrow q) \land p] \rightarrow q.$$

If the final column in the truth table for $[(p \rightarrow q) \land p] \rightarrow q$ is true in every case, then the statement is a tautology and the argument is valid. If the conditional statement in the last column is false in at least one case, then the statement is not a tautology, and the argument is invalid. The truth table is shown below.

p	*q*	$p \rightarrow q$	$(p \rightarrow q) \land p$	$[(p \rightarrow q) \land p] \rightarrow q$
T	T	T	T	T
T	F	F	F	T
F	T	T	F	T
F	F	T	F	T

The final column in the table is true in every case. The conditional statement is a tautology. This means that the true premises imply the conclusion. The conclusion necessarily follows from the premises. Therefore, the argument is valid.

The form of the prosecutor's argument in the Menendez case

$$p \rightarrow q$$
$$\underline{p}$$
$$\therefore q$$

is called **direct reasoning**. All arguments that have the direct reasoning form are valid regardless of the English statements that *p* and *q* represent.

Here's a step-by-step procedure to test the validity of an argument using truth tables:

> ### TESTING THE VALIDITY OF AN ARGUMENT WITH A TRUTH TABLE
> 1. Use a letter to represent each simple statement in the argument.
> 2. Express the premises and the conclusion symbolically.
> 3. Write a symbolic conditional statement of the form
>
> $$[(\text{premise 1}) \wedge (\text{premise 2}) \wedge \cdots \wedge (\text{premise } n)] \to \text{conclusion},$$
>
>   where n is the number of premises.
> 4. Construct a truth table for the conditional statement in step 3.
> 5. If the final column of the truth table has all trues, the conditional statement is a tautology and the argument is valid. If the final column does not have all trues, the conditional statement is not a tautology and the argument is invalid.

EXAMPLE 1   DID THE PICKIEST LOGICIAN IN THE GALAXY FOUL UP?

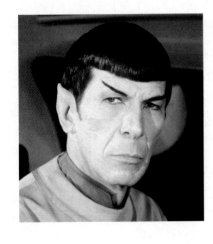

In an episode of the television series *Star Trek*, the starship *Enterprise* is hit by an ion storm, causing the power to go out. Captain Kirk wonders if Mr. Scott, the engineer, is aware of the problem. Mr. Spock, the paragon of extraterrestrial intelligence, replies, "If Mr. Scott is still with us, the power should be on momentarily." Moments later, the ship's power comes on and Spock arches his Vulcan brow: "Ah, Mr. Scott is still with us."

Spock's logic can be expressed in the form of an argument:

> If Mr. Scott is still with us, then the power will come on.
>
> The power comes on.
>
> Therefore, Mr. Scott is still with us.

Determine whether this argument is valid or invalid.

SOLUTION

Step 1. Use a letter to represent each simple statement in the argument. We introduce the following representations:

p: Mr. Scott is still with us.

q: The power will come on.

Step 2. Express the premises and the conclusion symbolically.

$p \to q$	If Mr. Scott is still with us, then the power will come on.
q	The power comes on.
$\therefore p$	Mr. Scott is still with us.

Step 3. Write a symbolic statement of the form

$$[(\textbf{premise 1}) \wedge (\textbf{premise 2})] \to \textbf{conclusion}.$$

The symbolic statement is

$$[(p \to q) \wedge q] \to p.$$

Step 4. Construct a truth table for the conditional statement in step 3.

p	q	$p \to q$	$(p \to q) \wedge q$	$[(p \to q) \wedge q] \to p$
T	T	T	T	T
T	F	F	F	T
F	T	T	T	F
F	F	T	F	T

Step 5. Use the truth values in the final column to determine if the argument is valid or invalid. The entries in the final column of the truth table are not all true, so the conditional statement is not a tautology. Spock's argument is invalid, or a fallacy.

The form of the argument in Spock's logical foul-up

$$p \rightarrow q$$
$$\underline{q}$$
$$\therefore p$$

is called the **fallacy of the converse**. It should remind you that a conditional is not equivalent to its converse. All arguments that have this form are invalid regardless of the English statements that p and q represent.

You may recall that a conditional statement is not equivalent to its inverse. Another invalid form of an argument is called the **fallacy of the inverse**:

$$p \rightarrow q$$
$$\underline{\sim p}$$
$$\therefore \sim q.$$

An example of such a fallacy is "If I study, I pass. I do not study. Therefore, I do not pass." For most students, the conclusion is true, but it does not have to be. If an argument is invalid, then the conclusion is not necessarily true. This, however, does not mean that the conclusion must be false.

 Use a truth table to determine whether the following argument is valid or invalid:

The United States must energetically support the development of solar-powered cars or suffer increasing atmospheric pollution.
The United States must not suffer increasing atmospheric pollution.
Therefore, the United States must energetically support the development of solar-powered cars.

EXAMPLE 2 DETERMINING VALIDITY WITH A TRUTH TABLE

Determine whether the following argument is valid or invalid:

"I can't have anything more to do with the operation. If I did, I'd have to lie to the Ambassador. And I can't do that."

— Henry Bromell, "I Know Your Heart, Marco Polo," *The New Yorker*

SOLUTION We can express the argument as follows:

If I had anything more to do with the operation, I'd have to lie to the Ambassador.
I can't lie to the Ambassador.
Therefore, I can't have anything more to do with the operation.

Step 1. Use a letter to represent each statement in the argument. We introduce the following representations:

p: I have more to do with the operation.

q: I have to lie to the Ambassador.

Step 2. Express the premises and the conclusion symbolically.

$p \rightarrow q$ If I had anything more to do with the operation, I'd have to lie to the Ambassador.

$\underline{\sim q}$ I can't lie to the Ambassador.

$\therefore \sim p$ Therefore, I can't have anything more to do with the operation.

Step 3. Write a symbolic statement of the form

$$[(\textbf{premise 1}) \wedge (\textbf{premise 2})] \rightarrow \textbf{conclusion}.$$

The symbolic statement is

$$[(p \rightarrow q) \wedge \sim q] \rightarrow \sim p.$$

Step 4. Construct a truth table for the conditional statement in step 3.

p	q	$p \rightarrow q$	$\sim q$	$(p \rightarrow q) \wedge \sim q$	$\sim p$	$[(p \rightarrow q) \wedge \sim q] \rightarrow \sim p$
T	T	T	F	F	F	T
T	F	F	T	F	F	T
F	T	T	F	F	T	T
F	F	T	T	T	T	T

Step 5. Use the truth values in the final column to determine if the argument is valid or invalid. The entries in the final column of the truth table are all true, so the conditional statement is a tautology. The given argument is valid.

The form of the argument in Example 2

$$p \rightarrow q$$
$$\underline{\sim q}$$
$$\therefore \sim p$$

should remind you that a conditional statement is equivalent to its contrapositive:

$$p \rightarrow q \equiv \sim q \rightarrow \sim p.$$

The form of this argument is called **contrapositive reasoning**.

 Use a truth table to determine whether the following argument is valid or invalid:

> I study for 5 hours or I fail.
> <u>I did not study for 5 hours.</u>
> Therefore, I failed.

EXAMPLE 3	THE DEFENSE ATTORNEY'S ARGUMENT AT THE MENENDEZ TRIAL

The defense attorney at the Menendez trial admitted that the brothers murdered their parents. However, she presented the following argument that resulted in a different conclusion about sentencing:

> If children murder parents because they fear abuse, there are mitigating circumstances to the murder.
> <u>If there are mitigating circumstances, then children deserve a lighter sentence.</u>
> Therefore, if children murder parents because they fear abuse, they deserve a lighter sentence.

(*Source*: Sherry Diestler, *Becoming a Critical Thinker, Fourth Edition*, Prentice Hall, 2005)

Determine whether this argument is valid or invalid.

SOLUTION

Step 1. Use a letter to represent each statement in the argument. We introduce the following representations:

p: Children murder parents because they fear abuse.

q: There are mitigating circumstances to the murder.

r: Children deserve a lighter sentence.

Step 2. **Express the premises and the conclusion symbolically.**

$p \rightarrow q$ If children murder parents because they fear abuse, there are mitigating circumstances to the murder.

$q \rightarrow r$ If there are mitigating circumstances, then children deserve a lighter sentence.

$\therefore p \rightarrow r$ Therefore, if children murder parents because they fear abuse, they deserve a lighter sentence.

Step 3. **Write a symbolic statement of the form**

$$[(\textbf{premise 1}) \wedge (\textbf{premise 2})] \rightarrow \textbf{conclusion}.$$

The symbolic statement is

$$[(p \rightarrow q) \wedge (q \rightarrow r)] \rightarrow (p \rightarrow r).$$

Step 4. **Construct a truth table for the conditional statement in step 3.**

p	q	r	$p \rightarrow q$	$q \rightarrow r$	$p \rightarrow r$	$(p \rightarrow q) \wedge (q \rightarrow r)$	$[(p \rightarrow q) \wedge (q \rightarrow r)] \rightarrow (p \rightarrow r)$
T	T	T	T	T	T	T	T
T	T	F	T	F	F	F	T
T	F	T	F	T	T	F	T
T	F	F	F	T	F	F	T
F	T	T	T	T	T	T	T
F	T	F	T	F	T	F	T
F	F	T	T	T	T	T	T
F	F	F	T	T	T	T	T

Step 5. **Use the truth values in the final column to determine if the argument is valid or invalid.** The entry in each of the eight rows in the final column of the truth table is true, so the conditional statement is a tautology. The defense attorney's argument is valid.

The form of the defense attorney's argument

$$p \rightarrow q$$
$$q \rightarrow r$$
$$\therefore p \rightarrow r$$

is called **transitive reasoning**. If p implies q and q implies r, then p must imply r. Because $p \rightarrow r$ is a valid conclusion, the contrapositive, $\sim r \rightarrow \sim p$, is also a valid conclusion. Not necessarily true are the converse, $r \rightarrow p$, and the inverse, $\sim p \rightarrow \sim r$.

 Use a truth table to determine whether the following argument is valid or invalid:

If you lower the fat in your diet, you lower your cholesterol.

If you lower your cholesterol, you reduce the risk of heart disease.

Therefore, if you do not lower the fat in your diet, you do not reduce the risk of heart disease.

We have seen two valid arguments that resulted in very different conclusions. The prosecutor in the Menendez case concluded that the brothers needed to be punished to the full extent of the law. The defense attorney concluded that they deserved a lighter sentence. This illustrates that the conclusion of a valid argument is true *relative to the premises*. The conclusion may follow from the premises, although one or more of the premises may not be true.

A valid argument with true premises is called a **sound argument**. The conclusion of a sound argument is true relative to the premises, but it is also true as a separate statement removed from the premises. When an argument is sound, its conclusion represents perfect certainty. Knowing how to assess the validity and soundness of arguments is a very important skill that will enable you to avoid being fooled into thinking that something is proven with certainty when it is not.

Table 3.17 contains the standard forms of commonly used valid and invalid arguments. If an English argument translates into one of these forms, you can immediately determine whether or not it is valid without using a truth table.

2 | Recognize and use forms of valid and invalid arguments.

TABLE 3.17 STANDARD FORMS OF ARGUMENTS

Valid Arguments

Direct Reasoning	Contrapositive Reasoning	Disjunctive Reasoning	Transitive Reasoning
$p \rightarrow q$ p $\therefore q$	$p \rightarrow q$ $\sim q$ $\therefore \sim p$	$p \vee q$ $\quad$ $p \vee q$ $\sim p$ $\quad$ $\sim q$ $\therefore q$ $\quad$ $\therefore p$	$p \rightarrow q$ $q \rightarrow r$ $\therefore p \rightarrow r$ $\therefore \sim r \rightarrow \sim p$

Invalid Arguments

Fallacy of the Converse	Fallacy of the Inverse	Misuse of Disjunctive Reasoning	Misuse of Transitive Reasoning
$p \rightarrow q$ q $\therefore p$	$p \rightarrow q$ $\sim p$ $\therefore \sim q$	$p \vee q$ $\quad$ $p \vee q$ p $\quad$ q $\therefore \sim q$ $\quad$ $\therefore \sim p$	$p \rightarrow q$ $q \rightarrow r$ $\therefore r \rightarrow p$ $\therefore \sim p \rightarrow \sim r$

EXAMPLE 4 DETERMINING VALIDITY WITHOUT TRUTH TABLES

Determine whether each argument is valid or invalid. Identify any sound arguments.

a. There is no need for surgery. I know this because if there is a tumor then there is need for surgery, but there is no tumor.

b. The emergence of democracy is a cause for hope or environmental problems will overshadow any promise of a bright future. Because environmental problems will overshadow any promise of a bright future, it follows that the emergence of democracy is not a cause for hope.

c. If evidence of the defendant's DNA is found at the crime scene, we can connect him with the crime. If we can connect him with the crime, we can have him stand trial. Therefore, if the defendant's DNA is found at the crime scene, we can have him stand trial.

SOLUTION

a. We introduce the following representations:

p: There is a tumor.
q: There is need for surgery.

We express the premises and conclusion symbolically.

If there is a tumor then there is need for surgery.	$p \rightarrow q$
There is no tumor.	$\sim p$
Therefore, there is no need for surgery.	$\therefore \sim q$

The argument is in the form of the fallacy of the inverse. Therefore, the argument is invalid.

b. We introduce the following representations:

   p: The emergence of democracy is a cause for hope.

   q: Environmental problems will overshadow any promise of a bright future.

We express the premises and conclusion symbolically.

The emergence of democracy is a cause for hope or environmental problems will overshadow any promise of a bright future.	$p \lor q$
Environmental problems will overshadow any promise of a bright future.	q
Therefore, the emergence of democracy is not a cause for hope.	$\therefore \sim p$

The argument is in a form that represents a misuse of disjunctive reasoning. Therefore, the argument is invalid.

c. We introduce the following representations:

   p: Evidence of the defendant's DNA is found at the crime scene.

   q: We can connect him with the crime.

   r: We can have him stand trial.

The argument can now be expressed symbolically.

If evidence of the defendant's DNA is found at the crime scene, we can connect him with the crime.	$p \rightarrow q$
If we can connect him with the crime, we can have him stand trial.	$q \rightarrow r$
Therefore, if the defendant's DNA is found at the crime scene, we can have him stand trial.	$\therefore \ p \rightarrow r$

The argument is in the form of transitive reasoning. Therefore, the argument is valid. Furthermore, the premises appear to be true statements, so this is a sound argument.

○

 Determine whether each argument is valid or invalid.

a. The emergence of democracy is a cause for hope or environmental problems will overshadow any promise of a bright future. Environmental problems will not overshadow any promise of a bright future. Therefore, the emergence of democracy is a cause for hope.

b. If the defendant's DNA is found at the crime scene, then we can have him stand trial. He is standing trial. Consequently, we found evidence of his DNA at the crime scene.

c. If you mess up, your self-esteem goes down. If your self-esteem goes down, everything else falls apart. So, if you mess up, everything else falls apart.

EXAMPLE 5   NIXON'S RESIGNATION

"The decision of the Supreme Court in *U.S. v. Nixon* (1974), handed down the first day of the Judiciary Committee's final debate, was critical. If the President defied the order, he would be impeached. If he obeyed the order, it was increasingly apparent he would be impeached on the evidence."

—Victoria Schuck, "Watergate," *The Key Reporter*

Richard Nixon's resignation on August 8, 1974, was the sixth anniversary of the day he had triumphantly accepted his party's nomination for his first term as president.

Based on this information, we can formulate the following argument:

> If Nixon did not obey the Supreme Court order, he would be impeached.
>
> If Nixon obeyed the Supreme Court order, he would be impeached.
>
> Therefore, Nixon's impeachment was certain.

Determine whether this argument is valid or invalid.

SOLUTION

Step 1. Use a letter to represent each simple statement in the argument. We introduce the following representations:

p: Nixon obeys the Supreme Court order.

q: Nixon is impeached.

Step 2. Express the premises and the conclusion symbolically.

$\sim p \rightarrow q$	If Nixon did not obey the Supreme Court order, he would be impeached.
$p \rightarrow q$	If Nixon obeyed the Supreme Court order, he would be impeached.
$\therefore q$	Therefore, Nixon's impeachment was certain.

Because this argument is not in the form of a recognizable valid or invalid argument, we will use a truth table to determine validity.

Step 3. Write a symbolic statement of the form

$$[(\textbf{premise 1}) \wedge (\textbf{premise 2})] \rightarrow \textbf{conclusion}.$$

The symbolic statement is

$$[(\sim p \rightarrow q) \wedge (p \rightarrow q)] \rightarrow q.$$

Step 4. Construct a truth table for the conditional statement in step 3.

p q	$\sim p$	$\sim p \rightarrow q$	$p \rightarrow q$	$(\sim p \rightarrow q) \wedge (p \rightarrow q)$	$[(\sim p \rightarrow q) \wedge (p \rightarrow q)] \rightarrow q$
T T	F	T	T	T	T
T F	F	T	F	F	T
F T	T	T	T	T	T
F F	T	F	T	F	T

Step 5. Use the truth values in the final column to determine if the argument is valid or invalid. The entries in the final column of the truth table are all true, so the conditional statement is a tautology. Thus, the given argument is valid. Because the premises are true statements, this is a sound argument, with impeachment a certainty. In a 16-minute broadcast on August 8, 1974, Richard Nixon yielded to the inevitability of the argument's conclusion and, staring sadly into the cameras, announced his resignation.

○

 Determine whether the following argument is valid or invalid:

> If people are good, laws are not needed to prevent wrongdoing.
>
> If people are not good, laws will not succeed in preventing wrongdoing.
>
> Therefore, laws are not needed to prevent wrongdoing or laws will not succeed in preventing wrongdoing.

A **logical** or **valid conclusion** is one that forms a valid argument when it follows a given set of premises. Suppose that the premises of an English argument translate into any one of the symbolic forms of premises for the valid arguments in Table 3.17 on page 172. The symbolic conclusion can be used to find a valid English conclusion. Example 6 shows how this is done.

EXAMPLE 6   DRAWING A LOGICAL CONCLUSION

Draw a valid conclusion from the following premises:

> If all people have the same idea of what is humorous, then no jokes bomb.
> Some jokes bomb.

SOLUTION

Let p be: All people have the same idea of what is humorous.
Let q be: No jokes bomb.

The form of the premises is

$$p \rightarrow q \quad \text{If all people have the same idea of what is humorous, then no jokes bomb.}$$

$$\underline{\sim q} \quad \text{Some jokes bomb. (Recall that the negation of "no" is "some.")}$$

$$\therefore \ ?$$

The conclusion $\sim p$ is valid because it forms the contrapositive reasoning of a valid argument when it follows the given premises. The conclusion $\sim p$ translates as

> Not all people have the same idea of what is humorous.

Because the negation of "all" is "some ... not," we can equivalently conclude that

> Some people do not have the same idea of what is humorous.

In the context of this discussion, *some* means *at least two*.

Draw a valid conclusion from the following premises:

> If all schools across the country are reexamining their educational objectives, then major educational reform is a national goal. Major educational reform is not a national goal.

E X E R C I S E   S E T   3 . 6

• Practice Exercises

In Exercises 1–14, use a truth table to determine whether the symbolic form of the argument is valid or invalid.

1. $p \rightarrow q$
$\underline{\sim p}$
$\therefore \sim q$

2. $p \rightarrow q$
$\underline{\sim p}$
$\therefore q$

3. $p \rightarrow \sim q$
$\underline{q}$
$\therefore \sim p$

4. $\sim p \rightarrow q$
$\underline{\sim q}$
$\therefore p$

5. $p \wedge \sim q$
$\underline{p}$
$\therefore \sim q$

6. $\sim p \vee q$
$\underline{p}$
$\therefore q$

7. $p \rightarrow q$
$\underline{q \rightarrow p}$
$\therefore p \wedge q$

8. $(p \rightarrow q) \wedge (q \rightarrow p)$
$\underline{p}$
$\therefore p \vee q$

9. $p \rightarrow q$
$\underline{q \rightarrow r}$
$\therefore r \rightarrow p$

10. $p \rightarrow q$
$\underline{q \rightarrow r}$
$\therefore \sim p \rightarrow \sim r$

11. $p \rightarrow q$
$\underline{q \wedge r}$
$\therefore p \vee r$

12. $\sim p \wedge q$
$\underline{p \leftrightarrow r}$
$\therefore p \wedge r$

13. $p \leftrightarrow q$
$\underline{q \rightarrow r}$
$\therefore \sim r \rightarrow \sim p$

14. $q \rightarrow \sim p$
$\underline{q \wedge r}$
$\therefore r \rightarrow p$

In Exercises 15–42, translate each argument into symbolic form. Then determine whether the argument is valid or invalid. You may use a truth table or, if applicable, compare the argument's symbolic form to a standard valid or invalid form. (You can ignore differences in past, present, and future tense.)

15. If it is cold, my motorcycle will not start.
$\underline{\text{My motorcycle started.}}$
$\therefore$ It is not cold.

16. If a metrorail system is not in operation, there are traffic delays.

Over the past year there have been no traffic delays.

∴ Over the past year a metrorail system has been in operation.

17. There must be a dam or there is flooding.

This year there is flooding.

∴ This year there is no dam.

18. You must eat well or you will not be healthy.

I eat well.

∴ I am healthy.

19. If we close the door, then there is less noise.

There is less noise.

∴ We closed the door.

20. If an argument is in the form of the fallacy of the inverse, then it is invalid.

This argument is invalid.

∴ This argument is in the form of the fallacy of the inverse.

21. If he was disloyal, his dismissal was justified.

If he was loyal, his dismissial was justified.

∴ His dismissal was justified.

22. If I tell you I cheated, I'm miserable.

If I don't tell you I cheated, I'm miserable.

∴ I'm miserable.

23. We criminalize drugs or we damage the future of young people.

We will not damage the future of young people.

∴ We criminalize drugs.

24. He is intelligent or an overachiever.

He is not intelligent.

∴ He is an overachiever.

25. If all people obey the law, then no jails are needed.

Some people do not obey the law.

∴ Some jails are needed.

26. If all people obey the law, then no jails are needed.

Some jails are needed.

∴ Some people do not obey the law.

27. If I'm tired, I'm edgy.

If I'm edgy, I'm nasty.

∴ If I'm tired, I'm nasty.

28. If I am at the beach, then I swim in the ocean.

If I swim in the ocean, then I feel refreshed.

∴ If I am at the beach, then I feel refreshed.

29. If I'm tired, I'm edgy.

If I'm edgy, I'm nasty.

∴ If I'm nasty, I'm tired.

30. If I'm at the beach, then I swim in the ocean.

If I swim in the ocean, then I feel refreshed.

∴ If I'm not at the beach, then I don't feel refreshed.

31. If Tim and Janet play, then the team wins.

Tim played and the team did not win.

∴ Janet did not play.

32. If *The Graduate* and *Midnight Cowboy* are shown, then the performance is sold out.

Midnight Cowboy was shown and the performance was not sold out.

∴ *The Graduate* was not shown.

33. If it rains or snows, then I read.

I am not reading.

∴ It is neither raining nor snowing.

34. If I am tired or hungry, I cannot concentrate.

I can concentrate.

∴ I am neither tired nor hungry.

35. If it rains or snows, then I read.

I am reading.

∴ It is raining or snowing.

36. If I am tired or hungry, I cannot concentrate.

I cannot concentrate.

∴ I am tired or hungry.

37. If it is hot and humid, I complain.

It is not hot or it is not humid.

∴ I am not complaining.

38. If I watch *Schindler's List* and *Brokeback Mountain*, I am aware of the destructive nature of intolerance.

Today I did not watch *Schindler's List* or I did not watch *Brokeback Mountain.*

∴ Today I am not aware of the destructive nature of intolerance.

39. If you tell me what I already understand, you do not enlarge my understanding.

If you tell me something that I do not understand, then your remarks are unintelligible to me.

∴ Whatever you tell me does not enlarge my understanding or is unintelligible to me.

40. If we are to have peace, we must not encourage the competitive spirit.

If we are to make progress, we must encourage the competitive spirit.

∴ We do not have peace and we do not make progress.

41. If some journalists learn about the invasion, the newspapers will print the news.

If the newspapers print the news, the invasion will not be a secret.

The invasion was a secret.

∴ No journalists learned about the invasion.

42. If some journalists learn about the invasion, the newspapers will print the news.

If the newspapers print the news, the invasion will not be a secret.

No journalists learned about the invasion.

∴ The invasion was a secret.

In Exercises 43–50, use the standard forms of valid arguments to draw a valid conclusion from the given premises.

43. If a person is a chemist, then that person has a college degree.

My best friend does not have a college degree.

Therefore, …

44. If the Westway Expressway is not in operation, automobile traffic makes the East Side Highway look like a parking lot.

On June 2, the Westway Expressway was completely shut down because of an overturned truck.

Therefore, …

45. The writers of *My Mother the Car* were told by the network to improve their scripts or be dropped from prime time.

The writers of *My Mother the Car* did not improve their scripts.

Therefore, …

46. You exercise or you do not feel energized.

I do not exercise.

Therefore, …

47. If all electricity is off, then no lights work.

Some lights work.

Therefore, …

48. If all houses meet the hurricane code, then none of them are destroyed by a category 4 hurricane.

Some houses were destroyed by Andrew, a category 4 hurricane.

Therefore, …

49. If I vacation in Paris, I eat French pastries.

If I eat French pastries, I gain weight.

Therefore, …

50. If I am a full-time student, I cannot work.

If I cannot work, I cannot afford a rental apartment costing more than $500 per month.

Therefore, …

• Practice Plus

In Exercises 51–58, translate each argument into symbolic form. Then determine whether the argument is valid or invalid.

51. If it was any of your business, I would have invited you. It is not, and so I did not.

52. If it was any of your business, I would have invited you. I did, and so it is.

53. It is the case that $x < 5$ or $x > 8$, but $x \geq 5$, so $x > 8$.

54. It is the case that $x < 3$ or $x > 10$, but $x \leq 10$, so $x < 3$.

55. Having a college degree is necessary for obtaining a teaching position. You have a college degree, so you have a teaching position.

56. Having a college degree is necessary for obtaining a teaching position. You do not obtain a teaching position, so you do not have a college degree.

57. "I do know that this pencil exists; but I could not know this if Hume's principles were true. Therefore, Hume's principles, one or both of them, are false."

— G. E. Moore, *Some Main Problems of Philosophy*

58. (In this exercise, determine if the argument is sound, valid but not sound, or invalid.)

If an argument is invalid, it does not produce truth, whereas a valid unsound argument also does not produce truth. Arguments are invalid or they are valid but unsound. Therefore, no arguments produce truth.

• Application Exercises

Exercises 59–60 illustrate arguments that have appeared in cartoons. Each argument is restated below the cartoon. Translate the argument into symbolic form and then determine whether it is valid or invalid.

59.

Peanuts reprinted by permission of United Feature Syndicate, Inc.

If you do not know how to read, you cannot read *War and Peace*. If you cannot read *War and Peace*, then Leo Tolstoy will hate you. Therefore, if you do not know how to read, Leo Tolstoy will hate you.

60.

Betty by Gary Delainey and Gery Rasmussen.
Reprinted by permission of Newspaper Enterprise Association, Inc.

If I say I'm in denial, then I'm not in denial. I am saying that I'm in denial, so I'm not in denial at all.

61. Conservative commentator Rush Limbaugh directed the passage on the next page at liberals and the way they think about crime.

Of course, liberals will argue that these actions [contemporary youth crime] can be laid at the foot of socioeconomic inequities, or poverty. However, the Great Depression caused a level of poverty unknown to exist in America today, and yet I have been unable to find any accounts of crime waves sweeping our large cities. Let the liberals chew on that.

(See, I Told You So, p. 83)

Limbaugh's passage can be expressed in the form of an argument:

> If poverty causes crime, then crime waves would have swept American cities during the Great Depression.
> Crime waves did not sweep American cities during the Great Depression.
> ∴ Poverty does not cause crime. (Liberals are wrong.)

Translate this argument into symbolic form and determine whether it is valid or invalid.

62. In the following passage, Martin Luther King, Jr. presents an argument with the conclusion "Segregation statutes are unjust." Use two premises, one a conditional statement and the other a simple statement, to rewrite King's argument in the format used throughout this section. Then determine if the argument is sound, valid but not sound, or invalid.

> *"Any law that uplifts human personality is just. Any law that degrades human personality is unjust. All segregation statutes are unjust because segregation distorts the soul and damages the personality. It gives the segregator a false sense of superiority, and the segregated a false sense of inferiority."*

—Martin Luther King, Jr., "Letter from a Birmingham Jail"

In addition to the forms of invalid arguments, fallacious reasoning occurs in everyday logic. Some people use the fallacies described below to intentionally deceive. Others use fallacies innocently; they are not even aware they are using them. Match each description below with the example from Exercises 63–74 that illustrates the fallacy. The matching is one-to-one.

Common Fallacies in Everyday Reasoning

a. *The* **fallacy of emotion** *consists of appealing to emotion (pity, force, etc.) in an argument.*

b. *The* **fallacy of inappropriate authority** *consists of claiming that a statement is true because a person cited as an authority says it's true or because most people believe it's true.*

c. *The* **fallacy of hasty generalization** *occurs when an inductive generalization is made on the basis of a few observations or an unrepresentative sample.*

d. *The* **fallacy of questionable cause** *consists of claiming that A caused B when it is known that A occurred before B.*

e. *The* **fallacy of ambiguity** *occurs when the conclusion of an argument is based on a word or phrase that is used in two different ways in the premises.*

f. *The* **fallacy of ignorance** *consists of claiming that a statement is true simply because it has not been proven false, or vice-versa.*

g. *The* **mischaracterization fallacy** *consists of misrepresenting an opponent's position or attacking the opponent rather than that person's ideas in order to refute his or her argument.*

h. *The* **slippery slope fallacy** *occurs when an argument reasons without justification that an event will set off a series of events leading to an undesirable consequence.*

i. *The* **either/or fallacy** *mistakenly presents only two solutions to a problem, negates one of these either/or alternatives, and concludes that the other must be true.*

j. *The* **fallacy of begging the question** *assumes that the conclusion is true within the premises.*

k. *The* **fallacy of composition** *occurs when an argument moves from premises about the parts of a group to a conclusion about the whole group. It also occurs when characteristics of an entire group are mistakenly applied to parts of the group.*

l. *The* **fallacy of the complex question** *consists of drawing a conclusion from a self-incriminating question.*

63. If we allow physician-assisted suicide for those who are terminally ill and request it, it won't be long before society begins pressuring the old and infirm to get out of the way and make room for the young. Before long the government will be deciding who should live and who should die.

64. Of course there are extraterrestrials. Haven't you read that article in the *National Enquirer* about those UFOs spotted in Texas last month?

65. Either you go to college and make something of yourself, or you'll end up as an unhappy street person. You cannot be an unhappy street person, so you should go to college.

66. Scientists have not proved that AIDS cannot be transmitted through casual contact. Therefore, we should avoid a casual contact with suspected AIDS carriers.

67. Each of my three uncles smoked two packs of cigarettes every day and they all lived into their 90s. Smoking can't be that bad for your health.

68. You once cheated on tests. I know this because when I asked you if you had stopped cheating on tests, you said yes.

69. My paper is late, but I know you'll accept it because I've been sick and my parents will kill me if I flunk this course.

70. We've all heard Professor Jones tell us about how economic systems should place human need above profit. But I'm not surprised that he neglected to tell you that he's a communist who has visited Cuba twice. How can he possibly speak the truth about economic systems?

71. It's easy to see that suicide is wrong. After all, no one is ever justified in taking his or her own life.

72. The reason I hurt your arm is because you hurt me just as much by telling Dad.

73. Statistics show that nearly every heroin user started out by using marijuana. It's reasonable to conclude that smoking marijuana leads to harder drugs.

74. I know, without even looking, that question #17 on this test is difficult. This is the case because the test was made up by Professor Flunkem and Flunkem's exams are always difficult.

• Writing in Mathematics

75. Describe what is meant by a valid argument.

76. If you are given an argument in words that contains two premises and a conclusion, describe how to determine if the argument is valid or invalid.

77. Write an original argument in words for the direct reasoning form.

78. Write an original argument in words for the contrapositive reasoning form.

79. Write an original argument in words for the transitive reasoning form.

80. What is a valid conclusion?

81. Write a valid argument on one of the following questions. If you can, write valid arguments on both sides.

   a. Should the death penalty be abolished?

   b. Should *Roe v. Wade* be overturned?

   c. Should women be allowed combat roles in the military?

   d. Should drugs be legalized?

   e. Should grades be abolished?

   f. Should same-sex marriage be legalized?

• Critical Thinking Exercises

82. Write an original argument in words that has a true conclusion, yet is invalid.

83. Draw a valid conclusion from the given premises. Then use a truth table to verify your answer.

If you only spoke when spoken to and I only spoke when spoken to, then nobody would ever say anything. Some people do say things. Therefore, …

84. Translate the argument at the top of the next column into symbolic form. Then use a truth table to determine if the argument is valid or invalid.

It's wrong to smoke in public if secondary cigarette smoke is a health threat. If secondary cigarette smoke were not a health threat, the American Lung Association would not say that it is. The American Lung Association says that secondary cigarette smoke is a health threat. Therefore, it's wrong to smoke in public.

85. Draw what you believe is a valid conclusion in the form of a disjunction for the following argument. Then verify that the argument is valid for your conclusion.

> "Inevitably, the use of the placebo involved built-in contradictions. A good patient–doctor relationship is essential to the process, but what happens to that relationship when one of the partners conceals important information from the other? If the doctor tells the truth, he destroys the base on which the placebo rests. If he doesn't tell the truth, he jeopardizes a relationship built on trust."
>
> —Norman Cousins, *Anatomy of an Illness*

• Group Exercise

86. In this section, we used a variety of examples, including arguments from the Menendez trial, the inevitability of Nixon's impeachment, Spock's (fallacious) logic on *Star Trek*, and even two cartoons, to illustrate symbolic arguments.

   a. From any source that is of particular interest to you (these can be the words of someone you truly admire or a person who really gets under your skin), select a paragraph or two in which the writer argues a particular point. Rewrite the reasoning in the form of an argument using words. Then translate the argument into symbolic form and use a truth table to determine if it is valid or invalid.

   b. Each group member should share the selected passage with other people in the group. Explain how it was expressed in argument form. Then tell why the argument is valid or invalid.

SECTION 3.7 • ARGUMENTS AND EULER DIAGRAMS

OBJECTIVE

1. Use Euler diagrams to determine validity.

William Shakespeare

Leonhard Euler

He is the Shakespeare of mathematics, yet he is unknown by the general public. Most people cannot even correctly pronounce his name. The Swiss mathematician Leonhard Euler (1707–1783), whose last name rhymes with *boiler*, not *ruler*, is the most prolific mathematician in history. His collected books and papers fill some 80 volumes; Euler published an average of 800 pages of new mathematics per year over a career that spanned six decades. Euler was also an astronomer, botanist, chemist, physicist, and linguist. His productivity was not at all slowed down by the total blindness he experienced the last 17 years of his life. An equation discovered by Euler, $e^{\pi i} + 1 = 0$, connected five of the most important numbers in mathematics in a totally unexpected way.

Euler invented an elegant way to determine the validity of arguments whose premises contain the words *all*, *some*, and *no*. The technique for doing this uses geometric ideas and involves four basic diagrams, known as **Euler diagrams**. Figure 3.4 illustrates how Euler diagrams represent four quantified statements.

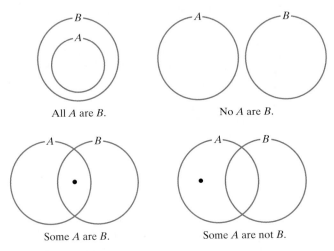

FIGURE 3.4 Euler diagrams for quantified statements

The Euler diagrams in Figure 3.4 are just like the Venn diagrams that we used in studying sets. However, there is no need to enclose the circles inside a rectangle representing a universal set. In these diagrams, circles are used to indicate relationships of premises to conclusions.

Here's a step-by-step procedure for using Euler diagrams to determine whether or not an argument is valid:

> **EULER DIAGRAMS AND ARGUMENTS**
>
> 1. Make an Euler diagram for the first premise.
> 2. Make an Euler diagram for the second premise on top of the one for the first premise.
> 3. The argument is valid if and only if every possible diagram illustrates the conclusion of the argument. If there is even *one* possible diagram that contradicts the conclusion, this indicates that the conclusion is not true in every case, so the argument is invalid.

The goal of this procedure is to produce, if possible, *a diagram that does **not** illustrate the argument's conclusion*. The method of Euler diagrams boils down to determining whether such a diagram is possible. If it is, this serves as a counterexample to the argument's conclusion, and the argument is immediately declared invalid. By contrast, if no such counterexample can be drawn, the argument is valid.

The technique of using Euler diagrams is illustrated in Examples 1–6.

EXAMPLE 1   ARGUMENTS AND EULER DIAGRAMS

Use Euler diagrams to determine whether the following argument is valid or invalid:

All people who arrive late cannot perform.

All people who cannot perform are ineligible for scholarships.

Therefore, all people who arrive late are ineligible for scholarships.

① Use Euler diagrams to determine validity.

SOLUTION

Step 1. Make an Euler diagram for the first premise. We begin by diagramming the premise

All people who arrive late cannot perform.

The region inside the smaller circle represents people who arrive late. The region inside the larger circle represents people who cannot perform.

Step 2. Make an Euler diagram for the second premise on top of the one for the first premise. We add to our previous figure the diagram for the second premise:

All people who cannot perform are ineligible for scholarships.

A third, larger, circle representing people who are ineligible for scholarships is drawn outside the circle representing people who cannot perform.

Step 3. The argument is valid if and only if every possible diagram illustrates the argument's conclusion. There is only one possible diagram. Let's see if this diagram illustrates the argument's conclusion, namely

All people who arrive late are ineligible for scholarships.

This is indeed the case because the Euler diagram shows the circle representing the people who arrive late contained within the circle of people who are ineligible for scholarships. The Euler diagram supports the conclusion and the given argument is valid.

 Use Euler diagrams to determine whether the following argument is valid or invalid:

All U.S. voters must register.

All people who register must be U.S. citizens.

Therefore, all U.S. voters are U.S. citizens.

EXAMPLE 2   ARGUMENTS AND EULER DIAGRAMS

Use Euler diagrams to determine whether the following argument is valid or invalid:

All poets appreciate language.

All writers appreciate language.

Therefore, all poets are writers.

SOLUTION

Step 1. Make an Euler diagram for the first premise. We begin by diagramming the premise

All poets appreciate language.

Up to this point, our work is similar to what we did in Example 1.

Step 2. Make an Euler diagram for the second premise on top of the one for the first premise. We add to our previous figure the diagram for the second premise:

All writers appreciate language.

A third circle representing writers must be drawn inside the circle representing people who appreciate language. There are four ways to do this.

Step 3. The argument is valid if and only if every possible diagram illustrates the argument's conclusion. The argument's conclusion is

All poets are writers.

This conclusion is not illustrated by every possible diagram shown above. One of these diagrams is repeated in the margin. This diagram shows "no poets are writers." There is no need to examine the other three diagrams.

The diagram on the left serves as a counterexample to the argument's conclusion. This means that the given argument is invalid. It would have suffed to draw only the counterexample on the left to determine that the argument is invalid.

○

CHECK POINT 2 Use Euler diagrams to determine whether the following argument is valid or invalid:

All baseball players are athletes.
All ballet dancers are athletes.
Therefore, no baseball players are ballet dancers.

●

EXAMPLE 3 ARGUMENTS AND EULER DIAGRAMS

Use Euler diagrams to determine whether the following argument is valid or invalid:

All freshmen live on campus.
No people who live on campus can own cars.
Therefore, no freshmen can own cars.

SOLUTION

Step 1. Make an Euler diagram for the first premise. The diagram for

All freshmen live on campus

is shown on the right. The region inside the smaller circle represents freshmen. The region inside the larger circle represents people who live on campus.

Step 2. Make an Euler diagram for the second premise on top of the one for the first premise. We add to our previous figure the diagram for the second premise:

No people who live on campus can own cars.

A third circle representing people who own cars is drawn outside the circle representing people who live on campus.

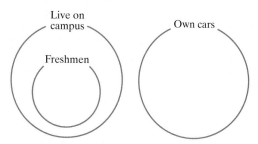

Step 3. The argument is valid if and only if every possible diagram illustrates the argument's conclusion. There is only one possible diagram. The argument's conclusion is

No freshmen can own cars.

This is supported by the diagram shown above because it shows the circle representing freshmen drawn outside the circle representing people who own cars. The Euler diagram supports the conclusion, and it is impossible to find a counterexample that does not. The given argument is valid.

 Use Euler diagrams to determine whether the following argument is valid or invalid:

All mathematicians are logical.

No poets are logical.

Therefore, no poets are mathematicians.

Let's see what happens to the validity if we reverse the second premise and the conclusion of the argument in Example 3.

EXAMPLE 4   EULER DIAGRAMS AND VALIDITY

Use Euler diagrams to determine whether the following argument is valid or invalid:

All freshmen live on campus.

No freshmen can own cars.

Therefore, no people who live on campus can own cars.

SOLUTION

Step 1. Make an Euler diagram for the first premise. We once again begin with the diagram for

All freshmen live on campus.

So far, our work is exactly the same as in the previous example.

Step 2. Make an Euler diagram for the second premise on top of the one for the first premise. We add to our previous figure the diagram for the second premise:

No freshmen can own cars.

The circle representing people who own cars is drawn outside the freshmen circle. At least two Euler diagrams, shown at the top of the next page, are possible.

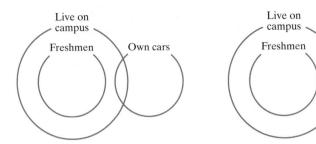

Step 3. The argument is valid if and only if every possible diagram illustrates the argument's conclusion. The argument's conclusion is

No people who live on campus can own cars.

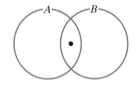

This conclusion is not supported by both diagrams shown above. The diagram that does not support the conclusion is repeated in the margin. Notice that the "live on campus" circle and the "own cars" circle intersect. This diagram serves as a counterexample to the argument's conclusion. This means that the argument is invalid. Once again, only the counterexample on the left is needed to conclude that the argument is invalid.

○

 Use Euler diagrams to determine whether the following argument is valid or invalid:

> All mathematicians are logical.
> No poets are mathematicians.
> Therefore, no poets are logical.

So far, the arguments that we have looked at have contained "all" or "no" in the premises and conclusions. The quantifier "some" is a bit trickier to work with. Because the statement "Some A are B" means there exists at least one A that is a B, we diagram this existence by showing a dot in the region where A and B intersect, illustrated in Figure 3.5.

Suppose that it is true that "Some A are not B," illustrated by the dot in Figure 3.6. This Euler diagram does not let us conclude that "Some B are not A" because there is not a dot in the part of the B circle that is not in the A circle. Conclusions with the word "some" must be shown by existence of at least one element represented by a dot in an Euler diagram.

Here is an example that shows the premise "Some A are not B" does not enable us to logically conclude that "Some B are not A."

Some U.S. citizens are not U.S. senators. (true)
∴ Some U.S. senators are not U.S. citizens. (false)

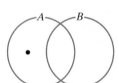

FIGURE 3.5 Some A are B.

FIGURE 3.6 Illustrated by the dot is some A are not B. We cannot validly conclude that some B are not A.

EXAMPLE 5	EULER DIAGRAMS AND THE QUANTIFIER "SOME"

Use Euler diagrams to determine whether the following argument is valid or invalid:

> All people are mortal.
> Some mortals are students.
> Therefore, some people are students.

SOLUTION

Step 1. Make an Euler diagram for the first premise.
Begin with the premise

All people are mortal.

The Euler diagram is shown on the right.

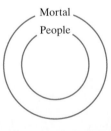

Step 2. Make an Euler diagram for the second premise on top of the one for the first premise. We add to our previous figure the diagram for the second premise:

Some mortals are students.

The circle representing students intersects the circle representing mortals. The dot in the region of intersection shows that at least one mortal is a student. Another diagram is possible, but if this serves as a counterexample then it is all we need. Let's check if it is a counterexample.

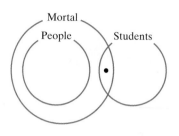

Step 3. The argument is valid if and only if every possible diagram illustrates the conclusion of the argument. The argument's conclusion is

Some people are students.

This conclusion is not supported by the Euler diagram. The diagram does not show the "people" circle and the "students" circle intersecting with a dot in the region of intersection. Although this conclusion is true in the real world, the Euler diagram serves as a counterexample that shows it does not follow from the premises. Therefore, the argument is invalid.

○

 Use Euler diagrams to determine whether the following argument is valid or invalid:

> All mathematicians are logical.
> Some poets are logical.
> Therefore, some poets are mathematicians.

Some arguments show existence without using the word "some." Instead, a particular person or thing is mentioned in one of the premises. This particular person or thing is represented by a dot. Here is an example:

All men are mortal.
Aristotle is a man.
Therefore, Aristotle is mortal.

The two premises can be represented by the following Euler diagrams:

 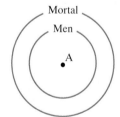

All men are mortal.   Aristotle (•) is a man.

The Euler diagram on the right uses a dot labeled A (for Aristotle). The diagram shows Aristotle (•) winding up in the "mortal" circle. The diagram supports the conclusion that Aristotle is mortal. This argument is valid.

EXAMPLE 6   AN ARGUMENT MENTIONING ONE PERSON

Use Euler diagrams to determine whether the following argument is valid or invalid:

All children love to swim.
Jeff Rouse loves to swim.
Therefore, Jeff Rouse is a child.

SOLUTION

Step 1. Make an Euler diagram for the first premise.
Begin with the premise

All children love to swim.

The Euler diagram is shown on the right.

Step 2. Make an Euler diagram for the second premise on top of the one for the first premise. We add to our previous figure the diagram for the second premise:

Jeff Rouse loves to swim.

Jeff Rouse is represented by a dot labeled J. The dot must be placed in the "love to swim" circle. At least two Euler diagrams are possible.

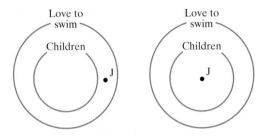

Step 3. The argument is valid if and only every possible diagram illustrates the conclusion of the argument. The argument's conclusion is

Jeff Rouse is a child.

This conclusion is not supported by the Euler diagram shown on the left. The dot representing Jeff Rouse is outside the "children" circle. Jeff Rouse might not be a child. This diagram serves as a counterexample to the argument's conclusion. The argument is invalid.

CHECK POINT 6 Use Euler diagrams to determine whether the following argument is valid or invalid:

> All mathematicians are logical.
> Euclid was logical.
> Therefore, Euclid was a mathematician.

EXERCISE SET 3.7 ●●●●●●

• Practice Exercises

In Exercises 1–24, use Euler diagrams to determine whether each argument is valid or invalid.

1. All writers appreciate language.
All poets are writers.
Therefore, all poets appreciate language.

2. All physicists are scientists.
All scientists attended college.
Therefore, all physicists attended college.

3. All clocks keep time accurately.
All time-measuring devices keep time accurately.
Therefore, all clocks are time-measuring devices.

4. All cowboys live on ranches.
All cowherders live on ranches.
Therefore, all cowboys are cowherders.

5. All insects have six legs.
No spiders have six legs.
Therefore, no spiders are insects.

6. All humans are warm-blooded.
No reptiles are warm-blooded.
Therefore, no reptiles are human.

7. All insects have six legs.
No spiders are insects.
Therefore, no spiders have six legs.

8. All humans are warm-blooded.
No reptiles are human.
Therefore, no reptiles are warm-blooded.

9. All professors are wise people.
Some wise people are actors.
Therefore, some professors are actors.

10. All comedians are funny people.
Some funny people are professors.
Therefore, some comedians are professors.

11. All professors are wise people.
Some professors are actors.
Therefore, some wise people are actors.

12. All comedians are funny people.
Some comedians are professors.
Therefore, some funny people are professors.

13. All dancers are athletes.
Savion Glover is a dancer.
Therefore, Savion Glover is an athlete.

14. All actors are artists.
Tom Hanks is an actor.
Therefore, Tom Hanks is an artist.

15. All dancers are athletes.
Savion Glover is an athlete.
Therefore, Savion Glover is a dancer.

16. All actors are artists.
Tom Hanks is an artist.
Therefore, Tom Hanks is an actor.

17. Some people enjoy reading.
Some people enjoy TV.
Therefore, some people who enjoy reading enjoy TV.

18. All thefts are immoral acts.
Some thefts are justifiable.
Therefore, some immoral acts are justifiable.

19. All dogs have fleas.
Some dogs have rabies.
Therefore, all dogs with rabies have fleas.

20. All logic problems make sense.
Some jokes make sense.
Therefore, some logic problems are jokes.

21. No blank disks contain data.
Some blank disks are formatted.
Therefore, some formatted disks do not contain data.

22. Some houses have two stories.
Some houses have air conditioning.
Therefore, some houses with air conditioning have two stories.

23. All multiples of 6 are multiples of 3.
Eight is not a multiple of 3.
Therefore, 8 is not a multiple of 6.

24. All multiples of 6 are multiples of 3.
Eight is not a multiple of 6.
Therefore, 8 is not a multiple of 3.

• Practice Plus

In Exercises 25–36, determine whether each argument is valid or invalid.

25. All natural numbers are whole numbers, all whole numbers are integers, and −4006 is not a whole number. Thus, −4006 is not an integer.

26. Some natural numbers are even, all natural numbers are whole numbers, and all whole numbers are integers. Thus, some integers are even.

27. All natural numbers are real numbers, all real numbers are complex numbers, but some complex numbers are not real numbers. The number $19 + 0i$ is a complex number, so it is not a natural number.

28. All rational numbers are real numbers, all real numbers are complex numbers, but some complex numbers are not real numbers. The number $\frac{1}{2} + 0i$ is a complex number, so it is not a rational number.

29. All A are B, all B are C, and all C are D. Thus, all A are D.

30. All A are B, no C are B, and all D are C. Thus, no A are D.

31. No A are B, some A are C, and all C are D. Thus, some D are B.

32. No A are B, some A are C, and all C are D. Thus, some D are C.

33. No A are B, no B are C, and no C are D. Thus, no A are D.

34. Some A are B, some B are C, and some C are D. Thus, some A are D.

35. All A are B, all A are C, and some B are D. Thus, some A are D.

36. Some A are B, all B are C, and some C are D. Thus, some A are D.

• Application Exercises

37. This is an excerpt from a 1967 speech in the U.S. House of Representatives by Representative Adam Clayton Powell:

> He who is without sin should cast the first stone. There is no one here who does not have a skeleton in his closet. I know, and I know them by name.

Powell's argument can be expressed as follows:

No sinner is one who should cast the first stone.
All people here are sinners.
Therefore, no person here is one who should cast the first stone.

Use an Euler diagram to determine whether the argument is valid or invalid.

38. In the *Sixth Meditation*, Descartes writes

> I first take notice here that there is a great difference between the mind and the body, in that the body, from its nature, is always divisible and the mind is completely indivisible.

Descartes's argument can be expressed as follows:

All bodies are divisible.
No minds are divisible.
Therefore, no minds are bodies.

Use an Euler diagram to determine whether the argument is valid or invalid.

39. In *Symbolic Logic*, Lewis Carroll presents the following argument:

> Babies are illogical. (All babies are illogical persons.)
> Illogical persons are despised. (All illogical persons are despised persons.)
> Nobody is despised who can manage a crocodile. (No persons who can manage crocodiles are despised persons.)
> Therefore, babies cannot manage crocodiles.

Use an Euler diagram to determine whether the argument is valid or invalid.

• Writing in Mathematics

40. Explain how to use Euler diagrams to determine whether or not an argument is valid.

41. Under what circumstances should Euler diagrams rather than truth tables be used to determine whether or not an argument is valid?

• Critical Thinking Exercises

42. Write an example of an argument with two quantified premises that is invalid but that has a true conclusion.

43. No animals that eat meat are vegetarians.
No cat is a vegetarian.
Felix is a cat.
Therefore, ...

 a. Felix is a vegetarian.

 b. Felix is not a vegetarian.

 c. Felix eats meat.

 d. All animals that do not eat meat are vegetarians.

44. Supply the missing first premise that will make this argument valid.

Some opera singers are terrible actors.
Therefore, some people who take voice lessons are terrible actors.

45. Supply the missing first premise that will make this argument valid.

All amusing people are entertaining.
Therefore, some teachers are entertaining.

●●●●●●● CHAPTER SUMMARY, REVIEW, AND TEST

● SUMMARY   DEFINITIONS AND CONCEPTS   EXAMPLES

3.1   Statements, Negations, and Quantified Statements

3.2   Compound Statements and Connectives

 a. A statement is a sentence that is either true or false, but not both simultaneously.

 b. Negations and equivalences of quantified statements are given in the following diagram. Each quantified statement's equivalent is written in parentheses below the statement. The statements diagonally opposite each other are negations.

Table 3.2, p. 112; Ex. 4, p. 112

All A are B.
(There are no A that are not B.)

No A are B.
(All A are not B.)

Some A are B.
(There exists at least one A that is a B.)

Some A are not B.
(Not all A are B.)

 c. The statements of symbolic logic and their translations are given as follows:

 • Negation

  $\sim p$: Not p. It is not true that p.

 • Conjunction

  $p \wedge q$: p and q. p but q. p yet q. p nevertheless q.

 • Disjunction

  $p \vee q$: p or q.

 • Conditional

  $p \rightarrow q$: If p, then q. q if p. p is sufficient for q. q is necessary for p. p only if q. Only if q, p.

 • Biconditional

  $p \leftrightarrow q$: p if and only if q. q if and only if p. If p then q, and if q then p. p is necessary and sufficient for q. q is necessary and sufficient for p.

Ex. 1, p. 115;
Ex. 2, p. 117;
Ex. 3, p. 117;
Ex. 4, p. 119;
Ex. 5, p. 120

d. Groupings in symbolic statements are determined as follows:

- Unless parentheses follow the negation symbol, ~, negates only the statement that immediately follows it.

- When translating symbolic statements into English, the simple statements in parentheses appear on the same side of the comma.

- If a symbolic statement appears without parentheses, group statements before and after the most dominant connective, where dominance is defined as follows:

Ex. 6, p. 121;
Ex. 7, p. 123;
Ex. 8, p. 124

1. Negation	2. Conjunction Disjunction	3. Conditional	4. Biconditional.

Least dominant   Most dominant

3.3 Truth Tables for Negation, Conjunction, and Disjunction
3.4 Truth Tables for the Conditional and the Biconditional

a. The definitions of symbolic logic are given by the truth values in the following table:

Table 3.11, p. 129;
Table 3.13, p. 130;
Ex. 1, p. 130

p q	Negation $\sim p$	Conjunction $p \wedge q$	Disjunction $p \vee q$	Conditional $p \rightarrow q$	Biconditional $p \leftrightarrow q$
T T	F	T	T	T	T
T F	F	F	T	F	F
F T	T	F	T	T	F
F F	T	F	F	T	T

Opposite truth values from p	True only when both component statements are true	False only when both component statements are false	False only when the antecedent is true and the consequent is false	True only when the component statements have the same truth value

b. A truth table for a compound statement shows when the statement is true and when it is false. The first few columns show the simple statements that comprise the compound statement and their possible truth values. The final column heading is the given compound statement. The truth values in each column are determined by looking back at appropriate columns and using one of the five definitions of symbolic logic. If a compound statement is always true, it is called a tautology.

Ex. 2, p. 132;
Ex. 3, p. 133;
Ex. 4, p. 134;
Ex. 5, p. 135;
Ex. 6, p. 136;
Ex. 1, p. 142;
Ex. 2, p. 144;
Ex. 3, p. 145;
Ex. 4, p. 147

c. To determine the truth value of a compound statement for a specific case, substitute the truth values of the simple statements into the symbolic form of the compound statement and then use the appropriate definitions.

Ex. 7, p. 138;
Ex. 5, p. 148

3.5 Equivalent Statements, Variations of Conditional Statements, and De Morgan's Laws

a. Two statements are equivalent, symbolized by $\equiv$, if they have the same truth value in every possible case.

Ex. 1, p. 152;
Ex. 2, p. 153;
Ex. 3, p. 154

b. Variations of the Conditional Statement $p \rightarrow q$
- $p \rightarrow q$ is equivalent to $\sim q \rightarrow \sim p$, the contrapositive: $p \rightarrow q \equiv \sim q \rightarrow \sim p$.
- $p \rightarrow q$ is not equivalent to $q \rightarrow p$, the converse.
- $p \rightarrow q$ is not equivalent to $\sim p \rightarrow \sim q$, the inverse.
- The negation of $p \rightarrow q$ is $p \wedge \sim q$: $\sim(p \rightarrow q) \equiv p \wedge \sim q$.

Ex. 4, p. 155;
Ex. 5, p. 157;
Ex. 6, p. 159

c. De Morgan's Laws

- $\sim(p \wedge q) \equiv \sim p \vee \sim q$: The negation of $p \wedge q$ is $\sim p \vee \sim q$.
- $\sim(p \vee q) \equiv \sim p \wedge \sim q$: The negation of $p \vee q$ is $\sim p \wedge \sim q$.

Ex. 7, p. 161;
Ex. 8, p. 161;
Ex. 9, p. 162;
Ex. 10, p. 162

3.6   Arguments and Truth Tables

a. An argument consists of two parts: the given statements, called the premises, and a conclusion. An argument is valid if the conclusion is true whenever the premises are assumed to be true. An argument that is not valid is called an invalid argument or a fallacy. A valid argument with true premises is called a sound argument.

b. A procedure to test the validity of an argument using a truth table is described in the box on page 168. If the argument contains n premises, write a conditional statement of the form

$$[(\text{premise } 1) \wedge (\text{premise } 2) \wedge \cdots \wedge (\text{premise } n)] \rightarrow \text{conclusion}$$

and construct a truth table. If the conditional statement is a tautology, the argument is valid; if not, the argument is invalid.

Ex. 1, p. 168;
Ex. 2, p. 169;
Ex. 3, p. 170;
Ex. 5, p. 173

c. Table 3.17 on page 172 contains the standard forms of commonly used valid and invalid arguments.

Ex. 4, p. 172;
Ex. 6, p. 175

3.7   Arguments and Euler Diagrams

a. Euler diagrams for quantified statements are given as follows:

    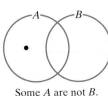

| All A are B. | No A are B. | Some A are B. | Some A are not B. |

b. To test the validity of an argument with an Euler diagram,
1. Make an Euler diagram for the first premise.
2. Make an Euler diagram for the second premise on top of the one for the first premise.
3. The argument is valid if and only if every possible diagram illustrates the conclusion of the argument.

Ex. 1, p. 180;
Ex. 2, p. 181;
Ex. 3, p. 182;
Ex. 4, p. 183;
Ex. 5, p. 184;
Ex. 6, p. 185

REVIEW EXERCISES

3.1 and 3.2

In Exercises 1–6, let p, q, and r represent the following simple statements:

> *p: The temperature is below 32°.*
> *q: We finished studying.*
> *r: We go to the movies.*

Express each symbolic compound statement in English. If a symbolic statement is given without parentheses, place them, as needed, before and after the most dominant connective and then translate into English.

1. $p \wedge q \rightarrow r$

2. $\sim r \rightarrow \sim p \vee \sim q$

3. $p \wedge (q \rightarrow r)$

4. $r \leftrightarrow (p \wedge q)$

5. $\sim(p \wedge q)$

6. $\sim r \leftrightarrow (\sim p \vee \sim q)$

In Exercises 7–12, let p, q, and r represent the following simple statements:

> *p: The outside temperature is at least 80°.*
> *q: The air conditioner is working.*
> *r: The house is hot.*

Express each English statement in symbolic form.

7. The outside temperature is at least 80° and the air conditioner is working, or the house is hot.

8. If the outside temperature is at least 80° or the air conditioner is not working, then the house is hot.

9. If the air conditioner is working, then the outside temperature is at least 80° if and only if the house is hot.

10. The house is hot, if and only if the outside temperature is at least 80° and the air conditioner is not working.

11. Having an outside temperature of at least 80° is sufficient for having a hot house.

12. Not having a hot house is necessary for the air conditioner to be working.

In Exercises 13–16, write the negation of each statement.

13. All houses are made with wood.

14. No students major in business.

15. Some crimes are motivated by passion.

16. Some Democrats are not registered voters.

17. The speaker stated that, "All new taxes are for education." We later learned that the speaker was not telling the truth. What can we conclude about new taxes and education?

3.3 and 3.4

In Exercises 18–25, construct a truth table for each statement. Then indicate whether the statement is a tautology, a self-contradiction, or neither.

18. $p \vee (\sim p \wedge q)$

19. $\sim p \vee \sim q$

20. $p \rightarrow (\sim p \vee q)$

21. $p \leftrightarrow \sim q$

22. $\sim(p \vee q) \rightarrow (\sim p \wedge \sim q)$

23. $(p \vee q) \rightarrow \sim r$

24. $(p \wedge q) \leftrightarrow (p \wedge r)$

25. $p \wedge [q \vee (r \rightarrow p)]$

In Exercises 26–27,

a. *Write each statement in symbolic form. Assign letters to simple statements that are not negated.*

b. *Construct a truth table for the symbolic statement in part (a).*

c. *Use the truth table to indicate one set of conditions that make the compound statement true, or state that no such conditions exist.*

26. I'm in class or I'm studying, and I'm not in class.

27. If you spit from a truck then it's legal, but if you spit from a car then it's not. (This law is still on the books in Georgia!)

In Exercises 28–31, determine the truth value for each statement when p is true, q is false, and r is false.

28. $\sim(q \leftrightarrow r)$

29. $(p \wedge q) \rightarrow (p \vee r)$

30. $(\sim q \rightarrow p) \vee (r \wedge \sim p)$

31. $\sim[(\sim p \vee r) \rightarrow (q \wedge r)]$

The bar graph shows the amount, in millions of dollars, that alcohol manufacturers spent on advertising during college sports programming.

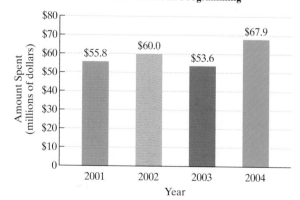

Amount Spent, in Millions of Dollars, Advertising Alcohol During College Football and Basketball Programming

Source: TNS Media Intelligence

In Exercises 32–34, write each statement in symbolic form. Then use the information in the graph to determine the truth value of the compound statement.

32. $60.0 million was spent in 2002 and it is not true that spending decreased from 2002 to 2003.

33. If more money was spent in 2003 than in 2004, then $67.9 million was spent in 2003 or $53.6 million was spent in 2004.

34. $55.8 million was spent in 2001 if and only if $60.0 million was spent in 2002, or it is not true that $67.9 was spent in 2004.

3.5

35. a. Use a truth table to show that $\sim p \vee q$ and $p \rightarrow q$ are equivalent.

b. Use the result from part (a) to write a statement that is equivalent to

The triangle is not isosceles or it has two equal sides.

36. Select the statement that is equivalent to

Joe grows mangos or oranges.

a. If Joe grows mangos, he does not grow oranges.

b. If Joe grows oranges, he does not grow mangos.

c. If Joe does not grow mangos, he grows oranges.

d. Joe grows both mangos and oranges.

In Exercises 37–38, use a truth table to determine whether the two statements are equivalent.

37. $\sim(p \leftrightarrow q), \sim p \vee \sim q$

38. $\sim p \wedge (q \vee r), (\sim p \wedge q) \vee (\sim p \wedge r)$

In Exercises 39–42, write the converse, inverse, and contrapositive of each statement.

39. If I am in Atlanta, then I am in the South.

40. If I am in class, then today is not a holiday.

41. If I work hard, then I pass all courses.

42. $\sim p \rightarrow \sim q$

In Exercises 43–45, write the negation of each conditional statement.

43. If an argument is sound, then it is valid.

44. If I do not work hard, then I do not succeed.

45. $\sim r \rightarrow p$

In Exercises 46–48, use De Morgan's laws to write a statement that is equivalent to each statement.

46. It is not true that both Chicago and Maine are cities.

47. It is not true that Ernest Hemingway was a musician or an actor.

48. If a number is not positive and not negative, the number is 0.

In Exercises 49–51, use De Morgan's laws to write the negation of each statement.

49. I work hard or I do not succeed.

50. She is not using her car and she is taking a bus.

51. $\sim p \vee q$

In Exercises 52–55, determine which, if any, of the three given statements are equivalent.

52. a. If it is hot, then I use the air conditioner.

b. If it is not hot, then I do not use the air conditioner.

c. It is not hot or I use the air conditioner.

53. **a.** If she did not play, then we lost.
    b. If we did not lose, then she played.
    c. She did not play and we did not lose.

54. **a.** He is here or I'm not.
    b. If I'm not here, he is.
    c. It is not true that he isn't here and I am.

55. **a.** If the class interests me and I like the teacher, then I enjoy studying.
    b. If the class interests me, then I like the teacher and I enjoy studying.
    c. The class interests me, or I like the teacher and I enjoy studying.

3.6

In Exercises 56–57, use a truth table to determine whether the symbolic form of the argument is valid or invalid.

56. $p \rightarrow q$
    $\underline{\sim q}$
    $\therefore p$

57. $p \wedge q$
    $\underline{q \rightarrow r}$
    $\therefore p \rightarrow r$

In Exercises 58–63, translate each argument into symbolic form. Then determine whether the argument is valid or invalid. You may use a truth table or, if applicable, compare the argument's symbolic form to a standard valid or invalid form.

58. If Tony plays, the team wins.
    The team won.
    $\therefore$ Tony played.

59. My plant is fertilized or it turns yellow.
    My plant is turning yellow.
    $\therefore$ My plant is not fertilized.

60. A majority of legislators vote for a bill or that bill does not become law.
    A majority of legislators did not vote for bill x.
    $\therefore$ Bill x did not become law.

61. Having good eye-hand coordination is necessary for being a good baseball player.
    Todd does not have good eye-hand coordination.
    $\therefore$ Todd is not a good baseball player.

62. If you love the person you marry, you can fall out of love with that person.
    If you do not love the person you marry, you can fall in love with that person.
    $\therefore$ You love the person you marry if and only if you can fall out of love with that person.

63. If I purchase season tickets to the football games, then I do not attend all lectures.
    If I do well in school, then I attend all lectures.
    $\therefore$ If I do not do well in school, then I purchased season tickets to the football games.

3.7

In Exercises 64–69, use Euler diagrams to determine whether each argument is valid or invalid.

64. All birds have feathers.
    All parrots have feathers.
    $\therefore$ All parrots are birds.

65. All botanists are scientists.
    All scientists have college degrees.
    $\therefore$ All botanists have college degrees.

66. All native desert plants can withstand severe drought.
    No tree ferns can withstand severe drought.
    $\therefore$ No tree ferns are native desert plants.

67. All native desert plants can withstand severe drought.
    No tree ferns are native desert plants.
    $\therefore$ No tree ferns can withstand severe drought.

68. All poets are writers.
    Some writers are wealthy.
    $\therefore$ Some poets are wealthy.

69. Some people enjoy reading.
    All people who enjoy reading appreciate language.
    $\therefore$ Some people appreciate language.

●●●●●● CHAPTER 3 TEST

Use the following representations in Exercises 1–6:

  p: I'm registered.
  q: I'm a citizen.
  r: I vote.

Express each compound statement in English.

1. $(p \wedge q) \rightarrow r$

2. $\sim r \leftrightarrow (\sim p \vee \sim q)$

3. $\sim (p \vee q)$

Express each English statement in symbolic form.

4. I am registered and a citizen, or I do not vote.

5. If I am not registered or not a citizen, then I do not vote.

6. Being a citizen is necessary for voting.

In Exercises 7–8, write the negation of the statement.

7. All numbers are divisible by 5.

8. Some people wear glasses.

In Exercises 9–11, construct a truth table for the statement.

9. $p \wedge (\sim p \vee q)$

10. $\sim (p \wedge q) \leftrightarrow (\sim p \vee \sim q)$

11. $p \leftrightarrow q \vee r$

12. Write the following statement in symbolic form and construct a truth table. Then indicate one set of conditions that make the compound statement false.

    If you break the law and change the law, then you have not broken the law.

In Exercises 13–14, determine the truth value for each statement when p is false, q is true, and r is false.

13. $\sim(q \rightarrow r)$

14. $(p \lor r) \leftrightarrow (\sim r \land p)$

15. The following statement pertains to life objectives of first-year college students in 2001 compared to 1969:

There was no decrease in the percentage of male students who considered "being very well off financially" essential, or there was a decrease in the percentage of female students who considered "developing a meaningful philosophy of life" and "raising a family" essential.

a. Write the statement in symbolic form.

b. Use the information in the following graph to determine the truth value of the statement in part (a).

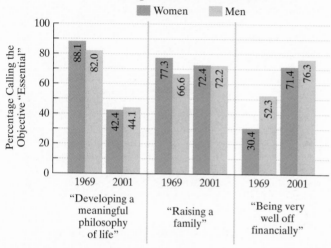

Comparing Life Objectives of First-Year U.S. College Students in 1969 and 2001

Source: UCLA Higher Education Research Institute

16. Select the statement below that is equivalent to
Gene is an actor or a musician.

a. If Gene is an actor, then he is not a musician.

b. If Gene is not an actor, then he is a musician.

c. It is false that Gene is not an actor or not a musician.

d. If Gene is an actor, then he is a musician.

17. Write the contrapositive of
If it is August, it does not snow.

18. Write the converse and the inverse of the following statement:
If the radio is playing, then I cannot concentrate.

19. Write the negation of the following statement:
If it is cold, we do not use the pool.

20. Write a statement that is equivalent to
It is not true that the test is today or the party is tonight.

21. Write the negation of the following statement:
The banana is green and it is not ready to eat.

In Exercises 22–23, determine which, if any, of the three given statements are equivalent.

22. a. If I'm not feeling well, I'm grouchy.

b. I'm feeling well or I'm grouchy.

c. If I'm feeling well, I'm not grouchy.

23. a. It is not true that today is a holiday or tomorrow is a holiday.

b. If today is not a holiday, then tomorrow is not a holiday.

c. Today is not a holiday and tomorrow is not a holiday.

Determine whether each argument in Exercises 24–29 is valid or invalid.

24. If a parrot talks, it is intelligent.
This parrot is intelligent.
∴ This parrot talks.

25. I am sick or I am tired.
I am not tired.
∴ I am sick.

26. I am going if and only if you are not.
You are going.
∴ I'm going.

27. All mammals are warm-blooded.
All dogs are warm-blooded.
∴ All dogs are mammals.

28. All conservationists are advocates of solar-powered cars.
No oil company executives are advocates of solar-powered cars.
∴ No conservationists are oil company executives.

29. All rabbis are Jewish.
Some Jews observe kosher dietary traditions.
∴ Some rabbis observe kosher dietary traditions.

Number Representation and Calculation

Adorable on the outside and clever on the inside, it's not hard to imagine friendly robots as our home-helping buddies. Built-in microchips with extraordinary powers based on ancient numeration systems enable your robot to recognize you, engage in (meaningful?) conversation, and perform household chores. If you find the idea of a friendship with a sophisticated machine a bit unsettling, consider a robot dog or cat. Scientists have designed these critters to blend computer technology with the cuddly appeal of animals. They move, play, and sleep like real pets, and can even be programmed to sing and dance. Without an understanding of how we represent numbers, none of this technology could exist.

••••••

Connections between binary numeration systems and computer technology are discussed in "Letters and Words in Base Two" on page 205, "Music in Base Two" on page 207, and "Base Two, Logic, and Computers" on page 214.

SECTION 4.1 • OUR HINDU-ARABIC SYSTEM AND EARLY POSITIONAL SYSTEMS

OBJECTIVES

1. Evaluate an exponential expression.

2. Write a Hindu-Arabic numeral in expanded form.

3. Express a number's expanded form as a Hindu-Arabic numeral.

4. Understand and use the Babylonian numeration system.

5. Understand and use the Mayan numeration system.

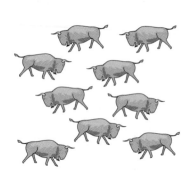

FIGURE 4.1

All of us have an intuitive understanding of *more* and *less*. As humanity evolved, this sense of more and less was used to develop a system of counting. A tribe needed to know how many sheep it had, and whether the flock was increasing or decreasing in number. The earliest way of keeping count probably involved some tally method, using one vertical mark on a cave wall for each sheep. Later, a variety of vocal sounds developed as a tally for the number of things in a group. Finally, written symbols, or numerals, were used to represent numbers.

A **number** is an abstract idea that addresses the question, "How many?" A **numeral** is a symbol used to represent a number. Different symbols may be used to represent the same number. Numerals used to represent how many buffalo are shown in Figure 4.1 include

|||| ||||	IX	9.
Tally method	Roman numeral	Hindu-Arabic numeral

We take numerals and the numbers that they represent for granted and use them every day. A **system of numeration** consists of a set of basic numerals and rules for combining them to represent numbers. It took humanity thousands of years to invent numeration systems that made computation a reasonable task. Today we use a system of writing numerals that was invented in India and brought to Europe by the Arabs. Our numerals are therefore called **Hindu-Arabic numerals**.

Like literature or music, a numeration system has a profound effect on the culture that created it. Computers, which affect our everyday lives, are based on an understanding of our Hindu-Arabic system of numeration. In this section, we study the characteristics of our numeration system. We also take a brief journey through history to look at two numeration systems that pointed the way toward an amazing cultural creation, our Hindu-Arabic system.

1 | Evaluate an exponential expression.

Exponential Notation

An understanding of *exponents* is important in understanding the characteristics of our numeration system.

EXPONENTIAL NOTATION

If n is a natural number $(1, 2, 3,$ and so on),

Exponent or Power

$$b^n = \underbrace{b \cdot b \cdot b \cdot \cdots \cdot b.}_{\substack{b \text{ appears as a} \\ \text{factor } n \text{ times.}}}$$

Base

b^n is read "the nth power of b" or "b to the nth power." Thus, the nth power of b is defined as the product of n factors of b. The expression b^n is called an **exponential expression**. Furthermore, $b^1 = b$.

EXAMPLE 1   UNDERSTANDING EXPONENTIAL NOTATION

Evaluate the following:

   a. 10^2 **b.** 10^3 **c.** 10^4 **d.** 2^6 **e.** 1^7 **f.** 7^1.

SOLUTION

   a. $10^2 = 10 \times 10 = 100$

   b. $10^3 = 10 \times 10 \times 10 = 1000$

   c. $10^4 = 10 \times 10 \times 10 \times 10 = 10,000$

   d. $2^6 = 2 \times 2 \times 2 \times 2 \times 2 \times 2 = 64$

   e. $1^7 = 1 \times 1 \times 1 \times 1 \times 1 \times 1 \times 1 = 1$

   f. $7^1 = 7$

 Evaluate the following:

   a. 7^2 **b.** 5^3 **c.** 1^4 **d.** 10^5 **e.** 10^6 **f.** 18^1.

---

2   Write a Hindu-Arabic numeral in expanded form.

Our Hindu-Arabic Numeration System

An important characteristic of our Hindu-Arabic system is that we can write the numeral for any number, large or small, using only ten symbols. The ten symbols that we use are

$$0, 1, 2, 3, 4, 5, 6, 7, 8, \text{ and } 9.$$

These symbols are called **digits**, from the Latin word for fingers.

   With the use of exponents, Hindu-Arabic numerals can be written in **expanded form** in which the value of the digit in each position is made clear. In a Hindu-Arabic numeral, the place value of the first digit on the right is 1. The place value of the second digit from the right is 10. The place value of the third digit from the right is 100, or 10^2. For example, we can write 663 in expanded form by thinking of 663 as six 100s plus six 10s plus three 1s. This means that 663 in expanded form is

$$663 = (6 \times 100) + (6 \times 10) + (3 \times 1)$$
$$= (6 \times 10^2) + (6 \times 10^1) + (3 \times 1).$$

   Because the value of a digit varies according to the position it occupies in a numeral, the Hindu-Arabic numeration system is called a **positional-value**, or **place-value**, system. The positional values in the system are based on powers of ten and are

$$\ldots, 10^5, 10^4, 10^3, 10^2, 10^1, 1.$$

BLITZER BONUS

Tally Sticks

This notched reindeer antler dates from 15,000 B.C. Humans learned how to keep track of numbers by tallying notches on bones with the same intelligence that led them to preserve and use fire, and at around the same time. Using tally sticks, early people grasped the idea that nine buffalo and nine sheep had something in common: the abstract idea of *nine*. As the human mind conceived of numbers separately from the things they represented, systems of numeration developed.

3 Express a number's expanded form as a Hindu-Arabic numeral.

EXAMPLE 2   WRITING HINDU-ARABIC NUMERALS IN EXPANDED FORM

Write each of the following in expanded form:

a. 3407   **b.** 53,525.

SOLUTION

a. $3407 = (3 \times 10^3) + (4 \times 10^2) + (0 \times 10^1) + (7 \times 1)$

 or $= (3 \times 1000) + (4 \times 100) + (0 \times 10) + (7 \times 1)$

Because $0 \times 10^1 = 0$, this term could be left out, but the expanded form is clearer when it is included.

b. $53,525 = (5 \times 10^4) + (3 \times 10^3) + (5 \times 10^2) + (2 \times 10^1) + (5 \times 1)$

 or $= (5 \times 10,000) + (3 \times 1000) + (5 \times 100) + (2 \times 10) + (5 \times 1)$

 Write each of the following in expanded form:

  a. 4026   **b.** 24,232.

EXAMPLE 3   EXPRESSING A NUMBER'S EXPANDED FORM AS A HINDU-ARABIC NUMERAL

Express each expanded form as a Hindu-Arabic numeral:

a. $(7 \times 10^3) + (5 \times 10^1) + (4 \times 1)$

b. $(6 \times 10^5) + (8 \times 10^1)$.

SOLUTION For clarification, we begin by showing all powers of ten, starting with the highest exponent given. Any power of ten that is left out is expressed as 0 times that power of ten.

a. $(7 \times 10^3) + (5 \times 10^1) + (4 \times 1)$

$= (7 \times 10^3) + (0 \times 10^2) + (5 \times 10^1) + (4 \times 1)$

$= 7054$

b. $(6 \times 10^5) + (8 \times 10^1)$

$= (6 \times 10^5) + (0 \times 10^4) + (0 \times 10^3) + (0 \times 10^2) + (8 \times 10^1) + (0 \times 1)$

$= 600,080$

 Express each expanded form as a Hindu-Arabic numeral:

  a. $(6 \times 10^3) + (7 \times 10^1) + (3 \times 1)$

  b. $(8 \times 10^4) + (9 \times 10^2)$.

Examples 2 and 3 show how there would be no Hindu-Arabic system without an understanding of zero and the invention of a symbol to represent nothingness. The system must have a symbol for zero to serve as a placeholder in case one or more powers of ten are not needed. The concept of zero was a new and radical invention, one that changed our ability to think about the world.

"It took men about five thousand years, counting from the beginning of number symbols, to think of a symbol for nothing."

ISAAC ASIMOV,
Asimov on Numbers

Early Positional Systems

Our Hindu-Arabic system developed over many centuries. Its digits can be found carved on ancient Hindu pillars over 2200 years old. In 1202, the Italian mathematician Leonardo Fibonacci (1170–1250) introduced the system to Europe, writing of its special characteristic: "With the nine Hindu digits and the Arab symbol 0, any number can be written." The Hindu-Arabic system came into widespread use only when printing was invented in the fifteenth century.

The Hindu-Arabic system uses powers of ten. However, positional systems can use powers of any number, not just 10. Think about our system of time, based on powers of 60:

Jasper Johns, *"Zero"*. © Jasper Johns/ Licensed by VAGA, New York, NY.

$$1 \text{ minute} = 60 \text{ seconds}$$
$$1 \text{ hour} = 60 \text{ minutes} = 60 \times 60 \text{ seconds} = 60^2 \text{ seconds}.$$

What is significant in a positional system is position and the powers that positions convey. The first early positional system that we will discuss uses powers of 60, just like those used for units of time.

4 | Understand and use the Babylonian numeration system.

The Babylonian Numeration System

The city of Babylon, 55 miles south of present-day Baghdad, was the center of Babylonian civilization that lasted for about 1400 years between 2000 B.C. and 600 B.C. The Babylonians used wet clay as a writing surface. Their clay tablets were heated and dried to give a permanent record of their work, which we are able to decipher and read today. Table 4.1 gives the numerals of this civilization's numeration system.

The place values in the Babylonian system use powers of 60. The place values are

$$..., \quad 60^3, \quad 60^2, \quad 60^1, \quad 1.$$

$60^3 = 60 \times 60 \times 60 = 216{,}000$ $60^2 = 60 \times 60 = 3600$

TABLE 4.1 BABYLONIAN NUMERALS

Babylonian numerals	∨	＜
Hindu-Arabic numerals	1	10

The Babylonians left a space to distinguish the various place values in a numeral from one another. For example,

∨   ＜   ∨∨

means

$$(1 \times 60^2) + (10 \times 60^1) + (1 + 1) \times 1$$
$$= (1 \times 3600) + (10 \times 60) + (2 \times 1)$$
$$= 3600 + 600 + 2 = 4202.$$

EXAMPLE 4   CONVERTING FROM A BABYLONIAN NUMERAL TO A HINDU-ARABIC NUMERAL

Write

∨∨   ＜∨   ＜＜∨∨

as a Hindu-Arabic numeral.

SOLUTION From left to right, the place values are 60^2, 60^1, and 1. Represent the numeral in each place as a familiar Hindu-Arabic numeral using Table 4.1. Multiply each Hindu-Arabic numeral by its respective place value. Then find the sum of these products.

$$\vee \vee \qquad\qquad \langle \vee \qquad\qquad \langle\langle \vee\vee$$

means

$$\downarrow \qquad\qquad \downarrow \qquad\qquad \downarrow$$

$$(1 + 1) \times 60^2 + (10 + 1) \times 60^1 + (10 + 10 + 1 + 1) \times 1$$

$$= (2 \times 60^2) + (11 \times 60^1) + (22 \times 1)$$

$$= (2 \times 3600) + (11 \times 60) + (22 \times 1)$$

$$= 7200 + 660 + 22 = 7882.$$

This sum indicates that the given Babylonian numeral is 7882 when written as a Hindu-Arabic numeral.

○

A major disadvantage of the Babylonian system is that it did not contain a symbol for zero. Some Babylonian tablets have a larger gap between the numerals or the insertion of the symbol ⩼ to indicate a missing place value, but this led to some ambiguity and confusion.

CHECK POINT 4 Write

$$\vee \vee \vee \quad \langle\langle \quad \langle\langle\langle \vee$$

as a Hindu-Arabic numeral.

─────────────────────────────────────●

5 | Understand and use the Mayan numeration system.

The Mayan Numeration System

The Maya, a tribe of Central American Indians, lived on the Yucatan Peninsula. At its peak, between 300 and 1000 A.D., their civilization covered an area including parts of Mexico, all of Belize and Guatemala, and part of Honduras. They were famous for their magnificent architecture, their astronomical and mathematical knowledge, and their excellence in the arts. Their numeration system was the first to have a symbol for zero. Table 4.2 gives the Mayan numerals.

TABLE 4.2 MAYAN NUMERALS

0	1	2	3	4	5	6	7	8	9

10	11	12	13	14	15	16	17	18	19

The place values in the Mayan system are

$$..., \qquad 18 \times 20^3, \qquad 18 \times 20^2, \qquad 18 \times 20, \qquad 20, \qquad 1$$

$18 \times 20 \times 20 \times 20 = 144{,}000$ $18 \times 20 \times 20 = 7200$ $18 \times 20 = 360$

Notice that instead of giving the third position a place value of 20^2, the Mayans used 18×20. This was probably done so that their calendar year of 360 days would be a basic part of the numeration system.

Numerals in the Mayan system are expressed vertically. The place value at the bottom of the column is 1.

Numbers and Bird Brains

Birds have large, well-developed brains and are more intelligent than is suggested by the slur "bird brain." Parakeets can learn to count to seven. They have been taught to identify a box of food by counting the number of small objects in front of the box. Some species of birds can tell the difference between two and three. If a nest contains four eggs and one is taken, the bird will stay in the nest to protect the remaining three eggs. However, if two of the four eggs are taken, the bird recognizes that only two remain and will desert the nest, leaving the remaining two eggs unprotected.

Birds easily master complex counting problems. The sense of *more* and *less* that led to the development of numeration systems is not limited to the human species.

EXAMPLE 5 USING THE MAYAN NUMERATION SYSTEM

Write

as a Hindu-Arabic numeral.

SOLUTION The given Mayan numeral has four places. From top to bottom, the place values are 7200, 360, 20, and 1. Represent the numeral in each row as a familiar Hindu-Arabic numeral using Table 4.2. Multiply each Hindu-Arabic numeral by its respective place value. Then find the sum of these products.

Mayan numeral		Hindu-Arabic numeral		Place value		
••••	=	14	×	7200	=	100,800
⊖	=	0	×	360	=	0
••	=	7	×	20	=	140
••	=	12	×	1	=	12
						100,952

The sum on the right indicates that the given Mayan numeral is 100,952 when written as a Hindu-Arabic numeral.

CHECK POINT 5 Write

as a Hindu-Arabic numeral.

EXERCISE SET 4.1 ●●●●●●

• Practice Exercises

In Exercises 1–8, evaluate the expression.

1. 5^2 **2.** 6^2 **3.** 2^3 **4.** 4^3

5. 3^4 **6.** 2^4 **7.** 10^5 **8.** 10^6

In Exercises 9–22, write each Hindu-Arabic numeral in expanded form.

9. 36 **10.** 65 **11.** 249 **12.** 698

13. 703 **14.** 902 **15.** 4856 **16.** 5749

17. 3070 **18.** 9007 **19.** 34,569 **20.** 67,943

21. 230,007,004 **22.** 909,006,070

In Exercises 23–32, express each expanded form as a Hindu-Arabic numeral.

23. $(7 \times 10^1) + (3 \times 1)$

24. $(9 \times 10^1) + (4 \times 1)$

25. $(3 \times 10^2) + (8 \times 10^1) + (5 \times 1)$

26. $(7 \times 10^2) + (5 \times 10^1) + (3 \times 1)$

27. $(5 \times 10^5) + (2 \times 10^4) + (8 \times 10^3) + (7 \times 10^2) + (4 \times 10^1) + (3 \times 1)$

28. $(7 \times 10^6) + (4 \times 10^5) + (2 \times 10^4) + (3 \times 10^3)$
$\qquad + (1 \times 10^2) + (9 \times 10^1) + (6 \times 1)$

29. $(7 \times 10^3) + (0 \times 10^2) + (0 \times 10^1) + (2 \times 1)$

30. $(9 \times 10^4) + (0 \times 10^3) + (0 \times 10^2) + (4 \times 10^1)$
$\qquad + (5 \times 1)$

31. $(6 \times 10^8) + (2 \times 10^3) + (7 \times 1)$

32. $(3 \times 10^8) + (5 \times 10^4) + (4 \times 1)$

In Exercises 33–40, use Table 4.1 on page 199 to write each Babylonian numeral as a Hindu-Arabic numeral.

33. ＜＜∨∨∨   **34.** ＜＜＜∨∨

35. ＜＜∨ ∨∨   **36.** ＜＜ ＜∨∨

37. ∨∨∨ ＜∨∨ ∨∨∨   **38.** ∨∨ ＜∨ ＜＜∨∨

39. ＜∨ ＜∨ ＜∨ ＜∨   **40.** ＜＜ ＜＜ ＜∨∨ ＜∨∨

In Exercises 41–50, use Table 4.2 on page 200 to write each Mayan numeral as a Hindu-Arabic numeral.

41. ⁞⁞⁞⁞   **42.** ⁞⁞⁞   **43.** ⁞⁞⁞⁞ / ═ / ◯   **44.** ⁞⁞⁞⁞ / ◯ / ──

45. ⁞⁞⁞ / ⁞⁞⁞ / ⁞⁞⁞   **46.** ⁑ / ⁑ / ⁑   **47.** ⁑ / ◯ / ◯ / ⁑   **48.** ⁞⁞⁞ / ═ / ◯

49. ═ / ⁞⁞⁞ / ◯ / ═   **50.** ═ / ◯ / ⁞⁞⁞ / ═

• Practice Plus

In Exercises 51–54, express the result of each addition as a Hindu-Arabic numeral in expanded form.

51. ∨ ＜＜ ＜＜∨ + ＜∨ ＜＜＜ ∨∨∨∨

52. ＜∨ ＜ ＜∨∨∨ + ∨∨∨ ＜＜ ∨∨

53. ⁞ / ⁞ / ⁞ + ── / ◯ / ⁞⁞⁞

54. ⁑ / ── / ⁑ + ⁞ / ═ / ◯

If n is a natural number, then $10^{-n} = \dfrac{1}{10^n}$. Negative powers of 10 can be used to write the decimal part of Hindu-Arabic numerals in expanded form. For example,

$0.8302 = (8 \times 10^{-1}) + (3 \times 10^{-2}) + (0 \times 10^{-3}) + (2 \times 10^{-4})$

$\qquad = \left(8 \times \dfrac{1}{10^1}\right) + \left(3 \times \dfrac{1}{10^2}\right) + \left(0 \times \dfrac{1}{10^3}\right) + \left(2 \times \dfrac{1}{10^4}\right)$

$\qquad = \left(8 \times \dfrac{1}{10}\right) + \left(3 \times \dfrac{1}{100}\right) + \left(0 \times \dfrac{1}{1000}\right) + \left(2 \times \dfrac{1}{10,000}\right).$

In Exercises 55–62, express each expanded form as a Hindu-Arabic numeral.

55. $(4 \times 10^{-1}) + (7 \times 10^{-2}) + (5 \times 10^{-3}) + (9 \times 10^{-4})$

56. $(6 \times 10^{-1}) + (8 \times 10^{-2}) + (1 \times 10^{-3}) + (2 \times 10^{-4})$

57. $(7 \times 10^{-1}) + (2 \times 10^{-4}) + (3 \times 10^{-6})$

58. $(8 \times 10^{-1}) + (3 \times 10^{-4}) + (7 \times 10^{-6})$

59. $(5 \times 10^3) + (3 \times 10^{-2})$

60. $(7 \times 10^4) + (5 \times 10^{-3})$

61. $(3 \times 10^4) + (7 \times 10^2) + (5 \times 10^{-2}) + (8 \times 10^{-3})$
$\qquad + (9 \times 10^{-5})$

62. $(7 \times 10^5) + (3 \times 10^2) + (2 \times 10^{-1}) + (2 \times 10^{-3})$
$\qquad + (1 \times 10^{-5})$

• Application Exercises

The Chinese "rod system" of numeration is a base ten positional system. The digits for 1 through 9 are shown as follows:

1 2 3 4 5 6 7 8 9
Ⅰ Ⅱ Ⅲ ⅢⅠ ⅢⅡ Ｔ ⊤Ⅰ ⊤Ⅱ ⊤Ⅲ
─ ═ ≡ ≣ ≣─ ⊥ ⊥─ ⊥═ ⊥≡

The vertical digits in the second row are used for place values of 1, 10^2, 10^4, and all even powers of 10. The horizontal digits in the third row are used for place values of 10^1, 10^3, 10^5, 10^7, and all odd powers of 10. A blank space is used for the digit zero. In Exercises 63–66, write each Chinese "rod system" numeral as a Hindu-Arabic numeral.

63. ≡ Ｔ ═ ⅢⅠ   **64.** ⊥ Ｔ ═ Ⅲ Ⅰ

65. ≡ ⊥ Ｔ   **66.** ⊥ Ⅲ Ⅱ

67. Humans have debated for decades about what messages should be sent to the stars to grab the attention of extraterrestrials and demonstrate our mathematical prowess. In the 1970s, Soviet scientists suggested we send the exponential message

$$10^2 + 11^2 + 12^2 = 13^2 + 14^2.$$

The Soviets called this equation "mind-catching." Evaluate the exponential expressions and verify that the sums on the two sides are equal. What is the significance of this sum?

• Writing in Mathematics

68. Describe the difference between a number and a numeral.

69. Explain how to evaluate 7^3.

70. What is the base in our Hindu-Arabic numeration system? What are the digits in the system?

71. Why is a symbol for zero needed in a positional system?

72. Explain how to write a Hindu-Arabic numeral in expanded form.

73. Describe one way that the Babylonian system is similar to the Hindu-Arabic system and one way that it is different from the Hindu-Arabic system.

74. Describe one way that the Mayan system is similar to the Hindu-Arabic system and one way that it is different from the Hindu-Arabic system.

75. **Research activity** Write a report on the history of the Hindu-Arabic system of numeration. Useful references include history of mathematics books, encyclopedias, and the World Wide Web.

• Critical Thinking Exercises

76. Write ⌄ <⌄⌄ <⌄ as a Mayan numeral.

77. Write •• as a Babylonian numeral.
        ••
        ••

78. Use Babylonian numerals to write the numeral that precedes and the numeral that follows:

<⌄ <<<<< ⌄⌄⌄⌄⌄⌄⌄⌄⌄.

• Group Exercise

79. Your group task is to create an original positional numeration system that is different from the three systems discussed in this section.

   a. Construct a table showing your numerals and the corresponding Hindu-Arabic numerals.

   b. Explain how to represent numbers in your system, and express a three-digit and a four-digit Hindu-Arabic numeral in your system.

SECTION 4.2 • NUMBER BASES IN POSITIONAL SYSTEMS

OBJECTIVES

1. Change numerals in bases other than ten to base ten.

2. Change base ten numerals to numerals in other bases.

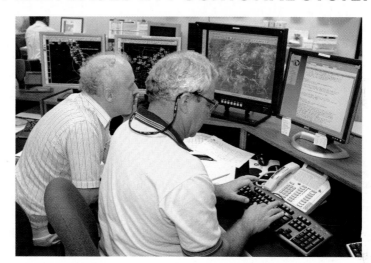

You are being drawn deeper into cyberspace, spending more time online each week. With constantly improving high-resolution images, cyberspace is reshaping your life by nourishing shared enthusiasms. The people who built your computer talk of "incredible bandwidth" that will give you the visual experience, in high-definition 3-D format, of being in the same room with a person who is actually in another city.

Because of our ten fingers and ten toes, the base ten Hindu-Arabic system seems to be an obvious choice. However, it is not base ten that computers use to process information and communicate with one another. Your experiences in cyberspace are sustained with a binary, or base two, system. In this section, we study numeration systems with bases other than ten. An understanding of such systems will help you to appreciate the nature of a positional system. You will also attain a better understanding of the computations you have used all of your life. You will even get to see how the world looks from a computer's point of view.

1 | Change numerals in bases other than ten to base ten.

Changing Numerals in Bases Other Than Ten to Base Ten

The base of a positional numeration system refers to the number of individual digit symbols that can be used in that system as well as to the number whose powers define the place values. For example, the digit symbols in a base five system are 0, 1, 2, 3, and 4. The place values in a base five system are powers of 5:

$$\ldots, 5^4, 5^3, 5^2, 5^1, 1$$
$$= \ldots, 5 \times 5 \times 5 \times 5, 5 \times 5 \times 5, 5 \times 5, 5, 1$$
$$= \ldots, 625, 125, 25, 5, 1.$$

When a numeral appears without a subscript, it is assumed that the base is ten. Bases other than ten are indicated with a spelled-out subscript, as in the numeral

$$122_{\text{five}}.$$

This numeral is read "one two two base five." Do not read it as "one hundred twenty two" because that terminology implies a base ten numeral, naming 122 in base ten.

We can convert 122_{five} to a base ten numeral by following the same procedure used in Section 4.1 to change the Babylonian and Mayan numerals to base ten Hindu-Arabic numerals. In the case of 122_{five}, the numeral has three places. From left to right, the place values are 5^2, 5^1, and 1. Multiply each digit in the numeral by its respective place value. Then add these products.

$$122_{\text{five}} = (1 \times 5^2) + (2 \times 5^1) + (2 \times 1)$$
$$= (1 \times 25) + (2 \times 5) + (2 \times 1)$$
$$= 25 + 10 + 2$$
$$= 37$$

Thus,

$$122_{\text{five}} = 37.$$

In base five, we do not need a digit symbol for 5 because

$$10_{\text{five}} = (1 \times 5^1) + (0 \times 1) = 5.$$

Likewise, the base ten numeral 6 is represented as 11_{five}, the base ten numeral 7 as 12_{five}, and so on. Table 4.3 shows base ten numerals from 0 through 20 and their base five equivalents.

In any base, the digit symbols begin at 0 and go up to one less than the base. In base b, the digit symbols begin at 0 and go up to $b - 1$. The place values in a base b system are powers of b:

$$\ldots, b^4, b^3, b^2, b, 1.$$

Table 4.4 shows the digit symbols and place values in various bases.

TABLE 4.3

Base Ten	Base Five
0	0
1	1
2	2
3	3
4	4
5	10
6	11
7	12
8	13
9	14
10	20
11	21
12	22
13	23
14	24
15	30
16	31
17	32
18	33
19	34
20	40

TABLE 4.4 DIGIT SYMBOLS AND PLACE VALUES IN VARIOUS BASES

Base	Digit Symbols	Place Values
two	$0, 1$	$\ldots, 2^4, 2^3, 2^2, 2^1, 1$
three	$0, 1, 2$	$\ldots, 3^4, 3^3, 3^2, 3^1, 1$
four	$0, 1, 2, 3$	$\ldots, 4^4, 4^3, 4^2, 4^1, 1$
five	$0, 1, 2, 3, 4$	$\ldots, 5^4, 5^3, 5^2, 5^1, 1$
six	$0, 1, 2, 3, 4, 5$	$\ldots, 6^4, 6^3, 6^2, 6^1, 1$
seven	$0, 1, 2, 3, 4, 5, 6$	$\ldots, 7^4, 7^3, 7^2, 7^1, 1$
eight	$0, 1, 2, 3, 4, 5, 6, 7$	$\ldots, 8^4, 8^3, 8^2, 8^1, 1$
nine	$0, 1, 2, 3, 4, 5, 6, 7, 8$	$\ldots, 9^4, 9^3, 9^2, 9^1, 1$
ten	$0, 1, 2, 3, 4, 5, 6, 7, 8, 9$	$\ldots, 10^4, 10^3, 10^2, 10^1, 1$

We have seen that in base five, 10_{five} represents one group of 5 and no groups of 1. Thus, $10_{\text{five}} = 5$. Similarly, in base six, 10_{six} represents one group of 6 and no groups of 1. Thus, $10_{\text{six}} = 6$. In general $10_{\text{base } b}$ represents one group of b and no groups of 1. This means that $10_{\text{base } b} = b$.

Here is the procedure for changing a numeral in a base other than ten to base ten:

> **CHANGING TO BASE TEN**
> To change a numeral in a base other than ten to a base ten numeral,
>
> 1. Find the place value for each digit in the numeral.
> 2. Multiply each digit in the numeral by its respective place value.
> 3. Find the sum of the products in step 2.

EXAMPLE 1   CONVERTING TO BASE TEN

Convert 4726_{eight} to base ten.

SOLUTION   The given base eight numeral has four places. From left to right, the place values are

$$8^3, 8^2, 8^1, \text{ and } 1.$$

Multiply each digit in the numeral by its respective place value. Then find the sum of these products.

Place value: 8^3	Place value: 8^2	Place value: 8^1	Place value: 1
4	7	2	6_{eight}

$$
\begin{aligned}
4726_{\text{eight}} &= (4 \times 8^3) + (7 \times 8^2) + (2 \times 8^1) + (6 \times 1) \\
&= (4 \times 8 \times 8 \times 8) + (7 \times 8 \times 8) + (2 \times 8) + (6 \times 1) \\
&= 2048 + 448 + 16 + 6 \\
&= 2518
\end{aligned}
$$

CHECK POINT 1   Convert 3422_{five} to base ten.

EXAMPLE 2   CONVERTING TO BASE TEN

Convert 100101_{two} to base ten.

SOLUTION   Multiply each digit in the numeral by its respective place value. Then find the sum of these products.

Place value: 2^5	Place value: 2^4	Place value: 2^3	Place value: 2^2	Place value: 2^1	Place value: 1
1	0	0	1	0	1_{two}

$$
\begin{aligned}
100101_{\text{two}} &= (1 \times 2^5) + (0 \times 2^4) + (0 \times 2^3) + (1 \times 2^2) + (0 \times 2^1) + (1 \times 1) \\
&= (1 \times 32) + (0 \times 16) + (0 \times 8) + (1 \times 4) + (0 \times 2) + (1 \times 1) \\
&= 32 + 0 + 0 + 4 + 0 + 1 \\
&= 37
\end{aligned}
$$

CHECK POINT 2   Convert 110011_{two} to base ten.

The word *digital* in computer technology refers to a method of encoding numbers, letters, visual images, and sounds using a **binary**, or base two, **system** of 0s and 1s. Because computers use electrical signals that are groups of on–off pulses of electricity, the digits in base two are convenient. In binary code, 1 indicates the passage of an electrical pulse ("on") and 0 indicates its interruption ("off"). For example, the number 37 (100101_{two}) becomes the binary code on–off–off–on–off–on. Microchips in a computer store and process these binary signals.

BLITZER BONUS

Letters and Words in Base Two

Wilhelm Leibniz (1646–1716)

Letters are converted into base two numbers for computer processing. A through Z are assigned 65 through 90, with each number expressed in base two. Thus, the binary code for A(65) is 1000001. Similarly, a through z are assigned 97 through 122 in base two.

The German mathematician Wilhelm Leibniz was the first modern thinker to promote the base two system. He never imagined that one day the base two system would enable computers to process information and communicate with one another.

In addition to base two, computer applications often involve base eight, called an **octal system**, and base sixteen, called a **hexadecimal system**. Base sixteen presents a problem because digit symbols are needed from 0 up to one less than the base. This means that we need more digit symbols than the ten (0, 1, 2, 3, 4, 5, 6, 7, 8, and 9) used in our base ten system. Computer programmers use the letters A, B, C, D, E, and F as base sixteen digit symbols for the numbers ten through fifteen, respectively.

Additional digit symbols in base sixteen:

A = 10   B = 11
C = 12   D = 13
E = 14   F = 15

EXAMPLE 3   CONVERTING TO BASE TEN

Convert $EC7_{sixteen}$ to base ten.

SOLUTION From left to right, the place values are
$$16^2, 16^1, \text{ and } 1.$$

The digit symbol E represents 14 and the digit symbol C represents 12. Although this numeral looks a bit strange, follow the usual procedure: Multiply each digit in the numeral by its respective place value. Then find the sum of these products.

Place value: 16^2 Place value: 16^1 Place value: 1

E   C $7_{sixteen}$

E = 14   C = 12

$$\begin{aligned}
EC7_{sixteen} &= (14 \times 16^2) + (12 \times 16^1) + (7 \times 1) \\
&= (14 \times 16 \times 16) + (12 \times 16) + (7 \times 1) \\
&= 3584 + 192 + 7 \\
&= 3783
\end{aligned}$$

 Convert $AD4_{sixteen}$ to base ten.

2 Change base ten numerals to numerals in other bases.

Changing Base Ten Numerals to Numerals in Other Bases

To convert a base ten numeral to a numeral in a base other than ten, we need to find how many groups of each place value are contained in the base ten numeral. When the base ten numeral consists of one or two digits, we can do this mentally. For example, suppose that we want to convert the base ten numeral 6 to a base four numeral. The place values in base four are

$$\ldots, 4^3, 4^2, 4, 1.$$

The place values that are less than 6 are 4 and 1. We can express 6 as one group of four and two ones:

$$6_{ten} = (1 \times 4) + (2 \times 1) = 12_{four}.$$

EXAMPLE 4   A MENTAL CONVERSION FROM BASE TEN TO BASE FIVE

Convert the base ten numeral 8 to a base five numeral.

SOLUTION The place values in base five are

$$\ldots, 5^3, 5^2, 5, 1.$$

The place values that are less than 8 are 5 and 1. We can express 8 as one group of five and three ones:

$$8_{ten} = (1 \times 5) + (3 \times 1) = 13_{five}.$$

 Convert the base ten numeral 6 to a base five numeral.

If a conversion cannot be performed mentally, you can use divisions to determine how many groups of each place value are contained in a base ten numeral.

EXAMPLE 5   USING DIVISIONS TO CONVERT FROM BASE TEN TO BASE EIGHT

Convert the base ten numeral 299 to a base eight numeral.

SOLUTION   The place values in base eight are

$$\ldots, 8^3, 8^2, 8^1, 1, \quad \text{or} \quad \ldots, 512, 64, 8, 1.$$

The place values that are less than 299 are 64, 8, and 1. We can use divisions to show
how many groups of each of these place values are contained in 299. Divide 299 by
64. Divide the remainder by 8.

4 groups of 64
$$
\begin{array}{r}
4 \\
64\overline{)299} \\
256 \\
\hline
43
\end{array}
$$

5 groups of 8
$$
\begin{array}{r}
5 \\
8\overline{)43} \\
40 \\
\hline
3
\end{array}
$$
3 ones left over

These divisions show that 299 can be expressed as 4 groups of 64, 5 groups of 8, and
3 ones:

$$
\begin{aligned}
299 &= (4 \times 64) + (5 \times 8) + (3 \times 1) \\
&= (4 \times 8^2) + (5 \times 8^1) + (3 \times 1) \\
&= 453_{\text{eight}}.
\end{aligned}
$$

 Convert the base ten numeral 365 to a base seven numeral.

EXAMPLE 6   USING DIVISIONS TO CONVERT FROM BASE TEN TO BASE SIX

Convert the base ten numeral 3444 to a base six numeral.

SOLUTION   The place values in base six are

$$\ldots, 6^5, 6^4, 6^3, 6^2, 6^1, 1, \quad \text{or} \quad \ldots, 7776, 1296, 216, 36, 6, 1.$$

We use the powers of 6 that are less than 3444 and perform successive divisions by
these powers.

2 groups of 1296
$$
\begin{array}{r}
2 \\
1296\overline{)3444} \\
2592 \\
\hline
852
\end{array}
$$

3 groups of 216
$$
\begin{array}{r}
3 \\
216\overline{)852} \\
648 \\
\hline
204
\end{array}
$$

5 groups of 36
$$
\begin{array}{r}
5 \\
36\overline{)204} \\
180 \\
\hline
24
\end{array}
$$

4 groups of 6
$$
\begin{array}{r}
4 \\
6\overline{)24} \\
24 \\
\hline
0
\end{array}
$$
0 ones left over

Using these four quotients and the final remainder, we can immediately write the
answer.

$$3444 = 23540_{\text{six}}$$

 Convert the base ten numeral 2763 to a base five numeral.

EXERCISE SET 4.2 ●●●●●○○

• Practice Exercises

In Exercises 1–18, convert the numeral to a numeral in base ten.

1. 43_{five}

2. 34_{five}

3. 52_{eight}

4. 67_{eight}

5. 132_{four}

6. 321_{four}

7. 1011_{two}

8. 1101_{two}

9. 2035_{six}

10. 2073_{nine}

11. 70355_{eight}

12. 41502_{six}

13. $2096_{sixteen}$

14. $3104_{fifteen}$

15. 110101_{two}

16. 101101_{two}

17. $ACE5_{sixteen}$

18. $EDF7_{sixteen}$

In Exercises 19–28, mentally convert each base ten numeral to a numeral in the given base.

19. 7 to base five

20. 9 to base five

21. 11 to base seven

22. 12 to base seven

23. 2 to base two

24. 3 to base two

25. 13 to base four

26. 19 to base four

27. 37 to base six

28. 25 to base six

In Exercises 29–40, use divisions to convert each base ten numeral to a numeral in the given base.

29. 87 to base five

30. 85 to base seven

31. 108 to base four

32. 199 to base four

33. 19 to base two

34. 23 to base two

35. 138 to base three

36. 129 to base three

37. 386 to base six

38. 428 to base nine

39. 1599 to base seven

40. 1346 to base eight

• Practice Plus

In Exercises 41–44, use Table 4.1 on page 199 to write each Hindu-Arabic numeral as a Babylonian numeral.

41. 3052

42. 6704

43. 23,546

44. 41,265

In Exercises 45–48, use Table 4.2 on page 200 to write each Hindu-Arabic numeral as a Mayan numeral.

45. 9307

46. 8703

47. 28,704

48. 34,847

49. Convert 34_{five} to base seven.

50. Convert 46_{eight} to base five.

51. Convert 110010011_{two} to base eight.

52. Convert 101110001_{two} to base eight.

• Application Exercises

Read the Blitzer Bonus on page 205. Then use the information in the essay to solve Exercises 53–60.

In Exercises 53–56, write the binary representation for each letter.

53. F

54. Y

55. m

56. p

In Exercises 57–58, break each binary sequence into groups of seven digits and write the word represented by the sequence.

57. 101000010000011001100

58. 1001100101010110000111001011

In Exercises 59–60, write a sequence of binary digits that represents each word.

59. Mom

60. Dad

• Writing in Mathematics

61. Explain how to determine the place values for a four-digit numeral in base six.

62. Describe how to change a numeral in a base other than ten to a base ten numeral.

63. Describe how to change a base ten numeral to a numeral in another base.

• Critical Thinking Exercises

In Exercises 64–65, write in the indicated base the counting numbers that precede and follow the number expressed by the given numeral.

64. 888_{nine}

65. $EC5_{sixteen}$

66. Arrange from smallest to largest:

$$11111011_{two}, 3A6_{twelve}, 673_{eight}.$$

• Group Exercises

The following topics are appropriate for either individual or group research projects. A report should be given to the class on the researched topic. Useful references include history of mathematics books, books whose purpose is to excite the reader about mathematics, encyclopedias, and the World Wide Web.

67. Societies that Use Numeration Systems with Bases Other Than Ten

68. The Use of Fingers to Represent Numbers

69. Applications of Bases Other Than Ten

70. Binary, Octal, Hexadecimal Bases and Computers

71. Babylonian and Mayan Civilizations and Their Contributions

SECTION 4.3 • COMPUTATION IN POSITIONAL SYSTEMS

O B J E C T I V E S

1. Add in bases other than ten.

2. Subtract in bases other than ten.

3. Multiply in bases other than ten.

4. Divide in bases other than ten.

People have always looked for ways to make calculations faster and easier. The Hindu-Arabic system of numeration made computation simpler and less mysterious. More people were able to perform computation with ease, leading to the widespread use of the system.

All computations in bases other than ten are performed exactly like those in base ten. However, when a computation is equal to or exceeds the given base, use the mental conversions discussed in the previous section to convert from the base ten numeral to a numeral in the desired base.

| 1 | Add in bases other than ten. |

The 4¹, or fours' column

The ones' column

$$33_{\text{four}}$$
$$+ 13_{\text{four}}$$

Addition

EXAMPLE 1   ADDITION IN BASE FOUR

Add:

$$33_{\text{four}}$$
$$+ 13_{\text{four}}.$$

SOLUTION   We will begin by adding the numbers in the right-hand column. In base four, the digit symbols are 0, 1, 2, and 3. If a sum in this, or any, column exceeds 3, we will have to convert this base ten number to base four. We begin by adding the numbers in the right-hand, or ones', column:

$$3_{\text{four}} + 3_{\text{four}} = 6.$$

6 is not a digit symbol in base four. However, we can express 6 as one group of four and two ones left over:

$$3_{\text{four}} + 3_{\text{four}} = 6_{\text{ten}} = (1 \times 4) + (2 \times 1) = 12_{\text{four}}.$$

Now we record the sum of the right-hand column, 12_{four}:

We place the digit on the left above the fours' column.

1
$$33_{\text{four}}$$
$$+ 13_{\text{four}}$$
2

$$12_{\text{four}}$$

We place the digit on the right under the ones' column.

Next, we add the three digits in the fours' column:

$$1_{\text{four}} + 3_{\text{four}} + 1_{\text{four}} = 5.$$

5 is not a digit symbol in base four. However, we can express 5 as one group of four and one left over:

$$1_{\text{four}} + 3_{\text{four}} + 1_{\text{four}} = 5_{\text{ten}} = (1 \times 4) + (1 \times 1) = 11_{\text{four}}.$$

Record the 11_{four}.

$$
\begin{array}{r}
\overset{1}{} \\
33_{\text{four}} \\
+\ 13_{\text{four}} \\
\hline
112_{\text{four}}
\end{array}
$$

This is the desired sum.

You can check the sum by converting 33_{four}, 13_{four}, and 112_{four} to base ten: $33_{\text{four}} = 15$, $13_{\text{four}} = 7$, and $112_{\text{four}} = 22$. Because $15 + 7 = 22$, our work is correct.

 1 Add:

$$
\begin{array}{r}
32_{\text{five}} \\
+\ 44_{\text{five}}
\end{array}.
$$

EXAMPLE 2   ADDITION IN BASE TWO

Add:

$$
\begin{array}{r}
111_{\text{two}} \\
+\ 101_{\text{two}}
\end{array}.
$$

SOLUTION We begin by adding the numbers in the right-hand, or ones', column:

$$1_{\text{two}} + 1_{\text{two}} = 2.$$

2 is not a digit symbol in base two. We can express 2 as one group of 2 and zero ones left over:

$$1_{\text{two}} + 1_{\text{two}} = 2_{\text{ten}} = (1 \times 2) + (0 \times 1) = 10_{\text{two}}.$$

Now we record the sum of the right-hand column, 10_{two}:

We place the digit on the left above the twos' column.

We place the digit on the right under the ones' column.

Next, we add the three digits in the twos' column:

$$1_{\text{two}} + 1_{\text{two}} + 0_{\text{two}} = 2_{\text{ten}} = (1 \times 2) + (0 \times 1) = 10_{\text{two}}.$$

Now we record the sum of the middle column, 10_{two}:

We place the digit on the left above the fours' column.

We place the digit on the right under the twos' column.

Finally, we add the three digits in the fours' column:

$$1_{\text{two}} + 1_{\text{two}} + 1_{\text{two}} = 3.$$

3 is not a digit symbol in base two. We can express 3 as one group of 2 and one 1 left over:

$$1_{\text{two}} + 1_{\text{two}} + 1_{\text{two}} = 3_{\text{ten}} = (1 \times 2) + (1 \times 1) = 11_{\text{two}}.$$

Record the 11_{two}.

$$
\begin{array}{r}
11 \\
111_{\text{two}} \\
+\ 101_{\text{two}} \\
\hline
1100_{\text{two}}
\end{array}
$$

This is the desired sum.

You can check the sum by converting to base ten: $111_{\text{two}} = 7$, $101_{\text{two}} = 5$, and $1100_{\text{two}} = 12$. Because $7 + 5 = 12$, our work is correct.

 2 Add:

$$
\begin{array}{r}
111_{\text{two}} \\
+\ 111_{\text{two}}
\end{array}
$$

Subtraction

To subtract in bases other than ten, we line up the digits with the same place values and subtract column by column, beginning with the column on the right. If "borrowing" is necessary to perform the subtraction, borrow the amount of the base. For example, when we borrow in base ten subtraction, we borrow 10s. Likewise, we borrow 2s in base two, 3s in base three, 4s in base four, and so on.

EXAMPLE 3   SUBTRACTION IN BASE FOUR

Subtract:

$$
\begin{array}{r}
31_{\text{four}} \\
-\ 12_{\text{four}}
\end{array}
$$

SOLUTION We start by performing subtraction in the right column, $1_{\text{four}} - 2_{\text{four}}$. Because 2_{four} is greater than 1_{four}, we need to borrow from the preceding column. We are working in base four, so we borrow one group of 4. This gives a sum of $4 + 1$, or 5, in base ten. Now we subtract 2 from 5, obtaining a difference of 3:

We borrow one group of 4. Now there are 2 groups of 4 for this place value, not 3.

$$
\begin{array}{r}
2\,5 \\
3\!\!\!/1_{\text{four}} \\
-\ 12_{\text{four}} \\
\hline
3_{\text{four}}
\end{array}
$$

We add the borrowed group of 4 to 1 in base ten: $1 + 4 = 5$.

Now we perform the subtraction in the second column from the right:

We subtract 1 from 2.

$$
\begin{array}{r}
2\,5 \\
3\!\!\!/1_{\text{four}} \\
-\ 12_{\text{four}} \\
\hline
13_{\text{four}}
\end{array}
$$

This is the desired difference.

You can check the difference by converting to base ten: $31_{\text{four}} = 13$, $12_{\text{four}} = 6$, and $13_{\text{four}} = 7$. Because $13 - 6 = 7$, our work is correct.

 3 Subtract:

$$
\begin{array}{r}
41_{\text{five}} \\
-\ 23_{\text{five}}
\end{array}
$$

Multiply in bases other than ten.

EXAMPLE 4 SUBTRACTION IN BASE FIVE

Subtract:

$$3431_{\text{five}} - 1242_{\text{five}}.$$

SOLUTION

Step 1. Borrow a group of 5 from the preceding column. This gives a sum of 5 + 1, or 6, in base ten.

$$\begin{array}{r} 2\,6 \\ 343\!\!\!/1_{\text{five}} \\ -\ 1242_{\text{five}} \\ \hline 4_{\text{five}} \end{array}$$

Step 2. 6 − 2 = 4

Step 3. Borrow a group of 5 from the preceding column. This gives a sum of 5 + 2, or 7, in base ten.

$$\begin{array}{r} 7 \\ 3\,2\,6 \\ 343\!\!\!/1_{\text{five}} \\ -\ 1242_{\text{five}} \\ \hline 34_{\text{five}} \end{array}$$

Step 4. 7 − 4 = 3

Step 5. No borrowing is needed for these two columns.

$$\begin{array}{r} 7 \\ 3\,2\,6 \\ 343\!\!\!/1_{\text{five}} \\ -\ 1242_{\text{five}} \\ \hline 2134_{\text{five}} \end{array}$$

Step 6. 3 − 2 = 1
Step 7. 3 − 1 = 2

Thus, $3431_{\text{five}} - 1242_{\text{five}} = 2134_{\text{five}}$.

CHECK POINT 4 Subtract: $5144_{\text{seven}} - 3236_{\text{seven}}$.

Multiplication

EXAMPLE 5 MULTIPLICATION IN BASE SIX

Multiply:

$$\begin{array}{r} 34_{\text{six}} \\ \times\ 2_{\text{six}} \end{array}$$

SOLUTION We multiply just as we do in base ten. That is, first we will multiply the digit 2 by the digit 4 directly above it. Then we will multiply the digit 2 by the digit 3 in the left column. Keep in mind that only the digit symbols 0, 1, 2, 3, 4, and 5 are permitted in base six. We begin with

$$2_{\text{six}} \times 4_{\text{six}} = 8_{\text{ten}} = (1 \times 6) + (2 \times 1) = 12_{\text{six}}.$$

Record the 2 and carry the 1:

$$\begin{array}{r} 1 \\ 34_{\text{six}} \\ \times\ 2_{\text{six}} \\ \hline 2_{\text{six}} \end{array}$$

Our next computation involves both multiplication and addition:

$$(2_{\text{six}} \times 3_{\text{six}}) + 1_{\text{six}} = 6 + 1 = 7_{\text{ten}} = (1 \times 6) + (1 \times 1) = 11_{\text{six}}.$$

Record the 11_{six}.

$$\begin{array}{r} 34_{\text{six}} \\ \times\ 2_{\text{six}} \\ \hline 112_{\text{six}} \end{array}$$
This is the desired product.

Let's check the product by converting to base ten: $34_{\text{six}} = 22$, $2_{\text{six}} = 2$, and $112_{\text{six}} = 44$. Because $22 \times 2 = 44$, our work is correct.

CHECK POINT 5 Multiply:

$$\begin{array}{r} 45_{\text{seven}} \\ \times\ 3_{\text{seven}} \end{array}$$

4 | Divide in bases other than ten.

Division

The answer in a division problem is called a **quotient**. A multiplication table showing products in the same base as the division problem is helpful.

EXAMPLE 6   DIVISION IN BASE FOUR

Use Table 4.5, showing products in base four, to perform the following division:

$$3_{four}\overline{)222_{four}}.$$

TABLE 4.5 MULTIPLICATION: BASE FOUR

×	0	1	2	3
0	0	0	0	0
1	0	1	2	3
2	0	2	10	12
3	0	3	12	21

SOLUTION We can use the same method to divide in base four that we use in base ten. Begin by dividing 22_{four} by 3_{four}. Use Table 4.5 to find in the vertical column headed by 3 the largest product that is less than or equal to 22_{four}. This product is 21_{four}. Because $3_{four} \times 3_{four} = 21_{four}$, the first number in the quotient is 3_{four}.

Divisor — $3_{four}\overline{)222_{four}}$ — First digit in the quotient — 3 — Dividend

Now multiply $3_{four} \times 3_{four}$ and write the product, 21_{four}, under the first two digits of the dividend.

$$\begin{array}{r} 3 \\ 3_{four}\overline{)222_{four}} \\ 21 \end{array}$$

Subtract: $22_{four} - 21_{four} = 1_{four}$.

$$\begin{array}{r} 3 \\ 3_{four}\overline{)222_{four}} \\ \underline{21} \\ 1 \end{array}$$

Bring down the next digit in the dividend, 2_{four}.

$$\begin{array}{r} 3 \\ 3_{four}\overline{)222_{four}} \\ \underline{21} \\ 12 \end{array}$$

We now return to Table 4.5. Find in the vertical column headed by 3 the largest product that is less than or equal to 12_{four}. Because $3_{four} \times 2_{four} = 12_{four}$, the next numeral in the quotient is 2_{four}. We use this information to finish the division.

This is the desired quotient.

$$\begin{array}{r} 32_{four} \\ 3_{four}\overline{)222_{four}} \\ \underline{21} \\ 12 \\ \underline{12} \\ 0 \end{array}$$

Let's check the quotient by converting to base ten: $3_{four} = 3, 222_{four} = 42$, and $32_{four} = 14$. Because $\dfrac{14}{3\overline{)42}}$, our work is correct.

○

Use Table 4.5, showing products in base four, to perform the following division:

$$2_{four}\overline{)112_{four}}.$$

BLITZER BONUS

Base Two, Logic, and Computers

Smaller than a fingernail, a computer's microchip operates like a tiny electronic brain. The microchip in Figure 4.2 is magnified almost 1200 times, revealing transistors with connecting tracks positioned above them. These tiny transistors switch on and off to control electronic signals, processing thousands of pieces of information per second. Since 1971, the number of transistors that can fit onto a single chip has increased from over 2000 to a staggering 500 million.

We have seen that communication inside a computer takes the form of sequences of on–off electric pulses that digitally represent numbers, words, sounds, and visual images. These binary streams are manipulated when they pass through the microchip's gates, shown in Figure 4.3. The **not gate** takes a digital sequence and changes all the 0s to 1s and all the 1s to 0s.

FIGURE 4.2

Before	After
11001101	00110010

The *and* and *or gates* take two input sequences and produce one output sequence. The **and gate** outputs a 1 if both sequences have a 1; otherwise, it outputs a 0.

Before	After
101001	100001
110101	

The **or gate** outputs a 1 if either sequence has a 1; otherwise, it outputs a 0.

Before	After
101001	111101
110101	

These gates are at the computational heart of a computer. They should remind you of negation, conjunction, and disjunction in logic, except that T is now 1 and F is now 0. Without the merging of base two and logic, computers as we know them would not exist.

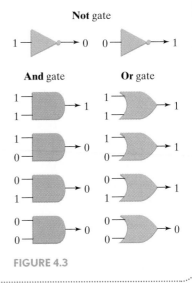

FIGURE 4.3

EXERCISE SET 4.3 ●●●●●●

• Practice Exercises

In Exercises 1–12, add in the indicated base.

1. 23_{four}
$+ 13_{\text{four}}$

2. 31_{four}
$+ 22_{\text{four}}$

3. 11_{two}
$+ 11_{\text{two}}$

4. 101_{two}
$+ \ 11_{\text{two}}$

5. 342_{five}
$+ 413_{\text{five}}$

6. 323_{five}
$+ 421_{\text{five}}$

7. 645_{seven}
$+ 324_{\text{seven}}$

8. 632_{seven}
$+ 564_{\text{seven}}$

9. 6784_{nine}
$+ 7865_{\text{nine}}$

10. 1021_{three}
$+ 2011_{\text{three}}$

11. 14632_{seven}
$+ \ 5604_{\text{seven}}$

12. $53B_{\text{sixteen}}$
$+ 694_{\text{sixteen}}$

In Exercises 13–24, subtract in the indicated base.

13. 32_{four}
$- 13_{\text{four}}$

14. 21_{four}
$- 12_{\text{four}}$

15. 23_{five}
$- 14_{\text{five}}$

16. 32_{seven}
$- 16_{\text{seven}}$

17. 475_{eight}
$- 267_{\text{eight}}$

18. 712_{nine}
$- 483_{\text{nine}}$

19. 563_{seven}
$- 164_{\text{seven}}$

20. 462_{eight}
$- 177_{\text{eight}}$

21. 1001_{two}
$- \ 111_{\text{two}}$

22. 1000_{two}
$- \ 101_{\text{two}}$

23. 1200_{three}
$- 1012_{\text{three}}$

24. $4C6_{\text{sixteen}}$
$- 198_{\text{sixteen}}$

In Exercises 25–34, multiply in the indicated base.

25. 25_{six}
$\times \ 4_{\text{six}}$

26. 34_{five}
$\times \ 3_{\text{five}}$

27. 11_{two}
$\times \ 1_{\text{two}}$

28. 21_{four}
$\times \ 3_{\text{four}}$

29. 543_{seven}
$\times \ 5_{\text{seven}}$

30. 243_{nine}
$\times \ 6_{\text{nine}}$

31. 623_{eight}
$\times \ 4_{\text{eight}}$

32. 543_{six}
$\times \ 5_{\text{six}}$

33. 21_{four}
$\times 12_{\text{four}}$

34. 32_{four}
$\times 23_{\text{four}}$

In Exercises 35–38, use the multiplication tables shown below to divide in the indicated base.

MULTIPLICATION: BASE FOUR

×	0	1	2	3
0	0	0	0	0
1	0	1	2	3
2	0	2	10	12
3	0	3	12	21

MULTIPLICATION: BASE FIVE

×	0	1	2	3	4
0	0	0	0	0	0
1	0	1	2	3	4
2	0	2	4	11	13
3	0	3	11	14	22
4	0	4	13	22	31

35. $2_{\text{four}} \overline{)100_{\text{four}}}$

36. $2_{\text{four}} \overline{)321_{\text{four}}}$

37. $3_{\text{five}} \overline{)224_{\text{five}}}$

38. $4_{\text{five}} \overline{)134_{\text{five}}}$

• Practice Plus

In Exercises 39–46, perform the indicated operations.

39. $10110_{\text{two}} + 10100_{\text{two}} + 11100_{\text{two}}$

40. $11100_{\text{two}} + 11111_{\text{two}} + 10111_{\text{two}}$

41. $11111_{\text{two}} + 10110_{\text{two}} - 101_{\text{two}}$

42. $10111_{\text{two}} + 11110_{\text{two}} - 111_{\text{two}}$

43. $1011_{\text{two}} \times 101_{\text{two}}$

44. $1101_{\text{two}} \times 110_{\text{two}}$

45. $D3_{\text{sixteen}} \times 8A_{\text{sixteen}}$

46. $B5_{\text{sixteen}} \times 2C_{\text{sixteen}}$

• Application Exercises

Read the Blitzer Bonus on page 214. Then use the information in the essay to solve Exercises 47–52. Each exercise shows the binary sequences 10011 and 11001 about to be manipulated by passing through a microchip's series of gates. Provide the result(s) of these computer manipulations, designated by **?** *in each diagram.*

47.

48.

49.

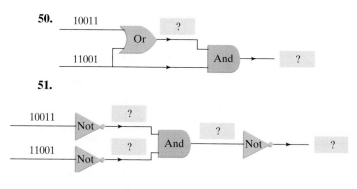

50.

51.

52.

53. Use the equivalence $p \rightarrow q \equiv \sim p \vee q$ to select the circuit in Exercises 47–52 that illustrates a conditional gate.

• Writing in Mathematics

54. Describe how to add two numbers in a base other than ten. How do you express and record the sum of numbers in a column if that sum exceeds the base?

55. Describe how to subtract two numbers in a base other than ten. How do you subtract a larger number from a smaller number in the same column?

56. Describe two difficulties that youngsters encounter when learning to add, subtract, multiply, and divide using Hindu-Arabic numerals. Base your answer on difficulties that are encountered when performing these computations in bases other than ten.

• Critical Thinking Exercises

57. Divide: $31_{\text{seven}} \overline{)2426_{\text{seven}}}$.

58. Use the Mayan numerals in Table 4.2 on page 200 to solve this exercise. Add $\overset{\cdot}{\underset{\cdot\cdot}{\text{—}}}$ and $\overset{\overline{\hspace{0.5em}}}{\underset{\equiv}{\ominus}}$ without converting to Hindu-Arabic numerals.

• Group Exercises

59. Group members should research various methods that societies have used to perform computations. Include finger multiplication, the galley method (sometimes called the Gelosia method), Egyptian duplation, subtraction by complements, Napier's bones, and other methods of interest in your presentation to the entire class.

60. Organize a debate. One side represents people who favor performing computations by hand, using the methods and procedures discussed in this section, but applied to base ten numerals. The other side represents people who favor the use of calculators for performing all computations. Include the merits of each approach in the debate.

SECTION 4.4 • LOOKING BACK AT EARLY NUMERATION SYSTEMS

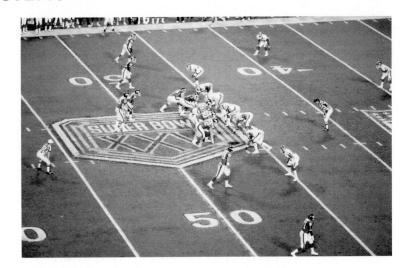

Super Bowl XXV, played on January 27, 1991, resulted in the closest score of all time: NY Giants: 20; Buffalo: 19. If you are intrigued by sports facts and figures, you are probably aware that major sports events, such as the Super Bowl, are named using Roman numerals. Perhaps you have seen the use of Roman numerals in dating movies and television shows, or on clocks and watches.

In this section, we embark on a brief journey through time and numbers. Our Hindu-Arabic numeration system, the focus of this chapter, is successful because it expresses numbers with just ten symbols and makes computation with these numbers relatively easy. By these standards, the early numeration systems discussed in this section, such as Roman numerals, are unsuccessful. By looking briefly at these systems, you will see that our system is outstanding when compared with other historical systems.

1 | Understand and use the Egyptian system.

The Egyptian Numeration System

Like most great civilizations, ancient Egypt had several numeration systems. The oldest is hieroglyphic notation, which developed around 3400 B.C. Table 4.6 lists the Egyptian hieroglyphic numerals with the equivalent Hindu-Arabic numerals. Notice that the numerals are powers of ten. Their numeral for 1,000,000, or 10^6, looks like someone who just won the lottery!

STUDY TIP

It is not necessary to memorize the symbols for the four numeration systems discussed in this section. Focus your attention on understanding the idea behind each system and how these ideas have been incorporated into our Hindu-Arabic system.

TABLE 4.6 EGYPTIAN HIEROGLYPHIC NUMERALS

Hindu-Arabic Numeral	Egyptian Numeral	Description
1		Staff
10		Heel bone
100		Spiral
1000		Lotus blossom
10,000		Pointing finger
100,000		Tadpole
1,000,000		Astonished person

It takes far more space to represent most numbers in the Egyptian system than in our system. This is because a number is expressed by repeating each numeral the required number of times. However, no numeral, except perhaps the astonished person, should be repeated more than nine times. If we were to use the Egyptian system to represent 764, we would need to write

100 100 100 100 100 100 100 10 10 10 10 10 10 1 1 1 1

and then represent each of these symbols with the appropriate hieroglyphic numeral from Table 4.6. Thus, 764 as an Egyptian numeral is

$$\text{۹۹۹۹۹۹۹∩∩∩∩∩∩IIII.}$$

The ancient Egyptian system is an example of an **additive system**, one in which the number represented is the sum of the values of the numerals.

EXAMPLE 1   USING THE EGYPTIAN NUMERATION SYSTEM

Write the following numeral as a Hindu-Arabic numeral:

$$\text{ᛉ∥∥∥∩∩∩∩IIIII.}$$

SOLUTION Using Table 4.6, find the value of each of the Egyptian numerals. Then add them.

$$1{,}000{,}000 + 10{,}000 + 10{,}000 + 10 + 10 + 10 + 1 + 1 + 1 + 1 = 1{,}020{,}034$$

○

CHECK POINT 1 Write the following numeral as a Hindu-Arabic numeral:

$$\text{↻ ↻ ↻ ↻ ۹۹∩∩III.}$$

EXAMPLE 2   USING THE EGYPTIAN NUMERATION SYSTEM

Write 1752 as an Egyptian numeral.

SOLUTION First break down the Hindu-Arabic numeral into quantities that match the Egyptian numerals:

$$\begin{aligned}
1752 &= 1000 + 700 + 50 + 2 \\
&= 1000 + 100 + 100 + 100 + 100 + 100 + 100 + 100 \\
&\quad + 10 + 10 + 10 + 10 + 10 + 1 + 1.
\end{aligned}$$

Now, use Table 4.6 to find the Egyptian symbol that matches each quantity. For example, the lotus blossom, ⚲, matches 1000. Write each of these symbols and leave out the addition signs. Thus, the number 1752 can be expressed as

$$\text{⚲۹۹۹۹۹۹۹∩∩∩∩∩II.}$$

○

CHECK POINT 2 Write 2563 as an Egyptian numeral.

The Roman Numeration System

The Roman numeration system was developed between 500 B.C. and 100 A.D. It evolved as a result of tax collecting and commerce in the vast Roman Empire. The Roman numerals shown in Table 4.7 were used throughout Europe until the eighteenth century. They are still commonly used in outlining, on clocks, for certain copyright dates, and in numbering some pages in books. Roman numerals are selected letters from the Roman alphabet.

TABLE 4.7 ROMAN NUMERALS

Roman numeral	I	V	X	L	C	D	M
Hindu-Arabic numeral	1	5	10	50	100	500	1000

If the symbols in Table 4.7 decrease in value from left to right, then add their values to obtain the value of the Roman numeral as a whole. For example, CX = 100 + 10 = 110. On the other hand, if symbols increase in value from left to right, then subtract the value of the symbol on the left from the symbol on the right. For example, IV means 5 − 1 = 4 and IX means 10 − 1 = 9.

Only the Roman numerals representing 1, 10, 100, 1000, ..., can be subtracted. Furthermore, they can be subtracted only from their next two greater Roman numerals.

Roman numeral (values that can be subtracted are shown in red)	I	V	X	L	C	D	M
Hindu-Arabic numeral	1	5	10	50	100	500	1000

I can be subtracted only from V and X.   X can be subtracted only from L and C.   C can be subtracted only from D and M.

EXAMPLE 3   USING ROMAN NUMERALS

Write CLXVII as a Hindu-Arabic numeral.

SOLUTION Because the numerals decrease in value from left to right, we add their values to find the value of the Roman numeral as a whole.

$$CLXVII = 100 + 50 + 10 + 5 + 1 + 1 = 167$$

 Write MCCCLXI as a Hindu-Arabic numeral.

EXAMPLE 4   USING ROMAN NUMERALS

Write MCMXCVI as a Hindu-Arabic numeral.

SOLUTION

$$
\begin{array}{ccccc}
M & CM & XC & V & I \\
\downarrow & \downarrow & \downarrow & \downarrow & \downarrow
\end{array}
$$
$$= 1000 + (1000 - 100) + (100 - 10) + 5 + 1$$
$$= 1000 + 900 + 90 + 5 + 1 = 1996$$

 Write MCDXLVII as a Hindu-Arabic numeral.

Because Roman numerals involve subtraction as well as addition, it takes far less space to represent most numbers than in the Egyptian system. It is never necessary to repeat any symbol more than three consecutive times. For example, we write 46 as a Roman numeral using

$$XLVI \quad \text{rather than} \quad XXXXVI.$$

XL = 50 − 10 = 40

EXAMPLE 5   USING ROMAN NUMERALS

Write 249 as a Roman numeral.

SOLUTION

$$
\begin{aligned}
249 &= \quad\ 200 \quad\ + \quad\ 40 \quad\ + \quad\ 9 \\
&= 100 + 100 + (50 - 10) + (10 - 1) \\
&\quad\ \downarrow \qquad \downarrow \qquad\quad \downarrow \qquad\qquad \downarrow \\
&= \ \text{C} \qquad \text{C} \qquad\ \text{XL} \qquad\quad \text{IX}
\end{aligned}
$$

Thus, 249 = CCXLIX.

CHECK POINT 5 Write 399 as a Roman numeral.

The Roman numeration system uses bars above numerals or groups of numerals to show that the numbers are to be multiplied by 1000. For example,

$$\overline{\text{L}} = 50 \times 1000 = 50{,}000 \quad \text{and} \quad \overline{\text{CM}} = 900 \times 1000 = 900{,}000.$$

Placing bars over Roman numerals reduces the number of symbols needed to represent large numbers.

The Traditional Chinese Numeration System

3 | Understand and use the traditional Chinese system.

The numerals used in the traditional Chinese numeration system are given in Table 4.8. At least two things are missing—a symbol for zero and a surprised lottery winner!

TABLE 4.8 TRADITIONAL CHINESE NUMERALS												
Traditional Chinese numerals	一	二	三	四	五	六	七	八	九	十	百	千
Hindu-Arabic numerals	1	2	3	4	5	6	7	8	9	10	100	1000

3
1000
2
100
6
10
4

Representing 3264 vertically is the first step in expressing it as a Chinese numeral.

So, how are numbers represented with this set of symbols? Chinese numerals are written vertically. Using our digits, the number 3264 is expressed as shown in the margin.

The next step is to replace each of these seven symbols with a traditional Chinese numeral from Table 4.8. Our next example illustrates this procedure.

Writing 3264 as a Chinese numeral

EXAMPLE 6 USING THE TRADITIONAL CHINESE NUMERATION SYSTEM

Write 3264 as a Chinese numeral.

SOLUTION First, break down the Hindu-Arabic numeral into quantities that match the Chinese numerals. Represent each quantity vertically. Then, use Table 4.8 on the previous page to find the Chinese symbol that matches each quantity. This procedure, with the resulting Chinese numeral, is shown in the margin.

The Chinese system does not need a numeral for zero because it is not positional. For example, we write 8006, using zeros as placeholders, to indicate that two powers of ten, namely 10^2, or 100, and 10^1, or 10, are not needed. The Chinese leave this out, writing

8
1000
6 , or .

CHECK POINT 6 Write 2693 as a Chinese numeral.

---

4 | Understand and use the Ionic Greek system.

The Ionic Greek Numeration System

The ancient Greeks, masters of art, architecture, theater, literature, philosophy, geometry, and logic, were not masters when it came to representing numbers. The Ionic Greek numeration system, which can be traced back as far as 450 B.C., used letters of their alphabet for numerals. Table 4.9 shows the many symbols (too many symbols!) used to represent numbers.

TABLE 4.9 IONIC GREEK NUMERALS								
1	α	alpha	10	ι	iota	100	ρ	rho
2	β	beta	20	κ	kappa	200	σ	sigma
3	γ	gamma	30	λ	lambda	300	τ	tau
4	δ	delta	40	μ	mu	400	υ	upsilon
5	ϵ	epsilon	50	ν	nu	500	ϕ	phi
6	ι	vau	60	ξ	xi	600	χ	chi
7	ζ	zeta	70	o	omicron	700	ψ	psi
8	η	eta	80	π	pi	800	ω	omega
9	θ	theta	90	Q	koph	900	⊤⊤	sampi

To represent a number from 1 to 999, the appropriate symbols are written next to one another. For example, the number 21 = 20 + 1. When 21 is expressed as a Greek numeral, the plus sign is left out:

$$21 = \kappa\alpha.$$

Similarly, the number 823 written as a Greek numeral is $\omega\kappa\gamma$.

EXAMPLE 7 USING THE IONIC GREEK NUMERATION SYSTEM

Write $\psi\lambda\delta$ as a Hindu-Arabic numeral.

SOLUTION $\psi = 700$, $\lambda = 30$, and $\delta = 4$. Adding these numbers gives 734.

CHECK POINT 7 Write $\omega\pi\epsilon$ as a Hindu-Arabic numeral.

One of the many unsuccessful features of the Greek numeration system is that new symbols have to be added to represent higher numbers. It is like an alphabet that gets bigger each time a new word is used and has to be written.

EXERCISE SET 4.4 ●●●●●●

• Practice Exercises

Use Table 4.6 on page 216 to solve Exercises 1–12.

In Exercises 1–6, write each Egyptian numeral as a Hindu-Arabic numeral.

1. ⟨Egyptian numeral⟩
2. ⟨Egyptian numeral⟩
3. ⟨Egyptian numeral⟩
4. ⟨Egyptian numeral⟩
5. ⟨Egyptian numeral⟩
6. ⟨Egyptian numeral⟩

In Exercises 7–12, write each Hindu-Arabic numeral as an Egyptian numeral.

7. 423
8. 825
9. 1846
10. 1425
11. 23,547
12. 2,346,031

Use Table 4.7 on page 218 to solve Exercises 13–36.

In Exercises 13–28, write each Roman numeral as a Hindu-Arabic numeral.

13. XI
14. CL
15. XVI
16. LVII
17. XL
18. CM
19. LIX
20. XLIV
21. CXLVI
22. CLXI
23. MDCXXI
24. MMCDXLV
25. MMDCLXXVII
26. MDCXXVI
27. $\overline{\text{IX}}$CDLVI
28. $\overline{\text{V}}$MCCXI

In Exercises 29–36, write each Hindu-Arabic numeral as a Roman numeral.

29. 43
30. 96
31. 129
32. 469
33. 1896
34. 4578
35. 6892
36. 5847

Use Table 4.8 on page 219 to solve Exercises 37–48.

In Exercises 37–42, write each traditional Chinese numeral as a Hindu-Arabic numeral.

37. 八十八
38. 七百
39. 五百二十七
40. 三千八十一
41. 二千七百五十六
42. 八千二百三十六

In Exercises 43–48, write each Hindu-Arabic numeral as a traditional Chinese numeral.

43. 43
44. 269
45. 583
46. 2965
47. 4870
48. 7605

Use Table 4.9 on page 220 to solve Exercises 49–56.

In Exercises 49–52, write each Ionic Greek numeral as a Hindu-Arabic numeral.

49. $\iota\beta$
50. $\phi\epsilon$
51. $\sigma\lambda\delta$
52. $\psi o\theta$

In Exercises 53–56, write each Hindu-Arabic numeral as an Ionic Greek numeral.

53. 43
54. 257
55. 483
56. 895

• Practice Plus

57. Write ⟨numerals⟩ as a Roman numeral and as a traditional Chinese numeral.
58. Write ⟨numerals⟩ as a Roman numeral and as a traditional Chinese numeral.
59. Write MDCCXLI as an Egyptian numeral and as a traditional Chinese numeral.
60. Write MMCCXLV as an Egyptian numeral and as a traditional Chinese numeral.

In Exercises 61–64, write each numeral as a numeral in base five.

61. ⟨Egyptian numeral⟩
62. ⟨Egyptian numeral⟩
63. CXCII
64. CMLXXIV

In Exercises 65–66, perform each subtraction without converting to Hindu-Arabic numerals.

65. ⟨Egyptian numeral⟩ − ⟨Egyptian numeral⟩
66. ⟨Egyptian numeral⟩ − ⟨Egyptian numeral⟩

• Application Exercises

67. Look at the back of a U.S. one dollar bill. What date is written in Roman numerals along the base of the pyramid with an eye? What is this date's significance?
68. A construction crew demolishing a very old building was surprised to find the numeral MCMLXXXIX inscribed on the cornerstone. Explain why they were surprised.

The Braille numeration system is a base ten positional system that uses raised dots in 2-by-3 cells as digit symbols.

Braille Digit Symbols   Other Symbols

0 1 2 3 4 5 6 7 8 9

Comma

Written before all numbers

In Exercises 69–70, use the digit symbols at the bottom of the previous page to express each Braille numeral as a Hindu-Arabic numeral and as a Roman numeral.

69.

70.

• Writing in Mathematics

71. Describe how a number is represented in the Egyptian numeration system.

72. If you are interpreting a Roman numeral, when do you add values and when do you subtract them? Give an example to illustrate each case.

73. Describe how a number is represented in the traditional Chinese numeration system.

74. Describe one disadvantage of the Ionic Greek numeration system.

75. If you could use only one system of numeration described in this section, which would you prefer? Discuss the reasons for your choice.

• Critical Thinking Exercises

76. Arrange these three numerals from smallest to largest.

四
百
二
十
八

CCCCXLIX   ꝯꝯꝯꝯ∩∩∩∩

77. Use Egyptian numerals to write the numeral that precedes and the numeral that follows

ꝯꝯ∩∩∩∩∩∩∩∩∩∩||||||.

78. After reading this section, a student had a numeration nightmare about selling flowers in a time-warped international market. She started out with 200 flowers, selling XLVI of them to a Roman,

∩∩∩||

to an Egyptian,

=
+

to a traditional Chinese family, and the remainder to a Greek. How many flowers were sold to the Greek? Express the answer in the Ionic Greek numeration system.

• Group Exercises

Take a moment to read the introduction to the group exercises on page 208. Exercises 79–83 list some additional topics for individual or group research projects.

79. A Time Line Showing Significant Developments in Numeration Systems

80. Animals and Number Sense

81. The Hebrew Numeration System (or any system not discussed in this chapter)

82. The Rhind Papyrus and What We Learned from It

83. Computation in an Early Numeration System

●●●●●● CHAPTER SUMMARY, REVIEW, AND TEST

● SUMMARY DEFINITIONS AND CONCEPTS	EXAMPLES

4.1 Our Hindu-Arabic System and Early Positional Systems

a. In a positional-value, or place-value, numeration system, the value of each symbol, called a digit, varies according to the position it occupies in the number.

b. The Hindu-Arabic numeration system is a base ten system with the digits 0, 1, 2, 3, 4, 5, 6, 7, 8, and 9. The place values in the system are

$$\ldots, 10^5, 10^4, 10^3, 10^2, 10^1, 1.$$

Ex. 2, p. 198; Ex. 3, p. 198

c. The Babylonian numeration system is a base 60 system, with place values given by

$$\ldots, \quad 60^3, \quad 60^2, \quad 60^1, \quad 1.$$
$$\text{or} \quad \text{or} \quad \text{or}$$
$$216{,}000 \quad 3600 \quad 60$$

Babylonian numerals are given in Table 4.1 on page 199.

Ex. 4, p. 199

d. The Mayan numeration system has place values given by

$$\ldots, \quad 18 \times 20^3, \quad 18 \times 20^2, \quad 18 \times 20, \quad 20, \quad 1.$$
$$\text{or} \quad \text{or} \quad \text{or}$$
$$144{,}000 \quad 7200 \quad 360$$

Mayan numerals are given in Table 4.2 on page 200.

Ex. 5, p. 201

4.2   Number Bases in Positional Systems

a. The base of a positional numeration system refers to the number of individual digit symbols used in the system as well as to the powers of the numbers used in place values. In base b, there are b digit symbols (from 0 through $b - 1$ inclusive) with place values given by

$$\ldots, b^4, b^3, b^2, b^1, 1.$$

b. To change a numeral in a base other than ten to a base ten numeral,

   1. Multiply each digit in the numeral by its respective place value.

   2. Find the sum of the products in step 1.

Ex. 1, p. 205;
Ex. 2, p. 205;
Ex. 3, p. 206

c. To change a base ten numeral to a base b numeral, use mental conversions or repeated divisions by powers of b to find how many groups of each place value are contained in the base ten numeral.

Ex. 4, p. 206;
Ex. 5, p. 207;
Ex. 6, p. 207

4.3   Computation in Positional Systems

a. Computations in bases other than ten are performed using the same procedures as in ordinary base ten arithmetic. When a computation is equal to or exceeds the given base, use mental conversions to convert from the base ten numeral to a numeral in the desired base.

Ex. 1, p. 209;
Ex. 2, p. 210;
Ex. 3, p. 211;
Ex. 4, p. 212;
Ex. 5, p. 212

b. To divide in bases other than ten, it is convenient to use a multiplication table for products in the required base.

Ex. 6, p. 213

4.4   Looking Back at Early Numeration Systems

a. A successful numeration system expresses numbers with relatively few symbols and makes computation with these numbers fairly easy.

b. By the standard in (a), the Egyptian system (Table 4.6 on page 216), the Roman system (Table 4.7 on page 218), the Chinese system (Table 4.8 on page 219), and the Greek system (Table 4.9 on page 220) are all unsuccessful. Unlike our Hindu-Arabic system, these systems are not positional and contain no symbol for zero.

Ex. 1, p. 217;
Ex. 2, p. 217;
Ex. 3, p. 218;
Ex. 4, p. 218;
Ex. 5, p. 219;
Ex. 6, p. 220;
Ex. 7, p. 220

REVIEW EXERCISES

4.1

In Exercises 1–2, evaluate the expression.

1. 11^2

2. 7^3

In Exercises 3–5, write each Hindu-Arabic numeral in expanded form.

3. 472

4. 8076

5. 70,329

In Exercises 6–7, express each expanded form as a Hindu-Arabic numeral.

6. $(7 \times 10^5) + (0 \times 10^4) + (6 \times 10^3) + (9 \times 10^2)$
$+ (5 \times 10^1) + (3 \times 1)$

7. $(7 \times 10^8) + (4 \times 10^7) + (3 \times 10^2) + (6 \times 1)$

Use Table 4.1 on page 199 to write each Babylonian numeral in Exercises 8–9 as a Hindu-Arabic numeral.

8. ‹ v   ‹ v v v

9. v v   ‹‹   ‹‹‹

Use Table 4.2 on page 200 to write each Mayan numeral in Exercises 10–11 as a Hindu-Arabic numeral.

10. $\cdot$ / $\cdots$ / $\equiv$

11. $\cdots\cdots$ / $\cdot\cdot$ / $\ominus$ / $\equiv$

12. Describe how a positional system is used to represent a number.

4.2

In Exercises 13–18, convert the numeral to a numeral in base ten.

13. 34_{five}

14. 110_{two}

15. 643_{seven}

16. 1084_{nine}

17. $FD3_{\text{sixteen}}$

18. 202202_{three}

In Exercises 19–24, convert each base ten numeral to a numeral in the given base.

19. 89 to base five

20. 21 to base two

21. 473 to base three

22. 7093 to base seven

23. 9348 to base six

24. 554 to base twelve

4.3

In Exercises 25–28, add in the indicated base.

25. 46_{seven}
$+53_{\text{seven}}$

26. 574_{eight}
$+605_{\text{eight}}$

27. 11011_{two}
$+10101_{\text{two}}$

28. $43C_{\text{sixteen}}$
$+694_{\text{sixteen}}$

In Exercises 29–32, subtract in the indicated base.

29. 34_{six}
-25_{six}

30. 624_{seven}
-246_{seven}

31. 1001_{two}
-110_{two}

32. 4121_{five}
-1312_{five}

In Exercises 33–35, multiply in the indicated base.

33. 32_{four}
$\times\ 3_{\text{four}}$

34. 43_{seven}
$\times\ 6_{\text{seven}}$

35. 123_{five}
$\times\ 4_{\text{five}}$

In Exercises 36–37, divide in the indicated base. Use the multiplication tables on page 215.

36. $2_{\text{four}}\overline{)332_{\text{four}}}$

37. $4_{\text{five}}\overline{)103_{\text{five}}}$

4.4

Use Table 4.6 on page 216 to solve Exercises 38–41.

In Exercises 38–39, write each Egyptian numeral as a Hindu-Arabic numeral.

38. 𓏲𓆼𓆼𓋹𓊖𓊖𓊖𓊖𓊖|||||

39. 𓎆𓏲𓏲𓆼𓆼𓆼𓆼𓆼𓊖𓊖𓊖||

In Exercises 40–41, write each Hindu-Arabic numeral as an Egyptian numeral.

40. 2486

41. 34,573

In Exercises 42–43, assume a system that represents numbers exactly like the Egyptian system, but with different symbols. In particular, A = 1, B = 10, C = 100, and D = 1000.

42. Write DDCCCBAAAA as a Hindu-Arabic numeral.

43. Write 5492 as a numeral in terms of A, B, C, and D.

44. Describe how the Egyptian system or the system in Exercises 42–43 is used to represent a number. Discuss one disadvantage of such a system when compared to our Hindu-Arabic system.

Use Table 4.7 on page 218 to solve Exercises 45–49.

In Exercises 45–47, write each Roman numeral as a Hindu-Arabic numeral.

45. CLXIII

46. MXXXIV

47. MCMXC

In Exercises 48–49, write each Hindu-Arabic numeral as a Roman numeral.

48. 49

49. 2965

50. Explain when to subtract the value of symbols when interpreting a Roman numeral. Give an example.

Use Table 4.8 on page 219 to solve Exercises 51–54.

In Exercises 51–52, write each traditional Chinese numeral as a Hindu-Arabic numeral.

51. 五
百
五
十
四

52. 八
千
二
百
五
十
三

In Exercises 53–54, write each Hindu-Arabic numeral as a traditional Chinese numeral.

53. 274

54. 3587

In Exercises 55–58, assume a system that represents numbers exactly like the traditional Chinese system, but with different symbols. The symbols are shown as follows:

Numerals in the System	A	B	C	D	E	F	G	H	I	X	Y	Z
Hindu-Arabic Numerals	1	2	3	4	5	6	7	8	9	10	100	1000

Express each numeral in Exercises 55–56 as a Hindu-Arabic numeral.

55. C
Y
F
X
E

56. D
Z
E
Y
B
X

Express each Hindu-Arabic numeral in Exercises 57–58 as a numeral in the system used for Exercises 55–56.

57. 793

58. 6854

59. Describe how the Chinese system or the system in Exercises 55–58 is used to represent a number. Discuss one disadvantage of such a system when compared to our Hindu-Arabic system.

Use Table 4.9 on page 220 to solve Exercises 60–63.

In Exercises 60–61, write each Ionic Greek numeral as a Hindu-Arabic numeral.

60. $\chi\nu\gamma$

61. $\chi o\eta$

In Exercises 62–63, write each Hindu-Arabic numeral as an Ionic Greek numeral.

62. 453

63. 902

In Exercises 64–68, assume a system that represents numbers exactly like the Greek Ionic system, but with different symbols. The symbols are shown as follows:

Decimal	1	2	3	4	5	6	7	8	9
Ones	A	B	C	D	E	F	G	H	I
Tens	J	K	L	M	N	O	P	Q	R
Hundreds	S	T	U	V	W	X	Y	Z	a
Thousands	b	c	d	e	f	g	h	i	j
Ten thousands	k	l	m	n	o	p	q	r	s

In Exercises 64–66, express each numeral as a Hindu-Arabic numeral.

64. UNG

65. mhZRD

66. rXJH

In Exercises 67–68, express each Hindu-Arabic numeral as a numeral in the system used for Exercises 64–66.

67. 597

68. 25,483

69. Discuss one disadvantage of the Greek Ionic system or the system described in Exercises 64–68 when compared to our Hindu-Arabic system.

●●●●●● ● CHAPTER 4 TEST

1. Evaluate 9^3.

2. Write 567 in expanded form.

3. Write 63,028 in expanded form.

4. Express as a Hindu-Arabic numeral:

$$(7 \times 10^3) + (4 \times 10^2) + (9 \times 10^1) + (3 \times 1).$$

5. Express as a Hindu-Arabic numeral:

$$(4 \times 10^5) + (2 \times 10^2) + (6 \times 1).$$

6. What is the difference between a number and a numeral?

7. Explain why a symbol for zero is needed in a positional system.

8. Place values in the Babylonian system are

$$\ldots, 60^3, 60^2, 60^1, 1.$$

Use the numerals shown to write the following Babylonian numeral as a Hindu-Arabic numeral:

$$<< \quad < \vee \vee \quad < \vee.$$

Babylonian	∨	<
Hindu-Arabic	1	10

9. Place values in the Mayan system are

$$\ldots, 18 \times 20^3, 18 \times 20^2, 18 \times 20, 20, 1.$$

Use the numerals shown to write the following Mayan numeral as a Hindu-Arabic numeral:

$$\overset{\bullet\bullet\bullet\bullet}{\underset{\ominus}{\bullet}}.$$

Mayan	⬯	•	••	•••	••••	▬	▬•
Hindu-Arabic	0	1	2	3	4	5	6

In Exercises 10–12, convert the numeral to a numeral in base ten.

10. 423_{five} **11.** 267_{nine} **12.** 110101_{two}

In Exercises 13–15, convert each base ten numeral to a numeral in the given base.

13. 77 to base three   **14.** 56 to base two

15. 1844 to base five

In Exercises 16–18, perform the indicated operation.

16. $\begin{array}{r} 234_{\text{five}} \\ + 423_{\text{five}} \\ \hline \end{array}$ **17.** $\begin{array}{r} 562_{\text{seven}} \\ - 145_{\text{seven}} \\ \hline \end{array}$ **18.** $\begin{array}{r} 54_{\text{six}} \\ \times \quad 3_{\text{six}} \\ \hline \end{array}$

19. Use the multiplication table shown to perform this division: $3_{\text{five}} \overline{)1213_{\text{five}}}$.

A MULTIPLICATION TABLE FOR BASE FIVE

×	0	1	2	3	4
0	0	0	0	0	0
1	0	1	2	3	4
2	0	2	4	11	13
3	0	3	11	14	22
4	0	4	13	22	31

Use the symbols in the tables shown below to solve Exercises 20–23.

Hindu-Arabic Numeral	Egyptian Numeral
1	|
10	∩
100	◉
1000	⚱
10,000	⌐
100,000	⌐
1,000,000	🧍

Hindu-Arabic Numeral	Roman Numeral
1	I
5	V
10	X
50	L
100	C
500	D
1000	M

20. Write the following numeral as a Hindu-Arabic numeral:

$$⌐⌐ ◉◉◉ |||.$$

21. Write 32,634 as an Egyptian numeral.

22. Write the Roman numeral MCMXCIV as a Hindu-Arabic numeral.

23. Express 459 as a Roman numeral.

24. Describe one difference between how a number is represented in the Egyptian system and the Roman system.

Number Theory and the Real Number System

While listening to the radio, you hear politicians discussing the problem of the $8.6 trillion national debt. They state that it's more than the gross domestic product of China, the world's second-richest nation, and four times greater than the combined net worth of America's 691 billionaires. They make it seem like the national debt is a real problem, but later you realize that you don't really know what a number like 8.6 trillion means. If the national debt were evenly divided among all citizens of the country, how much would every man, woman, and child have to pay?

Literacy with numbers, called *numeracy*, is a prerequisite for functioning in a meaningful way personally, professionally, and as a citizen. In this chapter, our focus is on understanding numbers, their properties, and their applications. The problem of placing the $8.6 trillion national debt in perspective appears as Example 9 in Section 5.6.

SECTION 5.1 • NUMBER THEORY: PRIME AND COMPOSITE NUMBERS

OBJECTIVES

1. Determine divisibility.
2. Write the prime factorization of a composite number.
3. Find the greatest common divisor of two numbers.
4. Solve problems using the greatest common divisor.
5. Find the least common multiple of two numbers.
6. Solve problems using the least common multiple.

Number Theory and Divisibility

You are organizing an intramural league at your school. You need to divide 40 men and 24 women into all-male and all-female teams so that each team has the same number of people. The men's teams should have the same number of players as the women's teams. What is the largest number of people that can be placed on a team?

This problem can be solved using a branch of mathematics called **number theory**. Number theory is primarily concerned with the properties of numbers used for counting, namely 1, 2, 3, 4, 5, and so on. The set of counting numbers is also called the set of **natural numbers**. We represent this set by the letter **N**.

> ### THE SET OF NATURAL NUMBERS
> $$\mathbf{N} = \{1, 2, 3, 4, 5, 6, 7, 8, 9, 10, 11, \dots\}$$

We can solve the intramural league problem. However, to do so we must understand the concept of divisibility. For example, there are a number of different ways to divide the 24 women into teams, including

1 team with all 24 women:	$1 \times 24 = 24$
2 teams with 12 women per team:	$2 \times 12 = 24$
3 teams with 8 women per team:	$3 \times 8 = 24$
4 teams with 6 women per team:	$4 \times 6 = 24$
6 teams with 4 women per team:	$6 \times 4 = 24$
8 teams with 3 women per team:	$8 \times 3 = 24$
12 teams with 2 women per team:	$12 \times 2 = 24$
24 teams with 1 woman per team:	$24 \times 1 = 24.$

The natural numbers that are multiplied together resulting in a product of 24 are called *factors* of 24. Any natural number can be expressed as a product of two or more natural numbers. The natural numbers that are multiplied are called the **factors** of the product. Notice that a natural number may have many factors.

$$2 \times 12 = 24 \qquad 3 \times 8 = 24 \qquad 6 \times 4 = 24$$

Factors of 24   Factors of 24   Factors of 24

The numbers 1, 2, 3, 4, 6, 8, 12, and 24 are all factors of 24. Each of these numbers divides 24 without a remainder.

In general, let a and b represent natural numbers. We say that a is **divisible** by b if the operation of dividing a by b leaves a remainder of 0.

A natural number is divisible by all of its factors. Thus, 24 is divisible by 1, 2, 3, 4, 6, 8, 12, and 24. Using the factor 8, we can express this divisibility in a number of ways:

24 is **divisible** by 8.

8 is a **divisor** of 24.

8 **divides** 24.

Mathematicians use a special notation to indicate divisibility.

> **DIVISIBILITY**
>
> If a and b are natural numbers, a is **divisible** by b if the operation of dividing a by b leaves a remainder of 0. This is the same as saying that b is a **divisor** of a, or b **divides** a. All three statements are symbolized by writing
>
> $$b \mid a.$$

Using this new notation, we can write

$$12 \mid 24.$$

Twelve divides 24 because 24 divided by 12 leaves a remainder of 0. By contrast, 13 does not divide 24 because 24 divided by 13 does not leave a remainder of 0. The notation

$$13 \nmid 24$$

means that 13 does not divide 24.

Table 5.1 shows some common rules for divisibility. Divisibility rules for 7 and 11 are difficult to remember and are not included in the table.

STUDY TIP

The words *factor* and *divisor* mean the same thing. Thus, 8 is a factor and a divisor of 24.

STUDY TIP

Do not confuse the notations $b \mid a$ and b/a. The symbol $b \mid a$ means b divides a. The symbol b/a means b divided by a (that is $b \div a$, the quotient of b and a). For example, $5 \mid 35$ means 5 divides 35, whereas $5/35$ means 5 divided by 35, which is the fraction $\frac{1}{7}$.

1 | Determine divisibility.

TABLE 5.1 RULES OF DIVISIBILITY		
Divisible By	**Test**	**Example**
2	The last digit is 0, 2, 4, 6, or 8.	5,892,796 is divisible by 2 because the last digit is 6.
3	The sum of the digits is divisible by 3.	52,341 is divisible by 3 because the sum of the digits is $5 + 2 + 3 + 4 + 1 = 15$, and 15 is divisible by 3.
4	The last two digits form a number divisible by 4.	3,947,136 is divisible by 4 because 36 is divisible by 4.
5	The number ends in 0 or 5.	28,160 and 72,805 end in 0 and 5, respectively. Both are divisible by 5.
6	The number is divisible by both 2 and 3. (In other words, the number is even and the sum of its digits is divisible by 3.)	954 is divisible by 2 because it ends in 4. 954 is also divisible by 3 because the digit sum is 18, which is divisible by 3. Because 954 is divisible by both 2 and 3, it is divisible by 6.
8	The last three digits form a number that is divisible by 8.	593,777,832 is divisible by 8 because 832 is divisible by 8.
9	The sum of the digits is divisible by 9.	5346 is divisible by 9 because the sum of the digits, 18, is divisible by 9.
10	The last digit is 0.	998,746,250 is divisible by 10 because the number ends in 0.
12	The number is divisible by both 3 and 4. (In other words, the sum of the digits is divisible by 3 and the last two digits form a number divisible by 4.)	614,608,176 is divisible by 3 because the digit sum is 39, which is divisible by 3. It is also divisible by 4 because the last two digits form 76, which is divisible by 4. Because 614,608,176 is divisible by both 3 and 4, it is divisible by 12.

TECHNOLOGY

CALCULATORS AND DIVISIBILITY

You can use a calculator to verify each result in Example 1. Consider part (a):

$$4|3,754,086.$$

Divide 3,754,086 by 4 using the following keystrokes:

3754086 ÷ 4.

Press = or ENTER . The number displayed is 938521.5. This is not a natural number. The 0.5 shows that the division leaves a nonzero remainder. Thus, 4 does not divide 3,754,086. The given statement is false.

Now consider part (b):

$$9|4,119,706,413.$$

Use your calculator to divide the number on the right by 9:

4119706413 ÷ 9.

Press = or ENTER . The display is 457745157. This is a natural number. The remainder of the division is 0, so 9 does divide 4,119,706,413. The given statement is false.

STUDY TIP

The number 2 is the only even prime number. Every other even number has at least three factors: 1, 2, and the number itself.

Write the prime factorization of a composite number.

EXAMPLE 1 USING THE RULES OF DIVISIBILITY

Which one of the following statements is true?

a. $4|3,754,086$ **b.** $9\!\!\!/\,4,119,706,413$ **c.** $8|677,840$

SOLUTION

a. $4|3,754,086$ states that 4 divides 3,754,086. Table 5.1 indicates that for 4 to divide a number, the last two digits must form a number that is divisible by 4. Because 86 is not divisible by 4, the given statement is false.

b. $9\!\!\!/\,4,119,706,413$ states that 9 does *not* divide 4,119,706,413. Based on Table 5.1, if the sum of the digits is divisible by 9, then 9 does indeed divide this number. The sum of the digits is $4 + 1 + 1 + 9 + 7 + 0 + 6 + 4 + 1 + 3 = 36$, which is divisible by 9. Because 4,119,706,413 is divisible by 9, the given statement is false.

c. $8|667,840$ states that 8 divides 677,840. Table 5.1 indicates that for 8 to divide a number, the last three digits must form a number that is divisible by 8. Because 840 is divisible by 8, then 8 divides 677,840, and the given statement is true.

The statement given in part (c) is the only true statement.

CHECK POINT 1 Which one of the following statements is true?

a. $8|48,324$ **b.** $6|48,324$ **c.** $4\!\!\!/\,48,324$

Prime Factorization

By developing some other ideas of number theory, we will be able to solve the intramural league problem. We begin with the definition of a prime number.

> **PRIME NUMBERS**
> A **prime number** is a natural number greater than 1 that has only itself and 1 as factors.

Using this definition, we see that the number 7 is a prime number because it has only 1 and 7 as factors. Said in another way, 7 is prime because it is divisible by only 1 and 7. The first ten prime numbers are 2, 3, 5, 7, 11, 13, 17, 19, 23, and 29. Each number in this list has exactly two divisors, itself and 1. By contrast, 9 is not a prime number; in addition to being divisible by 1 and 9, it is also divisible by 3. The number 9 is an example of a *composite number*.

> **COMPOSITE NUMBERS**
> A **composite number** is a natural number greater than 1 that is divisible by a number other than itself and 1.

Using this definition, the first ten composite numbers are 4, 6, 8, 9, 10, 12, 14, 15, 16, and 18. Each number in this list has at least three divisors.

Every composite number can be expressed as the product of prime numbers. For example, the composite number 45 can be expressed as

$$45 = 3 \times 3 \times 5.$$

Note that 3 and 5 are prime numbers. Expressing a composite number as the product of prime numbers is called **prime factorization**. The prime factorization of 45 is $3 \times 3 \times 5$. The order in which we write these factors does not matter. This means that

$$45 = 3 \times 3 \times 5$$
$$\text{or } 45 = 5 \times 3 \times 3$$
$$\text{or } 45 = 3 \times 5 \times 3.$$

In Chapter 1, we defined a **theorem** as a statement that can be proved using deductive reasoning. The ancient Greeks proved that if the order of the factors is disregarded, there is only one prime factorization possible for any given composite number. This statement is called the **Fundamental Theorem of Arithmetic**.

> **THE FUNDAMENTAL THEOREM OF ARITHMETIC**
> Every composite number can be expressed as a product of prime numbers in one and only one way (if the order of the factors is disregarded).

One method used to find the prime factorization of a composite number is called a **factor tree**. To use this method, begin by selecting any two numbers whose product is the number to be factored. If one or both of the factors are not prime numbers, continue to factor each composite number. Stop when all numbers are prime.

EXAMPLE 2	PRIME FACTORIZATION USING A FACTOR TREE

STUDY TIP

It does not matter how you begin a factor tree. For example, in Example 2 you can factor 700 by starting with 5 and 140. ($5 \times 140 = 700$)

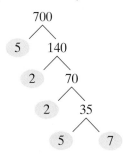

The prime factorization of 700 is

$$700 = 5 \times 2 \times 2 \times 5 \times 7$$
$$= 2^2 \times 5^2 \times 7.$$

This is the same prime factorization we obtained in Example 2.

Find the prime factorization of 700.

SOLUTION Start with any two numbers whose product is 700, such as 7 and 100. This forms the first branch of the tree. Continue factoring the composite number or numbers that result (in this case 100), branching until the end of each branch contains a prime number.

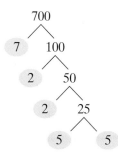

The prime factors are circled. Thus, the prime factorization of 700 is

$$700 = 7 \times 2 \times 2 \times 5 \times 5.$$

We can use exponents to show the repeated prime factors:

$$700 = 7 \times 2^2 \times 5^2.$$

Using a dot to indicate multiplication and arranging the factors from least to greatest, we can write

$$700 = 2^2 \cdot 5^2 \cdot 7.$$

  Find the prime factorization of 120.

---

3 Find the greatest common divisor of two numbers.

Greatest Common Divisor

The greatest common divisor of two or more natural numbers is the largest number that is a divisor (or factor) of all the numbers. For example, 8 is the greatest common divisor of 32 and 40 because it is the largest natural number that divides both 32 and 40. Some pairs of numbers have 1 as their greatest common divisor. Such number pairs are said to be **relatively prime**. For example, the greatest common divisor of 5 and 26 is 1. Thus, 5 and 26 are relatively prime.

The greatest common divisor can be found using prime factorizations.

> ### FINDING THE GREATEST COMMON DIVISOR OF TWO OR MORE NUMBERS USING PRIME FACTORIZATIONS
>
> To find the greatest common divisor of two or more numbers,
>
> 1. Write the prime factorization of each number.
> 2. Select each prime factor with the smallest exponent that is common to each of the prime factorizations.
> 3. Form the product of the numbers from step 2. The greatest common divisor is the product of these factors.

EXAMPLE 3   FINDING THE GREATEST COMMON DIVISOR

Find the greatest common divisor of 216 and 234.

SOLUTION

Step 1. Write the prime factorization of each number. Begin by writing the prime factorizations of 216 and 234.

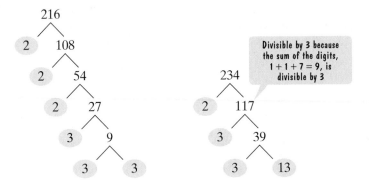

Divisible by 3 because the sum of the digits, $1 + 1 + 7 = 9$, is divisible by 3

The factor tree at the left indicates that

$$216 = 2^3 \times 3^3.$$

The factor tree at the right indicates that

$$234 = 2 \times 3^2 \times 13.$$

Step 2. Select each prime factor with the smallest exponent that is common to each of the prime factorizations. Look at the factorizations of 216 and 234 from step 1. Can you see that 2 is a prime number common to the factorizations of 216 and 234? Likewise, 3 is also a prime number common to the two factorizations. By contrast, 13 is a prime number that is not common to both factorizations.

$$216 = 2^3 \times 3^3$$
$$234 = 2 \times 3^2 \times 13$$

2 is a prime number common to both factorizations.

3 is a prime number common to both factorizations.

Now we need to use these prime factorizations to determine which exponent is appropriate for 2 and which exponent is appropriate for 3. The appropriate exponent is the smallest exponent associated with the prime number in the factorizations. The exponents associated with 2 in the factorizations are 1 and 3, so we select 1. Therefore, one factor for the greatest common divisor is 2^1, or 2. The exponents associated with 3 in the factorizations are 2 and 3, so we select 2. Therefore, another factor for the greatest common divisor is 3^2.

$$216 = 2^3 \times 3^3$$

Smallest exponent on 2 is 1.   Smallest exponent on 3 is 2.

$$234 = 2^1 \times 3^2 \times 13$$

Step 3. Form the product of the numbers from step 2. The greatest common divisor is the product of these factors.

$$\text{Greatest common divisor} = 2 \times 3^2 = 2 \times 9 = 18$$

The greatest common divisor of 216 and 234 is 18.

CHECK POINT 3 Find the greatest common divisor of 225 and 825.

4 | Solve problems using the greatest common divisor.

5 | Find the least common multiple of two numbers.

EXAMPLE 4 SOLVING A PROBLEM USING THE GREATEST COMMON DIVISOR

For an intramural league, you need to divide 40 men and 24 women into all-male and all-female teams so that each team has the same number of people. What is the largest number of people that can be placed on a team?

SOLUTION Because 40 men are to be divided into teams, the number of men on each team must be a divisor of 40. Because 24 women are to be divided into teams, the number of women placed on a team must be a divisor of 24. Although the teams are all-male and all-female, the same number of people must be placed on each team. The largest number of people that can be placed on a team is the largest number that will divide into 40 and 24 without a remainder. This is the greatest common divisor of 40 and 24.

To find the greatest common divisor of 40 and 24, begin with their prime factorizations.

 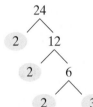

The factor trees indicate that

$$40 = 2^3 \times 5 \quad \text{and} \quad 24 = 2^3 \times 3.$$

We see that 2 is a prime number common to both factorizations. The exponents associated with 2 in the factorizations are 3 and 3, so we select 3.

$$\text{Greatest common divisor} = 2^3 = 2 \times 2 \times 2 = 8$$

The largest number of people that can be placed on a team is 8. Thus, the 40 men can form five teams with 8 men per team. The 24 women can form three teams with 8 women per team.

CHECK POINT 4 A choral director needs to divide 192 men and 288 women into all-male and all-female singing groups so that each group has the same number of people. What is the largest number of people that can be placed in each singing group?

Least Common Multiple

The **least common multiple** of two or more natural numbers is the smallest natural number that is divisible by all of the numbers. One way to find the least common multiple is to make a list of the numbers that are divisible by each number. This list represents the **multiples** of each number. For example, if we wish to find the least common multiple of 15 and 20, we can list the sets of multiples of 15 and multiples of 20.

$$\begin{cases} \text{Numbers Divisible by 15:} \\ \quad \text{Multiples of 15:} \qquad \{15, 30, 45, 60, 75, 90, 105, 120, \dots\} \end{cases}$$

$$\begin{cases} \text{Numbers Divisible by 20:} \\ \quad \text{Multiples of 20:} \qquad \{20, 40, 60, 80, 100, 120, 140, 160, \dots\} \end{cases}$$

Some common multiples of 15 and 20 are 60 and 120. The least common multiple is 60. Equivalently, 60 is the smallest number that is divisible by both 15 and 20.

Sometimes a partial list of the multiples for each of two numbers does not reveal the smallest number that is divisible by both given numbers. A more efficient method for finding the least common multiple is to use prime factorizations.

FINDING THE LEAST COMMON MULTIPLE USING PRIME FACTORIZATIONS

To find the least common multiple of two or more numbers,

1. Write the prime factorization of each number.
2. Select every prime factor that occurs, raised to the greatest power to which it occurs, in these factorizations.
3. Form the product of the numbers from step 2. The least common multiple is the product of these factors.

EXAMPLE 5   FINDING THE LEAST COMMON MULTIPLE

Find the least common multiple of 144 and 300.

SOLUTION

Step 1. Write the prime factorization of each number. Write the prime factorizations of 144 and 300.

$$144 = 2^4 \times 3^2$$
$$300 = 2^2 \times 3 \times 5^2$$

Step 2. Select every prime factor that occurs, raised to the greatest power to which it occurs, in these factorizations. The prime factors that occur are 2, 3, and 5. The greatest exponent that appears on 2 is 4, so we select 2^4. The greatest exponent that appears on 3 is 2, so we select 3^2. The greatest exponent that occurs on 5 is 2, so we select 5^2. Thus, we have selected 2^4, 3^2, and 5^2.

Step 3. Form the product of the numbers from step 2. The least common multiple is the product of these factors.

$$\text{Least common multiple} = 2^4 \times 3^2 \times 5^2 = 16 \times 9 \times 25 = 3600$$

The least common multiple of 144 and 300 is 3600. The smallest natural number divisible by 144 and 300 is 3600.

 5 Find the least common multiple of 18 and 30.

6 | Solve problems using the least common multiple.

EXAMPLE 6   SOLVING A PROBLEM USING THE LEAST COMMON MULTIPLE

A movie theater runs its films continuously. One movie runs for 80 minutes and a second runs for 120 minutes. Both movies begin at 4:00 P.M. When will the movies begin again at the same time?

SOLUTION The shorter movie lasts 80 minutes, or 1 hour, 20 minutes. It begins at 4:00, so it will be shown again at 5:20. The longer movie lasts 120 minutes, or 2 hours. It begins at 4:00, so it will be shown again at 6:00. We are asked to find when the movies will begin again at the same time. Therefore, we are looking for the least common multiple of 80 and 120. Find the least common multiple and then add this number of minutes to 4:00 P.M.

Begin with the prime factorizations of 80 and 120:

$$80 = 2^4 \times 5$$
$$120 = 2^3 \times 3 \times 5.$$

Now select each prime factor, with the greatest exponent from each factorization.

Least common multiple $= 2^4 \times 3 \times 5 = 16 \times 3 \times 5 = 240$

Therefore, it will take 240 minutes, or 4 hours, for the movies to begin again at the same time. By adding 4 hours to 4:00 P.M., they will start together again at 8:00 P.M.

○

STUDY TIP

Example 6 can also be solved by making a partial list of starting times for each movie.

Shorter Movie (Runs 1 hour, 20 minutes):

4:00,   5:20,   6:40,   8:00,...

Longer Movie (Runs 2 hours):

4:00,   6:00,   8:00,...

The list reveals that both movies start together again at 8:00 P.M.

CHECK POINT 6 A movie theater runs two documentary films continuously. One documentary runs for 40 minutes and a second documentary runs for 60 minutes. Both movies begin at 3:00 P.M. When will the movies begin again at the same time?

EXERCISE SET 5.1 ●●●●●●●

• Practice Exercises

Use rules of divisibility to determine whether each number given in Exercises 1–10 is divisible by

   a. 2   **b.** 3   **c.** 4   **d.** 5   **e.** 6
   f. 8   **g.** 9   **h.** 10   **i.** 12.

1. 6944   **2.** 7245   **3.** 21,408   **4.** 25,025

5. 26,428   **6.** 89,001   **7.** 374,832   **8.** 347,712

9. 6,126,120 **10.** 5,941,221

In Exercises 11–24, use a calculator to determine whether each statement is true or false. If the statement is true, explain why this is so using one of the rules of divisibility in Table 5.1 on page 229.

11. 3|5958   **12.** 3|8142   **13.** 4|10,612

14. 4|15,984   **15.** 5|38,814   **16.** 5|48,659

17. 6|104,538   **18.** 6|163,944   **19.** 8|20,104

20. 8|28,096   **21.** 9|11,378   **22.** 9|23,772

23. 12|517,872   **24.** 12|785,172

In Exercises 25–44, find the prime factorization of each composite number.

25. 75   **26.** 45   **27.** 56   **28.** 48

29. 105   **30.** 180   **31.** 500   **32.** 360

33. 663   **34.** 510   **35.** 885   **36.** 999

37. 1440   **38.** 1280   **39.** 1996   **40.** 1575

41. 3675   **42.** 8316   **43.** 85,800   **44.** 30,600

In Exercises 45–56, find the greatest common divisor of the numbers.

45. 42 and 56   **46.** 25 and 70   **47.** 16 and 42

48. 66 and 90   **49.** 60 and 108   **50.** 96 and 212

51. 72 and 120   **52.** 220 and 400   **53.** 342 and 380

54. 224 and 430   **55.** 240 and 285   **56.** 150 and 480

In Exercises 57–68, find the least common multiple of the numbers.

57. 42 and 56   **58.** 25 and 70   **59.** 16 and 42

60. 66 and 90   **61.** 60 and 108   **62.** 96 and 212

63. 72 and 120   **64.** 220 and 400   **65.** 342 and 380

66. 224 and 430   **67.** 240 and 285   **68.** 150 and 480

• Practice Plus

In Exercises 69–74, determine all values of d that make each statement true.

69. 9|12,34d   **70.** 9|23,42d   **71.** 8|76,523,45d

72. 8|88,888,82d   **73.** 4|963,23d   **74.** 4|752,67d

A **perfect number** is a natural number that is equal to the sum of its factors, excluding the number itself. In Exercises 75–78, determine whether or not each number is perfect.

75. 28   **76.** 6   **77.** 20   **78.** 50

A prime number is an **emirp** ("prime" spelled backward) if it becomes a different prime number when its digits are reversed. In Exercises 79–82, determine whether or not each prime number is an emirp.

79. 41   **80.** 43   **81.** 107   **82.** 113

A prime number p such that 2p + 1 is also a prime number is called a **Germain prime***, named after the German mathematician Sophie Germain (1776–1831), who made major contributions to number theory. In Exercises 83–86, determine whether or not each prime number is a Germain prime.*

83. 13   **84.** 11   **85.** 241   **86.** 97

87. Find the product of the greatest common divisor of 24 and 27 and the least common multiple of 24 and 27. Compare this result to the product of 24 and 27. Write a conjecture based on your observation.

88. Find the product of the greatest common divisor of 48 and 72 and the least common multiple of 48 and 72. Compare this result to the product of 48 and 72. Write a conjecture based on your observation.

• Application Exercises

89. In Carl Sagan's novel *Contact*, Ellie Arroway, the book's heroine, has been working at SETI, the Search for Extraterrestrial Intelligence, listening to the crackle of the cosmos. One night, as the radio telescopes are turned toward Vega, they suddenly pick up strange pulses through the background noise. Two pulses are followed by a pause, then three pulses, five, seven,

$$11, \quad 13, \quad 17, \quad 19, \quad 23, \quad 29, \quad 31, \dots$$

continuing through 97. Then it starts all over again. Ellie is convinced that only intelligent life could generate the structure in the sequence of pulses. "It's hard to imagine some radiating plasma sending out a regular set of mathematical signals like this." What is it about the structure of the pulses that the book's heroine recognizes as the sign of intelligent life? Asked in another way, what is significant about the number of pulses?

90. There are two species of insects, *Magicicada septendecim* and *Magicicada tredecim*, that live in the same environment. They have a life cycle of exactly 17 and 13 years, respectively. For all but their last year, they remain in the ground feeding on the sap of tree roots. Then, in their last year, they emerge en masse from the ground as fully formed cricketlike insects, taking over the forest in a single night. They chirp loudly, mate, eat, lay eggs, then die six weeks later.

(Source: Marcus du Sautoy, The Music of the Primes, HarperCollins, 2003)

a. Suppose that the two species have life cycles that are not prime, say 18 and 12 years, respectively. List the set of multiples of 18 that are less than or equal to 216. List the set of multiples of 12 that are less than or equal to 216. Over a 216-year period, how many times will the two species emerge in the same year and compete to share the forest?

b. Recall that both species have evolved prime-number life cycles, 17 and 13 years, respectively. Find the least common multiple of 17 and 13. How often will the two species have to share the forest?

c. Compare your answers to parts (a) and (b). What explanation can you offer for each species having a prime number of years as the length of its life cycle?

91. A relief worker needs to divide 300 bottles of water and 144 cans of food into groups that each contain the same number of items. Also, each group must have the same type of item (bottled water or canned food). What is the largest number of relief supplies that can be put in each group?

92. A choral director needs to divide 180 men and 144 women into all-male and all-female singing groups so that each group has the same number of people. What is the largest number of people that can be placed in each singing group?

93. You have in front of you 310 five-dollar bills and 460 ten-dollar bills. Your problem: Place the five-dollar bills and the ten-dollar bills in stacks so that each stack has the same number of bills, and each stack contains only one kind of bill (five-dollar or ten-dollar). What is the largest number of bills that you can place in each stack?

94. Harley collects sports cards. He has 360 football cards and 432 baseball cards. Harley plans to arrange his cards in stacks so that each stack has the same number of cards. Also, each stack must have the same type of card (football or baseball). Every card in Harley's collection is to be placed in one of the stacks. What is the largest number of cards that can be placed in each stack?

95. You and your brother both work the 4:00 P.M. to midnight shift. You have every sixth night off. Your brother has every tenth night off. Both of you were off on June 1. Your brother would like to see a movie with you. When will the two of you have the same night off again?

96. A movie theater runs its films continuously. One movie is a short documentary that runs for 40 minutes. The other movie is a full-length feature that runs for 100 minutes. Each film is shown in a separate theater. Both movies begin at noon. When will the movies begin again at the same time?

97. Two people are jogging around a circular track in the same direction. One person can run completely around the track in 15 minutes. The second person takes 18 minutes. If they both start running in the same place at the same time, how long will it take them to be together at this place if they continue to run?

98. Two people are in a bicycle race around a circular track. One rider can race completely around the track in 40 seconds. The other rider takes 45 seconds. If they both begin the race at a designated starting point, how long will it take them to be together at this starting point again if they continue to race around the track?

• Writing in Mathematics

99. If *a* is a factor of *c*, what does this mean?

100. Why is 45 divisible by 5?

101. What does "*a* is divisible by *b*" mean?

102. Describe the difference between a prime number and a composite number.

103. What does the Fundamental Theorem of Arithmetic state?

104. What is the greatest common divisor of two or more natural numbers?

105. Describe how to find the greatest common divisor of two numbers.

106. What is the least common multiple of two or more natural numbers?

107. Describe how to find the least common multiple of two natural numbers.

108. The process of finding the greatest common divisor of two natural numbers is similar to finding the least common multiple of the numbers. Describe how the two processes differ.

109. What does the Blitzer Bonus on page 232 have to do with Gödel's discovery about mathematics and logic, described on page 163?

• Critical Thinking Exercises

110. Write a four-digit natural number that is divisible by 4 and not by 8.

111. Find the greatest common divisor and the least common multiple of $2^{17} \cdot 3^{25} \cdot 5^{31}$ and $2^{14} \cdot 3^{37} \cdot 5^{30}$. Express answers in the same form as the numbers given.

112. A middle-age man observed that his present age was a prime number. He also noticed that the number of years in which his age would again be prime was equal to the number of years ago in which his age was prime. How old is the man?

113. A movie theater runs its films continuously. One movie runs for 85 minutes and a second runs for 100 minutes. The theater has a 15-minute intermission after each movie, at which point the movie is shown again. If both movies start at noon, when will the two movies start again at the same time?

114. The difference between consecutive prime numbers is always an even number, except for two particular prime numbers. What are those numbers?

• Technology Exercises

Use the divisibility rules listed in Table 5.1 on page 229 to answer the questions in Exercises 115–117. Then, using a calculator, perform the actual division to determine whether your answer is correct.

115. Is 67,234,096 divisible by 4?

116. Is 12,541,750 divisible by 3?

117. Is 48,201,651 divisible by 9?

• Group Exercises

The following topics from number theory are appropriate for either individual or group research projects. A report should be given to the class on the researched topic. Useful references include liberal arts mathematics textbooks, books about numbers and number theory, books whose purpose is to excite the reader about mathematics, history of mathematics books, encyclopedias, and the World Wide Web.

118. Euclid and Number Theory

119. An Unsolved Problem from Number Theory

120. Perfect Numbers

121. Deficient and Abundant Numbers

122. Formulas that Yield Primes

123. The Sieve of Eratosthenes

SECTION 5.2 • THE INTEGERS; ORDER OF OPERATIONS

OBJECTIVES

1. Define the integers.

2. Graph integers on a number line.

3. Use the symbols $<$ and $>$.

4. Find the absolute value of an integer.

5. Perform operations with integers.

6. Use the order of operations agreement.

From the political left and right, watchdogs of the federal budget are warning of fiscal trouble. David Walker, Comptroller General of the United States and the nation's top auditor, admits to being "terrified" about the budget deficit in coming decades. To hear him tell it, the United States can be likened to Rome before the fall of the empire. America's financial condition is "worse than advertised," he says. It has a "broken business model. It faces deficits in its budget, its balance of payments, and its savings." In this section, we use operations on a set of numbers called the *integers* to describe numerically the sad state of the nation's finances.

1 Define the integers.

Defining the Integers

In Section 5.1, we applied some ideas of number theory to the set of natural, or counting, numbers:

$$\text{Natural numbers} = \{1, 2, 3, 4, 5, \dots\}.$$

When we combine the number 0 with the natural numbers, we obtain the set of **whole numbers**:

$$\text{Whole numbers} = \{0, 1, 2, 3, 4, 5, \dots\}.$$

The whole numbers do not allow us to describe certain everyday situations. For example, if the balance in your checking account is $30 and you write a check for $35, your checking account is overdrawn by $5. We can write this as -5, read *negative* 5. The set consisting of the natural numbers, 0, and the negatives of the natural numbers is called the set of **integers**.

$$\text{Integers} = \{\dots, -4, -3, -2, -1, 0, 1, 2, 3, 4, \dots\}$$

Negative integers   Positive integers

Notice that the term *positive integers* is another name for the natural numbers. The positive integers can be written in two ways:

1. Use a "+" sign. For example, +4 is "positive four."
2. Do not write any sign. For example, 4 is assumed to be "positive four."

The Number Line; The Symbols < and >

The **number line** is a graph we use to visualize the set of integers, as well as sets of other numbers. The number line is shown in Figure 5.1.

Negative   Zero   Positive
numbers   numbers

```
←——+——+——+——+——+——+——+——+——+——+——→
  -5  -4  -3  -2  -1   0   1   2   3   4   5
```

FIGURE 5.1 The number line

The number line extends indefinitely in both directions, shown by the arrows on the left and the right. Zero separates the positive numbers from the negative numbers on the number line. The positive integers are located to the right of 0 and the negative integers are located to the left of 0. **Zero is neither positive nor negative.** For every positive integer on a number line, there is a corresponding negative integer on the opposite side of 0.

Integers are graphed on a number line by placing a dot at the correct location for each number.

2 Graph integers on a number line.

EXAMPLE 1   GRAPHING INTEGERS ON A NUMBER LINE

Graph: **a.** -3 **b.** 4   **c.** 0.

SOLUTION Place a dot at the correct location for each integer.

```
         (a)          (c)              (b)
←——+——+——•——+——+——•——+——+——•——+——→
  -5  -4  -3  -2  -1   0   1   2   3   4   5
```

 Graph:

a. -4 **b.** 0   **c.** 3.

3 | Use the symbols < and >.

We will use the following symbols for comparing two integers:

    < means "is less than."

    > means "is greater than."

On the number line, the integers increase from left to right. The *lesser* of two integers is the one farther to the *left* on a number line. The *greater* of two integers is the one farther to the *right* on a number line.

    Look at the number line in Figure 5.2. The integers -4 and -1 are graphed.

FIGURE 5.2

Observe that -4 is to the left of -1 on the number line. This means that -4 is less than -1.

$$-4 < -1 \qquad \boxed{\text{−4 is less than −1 because −4 is to the \textbf{left} of −1 on the number line.}}$$

In Figure 5.2, we can also observe that -1 is to the right of -4 on the number line. This means that -1 is greater than -4.

$$-1 > -4 \qquad \boxed{\text{−1 is greater than −4 because −1 is to the \textbf{right} of −4 on the number line.}}$$

The symbols < and > are called **inequality symbols**. These symbols always point to the lesser of the two real numbers when the inequality statement is true.

$$\boxed{\text{−4 is less than −1.}} \quad -4 < -1 \qquad \text{The symbol points to } -4, \text{ the lesser number.}$$

$$\boxed{\text{−1 is greater than −4.}} \quad -1 > -4 \qquad \text{The symbol still points to } -4, \text{ the lesser number.}$$

EXAMPLE 2   USING THE SYMBOLS < AND >

Insert either < or > in the shaded area between the integers to make each statement true:

  a. $-4 \blacksquare 3$ **b.** $-1 \blacksquare -5$ **c.** $-5 \blacksquare -2$ **d.** $0 \blacksquare -3$.

SOLUTION The solution is illustrated by the number line in Figure 5.3.

FIGURE 5.3

a. $-4 < 3$ (negative 4 is less than 3) because -4 is to the left of 3 on the number line.

b. $-1 > -5$ (negative 1 is greater than negative 5) because -1 is to the right of -5 on the number line.

c. $-5 < -2$ (negative 5 is less than negative 2) because -5 is to the left of -2 on the number line.

d. $0 > -3$ (zero is greater than negative 3) because 0 is to the right of -3 on the number line.

○

STUDY TIP

You can think of negative integers as amounts of money that you *owe*. It's better to owe less, so

$$-1 > -5.$$

CHECK POINT 2 Insert either < or > in the shaded area between the integers to make each statement true:

  a. $6 \blacksquare -7$ **b.** $-8 \blacksquare -1$ **c.** $-25 \blacksquare -2$ **d.** $-14 \blacksquare 0$.

The symbols $<$ and $>$ may be combined with an equal sign, as shown in the following table:

	Symbols	Meaning	Examples	Explanation
This inequality is true if either the $<$ part or the $=$ part is true.	$a \leq b$	a is less than or equal to b.	$2 \leq 9$ $9 \leq 9$	Because $2 < 9$ Because $9 = 9$
This inequality is true if either the $>$ part or the $=$ part is true.	$b \geq a$	b is greater than or equal to a.	$9 \geq 2$ $2 \geq 2$	Because $9 > 2$ Because $2 = 2$

4 Find the absolute value of an integer.

Absolute Value

Absolute value describes distance from 0 on a number line. If a represents an integer, the symbol $|a|$, represents its absolute value, read "the absolute value of a." For example,

$$|-5| = 5.$$

The absolute value of -5 is 5 because -5 is 5 units from 0 on a number line.

> **ABSOLUTE VALUE**
> The **absolute value** of an integer a, denoted by $|a|$, is the distance from 0 to a on the number line. Because absolute value describes a distance, it is never negative.

EXAMPLE 3   FINDING ABSOLUTE VALUE

Find the absolute value:

a. $|-3|$ **b.** $|5|$ **c.** $|0|$.

SOLUTION

a. $|-3| = 3$ *The absolute value of -3 is 3 because -3 is 3 units from 0.*

b. $|5| = 5$ *5 is 5 units from 0.*

c. $|0| = 0$ *0 is 0 units from itself.*

Example 3 illustrates that the absolute value of a positive integer or 0 is the number itself. The absolute value of a negative integer, such as -3, is the number without the negative sign. Zero is the only real number whose absolute value is 0: $|0| = 0$. **The absolute value of any integer other than 0 is always positive.**

 Find the absolute value:

a. $|-8|$ **b.** $|6|$.

5 Perform operations with integers.

Addition of Integers

It has not been a good day! First, you lost your wallet with $30 in it. Then, you borrowed $10 to get through the day, which you somehow misplaced. Your loss of $30 followed by a loss of $10 is an overall loss of $40. This can be written

$$-30 + (-10) = -40.$$

The result of adding two or more numbers is called the **sum** of the numbers. The sum of -30 and -10 is -40.

You can think of gains and losses of money to find sums. For example, to find $17 + (-13)$, think of a gain of $17 followed by a loss of $13. There is an overall gain of $4. Thus, $17 + (-13) = 4$. In the same way, to find $-17 + 13$, think of a loss of $17 followed by a gain of $13. There is an overall loss of $4, so $-17 + 13 = -4$.

Using gains and losses, we can develop the following rules for adding integers:

RULES FOR ADDITION OF INTEGERS

Rule

Examples

If the integers have the same sign,

1. Add their absolute values.

2. The sign of the sum is the same as the sign of the two numbers.

$-11 + (-15) = -26$

> Add absolute values:
> $11 + 15 = 26$.

Use the common sign.

If the integers have different signs,

1. Subtract the smaller absolute value from the larger absolute value.

2. The sign of the sum is the same as the sign of the number with the larger absolute value.

$-13 + 4 = -9$

> Subtract absolute values:
> $13 - 4 = 9$.

Use the sign of the number with the greater absolute value.

$13 + (-6) = 7$

> Subtract absolute values:
> $13 - 6 = 7$.

Use the sign of the number with the greater absolute value.

TECHNOLOGY

CALCULATORS AND ADDING INTEGERS

You can use a calculator to add integers. Here are the keystrokes for finding $-11 + (-15)$:

SCIENTIFIC CALCULATOR

11 $\boxed{+/_-}$ $\boxed{+}$ 15 $\boxed{+/_-}$ $\boxed{=}$

GRAPHING CALCULATOR

$\boxed{(-)}$ 11 $\boxed{+}$ $\boxed{(-)}$ 15 $\boxed{\text{ENTER}}$.

Here are the keystrokes for finding $-13 + 4$:

SCIENTIFIC CALCULATOR

13 $\boxed{+/_-}$ $\boxed{+}$ 4 $\boxed{=}$

GRAPHING CALCULATOR

$\boxed{(-)}$ 13 $\boxed{+}$ 4 $\boxed{\text{ENTER}}$.

STUDY TIP

In addition to gains and losses of money, another good analogy for adding integers is temperatures above and below zero on a thermometer. Think of the thermometer as a number line standing straight up. For example,

$-11 + (-15) = -26$

> If it's 11 below zero and the temperature falls 15 degrees, it will then be 26 below zero.

$-13 + 4 = -9$

> If it's 13 below zero and the temperature rises 4 degrees, the new temperature will be 9 below zero.

$13 + (-6) = 7.$

> If it's 13 above zero and the temperature falls 6 degrees, it will then be 7 above zero.

Using the analogies of gains and losses of money or temperatures can make the formal rules for addition of integers easy to use.

Can you guess what number is displayed if you use a calculator to find a sum such as $18 + (-18)$? If you gain 18 and then lose 18, there is neither an overall gain or loss. Thus,

$$18 + (-18) = 0.$$

We call 18 and -18 **additive inverses**. Additive inverses have the same absolute value, but lie on opposite sides of zero on the number line. Thus, -7 is the additive inverse of 7, and 5 is the additive inverse of -5. In general, the sum of any integer and its additive inverse is 0:

$$a + (-a) = 0.$$

Subtraction of Integers

Suppose that a computer that normally sells for $1500 has a price reduction of $600. The computer's reduced price, $900, can be expressed in two ways:

$$1500 - 600 = 900 \quad \text{or} \quad 1500 + (-600) = 900.$$

This means that

$$1500 - 600 = 1500 + (-600).$$

To subtract 600 from 1500, we add 1500 and the additive inverse of 600. Generalizing from this situation, we define subtraction as follows:

> **DEFINITION OF SUBTRACTION**
> For all integers a and b,
> $$a - b = a + (-b).$$
> In words, to subtract b from a, add the additive inverse of b to a. The result of subtraction is called the **difference**.

TECHNOLOGY

CALCULATORS AND SUBTRACTING INTEGERS

You can use a calculator to subtract integers. Here are the keystrokes for finding $17 - (-11)$:

SCIENTIFIC CALCULATOR

$17 \boxed{-} 11 \boxed{+/-} \boxed{=}$

GRAPHING CALCULATOR

$17 \boxed{-} \boxed{(-)} 11 \boxed{\text{ENTER}}$.

Here are the keystrokes for finding $-18 - (-5)$:

SCIENTIFIC CALCULATOR

$18 \boxed{+/-} \boxed{-} 5 \boxed{+/-} \boxed{=}$

GRAPHING CALCULATOR

$\boxed{(-)} 18 \boxed{-} \boxed{(-)} 5 \boxed{\text{ENTER}}$.

Don't confuse the subtraction key on a graphing calculator, $\boxed{-}$, with the sign change or additive inverse key, $\boxed{(-)}$. What happens if you do?

EXAMPLE 4   SUBTRACTING INTEGERS

Subtract:

a. $17 - (-11)$ **b.** $-18 - (-5)$ **c.** $-18 - 5$.

SOLUTION

a. $17 - (-11) = 17 + 11 = 28$

> Change the subtraction to addition.   Replace −11 with its additive inverse.

b. $-18 - (-5) = -18 + 5 = -13$

> Change the subtraction to addition.   Replace −5 with its additive inverse.

c. $-18 - 5 = -18 + (-5) = -23$

> Change the subtraction to addition.   Replace 5 with its additive inverse.

 CHECK POINT **4**   Subtract:

a. $30 - (-7)$ **b.** $-14 - (-10)$ **c.** $-14 - 10.$

STUDY TIP

You can think of subtracting a negative integer as taking away a debt. Let's apply this analogy to $17 - (-11)$. Your checking account balance is $17 after an erroneous $11 charge was made against your account. When you bring this error to the bank's attention, they will take away the $11 debit and your balance will go up to $28:

$$17 - (-11) = 28.$$

Subtraction is used to solve problems in which the word *difference* appears. The difference between integers *a* and *b* is expressed as $a - b$.

EXAMPLE 5	AN APPLICATION OF SUBTRACTION USING THE WORD *DIFFERENCE*

The bar graph in Figure 5.4 shows the budget surplus or deficit for the United States government from 2000 through 2005. What is the difference between the 2000 surplus and the 2005 deficit?

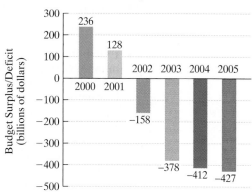

FIGURE 5.4
Source: Budget of the U.S. Government

SOLUTION

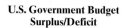

$$= 236 \quad - \quad (-427)$$
$$= 236 + 427 = 663$$

The difference between the 2000 surplus and the 2005 deficit is $663 billion.

 Use Figure 5.4 to find the difference between the 2004 deficit and the 2005 deficit.

Multiplication of Integers

The result of multiplying two or more numbers is called the **product** of the numbers. You can think of multiplication as repeated addition or subtraction that starts at 0. For example,

$$3(-4) = 0 + (-4) + (-4) + (-4) = -12$$

The numbers have different signs and the product is negative.

and

$$(-3)(-4) = 0 - (-4) - (-4) - (-4) = 0 + 4 + 4 + 4 = 12.$$

The numbers have the same sign and the product is positive.

These observations give us the following rules for multiplying integers:

RULES FOR MULTIPLYING INTEGERS

Rule	**Examples**
1. The product of two integers with different signs is found by multiplying their absolute values. The product is negative.	• $7(-5) = -35$
2. The product of two integers with the same sign is found by multiplying their absolute values. The product is positive.	• $(-6)(-11) = 66$
3. The product of 0 and any integer is 0: $a \cdot 0 = 0$ and $0 \cdot a = 0$.	• $-17(0) = 0$
4. If no number is 0, a product with an odd number of negative factors is found by multiplying absolute values. The product is negative.	• $-2(-3)(-5) = -30$ Three (odd) negative factors
5. If no number is 0, a product with an even number of negative factors is found by multiplying absolute values. The product is positive.	• $-2(3)(-5) = 30$ Two (even) negative factors

---

Exponential Notation

Because exponents indicate repeated multiplication, rules for multiplying real numbers can be used to evaluate exponential expressions.

EXAMPLE 6   EVALUATING EXPONENTIAL EXPRESSIONS

Evaluate: **a.** $(-6)^2$ **b.** -6^2 **c.** $(-5)^3$ **d.** $(-2)^4$.

SOLUTION

a. $(-6)^2 = (-6)(-6) = 36$

Base is −6.   Same signs give positive product.

b. $-6^2 = -(6 \cdot 6) = -36$

Base is 6. The negative is not inside parentheses and is not taken to the second power.

c. $(-5)^3 = (-5)(-5)(-5) = -125$

An odd number of negative factors gives a negative product.

d. $(-2)^4 = (-2)(-2)(-2)(-2) = 16$

An even number of negative factors gives a positive product.

 Evaluate:

a. $(-5)^2$ **b.** -5^2 **c.** $(-4)^3$ **d.** $(-3)^4$.

Exponential Representations of the Beast

The New Testament book of Revelation designates 666 as the Number of the Beast (the Antichrist):

"Here is wisdom. Let him that hath understanding count the number of the beast: for it is the number of a man; and his number is six hundred threescore and six." (Revelation 13:18)

Although your author has no idea of what this actually means, he is intrigued by the beast's curious exponential representations:

$$666 = 6 + 6 + 6 + 6^3 + 6^3 + 6^3$$
$$666 = 1^3 + 2^3 + 3^3 + 4^3 + 5^3 + 6^3 + 5^3 + 4^3 + 3^3 + 2^3 + 1^3$$
$$666 = 2^2 + 3^2 + 5^2 + 7^2 + 11^2 + 13^2 + 17^2$$

Sum of the squares of the first seven prime numbers

$$666 = 1^6 - 2^6 + 3^6.$$

The beast is even interesting in Roman numerals:

$$666 = \text{DCLXVI}.$$

Contains all Roman numerals from D(500) to I (1) in decending order

Division of Integers

The result of dividing the integer a by the nonzero integer b is called the **quotient** of the numbers. We can write this quotient as $a \div b$ or $\frac{a}{b}$.

A relationship exists between multiplication and division. For example,

$$\frac{-12}{4} = -3 \text{ means that } 4(-3) = -12.$$

$$\frac{-12}{-4} = 3 \text{ means that } -4(3) = -12.$$

Because of the relationship between multiplication and division, the rules for obtaining the sign of a quotient are the same as those for obtaining the sign of a product.

TECHNOLOGY

MULTIPLYING AND DIVIDING ON A CALCULATOR

Example: $(-173)(-256)$

SCIENTIFIC CALCULATOR

173 [+/−] [×] 256 [+/−] [=]

GRAPHING CALCULATOR

[(−)] 173 [×] [(−)] 256 [ENTER]

The number 44288 should be displayed.
Division is performed in the same manner, using [÷] instead of [×]. What happens when you divide by 0? Try entering

8 [÷] 0

and pressing [=] or [ENTER].

RULES FOR DIVIDING INTEGERS

Rule	Examples

1. The quotient of two integers with different signs is found by dividing their absolute values. The quotient is negative.

- $\frac{80}{-4} = -20$
- $\frac{-15}{5} = -3$

2. The quotient of two integers with the same sign is found by dividing their absolute values. The quotient is positive.

- $\frac{27}{9} = 3$
- $\frac{-45}{-3} = 15$

3. Zero divided by any nonzero integer is zero.

- $\frac{0}{-5} = 0$ (because $-5(0) = 0$)

4. Division by 0 is undefined.

- $\frac{-8}{0}$ is undefined (because 0 cannot be multiplied by an integer to obtain -8).

6 | Use the order of operations agreement.

Order of Operations

Suppose that you want to find the value of $3 + 7 \cdot 5$. Which procedure shown below is correct?

$$3 + 7 \cdot 5 = 3 + 35 = 38 \quad \text{or} \quad 3 + 7 \cdot 5 = 10 \cdot 5 = 50$$

If you know the answer, you probably know certain rules, called the **order of operations**, to make sure that there is only one correct answer. One of these rules states that if a problem contains no parentheses, perform multiplication before addition. Thus, the procedure on the left is correct because the multiplication of 7 and 5 is done first. Then the addition is performed. The correct answer is 38.

Here are the rules for determining the order in which operations should be performed:

> ### ORDER OF OPERATIONS
>
> 1. Perform all operations within grouping symbols.
> 2. Evaluate all exponential expressions.
> 3. Do all multiplications and divisions in the order in which they occur, working from left to right.
> 4. Finally, do all additions and subtractions in the order in which they occur, working from left to right.

In the third step, be sure to do all multiplications and divisions *as they occur* from left to right. For example,

$$8 \div 4 \cdot 2 = 2 \cdot 2 = 4$$

Do the division first because it occurs first.

$$8 \cdot 4 \div 2 = 32 \div 2 = 16.$$

Do the multiplication first because it occurs first.

EXAMPLE 7 USING THE ORDER OF OPERATIONS

Simplify: $6^2 - 24 \div 2^2 \cdot 3 + 1$.

SOLUTION There are no grouping symbols. Thus, we begin by evaluating exponential expressions. Then we multiply or divide. Finally, we add or subtract.

$$6^2 - 24 \div 2^2 \cdot 3 + 1$$

$= 36 - 24 \div 4 \cdot 3 + 1$ Evaluate exponential expressions: $6^2 = 6 \cdot 6 = 36$ and $2^2 = 2 \cdot 2 = 4$.

$= 36 - 6 \cdot 3 + 1$ Perform the multiplications and divisions from left to right. Start with $24 \div 4 = 6$.

$= 36 - 18 + 1$ Now do the multiplication: $6 \cdot 3 = 18$.

$= 18 + 1$ Finally, perform the additions and subtractions from left to right. Subtract: $36 - 18 = 18$.

$= 19$ Add: $18 + 1 = 19$.

○

CHECK POINT **7** Simplify: $7^2 - 48 \div 4^2 \cdot 5 + 2$.

EXAMPLE 8   USING THE ORDER OF OPERATIONS

Simplify: $(-6)^2 - (5 - 7)^2(-3)$.

SOLUTION   Because grouping symbols appear, we perform the operation within parentheses first.

$$(-6)^2 - (5 - 7)^2(-3)$$

$$= (-6)^2 - (-2)^2(-3)$$ Work inside parentheses first:
$5 - 7 = 5 + (-7) = -2.$

$$= 36 - 4(-3)$$ Evaluate exponential expressions:
$(-6)^2 = (-6)(-6) = 36$ and
$(-2)^2 = (-2)(-2) = 4.$

$$= 36 - (-12)$$ Multiply: $4(-3) = -12.$

$$= 48$$ Subtract: $36 - (-12) = 36 + 12 = 48.$

CHECK POINT **8**   Simplify $(-8)^2 - (10 - 13)^2(-2)$.

EXERCISE SET 5.2 ●●●●●●

• Practice Exercises

In Exercises 1–4, start by drawing a number line that shows integers from −5 to 5. Then graph each of the following integers on your number line.

1. 3   **2.** 5   **3.** −4   **4.** −2

In Exercises 5–12, insert either < or > in the shaded area between the integers to make the statement true.

5. −2 ■ 7   **6.** −1 ■ 13   **7.** −13 ■ −2   **8.** −1 ■ −13

9. 8 ■ −50   **10.** 7 ■ −9   **11.** −100 ■ 0   **12.** 0 ■ −300

In Exercises 13–18, find the absolute value.

13. $|-14|$ **14.** $|-16|$ **15.** $|14|$

16. $|16|$ **17.** $|-300,000|$ **18.** $|-1,000,000|$

In Exercises 19–30, find each sum.

19. $-7 + (-5)$ **20.** $-3 + (-4)$ **21.** $12 + (-8)$

22. $13 + (-5)$ **23.** $6 + (-9)$ **24.** $3 + (-11)$

25. $-9 + (+4)$ **26.** $-7 + (+3)$ **27.** $-9 + (-9)$

28. $-13 + (-13)$ **29.** $9 + (-9)$ **30.** $13 + (-13)$

In Exercises 31–42, perform the indicated subtraction.

31. $13 - 8$ **32.** $14 - 3$ **33.** $8 - 15$

34. $9 - 20$ **35.** $4 - (-10)$ **36.** $3 - (-17)$

37. $-6 - (-17)$ **38.** $-4 - (-19)$ **39.** $-12 - (-3)$

40. $-19 - (-2)$ **41.** $-11 - 17$ **42.** $-19 - 21$

In Exercises 43–52, find each product.

43. $6(-9)$ **44.** $5(-7)$ **45.** $(-7)(-3)$

46. $(-8)(-5)$ **47.** $(-2)(6)$ **48.** $(-3)(10)$

49. $(-13)(-1)$ **50.** $(-17)(-1)$ **51.** $0(-5)$

52. $0(-8)$

In Exercises 53–66, evaluate each exponential expression.

53. 5^2 **54.** 6^2 **55.** $(-5)^2$ **56.** $(-6)^2$

57. 4^3 **58.** 2^3 **59.** $(-5)^3$ **60.** $(-4)^3$

61. $(-5)^4$ **62.** $(-4)^4$ **63.** -3^4 **64.** -1^4

65. $(-3)^4$ **66.** $(-1)^4$

In Exercises 67–80, find each quotient, or, if applicable, state that the expression is undefined.

67. $\frac{-12}{4}$ **68.** $\frac{-40}{5}$ **69.** $\frac{21}{-3}$ **70.** $\frac{60}{-6}$

71. $\frac{-90}{-3}$ **72.** $\frac{-66}{-6}$ **73.** $\frac{0}{-7}$ **74.** $\frac{0}{-8}$

75. $\frac{-7}{0}$ **76.** $\frac{0}{0}$

77. $(-480) \div 24$ **78.** $(-300) \div 12$

79. $(465) \div (-15)$ **80.** $(-594) \div (-18)$

In Exercises 81–98, use the order of operations to find the value of each expression.

81. $7 + 6 \cdot 3$ **82.** $-5 + (-3) \cdot 8$

83. $(-5) - 6(-3)$ **84.** $-8(-3) - 5(-6)$

85. $6 - 4(-3) - 5$ **86.** $3 - 7(-1) - 6$

87. $3 - 5(-4 - 2)$ **88.** $3 - 9(-1 - 6)$

89. $(2 - 6)(-3 - 5)$ **90.** $9 - 5(6 - 4) - 10$

91. $3(-2)^2 - 4(-3)^2$ **92.** $5(-3)^2 - 2(-2)^3$

93. $(2 - 6)^2 - (3 - 7)^2$ **94.** $(4 - 6)^2 - (5 - 9)^3$

95. $6(3 - 5)^3 - 2(1 - 3)^3$

96. $-3(-6 + 8)^3 - 5(-3 + 5)^3$

97. $8^2 - 16 \div 2^2 \cdot 4 - 3$

98. $10^2 - 100 \div 5^2 \cdot 2 - (-3)$

• Practice Plus

In Exercises 99–104, use the order of operations to find the value of each expression.

99. $8 - 3[-2(2 - 5) - 4(8 - 6)]$

100. $8 - 3[-2(5 - 7) - 5(4 - 2)]$

101. $-2^2 + 4[16 \div (3 - 5)]$

102. $-3^2 + 2[20 \div (7 - 11)]$

103. $4|10 - (8 - 20)|$

104. $-5|7 - (20 - 8)|$

In Exercises 105–108, express each sentence as a single numerical expression. Then use the order of operations to simplify the expression.

105. Cube -2. Subtract this exponential expression from -10.

106. Cube -5. Subtract this exponential expression from -100.

107. Subtract 10 from 7. Multiply this difference by 2. Square this product.

108. Subtract 11 from 9. Multiply this difference by 2. Raise this product to the fourth power.

• Application Exercises

The bar graph shows the U.S. trade balance in goods and services, in billions of dollars, from 2000 through 2005. The most complete scorecard of the U.S. international trade performance deteriorated to a record $805 billion deficit in 2005. Use the information shown by the graph to solve Exercises 109–112. Express answers in billions of dollars.

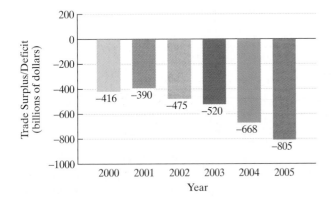

U.S. Trade Deficit

Source: Bureau of Economic Analysis

109. Find the difference between the 2000 trade deficit and the 2005 trade deficit.

110. Find the difference between the 2001 trade deficit and the 2005 trade deficit.

111. By how much did the 2005 deficit exceed twice the 2001 deficit?

112. Find the average trade deficit for 2003 and 2004 combined. By how much did the 2005 deficit exceed this average?

113. The peak of Mount Kilimanjaro, the highest point in Africa, is 19,321 feet above sea level. Qattara Depression, Egypt, the lowest point in Africa, is 436 feet below sea level. What is the difference in elevation between the peak of Mount Kilimanjaro and the Qattara Depression?

114. The peak of Mount Everest is 8848 meters above sea level. The Marianas Trench, on the floor of the Pacific Ocean, is 10,915 meters below sea level. What is the difference in elevation between the peak of Mount Everest and the Marianas Trench?

The following table shows the amount of money, in billions of dollars, collected and spent by the U.S. government from 2001 through 2005. Use the information from the table to solve Exercises 115–118. Express answers in billions of dollars.

Year	Money Collected (billions of dollars)	Money Spent (billions of dollars)
2001	$1991	$1863
2002	$1853	$2011
2003	$1782	$2160
2004	$1880	$2292
2005	$2053	$2479

Source: Budget of the U.S. Government

115. In 2002, what was the difference between the amount of money collected and the amount spent? Was there a budget surplus or deficit in 2002?

116. In 2003, what was the difference between the amount of money collected and the amount spent? Was there a budget surplus or deficit in 2003?

117. What is the difference between the 2001 surplus and the 2005 deficit?

118. What is the difference between the 2001 surplus and the 2004 deficit?

The way that we perceive the temperature on a cold day depends on both air temperature and wind speed. The windchill is what the air temperature would have to be with no wind to achieve the same chilling effect on the skin. In 2002, the National Weather Service issued new windchill temperatures, shown in the table below. Use the information from the table to solve Exercises 119–122.

New Windchill Temperature Index

	Air Temperature (°F)												
Wind Speed (miles per hour)		30	25	20	15	10	5	0	−5	−10	−15	−20	−25
5		25	19	13	7	1	−5	−11	−16	−22	−28	−34	−40
10		21	15	9	3	−4	−10	−16	−22	−28	−35	−41	−47
15		19	13	6	0	−7	−13	−19	−26	−32	−39	−45	−51
20		17	11	4	−2	−9	−15	−22	−29	−35	−42	−48	−55
25		16	9	3	−4	−11	−17	−24	−31	−37	−44	−51	−58
30		15	8	1	−5	−12	−19	−26	−33	−39	−46	−53	−60
35		14	7	0	−7	−14	−21	−27	−34	−41	−48	−55	−62
40		13	6	−1	−8	−15	−22	−29	−36	−43	−50	−57	−64
45		12	5	−2	−9	−16	−23	−30	−37	−44	−51	−58	−65
50		12	4	−3	−10	−17	−24	−31	−38	−45	−52	−60	−67
55		11	4	−3	−11	−18	−25	−32	−39	−46	−54	−61	−68
60		10	3	−4	−11	−19	−26	−33	−40	−48	−55	−62	−69

Frostbite occurs in 15 minutes or less.

Source: National Weather Service

119. What is the difference between how cold the temperature feels with winds at 10 miles per hour and 25 miles per hour when the air temperature is 15°F?

120. What is the difference between how cold the temperature feels with winds at 5 miles per hour and 30 miles per hour when the air temperature is 10°F?

121. What is the difference in the windchill temperature between an air temperature of 5°F with winds at 50 miles per hour and an air temperature of −10°F with winds at 5 miles per hour?

122. What is the difference in the windchill temperature between an air temperature of 5°F with winds at 55 miles per hour and an air temperature of −5°F with winds at 10 miles per hour?

• Writing in Mathematics

123. How does the set of integers differ from the set of whole numbers?

124. Explain how to graph an integer on a number line.

125. If you are given two integers, explain how to determine which one is smaller.

126. Explain how to add integers.

127. Explain how to subtract integers.

128. Explain how to multiply integers.

129. Explain how to divide integers.

130. Describe what it means to raise a number to a power. In your description, include a discussion of the difference between -5^2 and $(-5)^2$.

131. Why is $\frac{0}{4}$ equal to 0, but $\frac{4}{0}$ undefined?

• Critical Thinking Exercises

In Exercises 132–133, insert one pair of parentheses to make each calculation correct.

132. $8 - 2 \cdot 3 - 4 = 10$

133. $8 - 2 \cdot 3 - 4 = 14$

• Technology Exercises

Scientific calculators that have parentheses keys allow for the entry and computation of relatively complicated expressions in a single step. For example, the expression $15 + (10 - 7)^2$ can be evaluated by entering the following keystrokes:

$$15 \boxed{+} \boxed{(} \boxed{10} \boxed{-} \boxed{7} \boxed{)} \boxed{y^x} \boxed{2} \boxed{=} .$$

Find the value of each expression in Exercises 134–136 in a single step on your scientific calculator.

134. $8 - 2 \cdot 3 - 9$

135. $(8 - 2) \cdot (3 - 9)$

136. $5^3 + 4 \cdot 9 - (8 + 9 \div 3)$

SECTION 5.3 • THE RATIONAL NUMBERS

OBJECTIVES

1. Define the rational numbers.
2. Reduce rational numbers.
3. Convert between mixed numbers and improper fractions.
4. Express rational numbers as decimals.
5. Express decimals in the form $\frac{a}{b}$.
6. Multiply and divide rational numbers.
7. Add and subtract rational numbers.
8. Apply the density property of rational numbers.
9. Solve problems involving rational numbers.

You are making eight dozen chocolate chip cookies for a large neighborhood block party. The recipe lists the ingredients needed to prepare five dozen cookies, such as $\frac{3}{4}$ cup sugar. How do you adjust the amount of sugar, as well as each of the other ingredients, given in the recipe?

Adapting a recipe to suit a different number of portions usually involves working with numbers that are not integers. For example, the number describing the amount of sugar, $\frac{3}{4}$ (cup), is not an integer, although it consists of the quotient of two integers, 3 and 4. Before returning to the problem of changing the size of a recipe, we study a new set of numbers consisting of the quotient of integers.

1 | Define the rational numbers.

Defining the Rational Numbers

If two integers are added, subtracted, or multiplied, the result is always another integer. This, however, is not always the case with division. For example, 10 divided by 5 is the integer 2. By contrast, 5 divided by 10 is $\frac{1}{2}$, and $\frac{1}{2}$ is not an integer. To permit divisions such as $\frac{5}{10}$, we enlarge the set of integers, calling the new collection the *rational numbers*. The set of **rational numbers** consists of all the numbers that can be expressed as a quotient of two integers, with the denominator not 0.

> ### THE RATIONAL NUMBERS
> The set of **rational numbers** is the set of all numbers which can be expressed in the form $\frac{a}{b}$, where a and b are integers and b is not equal to 0. The integer a is called the **numerator** and the integer b is called the **denominator**.

2 Reduce rational numbers.

The following numbers are examples of rational numbers:

$$\frac{1}{2}, \frac{-3}{4}, 5, 0.$$

The integer 5 is a rational number because it can be expressed as the quotient of integers: $5 = \frac{5}{1}$. Similarly, 0 can be written as $\frac{0}{1}$.

In general, every integer a is a rational number because it can be expressed in the form $\frac{a}{1}$.

Reducing Rational Numbers

A rational number is **reduced to its lowest terms**, or **simplified**, when the numerator and denominator have no common divisors other than 1. Reducing rational numbers to lowest terms is done using the **Fundamental Principle of Rational Numbers**.

> ### THE FUNDAMENTAL PRINCIPLE OF RATIONAL NUMBERS
> If $\frac{a}{b}$ is a rational number and c is any number other than 0,
> $$\frac{a \cdot c}{b \cdot c} = \frac{a}{b}.$$
> The rational numbers $\frac{a}{b}$ and $\frac{a \cdot c}{b \cdot c}$ are called **equivalent fractions**.

When using the Fundamental Principle to reduce a rational number, the simplification can be done in one step by finding the greatest common divisor of the numerator and the denominator, and using it for c. Thus, **to reduce a rational number to its lowest terms, divide both the numerator and the denominator by their greatest common divisor**.

For example, consider the rational number $\frac{12}{100}$. The greatest common divisor of 12 and 100 is 4. We reduce to lowest terms as follows:

$$\frac{12}{100} = \frac{3 \cdot \cancel{4}}{25 \cdot \cancel{4}} = \frac{3}{25} \quad \text{or} \quad \frac{12}{100} = \frac{12 \div 4}{100 \div 4} = \frac{3}{25}.$$

EXAMPLE 1   REDUCING A RATIONAL NUMBER

Reduce $\frac{130}{455}$ to lowest terms.

SOLUTION Begin by finding the greatest common divisor of 130 and 455.

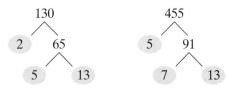

Thus, $130 = 2 \cdot 5 \cdot 13$ and $455 = 5 \cdot 7 \cdot 13$. The greatest common divisor is $5 \cdot 13$, or 65. Divide the numerator and the denominator of the given rational number by $5 \cdot 13$ or by 65.

$$\frac{130}{455} = \frac{2 \cdot \cancel{5} \cdot \cancel{13}}{\cancel{5} \cdot 7 \cdot \cancel{13}} = \frac{2}{7} \quad \text{or} \quad \frac{130}{455} = \frac{130 \div 65}{455 \div 65} = \frac{2}{7}$$

There are no common divisors of 2 and 7 other than 1. Thus, the rational number $\frac{2}{7}$ is in its lowest terms.

Reduce $\frac{72}{90}$ to lowest terms.

3 | Convert between mixed numbers and improper fractions.

STUDY TIP

The mixed number $3\frac{4}{5}$ is read "three and four-fifths."

Mixed Numbers and Improper Fractions

A **mixed number** consists of the sum of an integer and a rational number, expressed without the use of an addition sign. Here is an example of a mixed number:

$$3\frac{4}{5}.$$

The integer is 3 and the rational number is $\frac{4}{5}$. $3\frac{4}{5}$ means $3 + \frac{4}{5}$.

An **improper fraction** is a rational number whose numerator is greater than its denominator. An example of an improper fraction is $\frac{19}{5}$.

The mixed number $3\frac{4}{5}$ can be converted to the improper fraction $\frac{19}{5}$ using the following procedure:

> **CONVERTING A POSITIVE MIXED NUMBER TO AN IMPROPER FRACTION**
>
> 1. Multiply the denominator of the rational number by the integer and add the numerator to this product.
> 2. Place the sum in step 1 over the denominator in the mixed number.

EXAMPLE 2   CONVERTING FROM A MIXED NUMBER TO AN IMPROPER FRACTION

Convert $3\frac{4}{5}$ to an improper fraction.

SOLUTION

$$3\frac{4}{5} = \frac{5 \cdot 3 + 4}{5}$$

Multiply the denominator by the integer and add the numerator.

Place the sum over the mixed number's denominator.

$$= \frac{15 + 4}{5} = \frac{19}{5}$$

 Convert $2\frac{5}{8}$ to an improper fraction.

When converting a negative mixed number to an improper fraction, copy the negative sign and then follow the previous procedure. For example,

$$-2\frac{3}{4} = -\frac{4 \cdot 2 + 3}{4} = -\frac{8 + 3}{4} = -\frac{11}{4}.$$

Copy the negative sign from step to step and convert $2\frac{3}{4}$ to an improper fraction.

A positive improper fraction can be converted to a mixed number using the following procedure:

> **CONVERTING A POSITIVE IMPROPER FRACTION TO A MIXED NUMBER**
>
> 1. Divide the denominator into the numerator. Record the quotient and the remainder.
> 2. Write the mixed number using the following form:
>
> $$\text{quotient } \frac{\text{remainder}}{\text{original denominator}}.$$
>
> integer part   rational number part

| EXAMPLE 3 | CONVERTING FROM AN IMPROPER FRACTION TO A MIXED NUMBER |

Convert $\frac{42}{5}$ to a mixed number.

SOLUTION

Step 1. Divide the denominator into the numerator.

$$
\begin{array}{r}
8 \leftarrow \text{quotient} \\
5\overline{)42} \\
\underline{40} \\
2 \leftarrow \text{remainder}
\end{array}
$$

Step 2. Write the mixed number using quotient $\dfrac{\text{remainder}}{\text{original denominator}}$. Thus,

$$
\frac{42}{5} = 8\frac{2}{5}.
$$

with quotient 8, remainder 2, and original denominator 5.

 Convert $\frac{5}{3}$ to a mixed number.

When converting a negative improper fraction to a mixed number, copy the negative sign and then follow the previous procedure. For example,

$$
-\frac{29}{8} = -3\frac{5}{8}.
$$

Copy the negative sign.

Convert $\frac{29}{8}$ to a mixed number.

$$
\begin{array}{r}
3 \leftarrow \text{quotient} \\
8\overline{)29} \\
\underline{24} \\
5 \leftarrow \text{remainder}
\end{array}
$$

4 | Express rational numbers as decimals.

Rational Numbers and Decimals

We have seen that a rational number is the quotient of integers. Rational numbers can also be expressed as decimals. As shown in the place-value chart in the margin, it is convenient to represent rational numbers with denominators of 10, 100, 1000, and so on as decimals. For example,

$$
\frac{7}{10} = 0.7, \quad \frac{3}{100} = 0.03, \quad \text{and} \quad \frac{8}{1000} = 0.008.
$$

Any rational number $\frac{a}{b}$ can be expressed as a decimal by dividing the denominator, b, into the numerator, a.

Tens	Ones	.	Tenths	Hundredths	Thousandths	Ten-Thousandths	Hundred-Thousandths
10	1		$\frac{1}{10}$	$\frac{1}{100}$	$\frac{1}{1000}$	$\frac{1}{10,000}$	$\frac{1}{100,000}$

decimal point

| EXAMPLE 4 | EXPRESSING RATIONAL NUMBERS AS DECIMALS |

Express each rational number as a decimal:

a. $\frac{5}{8}$ **b.** $\frac{7}{11}$.

SOLUTION In each case, divide the denominator into the numerator.

a.
$$
\begin{array}{r}
0.625 \\
8\overline{)5.000} \\
\underline{4\,8} \\
20 \\
\underline{16} \\
40 \\
\underline{40} \\
0
\end{array}
$$

b.
$$
\begin{array}{r}
0.6363\ldots \\
11\overline{)7.0000\ldots} \\
\underline{6\,6} \\
40 \\
\underline{33} \\
70 \\
\underline{66} \\
40 \\
\underline{33} \\
70 \\
\vdots
\end{array}
$$

In Example 4, the decimal for $\frac{5}{8}$, namely 0.625, stops and is called a **terminating decimal**. Other examples of terminating decimals are

$$\frac{1}{4} = 0.25, \qquad \frac{2}{5} = 0.4, \qquad \text{and} \qquad \frac{7}{8} = 0.875.$$

By contrast, the division process for $\frac{7}{11}$ results in $0.6363\ldots$, with the digits 63 repeating over and over indefinitely. To indicate this, write a bar over the digits that repeat. Thus,

$$\frac{7}{11} = 0.\overline{63}.$$

The decimal for $\frac{7}{11}$, $0.\overline{63}$, is called a **repeating decimal**. Other examples of repeating decimals are

$$\frac{1}{3} = 0.333\ldots = 0.\overline{3} \qquad \text{and} \qquad \frac{2}{3} = 0.666\ldots = 0.\overline{6}.$$

RATIONAL NUMBERS AND DECIMALS

Any rational number can be expressed as a decimal. The resulting decimal will either terminate (stop), or it will have a digit that repeats or a block of digits that repeat.

 Express each rational number as a decimal:

a. $\dfrac{3}{8}$ **b.** $\dfrac{5}{11}$.

---

5   Express decimals in the form $\frac{a}{b}$.

Reversing Directions: Expressing Decimals as a Quotient of Two Integers

Terminating decimals can be expressed with denominators of 10, 100, 1000, 10,000, and so on. Use the place-value chart shown in the margin. The digits to the right of the decimal point are the numerator of the rational number. To find the denominator, observe the last digit to the right of the decimal point. The place-value of this digit will indicate the denominator.

Tens	Ones	Tenths	Hundredths	Thousandths	Ten-Thousandths	Hundred-Thousandths
10	1	$\frac{1}{10}$	$\frac{1}{100}$	$\frac{1}{1000}$	$\frac{1}{10,000}$	$\frac{1}{100,000}$

decimal point

EXAMPLE 5   EXPRESSING TERMINATING DECIMALS IN $\frac{a}{b}$ FORM

Express each terminating decimal as a quotient of integers:

a. 0.7   **b.** 0.49   **c.** 0.048.

SOLUTION

a. $0.7 = \frac{7}{10}$ because the 7 is in the tenths position.

b. $0.49 = \frac{49}{100}$ because the digit on the right, 9, is in the hundredths position.

c. $0.048 = \frac{48}{1000}$ because the digit on the right, 8, is in the thousandths position. Reducing to lowest terms, $\frac{48}{1000} = \frac{48 \div 8}{1000 \div 8} = \frac{6}{125}$.

○

 Express each terminating decimal as a quotient of integers, reduced to lowest terms:

a. 0.9   **b.** 0.86   **c.** 0.053.

If you are given a rational number as a repeating decimal, there is a technique for expressing the number as a quotient of integers. Although we will not be discussing algebra until Chapter 6, the basic algebra used in this technique should be familiar to you. We begin by illustrating the technique with an example. Then we will summarize the steps in the procedure and apply them to another example.

EXAMPLE 6　EXPRESSING A REPEATING DECIMAL IN $\frac{a}{b}$ FORM

Express $0.\overline{6}$ as a quotient of integers.

SOLUTION

Step 1.　Let n equal the repeating decimal. Let $n = 0.\overline{6}$, so that $n = 0.66666\ldots$.

Step 2.　If there is one repeating digit, multiply both sides of the equation in step 1 by 10.

$n = 0.66666\ldots$	This is the equation from step 1.
$10n = 10(0.66666\ldots)$	Multiply both sides by 10.
$10n = 6.66666\ldots$	Multiplying by 10 moves the decimal point one place to the right.

Step 3.　Subtract the equation in step 1 from the equation in step 2.

> **STUDY TIP**
>
> In step 3, be sure to line up the decimal points before subtracting.

Remember from algebra that n means $1n$. Thus, $10n - 1n = 9n$.

$$\begin{aligned} 10n &= 6.66666\ldots \\ -\ n &= 0.66666\ldots \\ \hline 9n &= 6 \end{aligned}$$

This is the equation from step 2.
This is the equation from step 1.

Step 4.　Divide both sides of the equation in step 3 by the number in front of n and solve for n. We solve $9n = 6$ for n by dividing both sides by 9.

$9n = 6$	This is the equation from step 3.
$\dfrac{9n}{9} = \dfrac{6}{9}$	Divide both sides by 9.
$n = \dfrac{6}{9} = \dfrac{2}{3}$	Reduce $\frac{6}{9}$ to lowest terms: $\dfrac{6}{9} = \dfrac{2 \cdot \cancel{3}}{3 \cdot \cancel{3}} = \dfrac{2}{3}$.

We began the solution process with $n = 0.\overline{6}$, and now we have $n = \frac{2}{3}$. Therefore,

$$0.\overline{6} = \frac{2}{3}.$$

Here are the steps for expressing a repeating decimal as a quotient of integers. Assume that the repeating digit or digits begin directly to the right of the decimal point.

EXPRESSING A REPEATING DECIMAL AS A QUOTIENT OF INTEGERS

Step 1. Let n equal the repeating decimal.

Step 2. Multiply both sides of the equation in step 1 by 10 if one digit repeats, by 100 if two digits repeat, by 1000 if three digits repeat, and so on.

Step 3. Subtract the equation in step 1 from the equation in step 2.

Step 4. Divide both sides of the equation in step 3 by the number in front of n and solve for n.

 Express $0.\overline{2}$ as a quotient of integers.

EXAMPLE 7   EXPRESSING A REPEATING DECIMAL IN $\frac{a}{b}$ FORM

Express $0.\overline{53}$ as a quotient of integers.

SOLUTION

Step 1. Let n equal the repeating decimal. Let $n = 0.\overline{53}$, so that $n = 0.535353\ldots$.

Step 2. If there are two repeating digits, multiply both sides of the equation in step 2 by 100.

$$n = 0.535353\ldots$$ This is the equation from step 1.
$$100n = 100(0.535353\ldots)$$ Multiply both sides by 100.
$$100n = 53.535353\ldots$$ Multiplying by 100 moves the decimal point two places to the right.

Step 3. Subtract the equation in step 1 from the equation in step 2.

$$100n = 53.535353\ldots$$ This is the equation from step 2.
$$-\quad n = 0.535353\ldots$$ This is the equation from step 1.
$$99n = 53$$

Step 4. Divide both sides of the equation in step 3 by the number in front of n and solve for n. We solve $99n = 53$ for n by dividing both sides by 99.

$$99n = 53$$ This is the equation from step 3.
$$\frac{99n}{99} = \frac{53}{99}$$ Divide both sides by 99.
$$n = \frac{53}{99}$$

Because n equals $0.\overline{53}$ and n equals $\frac{53}{99}$,

$$0.\overline{53} = \frac{53}{99}.$$

CHECK POINT Express $0.\overline{79}$ as a quotient of integers.

---

6 Multiply and divide rational numbers.

Multiplying and Dividing Rational Numbers

The product of two rational numbers is found as follows:

> **MULTIPLYING RATIONAL NUMBERS**
> The product of two rational numbers is the product of their numerators divided by the product of their denominators.
> If $\frac{a}{b}$ and $\frac{c}{d}$ are rational numbers, then $\frac{a}{b} \cdot \frac{c}{d} = \frac{a \cdot c}{b \cdot d}$.

EXAMPLE 8   MULTIPLYING RATIONAL NUMBERS

Multiply. If possible, reduce the product to its lowest terms:

a. $\frac{3}{8} \cdot \frac{5}{11}$ **b.** $\left(-\frac{2}{3}\right)\left(-\frac{9}{4}\right)$ **c.** $\left(3\frac{2}{3}\right)\left(1\frac{1}{4}\right)$.

SOLUTION

a. $\frac{3}{8} \cdot \frac{5}{11} = \frac{3 \cdot 5}{8 \cdot 11} = \frac{15}{88}$

b. $\left(-\frac{2}{3}\right)\left(-\frac{9}{4}\right) = \frac{(-2)(-9)}{3 \cdot 4} = \frac{18}{12} = \frac{3 \cdot 6}{2 \cdot 6} = \frac{3}{2}$ or $1\frac{1}{2}$

c. $\left(3\frac{2}{3}\right)\left(1\frac{1}{4}\right) = \frac{11}{3} \cdot \frac{5}{4} = \frac{11 \cdot 5}{3 \cdot 4} = \frac{55}{12}$ or $4\frac{7}{12}$

Multiply. If possible, reduce the product to its lowest terms:

a. $\frac{4}{11} \cdot \frac{2}{3}$ **b.** $\left(-\frac{3}{7}\right)\left(-\frac{14}{4}\right)$ **c.** $\left(3\frac{2}{5}\right)\left(1\frac{1}{2}\right)$.

STUDY TIP

You can divide numerators and denominators by common factors *before* performing multiplication. Then multiply the remaining factors in the numerators and multiply the remaining factors in the denominators. For example,

$$\frac{7}{15} \cdot \frac{20}{21} = \frac{\overset{1}{\cancel{7}}}{\underset{3}{\cancel{15}}} \cdot \frac{\overset{4}{\cancel{20}}}{\underset{3}{\cancel{21}}} = \frac{1 \cdot 4}{3 \cdot 3} = \frac{4}{9}.$$

Two numbers whose product is 1 are called **reciprocals**, or **multiplicative inverses**, of each other. Thus, the reciprocal of 2 is $\frac{1}{2}$ and the reciprocal of $\frac{1}{2}$ is 2 because $2 \cdot \frac{1}{2} = 1$. In general, if $\frac{c}{d}$ is a nonzero rational number, its reciprocal is $\frac{d}{c}$ because $\frac{c}{d} \cdot \frac{d}{c} = 1$.

Reciprocals are used to find the quotient of two rational numbers.

> ### DIVIDING RATIONAL NUMBERS
> The quotient of two rational numbers is the product of the first number and the reciprocal of the second number.
> If $\frac{a}{b}$ and $\frac{c}{d}$ are rational numbers and $\frac{c}{d}$ is not 0, then $\frac{a}{b} \div \frac{c}{d} = \frac{a}{b} \cdot \frac{d}{c} = \frac{a \cdot d}{b \cdot c}$.

EXAMPLE 9   DIVIDING RATIONAL NUMBERS

Divide. If possible, reduce the quotient to its lowest terms:

a. $\frac{4}{5} \div \frac{1}{10}$ **b.** $-\frac{3}{5} \div \frac{7}{11}$ **c.** $4\frac{3}{4} \div 1\frac{1}{2}$.

SOLUTION

a. $\frac{4}{5} \div \frac{1}{10} = \frac{4}{5} \cdot \frac{10}{1} = \frac{4 \cdot 10}{5 \cdot 1} = \frac{40}{5} = 8$

b. $-\frac{3}{5} \div \frac{7}{11} = -\frac{3}{5} \cdot \frac{11}{7} = \frac{-3(11)}{5 \cdot 7} = -\frac{33}{35}$

c. $4\frac{3}{4} \div 1\frac{1}{2} = \frac{19}{4} \div \frac{3}{2} = \frac{19}{4} \cdot \frac{2}{3} = \frac{19 \cdot 2}{4 \cdot 3} = \frac{38}{12} = \frac{19 \cdot \cancel{2}}{6 \cdot \cancel{2}} = \frac{19}{6}$ or $3\frac{1}{6}$

 Divide. If possible, reduce the quotient to its lowest terms:

a. $\frac{9}{11} \div \frac{5}{4}$ **b.** $-\frac{8}{15} \div \frac{2}{5}$ **c.** $3\frac{3}{8} \div 2\frac{1}{4}$.

---

7 | Add and subtract rational numbers.

Adding and Subtracting Rational Numbers

Rational expressions with identical denominators are added and subtracted using the following rules:

> ### ADDING AND SUBTRACTING RATIONAL NUMBERS WITH IDENTICAL DENOMINATORS
> The sum or difference of two rational numbers with identical denominators is the sum or difference of their numerators over the common denominator.
> If $\frac{a}{b}$ and $\frac{c}{b}$ are rational numbers, then $\frac{a}{b} + \frac{c}{b} = \frac{a + c}{b}$ and $\frac{a}{b} - \frac{c}{b} = \frac{a - c}{b}$.

| EXAMPLE 10 | ADDING AND SUBTRACTING RATIONAL NUMBERS WITH IDENTICAL DENOMINATORS |

Perform the indicated operations:

a. $\frac{3}{7} + \frac{2}{7}$ **b.** $\frac{11}{12} - \frac{5}{12}$ **c.** $-5\frac{1}{4} - \left(-2\frac{3}{4}\right)$.

SOLUTION

a. $\frac{3}{7} + \frac{2}{7} = \frac{3+2}{7} = \frac{5}{7}$

b. $\frac{11}{12} - \frac{5}{12} = \frac{11-5}{12} = \frac{6}{12} = \frac{1 \cdot 6}{2 \cdot 6} = \frac{1}{2}$

c. $-5\frac{1}{4} - \left(-2\frac{3}{4}\right) = -\frac{21}{4} - \left(-\frac{11}{4}\right) = -\frac{21}{4} + \frac{11}{4} = \frac{-21+11}{4} = \frac{-10}{4} = -\frac{5}{2}$ or $-2\frac{1}{2}$

 Perform the indicated operations:

a. $\frac{5}{12} + \frac{3}{12}$ **b.** $\frac{7}{4} - \frac{1}{4}$ **c.** $-3\frac{3}{8} - \left(-1\frac{1}{8}\right)$.

If the rational numbers to be added or subtracted have different denominators, we use the least common multiple of their denominators to rewrite the rational numbers. The least common multiple of the denominators is called the **least common denominator**.

Rewriting rational numbers with a least common denominator is done using the Fundamental Principle of Rational Numbers, discussed at the beginning of this section. Recall that if $\frac{a}{b}$ is a rational number and c is a nonzero number, then

$$\frac{a}{b} = \frac{a}{b} \cdot \frac{c}{c} = \frac{a \cdot c}{b \cdot c}.$$

Multiplying the numerator and the denominator of a rational number by the same nonzero number is equivalent to multiplying by 1, resulting in an equivalent fraction.

| EXAMPLE 11 | ADDING RATIONAL NUMBERS WITH UNLIKE DENOMINATORS |

Find the sum: $\frac{3}{4} + \frac{1}{6}$.

SOLUTION The smallest number divisible by both 4 and 6 is 12. Therefore, 12 is the least common multiple of 4 and 6, and will serve as the least common denominator. To obtain a denominator of 12, multiply the denominator and the numerator of the first rational number, $\frac{3}{4}$, by 3. To obtain a denominator of 12, multiply the denominator and the numerator of the second rational number, $\frac{1}{6}$, by 2.

$\frac{3}{4} + \frac{1}{6} = \frac{3}{4} \cdot \frac{3}{3} + \frac{1}{6} \cdot \frac{2}{2}$ *Rewrite each rational number as an equivalent fraction with a denominator of 12. $\frac{3}{3} = 1$ and $\frac{2}{2} = 1$, and multiplying by 1 does not change a number's value.*

$= \frac{9}{12} + \frac{2}{12}$ *Multiply.*

$= \frac{11}{12}$ *Add numerators and put this sum over the least common denominator.*

 Find the sum: $\frac{1}{5} + \frac{3}{4}$.

If the least common denominator cannot be found by inspection, use prime factorizations of the denominators and the method for finding their least common multiple, discussed in Section 5.1.

| EXAMPLE 12 | SUBTRACTING RATIONAL NUMBERS WITH UNLIKE DENOMINATORS |

Perform the indicated operation: $\frac{1}{15} - \frac{7}{24}$.

SOLUTION We need to first find the least common denominator, which is the least common multiple of 15 and 24. What is the smallest number divisible by both 15 and 24? The answer is not obvious, so we begin with the prime factorization of each number.

$$15 = 5 \cdot 3$$
$$24 = 8 \cdot 3 = 2^3 \cdot 3$$

The different factors are 5, 3, and 2. Using the greatest number of times each factor appears in any factorization, the least common multiple is $5 \cdot 3 \cdot 2^3 = 5 \cdot 3 \cdot 8 = 120$. We will now express each rational number with a denominator of 120, which is the least common denominator. For the first rational number, $\frac{1}{15}$, 120 divided by 15 is 8. Thus, we will multiply the numerator and denominator by 8. For the second rational number, $\frac{7}{24}$, 120 divided by 24 is 5. Thus, we will multiply the numerator and denominator by 5.

$$\frac{1}{15} - \frac{7}{24} = \frac{1}{15} \cdot \frac{8}{8} - \frac{7}{24} \cdot \frac{5}{5}$$

Rewrite each rational number as an equivalent fraction with a denominator of 120.

$$= \frac{8}{120} - \frac{35}{120}$$

Multiply.

$$= \frac{8 - 35}{120}$$

Subtract the numerators and put this difference over the least common denominator.

$$= \frac{-27}{120}$$

Perform the subtraction.

$$= \frac{-9 \cdot 3}{40 \cdot 3}$$

Reduce to lowest terms.

$$= -\frac{9}{40}$$

CHECK POINT 12 Perform the indicated operation: $\frac{3}{10} - \frac{7}{12}$.

Density of Rational Numbers

8 | Apply the density property of rational numbers.

It is always possible to find a rational number between any two given rational numbers. Mathematicians express this idea by saying that the set of rational numbers is **dense**.

> **DENSITY OF THE RATIONAL NUMBERS**
> If r and t represent rational numbers, with $r < t$, then there is a rational number s such that s is between r and t:
>
> $$r < s < t.$$

One way to find a rational number between two given rational numbers is to find the rational number halfway between them. Add the given rational numbers and divide their sum by 2, thereby finding the average of the numbers.

EXAMPLE 13   ILLUSTRATING THE DENSITY PROPERTY

Find a rational number halfway between $\frac{1}{2}$ and $\frac{3}{4}$.

SOLUTION   First, add $\frac{1}{2}$ and $\frac{3}{4}$.

$$\frac{1}{2} + \frac{3}{4} = \frac{2}{4} + \frac{3}{4} = \frac{5}{4}$$

Next, divide this sum by 2.

$$\frac{5}{4} \div \frac{2}{1} = \frac{5}{4} \cdot \frac{1}{2} = \frac{5}{8}$$

The number $\frac{5}{8}$ is halfway between $\frac{1}{2}$ and $\frac{3}{4}$. Thus,

$$\frac{1}{2} < \frac{5}{8} < \frac{3}{4}.$$

STUDY TIP

The inequality $\frac{1}{2} < \frac{5}{8} < \frac{3}{4}$ is more obvious if all denominators are changed to 8:

$$\frac{4}{8} < \frac{5}{8} < \frac{6}{8}.$$

We can repeat the procedure of Example 13 and find a rational number halfway between $\frac{1}{2}$ and $\frac{5}{8}$. Repeated application of this procedure implies the following surprising result:

Between any two given rational numbers are *infinitely many* rational numbers.

 Find a rational number halfway between $\frac{1}{3}$ and $\frac{1}{2}$.

9 | Solve problems involving rational numbers.

Problem Solving with Rational Numbers

A common application of rational numbers involves preparing food for a different number of servings than what the recipe gives. The amount of each ingredient can be found as follows:

Amount of ingredient needed

$$= \frac{\text{desired serving size}}{\text{recipe serving size}} \times \text{ingredient amount in the recipe.}$$

EXAMPLE 14   CHANGING THE SIZE OF A RECIPE

A chocolate-chip cookie recipe for five dozen cookies requires $\frac{3}{4}$ cup sugar. If you want to make eight dozen cookies, how much sugar is needed?

SOLUTION   Amount of sugar needed

$$= \frac{\text{desired serving size}}{\text{recipe serving size}} \times \text{sugar amount in recipe}$$

$$= \frac{8 \text{ dozen}}{5 \text{ dozen}} \times \frac{3}{4} \text{ cup}$$

The amount of sugar, in cups, needed is determined by multiplying the rational numbers:

$$\frac{8}{5} \times \frac{3}{4} = \frac{8 \cdot 3}{5 \cdot 4} = \frac{24}{20} = \frac{6 \cdot 4}{5 \cdot 4} = 1\frac{1}{5}.$$

Thus, $1\frac{1}{5}$ cups of sugar is needed. (Depending on the measuring cup you are using, you may need to round the sugar amount to $1\frac{1}{4}$ cups.)

14 A chocolate-chip cookie recipe for five dozen cookies requires two eggs. If you want to make seven dozen cookies, exactly how many eggs are needed? Now round your answer to a realistic number that does not involve a fractional part of an egg.

EXERCISE SET 5.3 ●●●●●●

• Practice Exercises

In Exercises 1–12, reduce each rational number to its lowest terms.

1. $\frac{10}{15}$ **2.** $\frac{18}{45}$ **3.** $\frac{15}{18}$ **4.** $\frac{16}{64}$

5. $\frac{24}{42}$ **6.** $\frac{32}{80}$ **7.** $\frac{60}{108}$ **8.** $\frac{112}{128}$

9. $\frac{342}{380}$ **10.** $\frac{210}{252}$ **11.** $\frac{308}{418}$ **12.** $\frac{144}{300}$

In Exercises 13–18, convert each mixed number to an improper fraction.

13. $2\frac{3}{8}$ **14.** $2\frac{7}{9}$ **15.** $-7\frac{3}{5}$

16. $-6\frac{2}{5}$ **17.** $12\frac{7}{16}$ **18.** $11\frac{5}{16}$

In Exercises 19–24, convert each improper fraction to a mixed number.

19. $\frac{23}{5}$ **20.** $\frac{47}{8}$ **21.** $-\frac{76}{9}$

22. $-\frac{59}{9}$ **23.** $\frac{711}{20}$ **24.** $\frac{788}{25}$

In Exercises 25–36, express each rational number as a decimal.

25. $\frac{3}{4}$ **26.** $\frac{3}{5}$ **27.** $\frac{7}{20}$ **28.** $\frac{3}{20}$

29. $\frac{7}{8}$ **30.** $\frac{5}{16}$ **31.** $\frac{9}{11}$ **32.** $\frac{3}{11}$

33. $\frac{22}{7}$ **34.** $\frac{20}{3}$ **35.** $\frac{2}{7}$ **36.** $\frac{5}{7}$

In Exercises 37–48, express each terminating decimal as a quotient of integers. If possible, reduce to lowest terms.

37. 0.3 **38.** 0.9 **39.** 0.4 **40.** 0.6

41. 0.39 **42.** 0.59 **43.** 0.82 **44.** 0.64

45. 0.725 **46.** 0.625 **47.** 0.5399 **48.** 0.7006

In Exercises 49–56, express each repeating decimal as a quotient of integers. If possible, reduce to lowest terms.

49. $0.\overline{7}$ **50.** $0.\overline{1}$ **51.** $0.\overline{9}$ **52.** $0.\overline{3}$

53. $0.\overline{36}$ **54.** $0.\overline{81}$ **55.** $0.\overline{257}$ **56.** $0.\overline{529}$

In Exercises 57–92, perform the indicated operations. If possible, reduce the answer to its lowest terms.

57. $\frac{3}{8} \cdot \frac{7}{11}$ **58.** $\frac{5}{8} \cdot \frac{3}{11}$ **59.** $\left(-\frac{1}{10}\right)\left(\frac{7}{12}\right)$

60. $\left(-\frac{1}{8}\right)\left(\frac{5}{9}\right)$ **61.** $\left(-\frac{2}{3}\right)\left(-\frac{9}{4}\right)$ **62.** $\left(-\frac{5}{4}\right)\left(-\frac{6}{7}\right)$

63. $\left(3\frac{3}{4}\right)\left(1\frac{3}{5}\right)$ **64.** $\left(2\frac{4}{5}\right)\left(1\frac{1}{4}\right)$ **65.** $\frac{5}{4} \div \frac{3}{8}$

66. $\frac{5}{8} \div \frac{4}{3}$ **67.** $-\frac{7}{8} \div \frac{15}{16}$ **68.** $-\frac{13}{20} \div \frac{4}{5}$

69. $6\frac{3}{5} \div 1\frac{1}{10}$ **70.** $1\frac{3}{4} \div 2\frac{5}{8}$ **71.** $\frac{2}{11} + \frac{3}{11}$

72. $\frac{5}{13} + \frac{2}{13}$ **73.** $\frac{5}{6} - \frac{1}{6}$ **74.** $\frac{7}{12} - \frac{5}{12}$

75. $\frac{7}{12} - \left(-\frac{1}{12}\right)$ **76.** $\frac{5}{16} - \left(-\frac{5}{16}\right)$ **77.** $\frac{1}{2} + \frac{1}{5}$

78. $\frac{1}{3} + \frac{1}{5}$ **79.** $\frac{3}{4} + \frac{3}{20}$ **80.** $\frac{2}{5} + \frac{2}{15}$

81. $\frac{5}{24} + \frac{7}{30}$ **82.** $\frac{7}{108} + \frac{55}{144}$ **83.** $\frac{13}{18} - \frac{2}{9}$

84. $\frac{13}{15} - \frac{2}{45}$ **85.** $\frac{4}{3} - \frac{3}{4}$ **86.** $\frac{3}{2} - \frac{2}{3}$

87. $\frac{1}{15} - \frac{27}{50}$ **88.** $\frac{4}{15} - \frac{1}{6}$ **89.** $3\frac{3}{4} - 2\frac{1}{3}$

90. $3\frac{2}{3} - 2\frac{1}{2}$ **91.** $\left(\frac{1}{2} - \frac{1}{3}\right) \div \frac{5}{8}$ **92.** $\left(\frac{1}{2} + \frac{1}{4}\right) \div \left(\frac{1}{2} + \frac{1}{3}\right)$

In Exercises 93–98, find a rational number halfway between the two numbers in each pair.

93. $\frac{1}{4}$ and $\frac{1}{3}$ **94.** $\frac{2}{3}$ and $\frac{5}{6}$ **95.** $\frac{1}{2}$ and $\frac{2}{3}$

96. $\frac{3}{5}$ and $\frac{2}{3}$ **97.** $-\frac{2}{3}$ and $-\frac{5}{6}$ **98.** -4 and $-\frac{7}{2}$

Different operations with the same rational numbers usually result in different answers. Exercises 99–100 illustrate some curious exceptions.

99. Show that $\frac{13}{4} + \frac{13}{9}$ and $\frac{13}{4} \times \frac{13}{9}$ give the same answer.

100. Show that $\frac{169}{30} + \frac{13}{15}$ and $\frac{169}{30} \div \frac{13}{15}$ give the same answer.

• Practice Plus

In Exercises 101–106, perform the indicated operations. If possible, reduce the answer to its lowest terms.

101. $-\frac{9}{4}\left(\frac{1}{2}\right) + \frac{3}{4} \div \frac{5}{6}$

102. $\left[-\frac{4}{7} - \left(-\frac{2}{5}\right)\right]\left[-\frac{3}{8} + \left(-\frac{1}{9}\right)\right]$

103. $\dfrac{\dfrac{7}{9} - 3}{\dfrac{5}{6}} \div \dfrac{3}{2} + \dfrac{3}{4}$

104. $\dfrac{\dfrac{17}{25}}{\dfrac{3}{5} - 4} \div \dfrac{1}{5} + \dfrac{1}{2}$

105. $\frac{1}{4} - 6(2 + 8) \div \left(-\frac{1}{3}\right)\left(-\frac{1}{9}\right)$

106. $\frac{3}{4} - 4(2 + 7) \div \left(-\frac{1}{2}\right)\left(-\frac{1}{6}\right)$

In Exercises 107–110, perform the indicated operations. Leave denominators in prime factorization form.

107. $\dfrac{5}{2^2 \cdot 3^2} - \dfrac{1}{2 \cdot 3^2}$ **108.** $\dfrac{7}{3^2 \cdot 5^2} - \dfrac{1}{3 \cdot 5^3}$

109. $\dfrac{1}{2^4 \cdot 5^3 \cdot 7} + \dfrac{1}{2 \cdot 5^4} - \dfrac{1}{2^3 \cdot 5^2}$

110. $\dfrac{1}{2^3 \cdot 17^8} + \dfrac{1}{2 \cdot 17^9} - \dfrac{1}{2^2 \cdot 3 \cdot 17^8}$

In Exercises 111–114, express each rational number as a decimal. Then insert either $<$ or $>$ in the shaded area between the rational numbers to make the statement true.

111. $\dfrac{6}{11}$ ▓ $\dfrac{7}{12}$ **112.** $\dfrac{29}{36}$ ▓ $\dfrac{28}{35}$

113. $-\dfrac{5}{6}$ ▓ $-\dfrac{8}{9}$ **114.** $-\dfrac{1}{125}$ ▓ $-\dfrac{3}{500}$

• Application Exercises

The circle graph shows the breakdown of the number of countries in the world that are free, partly free, or not free. Use the information in the graph to solve Exercises 115–116.

World's Countries by Status of Freedom

Source: Larry Berman and Bruce Murphy, *Approaching Democracy*, 4th Edition, Prentice Hall, 2003

115. What fractional part of the world's countries is free? Reduce the answer to its lowest terms.

116. What fractional part of the world's countries is not free? Reduce the answer to its lowest terms.

Use the following list of ingredients for chocolate brownies to solve Exercises 117–122.

Ingredients for 16 Brownies

$\frac{2}{3}$ cup butter, 5 ounces unsweetened chocolate, $1\frac{1}{2}$ cups sugar, 2 teaspoons vanilla, 2 eggs, 1 cup flour

117. How much of each ingredient is needed to make 8 brownies?

118. How much of each ingredient is needed to make 12 brownies?

119. How much of each ingredient is needed to make 20 brownies?

120. How much of each ingredient is needed to make 24 brownies?

121. With only one cup of butter, what is the greatest number of brownies that you can make? (Ignore part of a brownie.)

122. With only one cup of sugar, what is the greatest number of brownies that you can make? (Ignore part of a brownie.)

A mix for eight servings of instant potatoes requires $2\frac{2}{3}$ cups of water. Use this information to solve Exercises 123–124.

123. If you want to make 11 servings, how much water is needed?

124. If you want to make six servings, how much water is needed?

In most societies, women say they prefer to marry men who are older than themselves, whereas men say they prefer women who are younger. Evolutionary psychologists attribute these preferences to female concern with a partner's material resources and male concern with a partner's fertility (Source: David M. Buss, Psychological Inquiry, 6, 1–30). The graph shows the preferred age in a mate in five selected countries. Use the information in

the graph to solve Exercises 125–128. Express each answer as a mixed number.

Preferred Age in a Mate

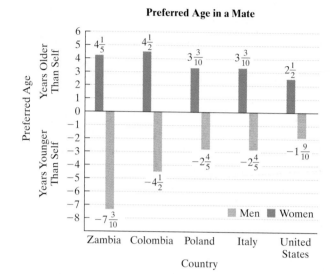

Source: Carole Wade and Carol Tavris, *Psychology*, 6th Edition, Prentice Hall, 2000

125. What is the difference between the preferred age in a mate for women in Italy and women in the United States?

126. What is the difference between the preferred age in a mate for women in Zambia and women in the United States?

127. What is the difference between the preferred age in a mate for men in Italy and men in the United States?

128. What is the difference between the preferred age in a mate for men in Colombia and men in the United States?

129. A franchise is owned by three people. The first owns $\frac{5}{12}$ of the business and the second owns $\frac{1}{4}$ of the business. What fractional part of the business is owned by the third person?

130. At a workshop on enhancing creativity, $\frac{1}{4}$ of the participants are musicians, $\frac{2}{5}$ are artists, $\frac{1}{10}$ are actors, and the remaining participants are writers. What fraction of the people attending the workshop are writers?

131. If you walk $\frac{3}{4}$ mile and then jog $\frac{2}{5}$ mile, what is the total distance covered? How much farther did you walk than jog?

132. Some companies pay people extra when they work more than a regular 40-hour work week. The overtime pay is often $1\frac{1}{2}$ times the regular hourly rate. This is called time and a half. A summer job for students pays $12 an hour and offers time and a half for the hours worked over 40. If a student works 46 hours during one week, what is the student's total pay before taxes?

133. A will states that $\frac{3}{5}$ of the estate is to be divided among relatives. Of the remaining estate, $\frac{1}{4}$ goes to the National Foundation for AIDS Research. What fraction of the estate goes to the National Foundation for AIDS Research?

134. The legend of a map indicates that 1 inch = 16 miles. If the distance on the map between two cities is $2\frac{3}{8}$ inches, how far apart are the cities?

• Writing in Mathematics

135. What is a rational number?

136. Explain how to reduce a rational number to its lowest terms.

137. Explain how to convert from a mixed number to an improper fraction. Use $7\frac{2}{3}$ as an example.

138. Explain how to convert from an improper fraction to a mixed number. Use $\frac{47}{5}$ as an example.

139. Explain how to write a rational number as a decimal.

140. Explain how to write 0.083 as a quotient of integers.

141. Explain how to write $0.\overline{9}$ as a quotient of integers.

142. Explain how to multiply rational numbers. Use $\frac{5}{6} \cdot \frac{1}{2}$ as an example.

143. Explain how to divide rational numbers. Use $\frac{5}{6} \div \frac{1}{2}$ as an example.

144. Explain how to add rational numbers with different denominators. Use $\frac{5}{6} + \frac{1}{2}$ as an example.

145. What does it mean when we say that the set of rational numbers is dense?

146. Explain what is wrong with this statement. "If you'd like to save some money, I'll be happy to sell you my computer system for only $\frac{3}{2}$ of the price I originally paid for it."

• Critical Thinking Exercises

147. Shown in the next column is a short excerpt from "The Star-Spangled Banner." The time is $\frac{3}{4}$, which means that each measure must contain notes that add up to $\frac{3}{4}$. The values of the different notes tell musicians how long to hold each note.

$$\circ = 1 \qquad \stackrel{}{\mathrel{\rule{0.4pt}{8pt}}} = \frac{1}{2} \qquad \stackrel{}{\mathrel{\rule{0.4pt}{8pt}}} = \frac{1}{4} \qquad \stackrel{}{\mathrel{\rule{0.4pt}{8pt}}} = \frac{1}{8}$$

Use vertical lines to divide this line of "The Star-Spangled Banner" into measures.

say does that Star-span-gled Ban-ner yet wave O'er the

148. Use inductive reasoning to predict the addition problem and the sum that will appear in the fourth row. Then perform the arithmetic to verify your conjecture.

$$\frac{1}{1 \cdot 2} + \frac{1}{2 \cdot 3} = \frac{2}{3}$$

$$\frac{1}{1 \cdot 2} + \frac{1}{2 \cdot 3} + \frac{1}{3 \cdot 4} = \frac{3}{4}$$

$$\frac{1}{1 \cdot 2} + \frac{1}{2 \cdot 3} + \frac{1}{3 \cdot 4} + \frac{1}{4 \cdot 5} = \frac{4}{5}$$

• Technology Exercises

149. Use a calculator to express the following rational numbers as decimals.

a. $\dfrac{197}{800}$ **b.** $\dfrac{4539}{3125}$ **c.** $\dfrac{7}{6250}$

150. Some calculators have a fraction feature. This feature allows you to perform operations with fractions and displays the answer as a fraction reduced to its lowest terms. If your calculator has this feature, use it to verify any five of the answers that you obtained in Exercises 57–92.

• Group Exercise

151. Each member of the group should present an application of rational numbers. The application can be based on research or on how the group member uses rational numbers in his or her life. If you are not sure where to begin, ask yourself how your life would be different if fractions and decimals were concepts unknown to our civilization.

SECTION 5.4 • THE IRRATIONAL NUMBERS

OBJECTIVES

1. Define the irrational numbers.
2. Simplify square roots.
3. Perform operations with square roots.
4. Rationalize the denominator.

Shown here is Renaissance artist Raphael Sanzio's (1483–1520) image of Pythagoras from *The School of Athens* mural. Detail of left side.
Stanza della Segnatura, Vatican Palace, Vatican State. Scala/Art Resource, NY.

Pythagoras

For the followers of the Greek mathematician Pythagoras in the sixth century B.C., numbers took on a life-and-death importance. The "Pythagorean Brotherhood" was a secret group whose members were convinced that properties of whole numbers were the key to understanding the universe. Members of the Brotherhood (which admitted women) thought that all numbers that were not whole numbers could be

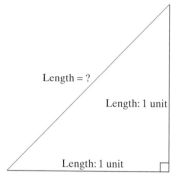

Length = ?

Length: 1 unit

Length: 1 unit

FIGURE 5.5

represented as the ratio of whole numbers. A crisis occurred for the Pythagoreans when they discovered the existence of a number that was not rational. Because the Pythagoreans viewed numbers with reverence and awe, the punishment for speaking about this number was death. However, a member of the Brotherhood revealed the secret of the number's existence. When he later died in a shipwreck, his death was viewed as punishment from the gods.

The triangle in Figure 5.5 led the Pythagoreans to the discovery of a number that could not be expressed as the quotient of integers. Based on their understanding of the relationship among the sides of this triangle, they knew that the length of the side shown in red had to be a number that, when squared, is equal to 2. The Pythagoreans discovered that this number seemed to be close to the rational numbers

$$\frac{14}{10}, \frac{141}{100}, \frac{1414}{1000}, \frac{14{,}141}{10{,}000}, \text{ and so on.}$$

However, they were shocked to find that there is no quotient of integers whose square is equal to 2.

The positive number whose square is equal to 2 is written $\sqrt{2}$. We read this "the square root of 2," or "radical 2." The symbol $\sqrt{\ }$ is called the **radical sign**. The number under the radical sign, in this case 2, is called the **radicand**. The entire symbol $\sqrt{2}$ is called a **radical**.

Using deductive reasoning, mathematicians have proved that $\sqrt{2}$ cannot be represented as a quotient of integers. This means that there is no terminating or repeating decimal that can be multiplied by itself to give 2. We can, however, give a decimal approximation for $\sqrt{2}$. We use the symbol $\approx$, which means "is approximately equal to." Thus,

$$\sqrt{2} \approx 1.414214.$$

We can verify that this is only an approximation by multiplying 1.414214 by itself. The product is not exactly 2:

$$1.414214 \times 1.414214 = 2.000001237796.$$

1 | Define the irrational numbers.

A number like $\sqrt{2}$, whose decimal representation does not come to an end and does not have a block of repeating digits, is an example of an **irrational number**.

> **THE IRRATIONAL NUMBERS**
> The set of **irrational numbers** is the set of numbers whose decimal representations are neither terminating nor repeating.

The Best and Worst of π

In 2002, Japanese mathematicians at Tokyo University calculated π to 1.24 trillion decimal places. The calculations used 400 hours of computer time, beating their previous record, set in 1999, of 206 billion places.

The most inaccurate version of π came from the 1897 General Assembly of Indiana. Bill No. 246 stated that "π was by law 4."

Perhaps the best known of all the irrational numbers is π (pi). This irrational number represents the distance around a circle (its circumference) divided by the diameter of the circle. In the *Star Trek* episode "Wolf in the Fold," Spock foils an evil computer by telling it to "compute the last digit in the value of π." Because π is an irrational number, there is no last digit in its decimal representation:

$$\pi = 3.14159265358979323846264433832795\ldots.$$

The nature of the irrational number π has fascinated mathematicians for centuries. Amateur and professional mathematicians have taken up the challenge of calculating π to more and more decimal places. Although such an exercise may seem pointless, it serves as the ultimate stress test for new high-speed computers and also as a test for the long-standing, but still unproven, conjecture that the distribution of digits in π is completely random.

TECHNOLOGY

You can obtain decimal approximations for irrational numbers using a calculator. For example, to approximate $\sqrt{2}$, use the following keystrokes:

Scientific Calculator

$2\ \boxed{\sqrt{}}$ or $2\ \boxed{\begin{matrix}2ND\\INV\end{matrix}}\ \boxed{x^2}$

Graphing Calculator

$\boxed{\sqrt{}}\ 2\ \boxed{ENTER}$ or $\boxed{\begin{matrix}2ND\\INV\end{matrix}}\ \boxed{x^2}\ 2\ \boxed{ENTER}$

Some graphing calculators show an open parenthesis after displaying $\sqrt{}$. In this case, enter a closed parenthesis, $\boxed{)}$, after **2**.

The display may read 1.41421356237, although your calculator may show more or fewer digits. Between which two integers would you graph $\sqrt{2}$ on a number line?

Square Roots

The U.N. building is designed with three golden rectangles.

The United Nations Building in New York was designed to represent its mission of promoting world harmony. Viewed from the front, the building looks like three rectangles stacked upon each other. In each rectangle, the width divided by the height is $\sqrt{5} + 1$ to 2, approximately 1.618 to 1. The ancient Greeks believed that such a rectangle, called a **golden rectangle**, was the most pleasing of all rectangles. The comparison 1.618 to 1 is approximate because $\sqrt{5}$ is an irrational number.

The **principal square root** of a nonnegative number n, written $\sqrt{n}$, is the positive number that when multiplied by itself gives n. Thus,

$$\sqrt{36} = 6 \text{ because } 6 \cdot 6 = 36$$

and

$$\sqrt{81} = 9 \text{ because } 9 \cdot 9 = 81.$$

Notice that both $\sqrt{36}$ and $\sqrt{81}$ are rational numbers because 6 and 9 are terminating decimals. Thus, **not all square roots are irrational**.

Numbers such as 36 and 81 are called *perfect squares*. A **perfect square** is a number that is the square of a whole number. The first few perfect squares are listed below.

$0 = 0^2$	$16 = 4^2$	$64 = 8^2$	$144 = 12^2$
$1 = 1^2$	$25 = 5^2$	$81 = 9^2$	$169 = 13^2$
$4 = 2^2$	$36 = 6^2$	$100 = 10^2$	$196 = 14^2$
$9 = 3^2$	$49 = 7^2$	$121 = 11^2$	$225 = 15^2$

The principal square root of a perfect square is a whole number. For example,

$$\sqrt{0} = 0, \sqrt{1} = 1, \sqrt{4} = 2, \sqrt{9} = 3, \sqrt{16} = 4, \sqrt{25} = 5, \sqrt{36} = 6,$$

and so on.

Simplifying Square Roots

2 Simplify square roots.

A rule for simplifying square roots can be generalized by comparing $\sqrt{25 \cdot 4}$ and $\sqrt{25} \cdot \sqrt{4}$. Notice that

$$\sqrt{25 \cdot 4} = \sqrt{100} = 10 \quad \text{and} \quad \sqrt{25} \cdot \sqrt{4} = 5 \cdot 2 = 10.$$

Because we obtain 10 in both situations, the original radicals must be equal. That is,

$$\sqrt{25 \cdot 4} = \sqrt{25} \cdot \sqrt{4}.$$

STUDY TIP

There are no addition or subtraction rules for square roots:

$$\sqrt{a+b} \neq \sqrt{a} + \sqrt{b}$$
$$\sqrt{a-b} \neq \sqrt{a} - \sqrt{b}.$$

For example, if $a = 9$ and $b = 16$,

$$\sqrt{9+16} = \sqrt{25} = 5$$

and

$$\sqrt{9} + \sqrt{16} = 3 + 4 = 7.$$

Thus,

$$\sqrt{9+16} \neq \sqrt{9} + \sqrt{16}.$$

This result is a particular case of the **product rule for square roots** that can be generalized as follows:

THE PRODUCT RULE FOR SQUARE ROOTS

If a and b represent nonnegative numbers, then

$$\sqrt{ab} = \sqrt{a} \cdot \sqrt{b} \quad \text{and} \quad \sqrt{a} \cdot \sqrt{b} = \sqrt{ab}.$$

The square root of a product is the product of the square roots.

Example 1 shows how the product rule is used to remove from the square root any perfect squares that occur as factors.

EXAMPLE 1   SIMPLIFYING SQUARE ROOTS

Simplify, if possible:

a. $\sqrt{75}$ **b.** $\sqrt{500}$ **c.** $\sqrt{17}$.

SOLUTION

a. $\sqrt{75} = \sqrt{25 \cdot 3}$ 25 is the greatest perfect square that is a factor of 75.

$\quad\quad = \sqrt{25} \cdot \sqrt{3}$ $\sqrt{ab} = \sqrt{a} \cdot \sqrt{b}$

$\quad\quad = 5\sqrt{3}$ Write $\sqrt{25}$ as 5.

b. $\sqrt{500} = \sqrt{100 \cdot 5}$ 100 is the greatest perfect square factor of 500.

$\quad\quad = \sqrt{100} \cdot \sqrt{5}$ $\sqrt{ab} = \sqrt{a} \cdot \sqrt{b}$

$\quad\quad = 10\sqrt{5}$ Write $\sqrt{100}$ as 10.

c. Because 17 has no perfect square factors (other than 1), $\sqrt{17}$ cannot be simplified.

 Simplify, if possible:

a. $\sqrt{12}$ **b.** $\sqrt{60}$ **c.** $\sqrt{55}$.

---

3 Perform operations with square roots.

Multiplying Square Roots

If a and b are nonnegative, then we can use the product rule

$$\sqrt{a} \cdot \sqrt{b} = \sqrt{a \cdot b}$$

to multiply square roots. The product of the square roots is the square root of the product. Once the square roots are multiplied, simplify the square root of the product when possible.

EXAMPLE 2   MULTIPLYING SQUARE ROOTS

Multiply:

a. $\sqrt{2} \cdot \sqrt{5}$ **b.** $\sqrt{7} \cdot \sqrt{7}$ **c.** $\sqrt{6} \cdot \sqrt{12}$.

SOLUTION

It is possible to multiply irrational numbers and obtain a rational number for the product.

a. $\sqrt{2} \cdot \sqrt{5} = \sqrt{2 \cdot 5} = \sqrt{10}$

b. $\sqrt{7} \cdot \sqrt{7} = \sqrt{7 \cdot 7} = \sqrt{49} = 7$

c. $\sqrt{6} \cdot \sqrt{12} = \sqrt{6 \cdot 12} = \sqrt{72} = \sqrt{36 \cdot 2} = \sqrt{36} \cdot \sqrt{2} = 6\sqrt{2}$

 Multiply:

a. $\sqrt{3} \cdot \sqrt{10}$ **b.** $\sqrt{10} \cdot \sqrt{10}$ **c.** $\sqrt{6} \cdot \sqrt{2}$.

A Radical Idea: Time Is Relative

What does travel in space have to do with square roots? Imagine that in the future we will be able to travel at velocities approaching the speed of light (approximately 186,000 miles per second). According to Einstein's theory of relativity, time would pass more quickly on Earth than it would in the moving spaceship. The square root expression

$$R_f\sqrt{1 - \left(\dfrac{v}{c}\right)^2}$$

gives the aging rate of an astronaut relative to the aging rate of a friend on Earth, R_f. In the expression, v is the astronaut's speed and c is the speed of light. As the astronaut's speed approaches the speed of light, we can substitute c for v:

$$R_f\sqrt{1 - \left(\dfrac{v}{c}\right)^2} \quad \text{Let } v = c.$$

$$= R_f\sqrt{1 - \left(\dfrac{c}{c}\right)^2}$$

$$= R_f\sqrt{1 - 1^2}$$

$$= R_f\sqrt{0} = 0.$$

Close to the speed of light, the astronaut's aging rate relative to a friend on Earth is nearly 0. What does this mean? As we age here on Earth, the space traveler would barely get older. The space traveler would return to a futuristic world in which friends and loved ones would be long dead.

Dividing Square Roots

Another property for square roots involves division.

> ### THE QUOTIENT RULE FOR SQUARE ROOTS
> If a and b represent nonnegative numbers and $b \neq 0$, then
>
> $$\dfrac{\sqrt{a}}{\sqrt{b}} = \sqrt{\dfrac{a}{b}} \quad \text{and} \quad \sqrt{\dfrac{a}{b}} = \dfrac{\sqrt{a}}{\sqrt{b}}.$$
>
> The quotient of two square roots is the square root of the quotient.

Once the square roots are divided, simplify the square root of the quotient when possible.

EXAMPLE 3   DIVIDING SQUARE ROOTS

Find the quotient:

a. $\dfrac{\sqrt{75}}{\sqrt{3}}$ **b.** $\dfrac{\sqrt{90}}{\sqrt{2}}$.

SOLUTION

a. $\dfrac{\sqrt{75}}{\sqrt{3}} = \sqrt{\dfrac{75}{3}} = \sqrt{25} = 5$

b. $\dfrac{\sqrt{90}}{\sqrt{2}} = \sqrt{\dfrac{90}{2}} = \sqrt{45} = \sqrt{9 \cdot 5} = \sqrt{9} \cdot \sqrt{5} = 3\sqrt{5}$

 Find the quotient:

a. $\dfrac{\sqrt{80}}{\sqrt{5}}$ **b.** $\dfrac{\sqrt{48}}{\sqrt{6}}$.

Adding and Subtracting Square Roots

The number that multiplies a square root is called the square root's **coefficient**. For example, in $3\sqrt{5}$, 3 is the coefficient of the square root.

Square roots with the same radicand can be added or subtracted by adding or subtracting their coefficients:

$$a\sqrt{c} + b\sqrt{c} = (a + b)\sqrt{c} \qquad\qquad a\sqrt{c} - b\sqrt{c} = (a - b)\sqrt{c}.$$

Sum of coefficients times the common square root

Difference of coefficients times the common square root

EXAMPLE 4   ADDING AND SUBTRACTING SQUARE ROOTS

Add or subtract as indicated:

a. $7\sqrt{2} + 5\sqrt{2}$ **b.** $2\sqrt{5} - 6\sqrt{5}$ **c.** $3\sqrt{7} + 9\sqrt{7} - \sqrt{7}$.

SOLUTION

a. $7\sqrt{2} + 5\sqrt{2} = (7 + 5)\sqrt{2}$
$$= 12\sqrt{2}$$

b. $2\sqrt{5} - 6\sqrt{5} = (2 - 6)\sqrt{5}$
$$= -4\sqrt{5}$$

c. $3\sqrt{7} + 9\sqrt{7} - \sqrt{7} = 3\sqrt{7} + 9\sqrt{7} - 1\sqrt{7}$ Write $\sqrt{7}$ as $1\sqrt{7}$.

$\qquad\qquad\qquad\quad = (3 + 9 - 1)\sqrt{7}$

$\qquad\qquad\qquad\quad = 11\sqrt{7}$

○

 Add or subtract as indicated:

$\quad$ **a.** $8\sqrt{3} + 10\sqrt{3}$ $\quad$ **b.** $4\sqrt{13} - 9\sqrt{13}$ $\quad$ **c.** $7\sqrt{10} + 2\sqrt{10} - \sqrt{10}.$

●

In some situations, it is possible to add and subtract square roots that do not contain a common square root by first simplifying.

<table>
<tr><td>**STUDY TIP**</td><td>**EXAMPLE 5**</td><td>ADDING AND SUBTRACTING SQUARE ROOTS BY FIRST SIMPLIFYING</td></tr>
</table>

STUDY TIP

Sums or differences of square roots that cannot be simplified and that do not contain a common square root cannot be combined into one term by adding or subtracting coefficients. Some examples:

- $5\sqrt{3} + 3\sqrt{5}$ cannot be combined by adding coefficients. The square roots, $\sqrt{3}$ and $\sqrt{5}$, are different.

- $28 + 7\sqrt{3}$, or $28\sqrt{1} + 7\sqrt{3}$, cannot be combined by adding coefficients. The square roots, $\sqrt{1}$ and $\sqrt{3}$, are different.

EXAMPLE 5 — ADDING AND SUBTRACTING SQUARE ROOTS BY FIRST SIMPLIFYING

Add or subtract as indicated:

a. $\sqrt{2} + \sqrt{8}$ $\qquad\qquad$ **b.** $4\sqrt{50} - 6\sqrt{32}.$

SOLUTION

a. $\sqrt{2} + \sqrt{8}$

$\quad = \sqrt{2} + \sqrt{4 \cdot 2}$ $\qquad$ Split 8 into two factors such that one is a perfect square.

$\quad = 1\sqrt{2} + 2\sqrt{2}$ $\qquad$ $\sqrt{4 \cdot 2} = \sqrt{4} \cdot \sqrt{2} = 2\sqrt{2}$

$\quad = (1 + 2)\sqrt{2}$ $\qquad$ Add coefficients and retain the common square root.

$\quad = 3\sqrt{2}$ $\qquad$ Simplify.

b. $4\sqrt{50} - 6\sqrt{32}$

$\quad = 4\sqrt{25 \cdot 2} - 6\sqrt{16 \cdot 2}$ $\qquad$ 25 is the greatest perfect square factor of 50 and 16 is the greatest perfect square factor of 32.

$\quad = 4 \cdot 5\sqrt{2} - 6 \cdot 4\sqrt{2}$ $\qquad$ $\sqrt{25 \cdot 2} = \sqrt{25}\sqrt{2} = 5\sqrt{2}$ and $\sqrt{16 \cdot 2} = \sqrt{16}\sqrt{2} = 4\sqrt{2}.$

$\quad = 20\sqrt{2} - 24\sqrt{2}$ $\qquad$ Multiply.

$\quad = (20 - 24)\sqrt{2}$ $\qquad$ Subtract coefficients and retain the common square root.

$\quad = -4\sqrt{2}$ $\qquad$ Simplify.

○

 Add or subtract as indicated:

$\quad$ **a.** $\sqrt{3} + \sqrt{12}$ $\qquad\qquad$ **b.** $4\sqrt{8} - 7\sqrt{18}.$

●

4 | Rationalize the denominator.

Rationalizing the Denominator

You can use a calculator to compare the approximate values for $\dfrac{1}{\sqrt{3}}$ and $\dfrac{\sqrt{3}}{3}$. The two approximations are the same. This is not a coincidence:

$$\frac{1}{\sqrt{3}} = \frac{1}{\sqrt{3}} \cdot \boxed{\frac{\sqrt{3}}{\sqrt{3}}} = \frac{\sqrt{3}}{\sqrt{9}} = \frac{\sqrt{3}}{3}$$

Any number divided by itself is 1. Multiplication by 1 does not change the value of $\dfrac{1}{\sqrt{3}}$.

This process involves rewriting a radical expression as an equivalent expression in which the denominator no longer contains any radicals. The process is called

Golden Rectangles

The early Greeks believed that the most pleasing of all rectangles were **golden rectangles**, whose ratio of width to height is

$$\frac{w}{h} = \frac{2}{\sqrt{5} - 1}.$$

The Parthenon at Athens fits into a golden rectangle once the triangular pediment is reconstructed.

STUDY TIP

You can rationalize the denominator of $\frac{12}{\sqrt{8}}$ by multiplying by $\frac{\sqrt{8}}{\sqrt{8}}$. However, it takes more work to simplify the result.

rationalizing the denominator. If the denominator contains the square root of a natural number that is not a perfect square, **multiply the numerator and the denominator by the smallest number that produces the square root of a perfect square in the denominator**.

EXAMPLE 6   RATIONALIZING DENOMINATORS

Rationalize the denominator:

a. $\dfrac{15}{\sqrt{6}}$ **b.** $\sqrt{\dfrac{3}{5}}$ **c.** $\dfrac{12}{\sqrt{8}}$.

SOLUTION

a. If we multiply numerator and denominator of $\dfrac{15}{\sqrt{6}}$ by $\sqrt{6}$, the denominator becomes $\sqrt{6} \cdot \sqrt{6} = \sqrt{36} = 6$. Therefore, we multiply by 1, choosing $\dfrac{\sqrt{6}}{\sqrt{6}}$ for 1.

$$\frac{15}{\sqrt{6}} = \frac{15}{\sqrt{6}} \cdot \frac{\sqrt{6}}{\sqrt{6}} = \frac{15\sqrt{6}}{\sqrt{36}} = \frac{15\sqrt{6}}{6} = \frac{5\sqrt{6}}{2}$$

Multiply by 1.

Simplify: $\frac{15}{6} = \frac{5 \cdot 3}{2 \cdot 3} = \frac{5}{2}$.

b. $\sqrt{\dfrac{3}{5}} = \dfrac{\sqrt{3}}{\sqrt{5}} = \dfrac{\sqrt{3}}{\sqrt{5}} \cdot \dfrac{\sqrt{5}}{\sqrt{5}} = \dfrac{\sqrt{15}}{\sqrt{25}} = \dfrac{\sqrt{15}}{5}$

Multiply by 1.

c. The *smallest* number that will produce a perfect square in the denominator of $\dfrac{12}{\sqrt{8}}$ is $\sqrt{2}$, because $\sqrt{8} \cdot \sqrt{2} = \sqrt{16} = 4$. We multiply by 1, choosing $\dfrac{\sqrt{2}}{\sqrt{2}}$ for 1.

$$\frac{12}{\sqrt{8}} = \frac{12}{\sqrt{8}} \cdot \frac{\sqrt{2}}{\sqrt{2}} = \frac{12\sqrt{2}}{\sqrt{16}} = \frac{12\sqrt{2}}{4} = 3\sqrt{2}$$

 CHECK POINT 6 Rationalize the denominator:

a. $\dfrac{25}{\sqrt{10}}$ **b.** $\sqrt{\dfrac{2}{7}}$ **c.** $\dfrac{5}{\sqrt{18}}$.

Irrational Numbers and Other Kinds of Roots

Irrational numbers appear in roots other than square roots. The symbol $\sqrt[3]{}$ represents the **cube root** of a number. For example,

$$\sqrt[3]{8} = 2 \text{ because } 2 \cdot 2 \cdot 2 = 8 \quad \text{and} \quad \sqrt[3]{64} = 4 \text{ because } 4 \cdot 4 \cdot 4 = 64.$$

Although these cube roots are rational numbers, most cube roots are not. For example,

$$\sqrt[3]{217} \approx 6.0092 \text{ because } (6.0092)^3 \approx 216.995, \text{ not exactly } 217.$$

There is no end to the kinds of roots for numbers. For example, $\sqrt[4]{}$ represents the **fourth root** of a number. Thus, $\sqrt[4]{81} = 3$ because $3 \cdot 3 \cdot 3 \cdot 3 = 81$. Although the fourth root of 81 is rational, most fourth roots, fifth roots, and so on tend to be irrational.

EXERCISE SET 5.4 ●●●●●●

• Practice Exercises

Evaluate each expression in Exercises 1–10.

1. $\sqrt{9}$ **2.** $\sqrt{16}$ **3.** $\sqrt{25}$ **4.** $\sqrt{49}$

5. $\sqrt{64}$ **6.** $\sqrt{100}$ **7.** $\sqrt{121}$ **8.** $\sqrt{144}$

9. $\sqrt{169}$ **10.** $\sqrt{225}$

In Exercises 11–16, use a calculator with a square root key to find a decimal approximation for each square root. Round the number displayed to the nearest **a.** *tenth,* **b.** *hundredth,* **c.** *thousandth.*

11. $\sqrt{173}$ **12.** $\sqrt{3176}$ **13.** $\sqrt{17{,}761}$

14. $\sqrt{779{,}264}$ **15.** $\sqrt{\pi}$ **16.** $\sqrt{2\pi}$

In Exercises 17–24, simplify the square root.

17. $\sqrt{20}$ **18.** $\sqrt{50}$ **19.** $\sqrt{80}$ **20.** $\sqrt{12}$

21. $\sqrt{250}$ **22.** $\sqrt{192}$ **23.** $7\sqrt{28}$ **24.** $3\sqrt{52}$

In Exercises 25–56, perform the indicated operation. Simplify the answer when possible.

25. $\sqrt{7}\cdot\sqrt{6}$ **26.** $\sqrt{19}\cdot\sqrt{3}$ **27.** $\sqrt{6}\cdot\sqrt{6}$

28. $\sqrt{5}\cdot\sqrt{5}$ **29.** $\sqrt{3}\cdot\sqrt{6}$ **30.** $\sqrt{12}\cdot\sqrt{2}$

31. $\sqrt{2}\cdot\sqrt{26}$ **32.** $\sqrt{5}\cdot\sqrt{50}$ **33.** $\dfrac{\sqrt{54}}{\sqrt{6}}$

34. $\dfrac{\sqrt{75}}{\sqrt{3}}$ **35.** $\dfrac{\sqrt{90}}{\sqrt{2}}$ **36.** $\dfrac{\sqrt{60}}{\sqrt{3}}$

37. $\dfrac{-\sqrt{96}}{\sqrt{2}}$ **38.** $\dfrac{-\sqrt{150}}{\sqrt{3}}$ **39.** $7\sqrt{3}+6\sqrt{3}$

40. $8\sqrt{5}+11\sqrt{5}$ **41.** $4\sqrt{13}-6\sqrt{13}$

42. $6\sqrt{17}-8\sqrt{17}$ **43.** $\sqrt{5}+\sqrt{5}$

44. $\sqrt{3}+\sqrt{3}$ **45.** $4\sqrt{2}-5\sqrt{2}+8\sqrt{2}$

46. $6\sqrt{3}+8\sqrt{3}-16\sqrt{3}$ **47.** $\sqrt{5}+\sqrt{20}$

48. $\sqrt{3}+\sqrt{27}$ **49.** $\sqrt{50}-\sqrt{18}$

50. $\sqrt{63}-\sqrt{28}$ **51.** $3\sqrt{18}+5\sqrt{50}$

52. $4\sqrt{12}+2\sqrt{75}$ **53.** $\dfrac{1}{4}\sqrt{12}-\dfrac{1}{2}\sqrt{48}$

54. $\dfrac{1}{5}\sqrt{300}-\dfrac{2}{3}\sqrt{27}$ **55.** $3\sqrt{75}+2\sqrt{12}-2\sqrt{48}$

56. $2\sqrt{72}+3\sqrt{50}-\sqrt{128}$

In Exercises 57–66, rationalize the denominator.

57. $\dfrac{5}{\sqrt{3}}$ **58.** $\dfrac{12}{\sqrt{5}}$ **59.** $\dfrac{21}{\sqrt{7}}$

60. $\dfrac{30}{\sqrt{5}}$ **61.** $\dfrac{12}{\sqrt{30}}$ **62.** $\dfrac{15}{\sqrt{50}}$

63. $\dfrac{15}{\sqrt{12}}$ **64.** $\dfrac{13}{\sqrt{40}}$ **65.** $\sqrt{\dfrac{2}{5}}$ **66.** $\sqrt{\dfrac{5}{7}}$

• Practice Plus

In Exercises 67–74, perform the indicated operations. Simplify the answer when possible.

67. $3\sqrt{8}-\sqrt{32}+3\sqrt{72}-\sqrt{75}$

68. $3\sqrt{54}-2\sqrt{24}-\sqrt{96}+4\sqrt{63}$

69. $3\sqrt{7}-5\sqrt{14}\cdot\sqrt{2}$

70. $4\sqrt{2}-8\sqrt{10}\cdot\sqrt{5}$

71. $\dfrac{\sqrt{32}}{5}+\dfrac{\sqrt{18}}{7}$ **72.** $\dfrac{\sqrt{27}}{2}+\dfrac{\sqrt{75}}{7}$

73. $\dfrac{\sqrt{2}}{\sqrt{3}}+\dfrac{\sqrt{3}}{\sqrt{2}}$ **74.** $\dfrac{\sqrt{2}}{\sqrt{7}}+\dfrac{\sqrt{7}}{\sqrt{2}}$

• Application Exercises

The formula

$$d=\sqrt{\dfrac{3h}{2}}$$

models the distance, d, in miles, that a person h feet high can see to the horizon. Use this formula to solve Exercises 75–76.

75. The pool deck on a cruise ship is 72 feet above the water. How far can passengers on the pool deck see? Write the answer in simplified radical form. Then use the simplified radical form and a calculator to express the answer to the nearest tenth of a mile.

76. The captain of a cruise ship is on the star deck, which is 120 feet above the water. How far can the captain see? Write the answer in simplified radical form. Then use the simplified radical form and a calculator to express the answer to the nearest tenth of a mile.

Police use the formula $v = 2\sqrt{5L}$ to estimate the speed of a car, v, in miles per hour, based on the length, L, in feet, of its skid marks upon sudden braking on a dry asphalt road. Use the formula to solve Exercises 77–78.

77. A motorist is involved in an accident. A police officer measures the car's skid marks to be 245 feet long. Estimate the speed at which the motorist was traveling before braking. If the posted speed limit is 50 miles per hour and the motorist tells the officer he was not speeding, should the officer believe him? Explain.

78. A motorist is involved in an accident. A police officer measures the car's skid marks to be 45 feet long. Estimate the speed at which the motorist was traveling before braking. If the posted speed limit is 35 miles per hour and the motorist tells the officer she was not speeding, should the officer believe her? Explain.

79. The graph shows the median heights for boys of various ages in the United States from birth through 60 months, or five years old.

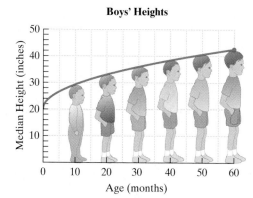

Boys' Heights

Source: Laura Walther Nathanson, *The Portable Pediatrician for Parents*

a. Use the graph at the bottom of the previous page to estimate the median height, to the nearest inch, of boys who are 50 months old.

b. The formula $h = 2.9\sqrt{x} + 20.1$ models the median height, h, in inches, of boys who are x months of age. According to the formula, what is the median height of boys who are 50 months old? Use a calculator and round to the nearest tenth of an inch. How well does your estimate from part (a) describe the median height obtained from the formula?

80. The graph shows the median heights for girls of various ages in the United States from birth through 60 months, or five years old.

Girls' Heights

Source: Laura Walther Nathanson, *The Portable Pediatrician for Parents*

a. Use the graph to estimate the median height, to the nearest inch, of girls who are 50 months old.

b. The formula $h = 3.1\sqrt{x} + 19$ models the median height, h, in inches, of girls who are x months of age. According to the formula, what is the median height of girls who are 50 months old? Use a calculator and round to the nearest tenth of an inch. How well does your estimate from part (a) describe the median height obtained from the formula?

Autism is a neurological disorder that impedes language and derails social and emotional development. New findings suggest that the condition is not a sudden calamity that strikes children at the age of 2 or 3, but a developmental problem linked to abnormally rapid brain growth during infancy. The graphs show that the heads of severely autistic children start out smaller than average and then go through a period of explosive growth. Exercises 81–82 involve mathematical models for the data shown by the graphs.

Developmental Differences between Healthy Children and Severe Autistics

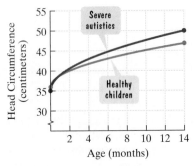

Source: The Journal of the American Medical Association

81. The data for one of the two groups shown by the graphs in the previous column can be modeled by

$$H = 2.9\sqrt{x} + 36,$$

where H is the head circumference, in centimeters, at age x months, $0 \le x \le 14$.

a. According to the model, what is the head circumference at birth?

b. According to the model, what is the head circumference at 9 months?

c. According to the model, what is the head circumference at 14 months? Use a calculator and round to the nearest tenth of a centimeter.

d. Use the values that you obtained in parts (a) through (c) and the graphs shown at the bottom of the previous column to determine if the given model describes healthy children or severe autistics.

82. The data for one of the two groups shown by the graphs in the previous column can be modeled by

$$H = 4\sqrt{x} + 35,$$

where H is the head circumference, in centimeters, at age x months, $0 \le x \le 14$.

a. According to the model, what is the head circumference at birth?

b. According to the model, what is the head circumference at 9 months?

c. According to the model, what is the head circumference at 14 months? Use a calculator and round to the nearest centimeter.

d. Use the values that you obtained in parts (a) through (c) and the graphs shown at the bottom of the previous column to determine if the given model describes healthy children or severe autistics.

The Blitzer Bonus on page 266 gives the square root expression

$$R_f\sqrt{1 - \left(\frac{v}{c}\right)^2}$$

for the aging rate of an astronaut relative to the aging rate of a friend on Earth, R_f, where v is the astronaut's speed and c is the speed of light. Take a few minutes to read the essay and then solve Exercises 83–84.

83. You are moving at 80% of the speed of light. Substitute $0.8c$ in the expression shown above. What is your aging rate relative to a friend on Earth? If 100 weeks have passed for your friend, how long were you gone?

84. You are moving at 90% of the speed of light. Substitute $0.9c$ in the expression shown above. What is your aging rate, correct to two decimal places, relative to a friend on Earth? If 100 weeks have passed for your friend, how long, to the nearest week, were you gone?

• Writing in Mathematics

85. Describe the difference between a rational number and an irrational number.

86. Describe what is wrong with this statement: $\pi = \frac{22}{7}$.

87. Using $\sqrt{50}$, explain how to simplify a square root.

88. Describe how to multiply square roots.

89. Explain how to add square roots with the same radicand.

90. Explain how to add $\sqrt{3} + \sqrt{12}$.

91. Describe what it means to rationalize a denominator. Use $\dfrac{2}{\sqrt{5}}$ in your explanation.

• Critical Thinking Exercises

92. Which one of the following is true?

  a. The product of any two irrational numbers is always an irrational number.

  b. $\sqrt{9} + \sqrt{16} = \sqrt{25}$

  c. $\sqrt{\sqrt{16}} = 2$

  d. $\dfrac{\sqrt{64}}{2} = \sqrt{32}$

In Exercises 93–95, insert either $<$ or $>$ in the shaded area between the numbers to make each statement true.

93. $\sqrt{2}\ \blacksquare\ 1.5$ **94.** $-\pi\ \blacksquare\ -3.5$ **95.** $-\dfrac{3.14}{2}\ \blacksquare\ -\dfrac{\pi}{2}$

96. How does doubling a number affect its square root?

97. Between which two consecutive integers is $-\sqrt{47}$?

98. Simplify: $\sqrt{2} + \sqrt{\dfrac{1}{2}}$.

99. Create a counterexample to show that the following statement is false: The difference between two irrational numbers is always an irrational number.

• Group Exercises

The following topics related to irrational numbers are appropriate for either individual or group research projects. A report should be given to the class on the researched topic.

100. A History of How Irrational Numbers Developed

101. Pi: Its History, Applications, and Curiosities

102. Proving That $\sqrt{2}$ Is Irrational

103. Imaginary Numbers: Their History, Applications, and Curiosities

104. The Golden Rectangle in Art and Architecture

SECTION 5.5 • REAL NUMBERS AND THEIR PROPERTIES

O B J E C T I V E S

1. Recognize subsets of the real numbers.

2. Recognize properties of real numbers.

Horror films offer the pleasure of vicarious terror, of being safely scared.

---

1 | Recognize subsets of the real numbers.

The Set of Real Numbers

The vampire legend is death as seducer; he/she sucks our blood to take us to a perverse immortality. The vampire resembles us, but appears only at night, hidden among mortals. In this section, you will find vampires in the world of numbers. Mathematicians even use the labels *vampire* and *weird* to describe sets of numbers. However, the label that appears most frequently is *real*. The union of the rational numbers and the irrational numbers is the set of **real numbers**.

    The sets that make up the real numbers are summarized in Table 5.2 on the next page. We refer to these sets as **subsets** of the real numbers, meaning that all elements in each subset are also elements in the set of real numbers.

Real numbers

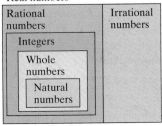

This diagram shows that every real number is rational or irrational.

TABLE 5.2 IMPORTANT SUBSETS OF THE REAL NUMBERS

Name	Description	Examples
Natural numbers	$\{1, 2, 3, 4, 5, \dots\}$ These are the numbers that we use for counting.	$2, 3, 5, 17$
Whole numbers	$\{0, 1, 2, 3, 4, 5, \dots\}$ The set of whole numbers includes 0 and the natural numbers.	$0, 2, 3, 5, 17$
Integers	$\{\dots, -5, -4, -3, -2, -1, 0, 1, 2, 3, 4, 5, \dots\}$ The set of integers includes the negatives of the natural numbers and the whole numbers.	$-17, -5, -3, -2, 0, 2, 3, 5, 17$
Rational numbers	$\left\{\dfrac{a}{b}\,\middle|\,a \text{ and } b \text{ are integers and } b \neq 0\right\}$ The set of rational numbers is the set of all numbers that can be expressed as a quotient of two integers, with the denominator not 0. Rational numbers can be expressed as terminating or repeating decimals.	$-17 = \frac{-17}{1}, -5 = \frac{-5}{1}, -3, -2,$ $0, 2, 3, 5, 17,$ $\frac{2}{5} = 0.4,$ $\frac{-2}{3} = -0.6666\dots = -0.\overline{6}$
Irrational numbers	The set of irrational numbers is the set of all numbers whose decimal representations are neither terminating nor repeating. Irrational numbers cannot be expressed as a quotient of integers.	$\sqrt{2} \approx 1.414214$ $-\sqrt{3} \approx -1.73205$ $\pi \approx 3.142$ $-\frac{\pi}{2} \approx -1.571$

EXAMPLE 1   CLASSIFYING REAL NUMBERS

Consider the following set of numbers:

$$\left\{-7, -\frac{3}{4}, 0, 0.\overline{6}, \sqrt{5}, \pi, 7.3, \sqrt{81}\right\}.$$

List the numbers in the set that are

a. natural numbers.   **b.** whole numbers.   **c.** integers.

d. rational numbers.   **e.** irrational numbers. **f.** real numbers.

SOLUTION

a. Natural numbers: The natural numbers are the numbers used for counting. The only natural number in the set is $\sqrt{81}$ because $\sqrt{81} = 9$. (9 multiplied by itself, or 9^2, is 81.)

b. Whole numbers: The whole numbers consist of the natural numbers and 0. The elements of the set that are whole numbers are 0 and $\sqrt{81}$.

c. Integers: The integers consist of the natural numbers, 0, and the negatives of the natural numbers. The elements of the set that are integers are $\sqrt{81}$, 0, and -7.

d. Rational numbers: All numbers in the set that can be expressed as the quotient of integers are rational numbers. These include $-7\left(-7 = \frac{-7}{1}\right)$, $-\frac{3}{4}$, $0\left(0 = \frac{0}{1}\right)$, and $\sqrt{81}\left(\sqrt{81} = \frac{9}{1}\right)$. Furthermore, all numbers in the set that are terminating or repeating decimals are also rational numbers. These include $0.\overline{6}$ and 7.3.

e. Irrational numbers: The irrational numbers in the set are $\sqrt{5}(\sqrt{5} \approx 2.236)$ and $\pi(\pi \approx 3.14)$. Both $\sqrt{5}$ and π are only approximately equal to 2.236 and 3.14, respectively. In decimal form, $\sqrt{5}$ and π neither terminate nor have blocks of repeating digits.

f. Real numbers: All the numbers in the given set are real numbers.

CHECK POINT 1 Consider the following set of numbers:

$$\left\{-9, -1.3, 0, 0.\overline{3}, \frac{\pi}{2}, \sqrt{9}, \sqrt{10}\right\}.$$

List the numbers in the set that are

a. natural numbers.   **b.** whole numbers.   **c.** integers.

d. rational numbers.   **e.** irrational numbers.   **f.** real numbers.

Vampire Numbers

Like legendary vampires that lie concealed among humans, vampire numbers lie hidden within the set of real numbers, mostly undetected. By definition, vampire numbers have an even number of digits. Furthermore, they are the product of two numbers whose digits all survive, in scrambled form, in the vampire. For example, 1260, 1435, and 2187 are vampire numbers.

$$21 \times 60 = 1260 \qquad 35 \times 41 = 1435 \qquad 27 \times 81 = 2187$$

> The digits 2, 1, 6, and 0 lie scrambled in the vampire number.

> The digits 3, 5, 4, and 1 lurk within the vampire number.

> The digits 2, 7, 8, and 1 survive in the vampire number.

As the real numbers grow increasingly larger, is it necessary to pull out a wooden stake with greater frequency? How often can you expect to find vampires hidden among the giants? And is it possible to find a weird vampire?

On the right of the equal sign is a 40-digit vampire number that was discovered using a Pascal program on a personal computer:

98,765,432,198,765,432,198 × 98,765,432,198,830,604,534 = 9,754,610,597,415,368,368,844,499,268,390,128,385,732.

Source: Clifford Pickover, *Wonders of Numbers*, Oxford University Press, 2001

---

2 Recognize properties of real numbers.

Properties of the Real Numbers

When you use your calculator to add two real numbers, you can enter them in either order. The fact that two real numbers can be added in either order is called the **commutative property of addition**. You probably use this property, as well as other properties of real numbers listed in Table 5.3, without giving it much thought. The properties of the real numbers are especially useful in algebra, as we shall see in Chapter 6.

The Associative Property and the English Language

In the English language, phrases can take on different meanings depending on the way the words are associated with commas. Here are three examples.

- Woman, without her man, is nothing.
  Woman, without her, man is nothing.
- What's the latest dope?
  What's the latest, dope?
- Population of Amsterdam broken down by age and sex
  Population of Amsterdam, broken down by age and sex

TABLE 5.3 PROPERTIES OF THE REAL NUMBERS

Name	Meaning	Examples
Closure Property of Addition	The sum of any two real numbers is a real number.	$4\sqrt{2}$ is a real number and $5\sqrt{2}$ is a real number, so $4\sqrt{2} + 5\sqrt{2}$, or $9\sqrt{2}$, is a real number.
Closure Property of Multiplication	The product of any two real numbers is a real number.	10 is a real number and $\frac{1}{2}$ is a real number, so $10 \cdot \frac{1}{2}$, or 5, is a real number.
Commutative Property of Addition	Changing order when adding does not affect the sum. $a + b = b + a$	$13 + 7 = 7 + 13$
Commutative Property of Multiplication	Changing order when multiplying does not affect the product. $ab = ba$	$13 \cdot 7 = 7 \cdot 13$ $\sqrt{2} \cdot \sqrt{5} = \sqrt{5} \cdot \sqrt{2}$
Associative Property of Addition	Changing grouping when adding does not affect the sum. $(a + b) + c = a + (b + c)$	$(7 + 2) + 5 = 7 + (2 + 5)$ $9 + 5 = 7 + 7$ $14 = 14$
Associative Property of Multiplication	Changing grouping when multiplying does not affect the product. $(ab)c = a(bc)$	$(7 \cdot 2) \cdot 5 = 7 \cdot (2 \cdot 5)$ $14 \cdot 5 = 7 \cdot 10$ $70 = 70$
Distributive Property of Multiplication over Addition	Multiplication distributes over addition. $a \cdot (b + c) = a \cdot b + a \cdot c$	$7(4 + \sqrt{3}) = 7 \cdot 4 + 7 \cdot \sqrt{3}$ $= 28 + 7\sqrt{3}$

STUDY TIP

Commutative: Changes *order*.
Associative: Changes *grouping*.

EXAMPLE 2   IDENTIFYING PROPERTIES OF THE REAL NUMBERS

Name the property illustrated:

a. $\sqrt{3} \cdot 7 = 7 \cdot \sqrt{3}$

b. $(4 + 7) + 6 = 4 + (7 + 6)$

c. $2(3 + \sqrt{5}) = 6 + 2\sqrt{5}$

d. $\sqrt{2} + (\sqrt{3} + \sqrt{7}) = \sqrt{2} + (\sqrt{7} + \sqrt{3})$.

SOLUTION

a. $\sqrt{3} \cdot 7 = 7 \cdot \sqrt{3}$ *Commutative property of multiplication*

b. $(4 + 7) + 6 = 4 + (7 + 6)$ *Associative property of addition*

c. $2(3 + \sqrt{5}) = 6 + 2\sqrt{5}$ *Distributive property of multiplication over addition*

d. $\sqrt{2} + (\sqrt{3} + \sqrt{7}) = \sqrt{2} + (\sqrt{7} + \sqrt{3})$ *The only change between the left and the right sides is in the order that $\sqrt{3}$ and $\sqrt{7}$ are added. The order is changed from $\sqrt{3} + \sqrt{7}$ to $\sqrt{7} + \sqrt{3}$ using the commutative property of addition.*   ○

CHECK POINT 2   Name the property illustrated:

a. $(4 \cdot 7) \cdot 3 = 4 \cdot (7 \cdot 3)$

b. $3(\sqrt{5} + 4) = 3(4 + \sqrt{5})$

c. $3(\sqrt{5} + 4) = 3\sqrt{5} + 12$

d. $2(\sqrt{3} + \sqrt{7}) = (\sqrt{3} + \sqrt{7})2$.

Although the entire set of real numbers is closed with respect to addition and multiplication, some of the subsets of the real numbers do not satisfy the closure property for a given operation. If an operation on a set results in just one number that is not in that set, then the set is not closed for that operation.

EXAMPLE 3   VERIFYING CLOSURE

a. Are the integers closed with respect to multiplication?

b. Are the irrational numbers closed with respect to multiplication?

c. Are the natural numbers closed with respect to division?

SOLUTION

a. Consider some examples of the multiplication of integers:

$$3 \cdot 2 = 6 \qquad 3(-2) = -6 \qquad -3(-2) = 6 \qquad -3 \cdot 0 = 0.$$

The product of any two integers is always a positive integer, a negative integer, or zero, which is an integer. Thus, the integers are closed under the operation of multiplication.

b. If we multiply two irrational numbers, must the product always be an irrational number? The answer is no. Here is an example:

$$\sqrt{7} \cdot \sqrt{7} = \sqrt{49} = 7.$$

Both irrational   Not an irrational number

This means that the irrational numbers are not closed under the operation of multiplication.

c. If we divide any two natural numbers, must the quotient always be a natural number? The answer is no. Here is an example:

$$4 \div 8 = \frac{1}{2}.$$

Both natural numbers

Not a natural number

Thus, the natural numbers are not closed under the operation of division.

a. Are the natural numbers closed with respect to multiplication?

b. Are the integers closed with respect to division?

The commutative property involves a change in order with no change in the final result. However, changing the order in which we subtract and divide real numbers can produce different answers. For example,

$$7 - 4 \neq 4 - 7 \quad \text{and} \quad 6 \div 2 \neq 2 \div 6.$$

Because the real numbers are not commutative with respect to subtraction and division, it is important that you enter numbers in the correct order when using a calculator to perform these operations.

The associative property does not hold for the operations of subtraction and division. The examples below show that if we change groupings when subtracting or dividing three numbers, the answer may change.

$$(6 - 1) - 3 \neq 6 - (1 - 3) \qquad (8 \div 4) \div 2 \neq 8 \div (4 \div 2)$$
$$5 - 3 \neq 6 - (-2) \qquad\qquad 2 \div 2 \neq 8 \div 2$$
$$2 \neq 8 \qquad\qquad\qquad 1 \neq 4$$

BLITZER BONUS

Beyond the Real Numbers

Only real numbers greater than or equal to zero have real number square roots. The square root of -1, $\sqrt{-1}$, is not a real number. This is because there is no real number that can be multiplied by itself that results in -1. Multiplying any real number by itself can never give a negative product. In the sixteenth century, mathematician Girolamo Cardano wrote that square roots of negative numbers would cause "mental tortures." In spite of these "tortures," mathematicians invented a new number, called i, to represent $\sqrt{-1}$. The number i is not a real number; it is called an **imaginary number**. Thus, $\sqrt{9} = 3$, $-\sqrt{9} = -3$, but $\sqrt{-9}$ is not a real number. However, $\sqrt{-9}$ is an imaginary number, represented by $3i$. The adjective *real* as a way of describing what we now call the real numbers was first used by the French mathematician and philosopher René Descartes (1596–1650) in response to the concept of imaginary numbers.

EXERCISE SET 5.5 ●●●●●●

• Practice Exercises

In Exercises 1–4, list all numbers from the given set that are

a. *natural numbers.*   **b.** *whole numbers.*   **c.** *integers.*

d. *rational numbers.*   **e.** *irrational numbers.*   **f.** *real numbers.*

1. $\left\{-9, -\frac{4}{5}, 0, 0.25, \sqrt{3}, 9.2, \sqrt{100}\right\}$

2. $\left\{-7, -0.\overline{6}, 0, \sqrt{49}, \sqrt{50}\right\}$

3. $\left\{-11, -\frac{5}{6}, 0, 0.75, \sqrt{5}, \pi, \sqrt{64}\right\}$

4. $\left\{-5, -0.\overline{3}, 0, \sqrt{2}, \sqrt{4}\right\}$

5. Give an example of a whole number that is not a natural number.

6. Give an example of an integer that is not a whole number.

7. Give an example of a rational number that is not an integer.

8. Give an example of a rational number that is not a natural number.

9. Give an example of a number that is an integer, a whole number, and a natural number.

10. Give an example of a number that is a rational number, an integer, and a real number.

11. Give an example of a number that is an irrational number and a real number.

12. Give an example of a number that is a real number, but not an irrational number.

Complete each statement in Exercises 13–15 to illustrate the commutative property.

13. $3 + (4 + 5) = 3 + (5 + \underline{\quad})$

14. $\sqrt{5} \cdot 4 = 4 \cdot \underline{\quad}$

15. $9 \cdot (6 + 2) = 9 \cdot (2 + \underline{\quad})$

Complete each statement in Exercises 16–17 to illustrate the associative property.

16. $(3 + 7) + 9 = \underline{\quad} + (7 + \underline{\quad})$

17. $(4 \cdot 5) \cdot 3 = \underline{\quad} \cdot (5 \cdot \underline{\quad})$

Complete each statement in Exercises 18–20 to illustrate the distributive property.

18. $3 \cdot (6 + 4) = 3 \cdot 6 + 3 \cdot \underline{\quad}$

19. $\underline{\quad} \cdot (4 + 5) = 7 \cdot 4 + 7 \cdot 5$

20. $2 \cdot (\underline{\quad} + 3) = 2 \cdot 7 + 2 \cdot 3$

Use the distributive property to simplify the radical expressions in Exercises 21–28.

21. $5\left(6 + \sqrt{2}\right)$

22. $4\left(3 + \sqrt{5}\right)$

23. $\sqrt{7}\left(3 + \sqrt{2}\right)$

24. $\sqrt{6}\left(7 + \sqrt{5}\right)$

25. $\sqrt{3}\left(5 + \sqrt{3}\right)$

26. $\sqrt{7}\left(9 + \sqrt{7}\right)$

27. $\sqrt{6}\left(\sqrt{2} + \sqrt{6}\right)$

28. $\sqrt{10}\left(\sqrt{2} + \sqrt{10}\right)$

In Exercises 29–38, state the name of the property illustrated.

29. $6 + (-4) = (-4) + 6$

30. $11 \cdot (7 + 4) = 11 \cdot 7 + 11 \cdot 4$

31. $6 + (2 + 7) = (6 + 2) + 7$

32. $6 \cdot (2 \cdot 3) = 6 \cdot (3 \cdot 2)$

33. $(2 + 3) + (4 + 5) = (4 + 5) + (2 + 3)$

34. $7 \cdot (11 \cdot 8) = (11 \cdot 8) \cdot 7$

35. $2(-8 + 6) = -16 + 12$

36. $-8(3 + 11) = -24 + (-88)$

37. $\left(2\sqrt{3}\right) \cdot \sqrt{5} = 2\left(\sqrt{3} \cdot \sqrt{5}\right)$

38. $\sqrt{2}\pi = \pi\sqrt{2}$

In Exercises 39–43, use two numbers to show that

39. the natural numbers are not closed with respect to subtraction.

40. the natural numbers are not closed with respect to division.

41. the integers are not closed with respect to division.

42. the irrational numbers are not closed with respect to subtraction.

43. the irrational numbers are not closed with respect to multiplication.

• Practice Plus

In Exercises 44–47, determine if each statement is true or false. Do not use a calculator.

44. $468(787 + 289) = 787 + 289(468)$

45. $468(787 + 289) = 787(468) + 289(468)$

46. $58 \cdot 9 + 32 \cdot 9 = (58 + 32) \cdot 9$

47. $58 \cdot 9 \cdot 32 \cdot 9 = (58 \cdot 32) \cdot 9$

In Exercises 48–49, name the property used to go from step to step each time that (why?) occurs.

48. $7 + 2(x + 9)$
$= 7 + (2x + 18)$ (why?)
$= 7 + (18 + 2x)$ (why?)
$= (7 + 18) + 2x$ (why?)
$= 25 + 2x$
$= 2x + 25$ (why?)

49. $5(x + 4) + 3x$
$= (5x + 20) + 3x$ (why?)
$= (20 + 5x) + 3x$ (why?)
$= 20 + (5x + 3x)$ (why?)
$= 20 + (5 + 3)x$ (why?)
$= 20 + 8x$
$= 8x + 20$ (why?)

• Application Exercises

In Exercises 50–53, use the definition of vampire numbers from the Blitzer Bonus on page 273 to determine which products are vampires.

50. $15 \times 93 = 1395$

51. $80 \times 86 = 6880$

52. $20 \times 51 = 1020$

53. $146 \times 938 = 136,948$

A **narcissistic number** is an n-digit number equal to the sum of each of its digits raised to the nth power. Here's an example:

$$153 = 1^3 + 5^3 + 3^3.$$

Three digits, so exponents are 3

In Exercises 54–57, determine which real numbers are narcissistic.

54. 370   **55.** 371   **56.** 372   **57.** 9474

58. Closure illustrates that a characteristic of a set is not necessarily a characteristic of all of its subsets. The real numbers are closed with respect to multiplication, but the irrational numbers, a subset of the real numbers, are not. Give an example of a set that is not mathematical that has a particular characteristic, but which has a subset without this characteristic.

59. The algebraic expressions

$$\frac{D(A + 1)}{24} \quad \text{and} \quad \frac{DA + D}{24}$$

describe the drug dosage for children between the ages of 2 and 13. In each algebraic expression, D stands for an adult dose and A represents the child's age.

a. Name the property that explains why these expressions are equal for all values of D and A.

b. If an adult dose of ibuprofen is 200 milligrams, what is the proper dose for a 12-year-old child? Use both forms of the algebraic expressions to answer the question. Which form is easier to use?

• Writing in Mathematics

60. What does it mean when we say that the rational numbers are a subset of the real numbers?

61. What does it mean if we say that a set is closed under a given operation?

62. State the commutative property of addition and give an example.

63. State the commutative property of multiplication and give an example.

64. State the associative property of addition and give an example.

65. State the associative property of multiplication and give an example.

66. State the distributive property of multiplication over addition and give an example.

67. Does $7 \cdot (4 \cdot 3) = 7 \cdot (3 \cdot 4)$ illustrate the commutative property or the associative property? Explain your answer.

• Critical Thinking Exercises

68. Which one of the following statements is true?

a. Every rational number is an integer.

b. Some whole numbers are not integers.

c. Some rational numbers are not positive.

d. Irrational numbers cannot be negative.

69. Which one of the following statements is true?

a. Subtraction is a commutative operation.

b. $(24 \div 6) \div 2 = 24 \div (6 \div 2)$

c. $7 \cdot a + 3 \cdot a = a \cdot (7 + 3)$

d. $2 \cdot a + 5 = 5 \cdot a + 2$

SECTION 5.6 • EXPONENTS AND SCIENTIFIC NOTATION

OBJECTIVES

1. Use properties of exponents.

2. Convert from scientific notation to decimal notation.

3. Convert from decimal notation to scientific notation.

4. Perform computations using scientific notation.

5. Solve applied problems using scientific notation.

We frequently encounter very large and very small numbers. Governments throughout the world are concerned about the billions of tons of carbon dioxide that the global population of 6.5 billion people release into the atmosphere each year. In the photo shown above, the national debt of the United States was about $8.2 trillion. A typical atom has a diameter of about one-ten-billionth of a meter. Exponents provide a way of putting these large and small numbers in perspective.

Properties of Exponents

We have seen that exponents are used to indicate repeated multiplication. Now consider the multiplication of two exponential expressions, such as $b^4 \cdot b^3$. We are multiplying 4 factors of b and 3 factors of b. We have a total of 7 factors of b:

4 factors of b   **3 factors of b**

$$b^4 \cdot b^3 = (b \cdot b \cdot b \cdot b)(b \cdot b \cdot b) = b^7.$$

Total: 7 factors of b

The product is exactly the same if we add the exponents:

$$b^4 \cdot b^3 = b^{4+3} = b^7.$$

Properties of exponents allow us to perform operations with exponential expressions without having to write out long strings of factors. Three such properties are given in Table 5.4.

TABLE 5.4 PROPERTIES OF EXPONENTS

Property	Meaning	Examples
The Product Rule $b^m \cdot b^n = b^{m+n}$	When multiplying exponential expressions with the same base, add the exponents. Use this sum as the exponent of the common base.	$9^6 \cdot 9^{12} = 9^{6+12} = 9^{18}$
The Power Rule $(b^m)^n = b^{m \cdot n}$	When an exponential expression is raised to a power, multiply the exponents. Place the product of the exponents on the base and remove the parentheses.	$(3^4)^5 = 3^{4 \cdot 5} = 3^{20}$ $(5^3)^8 = 5^{3 \cdot 8} = 5^{24}$
The Quotient Rule $\dfrac{b^m}{b^n} = b^{m-n}$	When dividing exponential expressions with the same base, subtract the exponent in the denominator from the exponent in the numerator. Use this difference as the exponent of the common base.	$\dfrac{5^{12}}{5^4} = 5^{12-4} = 5^8$ $\dfrac{9^{40}}{9^5} = 9^{40-5} = 9^{35}$

The third property in Table 5.4, the quotient rule, can lead to a zero exponent when subtracting exponents. Here is an example:

$$\frac{4^3}{4^3} = 4^{3-3} = 4^0.$$

We can see what this zero exponent means by evaluating 4^3 in the numerator and the denominator:

$$\frac{4^3}{4^3} = \frac{4 \cdot 4 \cdot 4}{4 \cdot 4 \cdot 4} = \frac{64}{64} = 1.$$

This means that 4^0 must equal 1. This example illustrates the zero exponent rule.

THE ZERO EXPONENT RULE
If b is any real number other than 0,

$$b^0 = 1.$$

EXAMPLE 1   USING THE ZERO EXPONENT RULE

Use the zero exponent rule to simplify:

a. 7^0 **b.** π^0 **c.** $(-5)^0$ **d.** -5^0.

SOLUTION

a. $7^0 = 1$ **b.** $\pi^0 = 1$ **c.** $(-5)^0 = 1$ **d.** $-5^0 = -1$

> Only 5 is raised to the 0 power.

○

 Use the zero exponent rule to simplify:

        a. 19^0 **b.** $(3\pi)^0$ **c.** $(-14)^0$ **d.** -14^0.

The quotient rule can result in a negative exponent. Consider, for example, $4^3 \div 4^5$:

$$\frac{4^3}{4^5} = 4^{3-5} = 4^{-2}.$$

STUDY TIP

$\dfrac{4^3}{4^5}$ and $\dfrac{4^5}{4^3}$ represent different numbers:

$$\frac{4^3}{4^5} = 4^{3-5} = 4^{-2} = \frac{1}{4^2} = \frac{1}{16}$$

$$\frac{4^5}{4^3} = 4^{5-3} = 4^2 = 16.$$

We can see what this negative exponent means by evaluating the numerator and the denominator:

$$\frac{4^3}{4^5} = \frac{\cancel{4} \cdot \cancel{4} \cdot \cancel{4}}{\cancel{4} \cdot \cancel{4} \cdot \cancel{4} \cdot 4 \cdot 4} = \frac{1}{4^2}.$$

Notice that $\dfrac{4^3}{4^5}$ equals both 4^{-2} and $\dfrac{1}{4^2}$. This means that 4^{-2} must equal $\dfrac{1}{4^2}$. This example is a particular case of the negative exponent rule.

THE NEGATIVE EXPONENT RULE

If b is any real number other than 0 and m is a natural number,

$$b^{-m} = \frac{1}{b^m}.$$

EXAMPLE 2   USING THE NEGATIVE EXPONENT RULE

Use the negative exponent rule to simplify:

a. 8^{-2} **b.** 5^{-3} **c.** 7^{-1}.

SOLUTION

a. $8^{-2} = \dfrac{1}{8^2} = \dfrac{1}{8 \cdot 8} = \dfrac{1}{64}$

b. $5^{-3} = \dfrac{1}{5^3} = \dfrac{1}{5 \cdot 5 \cdot 5} = \dfrac{1}{125}$

c. $7^{-1} = \dfrac{1}{7^1} = \dfrac{1}{7}$

○

 Use the negative exponent rule to simplify:

        a. 9^{-2} **b.** 6^{-3} **c.** 12^{-1}.

John Scott "*Invoking the Googolplex*" 1981, water-colour on paper, 24 × 18 in. *Source*: Photo courtesy of The Gallery, Stratford, Ontario.

Powers of Ten

Exponents and their properties allow us to represent and compute with numbers that are large or small. For example, one billion, or 1,000,000,000 can be written as 10^9. In terms of exponents, 10^9 might not look very large, but consider this: If you can count to 200 in one minute and decide to count for 12 hours a day at this rate, it would take you in the region of 19 years, 9 days, 5 hours, and 20 minutes to count to 10^9!

Powers of ten follow two basic rules:

1. **A positive exponent tells how many 0s follow the 1.** For example, 10^9 (one billion) is a 1 followed by nine zeros: 1,000,000,000. A googol, 10^{100}, is a 1 followed by one hundred zeros. (A googol far exceeds the number of protons, neutrons, and electrons in the universe.) A googol is a veritable pipsqueak compared to the googolplex, 10 raised to the googol power, or $10^{10^{100}}$; that's a 1 followed by a googol zeros. (If each zero in a googolplex were no larger than a grain of sand, there would not be enough room in the universe to represent the number.)

2. **A negative exponent tells how many places there are to the right of the decimal point.** For example, 10^{-9} (one billionth) has nine places to the right of the decimal point. The nine places contain eight 0s and the 1.

$$10^{-9} = 0.\underbrace{000000001}_{\text{nine places}}$$

Earthquakes and Powers of Ten

The earthquake that ripped through northern California on October 17, 1989, measured 7.1 on the Richter scale, killed more than 60 people, and injured more than 2400. Shown here is San Francisco's Marina district, where shock waves tossed houses off their foundations and into the street.

The Richter scale is misleading because it is not actually a 1 to 8, but rather a 1 to 10 million scale. Each level indicates a tenfold increase in magnitude from the previous level, making a 7.0 earthquake a million times greater than a 1.0 quake. The following is a translation of the Richter scale:

Richter number (R)	Magnitude (10^{R-1})
1	$10^{1-1} = 10^0 = 1$
2	$10^{2-1} = 10^1 = 10$
3	$10^{3-1} = 10^2 = 100$
4	$10^{4-1} = 10^3 = 1000$
5	$10^{5-1} = 10^4 = 10,000$
6	$10^{6-1} = 10^5 = 100,000$
7	$10^{7-1} = 10^6 = 1,000,000$
8	$10^{8-1} = 10^7 = 10,000,000$

TABLE 5.5 NAMES OF LARGE NUMBERS	
10^2	hundred
10^3	thousand
10^6	million
10^9	billion
10^{12}	trillion
10^{15}	quadrillion
10^{18}	quintillion
10^{21}	sextillion
10^{24}	septillion
10^{27}	octillion
10^{30}	nonillion
10^{100}	googol
10^{googol}	googolplex

Scientific Notation

As of December 2006, the national debt of the United States was about $8.6 trillion. This is the amount of money the government has had to borrow over the years, mostly by selling bonds, because it has spent more than it has collected in taxes. A stack of $1 bills equaling the national debt would rise to twice the distance from Earth to the moon. Because a trillion is 10^{12} (see Table 5.5), the national debt can be expressed as

$$8.6 \times 10^{12}.$$

The number 8.6×10^{12} is written in a form called *scientific notation*.

> **SCIENTIFIC NOTATION**
> A positive number is written in **scientific notation** when it is expressed in the form
> $$a \times 10^n,$$
> where a is a number greater than or equal to 1 and less than 10 ($1 \leq a < 10$) and n is an integer.

It is customary to use the multiplication symbol, $\times$, rather than a dot, when writing a number in scientific notation.

Here are two examples of numbers in scientific notation:

- Each day, 2.6×10^7 pounds of dust from the atmosphere settle on Earth.
- The length of the AIDS virus is 1.1×10^{-4} millimeter.

2 | Convert from scientific notation to decimal notation.

We can use n, the exponent on the 10 in $a \times 10^n$, to change a number in scientific notation to decimal notation. If n is **positive**, move the decimal point in a to the **right** n places. If n is **negative**, move the decimal point in a to the **left** $|n|$ places.

EXAMPLE 3   CONVERTING FROM SCIENTIFIC TO DECIMAL NOTATION

Write each number in decimal notation:

a. 2.6×10^7 **b.** 1.1×10^{-4}.

SOLUTION In each case, we use the exponent on the 10 to move the decimal point. In part (a), the exponent is positive, so we move the decimal point to the right. In part (b), the exponent is negative, so we move the decimal point to the left.

a. $2.6 \times 10^7 = 26{,}000{,}000$

$n = 7$

Move the decimal point 7 places to the right.

b. $1.1 \times 10^{-4} = 0.00011$

$n = -4$

Move the decimal point $|-4|$ places, or 4 places, to the left.

3   Write each number in decimal notation:

a. 7.4×10^9 **b.** 3.017×10^{-6}.

3 | Convert from decimal notation to scientific notation.

To convert a positive number from decimal notation to scientific notation, we reverse the procedure of Example 3.

CONVERTING FROM DECIMAL TO SCIENTIFIC NOTATION

Write the number in the form $a \times 10^n$.

- Determine a, the numerical factor. Move the decimal point in the given number to obtain a number greater than or equal to 1 and less than 10.
- Determine n, the exponent on 10^n. The absolute value of n is the number of places the decimal point was moved. The exponent n is positive if the given number is greater than 10 and negative if the given number is between 0 and 1.

EXAMPLE 4   CONVERTING FROM DECIMAL NOTATION TO SCIENTIFIC NOTATION

Write each number in scientific notation:

a. 4,600,000   **b.** 0.000023.

SOLUTION

a. $4{,}600{,}000 = 4.6 \times 10^6$

This number is greater than 10, so n is positive in $a \times 10^n$.	Move the decimal point in 4,600,000 to get $1 \le a < 10$.	The decimal point moved 6 places from 4,600,000 to 4.6.

b. $0.000023 = 2.3 \times 10^{-5}$

This number is less than 1, so n is negative in $a \times 10^n$.	Move the decimal point in 0.000023 to get $1 \le a < 10$.	The decimal point moved 5 places from 0.000023 to 2.3.

 CHECK POINT 4 Write each number in scientific notation:

a. 7,410,000,000   **b.** 0.000000092.

EXAMPLE 5 EXPRESSING THE NUMBER OF CELLPHONE SPAM MESSAGES IN SCIENTIFIC NOTATION

As feature-rich cellphones function more like PCs, digital intruders are targeting them with viruses, spam, and phishing scams. The bar graph in Figure 5.6 shows the number of cellphone spam messages, in millions, from 2002 through 2005. Express the number of spam messages in 2005 in scientific notation.

SOLUTION Because a million is 10^6, the number of cellphone spam messages in 2005 can be expressed as

$$500 \times 10^6.$$

This factor is not between 1 and 10, so the number is not in scientific notation.

The voice balloon indicates that we need to convert 500 to scientific notation.

$$500 \times 10^6 = (5 \times 10^2) \times 10^6 = 5 \times (10^2 \times 10^6) = 5 \times 10^{2+6} = 5 \times 10^8$$

There were 5×10^8 cellphone spam messages in 2005.

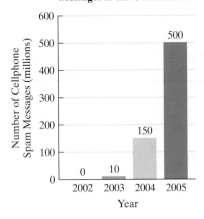

Number of Cellphone Spam Messages in the United States

FIGURE 5.6
Source: Ferris Research

STUDY TIP

Many of the large numbers we encounter in newspapers, magazines, and almanacs are expressed in millions (10^6), billions (10^9), and trillions (10^{12}). We can use exponential properties to describe the number of cellphone spam messages in 2005 using millions or billions.

$$500 \times 10^6 = 5 \times 10^8 = 0.5 \times 10^9$$

There were 500 million messages.	This expresses the number of messages in scientific notation.	There were half a billion messages.

 CHECK POINT 5 In 2005, the federal cost of social security was $519 billion. Express this amount in scientific notation.

Computations with Scientific Notation

4 Perform computations using scientific notation.

We use the product rule for exponents to multiply numbers in scientific notation:

$$(a \times 10^n) \times (b \times 10^m) = (a \times b) \times 10^{n+m}.$$

Add the exponents on 10 and multiply the other parts of the numbers separately.

EXAMPLE 6   MULTIPLYING NUMBERS IN SCIENTIFIC NOTATION

Multiply: $(3.4 \times 10^9)(2 \times 10^{-5})$. Write the product in decimal notation.

SOLUTION

$$\begin{aligned}(3.4 \times 10^9)(2 \times 10^{-5}) &= (3.4 \times 2) \times (10^9 \times 10^{-5}) && \text{Regroup factors.}\\ &= 6.8 \times 10^{9+(-5)} && \text{Add the exponents on 10 and multiply the other parts.}\\ &= 6.8 \times 10^4 && \text{Simplify.}\\ &= 68{,}000 && \text{Write the product in decimal notation.}\end{aligned}$$

TECHNOLOGY

$(3.4 \times 10^9)(2 \times 10^{-5})$ **on a Calculator:**

MANY SCIENTIFIC CALCULATORS

3.4 | EE | 9 | × | 2 | EE | 5 | +/− | = |

Display: 6.8   04

MANY GRAPHING CALCULATORS

3.4 | EE | 9 | × | 2 | EE | (−) | 5 | ENTER |

Display: 6.8 E 4

 CHECK POINT 6 Multiply: $(1.3 \times 10^7)(4 \times 10^{-2})$. Write the product in decimal notation.

We use the quotient rule for exponents to divide numbers in scientific notation:

$$\frac{a \times 10^n}{b \times 10^m} = \left(\frac{a}{b}\right) \times 10^{n-m}.$$

Subtract the exponents on 10 and divide the other parts of the numbers separately.

EXAMPLE 7   DIVIDING NUMBERS IN SCIENTIFIC NOTATION

Divide: $\dfrac{8.4 \times 10^{-7}}{4 \times 10^{-4}}$. Write the quotient in decimal notation.

SOLUTION

$$\begin{aligned}\frac{8.4 \times 10^{-7}}{4 \times 10^{-4}} &= \left(\frac{8.4}{4}\right) \times \left(\frac{10^{-7}}{10^{-4}}\right) && \text{Regroup factors.}\\ &= 2.1 \times 10^{-7-(-4)} && \text{Subtract the exponents on 10 and divide the other parts.}\\ &= 2.1 \times 10^{-3} && \text{Simplify: } -7 - (-4) = -7 + 4 = -3.\\ &= 0.0021 && \text{Write the quotient in decimal notation.}\end{aligned}$$

 CHECK POINT 7 Divide: $\dfrac{6.9 \times 10^{-8}}{3 \times 10^{-2}}$. Write the quotient in decimal notation.

Multiplication and division involving very large or very small numbers can be performed by first converting each number to scientific notation.

EXAMPLE 8   USING SCIENTIFIC NOTATION TO MULTIPLY

Multiply: $0.00064 \times 9{,}400{,}000{,}000$. Express the product in **a.** scientific notation and **b.** decimal notation.

SOLUTION

a. $0.00064 \times 9{,}400{,}000{,}000$

$$= 6.4 \times 10^{-4} \times 9.4 \times 10^{9}$$ Write each number in scientific notation.

$$= (6.4 \times 9.4) \times (10^{-4} \times 10^{9})$$ Regroup factors.

$$= 60.16 \times 10^{-4+9}$$ Add the exponents on 10 and multiply the other parts.

$$= 60.16 \times 10^{5}$$ Simplify.

$$= (6.016 \times 10) \times 10^{5}$$ Express 60.16 in scientific notation.

$$= 6.016 \times 10^{6}$$ Add exponents on 10: $10^{1} \times 10^{5} = 10^{1+5} = 10^{6}$.

b. The answer in decimal notation is obtained by moving the decimal point in 6.016 six places to the right. The product is 6,016,000.

 Multiply: $0.0036 \times 5{,}200{,}000$. Express the product in **a.** scientific notation and **b.** decimal notation.

---

5 | Solve applied problems using scientific notation.

Applications: Putting Numbers in Perspective

Due to tax cuts and spending increases, the United States began accumulating large deficits in the 1980s. To finance the deficit, the government had borrowed $8.6 trillion as of December 2006. The graph in Figure 5.7 shows the national debt increasing over time.

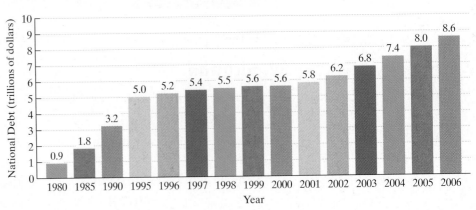

The National Debt

FIGURE 5.7
Source: Office of Management and Budget

Example 9 shows how we can use scientific notation to comprehend the meaning of a number such as 8.6 trillion.

Here is the keystroke sequence for solving Example 9 using a calculator:

8.4 $\boxed{\text{EE}}$ 12 $\boxed{÷}$ 3 $\boxed{\text{EE}}$ 8.

The quotient is displayed by pressing $\boxed{=}$ on a scientific calculator or $\boxed{\text{ENTER}}$ on a graphing calculator. The answer can be displayed in scientific or decimal notation. Consult your manual.

EXAMPLE 9 THE NATIONAL DEBT

As of December 2006, the national debt was \$8.6 trillion, or 8.6×10^{12} dollars. At that time, the U.S. population was approximately 300,000,000 (300 million), or 3×10^8. If the national debt was evenly divided among every individual in the United States, how much would each citizen have to pay?

SOLUTION The amount each citizen must pay is the total debt, 8.6×10^{12} dollars, divided by the number of citizens, 3×10^8.

$$\frac{8.6 \times 10^{12}}{3 \times 10^8} = \left(\frac{8.6}{3}\right) \times \left(\frac{10^{12}}{10^8}\right)$$
$$\approx 2.87 \times 10^{12-8}$$
$$= 2.87 \times 10^4$$
$$= 28,700$$

Every U.S. citizen would have to pay approximately \$28,700 to the federal government to pay off the national debt.

○

CHECK POINT 9 Pell Grants help low-income undergraduate students pay for college. In 2006, the federal cost of this program was \$13 billion (\$13 \times 10^9$) and there were 5.1 million (5.1×10^6) grant recipients. How much, to the nearest hundred dollars, was the average grant?

● ● ● ● ● ● ● ● ●

BLITZER BONUS

Fermat's Last Theorem

Pierre de Fermat (1601–1665) was a lawyer who enjoyed studying mathematics. In a margin of one of his books, he claimed that no natural numbers satisfy

$$a^n + b^n = c^n$$

if n is an integer greater than or equal to 3.

If $n = 2$, we can find numbers satisfying $a^n + b^n = c^n$, or $a^2 + b^2 = c^2$. For example,

$$3^2 + 4^2 = 5^2.$$

However, Fermat claimed that no natural numbers satisfy

$$a^3 + b^3 = c^3, \qquad a^4 + b^4 = c^4, \qquad a^5 + b^5 = c^5,$$

and so on.

Fermat claimed to have a proof of his conjecture, but added, "The margin of my book is too narrow to write it down." Some believe that he never had a proof and intended to frustrate his colleagues.

In June 1993, 40-year-old Princeton math professor Andrew Wiles claimed that he discovered a proof of the theorem. Subsequent study revealed flaws, but Wiles corrected them. In 1995, his final proof served as a classic example of how great mathematicians accomplish great things: a combination of genius, hard work, frustration, and trial and error.

(Andrew Wiles 1953–)

EXERCISE SET 5.6 ● ● ● ● ● ● ●

• Practice Exercises

In Exercises 1–12, use properties of exponents to simplify each expression. First express the answer in exponential form. Then evaluate the expression.

1. $2^2 \cdot 2^3$ **2.** $3^3 \cdot 3^2$ **3.** $4 \cdot 4^2$ **4.** $5 \cdot 5^2$

5. $(2^2)^3$ **6.** $(3^3)^2$ **7.** $(1^4)^5$ **8.** $(1^3)^7$

9. $\dfrac{4^7}{4^5}$ **10.** $\dfrac{6^7}{6^5}$ **11.** $\dfrac{2^8}{2^4}$ **12.** $\dfrac{3^8}{3^4}$

In Exercises 13–24, use the zero and negative exponent rules to simplify each expression.

13. 3^0 **14.** 9^0 **15.** $(-3)^0$ **16.** $(-9)^0$

17. -3^0 **18.** -9^0 **19.** 2^{-2} **20.** 3^{-2}

21. 4^{-3} **22.** 2^{-3} **23.** 2^{-5} **24.** 2^{-6}

In Exercises 25–30, use properties of exponents to simplify each expression. First express the answer in exponential form. Then evaluate the expression.

25. $3^4 \cdot 3^{-2}$ **26.** $2^5 \cdot 2^{-2}$ **27.** $3^{-3} \cdot 3$

28. $2^{-3} \cdot 2$ **29.** $\dfrac{2^3}{2^7}$ **30.** $\dfrac{3^4}{3^7}$

In Exercises 31–46, express each number in decimal notation.

31. 2.7×10^2 **32.** 4.7×10^3 **33.** 9.12×10^5

34. 8.14×10^4 **35.** 8×10^7 **36.** 7×10^6

37. 1×10^5 **38.** 1×10^8 **39.** 7.9×10^{-1}

40. 8.6×10^{-1} **41.** 2.15×10^{-2} **42.** 3.14×10^{-2}

43. 7.86×10^{-4} **44.** 4.63×10^{-5} **45.** 3.18×10^{-6}

46. 5.84×10^{-7}

In Exercises 47–66, express each number in scientific notation.

47. 370   **48.** 530   **49.** 3600   **50.** 2700

51. 32,000   **52.** 64,000   **53.** 220,000,000

54. 370,000,000,000   **55.** 0.027   **56.** 0.014

57. 0.0037   **58.** 0.00083   **59.** 0.00000293

60. 0.000000647   **61.** 820×10^5 **62.** 630×10^8

63. 0.41×10^6 **64.** 0.57×10^9 **65.** 2100×10^{-9}

66. $97,000 \times 10^{-11}$

In Exercises 67–80, perform the indicated operation and express each answer in decimal notation.

67. $(2 \times 10^3)(3 \times 10^2)$ **68.** $(5 \times 10^2)(4 \times 10^4)$

69. $(2 \times 10^9)(3 \times 10^{-5})$ **70.** $(4 \times 10^8)(2 \times 10^{-4})$

71. $(4.1 \times 10^2)(3 \times 10^{-4})$ **72.** $(1.2 \times 10^3)(2 \times 10^{-5})$

73. $\dfrac{12 \times 10^6}{4 \times 10^2}$ **74.** $\dfrac{20 \times 10^{20}}{10 \times 10^{15}}$

75. $\dfrac{15 \times 10^4}{5 \times 10^{-2}}$ **76.** $\dfrac{18 \times 10^2}{9 \times 10^{-3}}$

77. $\dfrac{6 \times 10^3}{2 \times 10^5}$ **78.** $\dfrac{8 \times 10^4}{2 \times 10^7}$

79. $\dfrac{6.3 \times 10^{-6}}{3 \times 10^{-3}}$ **80.** $\dfrac{9.6 \times 10^{-7}}{3 \times 10^{-3}}$

In Exercises 81–90, perform the indicated operation by first expressing each number in scientific notation. Write the answer in scientific notation.

81. $(82,000,000)(3,000,000,000)$

82. $(94,000,000)(6,000,000,000)$

83. $(0.0005)(6,000,000)$ **84.** $(0.000015)(0.004)$

85. $\dfrac{9,500,000}{500}$ **86.** $\dfrac{30,000}{0.0005}$

87. $\dfrac{0.00008}{200}$ **88.** $\dfrac{0.0018}{0.0000006}$

89. $\dfrac{480,000,000,000}{0.00012}$ **90.** $\dfrac{0.000000096}{16,000}$

• Practice Plus

In Exercises 91–94, perform the indicated operations. Express each answer as a fraction reduced to its lowest terms.

91. $\dfrac{2^4}{2^5} + \dfrac{3^3}{3^5}$ **92.** $\dfrac{3^5}{3^6} + \dfrac{2^3}{2^6}$

93. $\dfrac{2^6}{2^4} - \dfrac{5^4}{5^6}$ **94.** $\dfrac{5^6}{5^4} - \dfrac{2^4}{2^6}$

In Exercises 95–98, perform the indicated computations. Express answers in scientific notation.

95. $(5 \times 10^3)(1.2 \times 10^{-4}) \div (2.4 \times 10^2)$

96. $(2 \times 10^2)(2.6 \times 10^{-3}) \div (4 \times 10^3)$

97. $\dfrac{(1.6 \times 10^4)(7.2 \times 10^{-3})}{(3.6 \times 10^8)(4 \times 10^{-3})}$

98. $\dfrac{(1.2 \times 10^6)(8.7 \times 10^{-2})}{(2.9 \times 10^6)(3 \times 10^{-3})}$

• Application Exercises

The graph shows the net worth, in billions of dollars, of the five richest Americans. Use 10^9 for one billion and the figures shown to solve Exercises 99–102. Express all answers in scientific notation.

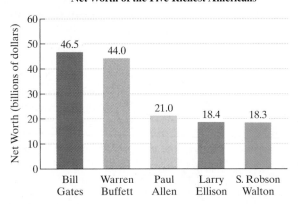

Net Worth of the Five Richest Americans

Source: Forbes Billionaires List, 2005

99. How much is Bill Gates worth?

100. How much is Warren Buffett worth?

101. By how much does Larry Ellison's worth exceed that of S. Robson Walton?

102. If each person doubled his net worth, by how much would Larry Ellison's worth exceed that of S. Robson Walton?

Our ancient ancestors hunted for their meat and expended a great deal of energy chasing it down. Today, our animal protein is raised in cages and on feedlots, delivered in great abundance nearly to our door. Use the numbers shown below to solve Exercises 103–106. Use 10^6 for one million and 10^9 for one billion.

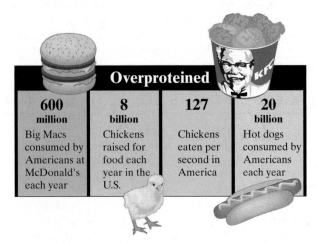

Overproteined

600 million	**8** billion	**127**	**20** billion
Big Macs consumed by Americans at McDonald's each year	Chickens raised for food each year in the U.S.	Chickens eaten per second in America	Hot dogs consumed by Americans each year

Source: Time, October 20, 2003

In Exercises 103–104, use 300 million, or 3×10^8, for the U.S. population. Express answers in decimal notation, rounded to the nearest whole number.

103. Find the number of hot dogs consumed by each American in a year.

104. If the consumption of Big Macs was divided evenly among all Americans, how many Big Macs would we each consume in a year?

In Exercises 105–106, use the Overproteined table and the fact that there are approximately 3.2×10^7 seconds in a year.

105. How many chickens are raised for food each second in the United States? Express the answer in scientific and decimal notations.

106. How many chickens are eaten per year in the United States? Express the answer in scientific notation.

The graph shows the cost, in billions of dollars, and the enrollment, in millions of people, for various federal social programs in 2005. Use the numbers shown to solve Exercises 107–109.

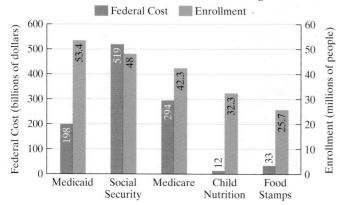

Cost and Enrollment for Federal Social Programs

Source: Office of Management and Budget

107. a. What was the average per person benefit for Social Security? Express the answer in scientific notation and in decimal notation, rounded to the nearest dollar.

b. What was the average monthly per person benefit, rounded to the nearest dollar, for Social Security?

108. a. What was the average per person benefit for the food stamps program? Express the answer in scientific notation and in decimal notation, rounded to the nearest dollar.

b. What was the average monthly per person benefit, rounded to the nearest dollar, for the food stamps program?

109. Medicaid provides health insurance for the poor. Medicare provides health insurance for people 65 and older, as well as younger people who are disabled. Which program provides the greater per person benefit? By how much, rounded to the nearest dollar?

110. The area of Alaska is approximately 3.66×10^8 acres. The state was purchased in 1867 from Russia for $7.2 million. What price per acre, to the nearest cent, did the United States pay Russia?

111. The mass of one oxygen molecule is 5.3×10^{-23} gram. Find the mass of 20,000 molecules of oxygen. Express the answer in scientific notation.

112. The mass of one hydrogen atom is 1.67×10^{-24} gram. Find the mass of 80,000 hydrogen atoms. Express the answer in scientific notation.

113. In Exercises 105–106, we used 3.2×10^7 as an approximation for the number of seconds in a year. Convert 365 days (one year) to hours, to minutes, and, finally, to seconds, to determine precisely how many seconds there are in a year. Express the answer in scientific notation.

• Writing in Mathematics

114. Explain the product rule for exponents. Use $2^3 \cdot 2^5$ in your explanation.

115. Explain the power rule for exponents. Use $(3^2)^4$ in your explanation.

116. Explain the quotient rule for exponents. Use $\dfrac{5^8}{5^2}$ in your explanation.

117. Explain the zero exponent rule and give an example.

118. Explain the negative exponent rule and give an example.

119. How do you know if a number is written in scientific notation?

120. Explain how to convert from scientific to decimal notation and give an example.

121. Explain how to convert from decimal to scientific notation and give an example.

122. Suppose you are looking at a number in scientific notation. Describe the size of the number you are looking at if the exponent on ten is **a.** positive, **b.** negative, **c.** zero.

123. Describe one advantage of expressing a number in scientific notation over decimal notation.

• Critical Thinking Exercises

124. Which one of the following is true?

a. $4^{-2} < 4^{-3}$

b. $5^{-2} > 2^{-5}$

c. $(-2)^4 = 2^{-4}$

d. $5^2 \cdot 5^{-2} > 2^5 \cdot 2^{-5}$

125. Which one of the following is true?

a. $534.7 = 5.347 \times 10^3$

b. $\dfrac{8 \times 10^{30}}{4 \times 10^{-5}} = 2 \times 10^{25}$

c. $(7 \times 10^5) + (2 \times 10^{-3}) = 9 \times 10^2$

d. $(4 \times 10^3) + (3 \times 10^2) = 43 \times 10^2$

126. Give an example of a number for which there is no advantage to using scientific notation instead of decimal notation. Explain why this is the case.

127. The mad Dr. Frankenstein has gathered enough bits and pieces (so to speak) for $2^{-1} + 2^{-2}$ of his creature-to-be. Write a fraction that represents the amount of his creature that must still be obtained.

• Technology Exercises

128. Use a calculator in a fraction mode to check your answers in Exercises 19–24.

129. Use a calculator to check any three of your answers in Exercises 31–46.

130. Use a calculator to check any three of your answers in Exercises 47–66.

131. Use a calculator with an $\boxed{\text{EE}}$ or $\boxed{\text{EXP}}$ key to check any four of your computations in Exercises 67–90. Display the result of the computation in scientific notation and in decimal notation.

• Group Exercises

132. Putting Numbers into Perspective. A large number can be put into perspective by comparing it with another number. For example, we put the $8.6 trillion national debt into perspective by comparing it to the number of U.S. citizens and computing the debt per person. For this project, each group member should consult an almanac, a newspaper, or the World Wide Web to find a number greater than one million. Explain to other members of the group the con-

text in which the large number is used. Express the number in scientific notation. Then put the number into perspective by comparing it with another number.

133. Fermat's most notorious theorem baffled the greatest minds for more than three centuries. In 1994, after ten years of work, Princeton University's Andrew Wiles proved Fermat's Last Theorem. *People* magazine put him on its list of "the 25 most intriguing people of the year," the Gap asked him to model jeans, and Barbara Walters chased him for an interview. "Who's Barbara Walters?" asked the bookish Wiles, who had somehow gone through life without a television.

Using the 1993 PBS documentary "Solving Fermat: Andrew Wiles" or information about Andrew Wiles on the Internet, research and present a group seminar on what Wiles did to prove Fermat's Last Theorem, problems along the way, and how Wiles overcame them.

SECTION 5.7 • ARITHMETIC AND GEOMETRIC SEQUENCES

OBJECTIVES

1. Write terms of an arithmetic sequence.
2. Use the formula for the general term of an arithmetic sequence.
3. Write terms of a geometric sequence.
4. Use the formula for the general term of a geometric sequence.

Sequences

Many creations in nature involve intricate mathematical designs, including a variety of spirals. For example, the arrangement of the individual florets in the head of a sunflower forms spirals. In some species, there are 21 spirals in the clockwise direction and 34 in the counterclockwise direction. The precise numbers depend on the species of sunflower: 21 and 34, or 34 and 55, or 55 and 89, or even 89 and 144.

This observation becomes even more interesting when we consider a sequence of numbers investigated by Leonardo of Pisa, also known as Fibonacci, an Italian mathematician of the thirteenth century. The **Fibonacci sequence** of numbers is an infinite sequence that begins as follows:

$$1, 1, 2, 3, 5, 8, 13, 21, 34, 55, 89, 144, 233, \ldots.$$

The first two terms are 1. Every term thereafter is the sum of the two preceding terms. For example, the third term, 2, is the sum of the first and second terms: $1 + 1 = 2$. The fourth term, 3, is the sum of the second and third terms: $1 + 2 = 3$, and so on. Did you know that the number of spirals in a daisy or a sunflower, 21 and 34, are two Fibonacci numbers? The number of spirals in a pinecone, 8 and 13, and a pineapple, 8 and 13, are also Fibonacci numbers.

We can think of a **sequence** as a list of numbers that are related to each other by a rule. The numbers in a sequence are called its **terms**. The letter a with a subscript is used to represent the terms of a sequence. Thus, a_1 represents the first term of the sequence, a_2 represents the second term, a_3 the third term, and so on. This notation is shown for the first six terms of the Fibonacci sequence:

1,   1,   2,   3,   5,   8.

$a_1 = 1$ $a_2 = 1$ $a_3 = 2$ $a_4 = 3$ $a_5 = 5$ $a_6 = 8$

Arithmetic Sequences

The bar graph in Figure 5.8 shows annual salaries, rounded to the nearest thousand dollars, of U.S. senators from 2000 to 2005. The graph illustrates that each year salaries increased by $4 thousand. The sequence of annual salaries

142, 146, 150, 154, 158, 162, ...

shows that each term after the first, 142, differs from the preceding term by a constant amount, namely 4. This sequence is an example of an *arithmetic sequence*.

Annual Salaries of U.S. Senators

FIGURE 5.8
Source: U.S. Senate

DEFINITION OF AN ARITHMETIC SEQUENCE

An **arithmetic sequence** is a sequence in which each term after the first differs from the preceding term by a constant amount. The difference between consecutive terms is called the **common difference** of the sequence.

The common difference, d, is found by subtracting any term from the term that directly follows it. In the following examples, the common difference is found by subtracting the first term from the second term: $a_2 - a_1$.

Arithmetic Sequence	**Common Difference**
142, 146, 150, 154, 158, ...	$d = 146 - 142 = 4$
$-5, -2, 1, 4, 7, ...$	$d = -2 - (-5) = -2 + 5 = 3$
$8, 3, -2, -7, -12, ...$	$d = 3 - 8 = -5$

If the first term of an arithmetic sequence is a_1, each term after the first is obtained by adding d, the common difference, to the previous term.

1 Write terms of an arithmetic sequence.

EXAMPLE 1 WRITING THE TERMS OF AN ARITHMETIC SEQUENCE

Write the first six terms of the arithmetic sequence with first term 6 and common difference 4.

SOLUTION The first term is 6. The second term is $6 + 4$, or 10. The third term is $10 + 4$, or 14, and so on. The first six terms are

6, 10, 14, 18, 22, and 26.

 Write the first six terms of the arithmetic sequence with first term 100 and common difference 20.

EXAMPLE 2 WRITING THE TERMS OF AN ARITHMETIC SEQUENCE

Write the first six terms of the arithmetic sequence with $a_1 = 5$ and $d = -2$.

SOLUTION The first term, a_1, is 5. The common difference, d, is -2. To find the second term, we add -2 to 5, giving 3. For the next term, we add -2 to 3, and so on. The first six terms are

5, 3, 1, −1, −3, and −5.

Write the first six terms of the arithmetic sequence with first term 8 and common difference −3.

2 | Use the formula for the general term of an arithmetic sequence.

The General Term of an Arithmetic Sequence

Consider an arithmetic sequence whose first term is a_1 and whose common difference is d. We are looking for a formula for the general term, a_n. Let's begin by writing the first six terms. The first term is a_1. The second term is $a_1 + d$. The third term is $a_1 + d + d$, or $a_1 + 2d$. Thus, we start with a_1 and add d to each successive term. The first six terms are

$$a_1, \quad a_1 + d, \quad a_1 + 2d, \quad a_1 + 3d, \quad a_1 + 4d, \quad a_1 + 5d.$$

a_1, first term a_2, second term a_3, third term a_4, fourth term a_5, fifth term a_6, sixth term

Applying inductive reasoning to the pattern of the terms results in the following formula for the general term, or the nth term, of an arithmetic sequence:

> **GENERAL TERM OF AN ARITHMETIC SEQUENCE**
> The nth term (the general term) of an arithmetic sequence with first term a_1 and common difference d is
> $$a_n = a_1 + (n - 1)d.$$

EXAMPLE 3   USING THE FORMULA FOR THE GENERAL TERM OF AN ARITHMETIC SEQUENCE

Find the eighth term of the arithmetic sequence whose first term is 4 and whose common difference is −7.

SOLUTION   To find the eighth term, a_8, we replace n in the formula with 8, a_1 with 4, and d with −7.

$$a_n = a_1 + (n - 1)d$$
$$a_8 = 4 + (8 - 1)(-7) = 4 + 7(-7) = 4 + (-49) = -45$$

The eighth term is −45. We can check this result by writing the first eight terms of the sequence:

$$4, -3, -10, -17, -24, -31, -38, -45.$$

Find the ninth term of the arithmetic sequence whose first term is 6 and whose common difference is −5.

In Chapter 1, we saw that the process of finding formulas to describe real-world phenomena is called mathematical modeling. Such formulas, together with the meaning assigned to the variables, are called mathematical models. Example 4 illustrates how the formula for the general term of an arithmetic sequence can be used to develop a mathematical model.

Changing Times in the U.S.

Percentage of Young Adults, Ages 18–24, Living with Parents

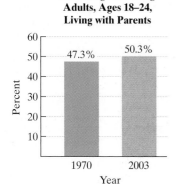

Number (in millions) Completing Four or More Years of College

FIGURE 5.9
Source: U.S. Census Bureau

EXAMPLE 4   USING AN ARITHMETIC SEQUENCE TO MODEL CHANGING TIMES

The top graph in Figure 5.9 shows that in 1970, 47.3% of young adults, ages 18–24, lived at home with their parents. On average, this has increased by approximately 0.09% per year.

a. Write a formula for the *n*th term of the arithmetic sequence that models the percentage of young adults living at home with their parents *n* years after 1969.

b. According to the model in part (a), what percentage of young adults will be living at home with their parents in 2009?

SOLUTION

a. We can express the percentage of young adults living with their parents by the following arithmetic sequence:

$$47.3, \qquad 47.39, \qquad 47.48, \ldots.$$

a_1: 47.3% lived with parents in 1970, 1 year after 1969.

a_2: 47.39% lived with parents in 1971, 2 years after 1969.

a_3: 47.48% lived with parents in 1972, 3 years after 1969.

In this sequence, a_1, the first term, represents the percentage of young adults who lived at home in 1970. Each subsequent year this increased by 0.09%, so $d = 0.09$. We use the formula for the general term of an arithmetic sequence to write the *n*th term of the sequence that describes the percentage of young adults living at home with their parents *n* years after 1969.

$a_n = a_1 + (n - 1)d$ This is the formula for the general term of an arithmetic sequence.

$a_n = 47.3 + (n - 1)0.09$ $a_1 = 47.3$ and $d = 0.09$.

$a_n = 47.3 + 0.09n - 0.09$ Distribute 0.09 to each term in parentheses.

$a_n = 0.09n + 47.21$ Simplify: $47.3 - 0.09 = 47.21$.

Thus, the percentage of young adults living at home with their parents *n* years after 1969 can be described by $a_n = 0.09n + 47.21$.

b. Now we need to find the percentage who will be living with their parents in 2009. The year 2009 is 40 years after 1969: That is, $2009 - 1969 = 40$. We substitute 40 for *n* in $a_n = 0.09n + 47.21$.

$$a_{40} = 0.09(40) + 47.21 = 50.81$$

The 40th term of the sequence is 50.81. Therefore, the model indicates that 50.81% of young adults will be living at home with their parents by the year 2009.

○

CHECK POINT 4   The bottom graph in Figure 5.9 shows that in 1970, 12.0 million Americans had completed four or more years of college. On average, this has increased by approximately 1.16 million people per year.

a. Write a formula for the *n*th term of the arithmetic sequence that models the number of Americans, in millions, completing four or more years of college *n* years after 1969.

b. According to the model in part (a), how many Americans, to the nearest tenth of a million, will have completed four or more years of college in 2019?

Geometric Sequences

Figure 5.10 shows a sequence in which the number of squares is increasing. From left to right, the number of squares is 1, 5, 25, 125, and 625. In this sequence, each term after the first, 1, is obtained by multiplying the preceding term by a constant amount, namely 5. This sequence of increasing numbers of squares is an example of a *geometric sequence*.

FIGURE 5.10 A geometric sequence of squares

> ### DEFINITION OF A GEOMETRIC SEQUENCE
> A **geometric sequence** is a sequence in which each term after the first is obtained by multiplying the preceding term by a fixed nonzero constant. The amount by which we multiply each time is called the **common ratio** of the sequence.

The common ratio, r, is found by dividing any term after the first term by the term that directly precedes it. In the examples below, the common ratio is found by dividing the second term by the first term: $\frac{a_2}{a_1}$.

Geometric sequence	Common ratio
$1, 5, 25, 125, 625, \ldots$	$r = \frac{5}{1} = 5$
$4, 8, 16, 32, 64, \ldots$	$r = \frac{8}{4} = 2$
$6, -12, 24, -48, 96, \ldots$	$r = \frac{-12}{6} = -2$
$9, -3, 1, -\frac{1}{3}, \frac{1}{9}, \ldots$	$r = \frac{-3}{9} = -\frac{1}{3}$

STUDY TIP

When the common ratio of a geometric sequence is negative, the signs of the terms alternate.

3 | Write terms of a geometric sequence.

How do we write out the terms of a geometric sequence when the first term and the common ratio are known? We multiply the first term by the common ratio to get the second term, multiply the second term by the common ratio to get the third term, and so on.

EXAMPLE 5 WRITING THE TERMS OF A GEOMETRIC SEQUENCE

Write the first six terms of the geometric sequence with first term 6 and common ratio $\frac{1}{3}$.

SOLUTION The first term is 6. The second term is $6 \cdot \frac{1}{3}$, or 2. The third term is $2 \cdot \frac{1}{3}$, or $\frac{2}{3}$. The fourth term is $\frac{2}{3} \cdot \frac{1}{3}$, or $\frac{2}{9}$, and so on. The first six terms are

$$6, 2, \frac{2}{3}, \frac{2}{9}, \frac{2}{27}, \text{ and } \frac{2}{81}.$$

○

 5 Write the first six terms of the geometric sequence with first term 12 and common ratio $-\frac{1}{2}$.

4 | Use the formula for the general term of a geometric sequence.

The General Term of a Geometric Sequence

Consider a geometric sequence whose first term is a_1 and whose common ratio is r. We are looking for a formula for the general term, a_n. Let's begin by writing the first six terms. The first term is a_1. The second term is $a_1 r$. The third term is $a_1 r \cdot r$, or $a_1 r^2$. The fourth term is $a_1 r^2 \cdot r$, or $a_1 r^3$, and so on. Starting with a_1 and multiplying each successive term by r, the first six terms are

$$a_1, \qquad a_1 r, \qquad a_1 r^2, \qquad a_1 r^3, \qquad a_1 r^4, \qquad a_1 r^5.$$

a_1, first term a_2, second term a_3, third term a_4, fourth term a_5, fifth term a_6, sixth term

Applying inductive reasoning to the pattern of the terms results in the following formula for the general term, or the nth term, of a geometric sequence:

> **GENERAL TERM OF A GEOMETRIC SEQUENCE**
> The nth term (the general term) of a geometric sequence with first term a_1 and common ratio r is
> $$a_n = a_1 r^{n-1}.$$

EXAMPLE 6   USING THE FORMULA FOR THE GENERAL TERM OF A GEOMETRIC SEQUENCE

Find the eighth term of the geometric sequence whose first term is -4 and whose common ratio is -2.

STUDY TIP

Be careful with the order of operations when evaluating

$$a_1 r^{n-1}.$$

First find r^{n-1}. Then multiply the result by a_1.

SOLUTION To find the eighth term, a_8, we replace n in the formula with 8, a_1 with -4, and r with -2.

$$a_n = a_1 r^{n-1}$$
$$a_8 = -4(-2)^{8-1} = -4(-2)^7 = -4(-128) = 512$$

The eighth term is 512. We can check this result by writing the first eight terms of the sequence:

$$-4, 8, -16, 32, -64, 128, -256, 512.$$

Find the seventh term of the geometric sequence whose first term is 5 and whose common ratio is -3.

EXAMPLE 7   GEOMETRIC POPULATION GROWTH

The table shows the population of the United States in 2000, with estimates given by the Census Bureau for 2001 through 2006.

Year	2000	2001	2002	2003	2004	2005	2006
Population (millions)	281.4	284.5	287.6	290.8	294.0	297.2	300.5

a. Show that the population is increasing geometrically.

b. Write the general term for the geometric sequence describing population growth for the United States n years after 1999.

c. Project the U.S. population, in millions, for the year 2009.

BLITZER BONUS

Geometric Population Growth

Economist Thomas Malthus (1766–1834) predicted that population growth would increase as a geometric sequence and food production would increase as an arithmetic sequence. He concluded that eventually population would exceed food production. If two sequences, one geometric and one arithmetic, are increasing, the geometric sequence will eventually overtake the arithmetic sequence, regardless of any head start that the arithmetic sequence might initially have.

SOLUTION

a. First, we use the sequence of population growth, 281.4, 284.5, 287.6, 290.8, and so on, to divide the population for each year by the population in the preceding year.

$$\frac{284.5}{281.4} \approx 1.011, \quad \frac{287.6}{284.5} \approx 1.011, \quad \frac{290.8}{287.6} \approx 1.011$$

Continuing in this manner, we will keep getting approximately 1.011. This means that the population is increasing geometrically with $r \approx 1.011$. In this situation, the common ratio is the growth rate, indicating that the population of the United States in any year shown in the sequence is approximately 1.011 times the population the year before.

b. The sequence of the U.S. population growth is

$$281.4, 284.5, 287.6, 290.8, 294.0, 297.2, 300.5, \ldots.$$

Because the population is increasing geometrically, we can find the general term of this sequence using

$$a_n = a_1 r^{n-1}.$$

In this sequence, $a_1 = 281.4$ and [from part (a)] $r \approx 1.011$. We substitute these values into the formula for the general term. This gives the general term for the geometric sequence describing the U.S. population n years after 1999.

$$a_n = 281.4(1.011)^{n-1}$$

c. We can use the formula for the general term, a_n, in part (b) to project the U.S. population for the year 2009. The year 2009 is 10 years after 1999—that is, $2009 - 1999 = 10$. Thus, $n = 10$. We substitute 10 for n in $a_n = 281.4(1.011)^{n-1}$.

$$a_{10} = 281.4(1.011)^{10-1} = 281.4(1.011)^9 \approx 310.5$$

The model projects that the United States will have a population of approximately 310.5 million in the year 2009.

7 Write the general term for the geometric sequence

$$3, 6, 12, 24, 48, \ldots.$$

Then use the formula for the general term to find the eighth term.

EXERCISE SET 5.7 ●●●●●●

• Practice Exercises

In Exercises 1–20, write the first six terms of the arithmetic sequence with the first term, a_1, and common difference, d.

1. $a_1 = 8, d = 2$
2. $a_1 = 5, d = 3$
3. $a_1 = 200, d = 20$
4. $a_1 = 300, d = 50$
5. $a_1 = -7, d = 4$
6. $a_1 = -8, d = 5$
7. $a_1 = -400, d = 300$
8. $a_1 = -500, d = 400$
9. $a_1 = 7, d = -3$
10. $a_1 = 9, d = -5$
11. $a_1 = 200, d = -60$
12. $a_1 = 300, d = -90$
13. $a_1 = \frac{5}{2}, d = \frac{1}{2}$
14. $a_1 = \frac{3}{4}, d = \frac{1}{4}$
15. $a_1 = \frac{3}{2}, d = \frac{1}{4}$
16. $a_1 = \frac{3}{2}, d = -\frac{1}{4}$
17. $a_1 = 4.25, d = 0.3$
18. $a_1 = 6.3, d = 0.25$
19. $a_1 = 4.5, d = -0.75$
20. $a_1 = 3.5, d = -1.75$

In Exercises 21–40, find the indicated term for the arithmetic sequence with first term, a_1, and common difference, d.

21. Find a_6, when $a_1 = 13, d = 4$.
22. Find a_{16}, when $a_1 = 9, d = 2$.
23. Find a_{50}, when $a_1 = 7, d = 5$.
24. Find a_{60}, when $a_1 = 8, d = 6$.
25. Find a_9, when $a_1 = -5, d = 9$.
26. Find a_{10}, when $a_1 = -8, d = 10$.
27. Find a_{200}, when $a_1 = -40, d = 5$.
28. Find a_{150}, when $a_1 = -60, d = 5$.
29. Find a_{10}, when $a_1 = -8, d = 10$.
30. Find a_{11}, when $a_1 = 10, d = -6$.
31. Find a_{60}, when $a_1 = 35, d = -3$.

32. Find a_{70}, when $a_1 = -32$, $d = 4$.

33. Find a_{12}, when $a_1 = 12$, $d = -5$.

34. Find a_{20}, when $a_1 = -20$, $d = -4$.

35. Find a_{90}, when $a_1 = -70$, $d = -2$.

36. Find a_{80}, when $a_1 = 106$, $d = -12$.

37. Find a_{12}, when $a_1 = 6$, $d = \frac{1}{2}$.

38. Find a_{14}, when $a_1 = 8$, $d = \frac{1}{4}$.

39. Find a_{50}, when $a_1 = 14$, $d = -0.25$.

40. Find a_{110}, when $a_1 = -12$, $d = -0.5$.

In Exercises 41–48, write a formula for the general term (the nth term) of each arithmetic sequence. Then use the formula for a_n to find a_{20}, the 20th term of the sequence.

41. $1, 5, 9, 13, \ldots$ **42.** $2, 7, 12, 17, \ldots$

43. $7, 3, -1, -5, \ldots$ **44.** $6, 1, -4, -9, \ldots$

45. $a_1 = 9$, $d = 2$ **46.** $a_1 = 6$, $d = 3$

47. $a_1 = -20$, $d = -4$ **48.** $a_1 = -70$, $d = -5$

In Exercises 49–70, write the first six terms of the geometric sequence with the first term, a_1, and common ratio, r.

49. $a_1 = 4$, $r = 2$ **50.** $a_1 = 2$, $r = 3$

51. $a_1 = 1000$, $r = 1$ **52.** $a_1 = 5000$, $r = 1$

53. $a_1 = 3$, $r = -2$ **54.** $a_1 = 2$, $r = -3$

55. $a_1 = 10$, $r = -4$ **56.** $a_1 = 20$, $r = -4$

57. $a_1 = 2000$, $r = -1$ **58.** $a_1 = 3000$, $r = -1$

59. $a_1 = -2$, $r = -3$ **60.** $a_1 = -4$, $r = -2$

61. $a_1 = -6$, $r = -5$ **62.** $a_1 = -8$, $r = -5$

63. $a_1 = \frac{1}{4}$, $r = 2$ **64.** $a_1 = \frac{1}{2}$, $r = 2$

65. $a_1 = \frac{1}{4}$, $r = \frac{1}{2}$ **66.** $a_1 = \frac{1}{5}$, $r = \frac{1}{2}$

67. $a_1 = -\frac{1}{16}$, $r = -4$ **68.** $a_1 = -\frac{1}{8}$, $r = -2$

69. $a_1 = 2$, $r = 0.1$ **70.** $a_1 = -1000$, $r = 0.1$

In Exercises 71–90, find the indicated term for the geometric sequence with first term, a_1, and common ratio, r.

71. Find a_7, when $a_1 = 4$, $r = 2$.

72. Find a_5, when $a_1 = 4$, $r = 3$.

73. Find a_{20}, when $a_1 = 2$, $r = 3$.

74. Find a_{20}, when $a_1 = 2$, $r = 2$.

75. Find a_{100}, when $a_1 = 50$, $r = 1$.

76. Find a_{200}, when $a_1 = 60$, $r = 1$.

77. Find a_7, when $a_1 = 5$, $r = -2$.

78. Find a_4, when $a_1 = 4$, $r = -3$.

79. Find a_{30}, when $a_1 = 2$, $r = -1$.

80. Find a_{40}, when $a_1 = 6$, $r = -1$.

81. Find a_6, when $a_1 = -2$, $r = -3$.

82. Find a_5, when $a_1 = -5$, $r = -2$.

83. Find a_8, when $a_1 = 6$, $r = \frac{1}{2}$.

84. Find a_8, when $a_1 = 12$, $r = \frac{1}{2}$.

85. Find a_6, when $a_1 = 18$, $r = -\frac{1}{3}$.

86. Find a_4, when $a_1 = 9$, $r = -\frac{1}{3}$.

87. Find a_{40}, when $a_1 = 1000$, $r = -\frac{1}{2}$.

88. Find a_{30}, when $a_1 = 8000$, $r = -\frac{1}{2}$.

89. Find a_8, when $a_1 = 1{,}000{,}000$, $r = 0.1$.

90. Find a_8, when $a_1 = 40{,}000$, $r = 0.1$.

In Exercises 91–98, write a formula for the general term (the nth term) of each geometric sequence. Then use the formula for a_n to find a_7, the seventh term of the sequence.

91. $3, 12, 48, 192, \ldots$ **92.** $3, 15, 75, 375, \ldots$

93. $18, 6, 2, \frac{2}{3}, \ldots$ **94.** $12, 6, 3, \frac{3}{2}, \ldots$

95. $1.5, -3, 6, -12, \ldots$ **96.** $5, -1, \frac{1}{5}, -\frac{1}{25}, \ldots$

97. $0.0004, -0.004, 0.04, -0.4, \ldots$

98. $0.0007, -0.007, 0.07, -0.7, \ldots$

Determine whether each sequence in Exercises 99–114 is arithmetic or geometric. Then find the next two terms.

99. $2, 6, 10, 14, \ldots$ **100.** $3, 8, 13, 18, \ldots$

101. $5, 15, 45, 135, \ldots$ **102.** $15, 30, 60, 120, \ldots$

103. $-7, -2, 3, 8, \ldots$ **104.** $-9, -5, -1, 3, \ldots$

105. $3, \frac{3}{2}, \frac{3}{4}, \frac{3}{8}, \ldots$ **106.** $6, 3, \frac{3}{2}, \frac{3}{4}, \ldots$

107. $\frac{1}{2}, 1, \frac{3}{2}, 2, \ldots$ **108.** $\frac{2}{3}, 1, \frac{4}{3}, \frac{5}{3}, \ldots$

109. $7, -7, 7, -7, \ldots$ **110.** $6, -6, 6, -6, \ldots$

111. $7, -7, -21, -35, \ldots$ **112.** $6, -6, -18, -30, \ldots$

113. $\sqrt{5}, 5, 5\sqrt{5}, 25, \ldots$ **114.** $\sqrt{3}, 3, 3\sqrt{3}, 9, \ldots$

• Practice Plus

The sum, S_n, of the first n terms of an arithmetic sequence is given by

$$S_n = \frac{n}{2}(a_1 + a_n),$$

in which a_1 is the first term and a_n is the nth term. The sum, S_n, of the first n terms of a geometric series is given by

$$S_n = \frac{a_1(1 - r^n)}{1 - r},$$

in which a_1 is the first term and r is the common ratio $(r \neq 1)$. In Exercises 115–122, determine whether each sequence is arithmetic or geometric. Then use the appropriate formula to find S_{10}, the sum of the first ten terms.

115. $4, 10, 16, 22, \ldots$ **116.** $7, 19, 31, 43, \ldots$

117. $2, 6, 18, 54, \ldots$ **118.** $3, 6, 12, 24, \ldots$

119. $3, -6, 12, -24, \ldots$ **120.** $4, -12, 36, -108, \ldots$

121. $-10, -6, -2, 2, \ldots$ **122.** $-15, -9, -3, 3, \ldots$

123. Use the appropriate formula shown above to find $1 + 2 + 3 + 4 + \cdots + 100$, the sum of the first 100 natural numbers.

124. Use the appropriate formula shown above to find $2 + 4 + 6 + 8 + \cdots + 200$, the sum of the first 100 positive even integers.

• Application Exercises

Use the formula for the nth term of an arithmetic sequence to solve Exercises 125–128.

The bar graphs show changes that have taken place in the United States from 1970 to 2002 or 2003. Exercises 125–126 involve developing arithmetic sequences that model the data.

Changing Times in the United States

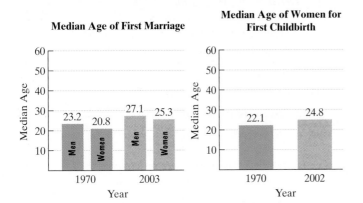

Source: U.S. Census Bureau

125. In 1970, the median age of first marriage for U.S. men was 23.2. On average, this age has increased by approximately 0.12 per year.

    a. Write a formula for the *n*th term of the arithmetic sequence that describes the median age of first marriage for U.S. men *n* years after 1969.

    b. According to the model in part (a), what will be the median age of first marriage for U.S. men in 2009?

126. In 1970, the median age of women for first childbirth was 22.1. On average, this age has increased by approximately 0.08 per year.

    a. Write a formula for the *n*th term of the arithmetic sequence that describes the median age for first childbirth for U.S. women *n* years after 1969.

    b. According to the model in part (a), what will be the median age for first childbirth for U.S. women in 2009?

127. Company A pays $24,000 yearly with raises of $1600 per year. Company B pays $28,000 yearly with raises of $1000 per year. Which company will pay more in year 10? How much more?

128. Company A pays $23,000 yearly with raises of $1200 per year. Company B pays $26,000 yearly with raises of $800 per year. Which company will pay more in year 10? How much more?

Use the formula for the nth term of a geometric sequence to solve Exercises 129–134.

In Exercises 129–130, suppose you save $1 the first day of a month, $2 the second day, $4 the third day, and so on. That is, each day you save twice as much as you did the day before.

129. What will you put aside for savings on the fifteenth day of the month?

130. What will you put aside for savings on the thirtieth day of the month?

131. A professional baseball player signs a contract with a beginning salary of $3,000,000 for the first year with an annual increase of 4% per year beginning in the second year. That is, beginning in year 2, the athlete's salary will be 1.04 times what it was in the previous year. What is the athlete's salary for year 7 of the contract? Round to the nearest dollar.

132. You are offered a job that pays $30,000 for the first year with an annual increase of 5% per year beginning in the second year. That is, beginning in year 2, your salary will be 1.05 times what it was in the previous year. What can you expect to earn in your sixth year on the job? Round to the nearest dollar.

133. The population of California from 1990 through 1997 is shown in the following table.

Year	1990	1991	1992	1993
Population in millions	29.76	30.15	30.54	30.94

Year	1994	1995	1996	1997
Population in millions	31.34	31.75	32.16	32.58

    a. Divide the population for each year by the population in the preceding year. Round to three decimal places and show that the population of California is increasing geometrically.

    b. Write the general term of the geometric sequence describing population growth for California *n* years after 1989.

    c. Estimate California's population, in millions, for the year 2000. According to the U.S. Census Bureau, California's population in 2000 was 33.87 million. How well does your geometric sequence describe the actual population?

134. The population of Texas from 1990 through 1997 is shown in the following table.

Year	1990	1991	1992	1993
Population in millions	16.99	17.35	17.71	18.08

Year	1994	1995	1996	1997
Population in millions	18.46	18.85	19.25	19.65

    a. Divide the population for each year by the population in the preceding year. Round to three decimal places and show that the population of Texas is increasing geometrically.

    b. Write the general term of the geometric sequence describing population growth for Texas *n* years after 1989.

    c. Estimate Texas's population, in millions, for the year 2000. According to the U.S. Census Bureau, Texas's population in 2000 was 20.85 million. How well does your geometric sequence describe the actual population?

• Writing in Mathematics

135. What is a sequence? Give an example with your description.

136. What is an arithmetic sequence? Give an example with your description.

137. What is the common difference in an arithmetic sequence?

138. What is a geometric sequence? Give an example with your description.

139. What is the common ratio in a geometric sequence?

140. If you are given a sequence that is arithmetic or geometric, how can you determine which type of sequence it is?

141. For the first 30 days of a flu outbreak, the number of students on your campus who become ill is increasing. Which is worse: The number of students with the flu is increasing arithmetically or is increasing geometrically? Explain your answer.

• Critical Thinking Exercises

142. Which one of the following is true?

 a. The common difference for the arithmetic sequence given by $1, -1, -3, -5, \ldots$ is 2.

 b. The sequence $1, 4, 8, 13, 19, 26, \ldots$ is an arithmetic sequence.

 c. The nth term of an arithmetic sequence whose first term is a_1 and whose common difference is d is $a_n = a_1 + nd$.

 d. If the first term of an arithmetic sequence is 5 and the third term is -3, then the fourth term is -7.

143. Which one of the following is true?

 a. The sequence $2, 6, 24, 120, \ldots$ is an example of a geometric sequence.

 b. Adjacent terms in a geometric sequence have a common difference.

 c. A sequence that is not arithmetic must be geometric.

 d. If a sequence is geometric, we can write as many terms as we want by repeatedly multiplying by the common ratio.

144. A person is investigating two employment opportunities. They both have a beginning salary of $20,000 per year. Company A offers an increase of $1000 per year. Company B offers 5% more than during the preceding year. Which company will pay more in the sixth year?

• Group Exercise

145. Enough curiosities involving the Fibonacci sequence exist to warrant a flourishing Fibonacci Association. It publishes a quarterly journal. Do some research on the Fibonacci sequence by consulting the research department of your library or the Internet, and find one property that interests you. After doing this research, get together with your group to share these intriguing properties.

●●●●●● CHAPTER SUMMARY, REVIEW, AND TEST

• SUMMARY   DEFINITIONS AND CONCEPTS

EXAMPLES

5.1   Number Theory: Prime and Composite Numbers

a. The set of natural numbers is $\{1, 2, 3, 4, 5, \ldots\}$. $b \mid a$ (b divides a: a is divisible by b) for natural numbers a and b if the operation of dividing a by b leaves a remainder of 0. Rules of divisibility are given in Table 5.1 on page 229.

Ex. 1, p. 230

b. A prime number is a natural number greater than 1 that has only itself and 1 as factors. A composite number is a natural number greater than 1 that is divisible by a number other than itself and 1. The Fundamental Theorem of Arithmetic: Every composite number can be expressed as a product of prime numbers in one and only one way (if the order of the factors is disregarded).

Ex. 2, p. 231

c. The greatest common divisor of two or more natural numbers is the largest number that is a divisor (or factor) of all the numbers. The procedure for finding the greatest common divisor is given in the box on page 232.

Ex. 3, p. 232;
Ex. 4, p. 233

d. The least common multiple of two or more natural numbers is the smallest natural number that is divisible by all of the numbers. The procedure for finding the least common multiple is given in the box on page 234.

Ex. 5, p. 234;
Ex. 6, p. 234

5.2   The Integers; Order of Operations

a. The set of whole numbers is $\{0, 1, 2, 3, 4, 5, \ldots\}$. The set of integers is $\{\ldots, -3, -2, -1, 0, 1, 2, 3, \ldots\}$. Integers are graphed on a number line by placing a dot at the correct location for each number.

Ex. 1, p. 238

b. $a < b$ (a is less than b) means a is to the left of b on a number line.

$a > b$ (a is greater than b) means a is to the right of b on a number line.

Ex. 2, p. 239

c. $|a|$, the absolute value of a, is the distance of a from 0 on a number line. The absolute value of a positive number is the number itself. The absolute value of 0 is 0: $|0| = 0$. The absolute value of a negative number is the number without the negative sign. For example, $|-8| = 8$.

Ex. 3, p. 240

d. Rules for performing operations with integers are given in the boxes on pages 241, 242, 244, and 245.

Ex. 4, p. 242;
Ex. 5, p. 243;
Ex. 6, p. 244

e. Order of Operations

   1. Perform all operations within grouping symbols.

   2. Evaluate all exponential expressions.

   3. Do all multiplications and divisions from left to right.

   4. Do all additions and subtractions from left to right.

Ex. 7, p. 246;
Ex. 8, p. 247

5.3   The Rational Numbers

a. The set of rational numbers is the set of all numbers which can be expressed in the form $\frac{a}{b}$, where a and b are integers and b is not equal to 0.

b. A rational number is reduced to its lowest terms, or simplified, by dividing both the numerator and the denominator by their greatest common divisor.

Ex. 1, p. 250

c. A mixed number consists of the sum of an integer and a rational number, expressed without the use of an addition sign. An improper fraction is a rational number whose numerator is greater than its denominator. Procedures for converting between these forms are given in the boxes on page 251.

Ex. 2, p. 251;
Ex. 3, p. 252

d. Any rational number can be expressed as a decimal. The resulting decimal will either terminate (stop), or it will have a digit that repeats or a block of digits that repeat. The rational number $\frac{a}{b}$ is expressed as a decimal by dividing b into a.

Ex. 4, p. 252

e. To express a terminating decimal as a quotient of integers, the digits to the right of the decimal point are the numerator. The place-value of the last digit to the right of the decimal point is the denominator.

Ex. 5, p. 253

f. To express a repeating decimal as a quotient of integers, use the boxed procedure on page 254.

Ex. 6, p. 254;
Ex. 7, p. 255

g. The product of two rational numbers is the product of their numerators divided by the product of their denominators.

Ex. 8, p. 255

h. Two numbers whose product is 1 are called reciprocals, or multiplicative inverses, of each other. The quotient of two rational numbers is the product of the first number and the reciprocal of the second number.

Ex. 9, p. 256

i. The sum or difference of two rational numbers with identical denominators is the sum or difference of their numerators over the common denominator.

Ex. 10, p. 257

j. Add or subtract rational numbers with unlike denominators by first expressing each rational number with the least common denominator and then following part (i) above.

Ex. 11, p. 257;
Ex. 12, p. 258

k. Density of the Rational Numbers
Given any two rational numbers, there is always a rational number between them. To find the rational number halfway between two rational numbers, add the rational numbers and divide their sum by 2.

Ex. 13, p. 259

5.4   The Irrational Numbers

a. The set of irrational numbers is the set of numbers whose decimal representations are neither terminating nor repeating. Examples of irrational numbers are $\sqrt{2} \approx 1.414$ and $\pi \approx 3.142$.

b. Simplifying square roots: Use the product rule, $\sqrt{ab} = \sqrt{a} \cdot \sqrt{b}$, to remove from the square root any perfect squares that occur as factors.

Ex. 1, p. 265

c. Multiplying square roots: $\sqrt{a} \cdot \sqrt{b} = \sqrt{ab}$. The product of square roots is the square root of the product.

Ex. 2, p. 265

d. Dividing square roots: $\dfrac{\sqrt{a}}{\sqrt{b}} = \sqrt{\dfrac{a}{b}}$. The quotient of the square roots is the square root of the quotient. Ex. 3, p. 266

e. Adding and subtracting square roots: If the radicals have the same radicand, add or subtract their coefficients. The answer is the sum or difference of the coefficients times the common square root. Addition or subtraction is sometimes possible by first simplifying the square roots. Ex. 4, p. 266; Ex. 5, p. 267

f. Rationalizing denominators: Multiply the numerator and denominator by the smallest number that produces a perfect square radicand in the denominator. Ex. 6, p. 268

5.5 Real Numbers and Their Properties

a. The set of real numbers is obtained by combining the rational numbers with the irrational numbers. The important subsets of the real numbers are summarized in Table 5.2 on page 272. A diagram representing the relationships among the subsets of the real numbers is given to the left of Table 5.2. Ex. 1, p. 272

b. Properties of real numbers, including closure properties ($a + b$ and ab are real numbers), commutative properties $(a + b = b + a; ab = ba)$, associative properties $[(a + b) + c = a + (b + c); (ab)c = a(bc)]$, and the distributive property $[a(b + c) = ab + ac]$, are summarized in Table 5.3 on page 273. Ex. 2, p. 274; Ex. 3, p. 274

5.6 Exponents and Scientific Notation

a. Properties of Exponents Table 5.4, p. 278; Ex. 1, p. 279; Ex. 2, p. 279

- Product rule: $b^m \cdot b^n = b^{m+n}$
- Zero exponent rule: $b^0 = 1, b \neq 0$
- Power rule: $(b^m)^n = b^{m \cdot n}$
- Negative exponent rule: $b^{-m} = \dfrac{1}{b^m}, b \neq 0$
- Quotient rule: $\dfrac{b^m}{b^n} = b^{m-n}, b \neq 0$

b. A positive number in scientific notation is expressed as $a \times 10^n$, where $1 \leq a < 10$ and n is an integer.

c. Changing from Scientific to Decimal Notation: If n is positive, move the decimal point in a to the right n places. If n is negative, move the decimal point in a to the left $|n|$ places. Ex. 3, p. 281

d. Changing from Decimal to Scientific Notation: Move the decimal point in the given number to obtain a, where $1 \leq a < 10$. The number of places the decimal point moves gives the absolute value of n in $a \times 10^n$; n is positive if the number is greater than 10 and negative if the number is less than 1. Ex. 4, p. 281

e. The product and quotient rules for exponents are used to multiply and divide numbers in scientific notation. Ex. 6, p. 283; Ex. 7, p. 283; Ex. 8, p. 284; Ex. 9, p. 285

5.7 Arithmetic and Geometric Sequences

a. In an arithmetic sequence, each term after the first differs from the preceding term by a constant, the common difference. Subtract any term from the term that directly follows to find the common difference. Ex. 1, p. 289; Ex. 2, p. 289

b. The general term or the nth term of an arithmetic sequence is Ex. 3, p. 290; Ex. 4, p. 291

$$a_n = a_1 + (n - 1)d,$$

where a_1 is the first term and d is the common difference.

c. In a geometric sequence, each term after the first is obtained by multiplying the preceding term by a nonzero constant, the common ratio. Divide any term after the first by the term that directly precedes it to find the common ratio. Ex. 5, p. 292

d. The general term or the nth term of a geometric sequence is Ex. 6, p. 293; Ex. 7, p. 293

$$a_n = a_1 r^{n-1},$$

where a_1 is the first term and r is the common ratio.

REVIEW EXERCISES

5.1

In Exercises 1 and 2, determine whether the number is divisible by each of the following numbers: 2, 3, 4, 5, 6, 8, 9, 10, and 12. If you are using a calculator, explain the divisibility shown by your calculator using one of the rules of divisibility.

1. 238,632

2. 421,153,470

In Exercises 3–5, find the prime factorization of each composite number.

3. 705

4. 960

5. 6825

In Exercises 6–8, find the greatest common divisor and the least common multiple of the numbers.

6. 30 and 48

7. 36 and 150

8. 216 and 254

9. For an intramural league, you need to divide 24 men and 60 women into all-male and all-female teams so that each team has the same number of people. What is the largest number of people that can be placed on a team?

10. The media center at a college runs videotapes of two lectures continuously. One videotape runs for 42 minutes and a second runs for 56 minutes. Both videotapes begin at 9:00 A.M. When will the videos of the two lectures begin again at the same time?

5.2

In Exercises 11–12, insert either $<$ or $>$ in the shaded area between the integers to make the statement true.

11. $-93 \blacksquare 17$

12. $-2 \blacksquare -200$

In Exercise 13–15, find the absolute value.

13. $|-860|$

14. $|53|$

15. $|0|$

Perform the indicated operations in Exercises 16–28.

16. $8 + (-11)$

17. $-6 + (-5)$

18. $-7 - 8$

19. $-7 - (-8)$

20. $(-9)(-11)$

21. $5(-3)$

22. $\frac{-36}{-4}$

23. $\frac{20}{-5}$

24. $-40 \div 5 \cdot 2$

25. $-6 + (-2) \cdot 5$

26. $6 - 4(-3 + 2)$

27. $28 \div (2 - 4^2)$

28. $36 - 24 \div 4 \cdot 3 - 1$

29. For the year 2015, the Congressional Budget Office projects a budget deficit of $-\$57$ billion. For the same year, the Brookings Institution forecasts a budget deficit of $-\$715$ billion. What is the difference between the CBO projection and the Brookings projection?

5.3

In Exercises 30–32, reduce each rational number to its lowest terms.

30. $\frac{40}{75}$

31. $\frac{36}{150}$

32. $\frac{165}{180}$

In Exercises 33–34, convert each mixed number to an improper fraction.

33. $5\frac{9}{11}$

34. $-3\frac{2}{7}$

In Exercises 35–36, convert each improper fraction to a mixed number.

35. $\frac{27}{5}$

36. $-\frac{17}{9}$

In Exercises 37–40, express each rational number as a decimal.

37. $\frac{4}{5}$

38. $\frac{3}{7}$

39. $\frac{5}{8}$

40. $\frac{9}{16}$

In Exercises 41–44, express each terminating decimal as a quotient of integers in lowest terms.

41. 0.6

42. 0.68

43. 0.588

44. 0.0084

In Exercises 45–47, express each repeating decimal as a quotient of integers in lowest terms.

45. $0.\overline{5}$

46. $0.\overline{34}$

47. $0.\overline{113}$

In Exercises 48–56, perform the indicated operations. Where possible, reduce the answer to lowest terms.

48. $\frac{3}{5} \cdot \frac{7}{10}$

49. $\left(3\frac{1}{3}\right)\left(1\frac{3}{4}\right)$

50. $\frac{4}{5} \div \frac{3}{10}$

51. $-1\frac{2}{3} \div 6\frac{2}{3}$

52. $\frac{2}{9} + \frac{4}{9}$

53. $\frac{7}{9} + \frac{5}{12}$

54. $\frac{3}{4} - \frac{2}{15}$

55. $\frac{1}{3} + \frac{1}{2} \cdot \frac{4}{5}$

56. $\frac{3}{8}\left(\frac{1}{2} + \frac{1}{3}\right)$

In Exercises 57–58, find a rational number halfway between the two numbers in each pair.

57. $\frac{1}{7}$ and $\frac{1}{8}$

58. $\frac{3}{4}$ and $\frac{3}{5}$

59. A recipe for coq au vin is meant for six people and requires $4\frac{1}{2}$ pounds of chicken. If you want to serve 15 people, how much chicken is needed?

60. The gas tank of a car is filled to its capacity. The first day, $\frac{1}{4}$ of the tank's gas is used for travel. The second day, $\frac{1}{3}$ of the tank's original amount of gas is used for travel. What fraction of the tank is filled with gas at the end of the second day?

5.4

In Exercises 61–64, simplify the square root.

61. $\sqrt{28}$

62. $\sqrt{72}$

63. $\sqrt{150}$

64. $\sqrt{300}$

In Exercises 65–73, perform the indicated operation. Simplify the answer when possible.

65. $\sqrt{6} \cdot \sqrt{8}$

66. $\sqrt{10} \cdot \sqrt{5}$

67. $\frac{\sqrt{24}}{\sqrt{2}}$

68. $\frac{\sqrt{27}}{\sqrt{3}}$

69. $\sqrt{5} + 4\sqrt{5}$

70. $7\sqrt{11} - 13\sqrt{11}$

71. $\sqrt{50} + \sqrt{8}$

72. $\sqrt{3} - 6\sqrt{27}$

73. $2\sqrt{18} + 3\sqrt{8}$

In Exercises 74–75, rationalize the denominator.

74. $\frac{30}{\sqrt{5}}$

75. $\sqrt{\frac{2}{3}}$

76. Paleontologists use the mathematical model $W = 4\sqrt{2x}$ to estimate the walking speed of a dinosaur, W, in feet per second, where x is the length, in feet, of the dinosaur's leg. What is the walking speed of a dinosaur whose leg length is 6 feet? Express the answer in simplified radical form. Then use your calculator to estimate the walking speed to the nearest tenth of a foot per second.

5.5

77. Consider the set

$$\left\{-17, -\frac{9}{13}, 0, 0.75, \sqrt{2}, \pi, \sqrt{81}\right\}.$$

List all numbers from the set that are **a.** natural numbers, **b.** whole numbers, **c.** integers, **d.** rational numbers, **e.** irrational numbers, **f.** real numbers.

78. Give an example of an integer that is not a natural number.

79. Give an example of a rational number that is not an integer.

80. Give an example of a real number that is not a rational number.

In Exercises 81–86, state the name of the property illustrated.

81. $3 + 17 = 17 + 3$

82. $(6 \cdot 3) \cdot 9 = 6 \cdot (3 \cdot 9)$

83. $\sqrt{3}\left(\sqrt{5} + \sqrt{3}\right) = \sqrt{15} + 3$

84. $(6 \cdot 9) \cdot 2 = 2 \cdot (6 \cdot 9)$

85. $\sqrt{3}\left(\sqrt{5} + \sqrt{3}\right) = \left(\sqrt{5} + \sqrt{3}\right)\sqrt{3}$

86. $(3 \cdot 7) + (4 \cdot 7) = (4 \cdot 7) + (3 \cdot 7)$

In Exercises 87–88, give on example to show that

87. The natural numbers are not closed with respect to division.

88. The whole numbers are not closed with respect to subtraction.

5.6

In Exercises 89–99, evaluate each expression.

89. $6 \cdot 6^2$

90. $2^3 \cdot 2^3$

91. $(2^2)^2$

92. $(3^3)^2$

93. $\dfrac{5^6}{5^4}$

94. 7^0

95. $(-7)^0$

96. 6^{-3}

97. 2^{-4}

98. $\dfrac{7^4}{7^6}$

99. $3^5 \cdot 3^{-2}$

In Exercises 100–103, express each number in decimal notation.

100. 4.6×10^2

101. 3.74×10^4

102. 2.55×10^{-3}

103. 7.45×10^{-5}

In Exercises 104–109, express each number in scientific notation.

104. 7520

105. $3{,}590{,}000$

106. 0.00725

107. 0.000000409

108. 420×10^{11}

109. 0.97×10^{-4}

In Exercises 110–117, perform the indicated operation and express each answer in decimal notation.

110. $(3 \times 10^7)(1.3 \times 10^{-5})$

111. $(5 \times 10^3)(2.3 \times 10^2)$

112. $\dfrac{6.9 \times 10^3}{3 \times 10^5}$

113. $\dfrac{2.4 \times 10^{-4}}{6 \times 10^{-6}}$

In Exercises 114–117, perform the indicated operation by first expressing each number in scientific notation. Write the answer in scientific notation.

114. $(60{,}000)(540{,}000)$

115. $(91{,}000)(0.0004)$

116. $\dfrac{8{,}400{,}000}{4000}$

117. $\dfrac{0.000003}{0.00000006}$

118. If you earned $1 million per year ($10^6$), how long would it take to accumulate $1 billion dollars ($10^9$)?

119. If the population of the United States is 3×10^8 and each person spends about $150 per year going to the movies (or renting movies), express the total annual spending on movies in scientific notation.

120. The world's population is approximately 6.5×10^9 people. Current projections double this population in 40 years. Write the population 40 years from now in scientific notation.

5.7

In Exercises 121–123, write the first six terms of the arithmetic sequence with the first term, a_1, and common difference, d.

121. $a_1 = 7, d = 4$

122. $a_1 = -4, d = -5$

123. $a_1 = \frac{3}{2}, d = -\frac{1}{2}$

In Exercises 124–126, find the indicated term for the arithmetic sequence with first term, a_1, and common difference, d.

124. Find a_6, when $a_1 = 5, d = 3$.

125. Find a_{12}, when $a_1 = -8, d = -2$.

126. Find a_{14}, when $a_1 = 14, d = -4$.

In Exercises 127–128, write a formula for the general term (the nth term) of each arithmetic sequence. Then use the formula for a_n to find a_{20}, the 20th term of the sequence.

127. $-7, -3, 1, 5, \ldots$

128. $a_1 = 200, d = -20$

In Exercises 129–131, write the first six terms of the geometric sequence with the first term, a_1, and common ratio, r.

129. $a_1 = 3, r = 2$ **130.** $a_1 = \frac{1}{2}, r = \frac{1}{2}$ **131.** $a_1 = 16, r = -\frac{1}{2}$

In Exercises 132–134, find the indicated term for the geometric sequence with first term, a_1, and common ratio, r.

132. Find a_4, when $a_1 = 2, r = 3$.

133. Find a_6, when $a_1 = 16, r = \frac{1}{2}$.

134. Find a_5, when $a_1 = -3, r = 2$.

In Exercises 135–136, write a formula for the general term (the nth term) of each geometric sequence. Then use the formula for a_n to find a_8, the eighth term of the sequence.

135. $1, 2, 4, 8, \ldots$

136. $100, 10, 1, \frac{1}{10}, \ldots$

Determine whether each sequence in Exercises 137–140 is arithmetic or geometric. Then find the next two terms.

137. $4, 9, 14, 19, \ldots$

138. $2, 6, 18, 54, \ldots$

139. $1, \frac{1}{4}, \frac{1}{16}, \frac{1}{64}, \ldots$

140. $0, -7, -14, -21, \ldots$

141. The graph shows the percentage of in-home dinners in the United States having various items as a side dish from 1993 through 2004.

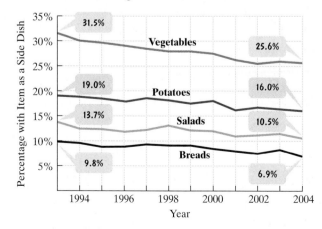

Percentage of U.S. In-Home Dinners Having Various Items as a Side Dish

Source: The NPD Group

In 1993, 31.5% of home dinners had vegetables as a side dish. On average, this decreased by approximately 0.54% per year since then.

a. Write a formula for the nth term of the arithmetic sequence that describes the percentage of dinners that included vegetables n years after 1992.

b. Use the model to predict the percentage of dinners that will include vegetables by the year 2010.

c. Repeat parts (a) and (b) for the change in another one of the items shown in the graph at the bottom of the previous page from 1993 to 2004.

142. Projections for the U.S. population, ages 85 and older, are shown in the following table.

Year	2000	2010	2020	2030	2040	2050
Projected Population in millions	4.2	5.9	8.3	11.6	16.2	22.7

Actual 2000 population

Source: U.S. Census Bureau

a. Show that the U.S. population, ages 85 and older, is projected to increase geometrically.

b. Write the general term of the geometric sequence describing the U.S. population, ages 85 and older, in millions, n decades after 1990.

c. Use the model in part (b) to project the U.S. population, ages 85 and older, in 2080.

• • • • • • CHAPTER 5 TEST

1. Which of the numbers 2, 3, 4, 5, 6, 8, 9, 10, and 12 divide 391,248?

2. Find the prime factorization of 252.

3. Find the greatest common divisor and the least common multiple of 48 and 72.

Perform the indicated operations in Exercises 4–6.

4. $-6 - (5 - 12)$

5. $(-3)(-4) \div (7 - 10)$

6. $(6 - 8)^2(5 - 7)^3$

7. Express $\frac{7}{12}$ as a decimal.

8. Express $0.\overline{64}$ as a quotient of integers in lowest terms.

In Exercises 9–11, perform the indicated operations. Where possible, reduce the answer to its lowest terms.

9. $\left(-\frac{3}{7}\right) \div \left(-2\frac{1}{7}\right)$ 10. $\frac{19}{24} - \frac{7}{40}$ 11. $\frac{1}{2} - 8\left(\frac{1}{4} + 1\right)$

12. Find a rational number halfway between $\frac{1}{2}$ and $\frac{2}{3}$.

13. Multiply and simplify: $\sqrt{10} \cdot \sqrt{5}$.

14. Add: $\sqrt{50} + \sqrt{32}$.

15. Rationalize the denominator: $\dfrac{6}{\sqrt{2}}$.

16. List all the rational numbers in this set:
$$\left\{-7, -\frac{4}{5}, 0, 0.25, \sqrt{3}, \sqrt{4}, \frac{22}{7}, \pi\right\}.$$

In Exercises 17–18, state the name of the property illustrated.

17. $3(2 + 5) = 3(5 + 2)$

18. $6(7 + 4) = 6 \cdot 7 + 6 \cdot 4$

In Exercises 19–21, evaluate each expression.

19. $3^3 \cdot 3^2$ 20. $\dfrac{4^6}{4^3}$ 21. 8^{-2}

22. Multiply and express the answer in decimal notation.
$$(3 \times 10^8)(2.5 \times 10^{-5})$$

23. Divide by first expressing each number in scientific notation. Write the answer in scientific notation.
$$\frac{49{,}000}{0.007}$$

24. In 2006, the U.S. government collected 2.18×10^{12} dollars in taxes. At that time, the U.S. population was approximately 300 million, or 3×10^8. If the total tax collections were evenly divided among all Americans, how much would each citizen pay? Express the answer in decimal notation, rounded to the nearest dollar.

25. Write the first six terms of the arithmetic sequence with first term, a_1, and common difference, d.
$$a_1 = 1, d = -5$$

26. Find a_9, the ninth term of the arithmetic sequence with the first term, a_1, and common difference, d.
$$a_1 = -2, d = 3$$

27. Write the first six terms of the geometric sequence with first term, a_1, and common ratio, r.
$$a_1 = 16, r = \frac{1}{2}$$

28. Find a_7, the seventh term of the geometric sequence with the first term, a_1, and common ratio, r.
$$a_1 = 5, r = 2$$

6

Algebra: Equations and Inequalities

America is a nation of immigrants. Since 1820, over 40 million people have immigrated to the United States from all over the world. They chose to come for various reasons, such as to live in freedom, to practice religion without persecution, to escape poverty or oppression, and to make better lives for themselves and their children. As a result, in 2003, 11.7% of the U.S. population was foreign-born. How can we use mathematical models to project when this percentage might grow to one in every five Americans, or even more?

In this chapter, you will learn to use formulas and mathematical models in new ways. With these skills, you will gain insights into a variety of issues, ranging from the growing diversity of the U.S. population to concerns about Social Security, and even the positive benefits that humor and laughter can have on our lives.

••••••
The foreign-born U.S. population model appears as Exercises 85–88 in Exercise Set 6.6. You will develop and use models for Social Security's income and outflow in Exercises 27–29 in the Chapter 6 Test. Humor opens Section 6.2, and the advantage of having a sense of humor becomes laughingly evident in the models in Example 6 on page 317.

SECTION 6.1 • ALGEBRAIC EXPRESSIONS AND FORMULAS

OBJECTIVES

1. Evaluate algebraic expressions.
2. Use mathematical models.
3. Understand the vocabulary of algebraic expressions.
4. Simplify algebraic expressions.

Algebraic Expressions

Feeling attractive with a suntan that gives you a "healthy glow"? Think again. Direct sunlight is known to promote skin cancer. Although sunscreens protect you from burning, dermatologists are concerned with the long-term damage that results from the sun even without sunburn.

Algebra uses letters, such as x and y, to represent numbers. If a letter is used to represent various numbers, it is called a **variable**. For example, we can let x represent the number of minutes that a person can stay in the sun without burning with no sunscreen. With a number 6 sunscreen, exposure time without burning is six times as long, or 6 times x. This can be written $6 \cdot x$, but it is usually expressed as $6x$. Placing a number and a letter next to one another indicates multiplication.

Notice that $6x$ combines the number 6 and the variable x using the operation of multiplication. A combination of variables and numbers using the operations of addition, subtraction, multiplication, or division, as well as powers or roots, is called an **algebraic expression**. Here are some examples of algebraic expressions:

$$x + 6, \quad x^2 - 6, \quad 6x, \quad \frac{x}{6}, \quad 3x + 5, \quad \sqrt{x} + 7.$$

Evaluating Algebraic Expressions

| 1 | Evaluate algebraic expressions.

Evaluating an algebraic expression means finding the value of the expression for a given value of the variable. For example, we can evaluate $6x$ (from the sunscreen example) when $x = 15$. We substitute 15 for x. We obtain $6 \cdot 15$, or 90. This means that if you can stay in the sun for 15 minutes without burning when you don't put on any lotion, then with a number 6 lotion, you can "cook" for 90 minutes without burning.

Many algebraic expressions contain more than one operation. Evaluating an algebraic expression correctly involves carefully applying the order of operations agreement that we studied in Chapter 5.

THE ORDER OF OPERATIONS AGREEMENT

1. Perform operations within the innermost parentheses and work outward. If the algebraic expression involves a fraction, treat the numerator and the denominator as if they were each enclosed in parentheses.
2. Evaluate all exponential expressions.
3. Perform multiplications and divisions as they occur, working from left to right.
4. Perform additions and subtractions as they occur, working from left to right.

EXAMPLE 1   EVALUATING AN ALGEBRAIC EXPRESSION

Evaluate $7 + 5(x - 4)^3$ for $x = 6$.

SOLUTION

$$\begin{aligned}
7 + 5(x - 4)^3 &= 7 + 5(6 - 4)^3 && \text{Replace x with 6.} \\
&= 7 + 5(2)^3 && \text{First work inside parentheses: } 6 - 4 = 2. \\
&= 7 + 5(8) && \text{Evaluate the exponential expression:} \\
&&& 2^3 = 2 \cdot 2 \cdot 2 = 8. \\
&= 7 + 40 && \text{Multiply: } 5(8) = 40. \\
&= 47 && \text{Add.}
\end{aligned}$$

 Evaluate $8 + 6(x - 3)^2$ for $x = 13$.

STUDY TIP

Notice the difference between the following evaluations:

- x^2 for $x = -6$

  $x^2 = (-6)^2$

  $\quad = (-6)(-6) = 36$

- $-x^2$ for $x = 6$

  $-x^2 = -6^2 = -6 \cdot 6 = -36$

  > The negative is not inside parentheses and is not taken to the second power.

Work carefully when evaluating algebraic expressions with exponents and negatives.

EXAMPLE 2   EVALUATING AN ALGEBRAIC EXPRESSION

Evaluate $x^2 + 5x - 3$ for $x = -6$.

SOLUTION We substitute -6 for each of the two occurrences of x. Then we use the order of operations to evaluate the algebraic expression.

$$\begin{aligned}
x^2 + 5x - 3 && \text{This is the given algebraic expression.} \\
= (-6)^2 + 5(-6) - 3 && \text{Substitute } -6 \text{ for each x.} \\
= 36 + 5(-6) - 3 && \text{Evaluate the exponential expression:} \\
&& (-6)^2 = (-6)(-6) = 36. \\
= 36 + (-30) - 3 && \text{Multiply: } 5(-6) = -30. \\
= 6 - 3 && \text{Add and subtract from left to right.} \\
&& \text{First add: } 36 + (-30) = 6. \\
= 3 && \text{Subtract.}
\end{aligned}$$

 Evaluate $x^2 + 4x - 7$ for $x = -5$.

EXAMPLE 3   EVALUATING AN ALGEBRAIC EXPRESSION

Evaluate $-2x^2 + 5xy - y^3$ for $x = 4$ and $y = -2$.

SOLUTION We substitute 4 for each x and -2 for each y. Then we use the order of operations to evaluate the algebraic expression.

$$\begin{aligned}
-2x^2 + 5xy - y^3 && \text{This is the given algebraic expression.} \\
= -2 \cdot 4^2 + 5 \cdot 4(-2) - (-2)^3 && \text{Substitute 4 for x and } -2 \text{ for y.} \\
= -2 \cdot 16 + 5(4)(-2) - (-8) && \text{Evaluate the exponential expressions:} \\
&& 4^2 = 4 \cdot 4 = 16 \text{ and} \\
&& (-2)^3 = (-2)(-2)(-2) = -8. \\
= -32 + (-40) - (-8) && \text{Multiply: } -2 \cdot 16 = -32 \text{ and} \\
&& 5(4)(-2) = 20(-2) = -40. \\
= -72 - (-8) && \text{Add and subtract from left to right. First add:} \\
&& -32 + (-40) = -72. \\
= -64 && \text{Subtract: } -72 - (-8) = -72 + 8 = -64.
\end{aligned}$$

 Evaluate $-3x^2 + 4xy - y^3$ for $x = 5$ and $y = -1$.

2 | Use mathematical models.

Formulas and Mathematical Models

An **equation** is formed when an equal sign is placed between two algebraic expressions. One aim of algebra is to provide a compact, symbolic description of the world. These descriptions involve the use of *formulas*. A **formula** is an equation that uses letters to express a relationship between two or more variables. Here is an example of a formula:

$$C = \frac{5}{9}(F - 32).$$

| Celsius temperature | is | $\frac{5}{9}$ of | the difference between Fahrenheit temperature and **32°**. |

> These important definitions are repeated from earlier chapters in case your course did not cover this material.

The process of finding formulas to describe real-world phenomena is called **mathematical modeling**. Such formulas, together with the meaning assigned to the variables, are called **mathematical models**. We often say that these formulas model, or describe, the relationships among the variables.

EXAMPLE 4   MODELING THE AMOUNT SPENT ON ONLINE DATING

In 2003, 28.5 million U.S. adults browsed Internet personals and 17.4 million posted online personal ads. The bar graph in Figure 6.1 shows the amount spent in the United States, in millions of dollars, on online dating. Here are three mathematical models for the data shown in the graph. In each formula, *D* represents the amount spent on online dating, in millions of dollars, *x* years after 2002.

Model 1	$D = 236(1.5)^x$
Model 2	$D = 127x + 239$
Model 3	$D = -54x^2 + 234x + 220$

Shopping for a Date: Millions of Dollars Spent in the U.S. on Online Dating

FIGURE 6.1
Source: Jupiter Research

Which model best describes the data for 2004?

SOLUTION Because 2004 is 2 years after 2002, we substitute 2 for *x* in each formula. Then we use the order of operations to find *D*, the amount spent, in millions of dollars, on online dating. The best model is the one that comes closest to giving the actual amount spent in 2004, namely $473 million.

Model 1	Model 2	Model 3
$D = 236(1.5)^x$	$D = 127x + 239$	$D = -54x^2 + 234x + 220$
$D = 236(1.5)^2$	$D = 127(2) + 239$	$D = -54 \cdot 2^2 + 234 \cdot 2 + 220$
$= 236(2.25)$	$= 254 + 239$	$= -54 \cdot 4 + 234 \cdot 2 + 220$
$= 531$	$= 493$	$= -216 + 468 + 220$
		$= 472$

> Figure 6.1 shows that $473 million was spent in **2004**.

The formula for model 3 indicates that in 2004, $472 million was spent on online dating. The number given in Figure 6.1 is $473 million, so model 3 best describes the data for that year.

In Example 4, model 1 does not provide a very good approximation for the 2004 data. If a mathematical model gives an estimate that is a poor approximation or is extended to include values of the variable that do not make sense, we say that **model breakdown** has occurred.

Use the three models in Example 4 to determine which model best describes the data for 2003.

3 | Understand the vocabulary of algebraic expressions.

The Vocabulary of Algebraic Expressions

We have seen that an algebraic expression combines numbers and variables. Here is another example of an algebraic expression:

$$7x - 9y - 3.$$

The **terms** of an algebraic expression are those parts that are separated by addition. For example, we can rewrite $7x - 9y - 3$ as

$$7x + (-9y) + (-3).$$

This expression contains three terms, namely $7x$, $-9y$, and -3.

The numerical part of a term is called its **coefficient**. In the term $7x$, the 7 is the coefficient. In the term $-9y$, the -9 is the coefficient.

Coefficients of 1 and -1 are not written. Thus, the coefficient of x, meaning $1x$, is 1. Similarly, the coefficient of $-y$, meaning $-1y$, is -1.

A term that consists of just a number is called a **numerical term** or a **constant**. The numerical term of $7x - 9y - 3$ is -3.

The parts of each term that are multiplied are called the **factors** of the term. The factors of the term $7x$ are 7 and x.

Like terms are terms that have the same variable factors. For example, $3x$ and $7x$ are like terms.

4 | Simplify algebraic expressions.

Simplifying Algebraic Expressions

The properties of real numbers that we discussed in Chapter 5 can be applied to algebraic expressions.

PROPERTIES OF REAL NUMBERS

Property	Example
Commutative Property of Addition	
$a + b = b + a$	$13x^2 + 7x = 7x + 13x^2$
Commutative Property of Multiplication	
$ab = ba$	$x \cdot 6 = 6x$
Associative Property of Addition	
$(a + b) + c = a + (b + c)$	$3 + (8 + x) = (3 + 8) + x = 11 + x$
Associative Property of Multiplication	
$(ab)c = a(bc)$	$-2(3x) = (-2 \cdot 3)x = -6x$
Distributive Property	
$a(b + c) = ab + ac$	$5(3x + 7) = 5 \cdot 3x + 5 \cdot 7 = 15x + 35$
$a(b - c) = ab - ac$	$4(2x - 5) = 4 \cdot 2x - 4 \cdot 5 = 8x - 20$

STUDY TIP

To combine like terms mentally, add or subtract the coefficients of the terms. Use this result as the coefficient of the terms' variable factor(s).

The distributive property in the form

$$ba + ca = (b + c)a$$

enables us to add or subtract like terms. For example,

$$3x + 7x = (3 + 7)x = 10x$$
$$7y^2 - y^2 = 7y^2 - 1y^2 = (7 - 1)y^2 = 6y^2.$$

This process is called **combining like terms.**

An algebraic expression is **simplified** when parentheses have been removed and like terms have been combined.

EXAMPLE 5   SIMPLIFYING AN ALGEBRAIC EXPRESSION

Simplify: $5(3x - 7) - 6x$.

SOLUTION

$$5(3x - 7) - 6x$$

$$= 5 \cdot 3x - 5 \cdot 7 - 6x \qquad \text{Use the distributive property to remove the parentheses.}$$

$$= 15x - 35 - 6x \qquad \text{Multiply.}$$

$$= (15x - 6x) - 35 \qquad \text{Group like terms.}$$

$$= 9x - 35 \qquad \text{Combine like terms: } 15x - 6x = (15 - 6)x = 9x.$$

CHECK POINT 5   Simplify: $7(2x - 3) - 11x$.

EXAMPLE 6   SIMPLIFYING AN ALGEBRAIC EXPRESSION

Simplify: $6(2x^2 + 4x) + 10(4x^2 + 3x)$.

SOLUTION

$$6(2x^2 + 4x) + 10(4x^2 + 3x)$$

$$= 6 \cdot 2x^2 + 6 \cdot 4x + 10 \cdot 4x^2 + 10 \cdot 3x$$

> $52x^2$ and $54x$ are not like terms. They contain different variable factors, x^2 and x, and cannot be combined.

$$= 12x^2 + 24x + 40x^2 + 30x \qquad \text{Use the distributive property to remove the parentheses.}$$

$$= (12x^2 + 40x^2) + (24x + 30x) \qquad \text{Multiply.}$$

$$= 52x^2 + 54x$$

Group like terms.

Combine like terms:
$12x^2 + 40x^2 = (12 + 40)x^2 = 52x^2$
and $24x + 30x = (24 + 30)x = 54x$.

CHECK POINT 6   Simplify: $7(4x^2 + 3x) + 2(5x^2 + x)$.

It is not uncommon to see algebraic expressions with parentheses preceded by a negative sign or subtraction. An expression of the form $-(a + b)$ can be simplified as follows:

$$-(a + b) = -1(a + b) = (-1)a + (-1)b = -a + (-b) = -a - b.$$

Do you see a fast way to obtain the simplified expression on the right? **If a negative sign or a subtraction symbol appears outside parentheses, drop the parentheses and change the sign of every term within the parentheses.** For example,

$$-(3x^2 - 7x - 4) = -3x^2 + 7x + 4.$$

EXAMPLE 7   SIMPLIFYING AN ALGEBRAIC EXPRESSION

Simplify: $8x + 2[5 - (x - 3)]$.

SOLUTION

$$8x + 2[5 - (x - 3)]$$
$$= 8x + 2[5 - x + 3]$$ Drop parentheses and change the sign of each term in parentheses: $-(x - 3) = -x + 3$.

$$= 8x + 2[8 - x]$$ Simplify inside brackets: $5 + 3 = 8$.
$$= 8x + 16 - 2x$$ Apply the distributive property:

$$2[8 - x] = 2 \cdot 8 - 2x = 16 - 2x.$$

$$= (8x - 2x) + 16$$ Group like terms.
$$= 6x + 16$$ Combine like terms:
$$8x - 2x = (8 - 2)x = 6x.$$

 Simplify: $6x + 4[7 - (x - 2)]$.

EXERCISE SET 6.1 ●●●●●●

• Practice Exercises

In Exercises 1–30, evaluate the algebraic expression for the given value or values of the variables.

1. $5x + 7$; $x = 4$
2. $9x + 6$; $x = 5$
3. $-7x - 5$; $x = -4$
4. $-6x - 13$; $x = -3$
5. $x^2 + 4$; $x = 5$
6. $x^2 + 9$; $x = 3$
7. $x^2 - 6$; $x = -2$
8. $x^2 - 11$; $x = -3$
9. $x^2 + 4x$; $x = 10$
10. $x^2 + 6x$; $x = 9$
11. $8x^2 + 17$; $x = 5$
12. $7x^2 + 25$; $x = 3$
13. $x^2 - 5x$; $x = -11$
14. $x^2 - 8x$; $x = -5$
15. $x^2 + 5x - 6$; $x = 4$
16. $x^2 + 7x - 4$; $x = 6$
17. $4 + 5(x - 7)^3$; $x = 9$
18. $6 + 5(x - 6)^3$; $x = 8$
19. $x^2 - 3(x - y)$; $x = 2, y = 8$
20. $x^2 - 4(x - y)$; $x = 3, y = 8$
21. $2x^2 - 5x - 6$; $x = -3$
22. $3x^2 - 4x - 9$; $x = -5$
23. $-5x^2 - 4x - 11$; $x = -1$
24. $-6x^2 - 11x - 17$; $x = -2$
25. $3x^2 + 2xy + 5y^2$; $x = 2, y = 3$
26. $4x^2 + 3xy + 2y^2$; $x = 3, y = 2$
27. $-x^2 - 4xy + 3y^3$; $x = -1, y = -2$
28. $-x^2 - 3xy + 4y^3$; $x = -3, y = -1$
29. $\dfrac{2x + 3y}{x + 1}$; $x = -2, y = 4$
30. $\dfrac{2x + y}{xy - 2x}$; $x = -2, y = 4$

The formula

$$C = \frac{5}{9}(F - 32)$$

expresses the relationship between Fahrenheit temperature, F, and Celsius temperature, C. In Exercises 31–32, use the formula to convert the given Fahrenheit temperature to its equivalent temperature on the Celsius scale.

31. $50°F$
32. $86°F$

A football was kicked vertically upward from a height of 4 feet with an initial speed of 60 feet per second. The formula

$$h = 4 + 60t - 16t^2$$

describes the ball's height above the ground, h, in feet, t seconds after it was kicked. Use this formula to solve Exercises 33–34.

33. What was the ball's height 2 seconds after it was kicked?
34. What was the ball's height 3 seconds after it was kicked?

In Exercises 35–52, simplify each algebraic expression.

35. $7x + 10x$
36. $5x + 13x$
37. $5x^2 - 8x^2$
38. $7x^2 - 10x^2$
39. $3(x + 5)$
40. $4(x + 6)$
41. $4(2x - 3)$
42. $3(4x - 5)$
43. $5(3x + 4) - 4$
44. $2(5x + 4) - 3$
45. $5(3x - 2) + 12x$
46. $2(5x - 1) + 14x$
47. $7(3y - 5) + 2(4y + 3)$
48. $4(2y - 6) + 3(5y + 10)$
49. $5(3y - 2) - (7y + 2)$
50. $4(5y - 3) - (6y + 3)$
51. $7 - 4[3 - (4y - 5)]$
52. $6 - 5[8 - (2y - 4)]$

• Practice Plus

In Exercises 53–56, simplify each algebraic expression.

53. $18x^2 + 4 - [6(x^2 - 2) + 5]$
54. $14x^2 + 5 - [7(x^2 - 2) + 4]$
55. $2(3x^2 - 5) - [4(2x^2 - 1) + 3]$
56. $4(6x^2 - 3) - [2(5x^2 - 1) + 1]$

In Exercises 57–64, write each English phrase as an algebraic expression. Then simplify the expression. Let x represent the number.

57. A number decreased by the sum of the number and four

58. A number decreased by the difference between eight and the number

59. Six times the product of negative five and a number

60. Ten times the product of negative four and a number

61. The difference between the product of five and a number and twice the number

62. The difference between the product of six and a number and negative two times the number

63. The difference between eight times a number and six more than three times the number

64. Eight decreased by three times the sum of a number and six

• Application Exercises

The bar graph shows the number of billionaires in the United States from 2000 through 2004.

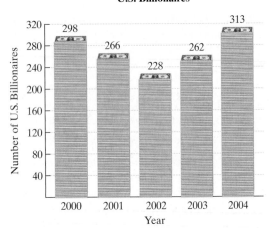

A Growing Club:
U.S. Billionaires

Source: Forbes magazine

The formula

$$N = 17x^2 - 65.4x + 302.2$$

models the number of billionaires, N, in the United States, x years after 2000. Use the formula to solve Exercises 65–68.

65. According to the formula, how many U.S. billionaires, to the nearest whole number, were there in 2004? How well does the formula model the actual data shown in the bar graph?

66. According to the formula, how many U.S. billionaires, to the nearest whole number, were there in 2003? How well does the formula model the actual data shown in the bar graph?

67. According to the formula, how many U.S. billionaires, to the nearest whole number, will there be in 2010?

68. According to the formula, how many U.S. billionaires, to the nearest whole number, will there be in 2008?

The bar graph shows the number of people in the United States, in millions, who do yoga.

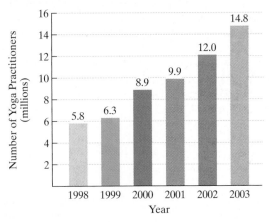

Yoga Stretch:
Number of U.S. Yoga Practitioners

Source: Yoga Journal

Here are four mathematical models for the data shown in the graph. In each formula, N represents the number of U.S. yoga practitioners, in millions, x years after 1998.

Model 1 $N = 1.8x + 5.1$

Model 2 $N = 5.6(1.2)^x$

Model 3 $N = 0.17x^2 + 0.95x + 5.68$

Model 4 $N = 0.01x^3 + 0.09x^2 + 1.1x + 5.64$

Use these models to solve Exercises 69–72.

69. Which model best describes the data for 2000?

70. Which model best describes the data for 1998?

71. How well does model 3 describe the data for 2003?

72. How well does model 4 describe the data for 2002?

The line graph shows the cost of inflation. What cost $10,000 in 1975 would cost the amount shown by the graph in subsequent years.

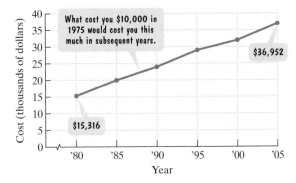

The Cost of Inflation

Source: Bureau of Labor Statistics

Here are two mathematical models for the data shown in the graph. In each formula, C represents the cost x years after 1980 of what cost $10,000 in 1975.

Model 1 $C = 865x + 15,316$

Model 2 $C = -2x^2 + 900x + 15,397$

Use these models to solve Exercises 73–75.

73. a. Use the graph to estimate the cost in 2000, to the nearest thousand dollars, of what cost $10,000 in 1975.
b. Use model 1 to determine the cost in 2000. How well does this describe your estimate from part (a)?
c. Use model 2 to determine the cost in 2000. How well does this describe your estimate from part (a)?

74. a. Use the graph to estimate the cost in 1990, to the nearest thousand dollars, of what cost $10,000 in 1975.
b. Use model 1 to determine the cost in 1990. How well does this describe your estimate from part (a)?
c. Use model 2 to determine the cost in 1990. How well does this describe your estimate from part (a)?

75. Which model is a better description for the cost in 2005 of what cost $10,000 in 1975?

• Writing in Mathematics

76. What is an algebraic expression? Provide an example with your description.
77. What does it mean to evaluate an algebraic expression? Provide an example with your description.
78. What is a term? Provide an example with your description.
79. What are like terms? Provide an example with your description.
80. Explain how to add like terms. Give an example.
81. What does it mean to simplify an algebraic expression?
82. An algebra student incorrectly used the distributive property and wrote $3(5x + 7) = 15x + 7$. If you were that student's teacher, what would you say to help the student avoid this kind of error?

• Critical Thinking Exercises

83. Which one of the following is true?
a. The term x has no coefficient.
b. $5 + 3(x - 4) = 8(x - 4) = 8x - 32$
c. $-x - x = -x + (-x) = 0$
d. $x - 0.02(x + 200) = 0.98x - 4$

84. Which one of the following is true?
a. $3 + 7x = 10x$
b. $b \cdot b = 2b$
c. $(3y - 4) - (8y - 1) = -5y - 3$
d. $-4y + 4 = -4(y + 4)$

85. A business that manufactures small alarm clocks has weekly fixed costs of $5000. The average cost per clock for the business to manufacture x clocks is described by

$$\frac{0.5x + 5000}{x}.$$

a Find the average cost when $x = 100$, 1000, and $10,000$.
b. Like all other businesses, the alarm clock manufacturer must make a profit. To do this, each clock must be sold for at least 50¢ more than what it costs to manufacture. Due to competition from a larger company, the clocks can be sold for $1.50 each and no more. Our small manufacturer can only produce 2000 clocks weekly. Does this business have much of a future? Explain.

SECTION 6.2 • LINEAR EQUATIONS IN ONE VARIABLE

O B J E C T I V E S
1. Solve linear equations.
2. Solve linear equations containing fractions.
3. Solve a formula for a variable.
4. Identify equations with no solution or infinitely many solutions.

Sense of Humor and Depression

FIGURE 6.2
Source: Steven Davis and Joseph Palladino, *Psychology,* 3rd Edition. Prentice Hall, 2003.

The belief that humor and laughter can have positive benefits on our lives is not new. The graphs in Figure 6.2 indicate that persons with a low sense of humor have higher levels of depression in response to negative life events than those with a high sense of humor. These graphs can be modeled by the following formulas:

Low-Humor Group

High-Humor Group

$$D = \frac{10}{9}x + \frac{53}{9} \qquad D = \frac{1}{9}x + \frac{26}{9}.$$

In each formula, x represents the intensity of a negative life event (from 1, low, to 10, high) and D is the level of depression in response to that event.

Suppose that the low-humor group averages a level of depression of 10 in response to a negative life event. We can determine the intensity of that event by substituting 10 for D in the low-humor model, $D = \dfrac{10}{9}x + \dfrac{53}{9}$:

$$10 = \dfrac{10}{9}x + \dfrac{53}{9}.$$

The two sides of an equation can be reversed. So, we can also express this equation as

$$\dfrac{10}{9}x + \dfrac{53}{9} = 10.$$

Notice that the highest exponent on the variable is 1. Such an equation is called a *linear equation in one variable*. In this section, we will study how to solve linear equations.

1 | Solve linear equations.

Solving Linear Equations in One Variable

We begin with a general definition of a linear equation in one variable.

DEFINITION OF A LINEAR EQUATION

A **linear equation in one variable** x is an equation that can be written in the form

$$ax + b = 0,$$

where a and b are real numbers, and $a \neq 0$.

An example of a linear equation in one variable is

$$4x + 12 = 0.$$

Solving an equation in x involves determining all values of x that result in a true statement when substituted into the equation. Such values are **solutions**, or **roots**, of the equation. For example, substitute -3 for x in $4x + 12 = 0$. We obtain

$$4(-3) + 12 = 0, \quad \text{or} \quad -12 + 12 = 0.$$

This simplifies to the true statement $0 = 0$. Thus, -3 is a solution of the equation $4x + 12 = 0$. We also say that -3 **satisfies** the equation $4x + 12 = 0$, because when we substitute -3 for x, a true statement results. The set of all such solutions is called the equation's **solution set**. For example, the solution set of the equation $4x + 12 = 0$ is $\{-3\}$.

Two or more equations that have the same solution set are called **equivalent equations**. For example, the equations

$$4x + 12 = 0 \quad \text{and} \quad 4x = -12 \quad \text{and} \quad x = -3$$

are equivalent equations because the solution set for each is $\{-3\}$. To solve a linear equation in x, we transform the equation into an equivalent equation one or more times. Our final equivalent equation should be of the form

$$x = \text{a number}.$$

The solution set of this equation is the set consisting of the number.

To generate equivalent equations, we will use the following properties:

THE ADDITION AND MULTIPLICATION PROPERTIES OF EQUALITY

THE ADDITION PROPERTY OF EQUALITY

The same real number or algebraic expression may be added to both sides of an equation without changing the equation's solution set.

$$a = b \text{ and } a + c = b + c \text{ are equivalent equations.}$$

THE MULTIPLICATION PROPERTY OF EQUALITY

The same nonzero real number may multiply both sides of an equation without changing the equation's solution set.

$$a = b \text{ and } ac = bc \text{ are equivalent equations as long as } c \neq 0.$$

Because subtraction is defined in terms of addition, the addition property also lets us subtract the same number from both sides of an equation without changing the equation's solution set. Similarly, because division is defined in terms of multiplication, the multiplication property of equality can be used to divide both sides of an equation by the same nonzero number to obtain an equivalent equation.

Table 6.1 illustrates how these properties are used to isolate x to obtain an equation of the form $x = $ a number.

TABLE 6.1 USING PROPERTIES OF EQUALITY TO SOLVE EQUATIONS

Equation	How to Isolate x	Solving the Equation	The Equation's Solution Set
$x - 3 = 8$	Add 3 to both sides.	$x - 3 + 3 = 8 + 3$ $x = 11$	$\{11\}$
$x + 7 = -15$	Subtract 7 from both sides.	$x + 7 - 7 = -15 - 7$ $x = -22$	$\{-22\}$
$6x = 30$	Divide both sides by 6 (or multiply both sides by $\frac{1}{6}$).	$\dfrac{6x}{6} = \dfrac{30}{6}$ $x = 5$	$\{5\}$
$\dfrac{x}{5} = 9$	Multiply both sides by 5.	$5 \cdot \dfrac{x}{5} = 5 \cdot 9$ $x = 45$	$\{45\}$

These equations are solved using the **Addition Property of Equality**.

These equations are solved using the **Multiplication Property of Equality**.

EXAMPLE 1   USING PROPERTIES OF EQUALITY TO SOLVE AN EQUATION

Solve and check: $2x + 3 = 17$.

SOLUTION Our goal is to obtain an equivalent equation with x isolated on one side and a number on the other side.

$$2x + 3 = 17 \qquad \text{This is the given equation.}$$

$$2x + 3 - 3 = 17 - 3 \qquad \text{Subtract 3 from both sides.}$$

$$2x = 14 \qquad \text{Simplify.}$$

$$\frac{2x}{2} = \frac{14}{2} \qquad \text{Divide both sides by 2.}$$

$$x = 7 \qquad \text{Simplify: } \frac{2x}{2} = 1x = x \text{ and } \frac{14}{2} = 7.$$

Now we check the proposed solution, 7, by replacing x with 7 in the original equation.

$$2x + 3 = 17 \qquad \text{This is the original equation.}$$

$$2 \cdot 7 + 3 \overset{?}{=} 17 \qquad \text{Substitute 7 for x. The question mark indicates that we do not yet know if the two sides are equal.}$$

$$14 + 3 \overset{?}{=} 17 \qquad \text{Multiply: } 2 \cdot 7 = 14.$$

This statement is true. $17 = 17 \qquad \text{Add: } 14 + 3 = 17.$

Because the check results in a true statement, we conclude that the solution set of the given equation is $\{7\}$.

 Solve and check: $4x + 5 = 29$.

Here is a step-by-step procedure for solving a linear equation in one variable. Not all of these steps are necessary to solve every equation.

SOLVING A LINEAR EQUATION

1. Simplify the algebraic expression on each side by removing grouping symbols and combining like terms.
2. Collect all the variable terms on one side and all the constants, or numerical terms, on the other side.
3. Isolate the variable and solve.
4. Check the proposed solution in the original equation.

EXAMPLE 2   SOLVING A LINEAR EQUATION

Solve and check: $2(x - 4) - 5x = -5$.

SOLUTION

Step 1. Simplify the algebraic expression on each side.

$$2(x - 4) - 5x = -5 \qquad \text{This is the given equation.}$$
$$2x - 8 - 5x = -5 \qquad \text{Use the distributive property.}$$
$$-3x - 8 = -5 \qquad \text{Combine like terms: } 2x - 5x = -3x.$$

Step 2. Collect variable terms on one side and constants on the other side. The only variable term, $-3x$, is already on the left side. We will collect constants on the right side by adding 8 to both sides.

$$-3x - 8 + 8 = -5 + 8 \qquad \text{Add 8 to both sides.}$$
$$-3x = 3 \qquad \text{Simplify.}$$

Step 3. Isolate the variable and solve. We isolate the variable, x, by dividing both sides of $-3x = 3$ by -3.

$$\frac{-3x}{-3} = \frac{3}{-3} \qquad \text{Divide both sides by } -3.$$

$$x = -1 \qquad \text{Simplify: } \frac{-3x}{-3} = 1x = x \text{ and } \frac{3}{-3} = -1.$$

Step 4. Check the proposed solution in the original equation. Substitute -1 for x in the original equation.

$$2(x - 4) - 5x = -5 \qquad \text{This is the original equation.}$$
$$2(-1 - 4) - 5(-1) \overset{?}{=} -5 \qquad \text{Substitute } -1 \text{ for } x.$$
$$2(-5) - 5(-1) \overset{?}{=} -5 \qquad \text{Simplify inside parentheses:}$$
$$\qquad\qquad\qquad\qquad -1 - 4 = -1 + (-4) = -5.$$
$$-10 - (-5) \overset{?}{=} -5 \qquad \text{Multiply: } 2(-5) = -10 \text{ and}$$
$$\qquad\qquad\qquad\qquad 5(-1) = -5.$$

This statement is true. $-5 = -5 \qquad -10 - (-5) = -10 + 5 = -5$

Because the check results in a true statement, we conclude that the solution set of the given equation is $\{-1\}$. ○

Solve and check: $6(x - 3) - 10x = -10$.

STUDY TIP

We simplify algebraic expressions. We solve algebraic equations. Although basic rules of algebra are used in both procedures, notice the differences between the procedures:

Simplifying an Algebraic Expression	**Solving an Algebraic Equation**
Simplify: $3(x - 7) - (5x - 11)$.	Solve: $3(x - 7) - (5x - 11) = 14$.

This is not an equation. There is no equal sign.

This is an equation. There is an equal sign.

Solution $\quad 3(x - 7) - (5x - 11)$

$\quad\quad = 3x - 21 - 5x + 11$

$\quad\quad = (3x - 5x) + (-21 + 11)$

$\quad\quad = -2x + (-10)$

$\quad\quad = -2x - 10$

Stop! Further simplification is not possible. Avoid the common error of setting $-2x - 10$ equal to 0.

Solution $3(x - 7) - (5x - 11) = 14$

$\quad\quad 3x - 21 - 5x + 11 = 14$

$\quad\quad\quad -2x - 10 = 14$

Add 10 to both sides.

$\quad\quad -2x - 10 + 10 = 14 + 10$

$\quad\quad\quad\quad -2x = 24$

Divide both sides by -2.

$\quad\quad\quad \dfrac{-2x}{-2} = \dfrac{24}{-2}$

$\quad\quad\quad\quad x = -12$

The solution set is $\{-12\}$.

EXAMPLE 3   SOLVING A LINEAR EQUATION

Solve and check: $5x - 12 = 8x + 24$.

SOLUTION

Step 1. Simplify the algebraic expression on each side. Neither side contains grouping symbols or like terms that can be combined. Therefore, we can skip this step.

STUDY TIP

You can solve

$\quad 5x - 12 = 8x + 24$

by collecting x-terms on the right and numbers on the left. To collect x-terms on the right, subtract $5x$ from both sides:

$5x - 12 - 5x = 8x + 24 - 5x$

$\quad\quad -12 = 3x + 24.$

To collect numbers on the left, subtract 24 from both sides:

$-12 - 24 = 3x + 24 - 24$

$\quad\quad -36 = 3x.$

Now isolate x by dividing both sides by 3:

$\quad \dfrac{-36}{3} = \dfrac{3x}{3}$

$\quad\quad -12 = x.$

This is the same solution that we obtained in Example 3.

Step 2. Collect variable terms on one side and constants on the other side. One way to do this is to collect variable terms on the left and constants on the right. This is accomplished by subtracting $8x$ from both sides and adding 12 to both sides.

$5x - 12 = 8x + 24$	This is the given equation.
$5x - 12 - 8x = 8x + 24 - 8x$	Subtract $8x$ from both sides.
$-3x - 12 = 24$	Simplify: $5x - 8x = -3x$.
$-3x - 12 + 12 = 24 + 12$	Add 12 to both sides and collect constants on the right side.
$-3x = 36$	Simplify.

Step 3. Isolate the variable and solve. We isolate the variable, x, by dividing both sides of $-3x = 36$ by -3.

$\dfrac{-3x}{-3} = \dfrac{36}{-3}$	Divide both sides by -3.
$x = -12$	Simplify.

Step 4. Check the proposed solution in the original equation. Substitute -12 for x in the original equation.

$5x - 12 = 8x + 24$	This is the original equation.
$5(-12) - 12 \stackrel{?}{=} 8(-12) + 24$	Substitute -12 for x.
$-60 - 12 \stackrel{?}{=} -96 + 24$	Multiply: $5(-12) = -60$ and $8(-12) = -96$.

This statement is true. $-72 = -72$

Add: $-60 + (-12) = -72$ and $-96 + 24 = -72$.

Because the check results in a true statement, we conclude that the solution set of the given equation is $\{-12\}$.

CHECK POINT 3 Solve the equation: $2x + 9 = 8x - 3$.

EXAMPLE 4   SOLVING A LINEAR EQUATION

Solve and check: $2(x - 3) - 17 = 13 - 3(x + 2)$.

SOLUTION

Step 1. Simplify the algebraic expression on each side.

> Do not begin with 13 − 3. Multiplication (the distributive property) is applied before subtraction.

$$2(x - 3) - 17 = 13 - 3(x + 2) \qquad \text{This is the given equation.}$$
$$2x - 6 - 17 = 13 - 3x - 6 \qquad \text{Use the distributive property.}$$
$$2x - 23 = -3x + 7 \qquad \text{Combine like terms.}$$

Step 2. Collect variable terms on one side and constants on the other side. We will collect variable terms on the left by adding $3x$ to both sides. We will collect the numbers on the right by adding 23 to both sides.

$$2x - 23 + 3x = -3x + 7 + 3x \qquad \text{Add 3x to both sides.}$$
$$5x - 23 = 7 \qquad \text{Simplify: 2x + 3x = 5x.}$$
$$5x - 23 + 23 = 7 + 23 \qquad \text{Add 23 to both sides.}$$
$$5x = 30 \qquad \text{Simplify.}$$

Step 3. Isolate the variable and solve. We isolate the variable, x, by dividing both sides of $5x = 30$ by 5.

$$\frac{5x}{5} = \frac{30}{5} \qquad \text{Divide both sides by 5.}$$
$$x = 6 \qquad \text{Simplify.}$$

Step 4. Check the proposed solution in the original equation. Substitute 6 for x in the original equation.

$$2(x - 3) - 17 = 13 - 3(x + 2) \qquad \text{This is the original equation.}$$
$$2(6 - 3) - 17 \stackrel{?}{=} 13 - 3(6 + 2) \qquad \text{Substitute 6 for x.}$$
$$2(3) - 17 \stackrel{?}{=} 13 - 3(8) \qquad \text{Simplify inside parentheses.}$$
$$6 - 17 \stackrel{?}{=} 13 - 24 \qquad \text{Multiply.}$$
$$-11 = -11 \qquad \text{Subtract.}$$

The true statement $-11 = -11$ verifies that the solution set is $\{6\}$.

CHECK POINT 4 Solve and check: $4(2x + 1) = 29 + 3(2x - 5)$.

---

2 | Solve linear equations containing fractions.

Linear Equations with Fractions

Equations are easier to solve when they do not contain fractions. How do we remove fractions from an equation? We begin by multiplying both sides of the equation by the least common denominator of the fractions in the equation. The least common denominator is the smallest number that all denominators will divide into. Multiplying every term on both sides of the equation by the least common denominator will eliminate the fractions in the equation. Example 5 shows how we "clear an equation of fractions."

EXAMPLE 5	SOLVING A LINEAR EQUATION INVOLVING FRACTIONS

Solve the equation: $\dfrac{3x}{2} = \dfrac{8x}{5} - \dfrac{39}{5}$.

SOLUTION The denominators are 2, 5, and 5. The smallest number that is divisible by 2, 5, and 5 is 10. We begin by multiplying both sides of the equation by 10, the least common denominator.

$$\frac{3x}{2} = \frac{8x}{5} - \frac{39}{5}$$ This is the given equation.

$$10 \cdot \frac{3x}{2} = 10\left(\frac{8x}{5} - \frac{39}{5}\right)$$ Multiply both sides by 10.

$$10 \cdot \frac{3x}{2} = 10 \cdot \frac{8x}{5} - 10 \cdot \frac{39}{5}$$ Use the distributive property. Be sure to multiply all terms by 10.

$$\overset{5}{\cancel{10}} \cdot \frac{3x}{\underset{1}{\cancel{2}}} = \overset{2}{\cancel{10}} \cdot \frac{8x}{\underset{1}{\cancel{5}}} - \overset{2}{\cancel{10}} \cdot \frac{39}{\underset{1}{\cancel{5}}}$$ Divide out common factors in the multiplications.

$$15x = 16x - 78$$ Complete the multiplications. The fractions are now cleared.

At this point, we have an equation similar to those we have previously solved. Collect the variable terms on one side and the constants on the other side.

$$15x - 16x = 16x - 16x - 78$$ Subtract 16x from both sides to get the variable terms on the left.

$$-x = -78$$ Simplify.

> We're not finished. A negative sign should not precede x.

Isolate x by multiplying or dividing both sides of this equation by -1.

$$\frac{-x}{-1} = \frac{-78}{-1}$$ Divide both sides by -1.

$$x = 78$$ Simplify.

Check the proposed solution. Substitute 78 for x in the original equation. You should obtain $117 = 117$. This true statement verifies that the solution set is $\{78\}$. ○

CHECK POINT 5 Solve the equation: $\dfrac{x}{4} = \dfrac{2x}{3} + \dfrac{5}{6}$.

Sense of Humor and Depression

Group's Average Level of Depression in Response to Negative Life Events

Low-Humor Group

High-Humor Group

Low   Average   High

Intensity of Negative Life Event

FIGURE 6.2 (repeated)

EXAMPLE 6	AN APPLICATION: RESPONDING TO NEGATIVE LIFE EVENTS

In the section opener, we used two formulas to model the level of depression, D, in response to the intensity of a negative life event, x, from 1, low, to 10, high:

Low-Humor Group	High-Humor Group
$D = \dfrac{10}{9}x + \dfrac{53}{9}$	$D = \dfrac{1}{9}x + \dfrac{26}{9}$.

If the high-humor group averages a level of depression of 3.5, or $\frac{7}{2}$, in response to a negative life event, what is the intensity of that event? How is the solution shown on the red line graph in Figure 6.2?

SOLUTION We are interested in the intensity of a negative life event with an average level of depression of $\frac{7}{2}$ for the high-humor group. We substitute $\frac{7}{2}$ for D in the high-humor model and solve for x, the intensity of the negative life event.

$$D = \frac{1}{9}x + \frac{26}{9}$$
This is the given formula for the high-humor group.

$$\frac{7}{2} = \frac{1}{9}x + \frac{26}{9}$$
Replace D with $\frac{7}{2}$.

$$18 \cdot \frac{7}{2} = 18\left(\frac{1}{9}x + \frac{26}{9}\right)$$
Multiply both sides by 18, the least common denominator.

$$18 \cdot \frac{7}{2} = 18 \cdot \frac{1}{9}x + 18 \cdot \frac{26}{9}$$
Use the distributive property.

$$\overset{9}{\cancel{18}} \cdot \frac{7}{\underset{1}{\cancel{2}}} = \overset{2}{\cancel{18}} \cdot \frac{1}{\underset{1}{\cancel{9}}}x + \overset{2}{\cancel{18}} \cdot \frac{26}{\underset{1}{\cancel{9}}}$$
Divide out common factors in the multiplications.

$$63 = 2x + 52$$
Complete the multiplications. The fractions are now cleared.

$$63 - 52 = 2x + 52 - 52$$
Subtract 52 from both sides to get constants on the left.

$$11 = 2x$$
Simplify.

$$\frac{11}{2} = \frac{2x}{2}$$
Divide both sides by 2.

$$\frac{11}{2} = x$$
Simplify.

FIGURE 6.3

The formula indicates that if the high-humor group averages a level of depression of 3.5 in response to a negative life event, the intensity of that event is $\frac{11}{2}$, or 5.5. This is illustrated on the line graph for the high-humor group in Figure 6.3.

CHECK POINT 6 Use the model for the low-humor group given in Example 6 on the previous page to solve this problem. If the low-humor group averages a level of depression of 10 in response to a negative life event, what is the intensity of that event? How is the solution shown on the blue line graph in Figure 6.2?

Solving a Formula for One of Its Variables

3 Solve a formula for a variable.

We know that solving an equation is the process of finding the number (or numbers) that make the equation a true statement. All of the equations we have solved contained only one letter, x.

By contrast, formulas contain two or more letters, representing two or more variables. An example is the formula for the perimeter of a rectangle:

$$2l + 2w = P.$$
A rectangle's perimeter is the sum of twice its length and twice its width.

We say that this formula is solved for the variable P because P is alone on one side of the equation and the other side does not contain a P.

Solving a formula for a variable means rewriting the formula so that the variable is isolated on one side of the equation. It does not mean obtaining a numerical value for that variable.

To solve a formula for one of its variables, treat that variable as if it were the only variable in the equation. Think of the other variables as if they were numbers. Isolate all terms with the specified variable on one side of the equation and all terms without the specified variable on the other side. Then divide both sides by the same nonzero quantity to get the specified variable alone. The next example shows how to do this.

EXAMPLE 7 SOLVING A FORMULA FOR A VARIABLE

Solve the formula $2l + 2w = P$ for l.

SOLUTION First, isolate $2l$ on the left by subtracting $2w$ from both sides. Then solve for l by dividing both sides by 2.

We need to isolate l.

$2l + 2w = P$	This is the given formula.
$2l + 2w - 2w = P - 2w$	Isolate 2l by subtracting 2w from both sides.
$2l = P - 2w$	Simplify.
$\dfrac{2l}{2} = \dfrac{P - 2w}{2}$	Solve for l by dividing both sides by 2.
$l = \dfrac{P - 2w}{2}$	Simplify.

 7 Solve the formula $2l + 2w = P$ for w.

EXAMPLE 8 SOLVING A FORMULA FOR A VARIABLE

The total price of an article purchased on a monthly deferred payment plan is described by the following formula:

$$T = D + pm.$$

In this formula, T is the total price, D is the down payment, p is the monthly payment, and m is the number of months one pays. Solve the formula for p.

SOLUTION First, isolate pm on the right by subtracting D from both sides. Then, isolate p from pm by dividing both sides of the formula by m.

We need to isolate p.

$T = D + pm$	This is the given formula. We want p alone.
$T - D = D - D + pm$	Isolate pm by subtracting D from both sides.
$T - D = pm$	Simplify.
$\dfrac{T - D}{m} = \dfrac{pm}{m}$	Now isolate p by dividing both sides by m.
$\dfrac{T - D}{m} = p$	Simplify: $\dfrac{pm}{m} = \dfrac{p\cancel{m}}{\cancel{m}} = \dfrac{p}{1} = p$.

 8 Solve the formula $T = D + pm$ for m.

4 Identify equations with no solution or infinitely many solutions.

Linear Equations with No Solution or Infinitely Many Solutions

Thus far, each equation that we have solved has had a single solution. However, some equations are not true for even one real number. By contrast, other equations are true for all real numbers.

If you attempt to solve an equation with no solution, you will eliminate the variable and obtain a false statement, such as $2 = 5$. If you attempt to solve an equation that is true for every real number, you will eliminate the variable and obtain a true statement, such as $4 = 4$.

EXAMPLE 9   SOLVING A LINEAR EQUATION

Solve: $2x + 6 = 2(x + 4)$.

SOLUTION

$$2x + 6 = 2(x + 4) \qquad \text{This is the given equation.}$$
$$2x + 6 = 2x + 8 \qquad \text{Use the distributive property.}$$
$$2x + 6 - 2x = 2x + 8 - 2x \qquad \text{Subtract 2x from both sides.}$$

Keep reading. 6 = 8 is not the solution. $\quad 6 = 8 \qquad$ Simplify.

The original equation, $2x + 6 = 2(x + 4)$, is equivalent to the statement $6 = 8$, which is false for every value of x. The equation has no solution. The solution set is $\emptyset$, the empty set.

 9 Solve: $3x + 7 = 3(x + 1)$.

EXAMPLE 10   SOLVING A LINEAR EQUATION

Solve: $4x + 6 = 6(x + 1) - 2x$.

SOLUTION

$$4x + 6 = 6(x + 1) - 2x \qquad \text{This is the given equation.}$$
$$4x + 6 = 6x + 6 - 2x \qquad \text{Apply the distributive property on the right side.}$$
$$4x + 6 = 4x + 6 \qquad \text{Combine like terms on the right side: } 6x - 2x = 4x.$$

Can you see that the equation $4x + 6 = 4x + 6$ is true for every value of x? Let's continue solving the equation by subtracting $4x$ from both sides.

$$4x - 4x + 6 = 4x - 4x + 6$$

Keep reading. 6 = 6 is not the solution. $\quad 6 = 6$

The original equation is equivalent to the statement $6 = 6$, which is true for every value of x. Thus, the solution set consists of the set of all real numbers, expressed in set-builder notation as $\{x \mid x \text{ is a real number}\}$. Try substituting any real number of your choice for x in the original equation. You will obtain a true statement.

STUDY TIP

Because of the fundamental role that sets play in mathematics, it's a good idea to use set notation to express an equation's solution set. If a linear equation has no solution, its solution set is $\emptyset$, the empty set. If a linear equation with variable x has infinitely many solutions, its solution set is $\{x \mid x \text{ is a real number}\}$.

 10 Solve: $7x + 9 = 9(x + 1) - 2x$.

EXERCISE SET 6.2 ●●●●●●

• Practice Exercises

In Exercises 1–42, solve each equation. Be sure to check your proposed solution by substituting it for the variable in the given equation.

1. $x - 7 = 3$

2. $x - 3 = -17$

3. $x + 5 = -12$

4. $x + 12 = -14$

5. $\dfrac{x}{3} = 4$

6. $\dfrac{x}{5} = 3$

7. $5x = 45$

8. $6x = 18$

9. $8x = -24$

10. $5x = -25$

11. $-8x = 2$

12. $-6x = 3$

13. $5x + 3 = 18$

14. $3x + 8 = 50$

15. $6x - 3 = 63$

16. $5x - 8 = 72$

17. $4x - 14 = -82$

18. $9x - 14 = -77$

19. $14 - 5x = -41$

20. $25 - 6x = -83$

21. $9(5x - 2) = 45$

22. $10(3x + 2) = 70$

23. $5x - (2x - 10) = 35$

24. $11x - (6x - 5) = 40$

25. $3x + 5 = 2x + 13$

26. $2x - 7 = 6 + x$

27. $8x - 2 = 7x - 5$

28. $13x + 14 = -5 + 12x$

29. $7x + 4 = x + 16$

30. $8x + 1 = x + 43$

31. $8y - 3 = 11y + 9$

32. $5y - 2 = 9y + 2$

33. $2(4 - 3x) = 2(2x + 5)$

34. $3(5 - x) = 4(2x + 1)$

35. $8(y + 2) = 2(3y + 4)$

36. $3(3y - 1) = 4(3 + 3y)$

37. $3(x + 1) = 7(x - 2) - 3$

38. $5x - 4(x + 9) = 2x - 3$

39. $5(2x - 8) - 2 = 5(x - 3) + 3$

40. $7(3x - 2) + 5 = 6(2x - 1) + 24$

41. $5(x - 2) - 2(2x + 1) = 2 + 5x$

42. $2(5x + 4) + 3(2x + 11) = 4x - 19$

Solve and check each equation in Exercises 43–50. Begin your work by rewriting each equation without fractions.

43. $\dfrac{x}{3} + \dfrac{x}{2} = \dfrac{5}{6}$

44. $\dfrac{x}{4} - 1 = \dfrac{x}{5}$

45. $\dfrac{x}{2} = 20 - \dfrac{x}{3}$

46. $\dfrac{x}{5} - \dfrac{1}{2} = \dfrac{x}{6}$

47. $\dfrac{3y}{4} - 3 = \dfrac{y}{2} + 2$

48. $y + \dfrac{1}{2} = 1 - \dfrac{y}{3}$

49. $\dfrac{3x}{5} - x = \dfrac{x}{10} - \dfrac{5}{2}$

50. $2x - \dfrac{2x}{7} = \dfrac{x}{2} + \dfrac{17}{2}$

In Exercises 51–68, solve each formula for the specified variable. Do you recognize the formula? If so, what does it describe?

51. $A = LW$ for L

52. $D = RT$ for R

53. $A = \frac{1}{2}bh$ for b

54. $V = \frac{1}{3}Bh$ for B

55. $I = Prt$ for P

56. $C = 2\pi r$ for r

57. $E = mc^2$ for m

58. $V = \pi r^2 h$ for h

59. $y = mx + b$ for m

60. $P = C + MC$ for M

61. $A = \frac{1}{2}(a + b)$ for a

62. $A = \frac{1}{2}(a + b)$ for b

63. $S = P + Prt$ for r

64. $S = P + Prt$ for t

65. $Ax + By = C$ for x

66. $Ax + By = C$ for y

67. $a_n = a_1 + (n - 1)d$ for n

68. $a_n = a_1 + (n - 1)d$ for d

In Exercises 69–84, solve each equation. Use set notation to express solution sets for equations with no solution or equations that are true for all real numbers.

69. $3x - 7 = 3(x + 1)$

70. $2(x - 5) = 2x + 10$

71. $2(x + 4) = 4x + 5 - 2x + 3$

72. $3(x - 1) = 8x + 6 - 5x - 9$

73. $7 + 2(3x - 5) = 8 - 3(2x + 1)$

74. $2 + 3(2x - 7) = 9 - 4(3x + 1)$

75. $4x + 1 - 5x = 5 - (x + 4)$

76. $5x - 5 = 3x - 7 + 2(x + 1)$

77. $4(x + 2) + 1 = 7x - 3(x - 2)$

78. $5x - 3(x + 1) = 2(x + 3) - 5$

79. $3 - x = 2x + 3$

80. $5 - x = 4x + 5$

81. $\dfrac{x}{3} + 2 = \dfrac{x}{3}$

82. $\dfrac{x}{4} + 3 = \dfrac{x}{4}$

83. $\dfrac{x}{2} - \dfrac{x}{4} + 4 = x + 4$

84. $\dfrac{x}{2} + \dfrac{2x}{3} + 3 = x + 3$

• Practice Plus

85. Evaluate $x^2 - x$ for the value of x satisfying $4(x - 2) + 2 = 4x - 2(2 - x)$.

86. Evaluate $x^2 - x$ for the value of x satisfying $2(x - 6) = 3x + 2(2x - 1)$.

87. Evaluate $x^2 - (xy - y)$ for x satisfying $\dfrac{x}{5} - 2 = \dfrac{x}{3}$ and y satisfying $-2y - 10 = 5y + 18$.

88. Evaluate $x^2 - (xy - y)$ for x satisfying $\dfrac{3x}{2} + \dfrac{3x}{4} = \dfrac{x}{4} - 4$ and y satisfying $5 - y = 7(y + 4) + 1$.

In Exercises 89–96, solve each equation.

89. $[(3 + 6)^2 \div 3] \cdot 4 = -54x$

90. $2^3 - [4(5 - 3)^3] = -8x$

91. $5 - 12x = 8 - 7x - [6 \div 3(2 + 5^3) + 5x]$

92. $2(5x + 58) = 10x + 4(21 \div 3.5 - 11)$

93. $0.7x + 0.4(20) = 0.5(x + 20)$

94. $0.5(x + 2) = 0.1 + 3(0.1x + 0.3)$

95. $4x + 13 - \{2x - [4(x - 3) - 5]\} = 2(x - 6)$

96. $-2\{7 - [4 - 2(1 - x) + 3]\} = 10 - [4x - 2(x - 3)]$

• Application Exercises

The bar graph shows the average amount of time, in hours, that each American aged 12 or older spent playing video games from 2001 through 2006.

Hours Spent per Person Playing Video Games

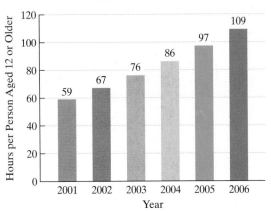

Source: U.S. Census Bureau

The data can be modeled by

$$H = 10x + 59,$$

where H is the annual hours spent playing video games per person x years after 2001. Use this formula to solve Exercises 97–98.

97. If trends continue, in which year will Americans average 179 hours per person playing video games?

98. If trends continue, in which year will Americans average 199 hours per person playing video games?

The formula

$$\frac{n}{2} + 80 = 2T$$

models the relationship between temperature, T, in degrees Fahrenheit, and the number of cricket chirps per minute, n, for the snow tree cricket. Use this mathematical model to solve Exercises 99–100.

99. Find the number of chirps per minute at a temperature of 70°F.

100. Find the number of chirps per minute at a temperature of 80°F.

The formula

$$p = 15 + \frac{5d}{11}$$

describes the pressure of sea water, p, in pounds per square foot, at a depth of d feet below the surface. Use the formula to solve Exercises 101–102.

101. The record depth for breath-held diving, by Francisco Ferreras (Cuba) off Grand Bahama Island, on November 14, 1993, involved pressure of 201 pounds per square foot. To what depth did Ferreras descend on this ill-advised venture? (He was underwater for 2 minutes and 9 seconds!)

102. At what depth is the pressure 20 pounds per square foot?

The line graphs show the average writing test scores for U.S. high school seniors. The graphs reflect general trends in which boys continue to fall behind girls in reading and writing proficiency, with fewer boys than girls going to college.

Average Writing Test Scores for High School Seniors

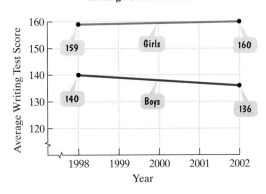

Source: Newsweek, January 30, 2006

The data can be modeled by the following formulas:

Girls $\quad W = \dfrac{1}{4}x + 159$ **Boys** $\quad W = -x + 140.$

In each formula, W is the average writing test score x years after 1998. Use the formulas to solve Exercises 103–108.

103. If current trends continue, when will the average test score for boys be 127?

104. If current trends continue, when will the average test score for boys be 126?

105. If current trends continue, when will the average test score for girls be 163?

106. If current trends continue, when will the average test score for girls be 164?

107. If current trends continue, when will the average test score for girls be 49 points higher than for boys?

108. If current trends continue, when will the average test score for girls be 54 points higher than for boys?

• Writing in Mathematics

109. What is the solution set of an equation?

110. State the addition property of equality and give an example.

111. State the multiplication property of equality and give an example.

112. How do you know if a linear equation has one solution, no solution, or infinitely many solutions?

113. What is the difference between solving an equation such as $2(x - 4) + 5x = 34$ and simplifying an algebraic expression such as $2(x - 4) + 5x$? If there is a difference, which topic should be taught first? Why?

114. Suppose that you solve $\frac{x}{5} - \frac{x}{2} = 1$ by multiplying both sides by 20, rather than the least common denominator of 5 and 2 (namely, 10). Describe what happens. If you get the correct solution, why do you think we clear the equation of fractions by multiplying by the *least* common denominator?

115. Suppose you are an algebra teacher grading the following solution on an examination:

$$\text{Solve: } -3(x - 6) = 2 - x.$$
$$\text{Solution: } -3x - 18 = 2 - x$$
$$-2x - 18 = 2$$
$$-2x = -16$$
$$x = 8.$$

You should note that 8 checks, and the solution set is {8}. The student who worked the problem therefore wants full credit. Can you find any errors in the solution? If full credit is 10 points, how many points should you give the student? Justify your position.

116. Although the formulas in Example 6 on page 317 are correct, some people object to representing the variables with numbers, such as a 1-to-10 scale for the intensity of a negative life event. What might be their objection to quantifying the variables in this situation?

● **Critical Thinking Exercises**

117. Which one of the following is true?

  a. If $3x + 7 = 0$, then $x = \frac{7}{3}$.

  b. Solving $A = LW$ for W gives $W = \frac{L}{A}$.

  c. The equation $6x = 0$ has exactly one solution.

  d. The final step in solving $x - b = 6x - c$ for x is $x = 6x - c + b$.

118. Write three equations whose solution set is {5}.

119. If x represents a number, write an English sentence about the number that results in an equation with no solution.

120. A woman's height, h, is related to the length of the femur, f (the bone from the knee to the hip socket), by the formula $f = 0.432h - 10.44$. Both h and f are measured in inches. A partial skeleton is found of a woman in which the femur is 16 inches long. Police find the skeleton in an area where a woman slightly over 5 feet tall has been missing for over a year. Can the partial skeleton be that of the missing woman? Explain.

Femur

f in.

h in.

SECTION 6.3 ● APPLICATIONS OF LINEAR EQUATIONS

OBJECTIVE

1. Use linear equations to solve problems.

The human race is undeniably becoming a faster race. Since the beginning of the past century, track-and-field records have fallen in everything from sprints to miles to marathons. The performance arc is clearly rising, but no one knows how much higher it can climb. At some point, even the best-trained body simply has to up and quit. The question is, just where is that point, and is it possible for athletes, trainers, and genetic engineers to push it higher? In this section, you will learn a problem-solving strategy that uses linear equations to determine if anyone will ever run a 3-minute mile.

1 | Use linear equations to solve problems.

Problem Solving with Linear Equations

We have seen that a model is a mathematical representation of a real-world situation. In this section, we will be solving problems that are presented in English. This means that we must obtain models by translating from the ordinary language of English into the language of algebraic equations. To translate, however, we must understand the English prose and be familiar with the forms of algebraic language. Here are some general steps we will follow in solving word problems:

> **STRATEGY FOR SOLVING WORD PROBLEMS**
>
> **Step 1.** Read the problem carefully at least twice. Attempt to state the problem in your own words and state what the problem is looking for. Let x (or any variable) represent one of the quantities in the problem.
>
> **Step 2.** If necessary, write expressions for any other unknown quantities in the problem in terms of x.
>
> **Step 3.** Write an equation in x that models the verbal conditions of the problem.
>
> **Step 4.** Solve the equation and answer the problem's question.
>
> **Step 5.** Check the solution *in the original wording* of the problem, not in the equation obtained from the words.

The most difficult step in this process is step 3 because it involves translating verbal conditions into an algebraic equation. Translations of some commonly used English phrases are listed in Table 6.2. We choose to use x to represent the variable, but we can use any letter.

STUDY TIP

Cover the right column in Table 6.2 with a sheet of paper and attempt to formulate the algebraic expression in the column on your own. Then slide the paper down and check your answer. Work through the entire table in this manner.

TABLE 6.2 ALGEBRAIC TRANSLATIONS OF ENGLISH PHRASES

English Phrase	Algebraic Expression
Addition	
The sum of a number and 7	$x + 7$
Five more than a number; a number plus 5	$x + 5$
A number increased by 6; 6 added to a number	$x + 6$
Subtraction	
A number minus 4	$x - 4$
A number decreased by 5	$x - 5$
A number subtracted from 8	$8 - x$
The difference between a number and 6	$x - 6$
The difference between 6 and a number	$6 - x$
Seven less than a number	$x - 7$
Seven minus a number	$7 - x$
Nine fewer than a number	$x - 9$
Multiplication	
Five times a number	$5x$
The product of 3 and a number	$3x$
Two-thirds of a number (used with fractions)	$\dfrac{2}{3}x$
Seventy-five percent of a number (used with decimals)	$0.75x$
Thirteen multiplied by a number	$13x$
A number multiplied by 13	$13x$
Twice a number	$2x$
Division	
A number divided by 3	$\dfrac{x}{3}$
The quotient of 7 and a number	$\dfrac{7}{x}$
The quotient of a number and 7	$\dfrac{x}{7}$
The reciprocal of a number	$\dfrac{1}{x}$
More than one operation	
The sum of twice a number and 7	$2x + 7$
Twice the sum of a number and 7	$2(x + 7)$
Three times the sum of 1 and twice a number	$3(1 + 2x)$
Nine subtracted from 8 times a number	$8x - 9$
Twenty-five percent of the sum of 3 times a number and 14	$0.25(3x + 14)$
Seven times a number, increased by 24	$7x + 24$
Seven times the sum of a number and 24	$7(x + 24)$

STUDY TIP

Here are three similar English phrases that have very different translations:

7 minus 10: $7 - 10$

7 less than 10: $10 - 7$

7 is less than 10: $7 < 10$.

Think carefully about what is expressed in English before you translate into the language of algebra.

EXAMPLE 1 SOLVING A WORD PROBLEM

Nine subtracted from eight times a number is 39. Find the number.

SOLUTION

Step 1. Let x represent one of the quantities. Because we are asked to find a number, let

$$x = \text{the number.}$$

Step 2. Represent other quantities in terms of x. There are no other unknown quantities to find, so we can skip this step.

Step 3. Write an equation in x that models the conditions.

$$8x \quad - \quad 9 \qquad = \qquad 39$$

Step 4. Solve the equation and answer the question.

$$8x - 9 = 39 \qquad \text{This is the equation that models the problem's conditions.}$$

$$8x - 9 + 9 = 39 + 9 \qquad \text{Add 9 to both sides.}$$

$$8x = 48 \qquad \text{Simplify.}$$

$$\frac{8x}{8} = \frac{48}{8} \qquad \text{Divide both sides by 8.}$$

$$x = 6 \qquad \text{Simplify.}$$

The number is 6.

Step 5. Check the proposed solution in the original wording of the problem. "Nine subtracted from eight times a number is 39." The proposed number is 6. Eight times 6 is $8 \cdot 6$, or 48. Nine subtracted from 48 is $48 - 9$, or 39. The proposed solution checks in the problem's wording, verifying that the number is 6.

 Four subtracted from six times a number is 68. Find the number.

EXAMPLE 2 WILL ANYONE EVER RUN A THREE-MINUTE MILE?

One yardstick for measuring how steadily—if slowly—athletic performance has improved is the mile run. In 1923, the record for the mile was a comparatively sleepy 4 minutes, 10.4 seconds. In 1954, Roger Bannister of Britain cracked the 4-minute mark, coming in at 3 minutes, 59.4 seconds. In the half-century since, about 0.3 second per year has been shaved off Bannister's record. If this trend continues, by which year will someone run a 3-minute mile?

SOLUTION In solving this problem, we will express time for the mile run in seconds. Our interest is in a time of 3 minutes, or 180 seconds.

Step 1. Let x represent one of the quantities. Here is the critical information in the problem:

- In 1954, the record was 3 minutes, 59.4 seconds, or 239.4 seconds.
- The record has decreased by 0.3 second per year since then.

We are interested in when the record will be 180 seconds. Let

$$x = \text{the number of years after 1954 when someone will run a 3-minute mile.}$$

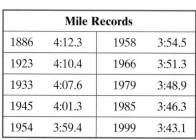

Mile Records			
1886	4:12.3	1958	3:54.5
1923	4:10.4	1966	3:51.3
1933	4:07.6	1979	3:48.9
1945	4:01.3	1985	3:46.3
1954	3:59.4	1999	3:43.1

Source: U.S.A. Track and Field

A Poky Species

For a species that prides itself on its athletic prowess, human beings are a pretty poky group. Lions can sprint at up to 50 miles per hour; cheetahs move even faster, flooring it to a sizzling 70 miles per hour. But most humans—with our willowy spines and awkward, upright gait—would have trouble cracking 20 miles per hour with a tail wind, a flat track, and a good pair of running shoes.

Step 2. Represent other quantities in terms of *x*. There are no other unknown quantities to find, so we can skip this step.

Step 3. Write an equation in *x* that models the conditions.

The 1954 record time	decreased by	0.3 second per year for *x* years	equals	the 3-minute, or 180-second, mile.
239.4	−	0.3*x*	=	180

Step 4. Solve the equation and answer the question.

$$239.4 - 0.3x = 180$$ This is the equation that models the problem's conditions.

$$239.4 - 239.4 - 0.3x = 180 - 239.4$$ Subtract 239.4 from both sides.

$$-0.3x = -59.4$$ Simplify.

$$\frac{-0.3x}{-0.3} = \frac{-59.4}{-0.3}$$ Divide both sides by −0.3.

$$x = 198$$ Simplify.

Using current trends, 198 years (gasp!) after 1954, or in 2152, someone will run a 3-minute mile.

Step 5. Check the proposed solution in the original wording of the problem. The problem states that the record time should be 180 seconds. Do we obtain 180 seconds if we decrease the 1954 record time, 239.4 seconds, by 0.3 second per year for 198 years, our proposed solution?

$$239.4 - 0.3(198) = 239.4 - 59.4 = 180$$

This verifies that, using current trends, the 3-minute mile will be run 198 years after 1954. ○

CHECK POINT 2   Got organic milk? Although organic milk accounts for only 1.2% of the market, consumption is increasing. In 2004, Americans purchased 40.7 million gallons of organic milk, increasing at a rate of 5.6 million gallons per year. If this trend continues, when will Americans purchase 79.9 million gallons of organic milk? (*Source:* National Dairy Council)

EXAMPLE 3   WALK IT OFF

Experts concerned with fitness and health suggest that we should walk 10,000 steps per day, about 5 miles. Depending on stride length, each mile ranges between 2000 and 2500 steps. The graph in Figure 6.4 shows the number of steps it takes to burn off various foods. (The data are based on a body weight of 150 to 165 pounds.)

The number of steps needed to burn off a cheeseburger exceeds the number needed to burn off a 12-ounce soda by 4140. The number needed to burn off a doughnut exceeds the number needed to burn off a 12-ounce soda by 2300. If you chow down a cheeseburger, doughnut, and 12-ounce soda, a 16,790-step walk is needed to burn off the calories (and perhaps alleviate the guilt). Determine the number of steps it takes to burn off a cheeseburger, a doughnut, and a 12-ounce soda.

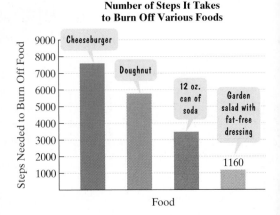

FIGURE 6.4
Source: The Step Diet Book

SOLUTION

Step 1. Let x represent one of the quantities. We know something about the number of steps needed to burn off a cheeseburger and a doughnut: The numbers exceed that of a 12-ounce soda by 4140 and 2300, respectively. We will let

x = the number of steps needed to burn off a 12-ounce soda.

Step 2. Represent other quantities in terms of x. Because the number of steps needed to burn off a cheeseburger exceeds the number needed to burn off a 12-ounce soda by 4140, let

$x + 4140$ = the number of steps needed to burn off a cheeseburger.

Because the number of steps needed to burn off a doughnut exceeds the number needed to burn off a 12-ounce soda by 2300, let

$x + 2300$ = the number of steps needed to burn off a doughnut.

Step 3. Write an equation in x that models the conditions. A 16,790-step walk is needed to burn off a "meal" consisting of a cheeseburger, a doughnut, and a 12-ounce soda.

Steps needed to burn off cheeseburger	plus	steps needed to burn off doughnut	plus	steps needed to burn off soda	equals	16,790.
$(x + 4140)$	$+$	$(x + 2300)$	$+$	x	$=$	$16{,}790$

Step 4. Solve the equation and answer the question.

$(x + 4140) + (x + 2300) + x = 16{,}790$ This is the equation that models the problem's conditions.

$3x + 6440 = 16{,}790$ Remove parentheses, regroup, and combine like terms.

$3x = 10{,}350$ Subtract 6440 from both sides.

$x = 3450$ Divide both sides by 3.

Thus,

the number of steps needed to burn off a 12-ounce soda = x = 3450.

the number of steps needed to burn off a cheeseburger

= $x + 4140 = 3450 + 4140 = 7590$.

the number of steps needed to burn off a doughnut

= $x + 2300 = 3450 + 2300 = 5750$.

It takes 7590 steps to burn off a cheeseburger, 5750 steps to burn off a doughnut, and 3450 steps to burn off a 12-ounce soda.

Step 5. Check the proposed solution in the original wording of the problem. The problem states that a 16,790-step walk is needed to burn off the calories in the three foods combined. By adding 7590, 5750, and 3450, the numbers that we found for each of the foods, we obtain

$$7590 + 5750 + 3450 = 16{,}790,$$

as specified by the problem's conditions.

STUDY TIP

Modeling with the word *exceeds* can be a bit tricky. It's helpful to identify the smaller quantity. Then add to this quantity to represent the larger quantity. For example, suppose that Tim's height exceeds Tom's height by a inches. Tom is the shorter person. If Tom's height is represented by x, then Tim's height is represented by $x + a$.

CHECK POINT 3 Basketball, bicycle riding, and football are the three sports and recreational activities in the United States with the greatest number of medically treated injuries. In 2004, the number of injuries from basketball exceeded those from football by 0.6 million. The number of injuries from bicycling exceeded those from football by 0.3 million. Combined, basketball, bicycling, and football accounted for 3.9 million injuries. Determine the number of medically treated injuries from each of these recreational activities in 2004.

(*Source:* U.S. Consumer Product Safety Commission)

STUDY TIP

There is great value in reasoning through a word problem. This value comes from the problem-solving skills that are attained and is often more important than the specific problem or its solution.

EXAMPLE 4   SELECTING A LONG-DISTANCE CARRIER

You are choosing between two long-distance telephone plans. Plan A has a monthly fee of $20 with a charge of $0.05 per minute for all long-distance calls. Plan B has a monthly fee of $5 with a charge of $0.10 per minute for all long-distance calls. For how many minutes of long-distance calls will the costs for the two plans be the same?

SOLUTION

Step 1. Let x represent one of the quantities. Let

$$x = \text{the number of minutes of long-distance calls}$$
$$\text{for which the two plans cost the same.}$$

Step 2. Represent other unknown quantities in terms of x. There are no other unknown quantities, so we can skip this step.

Step 3. Write an equation in x that models the conditions. The monthly cost for plan A is the monthly fee, $20, plus the per minute charge, $0.05, times the number of minutes of long-distance calls, x. The monthly cost for plan B is the monthly fee, $5, plus the per-minute charge, $0.10, times the number of minutes of long-distance calls, x.

The monthly cost for plan A	must equal	the monthly cost for plan B.
$20 + 0.05x$	$=$	$5 + 0.10x$

Step 4. Solve the equation and answer the question.

$$20 + 0.05x = 5 + 0.10x \qquad \text{This is the equation that models the problem's conditions.}$$
$$20 = 5 + 0.05x \qquad \text{Subtract } 0.05x \text{ from both sides.}$$
$$15 = 0.05x \qquad \text{Subtract 5 from both sides.}$$
$$\frac{15}{0.05} = \frac{0.05x}{0.05} \qquad \text{Divide both sides by 0.05.}$$
$$300 = x \qquad \text{Simplify.}$$

Because x represents the number of minutes of long-distance calls for which the two plans cost the same, the costs will be the same with 300 minutes of long-distance calls.

Step 5. Check the proposed solution in the original wording of the problem. The problem states that the costs for the two plans should be the same. Let's see if they are with 300 minutes of long-distance calls.

$$\text{Cost for plan A} = \$20 + \$0.05(300) = \$20 + \$15 = \$35$$

Monthly fee	Per-minute charge

$$\text{Cost for plan B} = \$5 + \$0.10(300) = \$5 + \$30 = \$35$$

With 300 minutes, or 5 hours, of long-distance calls, both plans cost $35 for the month. Thus, the proposed solution, 300 minutes, satisfies the problem's conditions.   ○

CHECK POINT 4   You are choosing between two long-distance telephone plans. Plan A has a monthly fee of $15 with a charge of $0.08 per minute for all long-distance calls. Plan B has a monthly fee of $3 with a charge of $0.12 per minute for all long-distance calls. For how many minutes of long-distance calls will the costs for the two plans be the same?

EXERCISE SET 6.3 ●●●●●●

• Practice and Application Exercises

In Exercises 1–24, use the five-step strategy to solve each problem.

1. When five times a number is decreased by 4, the result is 26. What is the number?

2. When two times a number is decreased by 3, the result is 11. What is the number?

3. One number exceeds another by 26. The sum of the numbers is 64. What are the numbers?

4. One number exceeds another by 24. The sum of the numbers is 58. What are the numbers?

According to one mathematical model, the average life expectancy for American men born in 1900 was 55 years. Life expectancy has increased by about 0.2 year for each birth year after 1900. Use this information to solve Exercises 5–6.

5. If this trend continues, for which birth year will the average life expectancy be 85 years?

6. If this trend continues, for which birth year will the average life expectancy be 91 years?

The graph shows the number of Americans without health insurance from 2000 through 2003.

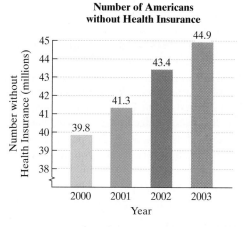

Number of Americans without Health Insurance

Source: U.S. Census Bureau

In 2000, there were 39.8 million Americans without health insurance. This number has increased at an average rate of 1.7 million people per year. Use this description to solve Exercises 7–8.

7. Determine when the number of Americans without health insurance will exceed the number in 2003 by 8.5 million.

8. Determine when the number of Americans without health insurance will exceed the number in 2003 by 10.2 million.

9. In 2000, the population of Greece was 10,600,000, with projections of a population decrease of 28,000 people per year. In the same year, the population of Belgium was 10,200,000, with projections of a population decrease of 12,000 people per year. (*Source*: United Nations) According to these projections, when will the two countries have the same population? What will be the population at that time?

10. In 2007, there were 13,300 students at college A, with a projected enrollment increase of 1000 students per year. In the same year, there were 26,800 students at college B, with a projected enrollment decline of 500 students per year. According to these projections, when will the colleges have the same enrollment? What will be the enrollment in each college at that time?

11. Each day, the number of births in the world exceeds the number of deaths by 229 thousand. The combined number of births and deaths is 521 thousand. Determine the number of births and the number of deaths per day.

Daily Growth of World Population

Source: "Population Update" 2000

12. The number of pages in the U.S. tax code exceeds the number of pages in the King James Bible by 18,528. The combined number of pages in the U.S. tax code and the King James Bible is 21,472. Determine the number of pages in each. (*Sources*: Amazon.com and Internal Revenue Service)

13. The bar graph shows the breakdown of the 7485 hate crimes reported in the United States in 2004. The number of hate crimes based on race exceeded three times the number based on sexual orientation by 127. Find the number of hate crimes reported in the United States in 2004 based on race and based on sexual orientation.

Hate Crimes in the U.S.

Source: FBI.

14. The bar graph on the next page shows the percentage of global energy used by the countries consuming the most energy. The percentage of global energy used by China exceeds Russia by 6% and the percentage of global energy used by the United States exceeds Russia by 16.4%.

Combined, the United States, China, and Russia consume 40.4% of the world's energy. Determine the percentage of global energy used by each country.

Countries Using the Most Energy

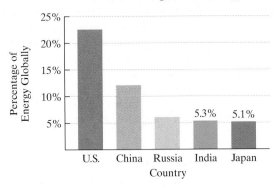

Source: World Bank Group

15. You are choosing between two health club plans. Plan A offers membership for a fee of $40 plus a monthly fee of $25. Plan B offers membership for a fee of $15 plus a monthly fee of $30. After how many months will the total cost for each plan be the same? What will be the total cost for each plan?

16. Video Store A charges $9 to rent a video game for one week. Although only members can rent from the store, membership is free. Video Store B charges only $4 to rent a video game for one week. Only members can rent from the store and membership is $50 per year. After how many video-game rentals will the total amount spent at each store be the same? What will be the total amount spent at each store?

17. The bus fare in a city is $1.25. People who use the bus have the option of purchasing a monthly coupon book for $15.00. With the coupon book, the fare is reduced to $0.75. Determine the number of times in a month the bus must be used so that the total monthly cost without the coupon book is the same as the total monthly cost with the coupon book.

18. A coupon book for a bridge costs $30 per month. The toll for the bridge is normally $5.00, but it is reduced to $3.50 for people who have purchased the coupon book. Determine the number of times in a month the bridge must be crossed so that the total monthly cost without the coupon book is the same as the total monthly cost with the coupon book.

19. You are choosing between two plans at a discount warehouse. Plan A offers an annual membership fee of $100 and you pay 80% of the manufacturer's recommended list price. Plan B offers an annual membership fee of $40 and you pay 90% of the manufacturer's recommended list price. How many dollars of merchandise would you have to purchase in a year to pay the same amount under both plans? What will be the cost for each plan?

20. You are choosing between two plans at a discount warehouse. Plan A offers an annual membership fee of $300 and you pay 70% of the manufacturer's recommended list price. Plan B offers an annual membership fee of $40 and you pay 90% of the manufacturer's recommended list

price. How many dollars of merchandise would you have to purchase in a year to pay the same amount under both plans? What will be the cost for each plan?

21. An automobile repair shop charged a customer $448, listing $63 for parts and the remainder for labor. If the cost of labor is $35 per hour, how many hours of labor did it take to repair the car?

22. A repair bill on a sailboat came to $1603, including $532 for parts and the remainder for labor. If the cost of labor is $63 per hour, how many hours of labor did it take to repair the sailboat?

23. A job pays an annual salary of $33,150, which includes a holiday bonus of $750. If paychecks are issued twice a month, what is the gross amount for each paycheck?

24. A bookcase is to be constructed as shown in the figure. The length is to be 3 times the height. If 60 feet of lumber is available for the entire unit, find the length and height of the bookcase.

• Writing in Mathematics

25. In your own words, describe a step-by-step approach for solving algebraic word problems.

26. Many students find solving linear equations much easier than solving algebraic word problems. Discuss some of the reasons why this is the case.

27. Did you have difficulties solving some of the problems that were assigned in this exercise set? Discuss what you did if this happened to you. Did your course of action enhance your ability to solve algebraic word problems?

28. The mile records in Example 2 on page 325 are a yardstick for measuring how athletes are getting better and better. Do you think that there is a limit to human performance? Explain your answer. If so, when might we reach it?

• Critical Thinking Exercises

29. An HMO pamphlet contains the following recommended weight for women: "Give yourself 100 pounds for the first 5 feet plus 5 pounds for every inch over 5 feet tall." Using this description, which height corresponds to an ideal weight of 135 pounds?

30. The rate for a particular international long distance telephone call is $0.55 for the first minute and $0.40 for each additional minute. Determine the length of a call that cost $6.95.

31. In a film, the actor Charles Coburn plays an elderly "uncle" character criticized for marrying a woman when he is 3 times her age. He wittily replies, "Ah, but in 20 years time I shall only be twice her age." How old are the "uncle" and the woman?

32. Suppose that we agree to pay you 8¢ for every problem in this chapter that you solve correctly and fine you 5¢ for every problem done incorrectly. If at the end of 26 problems we do not owe each other any money, how many problems did you solve correctly?

33. It was wartime when the Ricardos found out Mrs. Ricardo was pregnant. Ricky Ricardo was drafted and made out a will, deciding that $14,000 in a savings account was to be divided between his wife and his child-to-be. Rather strangely, and certainly with gender bias, Ricky stipulated that if the child were a boy, he would get twice the amount of the mother's portion. If it were a girl, the mother would get twice the amount the girl was to receive. We'll never know what Ricky was thinking of, for (as fate would have it) he did not return from war. Mrs. Ricardo gave birth to twins—a boy and a girl. How was the money divided?

34. A thief steals a number of rare plants from a nursery. On the way out, the thief meets three security guards, one after another. To each security guard, the thief is forced to give one-half the plants that he still has, plus 2 more. Finally, the thief leaves the nursery with 1 lone palm. How many plants were originally stolen?

• **Group Exercise**

35. One of the best ways to learn how to *solve* a word problem in algebra is to *design* word problems of your own. Creating a word problem makes you very aware of precisely how much information is needed to solve the problem. You must also focus on the best way to present information to a reader and on how much information to give. As you write your problem, you gain skills that will help you solve problems created by others.

   The group should design five different word problems that can be solved using algebraic equations. All of the problems should be on different topics. For example, the group should not have more than one problem on finding a number. The group should turn in both the problems and their algebraic solutions.

SECTION 6.4 • RATIO, PROPORTION, AND VARIATION

O B J E C T I V E S

1. Solve proportions.

2. Solve problems using proportions.

3. Solve direct variation problems.

4. Solve inverse variation problems.

The possibility of seeing a blue whale, the largest mammal ever to grace the Earth, increases the excitement of gazing out over the ocean's swell of waves. Blue whales were hunted to near extinction in the last half of the nineteenth and the first half of the twentieth centuries. Using a method for estimating wildlife populations that we discuss in this section, by the mid-1960s it was determined that the world population of blue whales was less than 1000. This led the International Whaling Commission to ban the killing of blue whales to prevent their extinction. A dramatic increase in blue whale sightings indicates an ongoing increase in their population and the success of the killing ban.

1 | Solve proportions.

Proportions

A **ratio** compares quantities by division. For example, a group contains 60 women and 30 men. The ratio of women to men is $\frac{60}{30}$. We can express this ratio as a fraction reduced to lowest terms:

$$\frac{60}{30} = \frac{2 \cdot 30}{1 \cdot 30} = \frac{2}{1}.$$

This ratio can be expressed as 2:1, or 2 to 1.

   A **proportion** is a statement that says that two ratios are equal. If the ratios are $\frac{a}{b}$ and $\frac{c}{d}$, then the proportion is

$$\frac{a}{b} = \frac{c}{d}.$$

We can clear this equation of fractions by multiplying both sides by bd, the least common denominator:

$$\frac{a}{b} = \frac{c}{d}$$ This is the given proportion.

$$bd \cdot \frac{a}{b} = bd \cdot \frac{c}{d}$$ Multiply both sides by bd ($b \neq 0$ and $d \neq 0$). Then simplify.

On the left, $\dfrac{\cancel{b}d}{1} \cdot \dfrac{a}{\cancel{b}} = da = ad$. On the right, $\dfrac{b\cancel{d}}{1} \cdot \dfrac{c}{\cancel{d}} = bc$.

$$ad = bc$$

We see that the following principle is true for any proportion:

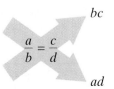

$$\frac{a}{b} = \frac{c}{d}$$

The cross-products principle: $ad = bc$

> **THE CROSS-PRODUCTS PRINCIPLE FOR PROPORTIONS**
>
> If $\dfrac{a}{b} = \dfrac{c}{d}$, then $ad = bc$. ($b \neq 0$ and $d \neq 0$.)
>
> The cross products ad and bc are equal.

For example, if $\frac{2}{3} = \frac{6}{9}$, we see that $2 \cdot 9 = 3 \cdot 6$, or $18 = 18$.

If three of the numbers in a proportion are known, the value of the missing quantity can be found by using the cross-products principle. This idea is illustrated in Example 1.

EXAMPLE 1   SOLVING PROPORTIONS

Solve each proportion for x:

a. $\dfrac{63}{x} = \dfrac{7}{5}$ **b.** $\dfrac{20}{x - 10} = \dfrac{30}{x}$.

SOLUTION

a.
$$\frac{63}{x} = \frac{7}{5}$$ This is the given proportion.

$$63 \cdot 5 = 7x$$ Apply the cross-products principle.

$$315 = 7x$$ Simplify.

$$\frac{315}{7} = \frac{7x}{7}$$ Divide both sides by 7.

$$45 = x$$ Simplify.

The solution set is $\{45\}$.

Check

$$\frac{63}{45} \overset{?}{=} \frac{7}{5}$$ Substitute 45 for x in $\dfrac{63}{x} = \dfrac{7}{5}$.

$$\frac{7 \cdot \cancel{9}}{5 \cdot \cancel{9}} \overset{?}{=} \frac{7}{5}$$ Reduce $\dfrac{63}{45}$ to lowest terms.

$$\frac{7}{5} = \frac{7}{5}$$ This true statement verifies that the solution set is $\{45\}$.

b.
$$\frac{20}{x - 10} = \frac{30}{x}$$ This is the given proportion.

$$20x = 30(x - 10)$$ Apply the cross-products principle.

$$20x = 30x - 30 \cdot 10$$ Use the distributive property.

$$20x = 30x - 300$$ Simplify.

$$20x - 30x = 30x - 300 - 30x \qquad \text{Subtract 30x from both sides.}$$
$$-10x = -300 \qquad \text{Simplify.}$$
$$\frac{-10x}{-10} = \frac{-300}{-10} \qquad \text{Divide both sides by } -10.$$
$$x = 30 \qquad \text{Simplify.}$$

Check

$$\frac{20}{30 - 10} \stackrel{?}{=} \frac{30}{30} \qquad \text{Substitute 30 for x in } \frac{20}{x - 10} = \frac{30}{x}.$$

$$\frac{20}{20} \stackrel{?}{=} \frac{30}{30} \qquad \text{Subtract: } 30 - 10 = 20.$$

$$1 = 1 \qquad \text{This true statement verifies that the solution is 30.}$$

The solution set is $\{30\}$.

Solve each proportion for x:

a. $\dfrac{10}{x} = \dfrac{2}{3}$ \qquad **b.** $\dfrac{11}{910 - x} = \dfrac{2}{x}.$

---

2 | Solve problems using proportions.

Applications of Proportions

We now turn to practical application problems that can be solved using proportions. Here is a procedure for solving these problems:

> ### SOLVING APPLIED PROBLEMS USING PROPORTIONS
>
> **1.** Read the problem and represent the unknown quantity by x (or any letter).
> **2.** Set up a proportion by listing the given ratio on one side and the ratio with the unknown quantity on the other side. Each respective quantity should occupy the same corresponding position on each side of the proportion.
> **3.** Drop units and apply the cross-products principle.
> **4.** Solve for x and answer the question.

EXAMPLE 2   APPLYING PROPORTIONS: CALCULATING TAXES

The property tax on a house whose assessed value is \$65,000 is \$825. Determine the property tax on a house with an assessed value of \$180,000, assuming the same tax rate.

STUDY TIP

Here are three other correct proportions you can use in step 2:

- $\dfrac{\$65,000 \text{ value}}{\$825 \text{ tax}} = \dfrac{\$180,000 \text{ value}}{\$x \text{ tax}}$

- $\dfrac{\$65,000 \text{ value}}{\$180,000 \text{ value}} = \dfrac{\$825 \text{ tax}}{\$x \text{ tax}}$

- $\dfrac{\$180,000 \text{ value}}{\$65,000 \text{ value}} = \dfrac{\$x \text{ tax}}{\$825 \text{ tax}}.$

Each proportion gives the same cross product obtained in step 3.

SOLUTION

Step 1. Represent the unknown by x. Let $x =$ the tax on a \$180,000 house.

Step 2. Set up a proportion. We will set up a proportion comparing taxes to assessed value.

Tax on \$65,000 house / Assessed value (\$65,000)   equals   Tax on \$180,000 house / Assessed value (\$180,000)

$$\text{Given ratio} \begin{cases} \dfrac{\$825}{\$65,000} \end{cases} = \dfrac{\$x}{\$180,000} \quad \begin{array}{l} \longleftarrow \text{Unknown} \\ \longleftarrow \text{Given quantity} \end{array}$$

Step 3. Drop the units and apply the cross-products principle. We drop the dollar signs and begin to solve for x.

$$\frac{825}{65,000} = \frac{x}{180,000}$$ This is the proportion that models the problem's conditions.

$$65,000x = (825)(180,000)$$ Apply the cross-products principle.

$$65,000x = 148,500,000$$ Multiply.

Step 4. Solve for x and answer the question.

$$\frac{65,000x}{65,000} = \frac{148,500,000}{65,000}$$ Divide both sides by 65,000.

$$x \approx 2284.62$$ Round the value of x to the nearest cent.

The property tax on the $180,000 house is approximately $2284.62.

○

CHECK POINT 2 The property tax on a house with an assessed value of $45,000 is $600. Determine the property tax on a house with an assessed value of $112,500, assuming the same tax rate.

Sampling in Nature

The method that was used to estimate the blue whale population described in the section opener is called the **capture-recapture method**. Because it is impossible to count each individual animal within a population, wildlife biologists randomly catch and tag a given number of animals. Sometime later they recapture a second sample of animals and count the number of recaptured tagged animals. The total size of the wildlife population is then estimated using the following proportion:

Initially unknown $(x) \longrightarrow$ $$\frac{\text{Original number of tagged animals}}{\text{Total number of animals in the population}} = \frac{\text{Number of recaptured tagged animals}}{\text{Number of animals in second sample}}.$$ } Known ratio

Although this is called the capture-recapture method, it is not necessary to recapture animals in order to observe whether or not they are tagged. This could be done from a distance, with binoculars for instance.

| EXAMPLE 3 | APPLYING PROPORTIONS: ESTIMATING WILDLIFE POPULATION |

Wildlife biologists catch, tag, and then release 135 deer back into a wildlife refuge. Two weeks later they observe a sample of 140 deer, 30 of which are tagged. Assuming the ratio of tagged deer in the sample holds for all deer in the refuge, approximately how many deer are in the refuge?

SOLUTION

Step 1. Represent the unknown by x. Let x = the total number of deer in the refuge.

Step 2. Set up a proportion.

Unknown $\longrightarrow$ $\dfrac{\text{Original number of tagged deer}}{\text{Total number of deer}}$ equals $\dfrac{\text{Number of tagged deer in the observed sample}}{\text{Total number of deer in the observed sample}}$ } Known ratio

$$\frac{135}{x} = \frac{30}{140}$$

Steps 3 and 4. Apply the cross-products principle, solve, and answer the question.

$$\frac{135}{x} = \frac{30}{140} \qquad \text{This is the proportion that models the problem's conditions.}$$

$$(135)(140) = 30x \qquad \text{Apply the cross-products principle.}$$

$$18{,}900 = 30x \qquad \text{Multiply.}$$

$$\frac{18{,}900}{30} = \frac{30x}{30} \qquad \text{Divide both sides by 30.}$$

$$630 = x \qquad \text{Simplify.}$$

There are approximately 630 deer in the refuge.

○

CHECK POINT 3 Wildlife biologists catch, tag, and then release 120 deer back into the wildlife refuge. Two weeks later they observe a sample of 150 deer, 25 of which are tagged. Assuming the ratio of tagged deer in the sample holds for all deer in the refuge, approximately how many deer are in the refuge?

───●

3 | Solve direct variation problems.

Direct Variation

In Example 2, we saw that as the assessed value on a house goes up, so do the taxes. When the assessed value is doubled, the taxes are doubled; when the assessed value is tripled, the taxes are tripled. Because of this, the tax on a house is said to **vary directly** as its assessed value. Direct variation situations can be solved using a proportion.

EXAMPLE 4   SOLVING A DIRECT VARIATION PROBLEM

An alligator's tail length varies directly as its body length. An alligator with a body length of 4 feet has a tail length of 3.6 feet. What is the tail length of an alligator whose body length is 6 feet?

|← ───────── Body length ─────────→|←───────── Tail length ─────────→|

SOLUTION

Step 1. Represent the unknown by x. Let x = the tail length of an alligator whose body length is 6 feet.

Step 2. Set up a proportion. We will set up a proportion comparing body length to tail length.

$$\underbrace{\frac{\text{Body length}}{\text{Tail length}}}_{\substack{\text{Given ratio: body}\\\text{length is 4 ft and}\\\text{tail length is 3.6 ft.}}} \quad \frac{4 \text{ ft}}{3.6 \text{ ft}} = \frac{6 \text{ ft}}{x \text{ ft}} \quad \underbrace{\frac{\text{Body length}}{\text{Tail length}}}_{\substack{\text{Ratio with unknown:}\\\text{Body length is 6 ft and}\\\text{we're seeking tail length.}}}$$

Steps 3 and 4. Apply the cross-products principle, solve, and answer the question.

$$\frac{4}{3.6} = \frac{6}{x}$$

This is the proportion that models the problem's conditions.

$$4x = (3.6)(6)$$ Apply the cross-products principle.

$$4x = 21.6$$ Multiply.

$$\frac{4x}{4} = \frac{21.6}{4}$$ Divide both sides by 4.

$$x = 5.4$$ Simplify.

An alligator whose body length is 6 feet has a tail length measuring 5.4 feet.

CHECK POINT 4 The number of gallons of water used when taking a shower varies directly as the time, in minutes, in the shower. A shower lasting 5 minutes uses 30 gallons of water. How much water is used in a shower lasting 11 minutes?

EXAMPLE 5   SOLVING A DIRECT VARIATION PROBLEM

The distance that the sky divers shown in the photograph fall varies directly as the square of the time in which they fall. The sky divers fall 64 feet in 2 seconds. How far will they fall in 5 seconds?

SOLUTION

Step 1. Represent the unknown by x. Let $x =$ the distance the sky divers fall in 5 seconds.

Step 2. Set up a proportion. We will set up a proportion comparing the distance that the sky divers fall to the square of the time in which they fall.

$$\frac{\text{Distance they fall in 2 seconds}}{\text{Square of the time they fall}} \quad \text{equals} \quad \frac{\text{Distance they fall in 5 seconds}}{\text{Square of the time they fall}}$$

$$\text{Given ratio} \left\{ \frac{64 \text{ feet}}{2^2 \text{ seconds}} \right. \qquad = \qquad \frac{x}{5^2 \text{ seconds}} \begin{array}{l} \leftarrow \text{Unknown} \\ \leftarrow \text{Given quantity} \end{array}$$

Steps 3 and 4. Apply the cross-products principle, solve, and answer the question.

$$\frac{64}{2^2} = \frac{x}{5^2}$$ This is the proportion that models the problem's conditions.

$$\frac{64}{4} = \frac{x}{25}$$ Square 2 and 5: $2^2 = 2 \cdot 2 = 4$ and $5^2 = 5 \cdot 5 = 25$.

$$4x = (64)(25)$$ Apply the cross-products principle.

$$4x = 1600$$ Multiply.

$$\frac{4x}{4} = \frac{1600}{4}$$ Divide both sides by 4.

$$x = 400$$ Simplify.

The sky divers will fall 400 feet in 5 seconds.

CHECK POINT 5 The distance required to stop a car varies directly as the square of its speed. If 200 feet are required to stop a car traveling 60 miles per hour, how many feet are required to stop a car traveling 100 miles per hour? Round to the nearest foot.

4 | Solve inverse variation problems.

Inverse Variation

So far, we have created models for situations in which an increase in one quantity is accompanied by an increase in a second quantity. However, there are other situations in which one quantity increases as the other decreases, or vice versa. For example, if you drive to campus, consider the rate at which you drive and the time it takes you to get there. As your driving rate increases, the time it takes you to get to campus decreases. This is an example of *inverse variation*. When two quantities **vary inversely**, as one quantity increases, the other decreases, and vice versa.

The distance from Atlanta, Georgia, to Orlando, Florida, is 450 miles. If you average 45 miles per hour, the time for the drive is 10 hours. If you average 75 miles per hour, the time for the drive is 6 hours. The following proportion represents this situation in which time varies inversely as driving rate:

$$\frac{\text{time at the slower rate}}{\text{the faster rate}} = \frac{\text{time at the faster rate}}{\text{the slower rate}}$$

$$\frac{10 \text{ hours}}{75 \text{ miles per hour}} = \frac{6 \text{ hours}}{45 \text{ miles per hour}}.$$

The cross products are equal:

$$\frac{10 \ \cancel{\text{hours}}}{1} \cdot \frac{45 \text{ miles}}{\cancel{\text{hour}}} = 10 \cdot 45 \text{ miles} = 450 \text{ miles}$$

$$\frac{75 \text{ miles}}{\cancel{\text{hour}}} \cdot \frac{6 \ \cancel{\text{hours}}}{1} = 75 \cdot 6 \text{ miles} = 450 \text{ miles}.$$

Because the product of rate and time is distance, each cross product gives the distance from Atlanta to Orlando.

There is something unusual about the placement of quantities in a proportion in an inverse variation situation:

These quantities correspond to each other.
6 hours is the travel time at 75 miles per hour.

$$\frac{10 \text{ hours}}{75 \text{ miles per hour}} = \frac{6 \text{ hours}}{45 \text{ miles per hour}}$$

These quantities correspond to each other.
10 hours is the travel time at 45 miles per hour.

In an inverse variation situation, corresponding values are not placed in the same ratio. *Placing corresponding values in opposite ratios* allows one quantity to increase while the other decreases, or vice versa.

STUDY TIP

When you apply the cross-products principle in an inverse variation proportion, you multiply corresponding quantities.

SETTING UP A PROPORTION WHEN y VARIES INVERSELY AS x

$$\frac{\text{The first value for } y}{\begin{array}{c}\text{The value for } x \text{ corresponding}\\ \text{to the second value for } y\end{array}} = \frac{\text{The second value for } y}{\begin{array}{c}\text{The value for } x \text{ corresponding}\\ \text{to the first value for } y\end{array}}$$

Doubling the pressure
halves the volume.

FIGURE 6.5

EXAMPLE 6   SOLVING AN INVERSE VARIATION PROBLEM

Figure 6.5 shows that a bicyclist tips the cycle when making a turn. The angle B, formed by the vertical direction and the bicycle, is called the banking angle. The banking angle varies inversely as the cycle's turning radius. When the turning radius is 4 feet, the banking angle is 28°. What is the banking angle when the turning radius is 3.5 feet?

SOLUTION

Step 1. Represent the unknown by x. Let

$$x = \text{the banking angle when the turning}$$
$$\text{radius is 3.5 feet.}$$

Step 2. Set up a proportion. We will set up a proportion comparing the banking angle to the turning radius. Because this is an inverse variation situation, we place corresponding values in opposite ratios.

> A banking angle of 28° corresponds to a turning radius of 4 ft.

> We must find the banking angle, $x°$, corresponding to a turning radius of 3.5 ft.

$$\frac{28°}{3.5 \text{ ft}} = \frac{x°}{4 \text{ ft}}$$

> banking angle
> turning radius

> banking angle
> turning radius

Steps 3 and 4. Apply the cross-products principle, solve, and answer the question.

$$\frac{28}{3.5} = \frac{x}{4} \qquad \text{This is the proportion that models the problem's conditions.}$$

$$3.5x = 28 \cdot 4 \qquad \text{Apply the cross-products principle.}$$

$$3.5x = 112 \qquad \text{Multiply.}$$

$$\frac{3.5x}{3.5} = \frac{112}{3.5} \qquad \text{Divide both sides by 3.5.}$$

$$x = 32 \qquad \text{Simplify.}$$

When the turning radius is 3.5 feet, the banking angle is 32°.

CHECK POINT 6 When you use a spray can and press the value at the top, you decrease the pressure of the gas in the can. This decrease of pressure causes the volume of the gas in the can to increase. Because the gas needs more room than is provided in the can, it expands in spray form through the small hole near the valve. In general, if the temperature is constant, the pressure of a gas in a container varies inversely as the volume of the container. The pressure of a gas sample in a container whose volume is 8 cubic inches is 12 pounds per square inch. If the sample expands to a volume of 22 cubic inches, what is the new pressure of the gas?

EXERCISE SET 6.4 ●●●●●●

• Practice Exercises

In Exercises 1–12, solve each proportion.

1. $\dfrac{24}{x} = \dfrac{12}{7}$

2. $\dfrac{56}{x} = \dfrac{8}{7}$

3. $\dfrac{x}{6} = \dfrac{18}{4}$

4. $\dfrac{x}{32} = \dfrac{3}{24}$

5. $\dfrac{x}{3} = -\dfrac{3}{4}$

6. $\dfrac{x}{2} = -\dfrac{1}{5}$

7. $\dfrac{-3}{8} = \dfrac{x}{40}$

8. $\dfrac{-3}{8} = \dfrac{6}{x}$

9. $\dfrac{x-2}{5} = \dfrac{3}{10}$

10. $\dfrac{x+4}{8} = \dfrac{3}{16}$

11. $\dfrac{y+10}{10} = \dfrac{y-2}{4}$

12. $\dfrac{2}{y-5} = \dfrac{3}{y+6}$

In Exercises 13–16, use a proportion to solve each variation problem.

13. y varies directly as x. $y = 65$ when $x = 5$. Find y when $x = 12$.

14. y varies directly as x. $y = 45$ when $x = 5$. Find y when $x = 13$.

15. y varies inversely as x. $y = 12$ when $x = 5$. Find y when $x = 2$.

16. y varies inversely as x. $y = 6$ when $x = 3$. Find y when $x = 9$.

• Practice Plus

In Exercises 17–22, solve each proportion for x.

17. $\dfrac{x}{a} = \dfrac{b}{c}$

18. $\dfrac{a}{x} = \dfrac{b}{c}$

19. $\dfrac{a + b}{c} = \dfrac{x}{d}$

20. $\dfrac{a - b}{c} = \dfrac{x}{d}$

21. $\dfrac{x + a}{a} = \dfrac{b + c}{c}$

22. $\dfrac{ax - b}{b} = \dfrac{c - d}{d}$

• Application Exercises

Use a proportion to solve Exercises 23–28.

23. The tax on a property with an assessed value of $65,000 is $725. Find the tax on a property with an assessed value of $100,000.

24. The maintenance bill for a shopping center containing 180,000 square feet is $45,000. What is the bill for a store in the center that is 4800 square feet?

25. St. Paul Island in Alaska has 12 fur seal rookeries (breeding places). In 1961, to estimate the fur seal pup population in the Gorbath rookery, 4963 fur seal pups were tagged in early August. In late August, a sample of 900 pups was observed and 218 of these were found to have been previously tagged. Estimate the total number of fur seal pups in this rookery.

26. To estimate the number of bass in a lake, wildlife biologists tagged 50 bass and released them in the lake. Later they netted 108 bass and found that 27 of them were tagged. Approximately how many bass are in the lake?

27. The ratio of monthly child support to a father's yearly income is 1:40. How much should a father earning $38,000 annually pay in monthly child support?

28. Many areas of Northern California depend on the snow-pack of the Sierra Nevada mountain range for their water supply. Meteorologists have determined that 250 cubic centimeters of snow will melt to 28 cubic centimeters of water. How much water does 1200 cubic centimeters of melting snow produce?

Exercises 29–42 involve direct and inverse variation. Use a proportion to solve each exercise.

29. An object's weight on the moon varies directly as its weight on Earth. Neil Armstrong, the first person to step on the moon on July 20, 1969, weighed 360 pounds on Earth (with all of his equipment on) and 60 pounds on the moon. What is the moon weight of a person who weighs 186 pounds on Earth?

30. The height that a ball bounces varies directly as the height from which it was dropped. A tennis ball dropped from 12 inches bounces 8.4 inches. From what height was the tennis ball dropped if it bounces 56 inches?

31. Height varies directly as foot length. A person whose foot length is 10 inches is 67 inches tall. In 1951, photos of large footprints were published. Some believed that these footprints were made by the "Abominable Snowman." Each footprint was 23 inches long. If indeed they belonged to the Abominable Snowman, how tall is the critter?

32. A person's hair length varies directly as the number of years it has been growing. After 2 years, a person's hair length is 8 inches. The longest moustache on record was grown by Kalyan Sain of India. Sain grew his moustache for 17 years. How long was it?

33. If all men had identical body types, their weights would vary directly as the cube of their heights. Shown is Robert Wadlow, who reached a record height of 8 feet 11 inches (107 inches) before his death at age 22. If a man who is 5 feet 10 inches tall (70 inches) with the same body type as Mr. Wadlow weighs 170 pounds, what was Robert Wadlow's weight shortly before his death?

34. The Mach number is a measurement of speed named after the man who suggested it, Ernst Mach (1838–1916). The speed of an aircraft varies directly as its Mach number. Shown here are two aircraft. Use the figures for the Concorde to determine the Blackbird's speed.

Concorde
Mach 2.03
Speed = 1502.2 miles per hour

SR-71 Blackbird
Mach 3.3
Speed = ?

35. On a dry asphalt road, a car's stopping distance varies directly as the square of its speed. A car traveling at 45 miles per hour can stop in 67.5 feet. What is the stopping distance for a car traveling at 60 miles per hour?

36. The distance that an object falls varies directly as the square of the time it has been falling. An object falls 144 feet in 3 seconds. Find how far it will fall in 7 seconds.

37. The water temperature of the Pacific Ocean varies inversely as the water's depth. At a depth of 1000 meters, the water temperature is 4.4° Celsius. What is the water temperature at a depth of 5000 meters?

38. The time that it takes you to get to campus varies inversely as your driving rate. Averaging 20 miles per hour in terrible traffic, it takes you 1.5 hours to get to campus. How long would the trip take averaging 60 miles per hour?

39. The volume of a gas in a container at a constant temperature varies inversely as the pressure. If the volume is 32 cubic centimeters at a pressure of 8 pounds, find the pressure when the volume is 40 cubic centimeters.

40. The current in a circuit varies inversely as the resistance. The current is 20 amperes when the resistance is 5 ohms. Find the current for a resistance of 16 ohms.

41. The loudness of a stereo speaker, measured in decibels, varies inversely as the square of your distance from the speaker. When you are 8 feet from the speaker, the loudness is 28 decibels. What is the loudness when you are 4 feet from the speaker?

42. Radiation machines, used to treat tumors, produce an intensity of radiation that varies inversely as the square of the distance from the machine. At 3 meters, the radiation intensity is 62.5 milliroentgens per hour. What is the intensity at a distance of 2.5 meters?

• Writing in Mathematics

43. What is a ratio? Give an example with your description.

44. What is a proportion? Give an example with your description.

45. Explain how to solve a proportion. Illustrate your explanation with an example.

46. Explain the meaning of this statement: A company's monthly sales vary directly as its advertising budget.

47. Explain the meaning of this statement: A company's monthly sales vary inversely as the price of its product.

48. Explain the difference between setting up proportions for direct and inverse variation problems.

• Critical Thinking Exercises

49. The front sprocket on a bicycle has 60 teeth and the rear sprocket has 20 teeth. For mountain biking, an owner needs a 5:1 front: rear ratio. If only one of the sprockets is to be replaced, describe the two ways in which this can be done.

50. My friend is 44 years old. My dog Phideaux is 7 years old. If Phideaux were human, he would be 56. Phideaux thinks my friend is another dog, which makes me wonder: If my friend were a dog, how old would my friend be?

51. In a hurricane, the wind pressure varies directly as the square of the wind velocity. If wind pressure is a measure of a hurricane's destructive capacity, what happens to this destructive power when the wind velocity doubles?

52. The illumination from a light source varies inversely as the square of the distance from the light source. If you raise a lamp from 15 inches to 30 inches over your desk, what happens to the illumination?

SECTION 6.5 • LINEAR INEQUALITIES IN ONE VARIABLE

OBJECTIVES

1. Graph subsets of real numbers on a number line.

2. Solve linear inequalities.

3. Solve applied problems using linear inequalities.

Rent-a-Heap, a car rental company, charges $125 per week plus $0.20 per mile to rent one of their cars. Suppose you are limited by how much money you can spend for the week: You can spend at most $335. If we let *x* represent the number of miles you drive the heap in a week, we can write an inequality that models the given conditions:

The weekly charge of $125	plus	the charge of $0.20 per mile for x miles	must be less than or equal to	$335.
125	+	0.20x	≤	335.

Notice that the highest exponent on the variable is 1. Such an inequality is called a *linear inequality in one variable*. The symbol between the two sides of an inequality can be ≤ (is less than or equal to), < (is less than), ≥ (is greater than or equal to), or > (is greater than).

In this section, we will study how to solve linear inequalities such as $125 + 0.20x \le 335$. **Solving an inequality** is the process of finding the set of numbers that make the inequality a true statement. These numbers are called the **solutions** of the inequality and we say that they **satisfy** the inequality. The set of all solutions is called the **solution set** of the inequality. We begin by discussing how to represent these solution sets, which are subsets of real numbers, on a number line.

<table>
<tr><td>1</td><td>Graph subsets of real numbers on a number line.</td></tr>
</table>

Graphing Subsets of Real Numbers on a Number Line

Table 6.3 shows how to represent various subsets of real numbers on a number line. Open dots ($\circ$) indicate that a number is not included in a set. Closed dots ($\bullet$) indicate that a number is included in a set.

TABLE 6.3 GRAPHS OF SUBSETS OF REAL NUMBERS

Let a and b be real numbers such that $a < b$.

Set-Builder Notation		Graph
$\{x \mid x < a\}$	x is a real number less than a.	
$\{x \mid x \le a\}$	x is a real number less than or equal to a.	
$\{x \mid x > b\}$	x is a real number greater than b.	
$\{x \mid x \ge b\}$	x is a real number greater than or equal to b.	
$\{x \mid a < x < b\}$	x is a real number greater than a and less than b.	
$\{x \mid a \le x \le b\}$	x is a real number greater than or equal to a and less than or equal to b.	
$\{x \mid a \le x < b\}$	x is a real number greater than or equal to a and less than b.	
$\{x \mid a < x \le b\}$	x is a real number greater than a and less than or equal to b.	

EXAMPLE 1 GRAPHING SUBSETS OF REAL NUMBERS

Graph each set:
a. $\{x \mid x < 3\}$ **b.** $\{x \mid x \ge -1\}$ **c.** $\{x \mid -1 < x \le 3\}$.

SOLUTION

a. $\{x \mid x < 3\}$ — x is a real number less than 3.

b. $\{x \mid x \ge -1\}$ — x is a real number greater than or equal to -1.

c. $\{x \mid -1 < x \le 3\}$ — x is a real number greater than -1 and less than or equal to 3.

 Graph each set:

a. $\{x \mid x < 4\}$ **b.** $\{x \mid x \ge -2\}$ **c.** $\{x \mid -4 \le x < 1\}$.

2 Solve linear inequalities.

Solving Linear Inequalities in One Variable

We know that a linear equation in x can be expressed as $ax + b = 0$. A **linear inequality in** x can be written in one of the following forms: $ax + b < 0$, $ax + b \leq 0$, $ax + b > 0$, $ax + b \geq 0$. In each form, $a \neq 0$. Back to our question that opened this section: How many miles can you drive your Rent-a-Heap car if you can spend at most $335 per week? We answer the question by solving

$$0.20x + 125 \leq 335$$

for x. The solution procedure is nearly identical to that for solving

$$0.20x + 125 = 335.$$

Our goal is to get x by itself on the left side. We do this by subtracting 125 from both sides to isolate $0.20x$:

$0.20x + 125 \leq 335$	This is the given inequality.
$0.20x + 125 - 125 \leq 335 - 125$	Subtract 125 from both sides.
$0.20x \leq 210.$	Simplify.

Finally, we isolate x from $0.20x$ by dividing both sides of the inequality by 0.20:

$\dfrac{0.20x}{0.20} \leq \dfrac{210}{0.20}$	Divide both sides by 0.20
$x \leq 1050.$	Simplify.

With at most $335 per week to spend, you can travel at most 1050 miles.

We started with the inequality $0.20x + 125 \leq 335$ and obtained the inequality $x \leq 1050$ in the final step. Both of these inequalities have the same solution set, namely $\{x \mid x \leq 1050\}$. Inequalities such as these, with the same solution set, are said to be **equivalent**.

We isolated x from $0.20x$ by dividing both sides of $0.20x \leq 210$ by 0.20, a positive number. Let's see what happens if we divide both sides of an inequality by a negative number. Consider the inequality $10 < 14$. Divide 10 and 14 by -2:

$$\frac{10}{-2} = -5 \quad \text{and} \quad \frac{14}{-2} = -7.$$

Because -5 lies to the right of -7 on the number line, -5 is greater than -7:

$$-5 > -7.$$

Notice that the direction of the inequality symbol is reversed:

$$10 < 14$$

Dividing by -2 changes the direction of the inequality symbol.

$$-5 > -7.$$

In general, **when we multiply or divide both sides of an inequality by a negative number, the direction of the inequality symbol is reversed**. When we reverse the direction of the inequality symbol, we say that we change the *sense* of the inequality.

We can summarize this discussion with the following statement:

STUDY TIP

English phrases such as "at least" and "at most" can be represented by inequalities.

English Sentence	Inequality
x is at least 5.	$x \geq 5$
x is at most 5.	$x \leq 5$
x is between 5 and 7.	$5 < x < 7$
x is no more than 5.	$x \leq 5$
x is no less than 5.	$x \geq 5$

SOLVING LINEAR INEQUALITIES

The procedure for solving linear inequalities is the same as the procedure for solving linear equations, with one important exception: When multiplying or dividing both sides of the inequality by a negative number, reverse the direction of the inequality symbol, changing the sense of the inequality.

EXAMPLE 2   SOLVING A LINEAR INEQUALITY

Solve and graph the solution set: $4x - 7 \geq 5$.

SOLUTION Our goal is to get x by itself on the left side. We do this by getting $4x$ by itself, adding 7 to both sides.

$$4x - 7 \geq 5 \qquad \text{This is the given inequality.}$$

$$4x - 7 + 7 \geq 5 + 7 \qquad \text{Add 7 to both sides.}$$

$$4x \geq 12 \qquad \text{Simplify.}$$

Next, we isolate x from $4x$ by dividing both sides by 4. The inequality symbol stays the same because we are dividing by a positive number.

$$\frac{4x}{4} \geq \frac{12}{4} \qquad \text{Divide both sides by 4.}$$

$$x \geq 3 \qquad \text{Simplify.}$$

The solution set consists of all real numbers that are greater than or equal to 3, expressed in set-builder notation as $\{x | x \geq 3\}$. The graph of the solution set is shown as follows:

We cannot check all members of an inequality's solution set, but we can take a few values to get an indication of whether or not it is correct. In Example 2, we found that the solution set of $4x - 7 \geq 5$ is $\{x | x \geq 3\}$. Show that 3 and 4 satisfy the inequality, whereas 2 does not.

 Solve and graph the solution set: $5x - 3 \leq 17$.

EXAMPLE 3   SOLVING LINEAR INEQUALITIES

Solve and graph the solution set:

a. $\dfrac{1}{3}x < 5$ **b.** $-3x < 21$.

SOLUTION In each case, our goal is to isolate x. In the first inequality, this is accomplished by multiplying both sides by 3. In the second inequality, we can do this by dividing both sides by -3.

a. $\dfrac{1}{3}x < 5$ This is the given inequality.

$3 \cdot \dfrac{1}{3}x < 3 \cdot 5$ Isolate x by multiplying by 3 on both sides.

⎵ The symbol $<$ stays the same because we are multiplying both sides by a positive number.

$x < 15$ Simplify.

The solution set is $\{x | x < 15\}$. The graph of the solution set is shown as follows:

b. $-3x < 21$ This is the given inequality.

$$\dfrac{-3x}{-3} > \dfrac{21}{-3}$$

Isolate x by dividing by −3 on both sides.
The symbol $<$ must be reversed because we are dividing both sides by a negative number.

$x > -7$ Simplify.

The solution set is $\{x | x > -7\}$. The graph of the solution set is shown as follows:

$$-8 \quad -7 \quad -6 \quad -5 \quad -4 \quad -3 \quad -2 \quad -1 \quad 0 \quad 1 \quad 2$$

CHECK POINT 3 Solve and graph the solution set:

a. $\dfrac{1}{4}x < 2$ **b.** $-6x < 18.$

EXAMPLE 4   SOLVING A LINEAR INEQUALITY

Solve and graph the solution set: $6x - 12 > 8x + 2.$

SOLUTION We will get x by itself on the left side. We begin by subtracting $8x$ from both sides so that the x-term appears on the left.

$6x - 12 > 8x + 2$ This is the given inequality.

$6x - 8x - 12 > 8x - 8x + 2$ Subtract 8x on both sides with the goal of isolating x on the left.

$-2x - 12 > 2$ Simplify.

Next, we get $-2x$ by itself, adding 12 to both sides.

$-2x - 12 + 12 > 2 + 12$ Add 12 to both sides.

$-2x > 14$ Simplify.

In the last step, we isolate x from $-2x$ by dividing both sides by -2. The direction of the inequality symbol must be reversed because we are dividing by a negative number.

$$\dfrac{-2x}{-2} < \dfrac{14}{-2}$$

Divide both sides by −2 and change the sense of the inequality.

$x < -7$ Simplify.

The solution set is $\{x | x < -7\}$. The graph of the solution set is shown as follows:

$$-9 \quad -8 \quad -7 \quad -6 \quad -5 \quad -4 \quad -3 \quad -2 \quad -1 \quad 0 \quad 1$$

CHECK POINT 4 Solve and graph the solution set: $7x - 3 > 13x + 33.$

EXAMPLE 5   SOLVING A LINEAR INEQUALITY

Solve and graph the solution set:

$$2(x - 3) + 5x \leq 8(x - 1).$$

SOLUTION Begin by simplifying the algebraic expression on each side.

$2(x - 3) + 5x \leq 8(x - 1)$ This is the given inequality.

$2x - 6 + 5x \leq 8x - 8$ Use the distributive property.

$7x - 6 \leq 8x - 8$ Add like terms on the left: 2x + 5x = 7x.

Left column is Study Tip. Right column is main body.

STUDY TIP

You can solve

$$7x - 6 \le 8x - 8$$

by isolating x on the right side. Subtract $7x$ from both sides and add 8 to both sides:

$$7x - 6 - 7x \le 8x - 8 - 7x$$
$$-6 \le x - 8$$
$$-6 + 8 \le x - 8 + 8$$
$$2 \le x.$$

This last inequality means the same thing as

$$x \ge 2.$$

We will get x by itself on the left side. Subtract $8x$ from both sides.

$$7x - 8x - 6 \le 8x - 8x - 8$$
$$-x - 6 \le -8$$

Next, we get $-x$ by itself, adding 6 to both sides.

$$-x - 6 + 6 \le -8 + 6$$
$$-x \le -2$$

To isolate x, we must eliminate the negative sign in front of the x. Because $-x$ means $-1x$, we can do this by dividing both sides of the inequality by -1. This reverses the direction of the inequality symbol.

$$\frac{-x}{-1} \ge \frac{-2}{-1} \qquad \text{Divide both sides by } -1 \text{ and change the}$$
$$\text{sense of the inequality.}$$

$$x \ge 2 \qquad \text{Simplify.}$$

The solution set is $\{x \mid x \ge 2\}$. The graph of the solution set is shown as follows:

○

 Solve and graph the solution set:

$$2(x - 3) - 1 \le 3(x + 2) - 14.$$

In our next example, the inequality has three parts:

$$-3 < 2x + 1 \le 3.$$

> $2x + 1$ is greater than -3
> and less than or equal to **3.**

By performing the same operation on all three parts of the inequality, our goal is to **isolate x in the middle**.

EXAMPLE 6   SOLVING A THREE-PART INEQUALITY

Solve and graph the solution set:

$$-3 < 2x + 1 \le 3.$$

SOLUTION We would like to isolate x in the middle. We can do this by first subtracting 1 from all three parts of the inequality. Then we isolate x from $2x$ by dividing all three parts of the inequality by 2.

$$-3 < 2x + 1 \le 3 \qquad \text{This is the given inequality.}$$
$$-3 - 1 < 2x + 1 - 1 \le 3 - 1 \qquad \text{Subtract 1 from all three parts.}$$
$$-4 < 2x \le 2 \qquad \text{Simplify.}$$
$$\frac{-4}{2} < \frac{2x}{2} \le \frac{2}{2} \qquad \text{Divide each part by 2.}$$
$$-2 < x \le 1 \qquad \text{Simplify.}$$

The solution set consists of all real numbers greater than -2 and less than or equal to 1, represented by $\{x \mid -2 < x \le 1\}$. The graph is shown as follows:

○

 Solve and graph the solution set on a number line: $1 \le 2x + 3 < 11$.

As you know, different professors may use different grading systems to determine your final course grade. Some professors require a final examination; others do not. In our next example, a final exam is required *and* it counts as two grades.

3 | Solve applied problems using linear inequalities.

EXAMPLE 7   AN APPLICATION: FINAL COURSE GRADE

To earn an A in a course, you must have a final average of at least 90%. On the first four examinations, you have grades of 86%, 88%, 92%, and 84%. If the final examination counts as two grades, what must you get on the final to earn an A in the course?

SOLUTION We will use our five-step strategy for solving algebraic word problems.

Steps 1 and 2. Represent unknown quantities in terms of x. Let $x =$ your grade on the final examination.

Step 3. Write an inequality in x that models the conditions. The average of the six grades is found by adding the grades and dividing the sum by 6.

$$\text{Average} = \frac{86 + 88 + 92 + 84 + x + x}{6}$$

Because the final counts as two grades, the x (your grade on the final examination) is added twice. This is also why the sum is divided by 6.

To get an A, your average must be at least 90. This means that your average must be greater than or equal to 90.

WHAT DO I NEED ON THE FINAL TO GET AN 'A'?

$E = mc^2$

| Your average | must be greater than or equal to | 90. |

$$\frac{86 + 88 + 92 + 84 + x + x}{6} \qquad \geq \qquad 90$$

Step 4. Solve the inequality and answer the problem's question.

$$\frac{86 + 88 + 92 + 84 + x + x}{6} \geq 90 \qquad \text{This is the inequality that models the given conditions.}$$

$$\frac{350 + 2x}{6} \geq 90 \qquad \text{Combine like terms in the numerator.}$$

$$6\left(\frac{350 + 2x}{6}\right) \geq 6(90) \qquad \text{Multiply both sides by 6, clearing the fraction.}$$

$$350 + 2x \geq 540 \qquad \text{Multiply.}$$

$$350 + 2x - 350 \geq 540 - 350 \qquad \text{Subtract 350 from both sides.}$$

$$2x \geq 190 \qquad \text{Simplify.}$$

$$\frac{2x}{2} \geq \frac{190}{2} \qquad \text{Divide both sides by 2.}$$

$$x \geq 95 \qquad \text{Simplify.}$$

You must get at least 95% on the final examination to earn an A in the course.

Step 5. Check. We can perform a partial check by computing the average with any grade that is at least 95. We will use 96. If you get 96% on the final examination, your average is

$$\frac{86 + 88 + 92 + 84 + 96 + 96}{6} = \frac{542}{6} = 90\frac{1}{3}.$$

Because $90\frac{1}{3} > 90$, you earn an A in the course.

○

CHECK POINT 7 To earn a B in a course, you must have a final average of at least 80%. On the first three examinations, you have grades of 82%, 74%, and 78%. If the final examination counts as two grades, what must you get on the final to earn a B in the course?

E X E R C I S E   S E T   6 . 5   ●●●●●●

• Practice Exercises

In Exercises 1–12, graph each set of real numbers on a number line.

1. $\{x \mid x > 6\}$ **2.** $\{x \mid x > -2\}$

3. $\{x \mid x < -4\}$ **4.** $\{x \mid x < 0\}$

5. $\{x \mid x \geq -3\}$ **6.** $\{x \mid x \geq -5\}$

7. $\{x \mid x \leq 4\}$ **8.** $\{x \mid x \leq 7\}$

9. $\{x \mid -2 < x \leq 5\}$ **10.** $\{x \mid -3 \leq x < 7\}$

11. $\{x \mid -1 < x < 4\}$ **12.** $\{x \mid -7 \leq x \leq 0\}$

In Exercises 13–66, solve each inequality and graph the solution set on a number line.

13. $x - 3 > 2$ **14.** $x + 1 < 5$

15. $x + 4 \leq 9$ **16.** $x - 5 \geq 1$

17. $x - 3 < 0$ **18.** $x + 4 \geq 0$

19. $4x < 20$ **20.** $6x \geq 18$

21. $3x \geq -15$ **22.** $7x < -21$

23. $2x - 3 > 7$ **24.** $3x + 2 \leq 14$

25. $3x + 3 < 18$ **26.** $8x - 4 > 12$

27. $\frac{1}{2}x < 4$ **28.** $\frac{1}{2}x > 3$

29. $\frac{x}{3} > -2$ **30.** $\frac{x}{4} < -1$

31. $-3x < 15$ **32.** $-7x > 21$

33. $-3x \geq -15$ **34.** $-7x \leq -21$

35. $3x + 4 \leq 2x + 7$ **36.** $2x + 9 \leq x + 2$

37. $5x - 9 < 4x + 7$ **38.** $3x - 8 < 2x + 11$

39. $-2x - 3 < 3$ **40.** $14 - 3x > 5$

41. $3 - 7x \leq 17$ **42.** $5 - 3x \geq 20$

43. $-x < 4$ **44.** $-x > -3$

45. $5 - x \leq 1$ **46.** $3 - x \geq -3$

47. $2x - 5 > -x + 6$ **48.** $6x - 2 \geq 4x + 6$

49. $2x - 5 < 5x - 11$ **50.** $4x - 7 > 9x - 2$

51. $3(x + 1) - 5 < 2x + 1$ **52.** $4(x + 1) + 2 \geq 3x + 6$

53. $8x + 3 > 3(2x + 1) - x + 5$

54. $7 - 2(x - 4) < 5(1 - 2x)$

55. $\frac{x}{4} - \frac{3}{2} \leq \frac{x}{2} + 1$ **56.** $\frac{3x}{10} + 1 \geq \frac{1}{5} - \frac{x}{10}$

57. $1 - \frac{x}{2} > 4$ **58.** $7 - \frac{4}{5}x < \frac{3}{5}$

59. $6 < x + 3 < 8$ **60.** $7 < x + 5 < 11$

61. $-3 \leq x - 2 < 1$ **62.** $-6 < x - 4 \leq 1$

63. $-11 < 2x - 1 \leq -5$ **64.** $3 \leq 4x - 3 < 19$

65. $-3 \leq \frac{2}{3}x - 5 < -1$ **66.** $-6 \leq \frac{1}{2}x - 4 < -3$

• Practice Plus

In Exercises 67–70, write an inequality with x isolated on the left side that is equivalent to the given inequality.

67. $Ax + By > C$; Assume $A > 0$.

68. $Ax + By \leq C$; Assume $A > 0$.

69. $Ax + By > C$; Assume $A < 0$.

70. $Ax + By \leq C$; Assume $A < 0$.

In Exercises 71–76, use set-builder notation to describe all real numbers satisfying the given conditions.

71. A number increased by 5 is at least two times the number.

72. A number increased by 12 is at least four times the number.

73. Twice the sum of four and a number is at most 36.

74. Three times the sum of five and a number is at most 48.

75. If the quotient of three times a number and five is increased by four, the result is no more than 34.

76. If the quotient of three times a number and four is decreased by three, the result is no less than 9.

• Application Exercises

The graphs show that the three components of love, namely passion, intimacy, and commitment, progress differently over time. Passion peaks early in a relationship and then declines. By contrast, intimacy and commitment build gradually. Use the graphs to solve Exercises 77–84. Assume that x represents years in a relationship.

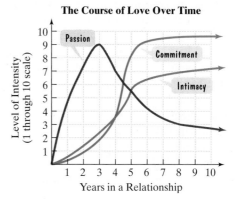

The Course of Love Over Time

Source: R. J. Sternberg, A Triangular Theory of Love, *Psychological Review*, 93, 119–135.

77. Use set-builder notation to write an inequality that expresses for which years in a relationship intimacy is greater that commitment.

78. Use set-builder notation to write an inequality that expresses for which years in a relationship passion is greater than or equal to intimacy.

79. What is the relationship between passion and intimacy for $\{x \mid 5 \leq x < 7\}$?

80. What is the relationship between intimacy and commitment for $\{x \mid 4 \leq x < 7\}$?

81. What is the relationship between passion and commitment for $\{x \mid 6 < x < 8\}$?

82. What is the relationship between passion and commitment for $\{x \mid 7 < x < 9\}$?

83. What is the maximum level of intensity for passion? After how many years in a relationship does this occur?

84. After approximately how many years do levels of intensity for commitment exceed the maximum level of intensity for passion?

The bar graph shows the percentage of U.S. college freshmen with no religious preference for selected years from 1984 through 2004.

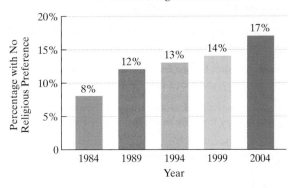

Percentage of U.S. College Freshmen with No Religious Preference

Source: UCLA Higher Education Research Institute

The data can be modeled by the formula

$$P = 0.4x + 8.8,$$

where P is the percentage of freshmen with no religious preference x years after 1984. Use this formula to solve Exercises 85–86.

85. If trends modeled by the formula continue, describe how many years after 1984 more than 20% of college freshmen will have no religious preference. What years are included in your description?

86. If trends modeled by the formula continue, describe how many years after 1984 more than 22% of college freshmen will have no religious preference. What years are included in your description?

87. On three examinations, you have grades of 88, 78, and 86. There is still a final examination, which counts as one grade.

   a. In order to get an A, your average must be at least 90. If you get 100 on the final, compute your average and determine if an A in the course is possible.

   b. To earn a B in the course, you must have a final average of at least 80. What must you get on the final to earn a B in the course?

88. On two examinations, you have grades of 86 and 88. There is an optional final examination, which counts as one grade. You decide to take the final in order to get a course grade of A, meaning a final average of at least 90.

   a. What must you get on the final to earn an A in the course?

   b. By taking the final, if you do poorly, you might risk the B that you have in the course based on the first two exam grades. If your final average is less than 80, you will lose your B in the course. Describe the grades on the final that will cause this to happen.

89. A car can be rented from Continental Rental for $80 per week plus 25 cents for each mile driven. How many miles can you travel if you can spend at most $400 for the week?

90. A car can be rented from Basic Rental for $60 per week plus 50 cents for each mile driven. How many miles can you travel if you can spend at most $600 for the week?

91. An elevator at a construction site has a maximum capacity of 3000 pounds. If the elevator operator weighs 245 pounds and each cement bag weighs 95 pounds, up to how many bags of cement can be safely lifted on the elevator in one trip?

92. An elevator at a construction site has a maximum capacity of 2800 pounds. If the elevator operator weighs 265 pounds and each cement bag weighs 65 pounds, up to how many bags of cement can be safely lifted on the elevator in one trip?

93. A basic cellular phone plan costs $20 per month for 60 calling minutes. Additional time costs $0.40 per minute. The formula

$$C = 20 + 0.40(x - 60)$$

gives the monthly cost for this plan, *C*, for *x* calling minutes, where $x > 60$. How many calling minutes are possible for a monthly cost of at least $28 and at most $40?

• Writing in Mathematics

94. When graphing the solutions of an inequality, what is the difference between an open dot and a closed dot?

95. When solving an inequality, when is it necessary to change the direction of the inequality symbol? Give an example.

96. Describe ways in which solving a linear inequality is similar to solving a linear equation.

97. Describe ways in which solving a linear inequality is different than solving a linear equation.

• Critical Thinking Exercises

98. A car can be rented from Basic Rental for $260 per week with no extra charge for mileage. Continental charges $80 per week plus 25 cents for each mile driven to rent the same car. How many miles must be driven in a week to make the rental cost for Basic Rental a better deal than Continental's?

99. A company manufactures and sells personalized stationery. The weekly fixed cost is $3000 and it cost $3.00 to produce each package of stationery. The selling price is $5.50 per package. How many packages of stationery must be produced and sold each week for the company to generate a profit?

SECTION 6.6 • QUADRATIC EQUATIONS

OBJECTIVES

1. Multiply binomials using the FOIL method.
2. Factor trinomials.
3. Solve quadratic equations by factoring.
4. Solve quadratic equations using the quadratic formula.
5. Solve problems modeled by quadratic equations.

Until fairly recently, many doctors believed that your blood pressure was theirs to know and yours to worry about. Today, however, people are encouraged to find out their blood pressure. That pumped-up cuff that squeezes against your upper arm measures blood pressure in millimeters (mm) of mercury (Hg). Blood pressure is given in two numbers: systolic pressure over diastolic pressure, such as 120 over 80. Systolic pressure is the pressure of blood against the artery walls when the heart contracts. Diastolic pressure is the pressure of blood against the artery walls when the heart is at rest.

There is a tendency for systolic pressure to increase with age as the arteries become less elastic. In this section, we will use equations to model normal systolic pressure based on age and gender. Unlike linear equations, these equations have a term in which the greatest exponent on the variable is 2. We focus on two methods for solving such equations: factoring and using a formula.

1 | Multiply binomials using the FOIL method.

Multiplying Two Binomials Using the FOIL Method

Before we learn about the first method, factoring, we need to consider the FOIL method for multiplying two binomials. A **binomial** is a simplified algebraic expression that contains two terms in which each exponent that appears on a variable is a whole number.

Examples of Binomials

$$x + 3, \quad x + 4, \quad 3x + 4, \quad 5x - 3$$

Two binomials can be quickly multiplied by using the FOIL method, in which **F** represents the product of the **first** terms in each binomial, **O** represents the product of the **outside** terms, **I** represents the product of the two **inside** terms, and **L** represents the product of the **last,** or second, terms in each binomial.

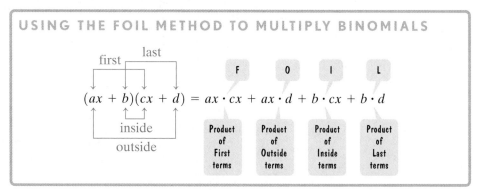

Once you have multiplied first, outside, inside, and last terms, combine all like terms.

EXAMPLE 1   USING THE FOIL METHOD

Multiply: $(x + 3)(x + 4)$.

SOLUTION

$$F : \text{First terms} \quad = x \cdot x = x^2 \quad (x + 3)(x + 4)$$
$$O: \text{Outside terms} = x \cdot 4 = 4x \quad (x + 3)(x + 4)$$
$$I : \text{Inside terms} \quad = 3 \cdot x = 3x \quad (x + 3)(x + 4)$$
$$L : \text{Last terms} \quad = 3 \cdot 4 = 12 \quad (x + 3)(x + 4)$$

$$\begin{aligned}
(x + 3)(x + 4) &= x \cdot x + x \cdot 4 + 3 \cdot x + 3 \cdot 4 \\
&= x^2 + 4x + 3x + 12 \\
&= x^2 + 7x + 12 \quad \text{Combine like terms.}
\end{aligned}$$

 Multiply: $(x + 5)(x + 6)$.

EXAMPLE 2   USING THE FOIL METHOD

Multiply: $(3x + 4)(5x - 3)$.

SOLUTION

$$\begin{aligned}
(3x + 4)(5x - 3) &= 3x \cdot 5x + 3x(-3) + 4 \cdot 5x + 4(-3) \\
&= 15x^2 - 9x + 20x - 12 \\
&= 15x^2 + 11x - 12 \quad \text{Combine like terms.}
\end{aligned}$$

 Multiply: $(7x + 5)(4x - 3)$.

---

2 | Factor trinomials.

Factoring a Trinomial Where the Coefficient of the Squared Term Is 1

The algebraic expression $x^2 + 7x + 12$ is called a trinomial. A **trinomial** is a simplified algebraic expression that contains three terms in which all variables have whole number exponents.

We can use the FOIL method to multiply two binomials to obtain the trinomial $x^2 + 7x + 12$:

$$\begin{array}{ccccc}
\textbf{Factored Form} & \textbf{F} & \textbf{O} \quad \textbf{I} & \textbf{L} & \textbf{Trinomial Form} \\
(x + 3)(x + 4) & = & x^2 + 4x + 3x + 12 & = & x^2 + 7x + 12
\end{array}$$

Because the product of $x + 3$ and $x + 4$ is $x^2 + 7x + 12$, we call $x + 3$ and $x + 4$ the **factors** of $x^2 + 7x + 12$. **Factoring** an algebraic expression containing the sum or difference of terms means finding an equivalent expression that is a product. Thus, to factor $x^2 + 7x + 12$, we write

$$x^2 + 7x + 12 = (x + 3)(x + 4).$$

We can make several important observations about the factors on the right side.

$$x^2 + 7x + 12 = (x + 3)(x + 4) \qquad x^2 + 7x + 12 = (x + 3)(x + 4) \qquad x^2 + 7x + 12 = (x + 3)(x + 4)$$

I: $3x$

O: $4x$

The first term of each factor is x. The product of the First terms is $x \cdot x = x^2$.

3 and 4 are factors of 12. The product of the Last terms is $3 \cdot 4 = 12$.

The sum of the Outside and Inside products is $4x + 3x = 7x$.

These observations provide us with a procedure for factoring $x^2 + bx + c$.

> **A STRATEGY FOR FACTORING** $x^2 + bx + c$
>
> **1.** Enter x as the first term of each factor.
> $$(x \quad)(x \quad) = x^2 + bx + c$$
>
> **2.** List pairs of factors of the constant c.
>
> **3.** Try various combinations of these factors. Select the combination in which the sum of the Outside and Inside products is equal to bx.
> $$(x + \square)(x + \square) = x^2 + bx + c$$
> I
> O
> Sum of O + I
>
> **4.** Check your work by multiplying the factors using the FOIL method. You should obtain the original trinomial.
>
> If none of the possible combinations yield an Outside product and an Inside product whose sum is equal to bx, the trinomial cannot be factored using integers and is called **prime**.

EXAMPLE 3   FACTORING A TRINOMIAL IN $x^2 + bx + c$ FORM

Factor: $x^2 + 6x + 8$.

SOLUTION

Step 1. Enter x as the first term of each factor.
$$x^2 + 6x + 8 = (x \quad)(x \quad)$$

To find the second term of each factor, we must find two integers whose product is 8 and whose sum is 6.

Step 2. List all pairs of factors of the constant, 8.

Factors of 8	8, 1	4, 2	$-8, -1$	$-4, -2$

Step 3. Try various combinations of these factors. The correct factorization of $x^2 + 6x + 8$ is the one in which the sum of the Outside and Inside products is equal to $6x$. Here is a list of the possible factorizations:

Possible Factorizations of $x^2 + 6x + 8$	Sum of Outside and Inside Products (Should Equal $6x$)
$(x + 8)(x + 1)$	$x + 8x = 9x$
$(x + 4)(x + 2)$	$2x + 4x = 6x$
$(x - 8)(x - 1)$	$-x - 8x = -9x$
$(x - 4)(x - 2)$	$-2x - 4x = -6x$

This is the required middle term.

Thus, $x^2 + 6x + 8 = (x + 4)(x + 2)$.

STUDY TIP

To factor $x^2 + bx + c$ when c is positive, find two numbers with the same sign as the middle term.

$$x^2 + 6x + 8 = (x + 2)(x + 4)$$

Same signs

$$x^2 - 5x + 6 = (x - 3)(x - 2)$$

Same signs

Using this observation, it is not necessary to list the last two factorizations in step 3 on the right.

We can check that $x^2 + 6x + 8 = (x + 4)(x + 2)$ by multiplying the right side using the FOIL method. You should obtain the original trinomial. Because of the commutative property, we can also say that

$$x^2 + 6x + 8 = (x + 2)(x + 4).$$

○

 Factor: $x^2 + 5x + 6$.

EXAMPLE 4   FACTORING A TRINOMIAL IN $x^2 + bx + c$ FORM

Factor: $x^2 + 2x - 35$.

SOLUTION

Step 1. Enter x as the first term of each factor.

$$x^2 + 2x - 35 = (x \quad)(x \quad)$$

To find the second term of each factor, we must find two integers whose product is -35 and whose sum is 2.

Step 2. List pairs of factors of the constant, -35.

Factors of -35	35, −1	−35, 1	−7, 5	7, −5

Step 3. Try various combinations of these factors. The correct factorization of $x^2 + 2x - 35$ is the one in which the sum of the Outside and Inside products is equal to $2x$. Here is a list of the possible factorizations:

Possible Factorizations of $x^2 + 2x - 35$	Sum of Outside and Inside Products (Should Equal $2x$)
$(x - 1)(x + 35)$	$35x - \quad x = 34x$
$(x + 1)(x - 35)$	$-35x + \quad x = -34x$
$(x - 7)(x + 5)$	$5x - 7x = -2x$
$(x + 7)(x - 5)$	$-5x + 7x = 2x$

This is the required middle term.

STUDY TIP

To factor $x^2 + bx + c$ when c is negative, find two numbers with opposite signs whose sum is the coefficient of the middle term.

$$x^2 + 2x - 35 = (x + 7)(x - 5)$$

Negative   Opposite signs

Thus, $x^2 + 2x - 35 = (x + 7)(x - 5)$ or $(x - 5)(x + 7)$.

Step 4. Verify the factorization using the FOIL method.

F   O   I   L

$$(x + 7)(x - 5) = x^2 - 5x + 7x - 35 = x^2 + 2x - 35$$

Because the product of the factors is the original trinomial, the factorization is correct.

○

Factor: $x^2 + 3x - 10$.

Factoring a Trinomial Where the Coefficient of the Squared Term Is Not 1

How do we factor a trinomial such as $3x^2 - 20x + 28$? Notice that the coefficient of the squared term is 3. We must find two binomials whose product is $3x^2 - 20x + 28$. The product of the First terms must be $3x^2$:

$$(3x \quad)(x \quad).$$

From this point on, the factoring strategy is exactly the same as the one we use to factor trinomials whose coefficient of the squared term is 1.

EXAMPLE 5   FACTORING A TRINOMIAL

Factor: $3x^2 - 20x + 28$.

SOLUTION

Step 1. Find two First terms whose product is $3x^2$.

$$3x^2 - 20x + 28 = (3x\quad)(x\quad)$$

Step 2. List all pairs of factors of the constant, 28. The number 28 has pairs of factors that are either both positive or both negative. Because the middle term, $-20x$, is negative, both factors must be negative. The negative factorizations of 28 are $-1(-28)$, $-2(-14)$, and $-4(-7)$.

Step 3. Try various combinations of these factors. The correct factorization of $3x^2 - 20x + 28$ is the one in which the sum of the Outside and Inside products is equal to $-20x$. Here is a list of the possible factorizations:

Possible Factorizations of $3x^2 - 20x + 28$	Sum of Outside and Inside Products (Should Equal $-20x$)
$(3x - 1)(x - 28)$	$-84x - x = -85x$
$(3x - 28)(x - 1)$	$-3x - 28x = -31x$
$(3x - 2)(x - 14)$	$-42x - 2x = -44x$
$(3x - 14)(x - 2)$	$-6x - 14x = -20x$
$(3x - 4)(x - 7)$	$-21x - 4x = -25x$
$(3x - 7)(x - 4)$	$-12x - 7x = -19x$

This is the required middle term.

Thus,

$$3x^2 - 20x + 28 = (3x - 14)(x - 2) \quad \text{or} \quad (x - 2)(3x - 14).$$

Step 4. Verify the factorization using the FOIL method.

$$(3x - 14)(x - 2) = \overset{F}{3x \cdot x} + \overset{O}{3x(-2)} + \overset{I}{(-14) \cdot x} + \overset{L}{(-14)(-2)}$$
$$= 3x^2 - 6x - 14x + 28$$
$$= 3x^2 - 20x + 28$$

Because this is the trinomial we started with, the factorization is correct.

Factor: $5x^2 - 14x + 8$.

EXAMPLE 6   FACTORING A TRINOMIAL

Factor: $8y^2 - 10y - 3$.

SOLUTION

Step 1. Find two first terms whose product is $8y^2$.

$$8y^2 - 10y - 3 \overset{?}{=} (8y\quad)(y\quad)$$
$$8y^2 - 10y - 3 \overset{?}{=} (4y\quad)(2y\quad)$$

Step 2. List all pairs of factors of the constant, -3. The possible factorizations are $1(-3)$ and $-1(3)$.

Step 3. Try various combinations of these factors. The correct factorization of $8y^2 - 10y - 3$ is the one in which the sum of the Outside and Inside products is equal to $-10y$. Here is a list of the possible factorizations:

Possible Factorizations of $8y^2 - 10y - 3$	Sum of Outside and Inside Products (Should Equal $-10y$)
$(8y + 1)(y - 3)$	$-24y + y = -23y$
$(8y - 3)(y + 1)$	$8y - 3y = 5y$
$(8y - 1)(y + 3)$	$24y - y = 23y$
$(8y + 3)(y - 1)$	$-8y + 3y = -5y$
$(4y + 1)(2y - 3)$	$-12y + 2y = -10y$
$(4y - 3)(2y + 1)$	$4y - 6y = -2y$
$(4y - 1)(2y + 3)$	$12y - 2y = 10y$
$(4y + 3)(2y - 1)$	$-4y + 6y = 2y$

> This is the required middle term.

Thus,

$$8y^2 - 10y - 3 = (4y + 1)(2y - 3) \quad \text{or} \quad (2y - 3)(4y + 1).$$

Show that this factorization is correct by multiplying the factors using the FOIL method. You should obtain the original trinomial.

 CHECK POINT 6 Factor: $6y^2 + 19y - 7$.

3 | Solve quadratic equations by factoring.

Solving Quadratic Equations by Factoring

We have seen that in a linear equation, the highest exponent on the variable is 1. We now define a quadratic equation, in which the greatest exponent on the variable is 2.

> **DEFINITION OF A QUADRATIC EQUATION**
> A **quadratic equation** in x is an equation that can be written in the form
> $$ax^2 + bx + c = 0,$$
> where a, b, and c are real numbers, with $a \neq 0$.

Here is an example of a quadratic equation:

$$x^2 - 7x + 10 = 0.$$

$a = 1 \quad b = -7 \quad c = 10$

Notice that we can factor the left side of this equation.

$$x^2 - 7x + 10 = 0$$
$$(x - 5)(x - 2) = 0$$

If a quadratic equation has zero on one side and a factored trinomial on the other side, it can be solved using the **zero-product principle**:

> **THE ZERO-PRODUCT PRINCIPLE**
> If the product of two factors is zero, then one (or both) of the factors must have a value of zero.
> $$\text{If } AB = 0, \text{ then } A = 0 \text{ or } B = 0.$$

> **EXAMPLE 7** SOLVING A QUADRATIC EQUATION USING THE ZERO-PRODUCT PRINCIPLE

Solve: $(x - 5)(x - 2) = 0$.

SOLUTION The product $(x - 5)(x - 2)$ is equal to zero. By the zero-product principle, the only way that this product can be zero is if at least one of the factors is zero. We set each individual factor equal to zero and solve each resulting equation for x.

$$(x - 5)(x - 2) = 0$$
$$x - 5 = 0 \quad \text{or} \quad x - 2 = 0$$
$$x = 5 \qquad\qquad x = 2$$

Check the proposed solutions by substituting each one separately for x in the original equation.

Check 5:	**Check** 2:
$(x - 5)(x - 2) = 0$	$(x - 5)(x - 2) = 0$
$(5 - 5)(5 - 2) \stackrel{?}{=} 0$	$(2 - 5)(2 - 2) \stackrel{?}{=} 0$
$0(3) \stackrel{?}{=} 0$	$-3(0) \stackrel{?}{=} 0$
$0 = 0, \quad$ true	$0 = 0, \quad$ true

The resulting true statements indicate that the solutions are 5 and 2. The solution set is $\{2, 5\}$.

○

 CHECK POINT 7 Solve: $(x + 6)(x - 3) = 0$.

STUDY TIP

The method on the right does not apply if $ax^2 + bx + c$ is not factorable, or prime.

SOLVING A QUADRATIC EQUATION BY FACTORING

1. If necessary, rewrite the equation in the form $ax^2 + bx + c = 0$, moving all terms to one side, thereby obtaining zero on the other side.
2. Factor.
3. Apply the zero-product principle, setting each factor equal to zero.
4. Solve the equations in step 3.
5. Check the solutions in the original equation.

> **EXAMPLE 8** SOLVING A QUADRATIC EQUATION BY FACTORING

Solve: $x^2 - 2x = 35$.

SOLUTION

Step 1. Move all terms to one side and obtain zero on the other side. Subtract 35 from both sides and write the equation in $ax^2 + bx + c = 0$ form.

$$x^2 - 2x = 35$$
$$x^2 - 2x - 35 = 35 - 35$$
$$x^2 - 2x - 35 = 0$$

Step 2. Factor. $\qquad (x - 7)(x + 5) = 0$

Steps 3 and 4. Set each factor equal to zero and solve each resulting equation.

$$x - 7 = 0 \quad \text{or} \quad x + 5 = 0$$
$$x = 7 \qquad\qquad x = -5$$

Step 5. Check the solutions in the original equation.

Check 7:	Check −5:
$x^2 - 2x = 35$	$x^2 - 2x = 35$
$7^2 - 2 \cdot 7 \overset{?}{=} 35$	$(-5)^2 - 2(-5) \overset{?}{=} 35$
$49 - 14 \overset{?}{=} 35$	$25 + 10 \overset{?}{=} 35$
$35 = 35$, true	$35 = 35$, true

The resulting true statements indicate that the solutions are 7 and −5. The solution set is $\{-5, 7\}$.

 Solve: $x^2 - 6x = 16$.

EXAMPLE 9	SOLVING A QUADRATIC EQUATION BY FACTORING

Solve: $5x^2 - 33x + 40 = 0$.

SOLUTION All terms are already on the left and zero is on the other side. Thus, we can factor the trinomial on the left side. $5x^2 - 33x + 40$ factors as $(5x - 8)(x - 5)$.

$$5x^2 - 33x + 40 = 0 \qquad \text{This is the given quadratic equation.}$$

$$(5x - 8)(x - 5) = 0 \qquad \text{Factor.}$$

$$5x - 8 = 0 \quad \text{or} \quad x - 5 = 0 \qquad \text{Set each factor equal to zero.}$$

$$5x = 8 \qquad\qquad x = 5 \qquad \text{Solve the resulting equations.}$$

$$x = \frac{8}{5}$$

Check these values in the original equation to confirm that the solution set is $\left\{\frac{8}{5}, 5\right\}$.

 Solve: $2x^2 + 7x - 4 = 0$.

---

4 | Solve quadratic equations using the quadratic formula.

Solving Quadratic Equations Using the Quadratic Formula

The solutions of a quadratic equation cannot always be found by factoring. Some trinomials are difficult to factor, and others cannot be factored (that is, they are prime). However, there is a formula that can be used to solve all quadratic equations, whether or not they contain factorable trinomials. The formula is called the *quadratic formula*.

STUDY TIP

The entire numerator of the quadratic formula must be divided by $2a$. Always write the fraction bar all the way across the numerator.

$$x = \frac{-b \pm \sqrt{b^2 - 4ac}}{2a}$$

THE QUADRATIC FORMULA

The solutions of a quadratic equation in the form $ax^2 + bx + c = 0$, with $a \neq 0$, are given by the **quadratic formula**

$$x = \frac{-b \pm \sqrt{b^2 - 4ac}}{2a}.$$

x equals negative b plus or minus the square root of $b^2 - 4ac$, all divided by 2a.

To Die at Twenty

Can the equations

$$7x^5 + 12x^3 - 9x + 4 = 0$$

and

$$8x^6 - 7x^5 + 4x^3 - 19 = 0$$

be solved using a formula similar to the quadratic formula? The first equation has five solutions and the second has six solutions, but they cannot be found using a formula. How do we know? In 1832, a 20-year-old Frenchman, Evariste Galois, wrote a proof showing that there is no general formula to solve equations when the exponent on the variable is 5 or greater.

Galois was jailed as a political activist several times while still a teenager. The day after his brilliant proof, he fought a duel over a woman. The duel was a political setup. As he lay dying, Galois told his brother, Alfred, of the manuscript that contained his proof: "Mathematical manuscripts are in my room. On the table. Take care of my work. Make it known. Important. Don't cry, Alfred. I need all my courage—to die at twenty."

(Our source is Leopold Infeld's biography of Galois, *Whom the Gods Love*. Some historians, however, dispute the story of Galois's ironic death the very day after his algebraic proof. Mathematical truths seem more reliable than historical ones!)

To use the quadratic formula, be sure that the quadratic equation is expressed with all terms on one side and zero on the other side. It may be necessary to begin by rewriting the equation in this form. Then determine the numerical values for a (the coefficient of the x^2-term), b (the coefficient of the x-term), and c (the constant term). Substitute the values of a, b, and c into the quadratic formula and evaluate the expression. The $\pm$ sign indicates that there are two solutions of the equation.

EXAMPLE 10   SOLVING A QUADRATIC EQUATION USING THE QUADRATIC FORMULA

Solve using the quadratic formula: $2x^2 + 9x - 5 = 0$.

SOLUTION   The given equation is in the desired form, with all terms on one side and zero on the other side. Begin by identifying the values for a, b, and c.

$$2x^2 + 9x - 5 = 0.$$

$$a = 2 \qquad b = 9 \qquad c = -5$$

Substituting these values into the quadratic formula and simplifying gives the equation's solutions.

$$x = \frac{-b \pm \sqrt{b^2 - 4ac}}{2a}$$ Use the quadratic formula.

$$x = \frac{-9 \pm \sqrt{9^2 - 4(2)(-5)}}{2(2)}$$ Substitute the values for a, b, and c: $a = 2$, $b = 9$, and $c = -5$.

$$= \frac{-9 \pm \sqrt{81 + 40}}{4}$$ $9^2 - 4(2)(-5) = 81 - (-40) = 81 + 40$

$$= \frac{-9 \pm \sqrt{121}}{4}$$ Add under the radical sign.

$$= \frac{-9 \pm 11}{4}$$ $\sqrt{121} = 11$

Now we will evaluate this expression in two different ways to obtain the two solutions. At the left, we will *add* 11 to -9. At the right, we will *subtract* 11 from -9.

$$x = \frac{-9 + 11}{4} \quad \text{or} \quad x = \frac{-9 - 11}{4}$$

$$= \frac{2}{4} = \frac{1}{2} \qquad\qquad = \frac{-20}{4} = -5$$

The solution set is $\left\{-5, \frac{1}{2}\right\}$.   ○

 CHECK POINT 10   Solve using the quadratic formula: $8x^2 + 2x - 1 = 0$.

The quadratic equation in Example 10 has rational solutions, namely -5 and $\frac{1}{2}$. The equation can also be solved by factoring. Take a few minutes to do this now and convince yourself that you will arrive at the same two solutions.

Any quadratic equation that has rational solutions can be solved by factoring or using the quadratic formula. However, quadratic equations with irrational solutions cannot be solved by factoring. These equations can be readily solved using the quadratic formula.

EXAMPLE 11   SOLVING A QUADRATIC EQUATION USING THE QUADRATIC FORMULA

Solve using the quadratic formula: $2x^2 = 4x + 1.$

SOLUTION The quadratic equation must have zero on one side to identify the values for a, b, and c. To move all terms to one side and obtain zero on the right, we subtract $4x + 1$ from both sides. Then we can identify the values for a, b, and c.

$$2x^2 = 4x + 1 \qquad \text{This is the given equation.}$$

$$2x^2 - 4x - 1 = 0. \qquad \text{Subtract } 4x + 1 \text{ from both sides.}$$

$$\boxed{a = 2} \qquad \boxed{b = -4} \qquad \boxed{c = -1}$$

Substituting these values into the quadratic formula and simplifying gives the equation's solutions.

$$x = \frac{-b \pm \sqrt{b^2 - 4ac}}{2a} \qquad \text{Use the quadratic formula.}$$

$$x = \frac{-(-4) \pm \sqrt{(-4)^2 - 4(2)(-1)}}{2(2)} \qquad \begin{array}{l} \text{Substitute the values for } a, b, \text{ and } c: \\ a = 2, b = -4, \text{ and } c = -1. \end{array}$$

$$= \frac{4 \pm \sqrt{16 - (-8)}}{4} \qquad (-4)^2 - 4(2)(-1) = 16 - (-8)$$

$$= \frac{4 \pm \sqrt{24}}{4} \qquad 16 - (-8) = 16 + 8 = 24$$

The solutions are $\dfrac{4 + \sqrt{24}}{4}$ and $\dfrac{4 - \sqrt{24}}{4}$. These solutions are irrational numbers.

You can use a calculator to obtain a decimal approximation for each solution. However, in situations such as this that do not involve applications, it is best to leave the irrational solutions in radical form as exact answers. In some cases, we can simplify this radical form. Using methods for simplifying square roots discussed in Section 5.4, we can simplify $\sqrt{24}$:

$$\sqrt{24} = \sqrt{4 \cdot 6} = \sqrt{4}\sqrt{6} = 2\sqrt{6}.$$

Now we can use this result to simplify the two solutions. First, use the distributive property to factor out 2 from both terms in the numerator. Then, divide the numerator and the denominator by 2.

$$x = \frac{4 \pm \sqrt{24}}{4} = \frac{4 \pm 2\sqrt{6}}{4} = \frac{\overset{1}{2}\left(2 \pm \sqrt{6}\right)}{\underset{2}{4}} = \frac{2 \pm \sqrt{6}}{2}$$

In simplified radical form, the equation's solution set is

$$\left\{ \frac{2 + \sqrt{6}}{2}, \frac{2 - \sqrt{6}}{2} \right\}.$$

Examples 10 and 11 illustrate that the solutions of quadratic equations can be rational or irrational numbers. In Example 10, the expression under the square root was 121, a perfect square ($\sqrt{121} = 11$), and we obtained rational solutions. In Example 11, this expression was 24, which is not a perfect square (although we simplified $\sqrt{24}$ to $2\sqrt{6}$), and we obtained irrational solutions. If the expression under the square root simplifies to a negative number, then the quadratic equation has **no real solution**. The solution set consists of *imaginary numbers*, discussed in the Blitzer Bonus on page 275.

 CHECK POINT 11 Solve using the quadratic formula: $2x^2 = 6x - 1.$

5 | Solve problems modeled by quadratic equations.

Applications

EXAMPLE 12   BLOOD PRESSURE AND AGE

The graphs in Figure 6.6 illustrate that a person's normal systolic blood pressure, measured in millimeters of mercury (mm Hg), depends on his or her age. The formula

$$P = 0.006A^2 - 0.02A + 120$$

models a man's normal systolic pressure, P, at age A.

a. Find the age, to the nearest year, of a man whose normal systolic blood pressure is 125 mm Hg.

b. Use the graphs in Figure 6.6 to describe the differences between the normal systolic blood pressures of men and women as they age.

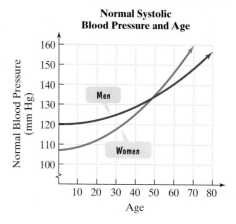

Normal Systolic Blood Pressure and Age

FIGURE 6.6

SOLUTION

a. We are interested in the age of a man with a normal systolic blood pressure of 125 millimeters of mercury. Thus, we substitute 125 for P in the given formula for men. Then we solve for A, the man's age.

$P = 0.006A^2 - 0.02A + 120$	This is the given formula for men.
$125 = 0.006A^2 - 0.02A + 120$	Substitute 125 for P.
$0 = 0.006A^2 - 0.02A - 5$	Subtract 125 from both sides and obtain zero on one side.

$$a = 0.006 \quad b = -0.02 \quad c = -5$$

Because the trinomial on the right side of the equation is prime, we solve using the quadratic formula.

TECHNOLOGY

On most calculators, here is how to approximate

$$\frac{0.02 + \sqrt{0.1204}}{0.012}.$$

MANY SCIENTIFIC CALCULATORS

(.02 + .1204 √)

÷ .012 =

MANY GRAPHING CALCULATORS

(.02 + √ .1204)

÷ .012 ENTER

If your calculator displays an open parenthesis after √ , you'll need to enter another closed parenthesis here.

Notice that the variable is A, rather than the usual x.

$$A = \frac{-b \pm \sqrt{b^2 - 4ac}}{2a}$$

Use the quadratic formula.

$$= \frac{-(-0.02) \pm \sqrt{(-0.02)^2 - 4(0.006)(-5)}}{2(0.006)}$$

Substitute the values for a, b, and c: $a = 0.006$, $b = -0.02$, and $c = -5$.

$$= \frac{0.02 \pm \sqrt{0.1204}}{0.012}$$

Use a calculator to simplify the expression under the square root.

$$\approx \frac{0.02 \pm 0.347}{0.012}$$

Use a calculator: $\sqrt{0.1204} \approx 0.347$.

$$A \approx \frac{0.02 + 0.347}{0.012} \quad \text{or} \quad A \approx \frac{0.02 - 0.347}{0.012}$$

$$A \approx 31 \qquad\qquad\qquad A \approx -27$$

Reject this solution. Age cannot be negative.

Use a calculator and round to the nearest integer.

The positive solution, $A \approx 31$, indicates that 31 is the approximate age of a man whose normal systolic blood pressure is 125 mm Hg. This is illustrated by the black lines with the arrows on the red graph representing men in Figure 6.7.

b. Take a second look at the graphs in Figure 6.7. Before approximately age 50, the blue graph representing women's normal systolic blood pressure lies below the red graph representing men's normal systolic blood pressure. Thus, up to age 50, women's normal systolic blood pressure is lower than men's, although it is increasing at a faster rate. After age 50, women's normal systolic blood pressure is higher than men's.

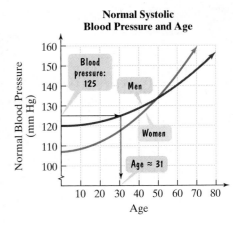

Normal Systolic Blood Pressure and Age

FIGURE 6.7

CHECK POINT 12 The formula $P = 0.01A^2 + 0.05A + 107$ models a woman's normal systolic blood pressure, P, at age A. Use this formula to find the age, to the nearest year, of a woman whose normal systolic blood pressure is 115 mm Hg. Use the blue graph in Figure 6.7 to verify your solution.

EXERCISE SET 6.6 ●●●●●●

Practice Exercises

Use FOIL to find the products in Exercises 1–8.

1. $(x + 3)(x + 5)$ **2.** $(x + 7)(x + 2)$

3. $(x - 5)(x + 3)$ **4.** $(x - 1)(x + 2)$

5. $(2x - 1)(x + 2)$ **6.** $(2x - 5)(x + 3)$

7. $(3x - 7)(4x - 5)$ **8.** $(2x - 9)(7x - 4)$

Factor the trinomials in Exercises 9–20, or state that the trinomial is prime. Check your factorization using FOIL multiplication.

9. $x^2 + 5x + 6$ **10.** $x^2 + 8x + 15$

11. $x^2 - 2x - 15$ **12.** $x^2 - 4x - 5$

13. $x^2 - 8x + 15$ **14.** $x^2 - 14x + 45$

15. $x^2 - 9x - 36$ **16.** $x^2 - x - 90$

17. $x^2 - 8x + 32$ **18.** $x^2 - 9x + 81$

19. $x^2 + 17x + 16$ **20.** $x^2 - 7x - 44$

Factor the trinomials in Exercises 21–32, or state that the trinomial is prime. Check your factorization using FOIL multiplication. Unlike the trinomials you factored in Exercises 9–20, the trinomials that follow have coefficients of squared terms that are not equal to 1.

21. $2x^2 + 7x + 3$ **22.** $3x^2 + 7x + 2$

23. $2x^2 - 17x + 30$ **24.** $5x^2 - 13x + 6$

25. $3x^2 - x - 2$ **26.** $2x^2 + 5x - 3$

27. $3x^2 - 25x - 28$ **28.** $3x^2 - 2x - 5$

29. $6x^2 - 11x + 4$ **30.** $6x^2 - 17x + 12$

31. $4x^2 + 16x + 15$ **32.** $8x^2 + 33x + 4$

In Exercises 33–36, solve each equation using the zero-product principle.

33. $(x - 8)(x + 3) = 0$ **34.** $(x + 11)(x - 5) = 0$

35. $(4x + 5)(x - 2) = 0$ **36.** $(x + 9)(3x - 1) = 0$

Solve the quadratic equations in Exercises 37–52 by factoring.

37. $x^2 + 8x + 15 = 0$ **38.** $x^2 + 5x + 6 = 0$

39. $x^2 - 2x - 15 = 0$ **40.** $x^2 + x - 42 = 0$

41. $x^2 - 4x = 21$ **42.** $x^2 + 7x = 18$

43. $x^2 + 9x = -8$ **44.** $x^2 - 11x = -10$

45. $x^2 - 12x = -36$ **46.** $x^2 - 14x = -49$

47. $2x^2 = 7x + 4$ **48.** $3x^2 = x + 4$

49. $5x^2 + x = 18$ **50.** $3x^2 - 4x = 15$

51. $x(6x + 23) + 7 = 0$ **52.** $x(6x + 13) + 6 = 0$

Solve the equations in Exercises 53–72 using the quadratic formula.

53. $x^2 + 8x + 15 = 0$ **54.** $x^2 + 8x + 12 = 0$

55. $x^2 + 5x + 3 = 0$ **56.** $x^2 + 5x + 2 = 0$

57. $x^2 + 4x = 6$ **58.** $x^2 + 2x = 4$

59. $x^2 + 4x - 7 = 0$ **60.** $x^2 + 4x + 1 = 0$

61. $x^2 - 3x = 18$ **62.** $x^2 - 3x = 10$

63. $6x^2 - 5x - 6 = 0$ **64.** $9x^2 - 12x - 5 = 0$

65. $x^2 - 2x - 10 = 0$ **66.** $x^2 + 6x - 10 = 0$

67. $x^2 - x = 14$ **68.** $x^2 - 5x = 10$

69. $6x^2 + 6x + 1 = 0$ **70.** $3x^2 = 5x - 1$

71. $4x^2 = 12x - 9$ **72.** $9x^2 + 6x + 1 = 0$

Practice Plus

In Exercises 73–80, solve each equation by the method of your choice.

73. $\dfrac{3x^2}{4} - \dfrac{5x}{2} - 2 = 0$ **74.** $\dfrac{x^2}{3} - \dfrac{x}{2} - \dfrac{3}{2} = 0$

75. $(x - 1)(3x + 2) = -7(x - 1)$

76. $x(x + 1) = 4 - (x + 2)(x + 2)$

77. $(2x - 6)(x + 2) = 5(x - 1) - 12$

78. $7x(x - 2) = 3 - 2(x + 4)$

79. $2x^2 - 9x - 3 = 9 - 9x$

80. $3x^2 - 6x - 3 = 12 - 6x$

81. When the sum of 6 and twice a positive number is subtracted from the square of the number, 0 results. Find the number.

82. When the sum of 1 and twice a negative number is subtracted from twice the square of the number, 0 results. Find the number.

Application Exercises

The formula

$$N = \frac{t^2 - t}{2}$$

describes the number of football games, N, that must be played in a league with t teams if each team is to play every other team once. Use this information to solve Exercises 83–84.

83. If a league has 36 games scheduled, how many teams belong to the league, assuming that each team plays every other team once?

84. If a league has 45 games scheduled, how many teams belong to the league, assuming that each team plays every other team once?

The bar graph shows the percentage of foreign-born Americans from 1930 through 2003. The percentage, P, of the U.S. population that was foreign-born x years after 1930 can be modeled by the formula

$$P = 0.005x^2 - 0.37x + 11.8.$$

Use the formula to solve Exercises 85–88.

Percentage of U.S. Population That Was Foreign-Born, 1930-2003

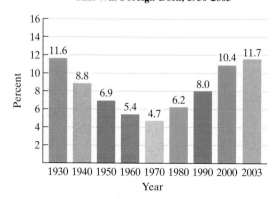

Source: U.S. Census Bureau

85. How well does the formula model the data for 2000?

86. How well does the formula model the data for 1940?

87. In which future year does the model project that 16% of the U.S. population will be foreign-born?

88. In which future year does the model project that 19% of the U.S. population will be foreign-born?

A driver's age has something to do with his or her chance of getting into a fatal car crash. The bar graph shows the number of fatal vehicle crashes per 100 million miles driven for drivers of various age groups. For example, 25-year-old drivers are involved in 4.1 fatal crashes per 100 million miles driven. Thus, when a group of 25-year-old Americans has driven a total of 100 million miles, approximately 4 have been in accidents in which someone died.

Age of U.S. Drivers and Fatal Crashes

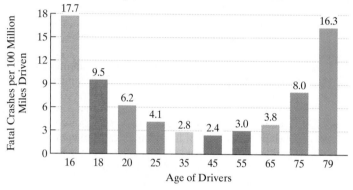

Source: Insurance Institute for Highway Safety

The number of fatal vehicle crashes per 100 million miles, N, for drivers of age x can be modeled by the formula

$$N = 0.013x^2 - 1.19x + 28.24.$$

Use the formula to solve Exercises 89–90. Use a calculator and round answers to the nearest year.

89. What age groups are expected to be involved in 3 fatal crashes per 100 million miles driven? How well does the formula model the trend in the actual data shown in the bar graph?

90. What age groups are expected to be involved in 10 fatal crashes per 100 million miles driven? How well does the formula model the trend in the actual data shown in the bar graph?

• Writing in Mathematics

91. Explain how to multiply two binomials using the FOIL method. Give an example with your explanation.

92. Explain how to factor $x^2 - 5x + 6$.

93. Explain how to solve a quadratic equation by factoring. Use the equation $x^2 + 6x + 8 = 0$ in your explanation.

94. Explain how to solve a quadratic equation using the quadratic formula. Use the equation $x^2 + 6x + 8 = 0$ in your explanation.

95. Describe the trend shown by the data for the percentage of foreign-born Americans in the graph for Exercises 85–88. Do you believe that this trend is likely to continue or might something occur that would make it impossible to extend the model into the future? Explain your answer.

• Critical Thinking Exercises

96. The radicand of the quadratic formula, $b^2 - 4ac$, can be used to determine whether $ax^2 + bx + c = 0$ has solutions that are rational, irrational, or not real numbers. Explain how this works. Is it possible to determine the kinds of answers that one will obtain to a quadratic equation without actually solving the equation? Explain.

In Exercises 97–98, find all positive integers b so that the trinomial can be factored.

97. $x^2 + bx + 15$

98. $x^2 + 4x + b$

99. Factor: $x^{2n} + 20x^n + 99$.

100. Solve: $x^2 + 2\sqrt{3}x - 9 = 0$.

•••••• CHAPTER SUMMARY, REVIEW, AND TEST

• S U M M A R Y DEFINITIONS AND CONCEPTS	EXAMPLES
6.1 Algebraic Expressions and Formulas	
a. An algebraic expression combines variables and numbers using addition, subtraction, multiplication, division, powers, or roots.	
b. Evaluating an algebraic expression means finding its value for a given value of the variable or for given values of the variables. Once these values are substituted, follow the order of operations agreement in the box on page 304.	Ex. 1, p. 305; Ex. 2, p. 305; Ex. 3, p. 305
c. An equation is a statement that two expressions are equal. Formulas are equations that express relationships among two or more variables. Mathematical modeling is the process of finding formulas to describe real-world phenomena. Such formulas, together with the meaning assigned to the variables, are called mathematical models. The formulas are said to model, or describe, the relationships among the variables.	Ex. 4, p. 306
d. Terms of an algebraic expression are separated by addition. Like terms have the same variables with the same exponents on the variables. To add or subtract like terms, add or subtract the coefficients and copy the common variable	
e. An algebraic expression is simplified when parentheses have been removed (using the distributive property) and like terms have been combined.	Ex. 5, p. 308; Ex. 6, p. 308; Ex. 7, p. 308
6.2 Linear Equations in One Variable	
a. A linear equation in one variable can be written in the form $ax + b = 0$, where a and b are real numbers, and $a \neq 0$.	
b. Solving a linear equation is the process of finding the set of numbers that make the equation a true statement. These numbers are the solutions. The set of all such solutions is the solution set.	
c. Equivalent equations have the same solution set. Properties for generating equivalent equations are given in the box on page 312.	Ex. 1, p. 313
d. A step-by-step procedure for solving a linear equation is given in the box on page 314.	Ex. 2, p. 314; Ex. 3, p. 315; Ex. 4, p. 316
e. If an equation contains fractions, begin by multiplying both sides of the equation by the least common denominator of the fractions in the equation, thereby clearing fractions.	Ex. 5, p. 317; Ex. 6, p. 317
f. Solving a formula for a variable means rewriting the formula so that the variable is isolated on one side of the equation.	Ex. 7, p. 319; Ex. 8, p. 319
g. If a false statement (such as $-6 = 7$) is obtained in solving a linear equation, the equation has no solution. The solution set is $\varnothing$, the empty set.	Ex. 9, p. 320
h. If a true statement (such as $-6 = -6$) is obtained in solving a linear equation, the equation has infinitely many solutions. The solution set is the set of all real numbers, written $\{x \mid x \text{ is a real number}\}$.	Ex. 10, p. 320

6.3 Applications of Linear Equations

a. Algebraic translations of English phrases are given in Table 6.2 on page 324.

b. A step-by-step strategy for solving word problems using linear equations is given in the box on page 324.

6.4 Ratio, Proportion, and Variation

a. The ratio of a to b is written $\dfrac{a}{b}$, or $a:b$.

b. A proportion is a statement in the form $\dfrac{a}{b} = \dfrac{c}{d}$.

c. The cross-products principle states that if $\dfrac{a}{b} = \dfrac{c}{d}$, then $ad = bc$.

d. A step-by-step procedure for solving applied problems using proportions is given in the box on page 333.

e. If two quantities vary directly, as one increases, so does the other. As one decreases, so does the other. Proportions can be used to solve direct variation problems.

f. If two quantities vary inversely, as one increases, the other decreases. As one decreases, the other increases. Proportions, as explained in the box on page 337, can be used to solve inverse variation problems.

6.5 Linear Inequalities in One Variable

A procedure for solving a linear inequality is given in the box on page 342. Remember to reverse the direction of the inequality symbol when multiplying or dividing both sides of an inequality by a negative number.

6.6 Quadratic Equations

a. A quadratic equation can be written in the form $ax^2 + bx + c = 0, a \neq 0$.

b. Some quadratic equations can be solved using factoring and the zero-product principle. A step-by-step procedure is given in the box on page 355.

c. All quadratic equations in the form $ax^2 + bx + c = 0$ can be solved using the quadratic formula:

$$x = \frac{-b \pm \sqrt{b^2 - 4ac}}{2a}.$$

REVIEW EXERCISES

6.1

In Exercises 1–3, evaluate the algebraic expression for the given value of the variable.

1. $6x + 9; x = 4$
2. $7x^2 + 4x - 5; x = -2$
3. $6 + 2(x - 8)^3; x = 5$

4. The bar graph on the right shows the number of music CD sales, in millions, in the United States from 1998 through 2002. The data can be modeled by the formula

$$N = -26x^2 + 143x + 740,$$

where N represents the number of music CD sales, in millions, x years after 1997. According to the formula, how many millions of CDs were sold in 2002? How well does the formula describe sales for that year shown by the graph?

Music CD Sales in the United States

CD Sales (millions of units)

1998 1999 2000 2001 2002
Year

Source: RIAA

In Exercises 5–7, simplify each algebraic expression.

5. $5(2x - 3) + 7x$

6. $3(4y - 5) - (7y - 2)$

7. $2(x^2 + 5x) + 3(4x^2 - 3x)$

6.2

In Exercises 8–14, solve each equation.

8. $4x + 9 = 33$

9. $5x - 3 = x + 5$

10. $3(x + 4) = 5x - 12$

11. $2(x - 2) + 3(x + 5) = 2x - 2$

12. $\dfrac{2x}{3} = \dfrac{x}{6} + 1$

13. $7x + 5 = 5(x + 3) + 2x$

14. $7x + 13 = 2(2x - 5) + 3x + 23$

In Exercises 15–18, solve each formula for the specified variable.

15. $Ax - By = C$ for x

16. $A = \frac{1}{2}bh$ for h

17. $A = \dfrac{B + C}{2}$ for B

18. $vt + gt^2 = s$ for g

19. The bar graph shows the average prescription-drug price in the United States from 2000 through 2004. The data can be modeled by the formula

$$P = 4.6x + 45.8,$$

where P is the average price of a prescription drug, in dollars, x years after 2000. In which year does this model project that the average prescription-drug price will be $101?

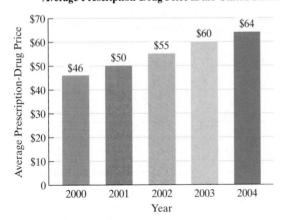

Average Prescription-Drug Price in the United States

Source: U.S. Census Bureau

6.3

In Exercises 20–24, use an equation to solve each problem.

20. When 7 times a number is decreased by 1, the result is 9 more than 5 times the number. Find the number.

21. The fast-food chains may be touting their "new and improved" salads, but how do they measure up in terms of calories?

Burger King
Chicken Caesar

Taco Bell
Express Taco Salad

Wendy's
Mandarin Chicken Salad

Number of calories exceeds the Chicken Caesar by 125.

Number of calories exceeds the Chicken Caesar by 95.

Source: Newsweek

Combined, the three salads contain 1705 calories. Determine the number of calories in each salad.

22. The bar graph shows the number of endangered plant species in the United States from 1998 through 2003. In 1998, there were 567 endangered species. For the period shown, the number of endangered plants increased at an average rate of 6.4 species per year. If this trend continues, in which year will there be 663 endangered plant species in the United States?

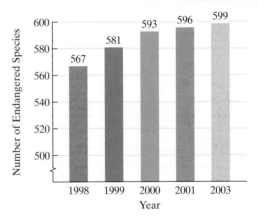

Endangered Plant Species in the United States

Source: U.S. Fish and Wildlife Service

23. You are choosing between two long-distance telephone plans. One plan has a monthly fee of $15 with a charge of $0.05 per minute. The other plan has a monthly fee of $5 with a charge of $0.07 per minute. For how many minutes of long-distance calls will the costs for the two plans be the same?

24. In 2004, the world's largest oil consumers were the United States and China. Oil consumption in the United States exceeded three times that of China by 1 million barrels per day. If the two countries combined consumed 27 million barrels of oil per day, determine the oil consumption, in millions of barrels per day, for each country.

(*Source*: Energy Information Administration)

6.4

In Exercises 25–28, solve each proportion.

25. $\dfrac{3}{x} = \dfrac{15}{25}$

26. $\dfrac{-7}{5} = \dfrac{91}{x}$

27. $\dfrac{x+2}{3} = \dfrac{4}{5}$

28. $\dfrac{5}{x+7} = \dfrac{3}{x+3}$

Use a proportion to solve Exercises 29–30.

29. If a school board determines that there should be 3 teachers for every 50 students, how many teachers are needed for an enrollment of 5400 students?

30. To determine the number of trout in a lake, a conservationist catches 112 trout, tags them, and returns them to the lake. Later, 82 trout are caught, and 32 of them are found to be tagged. How many trout are in the lake?

Exercises 31–33 involve direct and inverse variation. Use a proportion to solve each exercise.

31. An electric bill varies directly as the amount of electricity used. The bill for 1400 kilowatts of electricity is $98. What is the bill for 2200 kilowatts of electricity?

32. The distance that a body falls from rest varies directly as the square of the time of the fall. If skydivers fall 144 feet in 3 seconds, how far will they fall in 10 seconds?

33. The time it takes to drive a certain distance varies inversely as the rate of travel. If it takes 4 hours at 50 miles per hour to drive the distance, how long will it take at 40 miles per hour?

6.5

In Exercises 34–40, solve each inequality and graph the solution set on a number line.

34. $2x - 5 < 3$

35. $\frac{x}{2} > -4$

36. $3 - 5x \le 18$

37. $4x + 6 < 5x$

38. $6x - 10 \ge 2(x + 3)$

39. $4x + 3(2x - 7) \le x - 3$

40. $-1 < 4x + 2 \le 6$

41. To pass a course, a student must have an average on three examinations of at least 60. If a student scores 42 and 74 on the first two tests, what must be earned on the third test to pass the course?

6.6

Use FOIL to find the products in Exercises 42–43.

42. $(x + 9)(x - 5)$

43. $(4x - 7)(3x + 2)$

Factor the trinomials in Exercises 44–49, or state that the trinomial is prime.

44. $x^2 - x - 12$

45. $x^2 - 8x + 15$

46. $x^2 + 2x + 3$

47. $3x^2 - 17x + 10$

48. $6x^2 - 11x - 10$

49. $3x^2 - 6x - 5$

Solve the quadratic equations in Exercises 50–53 by factoring.

50. $x^2 + 5x - 14 = 0$

51. $x^2 - 4x = 32$

52. $2x^2 + 15x - 8 = 0$

53. $3x^2 = -21x - 30$

Solve the quadratic equations in Exercises 54–57 using the quadratic formula.

54. $x^2 - 4x + 3 = 0$

55. $x^2 - 5x = 4$

56. $2x^2 + 5x - 3 = 0$

57. $3x^2 - 6x = 5$

58. In 1945, 35.4% of taxes collected by the U.S. Treasury came from corporate income taxes. Since then, corporations have worked hard to convince lawmakers that they shouldn't pay taxes. The bar graph shows the percentage of federal taxes from corporate income taxes for selected years from 1985 through 2003. The data can be modeled by the formula

$$P = -0.035x^2 + 0.65x + 7.6,$$

where P represents the percentage of federal taxes from corporations x years after 1985. If these trends continue, by which year (to the nearest year) will corporations pay no taxes?

Percentage of Federal Taxes from Corporate Income Taxes

Source: White House Office of Management and Budget

● ● ● ● ● ● **CHAPTER 6 TEST**

1. Evaluate $x^3 - 4(x - 1)^2$ when $x = -2$.

2. Simplify: $5(3x - 2) - (x - 6)$.

3. The formula

$$F = 24t^2 - 260t + 816$$

models the number of police officers in the United States, F, convicted of felonies t years after 1990. How many convictions of police officers were there in 2000?

(*Source:* FBI)

In Exercises 4–7, solve each equation.

4. $12x + 4 = 7x - 21$

5. $3(2x - 4) = 9 - 3(x + 1)$

6. $3(x - 4) + x = 2(6 + 2x)$

7. $\dfrac{x}{5} - 2 = \dfrac{x}{3}$

8. Solve for y: $By - Ax = A$.

9. The formula $D = 0.12x + 5.44$ models the number of children in the United States with physical disabilities, D, in millions, x years after 2000. According to this model, in which year will there be 6.4 million children in the United States with physical disabilities?

In Exercises 10–13, use an equation to solve each problem.

10. The product of 5 and a number, decreased by 9, is 310. What is the number?

11. In New York City, a fitness trainer earns $22,870 more per year than a preschool teacher. The yearly average salaries for fitness trainers and preschool teachers combined are $79,030. Determine the average yearly salary of a fitness trainer and a preschool teacher in New York City.

(*Source: Time*, April 14, 2003)

12. You bought a new car for $13,805. Its value is decreasing by $1820 per year. After how many years will its value be $4705?

13. Photo Shop A charges $1.60 to develop a roll of film plus $0.11 for each print. Photo Shop B charges $1.20 to develop a roll of film plus $0.13 per print. For how many prints will the amount spent at each photo shop be the same? What will be that amount?

In Exercises 14–15, solve each proportion.

14. $\dfrac{5}{8} = \dfrac{x}{12}$

15. $\dfrac{x + 5}{8} = \dfrac{x + 2}{5}$

16. Park rangers catch, tag, and release 200 tule elk back into a wildlife refuge. Two weeks later they observe a sample of 150 elk, of which 5 are tagged. Assuming that the ratio of tagged elk in the sample holds for all elk in the refuge, how many elk are there in the park?

17. The pressure of water on an object below the surface varies directly as its distance below the surface. If a submarine experiences a pressure of 25 pounds per square inch 60 feet below the surface, how much pressure will it experience 330 feet below the surface?

18. The time required to accomplish a task varies inversely as the number of people working on the task. It takes 6 hours for 20 people to put a new roof on a porch. How long would it take 30 people to do the job?

In Exercises 19–21, solve each inequality and graph the solution set on a number line.

19. $6 - 9x \geq 33$

20. $4x - 2 > 2(x + 6)$

21. $-3 \leq 2x + 1 < 6$

22. A student has grades on three examinations of 76, 80, and 72. What must the student earn on a fourth examination in order to have an average of at least 80?

23. Use FOIL to find this product: $(2x - 5)(3x + 4)$.

24. Factor: $2x^2 - 9x + 10$.

25. Solve by factoring: $x^2 + 5x = 36$.

26. Solve using the quadratic formula: $2x^2 + 4x = -1$.

Without changes, the graphs show projections for the amount being paid in Social Security benefits and the amount going into the system. All data are expressed in billions of dollars.

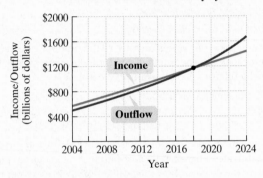

Social Insecurity: Projected Income and Outflow of the Social Security System

Source: 2004 Social Security Trustees Report

Exercises 27–29 are based on the data shown by the graphs.

27. In 2004, the system's income was $575 billion, projected to increase at an average rate of $43 billion per year. In which year will the system's income be $1177 billion?

28. The data for the system's outflow can be modeled by the formula

$$B = 0.07x^2 + 47.4x + 500,$$

where B represents the amount paid in benefits, in billions of dollars, x years after 2004. According to this model, when will the amount paid in benefits be $1177 billion? Round to the nearest year.

29. How well do your answers to Exercises 27 and 28 model the data shown by the graphs?

Algebra: Graphs, Functions, and Linear Systems

The most casual cruise on the Internet shows how people disagree when it comes to making predictions about the effects of the world's growing population. Some argue that there is a recent slowdown in the growth rate, economies remain robust, and famines in North Korea and Ethiopia are aberrations rather than signs of the future. Others say that the 6.5 billion people on Earth is twice as many as can be supported in middle-class comfort, and the world is running out of arable land and fresh water. How can we approach this debate mathematically?

Various models for the world's population growth appear in Example 2 of Section 7.6. on page 422.

SECTION 7.1 • GRAPHING AND FUNCTIONS

O B J E C T I V E S

1. Plot points in the rectangular coordinate system.
2. Graph equations in the rectangular coordinate system.
3. Use $f(x)$ notation.
4. Graph functions.
5. Use the vertical line test.
6. Obtain information about a function from its graph.

The beginning of the seventeenth century was a time of innovative ideas and enormous intellectual progress in Europe. English theatergoers enjoyed a succession of exciting new plays by Shakespeare. William Harvey proposed the radical notion that the heart was a pump for blood rather than the center of emotion. Galileo, with his new-fangled invention called the telescope, supported the theory of Polish astronomer Copernicus that the sun, not the Earth, was the center of the solar system. Monteverdi was writing the world's first grand operas. French mathematicians Pascal and Fermat invented a new field of mathematics called probability theory.

Into this arena of intellectual electricity stepped French aristocrat René Descartes (1596–1650). Descartes (pronounced "day cart"), propelled by the creativity surrounding him, developed a new branch of mathematics that brought together algebra and geometry in a unified way—a way that visualized numbers as points on a graph, equations as geometric figures, and geometric figures as equations. This new branch of mathematics, called *analytic geometry*, established Descartes as one of the founders of modern thought and among the most original mathematicians and philosophers of any age. We begin this section by looking at Descartes's deceptively simple idea, called the **rectangular coordinate system** or (in his honor) the **Cartesian coordinate system**.

1 | Plot points in the rectangular coordinate system.

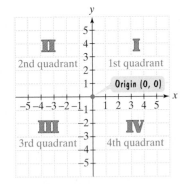

FIGURE 7.1 The rectangular coordinate system

STUDY TIP

The phrase *ordered pair* is used because order is important. The order in which coordinates appear makes a difference in a point's location. This is illustrated in Figure 7.2.

Points and Ordered Pairs

Descartes used two number lines that intersect at right angles at their zero points, as shown in Figure 7.1. The horizontal number line is the **x-axis**. The vertical number line is the **y-axis**. The point of intersection of these axes is their zero points, called the **origin**. Positive numbers are shown to the right and above the origin. Negative numbers are shown to the left and below the origin. The axes divide the plane into four quarters, called **quadrants**. The points located on the axes are not in any quadrant.

Each point in the rectangular coordinate system corresponds to an **ordered pair** of real numbers, (x, y). Examples of such pairs are $(-5, 3)$ and $(3, -5)$. The first number in each pair, called the **x-coordinate**, denotes the distance and direction from the origin along the x-axis. The second number in each pair, called the **y-coordinate**, denotes vertical distance and direction along a line parallel to the y-axis or along the y-axis itself.

Figure 7.2 shows how we **plot**, or locate, the points corresponding to the ordered pairs $(-5, 3)$ and $(3, -5)$. We plot $(-5, 3)$ by going 5 units from 0 to the left along the x-axis. Then we go 3 units up parallel to the y-axis. We plot $(3, -5)$ by going 3 units from 0 to the right along the x-axis and 5 units down parallel to the y-axis. The phrase "the points corresponding to the ordered pairs $(-5, 3)$ and $(3, -5)$" is often abbreviated as "the points $(-5, 3)$ and $(3, -5)$."

FIGURE 7.2 Plotting $(-5, 3)$ and $(3, -5)$

EXAMPLE 1	PLOTTING POINTS IN THE RECTANGULAR COORDINATE SYSTEM

Plot the points: $A(-3, 5)$, $B(2, -4)$, $C(5, 0)$, $D(-5, -3)$, $E(0, 4)$, and $F(0, 0)$.

SOLUTION See Figure 7.3. We move from the origin and plot the points in the following way:

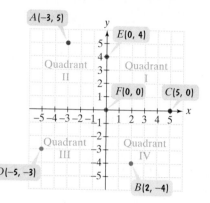

$A(-3, 5)$:   3 units left, 5 units up

$B(2, -4)$:   2 units right, 4 units down

$C(5, 0)$:   5 units right, 0 units up or down

$D(-5, -3)$: 5 units left, 3 units down

$E(0, 4)$:   0 units right or left, 4 units up

$F(0, 0)$:   0 units right or left, 0 units up or down

FIGURE 7.3 Plotting points

Plot the points: $A(-2, 4)$, $B(4, -2)$, $C(-3, 0)$, and $D(0, -3)$.

2	Graph equations in the rectangular coordinate system.

Graphs of Equations

A relationship between two quantities can sometimes be expressed as an **equation in two variables**, such as

$$y = 4 - x^2.$$

A **solution of an equation in two variables**, x and y, is an ordered pair of real numbers with the following property: When the x-coordinate is substituted for x and the y-coordinate is substituted for y in the equation, we obtain a true statement. For example, consider the equation $y = 4 - x^2$ and the ordered pair $(3, -5)$. When 3 is substituted for x and -5 is substituted for y, we obtain the statement $-5 = 4 - 3^2$, or $-5 = 4 - 9$, or $-5 = -5$. Because this statement is true, the ordered pair $(3, -5)$ is a solution of the equation $y = 4 - x^2$. We also say that $(3, -5)$ **satisfies** the equation.

We can generate as many ordered-pair solutions as desired to $y = 4 - x^2$ by substituting numbers for x and then finding the corresponding values for y. For example, suppose we let $x = 3$:

Start with x.	Compute y.	Form the ordered pair (x, y).
x	$y = 4 - x^2$	**Ordered Pair (x, y)**
3	$y = 4 - 3^2 = 4 - 9 = -5$	$(3, -5)$

Let $x = 3$. $(3, -5)$ is a solution of $y = 4 - x^2$.

The **graph of an equation in two variables** is the set of all points whose coordinates satisfy the equation. One method for graphing such equations is the **point-plotting method**. First, we find several ordered pairs that are solutions of the equation. Next, we plot these ordered pairs as points in the rectangular coordinate system. Finally, we connect the points with a smooth curve or line. This often gives us a picture of all ordered pairs that satisfy the equation.

EXAMPLE 2   GRAPHING AN EQUATION USING THE POINT-PLOTTING METHOD

Graph $y = 4 - x^2$. Select integers for x, starting with -3 and ending with $3 (-3 \leq x \leq 3)$.

SOLUTION For each value of x, we find the corresponding value for y.

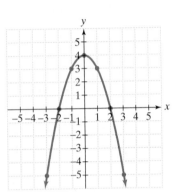

FIGURE 7.4 The graph of $y = 4 - x^2$

	Start with x.	Compute y.	Form the ordered pair (x, y).
	x	$y = 4 - x^2$	Ordered Pair (x, y)
We selected integers from -3 to 3, inclusive, to include three negative numbers, 0, and three positive numbers. We also wanted to keep the resulting computations for y relatively simple.	-3	$y = 4 - (-3)^2 = 4 - 9 = -5$	$(-3, -5)$
	-2	$y = 4 - (-2)^2 = 4 - 4 = 0$	$(-2, 0)$
	-1	$y = 4 - (-1)^2 = 4 - 1 = 3$	$(-1, 3)$
	0	$y = 4 - 0^2 = 4 - 0 = 4$	$(0, 4)$
	1	$y = 4 - 1^2 = 4 - 1 = 3$	$(1, 3)$
	2	$y = 4 - 2^2 = 4 - 4 = 0$	$(2, 0)$
	3	$y = 4 - 3^2 = 4 - 9 = -5$	$(3, -5)$

Now we plot the seven points and join them with a smooth curve, as shown in Figure 7.4. The graph of $y = 4 - x^2$ is a curve where the part of the graph to the right of the y-axis is a reflection of the part to the left of it and vice versa. The arrows on the left and the right of the curve indicate that it extends indefinitely in both directions.

 Graph $y = x^2 - 1$. Select integers for x, $-3 \leq x \leq 3$.

Part of the beauty of the rectangular coordinate system is that it allows us to "see" formulas and visualize the solution to a problem. This idea is demonstrated in Example 3.

EXAMPLE 3   AN APPLICATION USING GRAPHS OF EQUATIONS

The toll to a bridge costs $2.50. Commuters who use the bridge frequently have the option of purchasing a monthly coupon book for $21.00. With the coupon book, the toll is reduced to $1.00. The monthly cost, y, of using the bridge x times can be described by the following formulas:

Without the coupon book:

$$y = 2.5x$$ *The monthly cost, y, is $2.50 times the number of times, x, that the bridge is used.*

With the coupon book:

$$y = 21 + 1 \cdot x$$ *The monthly cost, y, is $21 for the book plus $1 times*
$$y = 21 + x.$$ *the number of times, x, that the bridge is used.*

a. Let $x = 0, 2, 4, 10, 12, 14,$ and 16. Make a table of values for each equation showing seven solutions for the equation.

b. Graph the equations in the same rectangular coordinate system.

c. What are the coordinates of the intersection point for the two graphs? Interpret the coordinates in practical terms.

SOLUTION

a. Tables of values showing seven solutions for each equation follow.

WITHOUT THE COUPON BOOK

x	$y = 2.5x$	(x, y)
0	$y = 2.5(0) = 0$	$(0, 0)$
2	$y = 2.5(2) = 5$	$(2, 5)$
4	$y = 2.5(4) = 10$	$(4, 10)$
10	$y = 2.5(10) = 25$	$(10, 25)$
12	$y = 2.5(12) = 30$	$(12, 30)$
14	$y = 2.5(14) = 35$	$(14, 35)$
16	$y = 2.5(16) = 40$	$(16, 40)$

WITH THE COUPON BOOK

x	$y = 21 + x$	(x, y)
0	$y = 21 + 0 = 21$	$(0, 21)$
2	$y = 21 + 2 = 23$	$(2, 23)$
4	$y = 21 + 4 = 25$	$(4, 25)$
10	$y = 21 + 10 = 31$	$(10, 31)$
12	$y = 21 + 12 = 33$	$(12, 33)$
14	$y = 21 + 14 = 35$	$(14, 35)$
16	$y = 21 + 16 = 37$	$(16, 37)$

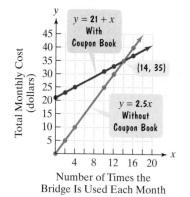

y = 21 + x
With
Coupon Book

(14, 35)

y = 2.5x
Without
Coupon Book

Total Monthly Cost (dollars)

Number of Times the Bridge Is Used Each Month

FIGURE 7.5 Options for a toll

b. Now we are ready to graph the two equations. Because the x- and y-coordinates are nonnegative, it is only necessary to use the origin, the positive portions of the x- and y-axes, and the first quadrant of the rectangular coordinate system. The x-coordinates begin at 0 and end at 16. We will let each tick-mark on the x-axis represent two units. However, the y-coordinates begin at 0 and get as large as 40 in the formula that describes the monthly cost without the coupon book. So that our y-axis does not get too long, we will let each tick mark on the y-axis represent five units. Using this setup and the two tables of values, we construct the graphs of $y = 2.5x$ and $y = 21 + x$, shown in Figure 7.5.

c. The graphs intersect at $(14, 35)$. This means that if the bridge is used 14 times in a month, the total monthly cost without the coupon book is the same as the total monthly cost with the coupon book, namely $35.

In Figure 7.5, look at the two graphs to the right of the intersection point $(14, 35)$. The red graph of $y = 21 + x$ lies below the blue graph of $y = 2.5x$. This means that if the bridge is used more than 14 times in a month $(x > 14)$, the (red) monthly cost, y, with the coupon book is less than the (blue) monthly cost, y, without the coupon book.

CHECK POINT

3 The toll to a bridge costs $2.00. If you use the bridge x times in a month, the monthly cost, y, is $y = 2x$. With a $10 coupon book, the toll is reduced to $1.00. The monthly cost, y, of using the bridge x times in a month with the coupon book is $y = 10 + x$.

a. Let $x = 0, 2, 4, 6, 8, 10,$ and 12. Make tables of values showing seven solutions of $y = 2x$ and seven solutions of $y = 10 + x$.

b. Graph the equations in the same rectangular coordinate system.

c. What are the coordinates of the intersection point for the two graphs? Interpret the coordinates in practical terms.

3 Use $f(x)$ notation.

Functions

Reconsider one of the equations from Example 3, $y = 2.5x$. Recall that this equation describes the monthly cost, y, of using the bridge x times, with a toll cost of $2.50 each time the bridge is used. The monthly cost, y, depends on the number of times the bridge is used, x. For each value of x, there is one and only one value of y. If an equation in two variables (x and y) yields precisely one value of y for each value of x, we say that y is a **function** of x.

The notation $y = f(x)$ indicates that the variable y is a function of x. The notation $f(x)$ is read "f of x."

For example, the formula for the cost of the bridge

$$y = 2.5x$$

can be expressed in function notation as

$$f(x) = 2.5x.$$

We read this as "f of x is equal to $2.5x$." If, say, x equals 10 (meaning that the bridge is used 10 times), we can find the corresponding value of y (monthly cost) using the equation $f(x) = 2.5x$.

STUDY TIP

The notation $f(x)$ does not mean "f times x." The notation describes the "output" for the function f when the "input" is x. Think of $f(x)$ as another name for y.

Input x

f

Output $f(x)$

$$f(x) = 2.5x$$
$$f(10) = 2.5(10) \qquad \text{To find f(10), read "f of 10," replace x with 10.}$$
$$= 25$$

Because $f(10) = 25$ (f of 10 equals 25), this means that if the bridge is used 10 times in a month, the total monthly cost is $25.

Table 7.1 compares our previous notation with the new notation of functions.

TABLE 7.1 FUNCTION NOTATION	
"y Equals" Notation	**"f(x) Equals" Notation**
$y = 2.5x$	$f(x) = 2.5x$
If $x = 10$, $\quad y = 2.5(10) = 25.$	$f(10) = 2.5(10) = 25$ f of 10 equals 25.

EXAMPLE 4   USING FUNCTION NOTATION

The wage gap is used to compare the status of women's earnings relative to men's. The wage gap is expressed as a percent and is calculated by dividing the median, or middlemost, annual earnings for women by the median annual earnings for men. The line graph in Figure 7.6 shows the wage gap for selected years from 1960 through 2003.

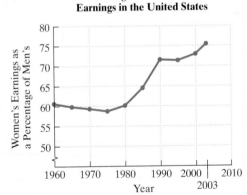

Median Women's Earnings as a Percentage of Median Men's Earnings in the United States

FIGURE 7.6
Source: U.S. Women's Bureau

a. Use the graph to estimate, to the nearest percent, women's earnings as a percentage of men's in 2003.

b. The function

$$f(x) = 0.012x^2 - 0.16x + 60$$

models median women's earnings as a percentage of men's earnings, $f(x)$, x years after 1960. Use this function to find women's earnings as a percentage of men's in 2003. Round to the nearest tenth of a percent.

SOLUTION

a. The data for 2003 is obtained using the point on the far right of the line graph in Figure 7.6. This point extends slightly above the tick mark representing 75 on the vertical axis. Thus, 76 is a reasonable estimate. We conclude that in 2003, women's earnings were approximately 76% of men's.

b. The given function models the wage gap x years after 1960. Because 2003 is 43 years after 1960 ($2003 - 1960 = 43$), we need to find $f(43)$. We can find $f(43)$, f of 43, by replacing each occurrence of x with 43. The arithmetic gets somewhat "messy," so it is probably a good idea to use a calculator.

TECHNOLOGY

On most calculators, here is how to find
$0.012(43)^2 - 0.16(43) + 60$.

MANY SCIENTIFIC CALCULATORS

.012 $\boxed{\times}$ 43 $\boxed{x^2}$ $\boxed{-}$

.16 $\boxed{\times}$ 43 $\boxed{+}$ 60 $\boxed{=}$

MANY GRAPHING CALCULATORS

.012 $\boxed{\times}$ 43 $\boxed{\wedge}$ 2 $\boxed{-}$

.16 $\boxed{\times}$ 43 $\boxed{+}$ 60 $\boxed{\text{ENTER}}$

$f(x) = 0.012x^2 - 0.16x + 60$	This is the given function.
$f(43) = 0.012(43)^2 - 0.16(43) + 60$	Replace each x with 43.
$= 0.012(1849) - 0.16(43) + 60$	Use the order of operations, evaluating the exponential expression.
$= 22.188 - 6.88 + 60$	Perform the multiplications.
$= 75.308$	Subtract and add as indicated.
≈ 75.3	As directed, we've rounded to the nearest tenth.

We see that $f(43) \approx 75.3$—that is, f of 43 is approximately 75.3. The model indicates that 43 years after 1960, in 2003, women's earnings were approximately 75.3% of men's.

In 2003, median annual earnings for U.S. women and men were $30,724 and $40,688, respectively. Women's earnings as a percentage of men's were

$$\frac{30,724}{40,688} \approx 0.755 = 75.5\%.$$

The actual wage gap was 75.5%. The values that we obtained from the function and the graph in Example 4, 75.3% and 76%, respectively, are quite close to this percent.

CHECK POINT 4

a. Use the graph in Figure 7.6 to estimate, to the nearest percent, women's earnings as a percentage of men's in 2000.

b. Use the function in Example 4(b) to find women's earnings as a percentage of men's in 2000.

4 | Graph functions.

Graphing Functions

The **graph of a function** is the graph of its ordered pairs. In our next example, we will graph two functions. It would be awkward to call both of them f. We will call one function f and the other g. These are the letters most frequently used to name functions.

EXAMPLE 5   GRAPHING FUNCTIONS

Graph the functions $f(x) = 2x$ and $g(x) = 2x + 4$ in the same rectangular coordinate system. Select integers for x, $-2 \leq x \leq 2$.

SOLUTION For each function, we use the suggested values for x to create a table of some of the coordinates. These tables are shown below. Now, we plot the five points in each table and connect them, as shown in Figure 7.7. The graph of each function is a straight line. Do you see a relationship between the two graphs? The graph of g is the graph of f shifted vertically up 4 units.

FIGURE 7.7

x	$f(x) = 2x$	(x, y) or $(x, f(x))$
-2	$f(-2) = 2(-2) = -4$	$(-2, -4)$
-1	$f(-1) = 2(-1) = -2$	$(-1, -2)$
0	$f(0) = 2 \cdot 0 = 0$	$(0, 0)$
1	$f(1) = 2 \cdot 1 = 2$	$(1, 2)$
2	$f(2) = 2 \cdot 2 = 4$	$(2, 4)$

Choose x.   Compute $f(x)$ by evaluating f at x.   Form the ordered pair.

x	$g(x) = 2x + 4$	(x, y) or $(x, g(x))$
-2	$g(-2) = 2(-2) + 4 = 0$	$(-2, 0)$
-1	$g(-1) = 2(-1) + 4 = 2$	$(-1, 2)$
0	$g(0) = 2 \cdot 0 + 4 = 4$	$(0, 4)$
1	$g(1) = 2 \cdot 1 + 4 = 6$	$(1, 6)$
2	$g(2) = 2 \cdot 2 + 4 = 8$	$(2, 8)$

Choose x.   Compute $g(x)$ by evaluating g at x.   Form the ordered pair.

CHECK POINT 5   Graph the functions $f(x) = 2x$ and $g(x) = 2x - 3$ in the same rectangular coordinate system. Select integers for x, $-2 \leq x \leq 2$. How is the graph of g related to the graph of f?

5 | Use the vertical line test.

The Vertical Line Test

Not every graph in the rectangular coordinate system is the graph of a function. The definition of a function specifies that no value of x can be paired with two or more different values of y. Consequently, if a graph contains two or more different points with the same first coordinate, the graph cannot represent a function. This is illustrated in Figure 7.8. Observe that points sharing a common first coordinate are vertically above or below each other.

This observation is the basis of a useful test for determining whether a graph defines y as a function of x. The test is called the **vertical line test**.

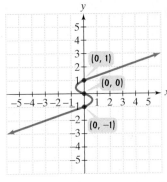

FIGURE 7.8 y is not a function of x because 0 is paired with three values of y, namely, 1, 0, and -1.

> ### THE VERTICAL LINE TEST FOR FUNCTIONS
> If any vertical line intersects a graph in more than one point, the graph does not define y as a function of x.

EXAMPLE 6   USING THE VERTICAL LINE TEST

Use the vertical line test to identify graphs in which y is a function of x.

SOLUTION y is a function of x for the graphs in (b) and (c).

a.

y **is not a function** of x.
Two values of y correspond to one x-value.

b.

y **is a function** of x.

c.

y **is a function** of x.

d.

y **is not a function** of x.
Two values of y correspond to one x-value.

○

CHECK POINT **6**   Use the vertical line test to identify graphs in which y is a function of x.

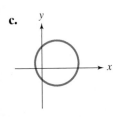

6 | Obtain information about a function from its graph.

Obtaining Information from Graphs

Example 7 illustrates how to obtain information about a function from its graph.

EXAMPLE 7   ANALYZING THE GRAPH OF A FUNCTION

Too late for that flu shot now! It's only 8 A.M. and you're feeling lousy. Fascinated by the way that algebra models the world (your author is projecting a bit here), you construct a graph showing your body temperature from 8 A.M. through 3 P.M. You decide to let x represent the number of hours after 8 A.M. and y represent your body temperature at time x. The graph is shown in Figure 7.9. The symbol $\dagger$ on the y-axis shows that there is a break in values between 0 and 98. Thus, the first tick mark on the y-axis represents a temperature of 98°F.

FIGURE 7.9 Body temperature from 8 A.M. through 3 P.M.

a. What is your temperature at 8 A.M.?

b. During which period of time is your temperature decreasing?

c. Estimate your minimum temperature during the time period shown. How many hours after 8 A.M. does this occur? At what time does this occur?

d. During which period of time is your temperature increasing?

e. Part of the graph is shown as a horizontal line segment. What does this mean about your temperature and when does this occur?

f. Explain why the graph defines y as a function of x.

SOLUTION

a. Because x is the number of hours after 8 A.M., your temperature at 8 A.M. corresponds to $x = 0$. Locate 0 on the horizontal axis and look at the point on the graph above 0. The first figure on the right shows that your temperature at 8 A.M. is 101°F.

b. Your temperature is decreasing when the graph falls from left to right. This occurs between $x = 0$ and $x = 3$, also shown in the first figure on the right. Because x represents the number of hours after 8 A.M., your temperature is decreasing between 8 A.M. and 11 A.M.

c. Your minimum temperature can be found by locating the lowest point on the graph. This point lies above 3 on the horizontal axis, shown in the second figure on the right. The y-coordinate of this point falls more than midway between 98 and 99, at approximately 98.6. The lowest point on the graph, (3, 98.6), shows that your minimum temperature, 98.6°F, occurs 3 hours after 8 A.M., at 11 A.M.

d. Your temperature is increasing when the graph rises from left to right. This occurs between $x = 3$ and $x = 5$, shown in the second figure. Because x represents the number of hours after 8 A.M., your temperature is increasing between 11 A.M. and 1 P.M.

e. The horizontal line segment shown in the figure on the right indicates that your temperature is neither increasing nor decreasing. Your temperature remains the same, 100°F, between $x = 5$ and $x = 7$. Thus, your temperature is at a constant 100°F between 1 P.M. and 3 P.M.

f. The complete graph of your body temperature from 8 A.M. through 3 P.M. is shown above in part (e). No vertical line can be drawn that intersects this blue graph more than once. By the vertical line test, the graph defines y as a function of x. In practical terms, this means that your body temperature is a function of time. Each hour (or fraction of an hour) after 8 A.M., represented by x, yields precisely one body temperature, represented by y.

CHECK POINT

7 When a person receives a drug injected into a muscle, the concentration of the drug in the body, measured in milligrams per 100 milliliters, depends on the time elapsed after the injection, measured in hours. The figure shows the graph of drug concentration over time, where x represents hours after the injection and y represents the drug concentration at time x.

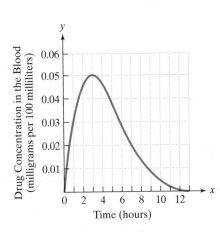

a. During which period of time is the drug concentration increasing?

b. During which period of time is the drug concentration decreasing?

c. What is the drug's maximum concentration and when does this occur?

d. What happens by the end of 13 hours?

e. Explain why the graph defines y as a function of x.

EXERCISE SET 7.1 ●●●●●●

• Practice Exercises

In Exercises 1–20, plot the given point in a rectangular coordinate system.

1. $(1, 4)$

2. $(2, 5)$

3. $(-2, 3)$

4. $(-1, 4)$

5. $(-3, -5)$

6. $(-4, -2)$

7. $(4, -1)$

8. $(3, -2)$

9. $(-4, 0)$

10. $(-5, 0)$

11. $(0, -3)$

12. $(0, -4)$

13. $(0, 0)$

14. $\left(-3, -1\frac{1}{2}\right)$

15. $\left(-2, -3\frac{1}{2}\right)$

16. $(-5, -2.5)$

17. $(3.5, 4.5)$

18. $(2.5, 3.5)$

19. $(1.25, -3.25)$

20. $(2.25, -4.25)$

Graph each equation in Exercises 21–32. Select integers for x, $-3 \le x \le 3$.

21. $y = x^2 - 2$

22. $y = x^2 + 2$

23. $y = x - 2$

24. $y = x + 2$

25. $y = 2x + 1$

26. $y = 2x - 4$

27. $y = -\frac{1}{2}x$

28. $y = -\frac{1}{2}x + 2$

29. $y = x^3$

30. $y = x^3 - 1$

31. $y = |x| + 1$

32. $y = |x| - 1$

In Exercises 33–42, find f of each given value of x.

33. $f(x) = x - 4$ **a.** $f(8)$ **b.** $f(1)$

34. $f(x) = x - 6$ **a.** $f(9)$ **b.** $f(2)$

35. $f(x) = 3x - 2$ **a.** $f(7)$ **b.** $f(0)$

36. $f(x) = 4x - 3$ **a.** $f(7)$ **b.** $f(0)$

37. $f(x) = x^2 + 1$ **a.** $f(2)$ **b.** $f(-2)$

38. $f(x) = x^2 + 4$ **a.** $f(3)$ **b.** $f(-3)$

39. $f(x) = 3x^2 + 5$ **a.** $f(4)$ **b.** $f(-1)$

40. $f(x) = 2x^2 - 4$ **a.** $f(5)$ **b.** $f(-1)$

41. $f(x) = 2x^2 + 3x - 1$ **a.** $f(3)$ **b.** $f(-4)$

42. $f(x) = 3x^2 + 4x - 2$ **a.** $f(2)$ **b.** $f(-1)$

In Exercises 43–50, evaluate $f(x)$ for the given values of x. Then use the ordered pairs $(x, f(x))$ from your table to graph the function.

43. $f(x) = x^2 - 1$

x	$f(x) = x^2 - 1$
-2	
-1	
0	
1	
2	

44. $f(x) = x^2 + 1$

x	$f(x) = x^2 + 1$
-2	
-1	
0	
1	
2	

45. $f(x) = x - 1$

x	$f(x) = x - 1$
-2	
-1	
0	
1	
2	

46. $f(x) = x + 1$

x	$f(x) = x + 1$
-2	
-1	
0	
1	
2	

47. $f(x) = (x - 2)^2$

x	$f(x) = (x - 2)^2$
0	
1	
2	
3	
4	

48. $f(x) = (x + 1)^2$

x	$f(x) = (x + 1)^2$
-3	
-2	
-1	
0	
1	

49. $f(x) = x^3 + 1$

x	$f(x) = x^3 + 1$
-3	
-2	
-1	
0	
1	

50. $f(x) = (x + 1)^3$

x	$f(x) = (x + 1)^3$
-3	
-2	
-1	
0	
1	

For Exercises 51–58, use the vertical line test to identify graphs in which y is a function of x.

51.

52.

53.

54.

55.

56.

57.

58.

• Practice Plus

In Exercises 59–60, let $f(x) = x^2 - x + 4$ and $g(x) = 3x - 5$.

59. Find $g(1)$ and $f(g(1))$.

60. Find $g(-1)$ and $f(g(-1))$.

In Exercises 61–62, let f and g be defined by the following table:

x	$f(x)$	$g(x)$
-2	6	0
-1	3	4
0	-1	1
1	-4	-3
2	0	-6

61. Find
$$\sqrt{f(-1) - f(0)} - [g(2)]^2 + f(-2) \div g(2) \cdot g(-1).$$

62. Find $|f(1) - f(0)| - [g(1)]^2 + g(1) \div f(-1) \cdot g(2)$.

In Exercises 63–66, write each English sentence as an equation in two variables. Then graph the equation.

63. The y-value is four more than twice the x-value.

64. The y-value is the difference between four and twice the x-value.

65. The y-value is three decreased by the square of the x-value.

66. The y-value is two more than the square of the x-value.

• Application Exercises

Afghanistan accounts for 76% of the world's illegal opium production. Opium-poppy cultivation nets big money in a country where most people earn less than $1 per day. (Source: Newsweek) The line graph shows opium-poppy cultivation, in thousands of acres, in Afghanistan from 1990 through 2004. Use the graph to solve Exercises 67–74.

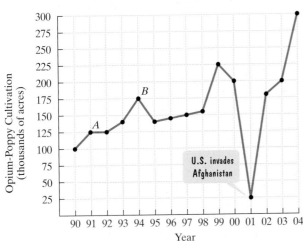

Afghanistan's Opium Crop

Source: U.N. Office on Drugs and Crime

67. What are the coordinates of point *A*? What does this mean in terms of the information given by the graph?

68. What are the coordinates of point *B*? What does this mean in terms of the information given by the graph?

69. In which year(s) were 200 thousand acres used for opium-poppy cultivation?

70. In which year were 150 thousand acres used for opium-poppy cultivation?

71. For the period shown, when did opium cultivation reach a minimum? How many thousands of acres were used to cultivate the illegal crop that year?

72. For the period shown, when did opium cultivation reach a maximum? How many thousands of acres were used to cultivate the illegal crop that year?

73. Between which two years did opium cultivation not change?

74. Between which two years did opium cultivation increase at the greatest rate? What is a reasonable estimate of the increase, in thousands of acres, used to cultivate the illegal crop during this period?

The male minority? The bar graph shows the number of bachelor's degrees, in thousands, awarded to men and women in the United States for selected years, with projections for 2010. The trend indicated by the graphs is among the hottest topics of debate among college-admissions officers. Some private liberal arts colleges have quietly begun special efforts to recruit men—including admissions preferences for them.

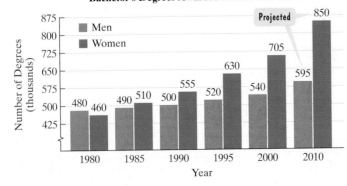

Bachelor's Degrees Awarded to Men and Women

Source: Department of Education

Graphs of Models for the Data

The function

$$M(x) = 3.5x + 472$$

models the number of bachelor's degrees, in thousands, awarded to men x years after 1980. The function

$$W(x) = 13.2x + 443$$

models the number of bachelor's degrees, in thousands, awarded to women x years after 1980. The graphs of functions M and W are shown to the right of the actual data. Use this information to solve Exercises 75–78.

75. a. Find and interpret $W(20)$. Identify this information as a point on the graph of the function for women.

b. How well does $W(20)$ model the actual data shown by the bar graph?

76. a. Find and interpret $M(20)$. Identify this information as a point on the graph of the function for men.

b. How well does $M(20)$ model the actual data shown by the bar graph?

77. a. Use the two functions to find and interpret $W(10) - M(10)$. Identify this information as an appropriate distance between the graphs of the functions for women and men.

b. How well does $W(10) - M(10)$ model the actual data shown by the bar graph?

78. a. Use the two functions to find and interpret $W(5) - M(5)$. Identify this information as an appropriate distance between the graphs of the functions for women and men.

b. How well does $W(5) - M(5)$ model the actual data shown by the bar graph?

The function

$$f(x) = 339x^3 - 2085x^2 + 2814x + 8123$$

models the number of hate-crime incidents reported by law enforcement agencies in the United States, $f(x)$, x years after 2000. The graph of f is shown in the figure. Use this information to solve Exercises 79–82.

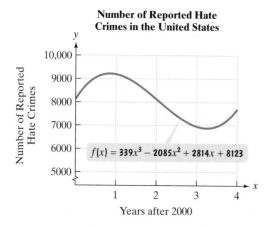

Number of Reported Hate Crimes in the United States

$f(x) = 339x^3 - 2085x^2 + 2814x + 8123$

Years after 2000

Source: Department of Justice

79. a. For the period shown, in which year did the number of hate crimes reach a maximum? Use the graph to find a reasonable estimate of the number of hate crimes for that year.

b. Use the function to find the number of hate crimes for the year in part (a).

80. a. For the period shown, in which year did the number of hate crimes reach a minimum? Use the graph to find a reasonable estimate of the number of hate crimes for that year.

b. Use the function to find the number of hate crimes for the year in part (a).

81. Use the function to find $f(2)$. Identify this information on the graph of f.

82. Use the function to find $f(4)$. Identify this information on the graph of f.

• Writing in Mathematics

83. What is the rectangular coordinate system?

84. Explain how to plot a point in the rectangular coordinate system. Give an example with your explanation.

85. Explain why $(5, -2)$ and $(-2, 5)$ do not represent the same ordered pair.

86. Explain how to graph an equation in the rectangular coordinate system.

87. What is a function?

88. Explain how the vertical line test is used to determine whether a graph represents a function.

• Critical Thinking Exercises

In Exercises 89–92, use the graphs of f and g to find each number.

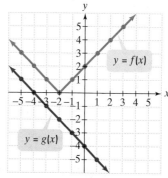

$y = f(x)$

$y = g(x)$

89. $f(-1) + g(-1)$ **90.** $f(1) + g(1)$

91. $f(g(-1))$ **92.** $f(g(1))$

• Technology Exercise

93. Use a graphing calculator to verify the graphs that you drew by hand in Exercises 43–50.

SECTION 7.2 • LINEAR FUNCTIONS AND THEIR GRAPHS

OBJECTIVES

1. Use intercepts to graph a linear equation.

2. Calculate slope.

3. Use the slope and y-intercept to graph a line.

4. Graph horizontal or vertical lines.

5. Interpret slope as rate of change.

6. Use slope and y-intercept to model data.

A best guess at the look of our nation in the next decades indicates that the number of men and women living alone will increase each year. Figure 7.10 shows that in 2003, approximately 12.5 million men and 16.9 million women lived alone, an increase over the numbers displayed for 1990.

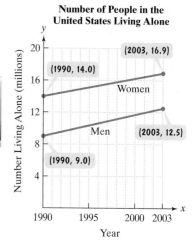

Number of People in the United States Living Alone

(2003, 16.9)

(1990, 14.0)

Women

(1990, 9.0)

Men

(2003, 12.5)

Year

FIGURE 7.10

Source: U.S. Census Bureau

The data for the men can be modeled by

$$y = 0.27x + 9,$$

where y represents the number of men living alone, in millions, x years after 1990. Using function notation, we can rewrite the equation as

$$f(x) = 0.27x + 9.$$

A function such as this, whose graph is a straight line, is called a **linear function**. In this section, we will study linear functions and their graphs.

<table>
<tr><td>1</td><td>Use intercepts to graph a linear equation.</td></tr>
</table>

Graphing Using Intercepts

There is another way that we can write the equation

$$y = 0.27x + 9.$$

We will collect the x- and y-terms on the left side. This is done by subtracting $0.27x$ from both sides:

$$-0.27x + y = 9.$$

All equations of the form $Ax + By = C$ are straight lines when graphed, as long as A and B are not both zero. Such equations are called **linear equations in two variables**. We can quickly obtain the graph for equations in this form by finding the points where the graph crosses the x-axis and the y-axis. The x-coordinate of the point where the graph crosses the x-axis is called the **x-intercept**. The y-coordinate of the point where the graph crosses the y-axis is called the **y-intercept**.

LOCATING INTERCEPTS

To locate the x-intercept, set $y = 0$ and solve the equation for x.

To locate the y-intercept, set $x = 0$ and solve the equation for y.

An equation of the form $Ax + By = C$ can be graphed by finding the x- and y-intercepts, plotting the intercepts, and drawing a straight line through these points. When graphing using intercepts, it is a good idea to use a third point, a checkpoint, before drawing the line. A checkpoint can be obtained by selecting a value for x, other than 0, and finding the corresponding value for y. The checkpoint should lie on the same line as the x- and y-intercepts. If it does not, recheck your work and find the error.

EXAMPLE 1 USING INTERCEPTS TO GRAPH A LINEAR EQUATION

Graph: $3x + 2y = 6$.

SOLUTION

Find the x-intercept by letting $y = 0$ and solving for x.	Find the y-intercept by letting $x = 0$ and solving for y.
$3x + 2y = 6$	$3x + 2y = 6$
$3x + 2 \cdot 0 = 6$	$3 \cdot 0 + 2y = 6$
$3x = 6$	$2y = 6$
$x = 2$	$y = 3$

The x-intercept is 2, so the line passes through the point $(2, 0)$. The y-intercept is 3, so the line passes through the point $(0, 3)$.

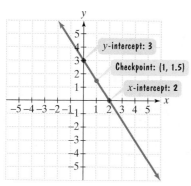

FIGURE 7.11 The graph of $3x + 2y = 6$

For our checkpoint, we will let $x = 1$ and find the corresponding value for y.

$$3x + 2y = 6 \qquad \text{This is the given equation.}$$
$$3 \cdot 1 + 2y = 6 \qquad \text{Substitute 1 for } x.$$
$$3 + 2y = 6 \qquad \text{Simplify.}$$
$$2y = 3 \qquad \text{Subtract 3 from both sides.}$$
$$y = \frac{3}{2} \qquad \text{Divide both sides by 2.}$$

The checkpoint is the ordered pair $\left(1, \frac{3}{2}\right)$, or $(1, 1.5)$.

The three points in Figure 7.11 lie along the same line. Drawing a line through the three points results in the graph of $3x + 2y = 6$.

 Graph: $2x + 3y = 6$.

2 | Calculate slope.

Slope

Mathematicians have developed a useful measure of the steepness of a line, called the *slope* of the line. Slope compares the vertical change (the **rise**) to the horizontal change (the **run**) when moving from one fixed point to another along the line. To calculate the slope of a line, we use a ratio that compares the change in y (the rise) to the change in x (the run).

DEFINITION OF SLOPE

The **slope** of the line through the distinct points (x_1, y_1) and (x_2, y_2) is

$$\frac{\text{Change in } y}{\text{Change in } x} = \frac{\text{Rise}}{\text{Run}}$$

$$= \frac{y_2 - y_1}{x_2 - x_1},$$

where $x_2 - x_1 \neq 0$.

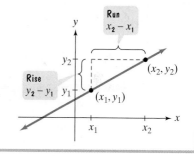

It is common notation to let the letter m represent the slope of a line. The letter m is used because it is the first letter of the French verb *monter*, meaning to rise, or to ascend.

EXAMPLE 2 USING THE DEFINITION OF SLOPE

Find the slope of the line passing through each pair of points:

a. $(-3, -1)$ and $(-2, 4)$ **b.** $(-3, 4)$ and $(2, -2)$.

SOLUTION

a. Let $(x_1, y_1) = (-3, -1)$ and $(x_2, y_2) = (-2, 4)$. We obtain the slope as follows:

$$m = \frac{\text{Change in } y}{\text{Change in } x} = \frac{y_2 - y_1}{x_2 - x_1} = \frac{4 - (-1)}{-2 - (-3)} = \frac{5}{1} = 5.$$

The situation is illustrated in Figure 7.12. The slope of the line is 5, indicating that there is a vertical change, a rise, of 5 units for each horizontal change, a run, of 1 unit. The slope is positive and the line rises from left to right.

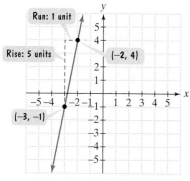

FIGURE 7.12 Visualizing a slope of 5

STUDY TIP

When computing slope, it makes no difference which point you call (x_1, y_1) and which point you call (x_2, y_2). If we let $(x_1, y_1) = (-2, 4)$ and $(x_2, y_2) = (-3, -1)$, the slope is still 5:

$$m = \frac{\text{Change in } y}{\text{Change in } x} = \frac{y_2 - y_1}{x_2 - x_1} = \frac{-1 - 4}{-3 - (-2)} = \frac{-5}{-1} = 5.$$

However, you should not subtract in one order in the numerator $(y_2 - y_1)$ and then in a different order in the denominator $(x_1 - x_2)$. The slope is *not* -5:

$$\frac{-1 - 4}{-2 - (-3)} = \frac{-5}{1} = -5. \qquad \text{Incorrect}$$

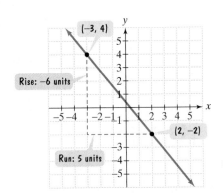

Rise: −6 units

Run: 5 units

(−3, 4)

(2, −2)

FIGURE 7.13 Visualizing a slope of $-\frac{6}{5}$

b. We can let $(x_1, y_1) = (-3, 4)$ and $(x_2, y_2) = (2, -2)$. The slope of the line shown in Figure 7.13 is computed as follows:

$$m = \frac{\text{Change in } y}{\text{Change in } x} = \frac{y_2 - y_1}{x_2 - x_1} = \frac{-2 - 4}{2 - (-3)} = \frac{-6}{5} = -\frac{6}{5}.$$

The slope of the line is $-\frac{6}{5}$. For every vertical change of -6 units (6 units down), there is a corresponding horizontal change of 5 units. The slope is negative and the line falls from left to right.

Find the slope of the line passing through each pair of points:

a. $(-3, 4)$ and $(-4, -2)$

b. $(4, -2)$ and $(-1, 5)$.

Example 2 illustrates that a line with a positive slope is rising from left to right and a line with a negative slope is falling from left to right. By contrast, a horizontal line neither rises nor falls and has a slope of zero. A vertical line has no horizontal change, so $x_2 - x_1 = 0$ in the formula for slope. Because we cannot divide by zero, the slope of a vertical line is undefined. This discussion is summarized in Table 7.2.

TABLE 7.2 POSSIBILITIES FOR A LINE'S SLOPE

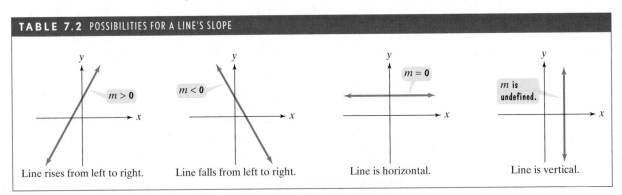

$m > 0$	$m < 0$	$m = 0$	m is undefined.
Line rises from left to right.	Line falls from left to right.	Line is horizontal.	Line is vertical.

3 Use the slope and y-intercept to graph a line.

The Slope-Intercept Form of the Equation of a Line

We can use the definition of slope to write the equation of any nonvertical line with slope m and y-intercept b. Because the y-intercept is b, the point $(0, b)$ lies on the line. Now, let (x, y) represent any other point on the line, shown in Figure 7.14. Keep in mind that the point (x, y) is arbitrary and is not in one fixed position. By contrast, the point $(0, b)$ is fixed.

Regardless of where the point (x, y) is located, the steepness of the line in Figure 7.14

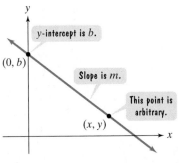

y-intercept is b.

Slope is m.

This point is arbitrary.

$(0, b)$

(x, y)

FIGURE 7.14 A line with slope m and y-intercept b

remains the same. Thus, the ratio for slope stays a constant m. This means that for all points along the line

$$m = \frac{\text{Change in } y}{\text{Change in } x} = \frac{y - b}{x - 0} = \frac{y - b}{x}.$$

We can clear the fraction by multiplying both sides by x, the least common denominator.

$$m = \frac{y - b}{x} \qquad \text{This is the slope of the line in Figure 7.14.}$$

$$mx = \frac{y - b}{x} \cdot x \qquad \text{Multiply both sides by x.}$$

$$mx = y - b \qquad \text{Simplify: } \frac{y - b}{\cancel{x}} \cdot \cancel{x} = y - b.$$

$$mx + b = y - b + b \qquad \text{Add b to both sides and solve for y.}$$

$$mx + b = y \qquad \text{Simplify.}$$

Now, if we reverse the two sides, we obtain the *slope-intercept form* of the equation of a line.

SLOPE-INTERCEPT FORM OF THE EQUATION OF A LINE

The **slope-intercept form of the equation** of a nonvertical line with slope m and y-intercept b is

$$y = mx + b.$$

The slope-intercept form of a line's equation, $y = mx + b$, can be expressed in function notation by replacing y with $f(x)$:

$$f(x) = mx + b.$$

We have seen that functions in this form are called **linear functions**. Thus, in the equation of a linear function, the x-coefficient is the line's slope and the constant term is the y-intercept. Here are two examples:

$$y = 2x - 4 \qquad\qquad f(x) = \frac{1}{2}x + 2.$$

The slope is 2.   The y-intercept is −4.   The slope is $\frac{1}{2}$.   The y-intercept is 2.

If a linear function's equation is in slope-intercept form, we can use the y-intercept and the slope to obtain its graph.

GRAPHING $y = mx + b$ USING THE SLOPE AND y-INTERCEPT

1. Plot the point containing the y-intercept on the y-axis. This is the point $(0, b)$.

2. Obtain a second point using the slope, m. Write m as a fraction, and use rise over run, starting at the point containing the y-intercept, to plot this point.

3. Use a straightedge to draw a line through the two points. Draw arrowheads at the ends of the line to show that the line continues indefinitely in both directions.

EXAMPLE 3 GRAPHING BY USING THE SLOPE AND y-INTERCEPT

Graph the linear function $y = \frac{2}{3}x + 2$ by using the slope and y-intercept.

SOLUTION The equation of the linear function is in the form $y = mx + b$. We can find the slope, m, by identifying the coefficient of x. We can find the y-intercept, b, by identifying the constant term.

$$y = \frac{2}{3}x + 2$$

The slope is $\frac{2}{3}$.   The y-intercept is 2.

Now that we have identified the slope and the y-intercept, we use the three-step procedure to graph the equation.

Step 1. Plot the point containing the y-intercept on the y-axis. The y-intercept is 2. We plot $(0, 2)$, shown in Figure 7.15.

Step 2. Obtain a second point using the slope, m. Write m as a fraction, and use rise over run, starting at the point containing the y-intercept, to plot this point. The slope, $\frac{2}{3}$, is already written as a fraction:

$$m = \frac{2}{3} = \frac{\text{Rise}}{\text{Run}}.$$

We plot the second point on the line by starting at $(0, 2)$, the first point. Based on the slope, we move 2 units *up* (the rise) and 3 units to the *right* (the run). This puts us at a second point on the line, $(3, 4)$, shown in Figure 7.15.

Step 3. Use a straightedge to draw a line through the two points. The graph of $y = \frac{2}{3}x + 2$ is shown in Figure 7.15. ○

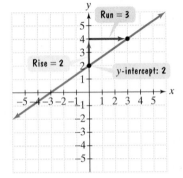

FIGURE 7.15 The graph of $y = \frac{2}{3}x + 2$

 Graph the linear function $y = \frac{3}{5}x + 1$ by using the slope and y-intercept.

Earlier in this section, we considered linear functions of the form $Ax + By = C$. We used x- and y-intercepts, as well as checkpoints, to graph these functions. It is also possible to obtain the graphs by using the slope and y-intercept. To do this, begin by solving $Ax + By = C$ for y. This will put the equation in slope-intercept form. Then use the three-step procedure to graph the equation. This is illustrated in Example 4.

EXAMPLE 4 GRAPHING BY USING THE SLOPE AND y-INTERCEPT

Graph the linear function $2x + 5y = 0$ by using the slope and y-intercept.

SOLUTION We put the equation in slope-intercept form by solving for y.

$2x + 5y = 0$	This is the given equation.
$2x - 2x + 5y = -2x + 0$	Subtract 2x from both sides.
$5y = -2x + 0$	Simplify.
$\dfrac{5y}{5} = \dfrac{-2x + 0}{5}$	Divide both sides by 5.
$y = \dfrac{-2x}{5} + \dfrac{0}{5}$	Divide each term in the numerator by 5.
$y = -\dfrac{2}{5}x + 0$	Simplify. Equivalently, $f(x) = -\frac{2}{5}x + 0$.

Now that the equation is in slope-intercept form, we can use the slope and y-intercept to obtain its graph. Examine the slope-intercept form:

$$y = -\frac{2}{5}x + 0.$$

slope: $-\frac{2}{5}$ y-intercept: 0

Note that the slope is $-\frac{2}{5}$ and the y-intercept is 0. Use the y-intercept to plot $(0, 0)$ on the y-axis. Then locate a second point by using the slope.

$$m = -\frac{2}{5} = \frac{-2}{5} = \frac{\text{Rise}}{\text{Run}}$$

Because the rise is -2 and the run is 5, move *down* 2 units and to the *right* 5 units, starting at the point $(0, 0)$. This puts us at a second point on the line, $(5, -2)$. The graph of $2x + 5y = 0$ is the line drawn through these points, shown in Figure 7.16.

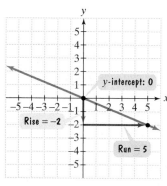

FIGURE 7.16 The graph of $2x + 5y = 0$, or $y = -\frac{2}{5}x$

If you try graphing $2x + 5y = 0$ by using intercepts, you will find that the x-intercept is 0 and the y-intercept is 0. This means that the graph passes through the origin. A second point must be found to graph the line. In Example 4, the line's slope gave us the second point.

 Graph the linear function $3x + 4y = 0$ by using the slope and y-intercept.

4 | Graph horizontal or vertical lines.

Equations of Horizontal and Vertical Lines

Some things change very little. For example, from 1997 through 2005, the federal minimum wage remained constant at $5.15 per hour, indicated by the brown bars in Figure 7.17. These bars show the minimum wage before it was adjusted for inflation. Also shown in the figure is a blue horizontal line segment that passes through the tops of the nine brown bars.

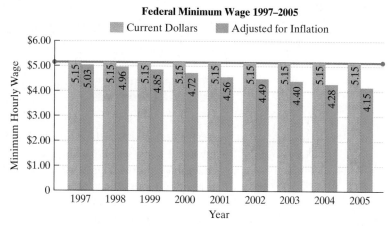

FIGURE 7.17
Source: Department of Labor

We can use $y = mx + b$, the slope-intercept form of a line's equation, to obtain an equation that models the federal minimum wage, y, in current dollars, in year x, where x is between 1997 and 2005, inclusive. The horizontal blue line segment in Figure 7.17 provides the values for m and b:

$$y = mx + b.$$

Because the line segment is horizontal, $m = 0$.   The y-intercept is shown as $5.15, so $b = 5.15$.

Thus, an equation that models the federal minimum wage between 1997 and 2005, inclusive, is

$$y = 0x + 5.15, \quad \text{or } y = 5.15.$$

The federal minimum wage remained constant at $5.15 per hour. Using function notation, we can write

$$f(x) = 5.15.$$

| For all year inputs, x, from 1997 through 2005, inclusive, | the output is a constant 5.15. |

In general, if a line is horizontal, its slope is zero: $m = 0$. Thus, the equation $y = mx + b$ becomes $y = b$, where b is the y-intercept. All horizontal lines have equations of the form $y = b$.

EXAMPLE 5 GRAPHING A HORIZONTAL LINE

Graph $y = -4$ in the rectangular coordinate system.

SOLUTION All ordered pairs that are solutions of $y = -4$ have a value of y that is always -4. Any value can be used for x. In the table on the right, we have selected three of the possible values for x: $-2, 0,$ and 3. The table shows that three ordered pairs that are solutions of $y = -4$ are $(-2, -4)$, $(0, -4)$, and $(3, -4)$. Drawing a line that passes through the three points gives the horizontal line shown in Figure 7.18.

x	$y = -4$	(x, y)
-2	-4	$(-2, -4)$
0	-4	$(0, -4)$
3	-4	$(3, -4)$

| For all choices of x, | y is a constant -4. |

FIGURE 7.18 The graph of $y = -4$ or $f(x) = -4$

CHECK POINT 5 Graph $y = 3$ in the rectangular coordinate system.

Next, let's see what we can discover about the graph of an equation of the form $x = a$ by looking at an example.

EXAMPLE 6 GRAPHING A VERTICAL LINE

Graph $x = 2$ in the rectangular coordinate system.

SOLUTION All ordered pairs that are solutions of $x = 2$ have a value of x that is always 2. Any value can be used for y. In the table on the right, we have selected three of the possible values for y: $-2, 0,$ and 3. The table shows that three ordered pairs that are solutions of $x = 2$ are $(2, -2)$, $(2, 0)$, and $(2, 3)$. Drawing a line that passes through the three points gives the vertical line shown in Figure 7.19.

For all choices of y,		
$x = 2$	y	(x, y)
2	-2	$(2, -2)$
2	0	$(2, 0)$
2	3	$(2, 3)$

x is always 2.

FIGURE 7.19 The graph of $x = 2$

Does a vertical line represent the graph of a linear function? No. Look at the graph of $x = 2$ in Figure 7.19. A vertical line drawn through $(2, 0)$ intersects the graph infinitely many times. This shows that infinitely many outputs are associated with the input 2. **No vertical line is a linear function.** All other lines are graphs of functions.

HORIZONTAL AND VERTICAL LINES

The graph of $y = b$ or $f(x) = b$ is a horizontal line. The y-intercept is b.

The graph of $x = a$ is a vertical line. The x-intercept is a.

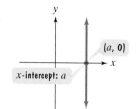

CHECK POINT 6 Graph $x = -2$ in the rectangular coordinate system.

---

5 | Interpret slope as rate of change.

Slope as Rate of Change

Slope is defined as the ratio of a change in y to a corresponding change in x. Our next example shows how slope can be interpreted as a **rate of change** in an applied situation.

EXAMPLE 7   SLOPE AS A RATE OF CHANGE

Shown, again, in Figure 7.10, are the line graphs for the number of U.S. men and women living alone from 1990 through 2003. Find the slope of the line segment for the women. Describe what the slope represents.

SOLUTION We let x represent a year and y the number of women living alone in that year. The two points shown on the line segment for women have the following coordinates:

$$(1990, 14.0) \quad \text{and} \quad (2003, 16.9).$$

In 1990, 14 million U.S. women lived alone.

In 2003, 16.9 million U.S. women lived alone.

Number of People in the United States Living Alone

(2003, 16.9)

(1990, 14.0)

Women

Men   (2003, 12.5)

(1990, 9.0)

Number Living Alone (millions)

Year

FIGURE 7.10 (repeated)

Now we compute the slope.

$$m = \frac{\text{Change in } y}{\text{Change in } x} = \frac{16.9 - 14.0}{2003 - 1990}$$

The unit in the numerator is million women.

$$= \frac{2.9}{13} \approx 0.22$$

The unit in the denominator is year.

The slope indicates that for the period from 1990 through 2003, the number of U.S. women living alone increased by approximately 0.22 million each year. The rate of change is approximately 0.22 million women per year.

CHECK POINT 7 Use the graph in Figure 7.10 to find the slope of the line segment for the men. Express the slope correct to two decimal places and describe what it represents.

6 | Use slope and *y*-intercept to model data.

Modeling Data with the Slope-Intercept Form of the Equation of a Line

Linear functions are useful for modeling data that fall on or near a line. For example, Figure 7.20 shows the number, in millions, of cars and SUVs sold by America's big three automakers from 1990 through 2003. Example 8 and Check Point 8 illustrate how we can use the equation $y = mx + b$ to develop models for the data. The red modifications below the *x*-axis show additions to the original display so that we can obtain these models.

**Cars in Reverse:
Millions of Cars and SUVs Sold**

FIGURE 7.20 Obtaining models from data

EXAMPLE 8   MODELING WITH THE SLOPE-INTERCEPT EQUATION

Find a function in the form $C(x) = mx + b$ that models car sales, $C(x)$, in millions, *x* years after 1990.

SOLUTION We will use the line segment passing through the points $(0, 9)$ and $(13, 7.2)$ to obtain a model. We need values for *m*, the slope, and *b*, the *y*-intercept.

$$C(x) = mx + b$$

$m = \dfrac{\text{Change in } y}{\text{Change in } x}$

$= \dfrac{7.2 - 9}{13 - 0} \approx -0.14$

The point $(0, 9)$ lies on the line segment, so the *y*-intercept is 9: $b = 9$.

Car sales, $C(x)$, in millions, *x* years after 1990 can be modeled by the linear function

$$C(x) = -0.14x + 9.$$

The slope, approximately -0.14, indicates a decrease in sales of about 0.14 million cars per year from 1990 through 2003.

CHECK POINT 8 Use Figure 7.20 to find a function in the form $S(x) = mx + b$ that models SUV sales, $S(x)$, in millions, *x* years after 1990.

EXERCISE SET 7.2 ●●●●●●

• **Practice Exercises**

In Exercises 1–8, use the x- and y-intercepts to graph each linear equation.

1. $x - y = 3$
2. $x + y = 4$
3. $3x - 4y = 12$
4. $2x - 5y = 10$
5. $2x + y = 6$
6. $x + 3y = 6$
7. $5x = 3y - 15$
8. $3x = 2y + 6$

In Exercises 9–20, calculate the slope of the line passing through the given points. If the slope is undefined, so state. Then indicate whether the line rises, falls, is horizontal, or is vertical.

9. $(2, 6)$ and $(3, 5)$
10. $(4, 2)$ and $(3, 4)$
11. $(-2, 1)$ and $(2, 2)$
12. $(-1, 3)$ and $(2, 4)$
13. $(-2, 4)$ and $(-1, -1)$
14. $(6, -4)$ and $(4, -2)$
15. $(5, 3)$ and $(5, -2)$
16. $(3, -4)$ and $(3, 5)$
17. $(2, 0)$ and $(0, 8)$
18. $(3, 0)$ and $(0, -9)$
19. $(5, 1)$ and $(-2, 1)$
20. $(-2, 3)$ and $(1, 3)$

In Exercises 21–32, graph each linear function using the slope and y-intercept.

21. $y = 2x + 3$
22. $y = 2x + 1$
23. $y = -2x + 4$
24. $y = -2x + 3$
25. $y = \frac{1}{2}x + 3$
26. $y = \frac{1}{2}x + 2$
27. $f(x) = \frac{2}{3}x - 4$
28. $f(x) = \frac{3}{4}x - 5$
29. $y = -\frac{3}{4}x + 4$
30. $y = -\frac{2}{3}x + 5$
31. $f(x) = -\frac{5}{3}x$
32. $f(x) = -\frac{4}{3}x$

In Exercises 33–40,

    a. *Put the equation in slope-intercept form by solving for y.*

    b. *Identify the slope and the y-intercept.*

    c. *Use the slope and y-intercept to graph the line.*

33. $3x + y = 0$ **34.** $2x + y = 0$

35. $3y = 4x$ **36.** $4y = 5x$

37. $2x + y = 3$ **38.** $3x + y = 4$

39. $7x + 2y = 14$ **40.** $5x + 3y = 15$

In Exercises 41–48, graph each horizontal or vertical line.

41. $y = 4$ **42.** $y = 2$

43. $y = -2$ **44.** $y = -3$

45. $x = 2$ **46.** $x = 4$

47. $x + 1 = 0$ **48.** $x + 5 = 0$

• Practice Plus

In Exercises 49–52, find the slope of the line passing through each pair of points or state that the slope is undefined. Assume that all variables represent positive real numbers. Then indicate whether the line through the points rises, falls, is horizontal, or is vertical.

49. $(0, a)$ and $(b, 0)$

50. $(-a, 0)$ and $(0, -b)$

51. (a, b) and $(a, b + c)$

52. $(a - b, c)$ and $(a, a + c)$

In Exercises 53–54, give the slope and y-intercept of each line whose equation is given. Assume that $B \neq 0$.

53. $Ax + By = C$

54. $Ax = By - C$

In Exercises 55–56, find the value of y if the line through the two given points is to have the indicated slope.

55. $(3, y)$ and $(1, 4)$, $m = -3$

56. $(-2, y)$ and $(4, -4)$, $m = \frac{1}{3}$

Use the figure to make the lists in Exercises 57–58.

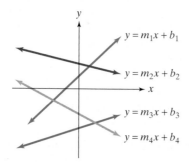

57. List the slopes m_1, m_2, m_3, and m_4 in order of decreasing size.

58. List the y-intercepts b_1, b_2, b_3, and b_4 in order of decreasing size.

• Application Exercises

59. The graph shows the nationwide average for unleaded regular gas from 2000 through 2005.

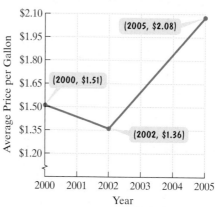

Average Retail Price for Unleaded Regular Gasoline in the United States

Source: Energy Information Administration

    a. Find the slope of the line through $(2000, 1.51)$ and $(2002, 1.36)$. What does this represent in terms of the rate of change in the average price for a gallon of gas from 2000 through 2002?

    b. Find the slope of the line through $(2002, 1.36)$ and $(2005, 2.08)$. What does this represent in terms of the rate of change in the average price for a gallon of gas from 2002 through 2005?

60. The graph shows the percentage of sales of recorded music in the United States for rock and rap/hip hop.

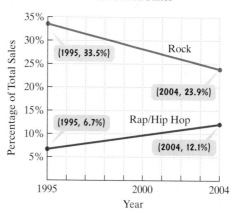

Sales of Recorded Music in the United States

Source: RIAA

    a. Find the slope of the line through $(1995, 33.5)$ and $(2004, 23.9)$. Round to one decimal place. What does this represent in terms of the rate of change in the percentage of total sales of rock for the period shown?

    b. Find the slope of the line through $(1995, 6.7)$ and $(2004, 12.1)$. What does this represent in terms of the rate of change in the percentage of total sales of rap/hip hop for the period shown?

61. The five points shown below represent the number of global HIV/AIDS cases, in millions, from 1999 through 2003. Also shown is the graph of a linear function that passes through or near the points.

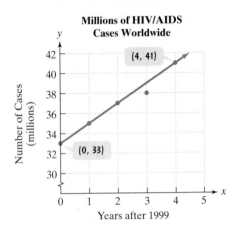

Millions of HIV/AIDS Cases Worldwide

(4, 41)

(0, 33)

Number of Cases (millions)

Years after 1999

Source: UNAIDS

a. According to the graph, what is the *y*-intercept? Describe what this represents in this situation.

b. Use the coordinates of the two points shown to compute the slope. What does this mean about the number of HIV/AIDS cases worldwide?

c. Use the *y*-intercept from part (a) and the slope from part (b) to write a linear function that models the number of HIV/AIDS cases worldwide, *y*, in millions, *x* years after 1999.

d. Use the linear function from part (c) to predict the number of HIV/AIDS cases worldwide, in millions, in 2010.

62. The five points shown below represent retail prescription drug sales in the United States, in billions of dollars, from 2000 through 2004. Also shown is the graph of a linear function that passes through or near the points.

Retail Prescription Drug Sales in the United States

(0, $146)

(4, $221)

Sales (billions of dollars)

Years after 2000

Source: U.S. Census Bureau

a. According to the graph, what is the *y*-intercept? Describe what this represents in this situation.

b. Use the coordinates of the two points shown to compute the slope. What does this mean about retail prescription drug sales in the United States?

c. Use the *y*-intercept from part (a) and the slope from part (b) to write a linear function that models prescription drug sales in the United States, *y*, in billions of dollars, *x* years after 2000.

d. Use the linear function from part (c) to predict prescription drug sales, in billions of dollars, in 2010.

• Writing in Mathematics

63. Describe how to find the *x*-intercept of a linear equation.

64. Describe how to find the *y*-intercept of a linear equation.

65. What is the slope of a line?

66. Describe how to calculate the slope of a line passing through two points.

67. Describe how to graph a line using the slope and *y*-intercept. Provide an original example with your description.

68. What does it mean if the slope of a line is 0?

69. What does it mean if the slope of a line is undefined?

70. What is the least number of points needed to graph a line? How many should actually be used? Explain.

71. Explain why the *y*-values can be any number for the equation $x = 5$. How is this shown in the graph of the equation?

• Critical Thinking Exercises

72. Which one of the following is true?

a. The equation $y = mx + b$ shows that no line can have a *y*-intercept that is numerically equal to its slope.

b. Every line in the rectangular coordinate system has an equation that can be expressed in slope-intercept form.

c. The line $3x + 2y = 5$ has slope $-\frac{3}{2}$.

d. The line $2y = 3x + 7$ has a *y*-intercept of 7.

73. The relationship between Celsius temperature, *C*, and Fahrenheit temperature, *F*, can be described by a linear equation in the form $F = mC + b$. The graph of this equation contains the point $(0, 32)$: Water freezes at 0°C or at 32°F. The line also contains the point $(100, 212)$: Water boils at 100°C or at 212°F. Write the linear equation expressing Fahrenheit temperature in terms of Celsius temperature.

• Technology Exercises

74. Use a graphing utility to verify any three of your hand-drawn graphs in Exercises 21–32.

75. Use a graphing utility to verify any three of your hand-drawn graphs in Exercises 33–40. Solve the equation for *y* before entering it.

SECTION 7.3 • SYSTEMS OF LINEAR EQUATIONS IN TWO VARIABLES

O B J E C T I V E S

1. Decide whether an ordered pair is a solution of a linear system.

2. Solve linear systems by graphing.

3. Solve linear systems by substitution.

4. Solve linear systems by addition.

5. Identify systems that do not have exactly one ordered-pair solution.

6. Solve problems using systems of linear equations.

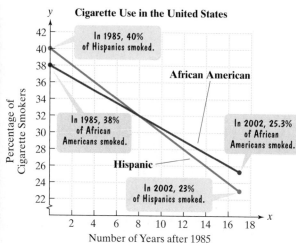

Cigarette Use in the United States

In 1985, 40% of Hispanics smoked.

African American

In 1985, 38% of African Americans smoked.

In 2002, 25.3% of African Americans smoked.

Hispanic

In 2002, 23% of Hispanics smoked.

Percentage of Cigarette Smokers

Number of Years after 1985

FIGURE 7.21
Source: Department of Health and Human Services

Although we still see celebrities smoking in movies, in music videos, and on television, there has been a remarkable decline in the percentage of cigarette smokers in the United States. The decline among African Americans and Hispanics, illustrated in Figure 7.21, can be analyzed using a pair of linear models in two variables.

In this section, you will learn to model your world with two equations in two variables. The methods you learn for solving these systems provide the foundation for solving complex problems involving thousands of equations containing thousands of variables. In the exercise set, you will apply these methods to analyze the linear decrease in cigarette use among whites, African Americans, and Hispanics.

1 | Decide whether an ordered pair is a solution of a linear system.

Systems of Linear Equations and Their Solutions

We have seen that all equations in the form $Ax + By = C$ are straight lines when graphed. Two such equations are called a **system of linear equations** or a **linear system**. A **solution to a system of linear equations in two variables** is an ordered pair that satisfies both equations in the system. For example, $(3, 4)$ satisfies the system

$$x + y = \ \ 7 \qquad (3 + 4 \text{ is, indeed, } 7.)$$
$$x - y = -1. \qquad (3 - 4 \text{ is, indeed, } -1.)$$

Thus, $(3, 4)$ satisfies both equations and is a solution of the system. The solution can be described by saying that $x = 3$ and $y = 4$. The solution can also be described using set notation. The solution set of the system is $\{(3, 4)\}$—that is, the set consisting of the ordered pair $(3, 4)$.

A system of linear equations can have exactly one solution, no solution, or infinitely many solutions. We begin with systems having exactly one solution.

EXAMPLE 1   DETERMINING WHETHER AN ORDERED PAIR IS A SOLUTION OF A SYSTEM

Determine whether $(1, 2)$ is a solution of the system:

$$2x - 3y = -4$$
$$2x + \ y = \ \ 4.$$

SOLUTION Because 1 is the x-coordinate and 2 is the y-coordinate of $(1, 2)$, we replace x with 1 and y with 2.

$2x - 3y = -4$	$2x + y = 4$
$2(1) - 3(2) \overset{?}{=} -4$	$2(1) + 2 \overset{?}{=} 4$
$2 - 6 \overset{?}{=} -4$	$2 + 2 \overset{?}{=} 4$
$-4 = -4,$ true	$4 = 4,$ true

The pair $(1, 2)$ satisfies both equations: It makes each equation true. Thus, the pair is a solution of the system.

 Determine whether $(-4, 3)$ is a solution of the system:

$$x + 2y = 2$$
$$x - 2y = 6.$$

---

2 | Solve linear systems by graphing.

Solving Linear Systems by Graphing

The solution to a system of linear equations can be found by graphing both of the equations in the same rectangular coordinate system. For a system with one solution, **the coordinates of the point of intersection of the lines is the system's solution**.

> ### EXAMPLE 2   SOLVING A LINEAR SYSTEM BY GRAPHING
>
> Solve by graphing:
>
> $$x + 2y = 2$$
> $$x - 2y = 6.$$

SOLUTION We find the solution by graphing both $x + 2y = 2$ and $x - 2y = 6$ in the same rectangular coordinate system. We will use intercepts to graph each equation.

$x + 2y = 2$

x-intercept: Set $y = 0$.
$$x + 2 \cdot 0 = 2$$
$$x = 2$$

The line passes through $(2, 0)$.

y-intercept: Set $x = 0$.
$$0 + 2y = 2$$
$$2y = 2$$
$$y = 1$$

The line passes through $(0, 1)$.

We graph $x + 2y = 2$ as a blue line in Figure 7.22.

$x - 2y = 6$

x-intercept: Set $y = 0$.
$$x - 2 \cdot 0 = 6$$
$$x = 6$$

The line passes through $(6, 0)$.

y-intercept: Set $x = 0$.
$$0 - 2y = 6$$
$$-2y = 6$$
$$y = -3$$

The line passes through $(0, -3)$.

We graph $x - 2y = 6$ as a red line in Figure 7.22.

The system is graphed in Figure 7.22. To ensure that the graph is accurate, check the coordinates of the intersection point, $(4, -1)$, in both equations. We replace x with 4 and y with -1.

$x + 2y = 2$	$x - 2y = 6$
$4 + 2(-1) \overset{?}{=} 2$	$4 - 2(-1) \overset{?}{=} 6$
$4 + (-2) \overset{?}{=} 2$	$4 - (-2) \overset{?}{=} 6$
$2 = 2,$ true	$4 + 2 \overset{?}{=} 6$
	$6 = 6,$ true

FIGURE 7.22 Visualizing a system's solution

All points are solutions of $x + 2y = 2.$

All points are solutions of $x - 2y = 6.$

Point of intersection $(4, -1)$ gives the common solution.

STUDY TIP

When solving linear systems by graphing, neatly drawn graphs are essential for determining points of intersection.

- Use rectangular coordinate graph paper.
- Use a ruler or straightedge.
- Use a pencil with a sharp point.

The pair $(4, -1)$ satisfies both equations—that is, it makes each equation true. This verifies that the system's solution set is $\{(4, -1)\}$.

⊙

CHECK POINT 2 Solve by graphing:

$$2x + 3y = 6$$
$$2x + y = -2.$$

3 Solve linear systems by substitution.

Solving Linear Systems by the Substitution Method

Finding the solution to a linear system by graphing equations may not be easy to do. For example, a solution of $\left(-\frac{2}{3}, \frac{157}{29}\right)$ would be difficult to "see" as an intersection point on a graph.

Let's consider a method that does not depend on finding a system's solution visually: the substitution method. This method involves converting the system to one equation in one variable by an appropriate substitution.

EXAMPLE 3   SOLVING A SYSTEM BY SUBSTITUTION

Solve by the substitution method:

$$y = -x - 1$$
$$4x - 3y = 24.$$

SOLUTION

Step 1. Solve either of the equations for one variable in terms of the other. This step has already been done for us. The first equation, $y = -x - 1$, is solved for y in terms of x.

Step 2. Substitute the expression from step 1 into the other equation. We substitute the expression $-x - 1$ for y into the other equation:

$$y = \boxed{-x - 1} \qquad 4x - 3\boxed{y} = 24 \qquad \text{Substitute } -x - 1 \text{ for } y.$$

This gives us an equation in one variable, namely

$$4x - 3(-x - 1) = 24.$$

The variable y has been eliminated.

Step 3. Solve the resulting equation containing one variable.

$4x - 3(-x - 1) = 24$	This is the equation containing one variable.
$4x + 3x + 3 = 24$	Apply the distributive property.
$7x + 3 = 24$	Combine like terms.
$7x = 21$	Subtract 3 from both sides.
$x = 3$	Divide both sides by 7.

TECHNOLOGY

A graphing calculator can be used to solve the system in Example 3. Graph each equation and use the intersection feature. The calculator displays the solution $(3, -4)$ as $x = 3, y = -4$.

[-10, 10, 1] by [-10, 10, 1]

Step 4. Back-substitute the obtained value into the equation from step 1. We now know that the x-coordinate of the solution is 3. To find the y-coordinate, we back-substitute the x-value into the equation from step 1,

$$y = -x - 1. \qquad \text{This is the equation from step 1.}$$

Substitute 3 for x.

$$y = -3 - 1$$
$$y = -4 \qquad \text{Simplify.}$$

With $x = 3$ and $y = -4$, the proposed solution is $(3, -4)$.

Step 5. Check the proposed solution, $(3, -4)$, in both of the system's given equations. Replace x with 3 and y with -4.

$$y = -x - 1 \qquad\qquad 4x - 3y = 24$$
$$-4 \overset{?}{=} -3 - 1 \qquad\qquad 4(3) - 3(-4) \overset{?}{=} 24$$
$$-4 = -4, \qquad \text{true} \qquad\qquad 12 + 12 \overset{?}{=} 24$$
$$\qquad\qquad\qquad\qquad\qquad\qquad 24 = 24, \qquad \text{true}$$

The pair $(3, -4)$ satisfies both equations. The system's solution set is $\{(3, -4)\}$.

 Solve by the substitution method:

$$y = 3x - 7$$
$$5x - 2y = 8.$$

Before considering additional examples, let's summarize the steps used in the substitution method.

SOLVING LINEAR SYSTEMS BY SUBSTITUTION

1. Solve either of the equations for one variable in terms of the other. (If one of the equations is already in this form, you can skip this step.)
2. Substitute the expression found in step 1 into the *other* equation. This will result in an equation in one variable.
3. Solve the equation containing one variable.
4. Back-substitute the value found from step 3 into the equation from step 1. Simplify and find the value of the remaining variable.
5. Check the proposed solution in both of the system's given equations.

EXAMPLE 4   SOLVING A SYSTEM BY SUBSTITUTION

Solve by the substitution method:

$$5x - 4y = 9$$
$$x - 2y = -3.$$

SOLUTION

Step 1. Solve either of the equations for one variable in terms of the other. We begin by isolating one of the variables in either of the equations. By solving for x in the second equation, which has a coefficient of 1, we can avoid fractions.

$$x - 2y = -3 \qquad \text{This is the second equation in the given system.}$$
$$x = 2y - 3 \qquad \text{Solve for x by adding 2y to both sides.}$$

Step 2. Substitute the expression from step 1 into the other equation. We substitute $2y - 3$ for x in the first equation.

$$x = \boxed{2y - 3} \qquad\qquad 5\boxed{x} - 4y = 9$$

This gives us an equation in one variable, namely

$$5(2y - 3) - 4y = 9.$$

The variable x has been eliminated.

Step 3. Solve the resulting equation containing one variable.

$$5(2y - 3) - 4y = 9 \qquad \text{This is the equation containing one variable.}$$
$$10y - 15 - 4y = 9 \qquad \text{Apply the distributive property.}$$
$$6y - 15 = 9 \qquad \text{Combine like terms: } 10y - 4y = 6y.$$
$$6y = 24 \qquad \text{Add 15 to both sides.}$$
$$y = 4 \qquad \text{Divide both sides by 6.}$$

Step 4. Back-substitute the obtained value into the equation from step 1. Now that we have the y-coordinate of the solution, we back-substitute 4 for y in the equation $x = 2y - 3$.

$$x = 2y - 3 \qquad \text{Use the equation obtained in step 1.}$$
$$x = 2(4) - 3 \qquad \text{Substitute 4 for y.}$$
$$x = 8 - 3 \qquad \text{Multiply.}$$
$$x = 5 \qquad \text{Subtract.}$$

With $x = 5$ and $y = 4$, the proposed solution is $(5, 4)$.

Step 5. Check. Take a moment to show that $(5, 4)$ satisfies both given equations. The solution set is $\{(5, 4)\}$.

 Solve by the substitution method:

$$3x + 2y = -1$$
$$x - y = 3.$$

---

4 | Solve linear systems by addition.

Solving Linear Systems by the Addition Method

The substitution method is most useful if one of the given equations has an isolated variable. A third, and frequently the easiest, method for solving a linear system is the addition method. Like the substitution method, the addition method involves eliminating a variable and ultimately solving an equation containing only one variable. However, this time we eliminate a variable by adding the equations.

For example, consider the following system of linear equations:

$$3x - 4y = 11$$
$$-3x + 2y = -7.$$

When we add these two equations, the x-terms are eliminated. This occurs because the coefficients of the x-terms, 3 and -3, are opposites (additive inverses) of each other:

$$3x - 4y = 11$$
$$\underline{-3x + 2y = -7}$$

Add: $-2y = 4$ $\boxed{\text{The sum is an equation in one variable.}}$

$$y = -2 \qquad \text{Solve for y, dividing both sides by } -2.$$

Now we can back-substitute -2 for y into one of the original equations to find x. It does not matter which equation we use: We will obtain the same value for x in either case. If we use either equation, we can show that $x = 1$ and the solution $(1, -2)$ satisfies both equations in the system.

When we use the addition method, we want to obtain two equations whose sum is an equation containing only one variable. The key step is to **obtain, for one of the variables, coefficients that differ only in sign**. To do this, we may need to multiply one or both equations by some nonzero number so that the coefficients of one of the variables, x or y, become opposites. Then when the two equations are added, this variable is eliminated.

STUDY TIP

Although the addition method is also known as the elimination method, variables are eliminated when using both the substitution and addition methods. The name *addition method* specifically tells us that the elimination of a variable is accomplished by adding two equations.

SOLVING LINEAR SYSTEMS BY ADDITION

1. If necessary, rewrite both equations in the form $Ax + By = C$.
2. If necessary, multiply either equation or both equations by appropriate nonzero numbers so that the sum of the x-coefficients or the sum of the y-coefficients is 0.
3. Add the equations in step 2. The sum is an equation in one variable.
4. Solve the equation in one variable.
5. Back-substitute the value obtained in step 4 into either of the given equations and solve for the other variable.
6. Check the solution in both of the original equations.

EXAMPLE 5 SOLVING A SYSTEM BY THE ADDITION METHOD

Solve by the addition method:

$$3x + 2y = 48$$
$$9x - 8y = -24.$$

SOLUTION

Step 1. Rewrite both equations in the form $Ax + By = C$. Both equations are already in this form. Variable terms appear on the left and constants appear on the right.

Step 2. If necessary, multiply either equation or both equations by appropriate numbers so that the sum of the x-coefficients or the sum of the y-coefficients is 0. We can eliminate x or y. Let's eliminate x. Consider the terms in x in each equation, that is, $3x$ and $9x$. To eliminate x, we can multiply each term of the first equation by -3 and then add the equations.

$$3x + 2y = 48 \xrightarrow{\text{Multiply by } -3.} -9x - 6y = -144$$

$$9x - 8y = -24 \xrightarrow{\text{No change}} \underline{9x - 8y = -24}$$

Step 3. Add the equations. Add: $-14y = -168$

Step 4. Solve the equation in one variable. We solve $-14y = -168$ by dividing both sides by -14.

$$\frac{-14y}{-14} = \frac{-168}{-14} \qquad \text{Divide both sides by } -14.$$

$$y = 12 \qquad \text{Simplify.}$$

Step 5. Back-substitute and find the value for the other variable. We can back-substitute 12 for y into either one of the given equations. We'll use the first one.

$$3x + 2y = 48 \qquad \text{This is the first equation in the given system.}$$
$$3x + 2(12) = 48 \qquad \text{Substitute 12 for } y.$$
$$3x + 24 = 48 \qquad \text{Multiply.}$$
$$3x = 24 \qquad \text{Subtract 24 from both sides.}$$
$$x = 8 \qquad \text{Divide both sides by 3.}$$

We found that $y = 12$ and $x = 8$. The proposed solution is $(8, 12)$.

Step 6. Check. Take a few minutes to show that $(8, 12)$ satisfies both of the original equations in the system. The solution set is $\{(8, 12)\}$.

 Solve by the addition method:

$$4x + 5y = 3$$
$$2x - 3y = 7.$$

EXAMPLE 6	SOLVING A SYSTEM BY THE ADDITION METHOD

Solve by the addition method:

$$7x = 5 \ - 2y$$
$$3y = 16 - 2x.$$

SOLUTION

Step 1. Rewrite both equations in the form $Ax + By = C$. We first arrange the system so that variable terms appear on the left and constants appear on the right. We obtain

$$7x + 2y = 5 \qquad \text{Add 2y to both sides of the first equation.}$$
$$2x + 3y = 16. \qquad \text{Add 2x to both sides of the second equation.}$$

Step 2. If necessary, multiply either equation or both equations by appropriate numbers so that the sum of the x-coefficients or the sum of the y-coefficients is 0. We can eliminate x or y. Let's eliminate y by multiplying the first equation by 3 and the second equation by -2.

$$7x + 2y = \ 5 \quad \xrightarrow{\text{Multiply by 3.}} \quad 21x + 6y = \ \ 15$$
$$2x + 3y = 16 \quad \xrightarrow{\text{Multiply by } -2.} \quad \underline{-4x - 6y = -32}$$

Step 3. Add the equations. $\qquad\qquad\qquad$ Add: $\quad 17x + 0y = -17$
$$17x = -17$$

Step 4. Solve the equation in one variable. We solve $17x = -17$ by dividing both sides by 17.

$$\frac{17x}{17} = \frac{-17}{17} \qquad \text{Divide both sides by 17.}$$

$$x = -1 \qquad \text{Simplify.}$$

Step 5. Back-substitute and find the value for the other variable. We can back-substitute -1 for x into either one of the given equations. We'll use the second one.

$$3y = 16 - 2x \qquad \text{This is the second equation in the given system.}$$
$$3y = 16 - 2(-1) \qquad \text{Substitute } -1 \text{ for x.}$$
$$3y = 16 + 2 \qquad \text{Multiply.}$$
$$3y = 18 \qquad \text{Add.}$$
$$y = 6 \qquad \text{Divide both sides by 3.}$$

With $x = -1$ and $y = 6$, the proposed solution is $(-1, 6)$.

Step 6. Check. Take a moment to show that $(-1, 6)$ satisfies both given equations. The solution is $(-1, 6)$ and the solution set is $\{(-1, 6)\}$.

 Solve by the addition method:

$$3x = 2 - 4y$$
$$5y = -1 - 2x.$$

5 | Identify systems that do not have exactly one ordered-pair solution.

Linear Systems Having No Solution or Infinitely Many Solutions

We have seen that a system of linear equations in two variables represents a pair of lines. The lines either intersect at one point, are parallel, or are identical. Thus, there are three possibilities for the number of solutions to a system of two linear equations.

THE NUMBER OF SOLUTIONS TO A SYSTEM OF TWO LINEAR EQUATIONS

The number of solutions to a system of two linear equations in two variables is given by one of the following. (See Figure 7.23.)

Number of Solutions	What This Means Graphically
Exactly one ordered-pair solution	The two lines intersect at one point.
No solution	The two lines are parallel.
Infinitely many solutions	The two lines are identical.

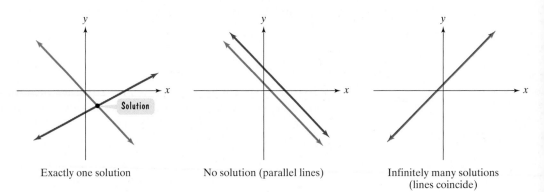

Exactly one solution   No solution (parallel lines)   Infinitely many solutions (lines coincide)

FIGURE 7.23 Possible graphs for a system of two linear equations in two variables

---

EXAMPLE 7   A SYSTEM WITH NO SOLUTION

Solve the system:

$$4x + 6y = 12$$
$$6x + 9y = 12.$$

SOLUTION Because no variable is isolated, we will use the addition method. To obtain coefficients of x that differ only in sign, we multiply the first equation by 3 and the second equation by -2.

$4x + 6y = 12$ $\xrightarrow{\text{Multiply by 3.}}$ $12x + 18y = 36$

$6x + 9y = 12$ $\xrightarrow{\text{Multiply by } -2.}$ $\underline{-12x - 18y = -24}$

Add: $ 0 = 12$

There are no values of x and y for which $0 = 12$. No values of x and y satisfy $0x + 0y = 12$.

The false statement $0 = 12$ indicates that the system has no solution. The solution set is the empty set, $\emptyset$.

The lines corresponding to the two equations in Example 7 are shown in Figure 7.24. The lines are parallel and have no point of intersection.

FIGURE 7.24 The graph of a system with no solution

 Solve the system:

$$x + 2y = 4$$
$$3x + 6y = 13.$$

EXAMPLE 8	A SYSTEM WITH INFINITELY MANY SOLUTIONS

Solve the system:

$$y = 3x - 2$$
$$15x - 5y = 10.$$

SOLUTION Because the variable y is isolated in $y = 3x - 2$, the first equation, we can use the substitution method. We substitute the expression for y into the second equation.

$y = \boxed{3x - 2}$ $15x - 5\boxed{y} = 10$ Substitute $3x - 2$ for y.

$15x - 5(3x - 2) = 10$ The substitution results in an equation in one variable.

$15x - 15x + 10 = 10$ Apply the distributive property.

This statement is true for all values of x and y. $10 = 10$ Simplify.

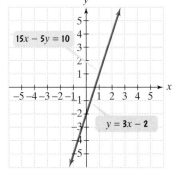

$15x - 5y = 10$

$y = 3x - 2$

FIGURE 7.25 The graph of a system with infinitely many solutions

In our final step, both variables have been eliminated and the resulting statement, $10 = 10$, is true. This true statement indicates that the system has infinitely many solutions. The solution set consists of all points (x, y) lying on either of the coinciding lines, $y = 3x - 2$ or $15x - 5y = 10$, as shown in Figure 7.25.

We express the solution set for the system in one of two equivalent ways:

$$\{(x, y) \mid y = 3x - 2\} \quad \text{or} \quad \{(x, y) \mid 15x - 5y = 10\}.$$

The set of all ordered pairs (x, y) such that $y = 3x - 2$

The set of all ordered pairs (x, y) such that $15x - 5y = 10$

STUDY TIP

Although the system in Example 8 has infinitely many solutions, this does not mean that any ordered pair of numbers you can form will be a solution. The ordered pair (x, y) must satisfy one of the system's equations, $y = 3x - 2$ or $15x - 5y = 10$, and there are infinitely many such ordered pairs. Because the graphs are coinciding lines, the ordered pairs that are solutions of one of the equations are also solutions of the other equation.

Solve the system:

$$y = 4x - 4$$
$$8x - 2y = 8.$$

LINEAR SYSTEMS HAVING NO SOLUTION OR INFINITELY MANY SOLUTIONS

If both variables are eliminated when a system of linear equations is solved by substitution or addition, one of the following is true:

1. There is no solution if the resulting statement is false.
2. There are infinitely many solutions if the resulting statement is true.

6 | Solve problems using systems of linear equations.

Modeling with Systems of Equations: Making Money (and Losing It)

What does every entrepreneur, from a kid selling lemonade to Donald Trump, want to do? Generate profit, of course. The profit made is the money taken in, or the revenue, minus the money spent, or the cost.

REVENUE AND COST FUNCTIONS

A company produces and sells x units of a product.

Revenue Function
$$R(x) = (\text{price per unit sold})x$$

Cost Function
$$C(x) = \text{fixed cost} + (\text{cost per unit produced})x$$

The point of intersection of the graphs of the revenue and cost functions is called the **break-even point**. The x-coordinate of the point reveals the number of units that a company must produce and sell so that money coming in, the revenue, is equal to money going out, the cost. The y-coordinate of the break-even point gives the amount of money coming in and going out. Example 9 illustrates how we obtain a mathematical model in the form of a system of equations that allows us to determine a company's break-even point.

EXAMPLE 9   FINDING A BREAK-EVEN POINT

A company is planning to manufacture radically different wheelchairs. Fixed cost will be $500,000 and it will cost $400 to produce each wheelchair. Each wheelchair will be sold for $600.

a. Write the cost function, C, of producing x wheelchairs.
b. Write the revenue function, R, from the sale of x wheelchairs.
c. Determine the break-even point. Describe what this means.

SOLUTION

a. The cost function is the sum of the fixed cost and variable cost.

> Fixed cost of $500,000   plus   Variable cost: $400 for each chair produced

$$C(x) = 500,000 + 400x$$

b. The revenue function is the money generated from the sale of x wheelchairs. We are given that each wheelchair will be sold for $600.

> Revenue per chair, $600, times   the number of chairs sold

$$R(x) = 600x$$

c. The break-even point occurs where the graphs of C and R intersect. Thus, we find this point by solving the system

$$C(x) = 500,000 + 400x \qquad\qquad y = 500,000 + 400x$$
$$R(x) = 600x \qquad\qquad\text{or}\qquad\qquad y = 600x.$$

Using substitution, we can substitute $600x$ for y in the first equation:

$$600x = 500,000 + 400x \qquad \text{Substitute } 600x \text{ for } y \text{ in } y = 500,000 + 400x.$$

$$200x = 500,000 \qquad \text{Subtract } 400x \text{ from both sides.}$$

$$x = 2500 \qquad \text{Divide both sides by 200.}$$

Back-substituting 2500 for x in either of the system's equations (or functions), we obtain

$$R(2500) = 600(2500) = 1,500,000.$$

> We used $R(x) = 600x$.

The break-even point is $(2500, 1,500,000)$. This means that the company will break even if it produces and sells 2500 wheelchairs. At this level, the money coming in is equal to the money going out: $1,500,000.

Figure 7.26 shows the graphs of the revenue and cost functions for the wheelchair business of Example 9. Similar graphs and models apply no matter how small or large a business venture may be.

FIGURE 7.26

The intersection point confirms that the company breaks even by producing and selling 2500 wheelchairs. Can you see what happens for $x < 2500$? The red cost graph lies above the blue revenue graph. The cost is greater than the revenue and the business is losing money. Thus, if they sell fewer than 2500 wheelchairs, the result is a *loss*. By contrast, look at what happens for $x > 2500$. The blue revenue graph lies above the red cost graph. The revenue is greater than the cost and the business is making money. Thus, if they sell more than 2500 wheelchairs, the result is a *gain*.

⊘ **Check Point 9** A company that manufactures running shoes has a fixed cost of $300,000. Additionally, it costs $30 to produce each pair of shoes. They are sold at $80 per pair.

    a. Write the cost function, C, of producing x pairs of running shoes.

    b. Write the revenue function, R, from the sale of x pairs of running shoes.

    c. Determine the break-even point. Describe what this means.

Once a business has modeled its revenue and cost with a system of equations, it can determine its *profit function*, $P(x)$.

THE PROFIT FUNCTION

The profit, $P(x)$, generated after producing and selling x units of a product is given by the **profit function**

$$P(x) = R(x) - C(x),$$

where R and C are the revenue and cost functions, respectively.

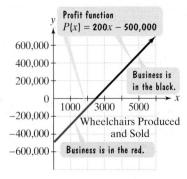

FIGURE 7.27

The profit function for the wheelchair business in Example 9 is

$$P(x) = R(x) - C(x)$$
$$= 600x - (500,000 + 400x)$$
$$= 200x - 500,000.$$

The graph of this profit function is shown in Figure 7.27. The red portion lies below the x-axis and shows a loss when fewer than 2500 wheelchairs are sold. The business is "in the red." The black portion lies above the x-axis and shows a gain when more than 2500 wheelchairs are sold. The wheelchair business is "in the black."

EXERCISE SET 7.3 ●●●●●●

• Practice Exercises

In Exercises 1–4, determine whether the given ordered pair is a solution of the system.

1. $(2, 3)$
$$x + 3y = 11$$
$$x - 5y = -13$$

2. $(-3, 5)$
$$9x + 7y = 8$$
$$8x - 9y = -69$$

3. $(2, 5)$
$$2x + 3y = 17$$
$$x + 4y = 16$$

4. $(8, 5)$
$$5x - 4y = 20$$
$$3y = 2x + 1$$

In Exercises 5–12, solve each system by graphing. Check the coordinates of the intersection point in both equations.

5. $x + y = 6$
$$x - y = 2$$

6. $x + y = 2$
$$x - y = 4$$

7. $2x - 3y = 6$
$$4x + 3y = 12$$

8. $4x + y = 4$
$$3x - y = 3$$

9. $y = x + 5$
$$y = -x + 3$$

10. $y = x + 1$
$$y = 3x - 1$$

11. $y = -x - 1$
$$4x - 3y = 24$$

12. $y = 3x - 4$
$$2x + y = 1$$

In Exercises 13–24, solve each system by the substitution method. Be sure to check all proposed solutions.

13. $x + y = 4$
$$y = 3x$$

14. $x + y = 6$
$$y = 2x$$

15. $x + 3y = 8$
$$y = 2x - 9$$

16. $2x - 3y = -13$
$$y = 2x + 7$$

17. $x + 3y = 5$
$$4x + 5y = 13$$

18. $y = 2x + 7$
$$2x - y = -15$$

19. $2x - y = -5$
$$x + 5y = 14$$

20. $2x + 3y = 11$
$$x - 4y = 0$$

21. $2x - y = 3$
$$5x - 2y = 10$$

22. $-x + 3y = 10$
$$2x + 8y = -6$$

23. $x + 8y = 6$
$$2x + 4y = -3$$

24. $-4x + y = -11$
$$2x - 3y = 5$$

In Exercises 25–36, solve each system by the addition method. Be sure to check all proposed solutions.

25. $x + y = 1$
$$x - y = 3$$

26. $x + y = 6$
$$x - y = -2$$

27. $2x + 3y = 6$
$$2x - 3y = 6$$

28. $3x + 2y = 14$
$$3x - 2y = 10$$

29. $x + 2y = 2$
$$-4x + 3y = 25$$

30. $2x - 7y = 2$
$$3x + y = -20$$

31. $4x + 3y = 15$
$$2x - 5y = 1$$

32. $3x - 7y = 13$
$$6x + 5y = 7$$

33. $3x - 4y = 11$
$$2x + 3y = -4$$

34. $2x + 3y = -16$
$$5x - 10y = 30$$

35. $2x = 3y - 4$
$$-6x + 12y = 6$$

36. $5x = 4y - 8$
$$3x + 7y = 14$$

In Exercises 37–44, solve by the method of your choice. Identify systems with no solution and systems with infinitely many solutions, using set notation to express their solution sets.

37. $x = 9 - 2y$
$$x + 2y = 13$$

38. $6x + 2y = 7$
$$y = 2 - 3x$$

39. $y = 3x - 5$
$$21x - 35 = 7y$$

40. $9x - 3y = 12$
$$y = 3x - 4$$

41. $3x - 2y = -5$
$$4x + y = 8$$

42. $2x + 5y = -4$
$$3x - y = 11$$

43. $x + 3y = 2$
$$3x + 9y = 6$$

44. $4x - 2y = 2$
$$2x - y = 1$$

• Practice Plus

Use the graphs of the linear functions to solve Exercises 45–46.

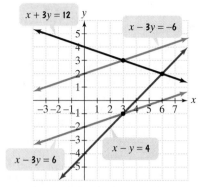

45. Write the linear system whose solution set is $\{(6, 2)\}$. Express each equation in the system in slope-intercept form.

46. Write the linear system whose solution set is $\varnothing$. Express each equation in the system in slope-intercept form.

In Exercises 47–48, solve each system for x and y, expressing either value in terms of a or b, if necessary. Assume that $a \neq 0$ and $b \neq 0$.

47. $5ax + 4y = 17$
$ax + 7y = 22$

48. $4ax + by = 3$
$6ax + 5by = 8$

49. For the linear function $f(x) = mx + b, f(-2) = 11$ and $f(3) = -9$. Find m and b.

50. For the linear function $f(x) = mx + b, f(-3) = 23$ and $f(2) = -7$. Find m and b.

• Application Exercises

The figure shows the graphs of the cost and revenue functions for a company that manufactures and sells small radios. Use the information in the figure to solve Exercises 51–56.

Radios Produced and Sold

51. How many radios must be produced and sold for the company to break even?

52. More than how many radios must be produced and sold for the company to have a profit?

53. Use the formulas shown in the voice balloons to find $R(200) - C(200)$. Describe what this means for the company.

54. Use the formulas shown in the voice balloons to find $R(300) - C(300)$. Describe what this means for the company.

55. a. Use the formulas shown in the voice balloons to write the company's profit function, P, from producing and selling x radios.

b. Find the company's profit if 10,000 radios are produced and sold.

56. a. Use the formulas shown in the voice balloons to write the company's profit function, P, from producing and selling x radios.

b. Find the company's profit if 20,000 radios are produced and sold.

Exercises 57–60 describe a number of business ventures. For each exercise,

a. *Write the cost function, C.*

b. *Write the revenue function, R.*

c. *Determine the break-even point. Describe what this means.*

57. A company that manufactures small canoes has a fixed cost of $18,000. It costs $20 to produce each canoe. The selling price is $80 per canoe. (In solving this exercise, let x represent the number of canoes produced and sold.)

58. A company that manufactures bicycles has a fixed cost of $100,000. It costs $100 to produce each bicycle. The selling price is $300 per bike. (In solving this exercise, let x represent the number of bicycles produced and sold.)

59. You invest in a new play. The cost includes an overhead of $30,000, plus production costs of $2500 per performance. A sold-out performance brings in $3125. (In solving this exercise, let x represent the number of sold-out performances.)

60. You invested $30,000 and started a business writing greeting cards. Supplies cost 2¢ per card and you are selling each card for 50¢. (In solving this exercise, let x represent the number of cards produced and sold.)

The bar graph shows the percentage of Americans who used cigarettes, by ethnicity, in 1985 and 2002. For each of the groups shown, cigarette use has been linearly decreasing. Use this information to solve Exercises 61–62.

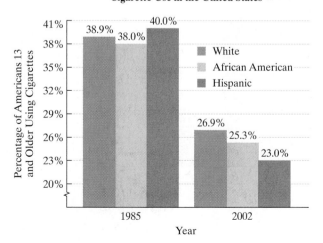

Source: Department of Health and Human Services

61. In this exercise, let x represent the number of years after 1985 and let y represent the percentage of Americans in one of the groups shown who used cigarettes.

a. Use the data points $(0, 38)$ and $(17, 25.3)$ to find the slope-intercept equation of the line that models the percentage of African Americans who used cigarettes, y, x years after 1985. Round the value of m to two decimal places.

b. Use the data points $(0, 40)$ and $(17, 23)$ to find the slope-intercept equation of the line that models the percentage of Hispanics who used cigarettes, y, x years after 1985.

c. Use the models from parts (a) and (b) to find the year during which cigarette use was the same for African Americans and Hispanics. What percentage of each group used cigarettes during that year?

62. In this exercise, refer to the bar graph at the bottom of the previous page. Let x represent the number of years after 1985 and let y represent the percentage of Americans in one of the groups shown who used cigarettes.

a. Use the data points $(0, 38.9)$ and $(17, 26.9)$ to find the slope-intercept equation of the line that models the percentage of whites who used cigarettes, y, x years after 1985. Round the value of m to two decimal places.

b. Use the data points $(0, 40)$ and $(17, 23)$ to find the slope-intercept equation of the line that models the percentage of Hispanics who used cigarettes, y, x years after 1985.

c. Use the models from parts (a) and (b) to find the year, to the nearest whole year, during which cigarette use was the same for whites and Hispanics. What percentage of each group, to the nearest percent, used cigarettes during that year?

Use a system of linear equations to solve Exercises 63–68.

The graph shows the calories in some favorite fast foods. Use the information in Exercises 63–64 to find the exact caloric content of the specified foods.

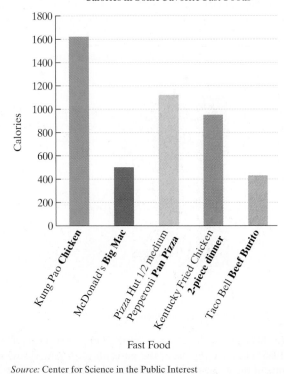

Calories in Some Favorite Fast Foods

Fast Food

Source: Center for Science in the Public Interest

63. One pan pizza and two beef burritos provide 1980 calories. Two pan pizzas and one beef burrito provide 2670 calories. Find the caloric content of each item.

64. One Kung Pao chicken and two Big Macs provide 2620 calories. Two Kung Pao chickens and one Big Mac provide 3740 calories. Find the caloric content of each item.

65. Cholesterol intake should be limited to 300 mg or less each day. One serving of scrambled eggs from McDonald's and one Double Beef Whopper from Burger King exceed this intake by 241 mg. Two servings of scrambled eggs and three Double Beef Whoppers provide 1257 mg of cholesterol. Determine the cholesterol content in each item.

66. Two medium eggs and three cups of ice cream contain 701 milligrams of cholesterol. One medium egg and one cup of ice cream exceed the suggested daily cholesterol intake of 300 milligrams by 25 milligrams. Determine the cholesterol content in each item.

67. A hotel has 200 rooms. Those with kitchen facilities rent for $100 per night and those without kitchen facilities rent for $80 per night. On a night when the hotel was completely occupied, revenues were $17,000. How many of each type of room does the hotel have?

68. A new restaurant is to contain two-seat tables and four-seat tables. Fire codes limit the restaurant's maximum occupancy to 56 customers. If the owners have hired enough servers to handle 17 tables of customers, how many of each kind of table should they purchase?

• Writing in Mathematics

69. What is a system of linear equations? Provide an example with your description.

70. What is the solution to a system of linear equations?

71. Explain how to solve a system of equations using graphing.

72. Explain how to solve a system of equations using the substitution method. Use $y = 3 - 3x$ and $3x + 4y = 6$ to illustrate your explanation.

73. Explain how to solve a system of equations using the addition method. Use $3x + 5y = -2$ and $2x + 3y = 0$ to illustrate your explanation.

74. What is the disadvantage to solving a system of equations using the graphing method?

75. When is it easier to use the addition method rather than the substitution method to solve a system of equations?

76. When using the addition or substitution method, how can you tell whether a system of linear equations has infinitely many solutions? What is the relationship between the graphs of the two equations?

77. When using the addition or substitution method, how can you tell whether a system of linear equations has no solution? What is the relationship between the graphs of the two equations?

• Critical Thinking Exercises

78. Write a system of equations having $\{(-2, 7)\}$ as a solution set. (More than one system is possible.)

79. One apartment is directly above a second apartment. The resident living downstairs calls his neighbor living above him and states, "If one of you is willing to come downstairs, we'll have the same number of people in both apartments." The upstairs resident responds, "We're all too tired to move. Why don't one of you come up here? Then we will have twice as many people up here as you've got down there." How many people are in each apartment?

80. A set of identical twins can only be recognized by the characteristic that one always tells the truth and the other always lies. One twin tells you of a lucky number pair: "When I multiply my first lucky number by 3 and my second lucky number by 6, the addition of the resulting numbers produces a sum of 12. When I add my first lucky number and twice my second lucky number, the sum is 5." Which twin is talking?

SECTION 7.4 • LINEAR INEQUALITIES IN TWO VARIABLES

OBJECTIVES

1. Graph a linear inequality in two variables.
2. Use mathematical models involving linear inequalities.
3. Graph a system of linear inequalities.

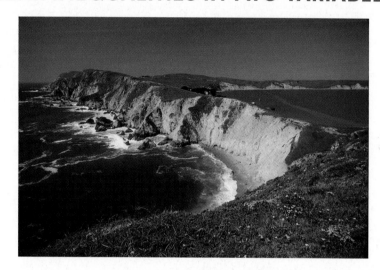

This book was written in Point Reyes National Seashore, 40 miles north of San Francisco. The park consists of 75,000 acres with miles of pristine surf-washed beaches, forested ridges, and bays bordered by white cliffs.

Like your author, many people are kept inspired and energized surrounded by nature's unspoiled beauty. In this section, you will see how systems of inequalities model whether a region's natural beauty manifests itself in forests, grasslands, or deserts.

Linear Inequalities in Two Variables and Their Solutions

We have seen that equations in the form $Ax + By = C$ are straight lines when graphed. If we change the symbol $=$ to $>$, $<$, $\geq$, or $\leq$, we obtain a **linear inequality in two variables**. Some examples of linear inequalities in two variables are $x + y < 2$ and $3x - 5y \geq 15$.

A **solution of an inequality in two variables**, x and y, is an ordered pair of real numbers with the following property: When the x-coordinate is substituted for x and the y-coordinate is substituted for y in the inequality, we obtain a true statement. For example, $(3, 1)$ is a solution of the inequality $x + y > 2$. When 3 is substituted for x and 1 is substituted for y, we obtain the true statement $3 + 1 > 2$, or $4 > 2$. Because there are infinitely many pairs of numbers that have a sum greater than 2, the inequality $x + y > 2$ has infinitely many solutions. Each ordered-pair solution is said to **satisfy** the inequality. Thus, $(3, 1)$ satisfies the inequality $x + y > 2$.

1   Graph a linear inequality in two variables.

The Graph of a Linear Inequality in Two Variables

We know that the graph of an equation in two variables is the set of all points whose coordinates satisfy the equation. Similarly, the **graph of an inequality in two variables** is the set of all points whose coordinates satisfy the inequality.

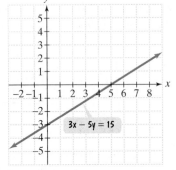

FIGURE 7.28

Let's use Figure 7.28 to get an idea of what the graph of a linear inequality in two variables looks like. Part of the figure shows the graph of the linear equation $x + y = 2$. The line divides the points in the rectangular coordinate system into three sets. First, there is the set of points along the line, satisfying $x + y = 2$. Next, there is the set of points in the green region above the line. Points in the green region satisfy the linear inequality $x + y > 2$. Finally, there is the set of points in the purple region below the line. Points in the purple region satisfy the linear inequality $x + y < 2$.

A **half-plane** is the set of all the points on one side of a line. In Figure 7.28, the green region is a half-plane. The purple region is also a half-plane. A half-plane is the graph of a linear inequality that involves $>$ or $<$. The graph of an inequality that involves $\geq$ or $\leq$ is a half-plane and a line. A solid line is used to show that the line is part of the graph. A dashed line is used to show that a line is not part of a graph.

GRAPHING A LINEAR INEQUALITY IN TWO VARIABLES

1. Replace the inequality symbol with an equal sign and graph the corresponding linear equation. Draw a solid line if the original inequality contains a $\leq$ or $\geq$ symbol. Draw a dashed line if the original inequality contains a $<$ or $>$ symbol.
2. Choose a test point in one of the half-planes that is not on the line. Substitute the coordinates of the test point into the inequality.
3. If a true statement results, shade the half-plane containing this test point. If a false statement results, shade the half-plane not containing this test point.

EXAMPLE 1	GRAPHING A LINEAR INEQUALITY IN TWO VARIABLES

Graph: $3x - 5y \geq 15$.

SOLUTION

Step 1. Replace the inequality symbol by = and graph the linear equation. We need to graph $3x - 5y = 15$. We can use intercepts to graph this line.

We set $y = 0$ to find the x-intercept.	We set $x = 0$ to find the y-intercept.
$3x - 5y = 15$	$3x - 5y = 15$
$3x - 5 \cdot 0 = 15$	$3 \cdot 0 - 5y = 15$
$3x = 15$	$-5y = 15$
$x = 5$	$y = -3$

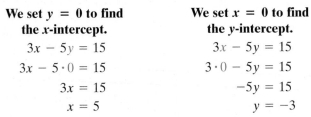

FIGURE 7.29 Preparing to graph $3x - 5y \geq 15$

The x-intercept is 5, so the line passes through $(5, 0)$. The y-intercept is -3, so the line passes through $(0, -3)$. Using the intercepts, the line is shown in Figure 7.29 as a solid line. This is because the inequality $3x - 5y \geq 15$ contains a $\geq$ symbol, in which equality is included.

Step 2. Choose a test point from one of the half-planes and not from the line. Substitute its coordinates into the inequality. The line $3x - 5y = 15$ divides the plane into three parts—the line itself and two half-planes. The points in one half-plane satisfy $3x - 5y > 15$. The points in the other half-plane satisfy $3x - 5y < 15$. We need to find which half-plane belongs to the solution of $3x - 5y \geq 15$. To do so, we test a point from either half-plane. The origin, $(0, 0)$, is the easiest point to test.

$$3x - 5y \geq 15 \qquad \text{This is the given inequality.}$$
$$3 \cdot 0 - 5 \cdot 0 \overset{?}{\geq} 15 \qquad \text{Test } (0, 0) \text{ by substituting 0 for } x \text{ and 0 for } y.$$
$$0 - 0 \overset{?}{\geq} 15 \qquad \text{Multiply.}$$
$$0 \geq 15 \qquad \text{This statement is false.}$$

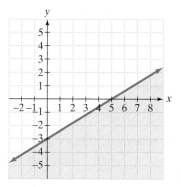

FIGURE 7.30 The graph of $3x - 5y \geq 15$

Step 3. If a false statement results, shade the half-plane not containing the test point. Because 0 is not greater than or equal to 15, the test point, $(0, 0)$, is not part of the solution set. Thus, the half-plane below the solid line $3x - 5y = 15$ is part of the solution set. The solution set is the line and the half-plane that does not contain the point $(0, 0)$, indicated by shading this half-plane. The graph is shown using green shading and a blue line in Figure 7.30.

 Graph: $2x - 4y \geq 8$.

When graphing a linear inequality, test a point that lies in one of the half-planes and *not on the line dividing the half-planes*. The test point $(0, 0)$ is convenient because it is easy to calculate when 0 is substituted for each variable. However, if $(0, 0)$ lies on the dividing line and not in a half-plane, a different test point must be selected.

> **EXAMPLE 2**   GRAPHING A LINEAR INEQUALITY IN TWO VARIABLES

Graph: $y > -\dfrac{2}{3}x$.

SOLUTION

Step 1. Replace the inequality symbol by = and graph the linear equation. Because we are interested in graphing $y > -\frac{2}{3}x$, we begin by graphing $y = -\frac{2}{3}x$. We can use the slope and the y-intercept to graph this linear function.

$$y = -\frac{2}{3}x + 0$$

Slope $= \dfrac{-2}{3} = \dfrac{\text{rise}}{\text{run}}$ y-intercept $= 0$

The y-intercept is 0, so the line passes through $(0, 0)$. Using the y-intercept and the slope, the line is shown in Figure 7.31 as a dashed line. This is because the inequality $y > -\frac{2}{3}x$ contains a $>$ symbol, in which equality is not included.

Step 2. Choose a test point from one of the half-planes and not from the line. Substitute its coordinates into the inequality. We cannot use $(0, 0)$ as a test point because it lies on the line and not in a half-plane. Let's use $(1, 1)$, which lies in the half-plane above the line.

$$y > -\frac{2}{3}x \qquad \text{This is the given inequality.}$$

$$1 \overset{?}{>} -\frac{2}{3} \cdot 1 \qquad \text{Test } (1, 1) \text{ by substituting 1 for } x \text{ and 1 for } y.$$

$$1 > -\frac{2}{3} \qquad \text{This statement is true.}$$

FIGURE 7.31 The graph of $y > -\frac{2}{3}x$

Step 3. If a true statement results, shade the half-plane containing the test point. Because 1 is greater than $-\frac{2}{3}$, the test point, $(1, 1)$, is part of the solution set. All the points on the same side of the line $y = -\frac{2}{3}x$ as the point $(1, 1)$ are members of the solution set. The solution set is the half-plane that contains the point $(1, 1)$, indicated by shading this half-plane. The graph is shown using green shading and a dashed blue line in Figure 7.31.

 Graph: $y > -\dfrac{3}{4}x$.

Graphing Linear Inequalities without Using Test Points

You can graph inequalities in the form $y > mx + b$ or $y < mx + b$ without using test points. The inequality symbol indicates which half-plane to shade.

- If $y > mx + b$, shade the half-plane above the line $y = mx + b$.
- If $y < mx + b$, shade the half-plane below the line $y = mx + b$.

It is also not necessary to use test points when graphing inequalities involving half-planes on one side of a vertical or a horizontal line.

For the Vertical Line $x = a$:

- If $x > a$, shade the half-plane to the right of $x = a$.
- If $x < a$, shade the half-plane to the left of $x = a$.

For the Horizontal Line $y = b$:

- If $y > b$, shade the half-plane above $y = b$.
- If $y < b$, shade the half-plane below $y = b$.

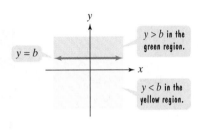

EXAMPLE 3   GRAPHING INEQUALITIES WITHOUT USING TEST POINTS

Graph each inequality in a rectangular coordinate system:

a. $y \leq -3$ **b.** $x > 2$.

SOLUTION

a. $y \leq -3$

Graph $y = -3$, a horizontal line with y-intercept -3. The line is solid because equality is included in $y \leq -3$. Because of the less than part of $\leq$, shade the half-plane below the horizontal line.

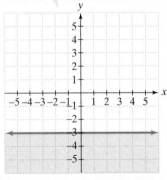

b. $x > 2$

Graph $x = 2$, a vertical line with x-intercept **2**. The line is dashed because equality is not included in $x > 2$. Because of $>$, the greater than symbol, shade the half-plane to the right of the vertical line.

Graph each inequality in a rectangular coordinate system:

a. $y > 1$ **b.** $x \leq -2$.

Modeling with Systems of Linear Inequalities

Just as two linear equations make up a system of linear equations, two or more linear inequalities make up a **system of linear inequalities**. A **solution of a system of linear inequalities** in two variables is an ordered pair that satisfies each inequality in the system.

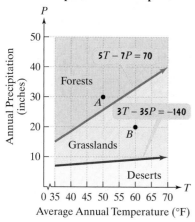

**Regions Resulting from Ranges of
Temperature and Precipitation**

FIGURE 7.32
Source: A. Miller and J. Thompson, *Elements of Meteorology*

EXAMPLE 4 — FORESTS, GRASSLANDS, DESERTS, AND SYSTEMS OF INEQUALITIES

Temperature and precipitation affect whether or not trees and forests can grow. At certain levels of precipitation and temperature, only grasslands and deserts will exist. Figure 7.32 shows three kinds of regions—deserts, grasslands, and forests—that result from various ranges of temperature, T, and precipitation, P.

Systems of inequalities can be used to model where forests, grasslands, and deserts occur. Because these regions occur when the average annual temperature, T, is 35°F or greater, each system contains the inequality $T \geq 35$.

Forests occur if	**Grasslands occur if**	**Deserts occur if**
$T \geq 35$	$T \geq 35$	$T \geq 35$
$5T - 7P < 70.$	$5T - 7P \geq 70$	$3T - 35P > -140.$
	$3T - 35P \leq -140.$	

Show that point A in Figure 7.32 is a solution of the system of inequalities that describes where forests occur.

SOLUTION Point A has coordinates $(50, 30)$. This means that if a region has an average annual temperature of 50°F and an average annual precipitation of 30 inches, a forest occurs. We can show that $(50, 30)$ satisfies the system of inequalities for forests by substituting 50 for T and 30 for P in each inequality in the system.

$$T \geq 35 \qquad\qquad 5T - 7P < 70$$

$$50 \geq 35, \quad \text{true} \qquad 5 \cdot 50 - 7 \cdot 30 \overset{?}{<} 70$$

$$250 - 210 \overset{?}{<} 70$$

$$40 < 70, \quad \text{true}$$

The coordinates $(50, 30)$ make each inequality true. Thus, $(50, 30)$ satisfies the system for forests.

Show that point B in Figure 7.32 is a solution of the system of inequalities given in Example 4 that models where grasslands occur.

---

3 | Graph a system of linear inequalities.

Graphing Systems of Linear Inequalities

The **solution set of a system of linear inequalities in two variables** is the set of all ordered pairs that satisfy each inequality in the system. Thus, to graph a system of inequalities in two variables, begin by graphing each individual inequality in the same rectangular coordinate system. Then find the region, if there is one, that is common to every graph in the system. This region of intersection gives a picture of the system's solution set.

EXAMPLE 5 — GRAPHING A SYSTEM OF LINEAR INEQUALITIES

Graph the solution set of the system:

$$x - y < 1$$
$$2x + 3y \geq 12.$$

SOLUTION Replacing each inequality symbol in $x - y < 1$ and $2x + 3y \geq 12$ with an equal sign indicates that we need to graph $x - y = 1$ and $2x + 3y = 12$. We can use intercepts to graph these lines.

$x - y = 1$		$2x + 3y = 12$

x-intercept: $x - 0 = 1$ 〔Set $y = 0$ in each equation.〕 x-intercept: $2x + 3 \cdot 0 = 12$

$x = 1$

$2x = 12$

The line passes through $(1, 0)$.

$x = 6$

The line passes through $(6, 0)$.

y-intercept: $0 - y = 1$ 〔Set $x = 0$ in each equation.〕 y-intercept: $2 \cdot 0 + 3y = 12$

$-y = 1$

$3y = 12$

$y = -1$

$y = 4$

The line passes through $(0, -1)$.   The line passes through $(0, 4)$.

Now we are ready to graph the solution set of the system of linear inequalities.

Graph $x - y < 1$. The blue line, $x - y = 1$, is dashed: Equality is not included in $x - y < 1$. Because $(0, 0)$ makes the inequality true $(0 - 0 < 1$, or $0 < 1$, is true), shade the half-plane containing $(0, 0)$ in yellow.

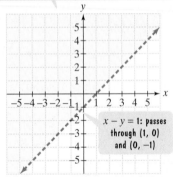

The graph of $x - y < 1$

Add the graph of $2x + 3y \geq 12$. The red line, $2x + 3y = 12$, is solid: Equality is included in $2x + 3y \geq 12$. Because $(0, 0)$ makes the inequality false $(2 \cdot 0 + 3 \cdot 0 \geq 12$, or $0 \geq 12$, is false), shade the half-plane not containing $(0, 0)$ using green vertical shading.

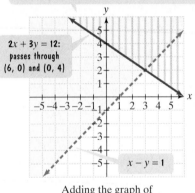

Adding the graph of $2x + 3y \geq 12$

The solution set of the system is graphed as the intersection (the overlap) of the two half-planes. This is the region in which the yellow shading and the green vertical shading overlap.

This open dot shows $(3, 2)$ is not in the solution set. It does not satisfy $x - y < 1$.

The graph of $x - y < 1$ and $2x + 3y \geq 12$

 CHECK POINT 5   Graph the solution set of the system:

$$x + 2y > 4$$
$$2x - 3y \leq -6.$$

EXAMPLE 6   GRAPHING A SYSTEM OF LINEAR INEQUALITIES

Graph the solution set of the system:

$$x \leq 4$$
$$y > -2.$$

SOLUTION

Graph $x \le 4$. The blue vertical line, $x = 4$, is solid. Graph $x < 4$, the half-plane to the left of the blue line, using yellow shading.

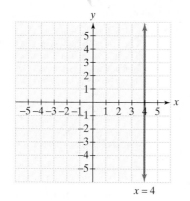

The graph of $x \le 4$

Add the graph of $y > -2$. The red horizontal line, $y = -2$, is dashed. Graph $y > -2$, the half-plane above the dashed red line, using green vertical shading.

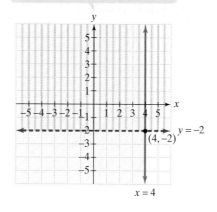

Adding the graph of $y > -2$

The solution set of the system is graphed as the intersection (the overlap) of the two half-planes. This is the region in which the yellow shading and the green vertical shading overlap.

This open dot shows $(4, -2)$ is not in the solution set. It does not satisfy $y > -2$.

The graph of $x \le 4$ and $y > -2$

 6 Graph the solution set of the system:

$$x < 3$$
$$y \ge -1.$$

EXERCISE SET 7.4 ●●●●●●

• Practice Exercises

In Exercises 1–22, graph each linear inequality.

1. $x + y \ge 2$ **2.** $x - y \le 1$

3. $3x - y \ge 6$ **4.** $3x + y \le 3$

5. $2x + 3y > 12$ **6.** $2x - 5y < 10$

7. $5x + 3y \le -15$ **8.** $3x + 4y \le -12$

9. $2y - 3x > 6$ **10.** $2y - x > 4$

11. $y > \dfrac{1}{3}x$ **12.** $y > \dfrac{1}{4}x$

13. $y \le 3x + 2$ **14.** $y \le 2x - 1$

15. $y < -\dfrac{1}{4}x$ **16.** $y < -\dfrac{1}{3}x$

17. $x \le 2$ **18.** $x \le -4$

19. $y > -4$ **20.** $y > -2$

21. $y \ge 0$ **22.** $x \ge 0$

In Exercises 23–38, graph the solution set of each system of inequalities.

23. $3x + 6y \le 6$
    $2x + y \le 8$

24. $x - y \ge 4$
    $x + y \le 6$

25. $2x + y < 3$
    $x - y > 2$

26. $x + y < 4$
    $4x - 2y < 6$

27. $2x + y < 4$
    $x - y > 4$

28. $2x - y < 3$
    $x + y < 6$

29. $x \ge 2$
    $y \le 3$

30. $x \ge 4$
    $y \le 2$

31. $x \le 5$
    $y > -3$

32. $x \le 3$
    $y > -1$

33. $x - y \le 1$
    $x \ge 2$

34. $4x - 5y \ge -20$
    $x \ge -3$

35. $y > 2x - 3$
    $y < -x + 6$

36. $y < -2x + 4$
    $y < x - 4$

37. $x + 2y \le 4$
    $y \ge x - 3$

38. $x + y \le 4$
    $y \ge 2x - 4$

• Practice Plus

In Exercises 39–40, write each sentence as an inequality in two variables. Then graph the inequality.

39. The y-variable is at least 4 more than the product of -2 and the x-variable.

40. The y-variable is at least 2 more than the product of -3 and the x-variable.

In Exercises 41–42, write the given sentences as a system of inequalities in two variables. Then graph the system.

41. The sum of the x-variable and the y-variable is at most 4. The y-variable added to the product of 3 and the x-variable does not exceed 6.

42. The sum of the x-variable and the y-variable is at most 3. The y-variable added to the product of 4 and the x-variable does not exceed 6.

The graphs of solution sets of systems of inequalities involve finding the intersection of the solution sets of two or more inequalities. By contrast, in Exercises 43–44, you will be graphing the union of the solution sets of two inequalities.

43. Graph the union of $y > \frac{3}{2}x - 2$ and $y < 4$.

44. Graph the union of $x - y \geq -1$ and $5x - 2y \leq 10$.

• Application Exercises

Maximum heart rate, H, in beats per minute, is a function of age, a, modeled by the formula

$$H = 220 - a,$$

where $10 \leq a \leq 70$. The bar graph shows the target heart rate ranges as a percentage of the maximum heart rate for four types of exercise goals.

Target Heart Rate Ranges for Exercise Goals

Source: Vitality

In Exercises 45–48, systems of inequalities will be used to model three of the target heart rate ranges shown in the bar graph. We begin with the target heart rate range for cardiovascular conditioning, modeled by the following system of inequalities:

$10 \leq a \leq 70$ — Heart rate ranges apply to ages 10 through 70, inclusive.

$H \geq 0.7(220 - a)$ — Target heart rate range is greater than or equal to 70% of maximum heart rate

$H \leq 0.8(220 - a)$. — and less than or equal to 80% of maximum heart rate.

The graph of this system is shown in the figure. Use the graph to solve Exercises 45–46.

45. a. What are the coordinates of point A and what does this mean in terms of age and heart rate?

b. Show that point A is a solution of the system of inequalities at the bottom of the previous column.

46. a. What are the coordinates of point B and what does this mean in terms of age and heart rate?

b. Show that point B is a solution of the system of inequalities at the bottom of the previous column.

47. Write a system of inequalities that models the target heart rate range shown by the bar graph on the left for the goal of losing weight.

48. Write a system of inequalities that models the target heart rate range shown by the bar graph on the left for improving overall health.

49. Many elevators have a capacity of 2000 pounds.

a. If a child averages 50 pounds and an adult 150 pounds, write an inequality that describes when x children and y adults will cause the elevator to be overloaded.

b. Graph the inequality. Because x and y must be positive, limit the graph to quadrant I only.

c. Select an ordered pair satisfying the inequality. What are its coordinates and what do they represent in this situation?

50. A patient is not allowed to have more than 330 milligrams of cholesterol per day from a diet of eggs and meat. Each egg provides 165 milligrams of cholesterol. Each ounce of meat provides 110 milligrams.

a. Write an inequality that describes the patient's dietary restrictions for x eggs and y ounces of meat.

b. Graph the inequality. Because x and y must be positive, limit the graph to quadrant I only.

c. Select an ordered pair satisfying the inequality. What are its coordinates and what do they represent in this situation?

The graph of an inequality in two variables is a region in the rectangular coordinate system. Regions in coordinate systems have numerous applications. For example, the regions in the following two graphs indicate whether a person is obese, overweight, borderline overweight, normal weight, or underweight.

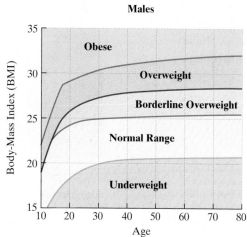

Source: Centers for Disease Control and Prevention

The horizontal axis shows a person's age. The vertical axis shows that person's body-mass index (BMI), computed using the following formula:

$$BMI = \frac{703W}{H^2}.$$

The variable W represents weight, in pounds. The variable H represents height, in inches. Use this information to solve Exercises 51–52.

51. A man is 20 years old, 72 inches (6 feet) tall, and weighs 200 pounds.

    a. Compute the man's BMI. Round to the nearest tenth.

    b. Use the man's age and his BMI to locate this information as a point in the coordinate system for males. Is this person obese, overweight, borderline overweight, normal weight, or underweight?

52. A woman is 25 years old, 66 inches (5 feet, 6 inches) tall, and weighs 105 pounds.

    a. Compute the woman's BMI. Round to the nearest tenth.

    b. Use the woman's age and her BMI to locate this information as a point in the coordinate system for females. Is this person obese, overweight, borderline overweight, normal weight, or underweight?

• Writing in Mathematics

53. What is a half-plane?

54. What does a dashed line mean in the graph of an inequality?

55. Explain how to graph $2x - 3y < 6$.

56. Compare the graphs of $3x - 2y > 6$ and $3x - 2y \leq 6$. Discuss similarities and differences between the graphs.

57. Describe how to solve a system of linear inequalities.

• Critical Thinking Exercises

In Exercises 58–59, write a system of inequalities for each graph.

58.

59.

Without graphing, in Exercises 60–63, determine if each system has no solution or infinitely many solutions.

60. $3x + y < 9$
    $3x + y > 9$

61. $6x - y \leq 24$
    $6x - y > 24$

62. $3x + y \leq 9$
    $3x + y \geq 9$

63. $6x - y \leq 24$
    $6x - y \geq 24$

SECTION 7.5 • LINEAR PROGRAMMING

West Berlin children at Tempelhof airport watch fleets of U.S. airplanes bringing in supplies to circumvent the Soviet blockade. The airlift began June 28, 1948 and continued for 15 months.

The Berlin Airlift (1948–1949) was an operation by the United States and Great Britain in response to military action by the former Soviet Union: Soviet troops closed all roads and rail lines between West Germany and Berlin, cutting off supply routes to the city. The Allies used a mathematical technique developed during World War II to maximize the amount of supplies transported. During the 15-month airlift, 278,228 flights provided basic necessities to blockaded Berlin, saving one of the world's great cities.

In this section, we will look at an important application of systems of linear inequalities. Such systems arise in **linear programming**, a method for solving problems in which a particular quantity that must be maximized or minimized is limited by other factors. Linear programming is one of the most widely used tools in management science. It helps businesses allocate resources to manufacture products in a way that will maximize profit. Linear programming accounts for more than 50% and perhaps as much as 90% of all computing time used for management decisions in business. The Allies used linear programming to save Berlin.

1 | Write an objective function describing a quantity that must be maximized or minimized.

Objective Functions in Linear Programming

Many problems involve quantities that must be maximized or minimized. Businesses are interested in maximizing profit. An operation in which bottled water and medical kits are shipped to earthquake victims needs to maximize the number of victims helped by this shipment. An **objective function** is an algebraic expression in two or more variables describing a quantity that must be maximized or minimized.

EXAMPLE 1   WRITING AN OBJECTIVE FUNCTION

Bottled water and medical supplies are to be shipped to victims of an earthquake by plane. Each container of bottled water will serve 10 people and each medical kit will aid 6 people. If x represents the number of bottles of water to be shipped and y represents the number of medical kits, write the objective function that describes the number of people who can be helped.

SOLUTION   Because each bottle of water serves 10 people and each medical kit aids 6 people, we have

The number of people helped	is	10 times the number of bottles of water	plus	6 times the number of medical kits.
=		$10x$	+	$6y.$

Using z to represent the number of people helped, the objective function is

$$z = 10x + 6y.$$

Unlike the functions that we have seen so far, the objective function is an equation in three variables. For a value of x and a value of y, there is one and only one value of z. Thus, z is a function of x and y.

CHECK POINT 1 A company manufactures bookshelves and desks for computers. Let x represent the number of bookshelves manufactured daily and y the number of desks manufactured daily. The company's profits are $25 per bookshelf and $55 per desk. Write the objective function that describes the company's total daily profit, z, from x bookshelves and y desks. (Check Points 2 through 4 are also related to this situation, so keep track of your answers.)

2 Use inequalities to describe limitations in a situation.

Constraints in Linear Programming

Ideally, the number of earthquake victims helped in Example 1 should increase without restriction so that every victim receives water and medical kits. However, the planes that ship these supplies are subject to weight and volume restrictions. In linear programming problems, such restrictions are called **constraints**. Each constraint is expressed as a linear inequality. The list of constraints forms a system of linear inequalities.

EXAMPLE 2   WRITING A CONSTRAINT

Each plane can carry no more than 80,000 pounds. The bottled water weighs 20 pounds per container and each medical kit weighs 10 pounds. Let x represent the number of bottles of water to be shipped and y the number of medical kits. Write an inequality that describes this constraint.

SOLUTION Because each plane can carry no more than 80,000 pounds, we have

The total weight of the water bottles	plus	the total weight of the medical kits	must be less than or equal to	80,000 pounds.
$20x$	$+$	$10y$	$\leq$	$80{,}000.$

Each bottle weighs 20 pounds.   Each kit weighs 10 pounds.

The plane's weight constraint is described by the inequality

$$20x + 10y \leq 80{,}000.$$

CHECK POINT 2 To maintain high quality, the company in Check Point 1 should not manufacture more than a total of 80 bookshelves and desks per day. Write an inequality that describes this constraint.

In addition to a weight constraint on its cargo, each plane has a limited amount of space in which to carry supplies. Example 3 demonstrates how to express this constraint.

EXAMPLE 3   WRITING A CONSTRAINT

Each plane can carry a total volume of supplies that does not exceed 6000 cubic feet. Each water bottle is 1 cubic foot and each medical kit also has a volume of 1 cubic foot. With x still representing the number of water bottles and y the number of medical kits, write an inequality that describes this second constraint.

SOLUTION Because each plane can carry a volume of supplies that does not exceed 6000 cubic feet, we have

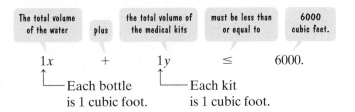

$$1x \quad + \quad 1y \quad \leq \quad 6000.$$

— Each bottle is 1 cubic foot.   — Each kit is 1 cubic foot.

The plane's volume constraint is described by the inequality $x + y \leq 6000$.

In summary, here's what we have described so far in this aid-to-earthquake-victims situation:

$$z = 10x + 6y$$ This is the objective function describing the number of people helped with x bottles of water and y medical kits.

$$20x + 10y \leq 80,000$$
$$x + y \leq 6000.$$ These are the constraints based on each plane's weight and volume limitations.

CHECK POINT 3 To meet customer demand, the company in Check Point 1 must manufacture between 30 and 80 bookshelves per day, inclusive. Furthermore, the company must manufacture at least 10 and no more than 30 desks per day. Write an inequality that describes each of these sentences. Then summarize what you have described about this company by writing the objective function for its profits and the three constraints.

---

3 | Use linear programming to solve problems.

Solving Problems with Linear Programming

The problem in the earthquake situation described previously is to maximize the number of victims who can be helped, subject to each plane's weight and volume constraints. The process of solving this problem is called *linear programming*, based on a theorem that was proven during World War II.

> **SOLVING A LINEAR PROGRAMMING PROBLEM**
>
> Let $z = ax + by$ be an objective function that depends on x and y. Furthermore, z is subject to a number of constraints on x and y. If a maximum or minimum value of z exists, it can be determined as follows:
>
> 1. Graph the system of inequalities representing the constraints.
> 2. Find the value of the objective function at each corner, or **vertex**, of the graphed region. The maximum and minimum of the objective function occur at one or more of the corner points.

EXAMPLE 4   SOLVING A LINEAR PROGRAMMING PROBLEM

Determine how many bottles of water and how many medical kits should be sent on each plane to maximize the number of earthquake victims who can be helped.

SOLUTION We must maximize $z = 10x + 6y$ subject to the following constraints:

$$20x + 10y \leq 80,000$$
$$x + y \leq 6000.$$

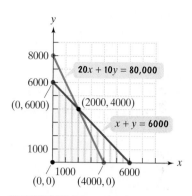

FIGURE 7.33 The region in quadrant I representing the constraints $20x + 10y \leq 80,000$ and $x + y \leq 6000$

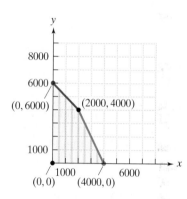

FIGURE 7.34

Step 1. Graph the system of inequalities representing the constraints. Because x (the number of bottles of water per plane) and y (the number of medical kits per plane) must be nonnegative, we need to graph the system of inequalities in quadrant I and its boundary only.

To graph the inequality $20x + 10y \leq 80,000$, we graph the equation $20x + 10y = 80,000$ as a solid blue line (Figure 7.33). Setting $y = 0$, the x-intercept is 4000 and setting $x = 0$, the y-intercept is 8000. Using $(0, 0)$ as a test point, the inequality is satisfied, so we shade below the blue line, as shown in yellow in Figure 7.33.

Now we graph $x + y \leq 6000$ by first graphing $x + y = 6000$ as a solid red line. Setting $y = 0$, the x-intercept is 6000. Setting $x = 0$, the y-intercept is 6000. Using $(0, 0)$ as a test point, the inequality is satisfied, so we shade below the red line, as shown using green vertical shading in Figure 7.33.

We use the addition method to find where the lines $20x + 10y = 80,000$ and $x + y = 6000$ intersect.

$$20x + 10y = 80,000 \quad \xrightarrow{\text{No change}} \quad 20x + 10y = 80,000$$

$$x + y = 6000 \quad \xrightarrow{\text{Multiply by } -10.} \quad \underline{-10x - 10y = -60,000}$$

$$\text{Add:} \quad 10x \qquad = 20,000$$

$$x \qquad = 2000$$

Back-substituting 2000 for x in $x + y = 6000$, we find $y = 4000$, so the intersection point is $(2000, 4000)$.

The system of inequalities representing the constraints is shown by the region in which the yellow shading and the green vertical shading overlap in Figure 7.33. The graph of the system of inequalities is shown again in Figure 7.34. The red and blue line segments are included in the graph.

Step 2. Find the value of the objective function at each corner of the graphed region. The maximum and minimum of the objective function occur at one or more of the corner points. We must evaluate the objective function, $z = 10x + 6y$, at the four corners, or vertices, of the region in Figure 7.34.

Corner (x, y)	Objective Function $z = 10x + 6y$
$(0, 0)$	$z = 10(0) + 6(0) = 0$
$(4000, 0)$	$z = 10(4000) + 6(0) = 40,000$
$(2000, 4000)$	$z = 10(2000) + 6(4000) = 44,000 \leftarrow$ maximum
$(0, 6000)$	$z = 10(0) + 6(6000) = 36,000$

Thus, the maximum value of z is 44,000 and this occurs when $x = 2000$ and $y = 4000$. In practical terms, this means that the maximum number of earthquake victims who can be helped with each plane shipment is 44,000. This can be accomplished by sending 2000 water bottles and 4000 medical kits per plane.

CHECK POINT 4 For the company in Check Points 1–3, how many bookshelves and how many desks should be manufactured per day to obtain a maximum profit? What is the maximum daily profit?

EXERCISE SET 7.5 ●●●●●●

• Practice Exercises

In Exercises 1–4, find the value of the objective function at each corner of the graphed region. What is the maximum value of the objective function? What is the minimum value of the objective function?

1. Objective Function
$z = 5x + 6y$

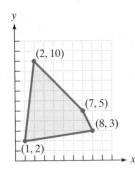

2. Objective Function
$z = 3x + 2y$

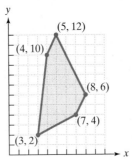

3. Objective Function
$z = 40x + 50y$

4. Objective Function
$z = 30x + 45y$

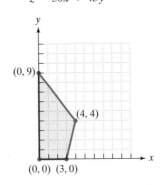

In Exercises 5–8, an objective function and a system of linear inequalities representing constraints are given.

a. *Graph the system of inequalities representing the constraints.*

b. *Find the value of the objective function at each corner of the graphed region.*

c. *Use the values in part (b) to determine the maximum value of the objective function and the values of x and y for which the maximum occurs.*

5. Objective Function
$z = x + y$
Constraints
$x \le 6$
$y \ge 1$
$2x - y \ge -1$

6. Objective Function
$z = 3x - 2y$
Constraints
$x \ge 1$
$x \le 5$
$y \ge 2$
$x - y \ge -3$

7. Objective Function
$z = 6x + 10y$
Constraints
$x + y \le 12$
$x + 2y \le 20$

$\left. \begin{array}{l} x \ge 0 \\ y \ge 0 \end{array} \right\}$ Quadrant 1 and its boundary

8. Objective Function
$z = x + 3y$
Constraints
$x + y \ge 2$
$x \le 6$
$y \le 5$

$\left. \begin{array}{l} x \ge 0 \\ y \ge 0 \end{array} \right\}$ Quadrant 1 and its boundary

• Practice Plus

Use the directions for Exercises 5–8 to solve Exercises 9–12.

9. Objective Function
$z = 5x - 2y$
Constraints
$0 \le x \le 5$
$0 \le y \le 3$
$x + y \ge 2$

10. Objective Function
$z = 3x - 2y$
Constraints
$1 \le x \le 5$
$y \ge 2$
$x - y \ge -3$

11. Objective Function
$z = 10x + 12y$
Constraints
$x \ge 0, y \ge 0$
$x + y \le 7$
$2x + y \le 10$
$2x + 3y \le 18$

12. Objective Function
$z = 5x + 6y$
Constraints
$x \ge 0, y \ge 0$
$2x + y \ge 10$
$x + 2y \ge 10$
$x + y \le 10$

• Application Exercises

13. a. A student earns $10 per hour for tutoring and $7 per hour as a teacher's aid. Let x = the number of hours each week spent tutoring and y = the number of hours each week spent as a teacher's aid. Write the objective function that describes total weekly earnings.

b. The student is bound by the following constraints:
- To have enough time for studies, the student can work no more 20 hours per week.
- The tutoring center requires that each tutor spend at least three hours per week tutoring.
- The tutoring center requires that each tutor spend no more than eight hours per week tutoring.

Write a system of three inequalities that describes these constraints.

c. Graph the system of inequalities in part (b). Use only the first quadrant and its boundary, because x and y are nonnegative.

d. Evaluate the objective function for total weekly earnings at each of the four vertices of the graphed region. [The vertices should occur at $(3, 0)$, $(8, 0)$, $(3, 17)$, and $(8, 12)$.]

e. Complete the missing portions of this statement: The student can earn the maximum amount per week by tutoring for _____ hours per week and working as a teacher's aid for _____ hours per week. The maximum amount that the student can earn each week is $_____.

14. A television manufacturer makes console and wide-screen televisions. The profit per unit is $125 for the console televisions and $200 for the wide-screen televisions.

a. Let x = the number of consoles manufactured in a month and y = the number of wide-screens manufactured in a month. Write the objective function that describes the total monthly profit.

b. The manufacturer is bound by the following constraints:

- Equipment in the factory allows for making at most 450 console televisions in one month.

- Equipment in the factory allows for making at most 200 wide-screen televisions in one month.

- The cost to the manufacturer per unit is $600 for the console televisions and $900 for the wide-screen televisions. Total monthly costs cannot exceed $360,000.

Write a system of three inequalities that describes these constraints.

c. Graph the system of inequalities in part (b). Use only the first quadrant and its boundary, because x and y must both be nonnegative.

d. Evaluate the objective function for total monthly profit at each of the five vertices of the graphed region. [The vertices should occur at $(0, 0)$, $(0, 200)$, $(300, 200)$, $(450, 100)$, and $(450, 0)$.]

e. Complete the missing portions of this statement: The television manufacturer will make the greatest profit by manufacturing _____ console televisions each month and _____ wide-screen televisions each month. The maximum monthly profit is $_____.

Use the two steps for solving a linear programming problem, given in the box on page 416, to solve the problems in Exercises 15–18.

15. Food and clothing are shipped to victims of a natural disaster. Each carton of food will feed 12 people, while each carton of clothing will help 5 people. Each 20-cubic-foot box of food weighs 50 pounds and each 10-cubic-foot box of clothing weighs 20 pounds. The commercial carriers transporting food and clothing are bound by the following constraints:

- The total weight per carrier cannot exceed 19,000 pounds.

- The total volume must be no more than 8000 cubic feet.

How many cartons of food and clothing should be sent with each plane shipment to maximize the number of people who can be helped?

16. You are about to take a test that contains computation problems worth 6 points each and word problems worth 10 points each. You can do a computation problem in 2 minutes and a word problem in 4 minutes. You have 40 minutes to take the test and may answer no more than 12 problems. Assuming you answer all the problems attempted correctly, how many of each type of problem must you answer to maximize your score? What is the maximum score?

17. A theater is presenting a program on drinking and driving for students and their parents. The proceeds will be donated to a local alcohol information center. Admission is $2.00 for parents and $1.00 for students. However, the situation has two constraints: The theater can hold no more than 150 people and every two parents must bring at least one student. How many parents and students should attend to raise the maximum amount of money?

18. On June 24, 1948, the former Soviet Union blocked all land and water routes through East Germany to Berlin. A gigantic airlift was organized using American and British planes to bring food, clothing, and other supplies to the more than 2 million people in West Berlin. The cargo capacity was 30,000 cubic feet for an American plane and 20,000 cubic feet for a British plane. To break the Soviet blockade, the Western Allies had to maximize cargo capacity, but were subject to the following restrictions:

- No more than 44 planes could be used.
- The larger American planes required 16 personnel per flight, double that of the requirement for the British planes. The total number of personnel available could not exceed 512.
- The cost of an American flight was $9000 and the cost of a British flight was $5000. Total weekly costs could not exceed $300,000.

Find the number of American and British planes that were used to maximize cargo capacity.

• Writing in Mathematics

19. What kinds of problems are solved using the linear programming method?

20. What is an objective function in a linear programming problem?

21. What is a constraint in a linear programming problem? How is a constraint represented?

22. In your own words, describe how to solve a linear programming problem.

23. Describe a situation in your life in which you would like to maximize something, but you are limited by at least two constraints. Can linear programming be used in this situation? Explain your answer.

• Critical Thinking Exercise

24. Suppose that you inherit $10,000. The will states how you must invest the money. Some (or all) of the money must be invested in stocks and bonds. The requirements are that at least $3000 be invested in bonds, with expected returns of $0.08 per dollar, and at least $2000 be invested in stocks, with expected returns of $0.12 per dollar. Because the stocks are medium risk, the final stipulation requires that the investment in bonds should never be less than the investment in stocks. How should the money be invested so as to maximize your expected returns?

• Group Exercises

25. Group members should choose a particular field of interest. Research how linear programming is used to solve problems in that field. If possible, investigate the solution of a specific practical problem. Present a report on your findings, including the contributions of George Dantzig, Narendra Karmarkar, and L. G. Khachion to linear programming.

26. Members of the group should interview a business executive who is in charge of deciding the product mix for a business. How are production policy decisions made? Are other methods used in conjunction with linear programming? What are these methods? What sort of academic background, particularly in mathematics, does this executive have? Present a group report addressing these questions, emphasizing the role of linear programming for the business.

SECTION 7.6 • APPROXIMATING REALITY WITH NONLINEAR MODELS

OBJECTIVES

1. Graph exponential functions.

2. Use exponential models.

3. Graph logarithmic functions.

4. Use logarithmic models.

5. Graph quadratic functions.

6. Use quadratic models.

7. Determine an appropriate function for modeling data.

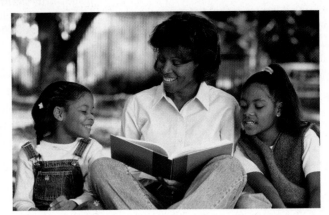

Is there a relationship between literacy and child mortality? As the percentage of adult females who are literate increases, does the mortality of children under five decrease? Figure 7.35, based on data from the United Nations, indicates that this is, indeed, the case. Each point in the figure represents one country.

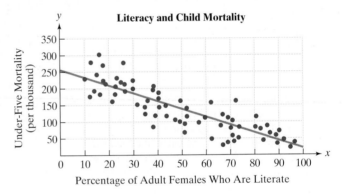

FIGURE 7.35
Source: United Nations

Data presented in a visual form as a set of points is called a **scatter plot**. Also shown in Figure 7.35 is a line that passes through or near the points. The line that best fits the data points in a scatter plot is called a **regression line**. We can use the line's slope and y-intercept to obtain a linear model for under-five mortality, y, per thousand, as a function of the percentage of literate adult females, x:

$$y = -2.3x + 255.$$

> For each percent increase in adult female literacy, under-five mortality decreases by 2.3 per thousand.

Using this model, we can make predictions about child mortality based on the percentage of literate adult females in a country.

In Figure 7.35, the data fall on or near a line. However, scatter plots are often curved in a way that indicates that the data do not fall near a line. In this section, we will use functions that are not linear functions to model such data and make predictions.

Modeling with Exponential Functions

The scatter plot in Figure 7.36 has a shape that indicates the data are increasing more and more rapidly. *Exponential functions* can be used to model this explosive growth, typically associated with populations, epidemics, and interest-bearing bank accounts.

FIGURE 7.36

> ### DEFINITION OF THE EXPONENTIAL FUNCTION
> The **exponential function** f **with base** b is defined by
>
> $$y = b^x \quad \text{or} \quad f(x) = b^x,$$
>
> where b is a positive constant other than 1 ($b > 0$ and $b \neq 1$) and x is any real number.

1 Graph exponential functions.

EXAMPLE 1   GRAPHING AN EXPONENTIAL FUNCTION

Graph: $f(x) = 2^x$.

SOLUTION   We start by selecting numbers for x and finding the corresponding values for $f(x)$.

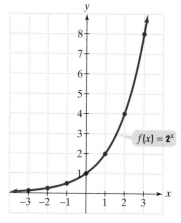

x	$f(x) = 2^x$	(x, y)
-3	$f(-3) = 2^{-3} = \frac{1}{8}$	$\left(-3, \frac{1}{8}\right)$
-2	$f(-2) = 2^{-2} = \frac{1}{4}$	$\left(-2, \frac{1}{4}\right)$
-1	$f(-1) = 2^{-1} = \frac{1}{2}$	$\left(-1, \frac{1}{2}\right)$
0	$f(0) = 2^0 = 1$	$(0, 1)$
1	$f(1) = 2^1 = 2$	$(1, 2)$
2	$f(2) = 2^2 = 4$	$(2, 4)$
3	$f(3) = 2^3 = 8$	$(3, 8)$

We plot these points, connecting them with a smooth curve. Figure 7.37 shows the graph of $f(x) = 2^x$.

FIGURE 7.37 The graph of $f(x) = 2^x$

All exponential functions of the form $y = b^x$, or $f(x) = b^x$, where b is a number greater than 1, have the shape of the graph shown in Figure 7.37. The graph approaches, but never touches, the negative portion of the x-axis.

CHECK POINT 1 Graph: $f(x) = 3^x$.

2 Use exponential models.

Figure 7.38(a) shows world population for seven selected years from 1950 through 2006. A scatter plot is shown in Figure 7.38(b).

World Population, 1950–2006

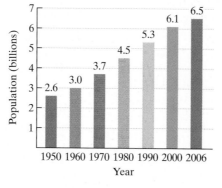

FIGURE 7.38(a)

Source: U.S. Census Bureau, International Database

FIGURE 7.38(b)

Because the data in the scatter plot appear to increase more and more rapidly, the shape suggests that an exponential function might be a good choice for modeling the data. Furthermore, we can probably draw a line that passes through or near the seven points. Thus, a linear function would also be a good choice for a model.

> ### EXAMPLE 2　COMPARING LINEAR AND EXPONENTIAL MODELS

The data for world population is shown in Table 7.3. After entering the data, a graphing calculator displays the linear model, $y = ax + b$, and the exponential model, $y = ab^x$, that best fit the data, shown in Figure 7.39.

TABLE 7.3

x, Number of Years after 1949	y, World Population (billions)
1 (1950)	2.6
11 (1960)	3.0
21 (1970)	3.7
31 (1980)	4.5
41 (1990)	5.3
51 (2000)	6.1
57 (2006)	6.5

FIGURE 7.39 A linear model and an exponential model for the data in Table 7.3

a. Use Figure 7.39 to express each model in function notation, with numbers rounded to three decimal places.

b. How well do the functions model world population in 2000?

c. By one projection, world population is expected to reach 8 billion in the year 2026. Which function serves as a better model for this prediction?

SOLUTION

a. Using Figure 7.39 and rounding to three decimal places, the functions

$$f(x) = 0.073x + 2.316 \quad \text{and} \quad g(x) = 2.569(1.017)^x$$

model world population, in billions, x years after 1949. We named the linear function f and the exponential function g, although any letters can be used.

b. Table 7.3 shows that world population in 2000 was 6.1 billion. The year 2000 is 51 years after 1949. Thus, we substitute 51 for x in each function's equation and then evaluate the resulting expressions with a calculator to see how well the functions describe world population in 2000.

$f(x) = 0.073x + 2.316$	This is the linear model.
$f(51) = 0.073(51) + 2.316$	Substitute 51 for x.
≈ 6.0	Use a calculator: .073 × 51 + 2.316 = .
$g(x) = 2.569(1.017)^x$	This is the exponential model.
$g(51) = 2.569(1.017)^{51}$	Substitute 51 for x.
≈ 6.1	Use a calculator: 2.569 × 1.017 y^x 51 = .

Because 6.1 billion was the actual world population in 2000, both functions model world population in 2000 extremely well.

STUDY TIP

Exponential functions of the form $y = ab^x$, $b > 1$, model growth in which quantities increase at a rate proportional to their size. Populations that are growing exponentially grow extremely rapidly as they get larger because there are more adults to have offspring.

c. Let's see which model comes closest to projecting a world population of 8 billion in the year 2026. Because 2026 is 77 years after 1949 ($2026 - 1949 = 77$), we substitute 77 for x in each function's equation.

$$f(x) = 0.073x + 2.316 \qquad \text{This is the linear model.}$$

$$f(77) = 0.073(77) + 2.316 \qquad \text{Substitute 77 for } x.$$

$$\approx 7.9 \qquad \text{Use a calculator:}$$
$$\boxed{.073} \times \boxed{77} + \boxed{2.316} = .$$

$$g(x) = 2.569(1.017)^x \qquad \text{This is the exponential model.}$$

$$g(77) = 2.569(1.017)^{77} \qquad \text{Substitute 77 for } x.$$

$$\approx 9.4 \qquad \text{Use a calculator:}$$
$$2.569 \times 1.017 \boxed{y^x} 77 = .$$

The linear function $f(x) = 0.073x + 2.316$ serves as a better model for a projected world population of 8 billion by 2026.

 Use the models in Example 2(a) to solve this problem.

a. World population in 1970 was 3.7 billion. Which function serves as a better model for this year?

b. By one projection, world population is expected to reach 7 billion by 2012. How well do the functions model this projection?

The Role of e in Applied Exponential Functions

An irrational number, symbolized by the letter e, appears as the base in many applied exponential functions. This irrational number is approximately equal to 2.72. More accurately,

$$e \approx 2.71828\ldots.$$

The number e is called the **natural base**. The function $f(x) = e^x$ is called the **natural exponential function**.

Use a scientific or graphing calculator with an $\boxed{e^x}$ key to evaluate e to various powers. For example, to find e^2, press the following keys on most calculators:

Scientific calculator: $2 \boxed{e^x}$

Graphing calculator: $\boxed{e^x} 2 \boxed{\text{ENTER}}$.

The display should be approximately 7.389.

$$e^2 \approx 7.389$$

The number e lies between 2 and 3. Because $2^2 = 4$ and $3^2 = 9$, it makes sense that e^2, approximately 7.389, lies between 4 and 9.

Because $2 < e < 3$, the graph of $y = e^x$ lies between the graphs of $y = 2^x$ and $y = 3^x$, shown in Figure 7.40.

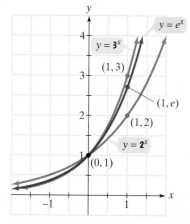

FIGURE 7.40 Graphs of three exponential functions

Visualizing the Relationship between Blood Alcohol Concentration and the Risk of a Car Accident

A blood alcohol concentration of 0.22 corresponds to near certainty, or a 100% probability, of a car accident.

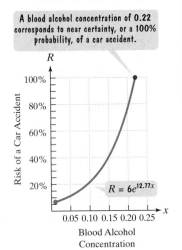

Blood Alcohol Concentration

EXAMPLE 3   ALCOHOL AND RISK OF A CAR ACCIDENT

Medical research indicates that the risk of having a car accident increases exponentially as the concentration of alcohol in the blood increases. The risk is modeled by

$$R = 6e^{12.77x},$$

where x is the blood alcohol concentration and R, given as a percent, is the risk of having a car accident. In many states, it is illegal to drive with a blood alcohol concentration of 0.08 or greater. What is the risk of a car accident with a blood alcohol concentration of 0.08?

SOLUTION For a blood alcohol concentration of 0.08, we substitute 0.08 for x in the exponential model's equation. Then we use a calculator to evaluate the resulting expression.

$$R = 6e^{12.77x} \qquad \text{This is the given exponential model.}$$

$$R = 6e^{12.77(0.08)} \qquad \text{Substitute 0.08 for x.}$$

Perform this computation on your calculator.

Scientific calculator: 6 $\times$ $($ 12.77 $\times$ $.08$ $)$ e^x $=$

Graphing calculator: 6 $\times$ e^x $($ 12.77 $\times$ $.08$ $)$ $\boxed{\text{ENTER}}$

The display should be approximately 16.665813. Rounding to one decimal place, the risk of a car accident is approximately 16.7% with a blood alcohol concentration of 0.08. This can be visualized as the point $(0.08, 16.7)$ on the graph of the model shown on the left.

CHECK POINT 3 Use the model in Example 3 to solve this problem. In many states, it is illegal for drivers under 21 years old to drive with a blood alcohol concentration of 0.01 or greater. What is the risk of a car accident with a blood alcohol concentration of 0.01? Round to one decimal place.

FIGURE 7.41

Modeling with Logarithmic Functions

The scatter plot in Figure 7.41 starts with rapid growth and then the growth begins to level off. This type of behavior can be modeled by *logarithmic functions*.

> ### DEFINITION OF THE LOGARITHMIC FUNCTION
> For $x > 0$ and $b > 0$, $b \neq 1$,
>
> $$y = \log_b x \text{ is equivalent to } b^y = x.$$
>
> The function $f(x) = \log_b x$ is the **logarithmic function with base b**.

The equations

$$y = \log_b x \quad \text{and} \quad b^y = x$$

are different ways of expressing the same thing. The first equation is in **logarithmic form** and the second equivalent equation is in **exponential form**.

Notice that a **logarithm, y, is an exponent**. You should learn the location of the base and exponent in each form.

> ## LOCATION OF BASE AND EXPONENT IN EXPONENTIAL AND LOGARITHMIC FORMS
>
> Exponent   Exponent
>
> Logarithmic Form: $y = \log_b x$ Exponential Form: $b^y = x$
>
> Base   Base

3 | Graph logarithmic functions.

EXAMPLE 4   GRAPHING A LOGARITHMIC FUNCTION

Graph: $y = \log_2 x$.

SOLUTION Because $y = \log_2 x$ means $2^y = x$, we will use the exponential form of the equation to obtain the function's graph. Using $2^y = x$, we start by selecting numbers for y and then we find the corresponding values for x.

STUDY TIP

The coordinates for the logarithmic function base 2 are the reverse of those for the exponential function base 2. In general, $y = \log_b x$ reverses the x- and y-coordinates of $y = b^x$.

Start with values for y.

$x = 2^y$	y	(x, y)
$2^{-2} = \frac{1}{4}$	-2	$\left(\frac{1}{4}, -2\right)$
$2^{-1} = \frac{1}{2}$	-1	$\left(\frac{1}{2}, -1\right)$
$2^0 = 1$	0	$(1, 0)$
$2^1 = 2$	1	$(2, 1)$
$2^2 = 4$	2	$(4, 2)$
$2^3 = 8$	3	$(8, 3)$

Compute x using $x = 2^y$.

FIGURE 7.42 The graph of the logarithmic function with base 2

We plot the six ordered pairs in the table, connecting the points with a smooth curve. Figure 7.42 shows the graph of $y = \log_2 x$.

All logarithmic functions of the form $y = \log_b x$, or $f(x) = \log_b x$, where $b > 1$, have the shape of the graph shown in Figure 7.42. The graph approaches, but never touches, the negative portion of the y-axis. Observe that the graph is increasing from left to right. However, the rate of increase is slowing down as the graph moves to the right. This is why logarithmic functions are often used to model growing phenomena with growth that is leveling off.

CHECK POINT 4 Rewrite $y = \log_3 x$ in exponential form. Then use the exponential form of the equation to obtain the function's graph. Select integers from -2 to 2, inclusive, for y.

Scientific and graphing calculators contain keys that can be used to evaluate the logarithmic function with base 10 and the logarithmic function with base e.

Key	Function the Key Is Used to Evaluate	
LOG	$y = \log_{10} x$	This is called the **common logarithmic function**, usually expressed as $y = \log x$.
LN	$y = \log_e x$	This is called the **natural logarithmic function**, usually expressed as $y = \ln x$.

4 | Use logarithmic models.

EXAMPLE 5

DANGEROUS HEAT: TEMPERATURE IN AN ENCLOSED VEHICLE

When the outside air temperature is anywhere from 72° to 96° Fahrenheit, the temperature in an enclosed vehicle climbs by 43° in the first hour. The bar graph in Figure 7.43 (a) shows the temperature increase throughout the hour. A scatter plot is shown in Figure 7.43(b).

Temperature Increase in an Enclosed Vehicle

FIGURE 7.43(a)

Source: Professor Jan Null, San Francisco State University

FIGURE 7.43(b)

Because the data in the scatter plot increase rapidly at first and then begin to level off a bit, the shape suggests that a logarithmic function is a good choice for a model. After entering the data, a graphing calculator displays the logarithmic model, $y = a + b \ln x$, shown in Figure 7.44.

a. Express the model in function notation, with numbers rounded to one decimal place.

b. Use the function to find the temperature increase, to the nearest degree, after 50 minutes. How well does the function model the actual increase shown in Figure 7.43(a)?

```
LnReg
 y=a+blnx
 a=-11.62862899
 b=13.42363186
```

FIGURE 7.44

SOLUTION

a. Using Figure 7.44 and rounding to one decimal place, the function

$$f(x) = -11.6 + 13.4 \ln x$$

models the temperature increase, $f(x)$, in degrees Fahrenheit, after x minutes.

b. We find the temperature increase after 50 minutes by substituting 50 for x and evaluating the function at 50.

$f(x) = -11.6 + 13.4 \ln x$ *This is the logarithmic model from part (a).*

$f(50) = -11.6 + 13.4 \ln 50$ *Substitute 50 for x.*

Perform this computation on your calculator.

Scientific calculator: 11.6 $\boxed{+/_-}$ $\boxed{+}$ 13.4 $\boxed{\times}$ 50 $\boxed{LN}$ $\boxed{=}$

Graphing calculator: $\boxed{(-)}$ 11.6 $\boxed{+}$ 13.4 $\boxed{LN}$ 50 $\boxed{ENTER}$

The display should be approximately 40.821108. Rounding to the nearest degree, the logarithmic model indicates that the temperature will have increased by approximately 41° after 50 minutes. Because the increase shown in Figure 7.43(a) is 41°, the function models the actual increase extremely well. ○

CHECK POINT **5** Use the model obtained in Example 5(a) to find the temperature increase, to the nearest degree, after 30 minutes. How well does the function model the actual increase shown in Figure 7.43(a)?

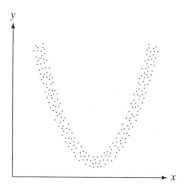

Modeling with Quadratic Functions

The scatter plot in Figure 7.45 has a shape that indicates the data are first decreasing and then increasing. This type of behavior can be modeled by *quadratic functions.*

> ### DEFINITION OF THE QUADRATIC FUNCTION
>
> A **quadratic function** is any function of the form
>
> $$y = ax^2 + bx + c \quad \text{or} \quad f(x) = ax^2 + bx + c,$$
>
> where a, b, and c are real numbers, with $a \neq 0$.

The graph of any quadratic function is called a **parabola**. Parabolas are shaped like cups, as shown in Figure 7.46. If the coefficient of x^2 (the value of a in $ax^2 + bx + c$) is positive, the parabola opens upward. If the coefficient of x^2 is negative, the graph opens downward. The **vertex** (or turning point) of the parabola is the lowest point on the graph when it opens upward and the highest point on the graph when it opens downward.

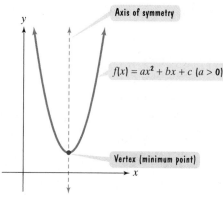

$a > 0$: Parabola opens upward.

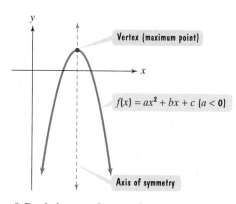

$a < 0$: Parabola opens downward.

FIGURE 7.46 Characteristics of graphs of quadratic functions

Look at the unusual image of the word "mirror" shown below. The artist, Scott Kim, has created the image so that the two halves of the whole are mirror images of each other. A parabola shares this kind of symmetry, in which a line through the vertex divides the figure in half. Parabolas are symmetric with respect to this line, called the **axis of symmetry**. If a parabola is folded along its axis of symmetry, the two halves match exactly.

When graphing quadratic functions or using them as models, it is frequently helpful to determine where the vertex, or turning point, occurs.

> ### THE VERTEX OF A PARABOLA
>
> The vertex of a parabola whose equation is $y = ax^2 + bx + c$ occurs when
>
> $$x = \frac{-b}{2a}.$$

5 | Graph quadratic functions.

Several points are helpful when graphing a quadratic function. These points are the x-intercepts (although not every parabola has x-intercepts), the y-intercept, and the vertex.

GRAPHING QUADRATIC FUNCTIONS

The graph of $y = ax^2 + bx + c$ or $f(x) = ax^2 + bx + c$, called a parabola, can be graphed using the following steps:

1. Determine whether the parabola opens upward or downward. If $a > 0$, it opens upward. If $a < 0$, it opens downward.
2. Determine the vertex of the parabola. The x-coordinate is $\dfrac{-b}{2a}$.

   The y-coordinate is found by substituting the x-coordinate into the parabola's equation and evaluating y.
3. Find any x-intercepts by replacing y or $f(x)$ with 0. Solve the resulting quadratic equation for x.
4. Find the y-intercept by replacing x with 0.
5. Plot the intercepts and the vertex.
6. Connect these points with a smooth curve.

EXAMPLE 6   GRAPHING A PARABOLA

Graph the quadratic function: $y = x^2 - 2x - 3$.

SOLUTION We can graph this function by following the steps in the box.

Step 1. Determine how the parabola opens. Note that a, the coefficient of x^2, is 1. Thus, $a > 0$; this positive value tells us that the parabola opens upward.

Step 2. Find the vertex. We know that the x-coordinate of the vertex is $\dfrac{-b}{2a}$. Let's identify the numbers a, b, and c in the given equation, which is in the form $y = ax^2 + bx + c$.

$$y = x^2 - 2x - 3$$

$$\boxed{a = 1} \quad \boxed{b = -2} \quad \boxed{c = -3}$$

Now we substitute the values of a and b into the equation for the x-coordinate:

$$x\text{-coordinate of vertex} = \frac{-b}{2a} = \frac{-(-2)}{2(1)} = \frac{2}{2} = 1.$$

The x-coordinate of the vertex is 1. We substitute 1 for x in the equation $y = x^2 - 2x - 3$ to find the y-coordinate:

$$y\text{-coordinate of vertex} = 1^2 - 2 \cdot 1 - 3 = 1 - 2 - 3 = -4.$$

The vertex is $(1, -4)$.

Step 3. Find the x-intercepts. Replace y with 0 in $y = x^2 - 2x - 3$. We obtain $0 = x^2 - 2x - 3$ or $x^2 - 2x - 3 = 0$. We can solve this equation by factoring.

$$x^2 - 2x - 3 = 0$$
$$(x - 3)(x + 1) = 0$$
$$x - 3 = 0 \quad \text{or} \quad x + 1 = 0$$
$$x = 3 \qquad\qquad x = -1$$

The x-intercepts are 3 and -1. The parabola passes through $(3, 0)$ and $(-1, 0)$.

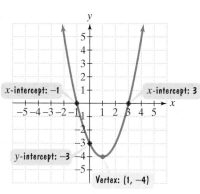

x-intercept: −1

x-intercept: 3

y-intercept: −3

Vertex: (1, −4)

FIGURE 7.47 The graph of $y = x^2 - 2x - 3$

Step 4. Find the y-intercept. Replace x with 0 in $y = x^2 - 2x - 3$:

$$y = 0^2 - 2 \cdot 0 - 3 = 0 - 0 - 3 = -3.$$

The y-intercept is -3. The parabola passes through $(0, -3)$.

Steps 5 and 6. Plot the intercepts and the vertex. Connect these points with a smooth curve. The intercepts and the vertex are shown as the four labeled points in Figure 7.47. Also shown is the graph of the quadratic function, obtained by connecting the points with a smooth curve.

 Graph the quadratic function: $y = x^2 + 6x + 5$.

6 | Use quadratic models.

EXAMPLE 7   MODELING WINE CONSUMPTION

The bar graph in Figure 7.48(a) shows per capita U.S. adult wine consumption, in gallons per person, for selected years from 1980 through 2003. A scatter plot is shown in Figure 7.48(b).

Wine Consumption per U.S. Adult

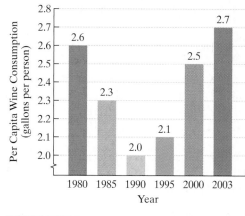

FIGURE 7.48(a)
Source: Adams Business Media

FIGURE 7.48(b)

FIGURE 7.49 Data (0, 2.6), (5, 2.3), (10, 2.0), (15, 2.1), (20, 2.5), (23, 2.7)

Because the data in the scatter plot first decrease and then increase, the shape suggests that a quadratic function is a good choice for a model. We let x represent the number of years after 1980 and y represent U.S. wine consumption, in gallons per person. After entering the data, a graphing calculator displays the quadratic function, $y = ax^2 + bx + c$, shown in Figure 7.49.

a. Express the model in function notation, with numbers rounded to three decimal places.

b. According to the function in part (a), in which year was wine consumption at a minimum? Round to the nearest year. What does the function give for per capita consumption, to the nearest tenth of a gallon, for that year? How well does this model the data shown in the bar graph in Figure 7.48(a)?

SOLUTION

a. Using Figure 7.49 and rounding to three decimal places, the function

$$f(x) = 0.005x^2 - 0.104x + 2.626$$

models U.S. wine consumption, $f(x)$, in gallons per person, x years after 1980.

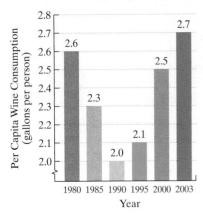

Wine Consumption per U.S. Adult

FIGURE 7.48(a) (repeated)

b. We can use the quadratic model to determine in which year wine consumption was at a minimum.

$$f(x) = 0.005x^2 - 0.104x + 2.626$$

$$a = 0.005 \qquad b = -0.104$$

Because the coefficient of x^2, 0.005, is positive, the parabola opens upward and the vertex is the lowest point on the graph. The x-coordinate of the vertex tells us when wine consumption was at a minimum.

$$x = \frac{-b}{2a} = \frac{-(-0.104)}{2(0.005)} = \frac{0.104}{0.01} \approx 10$$

The quadratic model indicates that wine consumption was at a minimum 10 years after 1980, in the year 1990. Let's see what the function gives for per capita consumption for that year.

$$f(x) = 0.005x^2 - 0.104x + 2.626 \qquad \text{This is the quadratic model.}$$
$$f(10) = 0.005(10)^2 - 0.104(10) + 2.626 \qquad \text{Substitute 10 for } x.$$
$$\approx 2.1 \qquad \text{Use a calculator.}$$

The vertex, approximately $(10, 2.1)$, shows that minimum U.S. wine consumption of 2.1 gallons per adult occurred 10 years after 1980, or in 1990. Because this is close to the 2.0 gallons shown in the bar graph for 1990 in Figure 7.48(a), the model's vertex describes the data fairly well.

○

CHECK POINT 7 The quadratic function $f(x) = 0.4x^2 - 36x + 1000$ models the number of car accidents, $f(x)$, per 50 million miles driven, as a function of a driver's age, x, in years, where $16 \leq x \leq 74$. According to this model, drivers at which age have the least number of car accidents? How many accidents does this age group have per 50 million miles driven?

7 Determine an appropriate function for modeling data.

Table 7.4 contains a description of the scatter plots we have encountered in this section, as well as the type of function that can serve as an appropriate model for each description.

TABLE 7.4 MODELING DATA

Description of Data Points in a Scatter Plot	Model
Lie on or near a line	Linear Function: $y = mx + b$ or $f(x) = mx + b$
Increasing more and more rapidly	Exponential Function: $y = b^x$ or $f(x) = b^x, b > 1$
Increasing, although rate of increase is slowing down	Logarithmic Function: $y = \log_b x$ or $f(x) = \log_b x, b > 1$ ($y = \log_b x$ means $b^y = x$.)
Decreasing and then increasing	Quadratic Function: $y = ax^2 + bx + c$ or $f(x) = ax^2 + bx + c, a > 0$ The vertex, $\left(\frac{-b}{2a}, f\left(\frac{-b}{2a}\right)\right)$, is a minimum point on the parabola.
Increasing and then decreasing	Quadratic Function: $y = ax^2 + bx + c$ or $f(x) = ax^2 + bx + c, a < 0$ The vertex, $\left(\frac{-b}{2a}, f\left(\frac{-b}{2a}\right)\right)$, is a maximum point on the parabola.

Once the type of model has been determined, the data can be entered into a graphing calculator. The calculator's regression feature will display the specific function of the type requested that best fits the data. That, in short, is how your author obtained the algebraic models you have encountered throughout this book. In this era of technology, the process of determining models that approximate reality is based on a knowledge of functions and their graphs and has nothing to do with long and tedious computations.

EXERCISE SET 7.6 ●●●●●●

• Practice Exercises

In Exercises 1–6, use a table of coordinates to graph each exponential function. Begin by selecting −2, −1, 0, 1, and 2 for x.

1. $f(x) = 4^x$ **2.** $f(x) = 5^x$

3. $y = 2^{x+1}$ **4.** $y = 2^{x-1}$

5. $f(x) = 3^{x-1}$ **6.** $f(x) = 3^{x+1}$

In Exercises 7–8,

  a. *Rewrite each equation in exponential form.*

  b. *Use a table of coordinates and the exponential form from part (a) to graph each logarithmic function. Begin by selecting −2, −1, 0, 1, and 2 for y.*

7. $y = \log_4 x$ **8.** $y = \log_5 x$

In Exercises 9–14,

  a. *Determine if the parabola whose equation is given opens upward or downward.*

  b. *Find the vertex.*

  c. *Find the x-intercepts.*

  d. *Find the y-intercept.*

  e. *Use (a)–(d) to graph the quadratic function.*

9. $y = x^2 + 8x + 7$ **10.** $y = x^2 + 10x + 9$

11. $f(x) = x^2 - 2x - 8$ **12.** $f(x) = x^2 + 4x - 5$

13. $y = -x^2 + 4x - 3$ **14.** $y = -x^2 + 2x + 3$

In Exercises 15–22,

  a. *Create a scatter plot for the data in each table.*

  b. *Use the shape of the scatter plot to determine if the data are best modeled by a linear function, an exponential function, a logarithmic function, or a quadratic function.*

15.

x	y
0	0
9	1
16	1.2
19	1.3
25	1.4

16.

x	y
0	0.3
8	1
15	1.2
18	1.3
24	1.4

17.

x	y
0	−3
1	2
2	7
3	12
4	17

18.

x	y
0	5
1	3
2	1
3	−1
4	−3

19.

x	y
0	4
1	1
2	0
3	1
4	4

20.

x	y
0	−4
1	−1
2	0
3	−1
4	−4

21.

x	y
0	−3
1	−2
2	0
3	4
4	12

22.

x	y
0	4
1	5
2	7
3	11
4	19

• Practice Plus

In Exercises 23–24, use a table of coordinates to graph each exponential function. Begin by selecting −2, −1, 0, 1, and 2 for x. Based on your graph, describe the shape of a scatter plot that can be modeled by $f(x) = b^x, 0 < b < 1$.

23. $f(x) = \left(\frac{1}{2}\right)^x$ (Equivalently, $y = 2^{-x}$)

24. $f(x) = \left(\frac{1}{3}\right)^x$ (Equivalently, $y = 3^{-x}$)

In Exercises 25–26, use the directions for Exercises 7–8 to graph each logarithmic function. Based on your graph, describe the shape of a scatter plot that can be modeled by $f(x) = \log_b x, 0 < b < 1$.

25. $y = \log_{\frac{1}{2}} x$ **26.** $y = \log_{\frac{1}{3}} x$

In Exercises 27–28, use the directions for Exercises 9–14 to graph each quadratic function. Use the quadratic formula to find x-intercepts, rounded to the nearest tenth.

27. $f(x) = -2x^2 + 4x + 5$ **28.** $f(x) = -3x^2 + 6x - 2$

In Exercises 29–30, find the vertex for the parabola whose equation is given by writing the equation in the form $y = ax^2 + bx + c$.

29. $y = (x - 3)^2 + 2$ **30.** $y = (x - 4)^2 + 3$

• Application Exercises

The bar graph shows the percentage of miscarriages for women at six selected ages. The graphing calculator screen displays an exponential function that models the data, where y represents the percentage of miscarriages at age x. Use this information to solve Exercises 31–32.

Percentage of Miscarriages in the United States, by Age

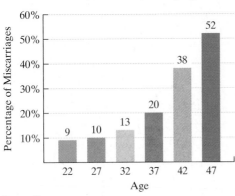

Source: Time

31. a. Explain why an exponential function was used to model the data displayed in the bar graph.

b. Use the graphing calculator screen to express the model in function notation, with numbers rounded to three decimal places.

c. According to the model, what is the percentage of miscarriages at age 37? Use a calculator with a $\boxed{y^x}$ key or a $\boxed{\wedge}$ key, and round to one decimal place. How well does this describe the actual data?

32. Repeat parts (a) and (b) of Exercise 31. For part (c), apply the model to the percentage of miscarriages at age 27 and follow the directions in Exercise 31(c).

Use a calculator with an $\boxed{e^x}$ key to solve Exercises 33–34. The graph shows the number of words, in millions, in the U.S. federal tax code for selected years from 1955 through 2000. The data can be modeled by

$$f(x) = 0.16x + 1.43 \quad \text{and} \quad g(x) = 1.8e^{0.04x},$$

in which $f(x)$ and $g(x)$ represent the number of words, in millions, in the federal tax code x years after 1955. Use these functions to solve Exercises 33–34.

Number of Words, in Millions, in the Federal Tax Code

Source: The Tax Foundation

33. Which function, the linear or the exponential, is a better model for the data in 2000?

34. Which function, the linear or the exponential, is a better model for the data in 1985?

Fed up with junk mail clogging your computer? Despite high-profile legislation and lawsuits, the bar graph shows that spam has flourished.

Spam Slam: Percentage of Inbound email in the U.S. Considered Spam

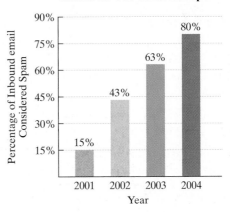

Source: Meta Group

The function $f(x) = 13.4 + 46.3 \ln x$ models the percentage of inbound email in the United States considered spam, $f(x)$, x years after 2000. Use this information to solve Exercises 35–36.

35. According to the model, what percentage of email was considered spam in 2003? Use a calculator with an $\boxed{\text{LN}}$ key and round to the nearest percent. How well does this describe the actual data?

36. According to the model, what percentage of email was considered spam in 2002? Use a calculator with an $\boxed{\text{LN}}$ key and round to the nearest percent. How well does this describe the actual data?

The percentage of adult height attained by a girl who is x years old can be modeled by

$$f(x) = 62 + 35 \log(x - 4),$$

where x represents the girl's age (from 5 to 15) and $f(x)$ represents the percentage of her adult height. Use the function to solve Exercises 37–38.

37. a. According to the model, what percentage of her adult height has a girl attained at age 13? Use a calculator with a $\boxed{\text{LOG}}$ key and round to the nearest tenth of a percent.

b. Why was a logarithmic function used to model the percentage of adult height attained by a girl from ages 5 to 15, inclusive?

38. a. According to the model, what percentage of her adult height has a girl attained at age ten? Use a calculator with a $\boxed{\text{LOG}}$ key and round to the nearest tenth of a percent.

b. Why was a logarithmic function used to model the percentage of adult height attained by a girl from ages 5 to 15, inclusive?

39. The bar graph shows the number of U.S. households, in millions, participating in the Food Stamp Program from 1999 through 2004. The graphing calculator screen displays a quadratic function that models the data, where y is the number of households, in millions, receiving food stamps x years after 1999.

Data:
$(0, 7.7), (1, 7.4), (2, 7.5),$
$(3, 8.2), (4, 9.2), (5, 10.6)$

U.S. Households on Food Stamps

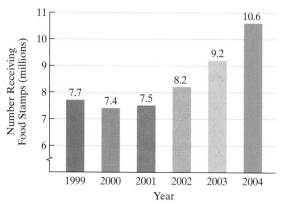

Source: Food Stamp Program

a. Explain why a quadratic function was used to model the data.

b. Use the graphing calculator screen to express the model in function notation, with numbers rounded to two decimal places.

c. According to the function in part (b), in which year was the number of households receiving food stamps at a minimum? Round to the nearest year. Use the model to find the number of households, in millions, for that year. How well does this model the data in the bar graph?

40. The bar graph shows the percentage of people in the United States living below the poverty level for selected years from 1990 through 2004. The quadratic function

$$f(x) = 0.04x^2 - 0.61x + 13.5$$

models the percentage below the poverty level, $f(x)$, x years after 1990.

Percentage of People in the U.S. Living Below the Poverty Level

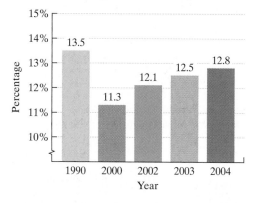

Source: Department of Health and Human Services

a. Explain why a quadratic function was used to model the data.

b. How well does the function model the data for 2004?

c. According to the function, in which year was the percentage living below the poverty level at a minimum? Round to the nearest year. What percentage of Americans lived below the poverty level in that year? Do these results seem consistent with the data displayed in the bar graph? Explain your answer.

• Writing in Mathematics

41. What is a scatter plot?

42. What is an exponential function?

43. Describe the shape of a scatter plot that suggests modeling the data with an exponential function.

44. Describe the shape of a scatter plot that suggests modeling the data with a logarithmic function.

45. Would you prefer that your salary be modeled exponentially or logarithmically? Explain your answer.

46. Describe the shape of a scatter plot that suggests modeling the data with a quadratic function.

• Critical Thinking Exercises

47. The exponential growth models describe the population of the indicated country, A, in millions, t years after 2003.

Canada $A = 32.2e^{0.003t}$

Uganda $A = 25.6e^{0.03t}$

According to these models, which one of the following is true?

a. In 2003, Uganda's population was ten times that of Canada's.

b. In 2003, Canada's population exceeded Uganda's by 660,000.

c. In 2012, Uganda's population will exceed Canada's.

d. None of these statements is true.

In Exercises 48–50, the value of a in $y = ax^2 + bx + c$ and the vertex of the parabola are given. How many x-intercepts does the parabola have? Explain how you arrived at this number.

48. $a = -2$; vertex at $(4, 8)$ **49.** $a = 1$; vertex at $(2, 0)$

50. $a = 3$; vertex at $(3, 1)$

• Technology Exercises

51. Use a graphing calculator to graph the exponential functions that you graphed by hand in Exercises 1–6. Describe similarities and differences between the graphs obtained by hand and those that appear in the calculator's viewing window.

52. Use a graphing calculator to graph the quadratic functions that you graphed by hand in Exercises 9–14.

Group Exercise

53. Each group member should consult an almanac, newspaper, magazine, or the Internet to find data that can be modeled by linear, exponential, logarithmic, or quadratic functions. Group members should select the two sets of data that are most interesting and relevant. Then consult a person who is familiar with graphing calculators to show you how to obtain a function that best fits each set of data. Once you have these functions, each group member should make one prediction based on one of the models, and then discuss a consequence of this prediction. What factors might change the accuracy of the prediction?

CHAPTER SUMMARY, REVIEW, AND TEST

● SUMMARY   DEFINITIONS AND CONCEPTS   EXAMPLES

7.1   Graphing and Functions

a. The rectangular coordinate system is formed using two number lines that intersect at right angles at their zero points. See Figure 7.1 on page 368. The horizontal line is the x-axis and the vertical line is the y-axis. Their point of intersection, $(0, 0)$, is the origin. Each point in the system corresponds to an ordered pair of real numbers, (x, y).

Ex. 1, p. 369

b. The graph of an equation in two variables is the set of all points whose coordinates satisfy the equation.

Ex. 2, p. 370;
Ex. 3, p. 370

c. If an equation in x and y yields one value of y for each value of x, then y is a function of x, indicated by writing $f(x)$ for y.

Ex. 4, p. 372

d. The graph of a function is the graph of its ordered pairs.

Ex. 5, p. 373

e. The Vertical Line Test: If any vertical line intersects a graph in more than one point, the graph does not define y as a function of x.

Ex. 6, p. 374

7.2   Linear Functions and Their Graphs

a. A function whose graph is a straight line is a linear function.

b. The graph of $Ax + By = C$, a linear equation in two variables, is a straight line. The line can be graphed using intercepts and a checkpoint. To locate the x-intercept, set $y = 0$ and solve for x. To locate the y-intercept, set $x = 0$ and solve for y.

Ex. 1, p. 380

c. The slope of the line through (x_1, y_1) and (x_2, y_2) is

$$m = \frac{\text{Rise}}{\text{Run}} = \frac{y_2 - y_1}{x_2 - x_1} = \frac{y_1 - y_2}{x_1 - x_2}.$$

Ex. 2, p. 381;
Ex. 7, p. 387

d. The equation $y = mx + b$ is the slope-intercept form of the equation of a line, in which m is the slope and b is the y-intercept.

Ex. 3, p. 384;
Ex. 4, p. 384;
Ex. 8, p. 388

e. Horizontal and Vertical Lines
  1. The graph of $y = b$ is a horizontal line that intersects the y-axis at $(0, b)$.
  2. The graph of $x = a$ is a vertical line that intersects the x-axis at $(a, 0)$.

Ex. 5, p. 386;
Ex. 6, p. 386

7.3   Systems of Linear Equations in Two Variables

a. Two equations in the form $Ax + By = C$ are called a system of linear equations. A solution of the system is an ordered pair that satisfies both equations in the system.

Ex. 1, p. 391

b. Linear systems with one solution can be solved by graphing. The coordinates of the point of intersection of the lines is the system's solution.

Ex. 2, p. 392

c. Systems of linear equations in two variables can be solved by eliminating a variable, using the substitution method (see the box on page 394) or the addition method (see the box on page 396).

Ex. 3, p. 393;
Ex. 4, p. 394;
Ex. 5, p. 396;
Ex. 6, p. 397

d. When solving by substitution or addition, if a false statement results, the linear system has no solution. If a true statement results, the system has infinitely many solutions.

Ex. 7, p. 398;
Ex. 8, p. 399

e. Functions of Business

Ex. 9, p. 400

$$R(x) = \text{(price per unit sold)}x$$
Revenue Function:
Cost Function: $C(x) = \text{fixed cost} + \text{(cost per unit produced)}x$
Profit Function: $P(x) = R(x) - C(x)$

The point of intersection of the graphs of R and C is the break-even point. The x-coordinate of the point reveals the number of units that a company must produce and sell so that the money coming in, the revenue, is equal to the money going out, the cost. The y-coordinate gives the amount of money coming in and going out.

7.4 Linear Inequalities in Two Variables

a. A linear inequality in two variables can be written in the form $Ax + By > C$, $Ax + By \geq C$, $Ax + By < C$, or $Ax + By \leq C$.

b. The procedure for graphing a linear inequality in two variables is given in the box on page 406.

Ex. 1, p. 406; Ex. 2, p. 407

c. Some inequalities can be graphed without using test points, including $y > mx + b$ (the half-plane above $y = mx + b$), $y < mx + b$, $x > a$ (the half-plane to the right of $x = a$), $x < a$, $y > b$ (the half-plane above $y = b$), and $y < b$.

Ex. 3, p. 408

d. Graphing Systems of Linear Inequalities
1. Graph each inequality in the system in the same rectangular coordinate system.
2. Find the intersection of the individual graphs.

Ex. 5, p. 409; Ex. 6, p. 410

7.5 Linear Programming

a. An objective function is an algebraic expression in three variables describing a quantity that must be maximized or minimized.

Ex. 1, p. 414

b. Constraints are restrictions, expressed as linear inequalities.

Ex. 2, p. 415; Ex. 3, p. 415

c. Steps for solving a linear programming problem are given in the box on page 416.

Ex. 4, p. 416

7.6 Approximating Reality with Nonlinear Models

a. The exponential function f with base b is defined by $y = b^x$ or $f(x) = b^x$, $b > 0$ and $b \neq 1$.

Ex. 1, p. 421

b. All exponential functions of the form $y = b^x$, where $b > 1$, have the shape of the graph in Figure 7.37 on page 421, making this function a good model for data points in a scatter plot that are increasing more and more rapidly.

Ex. 2, p. 422

c. The irrational number e, $e \approx 2.72$, appears in many applied exponential functions. The function $f(x) = e^x$ is called the natural exponential function.

Ex. 3, p. 424

d. The logarithmic function f with base b is defined by $y = \log_b x$ or $f(x) = \log_b x$, $x > 0, b > 0$, and $b \neq 1$. $y = \log_b x$ means $b^y = x$, so a logarithm is an exponent.

Ex. 4, p. 425

e. $y = \log x$ means $y = \log_{10} x$, the common logarithmic function. $y = \ln x$ means $y = \log_e x$, the natural logarithmic function. Calculators contain $\boxed{\text{LOG}}$ and $\boxed{\text{LN}}$ keys for evaluating these functions.

f. All logarithmic functions of the form $y = \log_b x$, where $b > 1$, have the shape of the graph in Figure 7.42 on page 425, making this function a good model for data points in a scatter plot that are increasing, but whose rate of increase is slowing down.

Ex. 5, p. 426

g. A quadratic function is any function of the form $y = ax^2 + bx + c$ or $f(x) = ax^2 + bx + c, a \neq 0$. The graph of a quadratic function is called a parabola.

Figure 7.46, p. 427

h. The x-coordinate of a parabola's vertex is $x = \frac{-b}{2a}$. The y-coordinate is found by substituting the x-coordinate into the parabola's equation. The vertex, or turning point, is the low point when the graph opens upward and the high point when the graph opens downward.   Ex. 7(b), p. 429

i. The six steps for graphing a parabola are given in the box on page 428.   Ex. 6, p. 428

j. All quadratic functions have the shape of one of the graphs in Figure 7.46 on page 427, making this function a good model for data points in a scatter plot that are decreasing and then increasing, or vice versa. See Table 7.4 on page 430.   Ex. 7, p. 429

REVIEW EXERCISES

7.1

In Exercises 1–4, plot the given point in a rectangular coordinate system.

1. $(2, 5)$ **2.** $(-4, 3)$

3. $(-5, -3)$ **4.** $(2, -5)$

Graph each equation in Exercises 5–7. Let $x = -3, -2, -1, 0, 1, 2,$ and 3.

5. $y = 2x - 2$ **6.** $y = |x| + 2$ **7.** $y = x$

8. If $f(x) = 4x + 11$, find $f(-2)$.

9. If $f(x) = -7x + 5$, find $f(-3)$.

10. If $f(x) = 3x^2 - 5x + 2$, find $f(4)$.

11. If $f(x) = -3x^2 + 6x + 8$, find $f(-4)$.

In Exercises 12–13, evaluate $f(x)$ for the given values of x. Then use the ordered pairs $(x, f(x))$ from your table to graph the function.

12. $f(x) = \frac{1}{2}|x|$

x	$f(x) = \frac{1}{2}|x|$
-6	
-4	
-2	
0	
2	
4	
6	

13. $f(x) = x^2 - 2$

x	$f(x) = x^2 - 2$
-2	
-1	
0	
1	
2	

In Exercises 14–15, use the vertical line test to identify graphs in which y is a function of x.

14.

15.

16. The figure shows the percentage of Jewish Americans in the U.S. population, $f(x)$, x years after 1900.

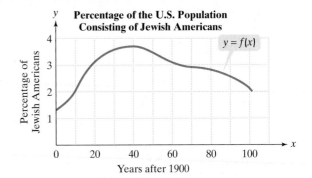

Source: American Jewish Yearbook

a. Use the graph to find a reasonable estimate of $f(60)$. What does this mean in terms of the variables in this situation?

b. In which year did the percentage of Jewish Americans in the U.S. population reach a maximum? What is a reasonable estimate of the percentage for that year?

c. In which year was the percentage of Jewish Americans in the U.S. population at a minimum? What is a reasonable estimate of the percentage for that year?

d. Explain why f represents the graph of a function.

e. Describe the general trend shown by the graph.

7.2

In Exercises 17–19, use the x- and y-intercepts to graph each linear equation.

17. $2x + y = 4$ **18.** $2x - 3y = 6$ **19.** $5x - 3y = 15$

In Exercises 20–23, calculate the slope of the line passing through the given points. If the slope is undefined, so state. Then indicate whether the line rises, falls, is horizontal, or is vertical.

20. $(3, 2)$ and $(5, 1)$ **21.** $(-1, 2)$ and $(-3, -4)$

22. $(-3, 4)$ and $(6, 4)$ **23.** $(5, 3)$ and $(5, -3)$

In Exercises 24–27, graph each linear function using the slope and y-intercept.

24. $y = 2x - 4$ **25.** $y = -\frac{2}{3}x + 5$

26. $f(x) = \frac{3}{4}x - 2$ **27.** $y = \frac{1}{2}x + 0$

In Exercises 28–30, **a.** Put the equation in slope-intercept form by solving for y; **b.** Identify the slope and the y-intercept; **c.** Use the slope and y-intercept to graph the line.

28. $2x + y = 0$ **29.** $3y = 5x$ **30.** $3x + 2y = 4$

In Exercises 31–33, graph each horizontal or vertical line.

31. $x = 3$ **32.** $y = -4$ **33.** $x + 2 = 0$

34. The eight points below show the mounting debt on credit cards for the period from 1990 through 2004. Also shown is the graph of a linear function that passes through or near the points.

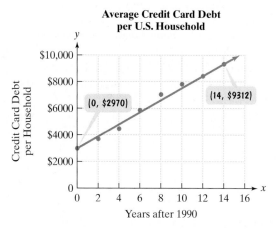

Average Credit Card Debt per U.S. Household

Source: CardWeb.com

a. According to the graph, what is the y-intercept? Describe what this represents in this situation.

b. Use the coordinates of the two points shown to compute the slope. What does this represent in terms of the rate of change in credit card debt for the period shown?

c. Use the y-intercept from part (a) and the slope from part (b) to write a linear function that models the average credit card debt per U.S. household, y, in dollars, x years after 1990.

d. Use the linear function from part (c) to predict the average credit card debt per household in 2010.

7.3

In Exercises 35–37, solve each system by graphing. Check the coordinates of the intersection point in both equations.

35. $x + y = 5$
     $3x - y = 3$

36. $2x - y = -1$
     $x + y = -5$

37. $y = -x + 5$
     $2x - y = 4$

In Exercises 38–40, solve each system by the substitution method.

38. $2x + 3y = 2$
     $x = 3y + 10$

39. $y = 4x + 1$
     $3x + 2y = 13$

40. $x + 4y = 14$
     $2x - y = 1$

In Exercises 41–43, solve each system by the addition method.

41. $x + 2y = -3$
     $x - y = -12$

42. $2x - y = 2$
     $x + 2y = 11$

43. $5x + 3y = 1$
     $3x + 4y = -6$

In Exercises 44–46, solve by the method of your choice. Identify systems with no solution and systems with infinitely many solutions, using set notation to express their solution sets.

44. $y = -x + 4$
     $3x + 3y = -6$

45. $3x + y = 8$
     $2x - 5y = 11$

46. $3x - 2y = 6$
     $6x - 4y = 12$

47. A company is planning to manufacture computer desks. The fixed cost will be $60,000 and it will cost $200 to produce each desk. Each desk will be sold for $450.

a. Write the cost function, C, of producing x desks.

b. Write the revenue function, R, from the sale of x desks.

c. Determine the break-even point. Describe what this means.

48. The bar graph shows the five countries with the longest healthy life expectancy at birth. (The healthy life expectancy in the United States is 67.6 years.) Combined, people in Japan and Switzerland can expect to spend 146.4 years in good health. The difference between healthy life expectancy between these two countries is 0.8 year. Find the healthy life expectancy at birth in Japan and Switzerland.

Countries with the Longest Healthy Life Expectancy

Source: World Health Organization

7.4

In Exercises 49–55, graph each linear inequality.

49. $x - 3y \le 6$ **50.** $2x + 3y \ge 12$ **51.** $2x - 7y > 14$

52. $y > \frac{3}{5}x$ **53.** $y \le -\frac{1}{2}x + 2$ **54.** $x \le 2$

55. $y > -3$

In Exercises 56–61, graph the solution set of each system of linear inequalities.

56. $3x - y \le 6$
     $x + y \ge 2$

57. $x + y < 4$
     $x - y < 4$

58. $x \le 3$
     $y > -2$

59. $4x + 6y \le 24$
     $y > 2$

60. $x + y \le 6$
     $y \ge 2x - 3$

61. $y < -x + 4$
     $y > x - 4$

7.5

62. Find the value of the objective function $z = 2x + 3y$ at each corner of the graphed region shown. What is the maximum value of the objective function? What is the minimum value of the objective function?

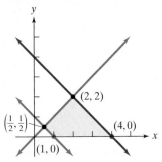

63. Consider the objective function $z = 2x + 3y$ and the following constraints:

$$x \le 6,\ y \le 5,\ x + y \ge 2,\ \underbrace{x \ge 0,\ y \ge 0.}_{\substack{\text{Quadrant 1 and} \\ \text{its boundary}}}$$

a. Graph the system of inequalities representing the constraints.

b. Find the value of the objective function at each corner of the graphed region.

c. Use the values in part (b) to determine the maximum and minimum values of the objective function and the values of x and y for which they occur.

64. A paper manufacturing company converts wood pulp to writing paper and newsprint. The profit on a unit of writing paper is $500 and the profit on a unit of newsprint is $350.

a. Let x represent the number of units of writing paper produced daily. Let y represent the number of units of newsprint produced daily. Write the objective function that models total daily profit.

b. The manufacturer is bound by the following constraints:
   - Equipment in the factory allows for making at most 200 units of paper (writing paper and newsprint) in a day.
   - Regular customers require at least 10 units of writing paper and at least 80 units of newsprint daily.
   Write a system of inequalities that models these constraints.

c. Graph the inequalities in part (b). Use only the first quadrant and its boundary, because x and y must both be nonnegative. (*Suggestion:* Let each unit along the x- and y-axes represent 20.)

d. Evaluate the objective profit function at each of the three vertices of the graphed region.

e. Complete the missing portions of this statement: The company will make the greatest profit by producing _____ units of writing paper and _____ units of newsprint each day. The maximum daily profit is $_____.

7.6

In Exercises 65–66, use a table of coordinates to graph each exponential function. Begin by selecting −2, −1, 0, 1, and 2 for x.

65. $f(x) = 2^x$ **66.** $y = 2^{x+1}$

67. Graph $y = \log_2 x$ by rewriting the equation in exponential form. Use a table of coordinates and select −2, −1, 0, 1, and 2 for y.

In Exercises 68–69,

a. Determine if the parabola whose equation is given opens upward or downward.

b. Find the vertex.

c. Find the x-intercepts.

d. Find the y-intercept.

e. Use (a)–(d) to graph the quadratic function.

68. $y = x^2 - 6x - 7$ **69.** $f(x) = -x^2 - 2x + 3$

In Exercises 70–73,

a. Create a scatter plot for the data in each table.

b. Use the shape of the scatter plot to determine if the data are best modeled by a linear function, an exponential function, a logarithmic function, or a quadratic function.

70. PERCENTAGE OF U.S. HIGH SCHOOL SENIORS TAKING STEROIDS

Year	Percent
2000	2.5%
2001	3.8%
2002	4.1%
2003	3.5%

Source: University of Michigan

71. HYBRID CAR SALES IN THE UNITED STATES

Year	Hybrid Cars Sold (thousands)
2000	8
2001	20
2002	36
2003	47
2004	83

Source: R. L. Polk and Co.

72. PERCENTAGE OF U.S. HOUSEHOLDS WITH TVs WITH CABLE TELEVISION

Year	Percent
1980	23%
1985	46%
1990	59%
1995	65%
2000	68%
2005	69%

Source: Nielsen Media Research

73. AVERAGE MONTHLY CELLPHONE BILLS

Year	Average Monthly Bill
2000	$45
2001	$47
2002	$48
2003	$50
2004	$51

Source: U.S. Census Bureau

74. Use a calculator with an $\boxed{y^x}$ key or a $\boxed{\wedge}$ key to solve this exercise.

The amount of carbon dioxide in the atmosphere, measured in parts per million, has been increasing as a result of the burning of oil and coal. The buildup of gases and particles traps heat and raises the planet's temperature, a phenomenon called the greenhouse effect. Carbon dioxide accounts for about half of the warming. The function $f(x) = 364(1.005)^x$ projects carbon dioxide concentration, $f(x)$, in parts per million, x years after 2000. According to the model, what will be the concentration in the year 2086? Round to the nearest part per million. How does this compare with the preindustrial level of 280 parts per million?

75. In 2003, Mexico's population was approximately 104.9 million, with a projected growth rate of 1.7% per year. The function

$$f(x) = 104.9e^{0.017x}$$

models Mexico's projected population, $f(x)$, in millions, x years after 2003. According to this model, what will Mexico's population be in 2044? Use a calculator with an $\boxed{e^x}$ key and round to one decimal place. How does this compare with the 2003 population of 104.9 million?

76. The bar graph shows the percentage of U.S. companies that performed drug tests on employees or job applicants in five selected years from 1998 through 2003. The data can be modeled by

$$f(x) = -1.7x + 74.5 \text{ and } g(x) = -4.9 \ln x + 73.8,$$

in which $f(x)$ and $g(x)$, model the percentage of such companies x years after 1997.

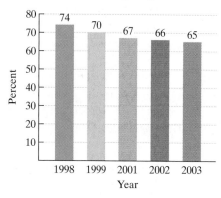

Percentage of U.S. Companies Performing Drug Tests

Source: American Management Association

a. What is the slope of the linear model? What does this mean in terms of the change in the percentage of companies that performed drug tests?

b. Which function, the linear or the logarithmic, is a better model for the data in 2003?

● ● ● ● ● ● CHAPTER 7 TEST

1. Graph $y = |x| - 2$. Let $x = -3, -2, -1, 0, 1, 2,$ and 3.

2. If $f(x) = 3x^2 - 7x - 5$, find $f(-2)$.

In Exercises 3–4, use the vertical line test to identify graphs in which y is a function of x.

3.

4.

5. The graph shows the height, in meters, of an eagle in terms of its time, in seconds, in flight.

(Be sure to refer to the graph at the bottom of the previous page.)

a. Is the eagle's height a function of time? Use the graph to explain why or why not.

b. Find $f(15)$. Describe what this means in practical terms.

c. What is a reasonable estimate of the eagle's maximum height?

d. During which period of time was the eagle descending?

6. Use the x- and y-intercepts to graph $4x - 2y = -8$.

7. Find the slope of the line passing through $(-3, 4)$ and $(-5, -2)$.

In Exercises 8–9, graph each linear function using the slope and y-intercept.

8. $y = \frac{2}{3}x - 1$ **9.** $f(x) = -2x + 3$

10. The six points below show the decreasing number of hours that Americans spent each year reading a daily newspaper. Also shown is the graph of a linear function that passes through or near the points.

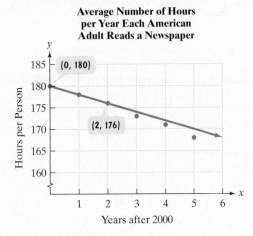

Average Number of Hours per Year Each American Adult Reads a Newspaper

Source: U.S. Census Bureau

a. According to the graph, what is the y-intercept? Describe what this represents in this situation.

b. Use the coordinates of the two points shown to compute the slope. What does this represent in terms of the rate of change in the hours per year spent reading a newspaper for the period shown?

c. Use the y-intercept from part (a) and the slope from part (b) to write a linear function that models the average number of hours per year, y, that each American adult spent reading a newspaper x years after 2000.

d. Use the linear function from part (c) to predict the average number of hours that each American will spend reading a newspaper in 2012.

11. Solve by graphing:

$$x + y = 6$$
$$4x - y = 4.$$

12. Solve by substitution:

$$x = y + 4$$
$$3x + 7y = -18.$$

13. Solve by addition:

$$5x + 4y = 10$$
$$3x + 5y = -7.$$

14. A company is planning to produce and sell a new line of computers. The fixed cost will be $360,000 and it will cost $850 to produce each computer. Each computer will be sold for $1150.

a. Write the cost function, C, of producing x computers.

b. Write the revenue function, R, from the sale of x computers.

c. Determine the break-even point. Describe what this means.

Graph each linear inequality in Exercises 15–17.

15. $3x - 2y < 6$ **16.** $y \le \frac{1}{2}x - 1$ **17.** $y > -1$

18. Graph the system of linear inequalities:

$$2x - y \le 4$$
$$2x - y > -1.$$

19. Find the value of the objective function $z = 3x + 2y$ at each corner of the graphed region shown. What is the maximum value of the objective function? What is the minimum value of the objective function?

20. Find the maximum value of the objective function $z = 3x + 5y$ subject to the following constraints: $x \ge 0, y \ge 0, x + y \le 6, x \ge 2$.

21. A manufacturer makes two types of jet skis, regular and deluxe. The profit on a regular jet ski is $200 and the profit on the deluxe model is $250. To meet customer demand, the company must manufacture at least 50 regular jet skis per week and at least 75 deluxe models. To maintain high quality, the total number of both models of jet skis manufactured by the company should not exceed 150 per week. How many jet skis of each type should be manufactured per week to obtain maximum profit? What is the maximum weekly profit?

22. Graph $f(x) = 3^x$. Use $-2, -1, 0, 1,$ and 2 for x and find the corresponding values for y.

23. Graph $y = \log_3 x$ by rewriting the equation in exponential form. Use a table of coordinates and select $-2, -1, 0, 1,$ and 2 for y.

24. Use the vertex and intercepts to graph the quadratic function $f(x) = x^2 - 2x - 8$.

In Exercises 25–28, determine whether the values in each table belong to an exponential function, a logarithmic function, a linear function, or a quadratic function.

25.

x	y
0	3
1	1
2	-1
3	-3
4	-5

26.

x	y
$\frac{1}{3}$	-1
1	0
3	1
9	2
27	3

27.

x	y
0	1
1	5
2	25
3	125
4	625

28.

x	y
0	12
1	3
2	0
3	3
4	12

29. The bar graph shows the number, in millions, of cellphone subscribers in the United States from 2000 through 2004. The data can be modeled by the exponential function

$$f(x) = 110.5(1.13)^x,$$

in which $f(x)$ represents the number of cellphone subscribers, in millions, x years after 2000.

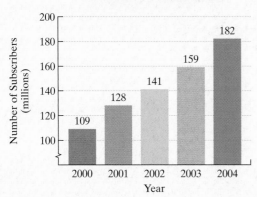

Number of Cellphone Subscribers in the United States

Source: CTIA

a. How well does the function model the data for 2003? Use a calculator and round to the nearest whole number.

b. Use the model to project the number of cellphone subscribers, in millions, in 2010.

30. The bar graph shows the number, in millions, of Internet users in the United States from 2000 through 2003. The data can be modeled by

$$f(x) = 15.3x + 106.7 \text{ and } g(x) = 34.1 \ln x + 117.7,$$

in which $f(x)$ and $g(x)$ represent the number of Internet users, in millions, x years after 1999.

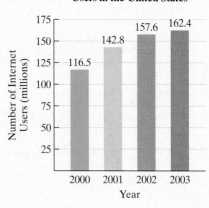

Number of Internet Users in the United States

Source: Jupiter Media

a. What is the slope of the linear model? What does this mean in terms of the change in the number of Internet users?

b. Based on the shape of the graph, which function, the linear or the logarithmic, is a better model for the data? Explain your answer.

c. Use each function to find the number of Internet users, in millions, in 2001. To evaluate the logarithmic function, use a calculator with an $\boxed{\text{LN}}$ key and round to one decimal place. Which function serves as the better model for 2001? Is this consistent with your answer in part (b)?

CHAPTER **8**

Consumer Mathematics and Financial Management

"I realize, of course, that it's no shame to be poor, but it's no great honor either. So what would have been so terrible if I had a small fortune?"

—TEVYE, A POOR DAIRYMAN, IN THE MUSICAL *FIDDLER ON THE ROOF*

We all want a wonderful life with fulfilling work, good health, and loving relationships. And let's be honest: Financial security, or even a small fortune, wouldn't hurt! Achieving this goal depends on understanding basic ideas about savings, loans, and investments. A solid understanding of the topics in this chapter can pay, literally, by making your financial goals a reality.

A number of examples illustrate how to attain fortunes ranging from over a half-million dollars to $4 million through regular savings. See Example 3 in Section 8.4 and Exercises 35–36 in Exercise Set 8.4.

SECTION 8.1 • PERCENT, SALES TAX, AND INCOME TAX

OBJECTIVES

1. Express a fraction as a percent.
2. Express a decimal as a percent.
3. Express a percent as a decimal.
4. Solve applied problems involving sales tax and discounts.
5. Compute income tax.
6. Determine percent increase or decrease.
7. Investigate some of the ways percent can be abused.

"And if elected, it is my solemn pledge to cut your taxes by 10% for each of my first three years in office, for a total cut of 30%."

Did you know that one of the most common ways that you are given numerical information is with percents? This section will provide you with the tools to make sense of the politician's promise, as we present the uses, and abuses, of percent.

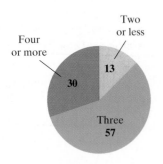

Source: U.S. Census Bureau and HUD

FIGURE 8.1 Number of bedrooms in privately owned single-family U.S. houses per 100 houses

Basics of Percent

Percents are the result of expressing numbers as a part of 100. The word *percent* means *per hundred*. For example, the circle graph in Figure 8.1 shows that 57 out of every 100 single-family homes have three bedrooms. Thus, $\frac{57}{100} = 57\%$, indicating that 57% of the houses have three bedrooms. The percent sign, %, is used to indicate the number of parts out of one hundred parts.

A fraction can be expressed as a percent using the following procedure:

> **EXPRESSING A FRACTION AS A PERCENT**
> 1. Divide the numerator by the denominator.
> 2. Multiply the quotient by 100. This is done by moving the decimal point in the quotient two places to the right.
> 3. Add a percent sign.

1 | Express a fraction as a percent.

EXAMPLE 1 EXPRESSING A FRACTION AS A PERCENT

Express $\frac{5}{8}$ as a percent.

SOLUTION

Step 1. Divide the numerator by the denominator.
$$5 \div 8 = 0.625$$

Step 2. Multiply the quotient by 100.
$$0.625 \times 100 = 62.5$$

Step 3. Add a percent sign.
$$62.5\%$$

Thus, $\frac{5}{8} = 62.5\%$.

 Express $\frac{1}{8}$ as a percent.

2 | Express a decimal as a percent.

Our work in Example 1 shows that $0.625 = 62.5\%$. This illustrates the procedure for expressing a decimal number as a percent.

> **EXPRESSING A DECIMAL NUMBER AS A PERCENT**
> **1.** Move the decimal point two places to the right.
> **2.** Attach a percent sign.

EXAMPLE 2   EXPRESSING A DECIMAL AS A PERCENT

Express 0.47 as a percent.

SOLUTION

Move decimal point two places right.

$0.47\ \%$ Add a percent sign.

Thus, $0.47 = 47\%$.

CHECK POINT 2 Express 0.023 as a percent.

3 | Express a percent as a decimal.

We reverse the procedure of Example 2 to express a percent as a decimal number.

> **EXPRESSING A PERCENT AS A DECIMAL NUMBER**
> **1.** Move the decimal point two places to the left.
> **2.** Remove the percent sign.

EXAMPLE 3   EXPRESSING PERCENTS AS DECIMALS

Express each percent as a decimal:

a. 19%   **b.** 180%.

SOLUTION Use the two steps in the box.

a.

$$19\% = 19.\% = 0.19\ \%$$

The decimal point starts at the far right.

The decimal point is moved two places to the left.

The percent sign is removed.

Thus, $19\% = 0.19$.
b. $180\% = 1.80\% = 1.80$ or 1.8.

CHECK POINT 3 Express each percent as a decimal:

a. 67%   **b.** 250%.

If a fraction is part of a percent, as in $\frac{1}{4}\%$, begin by expressing the fraction as a decimal, retaining the percent sign. Then, use the two steps in the box to express the percent as a decimal number. For example,

$$\frac{1}{4}\% = 0.25\% = 00.25\% = 0.0025.$$

4   Solve applied problems involving sales tax and discounts.

Percent, Sales Tax, and Discounts

Many applications involving percent are based on the following formula:

A is *P* percent of *B*.

$$A = P \cdot B.$$

Note that the word *of* implies multiplication.

We can use this formula to determine the **sales tax** collected by states, counties, and cities on sales of items to customers. The sales tax is a percent of the cost of an item.

> Sales tax amount = tax rate × item's cost

EXAMPLE 4   PERCENT AND SALES TAX

Suppose that the local sales tax rate is 7.5% and you purchase a bicycle for $394.

a. How much tax is paid?

b. What is the bicycle's total cost?

SOLUTION

a.   Sales tax amount = tax rate × item's cost

$$= 7.5\% \times \$394 = 0.075 \times \$394 = \$29.55$$

> 7.5% of the item's cost, or 7.5% of $394

The tax paid is $29.55.

b. The bicycle's total cost is the purchase price, $394, plus the sales tax, $29.55.

$$\text{Total cost} = \$394.00 + \$29.55 = \$423.55$$

The bicycle's total cost is $423.55.

 Suppose that the local sales tax rate is 6% and you purchase a computer for $1260.

a. How much tax is paid?

b. What is the computer's total cost?

None of us is thrilled about sales tax, but we do like buying things that are *on sale*. Businesses reduce prices, or **discount**, to attract customers and to reduce inventory. The discount rate is a percent of the original price.

> Discount amount = discount rate × original price

EXAMPLE 5   PERCENT AND SALES PRICE

A computer with an original price of $1460 is on sale at 15% off.

a. What is the discount amount?

b. What is the computer's sale price?

SOLUTION

a.   Discount amount = discount rate × original price

$$= 15\% \times \$1460 = 0.15 \times \$1460 = \$219$$

> 15% of the original price, or 15% of $1460

The discount amount is $219.

A calculator is useful, and sometimes essential, in this chapter. The keystroke sequence that gives the sale price in Example 5 is

1460 $\boxed{-}$ .15 $\boxed{\times}$ 1460.

Press $\boxed{=}$ on a scientific calculator or $\boxed{\text{ENTER}}$ on a graphing calculator to display the answer, 1241.

b. The computer's sale price is the original price, $1460, minus the discount amount, $219.

$$\text{Sale price} = \$1460 - \$219 = \$1241$$

The computer's sale price is $1241.

> **CHECK POINT 5** A CD player with an original price of $380 is on sale at 35% off.
>
> **a.** What is the discount amount?
>
> **b.** What is the CD player's sale price?

Percent and Income Tax

We have seen how tax rates determine the amount of sales tax on an item. They also determine the amount that we must each pay in income tax.

> ### CALCULATING INCOME TAX
>
> **1.** Determine your adjusted gross income:
>
> $$\text{Adjusted gross income} = \text{Gross income} - \text{Adjustments.}$$
>
> > All income for the year, including wages, tips, earnings from investments, and unemployment compensation
>
> > Includes payments to tax-deferred savings plans
>
> **2.** Determine your taxable income:
>
> $$\text{Taxable income} = \text{Adjusted gross income} - (\text{Exemptions} + \text{Deductions}).$$
>
> > A fixed amount for yourself ($3200 in 2005) and the same amount for each dependent
>
> > Choose the greater of a standard deduction or an itemized deduction, which includes interest on home mortgages, state income taxes, property taxes, charitable contributions, and medical expenses exceeding 7.5% of adjusted gross income.
>
> **3.** Determine the income tax:
>
> $$\text{Income tax} = \text{Tax computation} - \text{Tax credits.}$$
>
> > Use your taxable income and tax rates for your filing status (single, married, etc.) to determine this amount.
>
> > May include up to $1000 per child, the cost of child care so a parent can work, and adoption credits for qualified expenses.

Tax Rate	Single
10%	up to $7300
15%	$7301 to $29,700

A portion of Table 8.1. (The complete table appears on the next page.)

Table 8.1 on the next page shows 2005 tax rates, standard deductions, and exemptions for the four **filing status** categories described in the voice balloons. The tax rates in the left column, called **marginal tax rates**, are assigned to various income ranges, called **margins**. For example, suppose you are single and your taxable income is $25,000. The singles column of the table shows that you must pay 10% tax on the first $7300, which is

$$10\% \text{ of } \$7300 = 0.10 \times \$7300 = \$730.$$

You must also pay 15% tax on the remaining $17,700 ($25,000 − $7300 = $17,700), which is

$$15\% \text{ of } \$17,700 = 0.15 \times \$17,700 = \$2655.$$

Your total tax is $730 + $2655 = $3385. In this scenario, your *marginal rate* is 15% and you are in the 15% *tax bracket*.

TABLE 8.1 2005 MARGINAL TAX RATES, STANDARD DEDUCTIONS, AND EXEMPTIONS

	Unmarried, divorced, or legally separated	Married and each partner files a separate tax return	Married and both partners file a single tax return	Unmarried and paying more than half the cost of supporting a child or parent
Tax Rate	**Single**	**Married Filing Separately**	**Married Filing Jointly**	**Head of Household**
10%	up to $7300	up to $7300	up to $14,600	up to $10,450
15%	$7301 to $29,700	$7301 to $29,700	$14,601 to $59,400	$10,451 to $39,800
25%	$29,701 to $71,950	$29,701 to $59,975	$59,401 to $119,950	$39,801 to $102,800
28%	$71,951 to $150,150	$59,976 to $91,400	$119,951 to $182,800	$102,801 to $166,450
33%	$150,151 to $326,450	$91,401 to $163,225	$182,801 to $326,450	$166,451 to $326,450
35%	more than $326,450	more than $163,225	more than $326,450	more than $326,450
Standard Deduction	$5000	$5000	$10,000	$7300
Exemptions (per person)	$3200	$3200	$3200	$3200

SINGLE WOMAN WITH NO DEPENDENTS

Gross income: $52,000

Adjustments: $4000 paid to a tax-deferred IRA (Individual Retirement Account)

Deductions:
- $7500: mortgage interest
- $2200: property taxes
- $2400: charitable contributions
- $1500: medical expenses not covered by insurance

Tax credit: $500

EXAMPLE 6   COMPUTING INCOME TAX

Calculate the income tax owed by a single woman with no dependents whose gross income, adjustments, deductions, and credits are given in the margin. Use the 2005 marginal tax rates in Table 8.1.

SOLUTION

Step 1. **Determine the adjusted gross income.**

$$\text{Adjusted gross income} = \text{Gross income} - \text{Adjustments}$$
$$= \$52,000 - \$4000$$
$$= \$48,000$$

Step 2. **Determine the taxable income.**

$$\text{Taxable income} = \text{Adjusted gross income} - (\text{Exemptions} + \text{Deductions})$$
$$= \$48,000 - (\$3200 + \text{Deductions})$$

The singles column in Table 8.1 shows a personal exemption of $3200.

The singles column in Table 8.1 shows a $5000 standard deduction. A greater deduction can be obtained by itemizing.

Itemized Deductions

$7500 : mortgage interest

$2200 : property taxes

$2400 : charitable contributions

$1500 : medical expenses

Can only deduct amount in excess of 7.5% of gross income:
$0.075 \times \$52,000 = \$3900$

$12,100 : total of deductible expenditures

We substitute $12,100 for deductions in the formula for taxable income.

$$\text{Taxable income} = \text{Adjusted gross income} - (\text{Exemptions} + \text{Deductions})$$
$$= \$48,000 - (\$3200 + \$12,100)$$
$$= \$48,000 - \$15,300$$
$$= \$32,700$$

Step 3. Determine the income tax.

$$\text{Income Tax} = \text{Tax computation} - \text{Tax credits}$$
$$= \text{Tax computation} - \$500$$

Tax Rate	Single
10%	up to $7300
15%	$7301 to $29,700
25%	$29,701 to $71,950

A portion of Table 8.1 (repeated)

We perform the tax computation using the singles rates in Table 8.1. Our taxpayer is in the 25% tax bracket because her taxable income, $32,700, is in the $29,701 to $71,950 income range. This means that she owes 10% on the first $7300 of her taxable income, 15% on her taxable income between $7301 and $29,700, inclusive, and 25% on her taxable income above $29,700.

| 10% marginal rate on first $7300 of taxable income | 15% marginal rate on taxable income between $7301 and $29,700 | 25% marginal rate on taxable income above $29,700 |

$$\text{Tax computation} = 0.10 \times \$7300 + 0.15 \times (\$29,700 - \$7300) + 0.25 \times (\$32,700 - \$29,700)$$
$$= 0.10 \times \$7300 + 0.15 \times \$22,400 + 0.25 \times \$3000$$
$$= \$730 + \$3360 + \$750$$
$$= \$4840$$

We substitute $4840 for the tax computation in the formula for income tax.

$$\text{Income tax} = \text{Tax computation} - \text{Tax credits}$$
$$= \$4840 - \$500$$
$$= \$4340$$

The income tax owed is $4340.

STUDY TIP

A tax credit is not the same thing as a tax deduction. The *tax credit* of $500 in Example 6 *reduces the income tax owed by the full dollar-for-dollar amount*, namely, $500. The *tax deduction* of $12,100 *reduces the taxable income* by $12,100, thereby saving only a percentage of $12,100 in taxes.

CHECK POINT 6 Use the 2005 marginal tax rates in Table 8.1 to calculate the tax owed by a single man with no dependents whose gross income, adjustments, deductions, and credits are given as follows:

Gross income: $40,000

Adjustments: $1000

Deductions: $3000: charitable contributions
$1500: theft loss
$300: cost of tax preparation

Tax credit: none.

6 Determine percent increase or decrease.

Percent and Change

Percents are used for comparing changes, such as increases or decreases in sales, population, prices, and production. If a quantity changes, its **percent increase** or its **percent decrease** can be found as follows:

FINDING PERCENT INCREASE OR PERCENT DECREASE

1. Find the fraction for the percent increase or the percent decrease:

$$\frac{\text{amount of increase}}{\text{original amount}} \quad \text{or} \quad \frac{\text{amount of decrease}}{\text{original amount}}.$$

2. Find the percent increase or the percent decrease by expressing the fraction in step 1 as a percent.

EXAMPLE 7 FINDING PERCENT INCREASE AND DECREASE

In 2000, world population was approximately 6 billion. Figure 8.2 shows world population projections through the year 2150. The data are from the United Nations Family Planning Program and are based on optimistic or pessimistic expectations for successful control of human population growth.

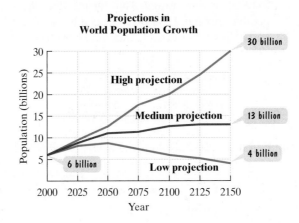

Projections in World Population Growth

FIGURE 8.2
Source: United Nations

a. Find the percent increase in world population from 2000 to 2150 using the high projection data.

b. Find the percent decrease in world population from 2000 to 2150 using the low projection data.

SOLUTION

a. Use the data shown on the blue, high-projection, graph.

$$\text{Percent increase} = \frac{\text{amount of increase}}{\text{original amount}}$$

$$= \frac{30 - 6}{6} = \frac{24}{6} = 4 = 400\%$$

The projected percent increase in world population is 400%.

b. Use the data shown on the green, low-projection, graph.

$$\text{Percent decrease} = \frac{\text{amount of decrease}}{\text{original amount}}$$

$$= \frac{6 - 4}{6} = \frac{2}{6} = \frac{1}{3} = 0.33\frac{1}{3} = 33\frac{1}{3}\%$$

The projected percent decrease in world population is $33\frac{1}{3}\%$.

In Example 7, we expressed the percent decrease as $33\frac{1}{3}\%$ because of the familiar conversion $\frac{1}{3} = 0.33\frac{1}{3}$. However, in many situations, rounding is needed. We suggest that you round to the nearest tenth of a percent. Carry the division in the fraction for percent increase or decrease to four places after the decimal point. Then round the decimal to three places, or to the nearest thousandth. Expressing this rounded decimal as a percent gives percent increase or decrease to the nearest tenth of a percent.

a. If 6 is increased to 10, find the percent increase.

b. If 10 is decreased to 6, find the percent decrease.

EXAMPLE 8   FINDING PERCENT DECREASE

A jacket regularly sells for $135.00. The sale price is $60.75. Find the percent decrease of the sale price from the regular price.

SOLUTION

$$\text{Percent decrease} = \frac{\text{amount of decrease}}{\text{original amount}}$$

$$= \frac{135.00 - 60.75}{135} = \frac{74.25}{135} = 0.55 = 55\%$$

The percent decrease of the sale price from the regular price is 55%. This means that the sale price of the jacket is 55% lower than the regular price.

○

 A television regularly sells for $940. The sale price is $611. Find the percent decrease of the sale price from the regular price.

7   Investigate some of the ways percent can be abused.

Abuses of Percent

In our next examples, we look at a few of the many ways that percent can be used incorrectly. Confusion often arises when percent increase (or decrease) refers to a changing quantity that is itself a percent.

EXAMPLE 9   PERCENTS OF PERCENTS

John Tesh, while he was still coanchoring *Entertainment Tonight*, reported that the PBS series *The Civil War* had an audience of 13% versus the usual 4% PBS audience, "an increase of more than 300%." Did Tesh report the percent increase correctly?

SOLUTION We begin by finding the percent increase.

$$\text{Percent increase} = \frac{\text{amount of increase}}{\text{original amount}}$$

$$= \frac{13\% - 4\%}{4\%} = \frac{9\%}{4\%} = \frac{9}{4} = 2.25 = 225\%$$

The percent increase for PBS was 225%. This is not more than 300%, so Tesh did not report the percent increase correctly.

○

 An episode of a television series had an audience of 12% versus its usual 10%. What was the percent increase for this episode?

EXAMPLE 10   PROMISES OF A POLITICIAN

A politician states, "If you elect me to office, I promise to cut your taxes for each of my first three years in office by 10% each year, for a total reduction of 30%." Evaluate the accuracy of the politician's statement.

SOLUTION To make things simple, let's assume that a taxpayer paid $100 in taxes in the year previous to the politician's election. A 10% reduction during year 1 is 10% of $100.

$$10\% \text{ of previous year tax} = 10\% \text{ of } \$100 = 0.10 \times \$100 = \$10$$

BLITZER BONUS

Percents and Tax Rates

In 1944 and 1945, the highest marginal tax rate in the United States was a staggering 94%. (Does a 94% tax bracket qualify as an abuse of percent?) The tax rate on the highest-income Americans remained at approximately 90% throughout the 1950s, decreased to 70% in the 1960s and 1970s, and to 50% in the early 1980s before reaching a post–World War II low of 28% in 1998. (*Source*: IRS) In 2006, Denmark had the world's highest tax rate, starting at 43.7% and climbing to 62.9% for its wealthiest taxpayers.

With a 10% reduction the first year, the taxpayer will pay only $100 − $10, or $90, in taxes during the politician's first year in office.

The following table shows how we calculate the new, reduced tax for each of the first three years in office:

Year	Tax Paid the Year Before	10% Reduction	Taxes Paid This Year
1	$100	$0.10 \times \$100 = \$10$	$\$100 - \$10 = \$90$
2	$90	$0.10 \times \ \$90 = \$9$	$\$90 - \$9 = \$81$
3	$81	$0.10 \times \ \$81 = \$8.10$	$\$81 - \$8.10 = \$72.90$

Now, we determine the percent decrease in taxes over the three years.

$$\text{Percent decrease} = \frac{\text{amount of decrease}}{\text{original amount}}$$

$$= \frac{\$100 - \$72.90}{\$100} = \frac{\$27.10}{\$100} = \frac{27.1}{100} = 0.271 = 27.1\%$$

The taxes decline by 27.1%, not by 30%. The politician is ill-informed in saying that three consecutive 10% cuts add up to a total tax cut of 30%. In our calculation, which serves as a counterexample to the promise, the total tax cut is only 27.1%.

CHECK POINT 10 Suppose you paid $1200 in taxes. During year 1, taxes decrease by 20%. During year 2, taxes increase by 20%.

a. What do you pay in taxes for year 2?

b. How do your taxes for year 2 compare with what you originally paid, namely $1200? If the taxes are not the same, find the percent increase or decrease.

EXERCISE SET 8.1 ●●●●●●

• Practice Exercises

In Exercises 1–10, express each fraction as a percent.

1. $\frac{2}{5}$ **2.** $\frac{3}{5}$ **3.** $\frac{1}{4}$ **4.** $\frac{3}{4}$

5. $\frac{3}{8}$ **6.** $\frac{7}{8}$ **7.** $\frac{1}{40}$ **8.** $\frac{3}{40}$

9. $\frac{9}{80}$ **10.** $\frac{13}{80}$

In Exercises 11–20, express each decimal as a percent.

11. 0.59   **12.** 0.96   **13.** 0.3844   **14.** 0.003

15. 2.87   **16.** 9.83   **17.** 14.87   **18.** 19.63

19. 100   **20.** 95

In Exercises 21–34, express each percent as a decimal.

21. 72%   **22.** 38%   **23.** 43.6%   **24.** 6.25%

25. 130%   **26.** 260%   **27.** 2%   **28.** 6%

29. $\frac{1}{2}$%   **30.** $\frac{3}{4}$%   **31.** $\frac{5}{8}$%   **32.** $\frac{1}{8}$%

33. $62\frac{1}{2}$%   **34.** $87\frac{1}{2}$%

Use the percent formula, $A = PB$: A is P percent of B, to solve Exercises 35–38.

35. What is 3% of 200?   **36.** What is 8% of 300?

37. What is 18% of 40?   **38.** What is 16% of 90?

• Practice Plus

There are three basic types of percent problems that can be solved using the percent formula $A = PB$.

Question	Given	Percent Formula
What is P percent of B?	P and B	Solve for A.
A is P percent of what?	A and P	Solve for B.
A is what percent of B?	A and B	Solve for P.

Exercises 35–38 involved using the formula to answer the first question. In Exercises 39–46, use the percent formula to answer the second or third question.

39. 3 is 60% of what?

40. 8 is 40% of what?

41. 24% of what number is 40.8?

42. 32% of what number is 51.2?

43. 3 is what percent of 15?

44. 18 is what percent of 90?

45. What percent of 2.5 is 0.3?

46. What percent of 7.5 is 0.6?

• Application Exercises

47. Suppose that the local sales tax rate is 6% and you purchase a car for $16,800.

 a. How much tax is paid?

 b. What is the car's total cost?

48. Suppose that the local sales tax rate is 7% and you purchase a graphing calculator for $96.

 a. How much tax is paid?

 b. What is the calculator's total cost?

49. An exercise machine with an original price of $860 is on sale at 12% off.

 a. What is the discount amount?

 b. What is the exercise machine's sale price?

50. A dictionary that normally sells for $16.50 is on sale at 40% off.

 a. What is the discount amount?

 b. What is the dictionary's sale price?

In Exercises 51–54, use the 2005 marginal tax rates in Table 8.1 on page 448 to calculate the income tax owed by each person.

51. Single male, no dependents

 Gross income: $75,000

 Adjustments: $4000

 Deductions:

   $28,000 mortgage interest

   $4200 property taxes

   $3000 charitable contributions

 Tax credit: none

52. Single female, no dependents

 Gross income: $70,000

 Adjustments: $2000

 Deductions:

   $10,000 mortgage interest

   $2500 property taxes

   $1200 charitable contributions

 Tax credit: none

53. Unmarried head of household with two dependent children

 Gross income: $50,000

 Adjustments: none

 Deductions:

   $4500 state taxes

   $2000 theft loss

 Tax credit: $2000

54. Unmarried head of household with one dependent child

 Gross income: $40,000

 Adjustments: $1500

 Deductions:

   $3600 state taxes

   $800 charitable contributions

 Tax credit: $2500

In addition to income tax, we are required to pay the federal government FICA (Federal Insurance Contribution Act) taxes that are used for Social Security and Medicare benefits. For people who are not self-employed, the 2005 FICA tax rates were as follows:

 • *7.65% on the first $90,000 from wages and tips*

 • *1.45% on income in excess of $90,000.*

The individual's employer must also pay matching amounts of FICA taxes. People who are self-employed pay double the rates shown above. Taxpayers are not permitted to subtract adjustments, exemptions, or deductions when determining FICA taxes. Use this information to solve Exercises 55–60.

55. If you are not self-employed and earn $100,000, what are your FICA taxes?

56. If you are not self-employed and earn $120,000, what are your FICA taxes?

57. If you are self-employed and earn $140,000, what are your FICA taxes?

58. If you are self-employed and earn $160,000, what are your FICA taxes?

59. In 2005, to help pay for college, you worked part-time at a local restaurant, earning $20,000 in wages and tips.

 a. Calculate your FICA taxes.

 b. Use Table 8.1 on page 448 to calculate your income tax. Assume you are single with no dependents, have no adjustments or tax credit, and you take the standard deduction.

 c. Including both FICA and income tax, what percent of your gross income are your federal taxes? Round to the nearest tenth of a percent.

60. In 2005, to help pay for college, you worked part-time at a local restaurant, earning $18,000 in wages and tips.

 a. Calculate your FICA taxes.

 b. Use Table 8.1 on page 448 to calculate your income tax. Assume you are single with no dependents, have no adjustments or tax credit, and take the standard deduction.

 c. Including both FICA and income tax, what percent of your gross income are your federal taxes? Round to the nearest tenth of a percent.

The table shows the fastest-growing U.S. jobs, by number of 2004 employees and expected employees in 2014.

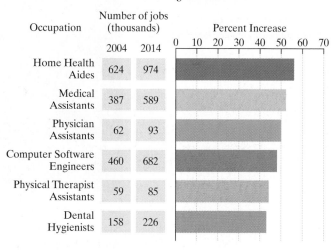

Fastest-Growing U.S. Jobs

Source: Bureau of Labor Statistics

In Exercises 61–64, use the number of jobs given at the bottom of the previous page to find the percent increase, to the nearest tenth of a percent, in the number of employees in the given occupation from 2004 to 2014.

61. home health aides

62. medical assistants

63. physician assistants

64. computer software engineers

65. A sofa regularly sells for $840. The sale price is $714. Find the percent decrease of the sale price from the regular price.

66. A FAX machine regularly sells for $380. The sale price is $266. Find the percent decrease of the sale price from the regular price.

67. Suppose that you have $10,000 in a rather risky investment recommended by your financial advisor. During the first year, your investment decreases by 30% of its original value. During the second year, your investment increases by 40% of its first-year value. Your advisor tells you that there must have been a 10% overall increase of your original $10,000 investment. Is your financial advisor using percentages properly? If not, what is your actual percent gain or loss of your original $10,000 investment?

68. The price of a color printer is reduced by 30% of its original price. When it still does not sell, its price is reduced by 20% of the reduced price. The salesperson informs you that there has been a total reduction of 50%. Is the salesperson using percentages properly? If not, what is the actual percent reduction from the original price?

• Writing in Mathematics

69. What is a percent?

70. Describe how to express a decimal number as a percent and give an example.

71. Describe how to express a percent as a decimal number and give an example.

72. Explain how to use the sales tax rate to determine an item's total cost.

73. A common complaint about income tax is "I can't afford to work more because it will put me in a higher tax bracket." Is it possible that being in a higher bracket means you actually lose money? Explain your answer.

74. Because of the mortgage interest tax deduction, is it possible to save money buying a house rather than renting, even though rent payments are lower than mortgage payments? Explain your answer.

75. Describe how to find percent increase and give an example.

• Critical Thinking Exercises

76. Which one of the following is true?
   a. If your weight increases by 5% this year and 5% next year, the increase in weight over two years is 10%.
   b. A grade point average that increases by 10% this semester and decreases by 10% next semester will be unchanged after two semesters.
   c. If $\frac{1}{10}$ of a person's salary is spent for clothing, $\frac{1}{3}$ for food, and $\frac{1}{5}$ for rent, the percent of the salary that is left is $36\frac{2}{3}\%$.
   d. If the amount that a person spends on rent increases from 20% to 30% of that person's income, the percent increase is 10%.

77. A condominium is taxed based on its $78,500 value. The tax rate is $3.40 for every $100 of value. If the tax is paid before March 1, 3% of the normal tax is given as a discount. How much tax is paid if the condominium owner takes advantage of the discount?

78. In January, each of 60 people purchased a $200 washing machine. In February, 10% fewer customers purchased the same washing machine that had increased in price by 20%. What was the change in sales from January to February?

• Group Exercise

79. Group members should research and present a report on the Alternative Minimum Tax (AMT). How do the AMT calculations differ from the income tax calculations that we discussed in this section? What are some of the hot political issues surrounding the AMT? On whom will it have the greatest financial impact?

SECTION 8.2 • SIMPLE INTEREST

OBJECTIVES

1. Calculate simple interest.

2. Use the future value formula.

3. Use the simple interest formula on discounted loans.

In 1626, Peter Minuit convinced the Wappinger Indians to sell him Manhattan Island for $24. If the native Americans had put the $24 into a bank account at a 5% interest rate compounded monthly, by the year 2006 there would be well over $4 billion in the account!

Although you may not yet understand terms such as *interest rate* and *compounded monthly*, one thing seems clear: Money in certain savings accounts grows in remarkable ways. You, too, can take advantage of such accounts with astonishing results. In the next two sections, we will show you how.

1 Calculate simple interest.

Simple Interest

Interest is the dollar amount that we get paid for lending money or pay for borrowing money. When we deposit money in a savings institution, the institution pays us interest for its use. When we borrow money, interest is the price we pay for the privilege of using the money until we repay it.

The amount of money that we deposit or borrow is called the **principal**. For example, if you deposit $2000 in a savings account, then $2000 is the principal. The amount of interest depends on the principal, the interest **rate**, which is given as a percent and varies from bank to bank, and the length of time for which the money is deposited. In this section, the rate is assumed to be per year.

Simple interest involves interest calculated only on the principal. The following formula is used to find simple interest:

CALCULATING SIMPLE INTEREST

$$\text{Interest} = \text{principal} \times \text{rate} \times \text{time}$$
$$I = Prt$$

The rate, r, is expressed as a decimal when calculating simple interest.

EXAMPLE 1   CALCULATING SIMPLE INTEREST FOR A YEAR

You deposit $2000 in a savings account at Hometown Bank, which has a rate of 6%. Find the interest at the end of the first year.

SOLUTION To find the interest at the end of the first year, we use the simple interest formula.

$$I = Prt = (2000)(0.06)(1) = 120$$

| Principal, or amount deposited, is $2000. | Rate is 6% = 0.06. | Time is 1 year. |

At the end of the first year, the interest is $120. You can withdraw the $120 interest and you still have $2000 in the savings account.

1 You deposit $3000 in a savings account at Yourtown Bank, which has a rate of 5%. Find the interest at the end of the first year.

EXAMPLE 2   CALCULATING SIMPLE INTEREST FOR MORE THAN A YEAR

A student took out a simple interest loan for $1800 for two years at a rate of 8% to purchase a used car. What is the interest on the loan?

SOLUTION To find the interest on the loan, we use the simple interest formula.

$$I = Prt = (1800)(0.08)(2) = 288$$

| Principal, or amount borrowed, is $1800. | Rate is 8% = 0.08. | Time is 2 years. |

The interest on the loan is $288.

2 A student took out a simple interest loan for $2400 for two years at a rate of 7%. What is the interest on the loan?

---

2 | Use the future value formula.

Future Value: Principal Plus Interest

When a loan is repaid, the interest is added to the original principal to find the total amount due. In Example 2, at the end of two years, the student will have to repay

$$\text{principal} + \text{interest} = \$1800 + \$288 = \$2088.$$

In general, if a principal P is borrowed at a simple interest rate r, then after t years the amount due, A, can be determined as follows:

$$A = P + I = P + Prt = P(1 + rt).$$

The amount due, A, is called the **future value** of the loan. The principal borrowed now, P, is also known as the loan's **present value**.

> **CALCULATING FUTURE VALUE FOR SIMPLE INTEREST**
> The future value, A, of P dollars at simple interest rate r (as a decimal) for t years is given by
> $$A = P(1 + rt).$$

STUDY TIP

Throughout this chapter, keep in mind that all given rates are assumed to be *per year*, unless otherwise stated.

EXAMPLE 3   CALCULATING FUTURE VALUE

A loan of $1060 has been made at 6.5% for three months. Find the loan's future value.

SOLUTION The amount borrowed, or principal, P, is $1060. The rate, r, is 6.5%, or 0.065. The time, t, is given as 3 months. We need to express the time in years because the rate is understood to be 6.5% per year. Because 3 months is $\frac{3}{12}$ of a year, $t = \frac{3}{12} = \frac{1}{4} = 0.25$.

The loan's future value, or the total amount due after three months, is

$$A = P(1 + rt) = 1060[1 + (0.065)(0.25)] \approx \$1077.23.$$

Rounded to the nearest cent, the loan's future value is $1077.23.

3 A loan of $2040 has been made at 7.5% for four months. Find the loan's future value.

Simple interest is used for many short-term loans, including automobile and consumer loans. Imagine that a short-term loan is taken for 125 days. The time of the loan is $\frac{125}{365}$ because there are 365 days in a year. However, the **Banker's rule** allows financial institutions to use 360 in the denominator of such a fraction, claiming that this simplifies the interest calculation. The time, t, for a 125-day short-term loan is

$$\frac{125 \text{ days}}{360 \text{ days}} = \frac{125}{360}.$$

Consumer groups question whether a year should be simplified to 360 days. Why? Compare the values for time, t, for a 125-day short-term loan using denominators of 360 and 365.

$$\frac{125}{360} \approx 0.347 \qquad \frac{125}{365} \approx 0.342$$

The denominator of 360 benefits the bank by resulting in a greater period of time for the loan, and consequently more interest.

The formula for future value, $A = P(1 + rt)$, has four variables. If we are given values for any three of these variables, we can solve for the fourth.

EXAMPLE 4   DETERMINING A SIMPLE INTEREST RATE

You borrow $2500 from a friend and promise to pay back $2655 in six months. What simple interest rate will you pay?

SOLUTION We use the formula for future value, $A = P(1 + rt)$. You borrow $2500: $P = 2500$. You will pay back $2655, so this is the future value: $A = 2655$. You will do this in six months, which must be expressed in years: $t = \frac{6}{12} = \frac{1}{2} = 0.5$. To determine the simple interest rate you will pay, we solve the future value formula for r.

$$A = P(1 + rt)$$ This is the formula for future value.

$$2655 = 2500[1 + r(0.5)]$$ Substitute the given values.

$$2655 = 2500 + 1250r$$ Use the distributive property.

$$155 = 1250r$$ Subtract 2500 from both sides.

$$\frac{155}{1250} = \frac{1250r}{1250}$$ Divide both sides by 1250.

$$r = 0.124 = 12.4\%$$ Express $\frac{155}{1250}$ as a percent.

You will pay a simple interest rate of 12.4%.

○

You borrow $5000 from a friend and promise to pay back $6800 in two years. What simple interest rate will you pay?

EXAMPLE 5   DETERMINING A PRESENT VALUE

You plan to save $2000 for a trip to Europe in two years. You decide to purchase a certificate of deposit (CD) from your bank that pays a simple interest rate of 4%. How much must you put in this CD now in order to have the $2000 in two years?

SOLUTION We use the formula for future value, $A = P(1 + rt)$. We are interested in finding the principal, P, or the present value.

$$A = P(1 + rt)$$ This is the formula for future value.

$$2000 = P[1 + (0.04)(2)]$$ A(future value) = $2000,
r(interest rate) = 0.04, and
t = 2 (you want $2000 in two years).

$$2000 = 1.08P$$ Simplify: 1 + (0.04)(2) = 1.08.

$$\frac{2000}{1.08} = \frac{1.08P}{1.08}$$ Divide both sides by 1.08.

$$P \approx 1851.852$$ Simplify.

To make sure you will have enough money for the vacation, let's round this principal *up* to $1851.86. Thus, you should put $1851.86 in the CD now to have $2000 in two years.

○

How much should you put in an investment paying a simple interest rate of 8% if you need $4000 in six months?

3 | Use the simple interest formula on discounted loans.

Discounted Loans

Some lenders collect the interest from the amount of the loan at the time that the loan is made. This type of loan is called a **discounted loan**. The interest that is deducted from the loan is the **discount**.

EXAMPLE 6   A DISCOUNTED LOAN

You borrow $10,000 on a 10% discounted loan for a period of 8 months.

a. What is the loan's discount?

b. Determine the net amount of money you receive.

c. What is the loan's actual interest rate?

SOLUTION

a. Because the loan's discount is the deducted interest, we use the simple interest formula.

$$I = Prt = (10{,}000)(0.10)\left(\tfrac{2}{3}\right) \approx 666.67$$

| Principal is $10,000. | Rate is 10% = 0.10. | Time is 8 months $= \tfrac{8}{12} = \tfrac{2}{3}$ year. |

The loan's discount is $666.67.

b. The net amount that you receive is the amount of the loan, $10,000, minus the discount, $666.67:

$$10{,}000 - 666.67 = 9333.33.$$

Thus, you receive $9333.33.

c. We can calculate the loan's actual interest rate, rather than the stated 10%, by using the simple interest formula.

$$I = Prt$$

This is the simple interest formula.

$$666.67 = (9333.33)r\left(\frac{2}{3}\right)$$

I (interest) = $666.67, P (principal, or the net amount received) = $9333.33, and $t = \dfrac{2}{3}$ year.

$$666.67 = 6222.22r$$

Simplify: $9333.33\left(\dfrac{2}{3}\right) = 6222.22$.

$$r = \frac{666.67}{6222.22} \approx 0.107 = 10.7\%$$

Solve for r and express r to the nearest tenth of a percent.

The actual rate of interest on the 10% discounted loan is approximately 10.7%.

○

CHECK POINT 6   You borrow $5000 on a 12% discounted loan for a period of two years. Determine: **a.** the loan's discount; **b.** the net amount you receive; **c.** the actual interest rate.

EXERCISE SET 8.2 ●●●●●●

• Practice Exercises

In Exercises 1–8, the principal P is borrowed at simple interest rate r for a period of time t. Find the simple interest owed for the use of the money. Assume 360 days in a year and round answers to the nearest cent.

1. $P = \$4000, r = 6\%, t = 1$ year

2. $P = \$7000, r = 5\%, t = 1$ year

3. $P = \$180, r = 3\%, t = 2$ years

4. $P = \$260, r = 4\%, t = 3$ years

5. $P = \$5000, r = 8.5\%, t = 9$ months

6. $P = \$18{,}000, r = 7.5\%, t = 18$ months

7. $P = \$15{,}500, r = 11\%, t = 90$ days

8. $P = \$12{,}600, r = 9\%, t = 60$ days

In Exercises 9–14, the principal P is borrowed at simple interest rate r for a period of time t. Find the loan's future value, A, or the total amount due at time t. Round answers to the nearest cent.

9. $P = \$3000, r = 7\%, t = 2$ years

10. $P = \$2000, r = 6\%, t = 3$ years

11. $P = \$26{,}000, r = 9.5\%, t = 5$ years

12. $P = \$24{,}000, r = 8.5\%, t = 6$ years

13. $P = \$9000, r = 6.5\%, t = 8$ months

14. $P = \$6000, r = 4.5\%, t = 9$ months

In Exercises 15–20, the principal P is borrowed and the loan's future value, A, at time t is given. Determine the loan's simple interest rate, r, to the nearest tenth of a percent.

15. $P = \$2000, A = \$2150, t = 1$ year

16. $P = \$3000, A = \$3180, t = 1$ year

17. $P = \$5000, A = \$5900, t = 2$ years

18. $P = \$10{,}000, A = \$14{,}060, t = 2$ years

19. $P = \$2300, A = \$2840, t = 9$ months

20. $P = \$1700, A = \$1820, t = 6$ months

In Exercises 21–26, determine the present value, P, you must invest to have the future value, A, at simple interest rate r after time t. Round answers up to the nearest cent.

21. $A = \$6000, r = 8\%, t = 2$ years

22. $A = \$8500, r = 7\%, t = 3$ years

23. $A = \$14{,}000, r = 9.5\%, t = 6$ years

24. $A = \$16{,}000, r = 11.5\%, t = 5$ years

25. $A = \$5000, r = 14.5\%, t = 9$ months

26. $A = \$2000, r = 12.6\%, t = 8$ months

Exercises 27–30 involve discounted loans. In each exercise, determine

    a. *the loan's discount.*

    b. *the net amount of money you receive.*

    c. *the loan's actual interest rate, to the nearest tenth of a percent.*

27. You borrow $2000 on a 7% discounted loan for a period of 8 months.

28. You borrow $3000 on an 8% discounted loan for a period of 9 months.

29. You borrow $12,000 on a 6.5% discounted loan for a period of two years.

30. You borrow $20,000 on an 8.5% discounted loan for a period of three years.

• Practice Plus

31. Solve for r: $A = P(1 + rt)$.

32. Solve for t: $A = P(1 + rt)$.

33. Solve for P: $A = P(1 + rt)$.

34. Solve for P: $A = P\left(1 + \frac{r}{n}\right)^{nt}$. (We will be using this formula in the next section.)

• Application Exercises

35. In order to start a small business, a student takes out a simple interest loan for $4000 for 9 months at a rate of 8.25%.

    a. How much interest must the student pay?

    b. Find the future value of the loan.

36. In order to pay for baseball uniforms, a school takes out a simple interest loan for $20,000 for 7 months at a rate of 12%.

    a. How much interest must the school pay?

    b. Find the future value of the loan.

37. You borrow $1400 from a friend and promise to pay back $2000 in two years. What simple interest rate, to the nearest tenth of a percent, will you pay?

38. Treasury bills (T-bills) can be purchased from the U.S. Treasury Department. You buy a T-bill for $981.60 that pays $1000 in 13 weeks. What simple interest rate, to the nearest tenth of a percent, does this T-bill earn?

39. A bank offers a CD that pays a simple interest rate of 6.5%. How much must you put in this CD now in order to have $3000 for a home-entertainment center in two years? Round *up* to the nearest cent.

40. A bank offers a CD that pays a simple interest rate of 5.5%. How much must you put in this CD now in order to have $8000 for a kitchen remodeling project in two years? Round *up* to the nearest cent.

• Writing in Mathematics

41. Explain how to calculate simple interest.

42. What is the future value of a loan and how is it determined?

43. What is a discounted loan? How is the net amount of money received from such a loan determined?

• Critical Thinking Exercises

44. Use the future value formula to show that the time required for an amount of money P to double in value to $2P$ is given by

$$t = \frac{1}{r}.$$

45. You deposit $5000 in an account that earns 5.5% simple interest.

    a. Express the future value in the account as a linear function of time, t.

    b. Determine the slope of the function in part (a) and describe what this means. Use the phrase "rate of change" in your description.

SECTION 8.3 • COMPOUND INTEREST

O B J E C T I V E S

1. Use compound interest formulas.

2. Calculate present value.

3. Understand and compute effective annual yield.

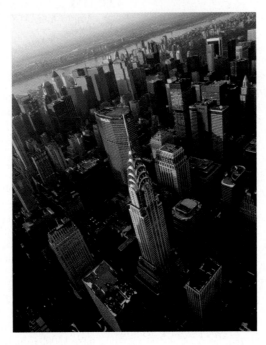

So, how did the present value of Manhattan in 1626—that is, the $24 paid to the native Americans—attain a future value of over $4 billion in 2006, 380 years later, at a mere 5% interest rate? After all, the future value on $24 for 380 years at 5% simple interest is

$$A = P(1 + rt)$$
$$= 24[1 + (0.05)(380)] = 480,$$

or a paltry $480, compared to over $4 billion. To understand this dramatic difference in future value, we turn to the concept of *compound interest*.

1 | Use compound interest formulas.

Compound Interest

Compound interest is interest computed on the original principal as well as on any accumulated interest. Many savings accounts pay compound interest. For example, suppose you deposit $1000 in a savings account at a rate of 5%. Table 8.2 shows how the investment grows if the interest earned is automatically added on to the principal.

TABLE 8.2 CALCULATING THE AMOUNT IN AN ACCOUNT SUBJECT TO COMPOUND INTEREST

Year	Starting Balance	Amount in the Account at Year's End
		Use $A = P(1 + rt)$ with $r = 0.05$ and $t = 1$, or $A = P(1 + 0.05)$.
1	$1000	$A = \$1000(1 + 0.05) = \$1050$
2	$1050 or $1000(1 + 0.05)$	$A = \$1050(1 + 0.05) = \$1102.50$ or $A = \$1000(1 + 0.05)(1 + 0.05) = \$1000(1 + 0.05)^2$
3	$1102.50 or $1000(1 + 0.05)^2$	$A = \$1102.50(1 + 0.05) \approx \$1157.63$ or $A = \$1000(1 + 0.05)^2(1 + 0.05) = \$1000(1 + 0.05)^3$

Using inductive reasoning, the amount, A, in the account after t years is the original principal, $1000, times $(1 + 0.05)^t$: $A = 1000(1 + 0.05)^t$.

If the original principal is P and the interest rate is r, we can use this same approach to determine the amount, A, in an account subject to compound interest.

> **CALCULATING THE AMOUNT IN AN ACCOUNT FOR COMPOUND INTEREST PAID ONCE A YEAR**
>
> If you deposit P dollars at rate r, in decimal form, subject to compound interest, then the amount, A, of money in the account after t years is given by
>
> $$A = P(1 + r)^t.$$
>
> The amount A is called the account's **future value** and the principal P is called its **present value**.

EXAMPLE 1   USING THE COMPOUND INTEREST FORMULA

You deposit $2000 in a savings account at Hometown Bank, which has a rate of 6%.

a. Find the amount, A, of money in the account after 3 years subject to compound interest.

b. Find the interest.

SOLUTION

a. The amount deposited, or principal, P, is $2000. The rate, r, is 6%, or 0.06. The time of the deposit, t, is three years. The amount in the account after three years is

$$A = P(1 + r)^t = 2000(1 + 0.06)^3 = 2000(1.06)^3 \approx 2382.03.$$

Rounded to the nearest cent, the amount in the savings account after three years is $2382.03.

b. Because the amount in the account is $2382.03 and the original principal is $2000, the interest is $2382.03 − $2000, or $382.03.

You deposit $1000 in a savings account at a bank that has a rate of 4%.

    a. Find the amount, A, of money in the account after 5 years subject to compound interest. Round to the nearest cent.

    b. Find the interest.

TECHNOLOGY

Here are the calculator keystrokes to compute $2000(1.06)^3$:

MANY SCIENTIFIC CALCULATORS

2000 ☒ 1.06 $\boxed{y^x}$ 3 $\boxed{=}$

MANY GRAPHING CALCULATORS

2000 ☒ 1.06 $\boxed{\wedge}$ 3 $\boxed{\text{ENTER}}$.

Compound Interest Paid More Than Once a Year

The period of time between two interest payments is called the **compounding period**. When compound interest is paid once per year, the compounding period is one year. We say that the interest is **compounded annually**.

Most savings institutions have plans in which interest is paid more than once per year. If compound interest is paid twice per year, the compounding period is six months. We say that the interest is **compounded semiannually**. When compound interest is paid four times per year, the compounding period is three months and the interest is said to be **compounded quarterly**. Some plans allow for monthly compounding or daily compounding.

In general, when compound interest is paid n times per year, we say that there are **n compounding periods per year**. The following formula is used to calculate the amount in an account subject to compound interest with n compounding periods per year:

CALCULATING THE AMOUNT IN AN ACCOUNT FOR
COMPOUND INTEREST PAID n TIMES A YEAR

If you deposit P dollars at rate r, in decimal form, subject to compound interest paid n times per year, then the amount, A, of money in the account after t years is given by

$$A = P\left(1 + \frac{r}{n}\right)^{nt}.$$

A is the account's **future value** and the principal P is its **present value**.

EXAMPLE 2   USING THE COMPOUND INTEREST FORMULA

You deposit $7500 in a savings account that has a rate of 6%. The interest is compounded monthly.

    a. How much money will you have after five years?

    b. Find the interest after five years.

Here are the calculator keystrokes to compute

$$7500\left(1 + \frac{0.06}{12}\right)^{12\cdot5}:$$

MANY SCIENTIFIC CALCULATORS

7500 × (1 + .06 ÷ 12)

y^x (12 × 5) =

MANY GRAPHING CALCULATORS

7500 (1 + .06 ÷ 12)

∧ (12 × 5) ENTER .

SOLUTION

a. The amount deposited, or principal, P, is $7500. The rate, r, is 6%, or 0.06. Because interest is compounded monthly, there are 12 compounding periods per year, so $n = 12$. The time of the deposit, t, is five years. The amount in the account after five years is

$$A = P\left(1 + \frac{r}{n}\right)^{nt} = 7500\left(1 + \frac{0.06}{12}\right)^{12\cdot5} = 7500(1.005)^{60} \approx 10{,}116.38.$$

Rounded to the nearest cent, you will have $10,116.38 after five years.

b. Because the amount in the account is $10,116.38 and the original principal is $7500, the interest after five years is $10,116.38 − $7500, or $2616.38.

2 You deposit $4200 in a savings account that has a rate of 4%. The interest is compounded quarterly.

    a. How much money will you have after ten years? Round to the nearest cent.

    b. Find the interest after ten years.

Continuous Compounding

Some banks use **continuous compounding**, where the compounding periods increase infinitely (compounding interest every trillionth of a second, every quadrillionth of a second, etc.). As n, the number of compounding periods in a year, increases without bound, the expression $\left(1 + \frac{1}{n}\right)^n$ approaches the irrational number e: $e \approx 2.71828$. This is illustrated in Table 8.3. As a result, the formula for the balance in an account with n compoundings per year, $A = P\left(1 + \frac{r}{n}\right)^{nt}$, becomes $A = Pe^{rt}$ with continuous compounding. Although continuous compounding sounds terrific, it yields only a fraction of a percent more interest over a year than daily compounding.

TABLE 8.3 AS n TAKES ON INCREASINGLY LARGE VALUES, THE EXPRESSION $\left(1 + \frac{1}{n}\right)^n$ APPROACHES THE IRRATIONAL NUMBER e.

n	$\left(1 + \dfrac{1}{n}\right)^n$
1	2
2	2.25
5	2.48832
10	2.59374246
100	2.704813829
1000	2.716923932
10,000	2.718145927
100,000	2.718268237
1,000,000	2.718280469
1,000,000,000	2.718281827

> **FORMULAS FOR COMPOUND INTEREST**
>
> After t years, the balance, A, in an account with principal P and annual interest rate r (in decimal form) is given by the following formulas:
>
> **1.** For n compoundings per year: $A = P\left(1 + \frac{r}{n}\right)^{nt}$
>
> **2.** For continuous compounding: $A = Pe^{rt}$.

You can compute e to a power using the $\boxed{e^x}$ key on your calculator. Use the key to enter e^1 and verify that e is approximately equal to 2.71828.

Scientific Calculators	**Graphing Calculators**
1 $\boxed{e^x}$	$\boxed{e^x}$ 1 ENTER

EXAMPLE 3   CHOOSING BETWEEN INVESTMENTS

You decide to invest $8000 for 6 years and you have a choice between two accounts. The first pays 7% per year, compounded monthly. The second pays 6.85% per year, compounded continuously. Which is the better investment?

SOLUTION The better investment is the one with the greater balance in the account after 6 years. Let's begin with the account with monthly compounding. We use the compound interest formula with $P = 8000, r = 7\% = 0.07, n = 12$ (monthly compounding means 12 compoundings per year), and $t = 6$.

$$A = P\left(1 + \frac{r}{n}\right)^{nt} = 8000\left(1 + \frac{0.07}{12}\right)^{12 \cdot 6} \approx 12{,}160.84$$

The balance in this account after 6 years would be $12,160.84.

For the second investment option, we use the formula for continuous compounding with $P = 8000, r = 6.85\% = 0.0685$, and $t = 6$.

$$A = Pe^{rt} = 8000e^{0.0685(6)} \approx 12{,}066.60$$

The balance in this account after 6 years would be $12,066.60, slightly less than the previous amount. Thus, the better investment is the 7% monthly compounding option.

3 A sum of $10,000 is invested at an annual rate of 8%. Find the balance in the account after 5 years subject to **a.** quarterly compounding and **b.** continuous compounding.

2 | Calculate present value.

Planning for the Future with Compound Interest

Just as we did in Section 8.2, we can determine P, the principal or present value, that should be deposited now in order to have a certain amount, A, in the future. If an account earns compound interest, the amount of money that should be invested today to obtain a future value of A dollars can be determined by solving the compound interest formula for P:

> ### CALCULATING PRESENT VALUE
> If A dollars are to be accumulated in t years in an account that pays rate r compounded n times per year, then the present value, P, that needs to be invested now is given by
>
> $$P = \frac{A}{\left(1 + \dfrac{r}{n}\right)^{nt}}.$$

EXAMPLE 4   CALCULATING PRESENT VALUE

How much money should be deposited in an account today that earns 8% compounded monthly so that it will accumulate to $20,000 in five years?

SOLUTION The amount we need today, or the present value, is determined by the present value formula. Because the interest is compounded monthly, $n = 12$. Furthermore, A (the future value) = $20,000, r (the rate) = 8% = 0.08, and t (time in years) = 5.

$$P = \frac{A}{\left(1 + \dfrac{r}{n}\right)^{nt}} = \frac{20{,}000}{\left(1 + \dfrac{0.08}{12}\right)^{12 \cdot 5}} \approx 13{,}424.21$$

Approximately $13,424.21 should be invested today in order to accumulate to $20,000 in five years.

4 How much money should be deposited in an account today that earns 6% compounded weekly so that it will accumulate to $10,000 in eight years?

3 | Understand and compute effective annual yield.

Effective Annual Yield

As we've seen before, a common problem in financial planning is selecting the best investment from two or more investments. For example, is an investment that pays 8.25% interest compounded quarterly better than one that pays 8.3% interest compounded semiannually? Another way to answer the question is to compare their *effective rates*, also called their *effective annual yields*.

> **EFFECTIVE ANNUAL YIELD**
> The **effective annual yield**, or the **effective rate**, is the simple interest rate that produces the same amount of money in an account at the end of one year as when the account is subjected to compound interest at a stated rate.

EXAMPLE 5   UNDERSTANDING EFFECTIVE ANNUAL YIELD

You deposit $4000 in an account that pays 8% interest compounded monthly.

a. Find the future value after one year.

b. Use the future value formula for simple interest to determine the effective annual yield.

SOLUTION

a. We use the compound interest formula to find the account's future value after one year.

$$A = P\left(1 + \frac{r}{n}\right)^{nt} = 4000\left(1 + \frac{0.08}{12}\right)^{12 \cdot 1} \approx \$4332.00$$

Principal is $4000.   Stated rate is 8% = 0.08.   Monthly compounding: $n = 12$ Time is one year: $t = 1$.

Rounded to the nearest cent, the future value after one year is $4332.00.

b. The effective annual yield, or effective rate, **is a simple interest rate**. We use the future value formula for simple interest to determine the simple interest rate that produces a future value of $4332 for a $4000 deposit after one year.

$A = P(1 + rt)$	This is the future value formula for simple interest.
$4332 = 4000(1 + r \cdot 1)$	Substitute the given values.
$4332 = 4000 + 4000r$	Use the distributive property.
$332 = 4000r$	Subtract 4000 from both sides.
$\dfrac{332}{4000} = \dfrac{4000r}{4000}$	Divide both sides by 4000.
$r = \dfrac{332}{4000} = 0.083 = 8.3\%$	Express r as a percent.

The effective annual yield, or effective rate, is 8.3%. This means that money invested at 8.3% simple interest earns the same amount in one year as money invested at 8% interest compounded monthly.

In Example 5, the stated 8% rate is called the **nominal rate**. The 8.3% rate is the effective rate and is a simple interest rate.

 You deposit $6000 in an account that pays 10% interest compounded monthly.

a. Find the future value after one year.

b. Determine the effective annual yield.

Generalizing the procedure of Example 5 and Check Point 5 gives a formula for effective annual yield:

> ### CALCULATING EFFECTIVE ANNUAL YIELD
> Suppose that an investment has a nominal interest rate, r, in decimal form, and pays compound interest n times per year. The investment's effective annual yield, Y, is given by
> $$Y = \left(1 + \frac{r}{n}\right)^n - 1.$$

TECHNOLOGY

Here are the keystrokes for Example 6:

MANY SCIENTIFIC CALCULATORS

$\boxed{(}\ 1\ \boxed{+}\ .05\ \boxed{\div}\ 360\ \boxed{)}\ \boxed{y^x}\ 360$

$\boxed{-}\ 1\ \boxed{=}$

MANY GRAPHING CALCULATORS

$\boxed{(}\ 1\ \boxed{+}\ .05\ \boxed{\div}\ 360\ \boxed{)}\ \boxed{\wedge}\ 360$

$\boxed{-}\ 1\ \boxed{ENTER}$.

Given the nominal rate and the number of compounding periods per year, some graphing calculators display the effective annual yield. The screen shows the calculation of the effective rate in Example 6 on the TI-83 Plus.

Nominal rate is 5% compounded 360 times per year.

Effective rate is displayed as a percent.

EXAMPLE 6   CALCULATING EFFECTIVE ANNUAL YIELD

A passbook savings account has a nominal rate of 5%. The interest is compounded daily. Find the account's effective annual yield. (Assume 360 days in a year.)

SOLUTION The rate, r, is 5%, or 0.05. Because interest is compounded daily and we assume 360 days in a year, $n = 360$. The account's effective annual yield is

$$Y = \left(1 + \frac{r}{n}\right)^n - 1 = \left(1 + \frac{0.05}{360}\right)^{360} - 1 \approx 0.0513 = 5.13\%.$$

The effective annual yield is 5.13%. Thus, money invested at 5.13% simple interest earns the same amount of interest in one year as money invested at 5% interest, the nominal rate, compounded daily.

CHECK POINT 6 What is the effective annual yield of an account paying 8% compounded quarterly?

The effective annual yield is often included in the information about investments or loans. Because it's the true interest rate you're earning or paying, it's the number you should pay attention to. **If you are selecting the best investment from two or more investments, the best choice is the account with the greatest effective annual yield.** However, there are differences in the types of accounts that you need to take into consideration. Some pay interest from the day of deposit to the day of withdrawal. Other accounts start paying interest the first day of the month that follows the day of deposit. Some savings institutions stop paying interest if the balance in the account falls below a certain amount.

When borrowing money, the effective rate or effective annual yield is usually called the **annual percentage rate**. If all other factors are equal and you are borrowing money, select the option with the least annual percentage rate. In the section on installment buying, we will discuss annual percentage rates in more detail.

EXERCISE SET 8.3 ●●●●●●

• Practice Exercises

In Exercises 1–12, the principal represents an amount of money deposited in a savings account subject to compound interest at the given rate.

  a. *Use the formula $A = P(1 + r)^t$ for one compounding period per year or $A = P\left(1 + \frac{r}{n}\right)^{nt}$ for n compounding periods per year to find how much money there will be in the account after the given number of years. (Assume 360 days in a year.)*

  b. *Find the interest earned.*

Round answers to the nearest cent.

	Principal	Rate	Compounded	Time
1.	$10,000	4%	annually	2 years
2.	$8000	6%	annually	3 years
3.	$3000	5%	semiannually	4 years
4.	$4000	4%	semiannually	5 years
5.	$9500	6%	quarterly	5 years
6.	$2500	8%	quarterly	6 years
7.	$4500	4.5%	monthly	3 years
8.	$2500	6.5%	monthly	4 years
9.	$1500	8.5%	daily	2.5 years
10.	$1200	8.5%	daily	3.5 years
11.	$20,000	4.5%	daily	20 years
12.	$25,000	5.5%	daily	20 years

Use the compound interest formulas $A = P\left(1 + \dfrac{r}{n}\right)^{nt}$ and $A = Pe^{rt}$ to solve Exercises 13–16. Round answers to the nearest cent.

13. Find the accumulated value of an investment of $10,000 for 5 years at an interest rate of 5.5% if the money is **a.** compounded semiannually; **b.** compounded quarterly; **c.** compounded monthly; **d.** compounded continuously.

14. Find the accumulated value of an investment of $5000 for 10 years at an interest rate of 6.5% if the money is **a.** compounded semiannually; **b.** compounded quarterly; **c.** compounded monthly; **d.** compounded continuously.

15. Suppose that you have $12,000 to invest. Which investment yields the greater return over 3 years: 7% compounded monthly or 6.85% compounded continuously?

16. Suppose that you have $6000 to invest. Which investment yields the greater return over 4 years: 8.25% compounded quarterly or 8.3% compounded semiannually?

Solve Exercises 17–20 using the present value formula:

$$P = \dfrac{A}{\left(1 + \dfrac{r}{n}\right)^{nt}}.$$

Round answers up to the nearest cent.

17. How much money should be deposited today in an account that earns 6% compounded semiannually so that it will accumulate to $10,000 in three years?

18. How much money should be deposited today in an account that earns 7% compounded semiannually so that it will accumulate to $12,000 in four years?

19. How much money should be deposited today in an account that earns 9.5% compounded monthly so that it will accumulate to $10,000 in three years?

20. How much money should be deposited today in an account that earns 10.5% compounded monthly so that it will accumulate to $22,000 in four years?

21. You deposit $10,000 in an account that pays 4.5% interest compounded quarterly.
    a. Find the future value after one year.
    b. Use the future value formula for simple interest to determine the effective annual yield.

22. You deposit $12,000 in an account that pays 6.5% interest compounded quarterly.
    a. Find the future value after one year.
    b. Use the future value formula for simple interest to determine the effective annual yield.

Solve Exercises 23–28 using the effective annual yield formula:

$$Y = \left(1 + \dfrac{r}{n}\right)^{n} - 1.$$

A passbook savings account has a rate of 6%. Find the effective annual yield, rounded to the nearest tenth of a percent, if the interest is compounded

23. semiannually.   24. quarterly.

25. monthly.

26. daily. (Assume 360 days in a year.)

27. 1000 times per year.

28. 100,000 times per year.

In Exercises 29–32, determine the effective annual yield, to the nearest tenth of a percent, for each investment. Then select the better investment. Assume 360 days in a year.

29. 8% compounded monthly; 8.25% compounded annually

30. 5% compounded monthly; 5.25% compounded quarterly

31. 5.5% compounded semiannually; 5.4% compounded daily

32. 7% compounded annually; 6.85% compounded daily

• Practice Plus

In Exercises 33–38, assume that you place money in an account subject to interest compounded annually. Use the formula $A = P(1 + r)^{t}$, a calculator, and trial and error to answer each question. Give answers to the nearest tenth of a year.

33. How long will it take for the investment to triple at an interest rate of 5%?

34. How long will it take for the investment to triple at an interest rate of 10%?

35. How long will it take for the investment to increase by 50% at an interest rate of 10%?

36. How long will it take for the investment to increase by 50% at an interest rate of 5%?

37. How long will it take for the investment to increase by 90% at an interest rate of 8%?

38. How long will it take for the investment to increase by 90% at an interest rate of 12%?

• Application Exercises

39. In 1626, Peter Minuit convinced the Wappinger Indians to sell him Manhattan Island for $24. If the Native Americans had put the $24 into a bank account paying compound interest at a 5% rate, how much would the investment be worth in the year 2006 ($t = 380$ years) if interest were compounded **a.** monthly? **b.** 360 times per year?

40. In 1777, Jacob DeHaven loaned George Washington's army $450,000 in gold and supplies. Due to a disagreement over the method of repayment (gold versus Continental money), DeHaven was never repaid, dying penniless. In 1989, his descendants sued the U.S. government over the 212-year-old debt. If the DeHavens used an interest rate of 6% and daily compounding (the rate offered by the Continental Congress in 1777), how much money did the DeHaven family demand in their suit? (*Hint:* Use the compound interest formula with $n = 360$ and $t = 212$ years.)

41. At the time of her grandson's birth, a grandmother deposits $10,000 in an account that pays 9% compounded monthly. What will be the value of the account at the child's twenty-first birthday, assuming that no other deposits or withdrawals are made during this period?

42. Parents wish to have $80,000 available for a child's education. If the child is now 5 years old, how much money must be set aside at 6% compounded semiannually to meet their financial goal when the child is 18?

43. A 30-year-old worker plans to retire at age 65. He believes that $500,000 is needed to retire comfortably. How much should be deposited now at 9% compounded monthly to meet the $500,000 retirement goal?

44. In 2001, First Internet Bank of Indiana offered a money market account paying 4.5% interest compounded monthly. NetBank offered a money market account paying 4.4% interest compounded daily. (*Source:* www.bankrate.com) Which account is the better investment?

• Writing in Mathematics

45. Describe the difference between simple and compound interest.

46. Give two examples that illustrate the difference between a compound interest problem involving future value and a compound interest problem involving present value.

47. What is effective annual yield?

48. Explain how to select the best investment from two or more investments.

49. Shown are figures in an actual advertisement for Great Western Bank. Explain the meaning of the given percents, as well as the statement below these percents.

9.21%	8.85%
Yield	Rate

Interest compounded monthly

• Critical Thinking Exercises

50. A depositor opens a new savings account with $6000 at 5% compounded semiannually. At the beginning of year 3, an additional $4000 is deposited. At the end of six years, what is the balance in the account?

51. A depositor opens a money market account with $5000 at 8% compounded monthly. After two years, $1500 is withdrawn from the account to buy a new computer. A year later, $2000 is put in the account. What will be the ending balance if the money is kept in the account for another three years?

52. Use the future value formulas for simple and compound interest in one year to derive the formula for effective annual yield.

• Group Exercise

53. This activity is a group research project intended for four or five people. Present your research in a seminar on the history of interest and banking. The seminar should last about 30 minutes. Address the following questions:

When was interest first charged on loans? How was lending money for a fee opposed historically? What is usury? What connection did banking and interest rates play in the historic European rivalries between Christians and Jews? When and where were some of the highest interest rates charged? What were the rates? Where does the word *interest* come from? What is the origin of the word *shylock*? What is the difference between usury and interest in modern times? What is the history of a national bank in the United States?

SECTION 8.4 • ANNUITIES, STOCKS, AND BONDS

O B J E C T I V E S

1. Determine the value of an annuity.

2. Determine regular annuity payments needed to achieve a financial goal.

3. Understand stocks and bonds as investments.

4. Read stock tables.

"Good Times Are Predicted in 1929"
—THE WASHINGTON POST, JAN. 1, 1929

"In a few months, I expect to see the stock market much higher than today."
—ESTEEMED ECONOMIST IRVING FISHER: OCT. 14, 1929

Date on which the stock market crashed and began the Depression: Oct. 29, 1929

According to the *Forbes Billionaires List*, in 2005 the two richest Americans were Bill Gates (net worth: $46.5 billion) and Warren Buffett (net worth: $44 billion). In May 1965, Buffett's new company, Berkshire Hathaway, was selling one share of stock for $18. By the end of 2004, the price of a share had increased to $86,300. If you purchased one share, your **return**, or percent increase, would be

$$\frac{\text{amount of increase}}{\text{original amount}} = \frac{\$86,300 - \$18}{\$18} \approx 4793.44 = 479,344\%.$$

What does a return of nearly 480,000% mean? If you invested $250 in Warren Buffett's company in May 1965, your shares would have been worth over $1.1 million by December 2004. (*Source*: *Pensions and Investments*)

Of course, investments that potentially offer outrageous returns come with great risk of losing part or all of the principal. The bottom line: Is there a safe way to save regularly and have an investment worth one million dollars or more? In this section, we consider such savings plans, some of which come with special tax treatment, as well as riskier investments in stocks and bonds.

1 Determine the value of an annuity.

Annuities

The compound interest formula

$$A = P(1 + r)^t$$

gives the future value, A, after t years, when a fixed amount of money, P, the principal, is deposited in an account that pays an annual interest rate r (in decimal form) compounded once a year. However, money is often invested in small amounts at periodic intervals. For example, to save for retirement, you might decide to place $1000 into an Individual Retirement Account (IRA) at the end of each year until you retire. An **annuity** is a sequence of equal payments made at equal time periods. An IRA is an example of an annuity.

The **value of an annuity** is the sum of all deposits plus all interest paid. Our first example illustrates how to find this value.

EXAMPLE 1 DETERMINING THE VALUE OF AN ANNUITY

You deposit $1000 into a savings plan at the end of each year for three years. The interest rate is 8% per year compounded annually.

a. Find the value of the annuity after three years.

b. Find the interest.

SOLUTION

a. The value of the annuity after three years is the sum of all deposits made plus all interest paid over three years.

> This is the $1000 deposit at year's end.

Value at end of year 1 = $1000

> This is the first-year deposit with interest earned for a year.

> This is the $1000 deposit at year's end.

Value at end of year 2 = $1000(1 + 0.08) + $1000

= $1080 + $1000 = $2080

> Use $A = P(1 + r)^t$ with $r = 0.08$ and $t = 1$, or $A = P(1 + 0.08)$.

> This is the second-year balance, $2080, with interest earned for a year.

> This is the $1000 deposit at year's end.

Value at end of year 3 = $2080(1 + 0.08) + $1000

= $2246.40 + $1000 = $3246.40

The value of the annuity at the end of three years is $3246.40.

b. You made three payments of $1000 each, depositing a total of 3 × $1000, or $3000. Because the value of the annuity is $3246.40, the interest is $3246.40 − $3000, or $246.40.

You deposit $2000 into a savings plan at the end of each year for three years. The interest rate is 10% per year compounded annually.

a. Find the value of the annuity after three years.

b. Find the interest.

Suppose that you deposit P dollars into an account at the end of each year. The account pays an annual interest rate, r, compounded annually. At the end of the first year, the account contains P dollars. At the end of the second year, P dollars is deposited again. At the time of this deposit, the first deposit has received interest earned during the second year. Thus, the value of the annuity after two years is

$$P + P(1 + r).$$

| Deposit of P dollars at end of second year | First-year deposit of P dollars with interest earned for a year |

The value of the annuity after three years is

$$P \quad + \quad P(1 + r) \quad + \quad P(1 + r)^2.$$

| Deposit of P dollars at end of third year | Second-year deposit of P dollars with interest earned for a year | First-year deposit of P dollars with interest earned over two years |

The value of the annuity after t years is

$$P + P(1 + r) + P(1 + r)^2 + P(1 + r)^3 + \cdots + P(1 + r)^{t-1}.$$

| Deposit of P dollars at end of year t | First-year deposit of P dollars with interest earned over $t - 1$ years |

Each term in this sum is obtained by multiplying the preceding term by $(1 + r)$. Thus, the terms form a geometric sequence. Using a formula for the sum of the terms of a geometric sequence, we can obtain the following formula that gives the value of this annuity:

VALUE OF AN ANNUITY: INTEREST COMPOUNDED ONCE A YEAR

If P is the deposit made at the end of each year for an annuity that pays an annual interest rate r (in decimal form) compounded once a year, the value, A, of the annuity after t years is

$$A = \frac{P[(1 + r)^t - 1]}{r}.$$

EXAMPLE 2   DETERMINING THE VALUE OF AN ANNUITY

To save for retirement, you decide to deposit $1000 into an IRA at the end of each year for the next 30 years. If you can count on an interest rate of 10% per year compounded annually,

a. How much will you have from the IRA after 30 years?

b. Find the interest.

SOLUTION

a. The amount that you will have from the IRA is its value after 30 years.

$$A = \frac{P[(1 + r)^t - 1]}{r}$$

Use the formula for the value of an annuity.

$$A = \frac{1000[(1 + 0.10)^{30} - 1]}{0.10}$$

The annuity involves year-end deposits of $1000: $P = 1000$. The interest rate is 10%: $r = 0.10$. The number of years is 30: $t = 30$.

$$= \frac{1000[(1.10)^{30} - 1]}{0.10}$$

Using parentheses keys on a graphing calculator, this calculation can be done in a single step.

$$\approx \frac{1000(17.4494 - 1)}{0.10}$$

Use a calculator to find $(1.10)^{30}$:

1.1 $\boxed{y^x}$ 30 $\boxed{=}$.

$$= \frac{1000(16.4494)}{0.10}$$

$$= 164,494$$

After 30 years, you will have approximately $164,494 from the IRA.

b. You made 30 payments of $1000 each, depositing a total of $30 \times \$1000$, or $30,000. Because the value of the annuity is approximately $164,494, the interest is approximately

$$\$164,494 - \$30,000, \text{ or } \$134,494.$$

The interest is nearly $4\frac{1}{2}$ times the amount of your payments, illustrating the power of compounding. ○

 You deposit $3000 into an IRA at the end of each year for the next 40 years. If you can count on an interest rate of 8% per year compounded annually,

a. How much will you have from the IRA after 40 years?

b. Find the interest.

We can adjust the formula for the value of an annuity if equal payments are made at the end of each of n yearly compounding periods.

STUDY TIP

Annuities can be categorized by when payments are made. The formula in the box describes **ordinary annuities**, where payments are made at the end of each period. The formula assumes the same number of yearly payments and yearly compounding periods. An annuity plan in which the payments are made at the beginning of each period is called an **annuity due**.

VALUE OF AN ANNUITY: INTEREST COMPOUNDED n TIMES PER YEAR

If P is the deposit made at the end of each compounding period for an annuity that pays an annual interest rate r (in decimal form) compounded n times per year, the value, A, of the annuity after t years is

$$A = \frac{P\left[\left(1 + \dfrac{r}{n}\right)^{nt} - 1\right]}{\dfrac{r}{n}}.$$

EXAMPLE 3 DETERMINING THE VALUE OF AN ANNUITY

At age 25, to save for retirement, you decide to deposit $200 at the end of each month into an IRA that pays 7.5% compounded monthly.

a. How much will you have from the IRA when you retire at age 65?

b. Find the interest.

SOLUTION

a. Because you are 25, the amount that you will have from the IRA when you retire at 65 is its value after 40 years.

$$A = \dfrac{P\left[\left(1 + \dfrac{r}{n}\right)^{nt} - 1\right]}{\dfrac{r}{n}}$$

Use the formula for the value of an annuity.

$$A = \dfrac{200\left[\left(1 + \dfrac{0.075}{12}\right)^{12\cdot40} - 1\right]}{\dfrac{0.075}{12}}$$

The annuity involves month-end deposits of $200: $P = 200$. The interest rate is 7.5%: $r = 0.075$. The interest is compounded monthly: $n = 12$. The number of years is 40: $t = 40$.

$$= \dfrac{200[(1 + 0.00625)^{480} - 1]}{0.00625}$$

Using parentheses keys, this can be performed in a single step on a graphing calculator.

$$= \dfrac{200[(1.00625)^{480} - 1]}{0.00625}$$

$$\approx \dfrac{200(19.8989 - 1)}{0.00625}$$

Use a calculator to find $(1.00625)^{480}$:

1.00625 $\boxed{y^x}$ 480 $\boxed{=}$.

$$\approx 604{,}765$$

After 40 years, you will have approximately $604,765 when retiring at age 65.

b. Interest = Value of the IRA − Total deposits

$\approx \$604{,}765 - \$200 \cdot 12 \cdot 40$

$200 per month × 12 months per year × 40 years

$= \$604{,}765 - \$96{,}000 = \$508{,}765$

The interest is approximately $508,765, more than five times the amount of your contributions to the IRA.

○

 3 At age 30, to save for retirement, you decide to deposit $100 at the end of each month into an IRA that pays 9.5% compounded monthly.

    a. How much will you have from the IRA when you retire at age 65?

    b. Find the interest.

2 | Determine regular annuity payments needed to achieve a financial goal.

Planning for the Future with an Annuity

By solving the annuity formula for P, we can determine the amount of money that should be deposited at the end of each compounding period so that an annuity has a future value of A dollars. The following formula gives the regular payments, P, needed to reach a financial goal, A:

> ### REGULAR PAYMENTS NEEDED TO ACHIEVE A FINANCIAL GOAL
>
> The deposit, P, that must be made at the end of each compounding period into an annuity that pays an annual interest rate r (in decimal form) compounded n times per year in order to achieve a value of A dollars after t years is
>
> $$P = \dfrac{A\left(\dfrac{r}{n}\right)}{\left[\left(1 + \dfrac{r}{n}\right)^{nt} - 1\right]}.$$

EXAMPLE 4   ACHIEVING A FINANCIAL GOAL

You would like to have $20,000 to use as a down payment for a home in five years by making regular, end-of-month deposits in an annuity that pays 8% compounded monthly.

a. How much should you deposit each month?

b. How much of the $20,000 down payment comes from deposits and how much comes from interest?

SOLUTION

a.
$$P = \frac{A\left(\dfrac{r}{n}\right)}{\left[\left(1 + \dfrac{r}{n}\right)^{nt} - 1\right]}$$

Use the formula for regular payments, P, needed to achieve a financial goal, A.

$$P = \frac{20{,}000\left(\dfrac{0.08}{12}\right)}{\left[\left(1 + \dfrac{0.08}{12}\right)^{12\cdot5} - 1\right]}$$

Your goal is to accumulate $20,000 (A = 20,000) over five years (t = 5). The interest rate is 8% (r = 0.08) compounded monthly (n = 12).

$$\approx 273$$

Use a calculator and round up to the nearest dollar to be certain you do not fall short of your goal.

You should deposit $273 each month to be certain of having $20,000 for a down payment on a home.

b.   Total deposits = $273 · 12 · 5 = $16,380

> **$273 per month × 12 months per year × 5 years**

Interest = $20,000 − $16,380 = $3620

We see that $16,380 of the $20,000 comes from your deposits and the remainder, $3620, comes from interest.

CHECK POINT 4   Parents of a baby girl are in a financial position to begin saving for her college education. They plan to have $100,000 in a college fund in 18 years by making regular, end-of-month deposits in an annuity that pays 9% compounded monthly.

a. How much should they deposit each month? Round up to the nearest dollar.

b. How much of the $100,000 college fund comes from deposits and how much comes from interest?

STUDY TIP

In Example 4 of Section 8.3, we saw that a lump-sum deposit of approximately $13,424 at 8% compounded monthly would accumulate to $20,000 in five years. In Example 4 on the right, we see that total deposits of $16,380 are required to reach the same goal. With the same interest rate, compounding period, and time period, a lump-sum deposit will generate more interest than an annuity. If you don't have a large sum of money to open an account, an annuity is a realistic, although more expensive, option to a lump-sum deposit for achieving the same financial goal.

3 | Understand stocks and bonds as investments.

Investments

When you deposit money into a bank account, you are making a **cash investment**. Bank accounts up to $100,000 are insured by the federal government, so there is no risk of losing the principal you've invested. The account's interest rate guarantees a certain percent increase in your investment, called its **return**. For example, if you deposit $7500 in a savings account that has a rate of 4% compounded annually, the annual return is 4%. There are other kinds of investments that are riskier, meaning that it is possible to lose all or part of your principal. These investments include **stocks** and **bonds**.

Risk

Danger   Opportunity

The Chinese define *risk* as a combination of danger and opportunity. Investments in which all or part of the principal is in danger frequently offer the opportunity of a greater return. Table 8.4 includes five types of investments, listed from no risk to high risk, and their average annual returns from 1926 through 2004. Although stocks offer the prospects of greater returns, large-company shareholders lost money for 22 of the 79 years shown in the table.

TABLE 8.4 INVESTMENTS FROM NO RISK TO HIGH RISK AND THEIR RETURNS: 1926-2004

Investment Type	Average Annual Return
U.S. Treasury Bills (Federally insured and risk free)	3.8%
Long-Term Government Bonds	5.8%
Long-Term Corporate Bonds	6.2%
Large-Company Stocks	12.4%
Small-Company Stocks	17.5%

Source: Summary Statistics of Annual Total Returns: 1926 to 2004 Yearbook, Ibbotson Associates, Chicago

Stocks

Investors purchase **stock**, shares of ownership in a company. The shares indicate the percent of ownership. For example, if a company has issued a total of one million shares and an investor owns 20,000 of these shares, that investor owns

$$\frac{20,000 \text{ shares}}{1,000,000 \text{ shares}} = 0.02$$

or 2% of the company. Any investor who owns some percentage of the company is called a **shareholder**.

Buying or selling stock is referred to as **trading**. Shares of stock need both a seller and a buyer to be traded. Stocks are traded on a **stock exchange**. The price of a share of stock is determined by the law of supply and demand. If a company is prospering, investors will be willing to pay a good price for its stock, and so the stock price goes up. If the company does not do well, investors may decide to sell, and the stock price goes down. Stock prices indicate the performance of the companies they represent, as well as the state of the national and global economies.

There are two ways to make money by investing in stock:

- You sell the shares for more money than what you paid for them, in which case you have a **capital gain** on the sale of stock. (There can also be a capital loss by selling for less than what you paid, or if the company goes bankrupt.)

- While you own the stock, the company distributes all or part of its profits to shareholders as **dividends**. Each share is paid the same dividend, so the amount you receive depends on the number of shares owned. (Some companies reinvest all profits and do not distribute dividends.)

When more and more average Americans began investing and making money in stocks in the 1990s, the federal government cut the capital-gains tax rate in 1997. Long-term capital gains (profits on items held for more than a year before being sold) and dividends are taxed at lower rates than wages and interest earnings.

Bonds

People who buy stock become part owners in a company. In order to raise money and not dilute the ownership of current stockholders, companies sell **bonds**. People who buy a bond are **lending money** to the company from which they buy the bond. Bonds are a commitment from a company to pay the price an investor pays for the bond at the time it was purchased, called the **face value**, along with interest payments at a given rate.

There are many reasons for issuing bonds. A company might need to raise money for research on a drug that has the potential for curing AIDS, so it issues bonds. The U.S. Treasury Department issues 30-year bonds at a fixed 7% annual rate to borrow money to cover possible federal deficits. Local governments often issue bonds to borrow money to build schools, parks, and libraries.

Bonds are traded like stock, and their price is a function of supply and demand. If a company goes bankrupt, bondholders are the first to claim the company's assets. They make their claims before the stockholders, even though (unlike stockholders) they do not own a share of the company. Buying and selling bonds is frequently done through online investing.

Generally speaking, investing in bonds is less risky than investing in stocks, although the return is lower. A listing of all the investments that a person holds is called a **financial portfolio**. Most financial advisors recommend a portfolio with a mixture of low-risk and high-risk investments, called a **diversified portfolio**.

4 | Read stock tables.

Reading Stock Tables

Daily newspapers and online services give current stock prices and other information about stocks. We will use Citigroup stock to learn how to read these daily stock tables. Look at the following newspaper listing of Citigroup stock.

52-Week High	Low	Stock	SYM	Div	Yld %	PE	Vol 100s	Hi	Lo	Close	Net Chg
77	28.50	Citigroup	C	.84	1.1	29	64981	76	74.44	74.56	−0.94

The headings indicate the meanings of the numbers across the row.

52-Week High
77

The heading **52-Week High** refers to the *highest price* at which Citigroup stock traded during the past 52 weeks. The highest price was $77.00 per share. This means that during the past 52 weeks an investor was willing to pay $77.00 for a share of stock. Notice that 77 represents a quantity in dollars, although the stock table does not show the dollar sign.

52-Week Low
28.50

The heading **52-Week Low** refers to the *lowest price* that Citigroup stock reached during the past 52 weeks. This price is $28.50.

Stock	SYM
Citigroup	C

The heading **Stock** is the *company name*, Citigroup. The heading **SYM** is the *symbol* the company uses for trading. Citigroup uses the symbol C.

Div
.84

The heading **Div** refers to *dividends* paid per share to stockholders last year. Citigroup paid a dividend of $0.84 per share. Once again, the dollar symbol does not appear in the table. Thus, if you owned 100 shares, you received a dividend of $0.84 × 100, or $84.00.

Yld %
1.1

The heading **Yld %** stands for *percent yield*. In this case, the percent yield is 1.1%. (The stock table does not show the percent sign.) This means that the dividends alone give investors an annual return of 1.1%. This is much lower than interest rates offered by most banks. However, this percent does not take into account the fact that Citigroup stock prices might rise. If an investor sells shares for more than what they were paid for, the gain will probably make Citigroup stock a much better investment than a bank account.

In order to understand the meaning of the heading PE, we need to understand some of the other numbers in the table. We will return to this column.

Vol 100s
64981

The heading **Vol 100s** stands for *sales volume in hundreds*. This is the number of shares traded yesterday, in hundreds. The number in the table is 64,981. This means that yesterday, a total of 64,981 × 100, or 6,498,100 shares of Citigroup were traded.

Hi
76

The heading **Hi** stands for the *highest price* at which Citigroup stock traded *yesterday*. This number is 76. Yesterday, Citigroup's highest trading price was $76 a share.

Lo
74.44

The heading **Lo** stands for the *lowest price* at which Citigroup stock traded *yesterday*. This number is 74.44. Yesterday, Citigroup's lowest trading price was $74.44 a share.

Close
74.56

The heading **Close** stands for the *price* at which shares traded *when the stock exchange closed yesterday*. This number is 74.56. Thus, the the price at which shares of Citigroup traded when the stock exchange closed yesterday was $74.56 per share. This is called yesterday's **closing price**.

Net Chg
−0.94

The heading **Net Chg** stands for *net change*. This is the change in price from the market close two days ago to yesterday's market close. This number is −0.94. Thus, the price of a share of Citigroup stock went down by $0.94. For some stock listings, the notation . . . appears under Net Chg. This means that there was *no change in price* for a share of stock from the market close two days ago to yesterday's market close.

PE
29

Now, we are ready to return to the heading **PE**, standing for the *price-to-earnings ratio*.

$$\text{PE ratio} = \frac{\text{Yesterday's closing price per share}}{\text{Annual earnings per share}}$$

This can be expressed as

$$\text{Annual earnings per share} = \frac{\text{Yesterday's closing price per share}}{\text{PE ratio}}.$$

Close
74.56

PE
29

The PE ratio for Citigroup is given to be 29. Yesterday's closing price per share was 74.56. We can substitute these numbers into the formula to find annual earnings per share:

$$\text{Annual earnings per share} = \frac{74.56}{29} \approx 2.57.$$

The annual earnings per share for Citigroup are $2.57. The PE ratio, 29, tells us that yesterday's closing price per share, $74.56, is 29 times greater than the earnings per share, $2.57.

EXAMPLE 5   READING STOCK TABLES

| 52-Week | | Stock | SYM | Div | Yld % | PE | Vol 100s | Hi | Lo | Close | Net Chg |
High	Low										
42.38	22.50	Disney	DIS	.21	.6	43	115900	32.50	31.25	32.50	...

Use the stock table for Disney to answer the following questions.

a. What were the high and low prices for the past 52 weeks?

b. If you owned 3000 shares of Disney stock last year, what dividend did you receive?

c. What is the annual return for dividends alone? How does this compare to a bank account offering a 3.5% interest rate?

d. How many shares of Disney were traded yesterday?

e. What were the high and low prices for Disney shares yesterday?

f. What was the price at which Disney shares traded when the stock exchange closed yesterday?

g. What does ... in the net change column mean?

h. Compute Disney's annual earnings per share using

$$\text{Annual earnings per share} = \frac{\text{Yesterday's closing price per share}}{\text{PE ratio}}.$$

SOLUTION

a. We find the high price for the past 52 weeks by looking under the heading **High**. The price is listed in dollars, given as 42.38. Thus, the high price for a share of stock for the past 52 weeks was $42.38. We find the low price for the past 52 weeks by looking under the heading **Low**. This price is also listed in dollars, given as 22.50. Thus, the low price for a share of Disney stock for the past 52 weeks was $22.50.

b. We find the dividend paid for a share of Disney stock last year by looking under the heading **Div**. The price is listed in dollars, given as .21. Thus, Disney paid a dividend of $0.21 per share to stockholders last year. If you owned 3000 shares, you received a dividend of $0.21 × 3000, or $630.

c. We find the annual return for dividends alone by looking under the heading **Yld %**, standing for percent yield. The number in the table, .6, is a percent. This means that the dividends alone give Disney investors an annual return of 0.6%. This is much lower than a bank account paying a 3.5% interest rate. However, if Disney shares increase in value, the gain might make Disney stock a better investment than the bank account.

| 52-Week | | | | | Yld | | Vol | | | | Net |
High	Low	Stock	SYM	Div	%	PE	100s	Hi	Lo	Close	Chg
42.38	22.50	Disney	DIS	.21	.6	43	115900	32.50	31.25	32.50	...

Disney stock table (repeated)

d. We find the number of shares of Disney traded yesterday by looking under the heading **Vol 100s**, standing for sales volume in hundreds. The number in the table is 115900. This means that yesterday, a total of 115,900 × 100, or 11,590,000 shares, were traded.

e. We find the high and low prices for Disney shares yesterday by looking under the headings **Hi** and **Lo**. Both prices are listed in dollars, given as 32.50 and 31.25. Thus, the high and low prices for Disney shares yesterday were $32.50 and $31.25, respectively.

f. We find the price at which Disney shares traded when the stock exchange closed yesterday by looking under the heading **Close**. The price is listed in dollars, given as 32.50. Thus, when the stock exchange closed yesterday, the price of a share of Disney stock was $32.50.

g. The ... under **Net Chg** means that there was no change in price in Disney stock from the market close two days ago to yesterday's market close. In part (f), we found that the price of a share of Disney stock at yesterday's close was $32.50, so the price at the market close two days ago was also $32.50.

h. We are now ready to use

$$\text{Annual earnings per share} = \frac{\text{Yesterday's closing price per share}}{\text{PE ratio}}$$

to compute Disney's annual earnings per share. We found that yesterday's closing price per share was $32.50. We find the PE ratio under the heading **PE**. The given number is 43. Thus,

$$\text{Annual earnings per share} = \frac{\$32.50}{43} \approx \$0.76.$$

The annual earnings per share for Disney are $0.76. The PE ratio, 43, tells us that yesterday's closing price per share, $32.50, is 43 times greater than the earnings per share, approximately $0.76.

 Use the stock table for Coca Cola to solve parts (a) through (h) in Example 5.

| 52-Week | | | | Yld | | Vol | | | | Net |
High	Low	Stock	Div	%	PE	100s	Hi	Lo	Close	Chg
63.38	42.37	CocaCl	.72	1.5	37	72032	49.94	48.33	49.50	+0.03

Ways to Invest in Annuities, Stocks, and Bonds

Investments in annuities, stocks, and bonds can be bought directly, which means making these investments on your own. You can open an IRA at a bank, purchase stock through stockbrokers, who charge a commission for their services, or buy bonds from the government.

It is not an easy job to determine which stocks and bonds to buy or sell, or when to do so. Even IRAs can be funded by mixing stocks and bonds. Many small investors have decided that they do not have the time to stay informed about the progress of corporations, even with the help of online industry research. Instead, they invest in a **mutual fund**. A mutual fund is a group of stocks and/or bonds managed by a professional investor. When you purchase shares in a mutual fund, you give your money to the **fund manager**. Your money is combined with the money of other investors in the mutual fund. The fund manager invests this pool of money, buying and selling shares of stocks and bonds to obtain the maximum possible returns.

Investors in mutual funds own a small portion of many different companies, which may protect them against the poor performance of a single company. When comparing mutual funds, consider both the fees charged for investing and how well the fund manager is doing with the fund's money. Newspapers publish ratings from 1 (worst) to 5 (best) of mutual fund performance based on whether the manager is doing a good job with its investors' money. Two numbers are given. The first number compares the performance of the mutual fund to a large group of similar funds. The second number compares the performance to funds that are nearly identical. The best rating a fund manager can receive is 5/5; the worst is 1/1.

EXERCISE SET 8.4 ●●●●●●

• Practice Exercises

In Exercises 1–10,

   a. *Use the formula*

$$A = \frac{P[(1 + r)^t - 1]}{r} \quad \text{or} \quad A = \frac{P\left[\left(1 + \dfrac{r}{n}\right)^{nt} - 1\right]}{\dfrac{r}{n}}$$

   to find the value of each annuity. Round to the nearest dollar.
   b. *Find the interest.*

Periodic Deposit	Rate	Time
1. $2000 at the end of each year	5% compounded annually	20 years
2. $3000 at the end of each year	4% compounded annually	20 years
3. $4000 at the end of each year	6.5% compounded annually	40 years
4. $4000 at the end of each year	5.5% compounded annually	40 years
5. $50 at the end of each month	6% compounded monthly	30 years
6. $60 at the end of each month	5% compounded monthly	30 years
7. $100 at the end of every six months	4.5% compounded semiannually	25 years
8. $150 at the end of every six months	6.5% compounded semiannually	25 years
9. $1000 at the end of every three months	6.25% compounded quarterly	6 years
10. $1200 at the end of every three months	3.25% compounded quarterly	6 years

In Exercises 11–18,

   a. *Use the formula*

$$P = \frac{A\left(\dfrac{r}{n}\right)}{\left[\left(1 + \dfrac{r}{n}\right)^{nt} - 1\right]}$$

   to determine the periodic deposit. Round up to the nearest dollar.
   b. *How much of the financial goal comes from deposits and how much comes from interest?*

Periodic Deposit	Rate	Time	Financial Goal
11. $? at the end of each year	6% compounded annually	18 years	$140,000
12. $? at the end of each year	5% compounded annually	18 years	$150,000
13. $? at the end of each month	4.5% compounded monthly	10 years	$200,000
14. $? at the end of each month	7.5% compounded monthly	10 years	$250,000
15. $? at the end of each month	7.25% compounded monthly	40 years	$1,000,000
16. $? at the end of each month	8.25% compounded monthly	40 years	$1,500,000
17. $? at the end of every three months	3.5% compounded quarterly	5 years	$20,000
18. $? at the end of every three months	4.5% compounded quarterly	5 years	$25,000

Exercises 19 and 20 refer to the stock tables for Goodyear (the tire company) and JC Penney (the department store) given below. In each exercise, use the stock table to answer the following questions. Where necessary, round dollar amounts to the nearest cent.

a. What were the high and low prices for a share for the past 52 weeks?

b. If you owned 700 shares of this stock last year, what dividend did you receive?

c. What is the annual return for the dividends alone? How does this compare to a bank offering a 3% interest rate?

d. How many shares of this company's stock were traded yesterday?

e. What were the high and low prices for a share yesterday?

f. What was the price at which a share traded when the stock exchange closed yesterday?

g. What was the change in price for a share of stock from the market close two days ago to yesterday's market close?

h. Compute the company's annual earnings per share using

Annual earnings per share =
$$\frac{Yesterday's\ closing\ price\ per\ share}{PE\ ratio}.$$

19.

52-Week High	Low	Stock	SYM	Div	Yld %	PE	Vol 100s	Hi	Lo	Close	Net Chg
73.25	45.44	Goodyear	GT	1.20	2.2	17	5915	56.38	54.38	55.50	+1.25

20.

52-Week High	Low	Stock	SYM	Div	Yld %	PE	Vol 100s	Hi	Lo	Close	Net Chg
78.34	35.38	Penney JC	JCP	2.18	4.7	22	7473	48.19	46.63	46.88	−1.31

• Practice Plus

In Exercises 21–22, round all answers to the nearest dollar.

21. Here are two ways of investing $30,000 for 20 years.

Lump-Sum Deposit	Rate	Time
$30,000	5% compounded annually	20 years

Periodic Deposit	Rate	Time
$1500 at the end of each year	5% compounded annually	20 years

a. After 20 years, how much more will you have from the lump-sum investment than from the annuity?

b. After 20 years, how much more interest will be earned from the lump-sum investment than from the annuity?

22. Here are two ways of investing $40,000 for 25 years.

Lump-Sum Deposit	Rate	Time
$40,000	6.5% compounded annually	25 years

Periodic Deposit	Rate	Time
$1600 at the end of each year	6.5% compounded annually	25 years

a. After 25 years, how much more will you have from the lump-sum investment than from the annuity?

b. After 25 years, how much more interest will be earned from the lump-sum investment than from the annuity?

In Exercises 23–24,

a. Determine the deposit at the end of each month. Round up to the nearest dollar.

b. Assume that the annuity in part (a) is a tax-deferred IRA belonging to a man whose gross income in 2005 was $50,000. Use Table 8.1 on page 448 to calculate his 2005 taxes first with and then without the IRA. Assume the man is single with no dependents, has no tax credits, and takes the standard deduction.

c. What percent of his gross income are the man's federal taxes with and without the IRA? Round to the nearest tenth of a percent.

	Periodic Deposit	Rate	Time	Financial Goal
23.	$? at the end of each month	8% compounded monthly	40 years	$1,000,000
24.	$? at the end of each month	7% compounded monthly	40 years	$650,000

25. Solve for P:

$$A = \frac{P[(1+r)^t - 1]}{r}.$$

What does the resulting formula describe?

26. Solve for P:

$$A = \frac{P\left[\left(1+\frac{r}{n}\right)^{nt} - 1\right]}{\frac{r}{n}}.$$

What does the resulting formula describe?

Application Exercises

In Exercises 27–32, use the formula

$$A = \frac{P[(1 + r)^t - 1]}{r} \quad \text{or} \quad A = \frac{P\left[\left(1 + \dfrac{r}{n}\right)^{nt} - 1\right]}{\dfrac{r}{n}}.$$

Round to the nearest dollar.

27. To save money for a sabbatical to earn a master's degree, you deposit $2000 at the end of each year in an annuity that pays 7.5% compounded annually.
   a. How much will you have saved at the end of five years?
   b. Find the interest.

28. To save money for a sabbatical to earn a master's degree, you deposit $2500 at the end of each year in an annuity that pays 6.25% compounded annually.
   a. How much will you have saved at the end of five years?
   b. Find the interest.

29. At age 25, to save for retirement, you decide to deposit $50 at the end of each month in an IRA that pays 5.5% compounded monthly.
   a. How much will you have from the IRA when you retire at age 65?
   b. Find the interest.

30. At age 25, to save for retirement, you decide to deposit $75 at the end of each month in an IRA that pays 6.5% compounded monthly.
   a. How much will you have from the IRA when you retire at age 65?
   b. Find the interest.

31. To offer scholarship funds to children of employees, a company invests $10,000 at the end of every three months in an annuity that pays 10.5% compounded quarterly.
   a. How much will the company have in scholarship funds at the end of ten years?
   b. Find the interest.

32. To offer scholarship funds to children of employees, a company invests $15,000 at the end of every three months in an annuity that pays 9% compounded quarterly.
   a. How much will the company have in scholarship funds at the end of ten years?
   b. Find the interest.

In Exercises 33–36, use the formula

$$P = \frac{A\left(\dfrac{r}{n}\right)}{\left[\left(1 + \dfrac{r}{n}\right)^{nt} - 1\right]}.$$

Round up to the nearest dollar.

33. You would like to have $3500 in four years for a special vacation following graduation by making deposits at the end of every six months in an annuity that pays 5% compounded semiannually.
   a. How much should you deposit at the end of every six months?
   b. How much of the $3500 comes from deposits and how much comes from interest?

34. You would like to have $4000 in four years for a special vacation following graduation by making deposits at the end of every six months in an annuity that pays 7% compounded semiannually.
   a. How much should you deposit at the end of every six months?
   b. How much of the $4000 comes from deposits and how much comes from interest?

35. How much should you deposit at the end of each month into an IRA that pays 8.5% compounded monthly to have $4 million when you retire in 45 years? How much of the $4 million comes from interest?

36. How much should you deposit at the end of each month into an IRA that pays 6.5% compounded monthly to have $2 million when you retire in 45 years? How much of the $2 million comes from interest?

• Writing in Mathematics

37. What is an annuity?

38. What is meant by the value of an annuity?

39. Write a problem involving the formula for regular payments needed to achieve a financial goal. The problem should be similar to Example 4 on page 472. However, the problem should be unique to your situation. Include something for which you would like to save, how much you need to save, and how long it will take to achieve your goal. Then solve the problem.

40. What is stock?

41. Describe how to find the percent ownership that a shareholder has in a company.

42. Describe the two ways that investors make money with stock.

43. What is a bond? Describe the difference between a stock and a bond.

44. Using a recent newspaper, copy the stock table for a company of your choice. Then explain the meaning of the numbers in the columns.

45. If an investor sees that the dividends for a stock have a lower annual rate than those for a no-risk bank account, should the stock be sold and the money placed in the bank account? Explain your answer.

Use the following investments to answer Exercises 46–49.

Investment 1: 1000 shares of IBM stock
Investment 2: A 5-year bond with a 22% interest rate issued by a small company that is testing and planning to sell delicious, nearly zero-calorie desserts
Investment 3: A 30-year U.S. treasury bond at a fixed 7% annual rate

46. Which of these investments has the greatest risk? Explain why.

47. Which of these investments has the least risk? Explain why.

48. Which of these investments has the possibility of the greatest return? Explain why.

49. If you could be given one of these investments as a gift, which one would you choose? Explain why.

• Critical Thinking Exercise

50. How much should you deposit at the end of each month in an IRA that pays 8% compounded monthly to earn $60,000 per year from interest alone, while leaving the principal untouched, when you retire in 30 years?

• Group Exercises

51. Each group should have a newspaper with current stock quotations. Choose nine stocks that group members think would make good investments. Imagine that you invest $1000 in each of these nine investments. Check the value of your stock each day over the next five weeks and then sell the nine stocks after five weeks. What is the group's profit or loss over the five-week period? Compare this figure with the profit or loss of other groups in your class for this activity.

52. This activity is a group research project intended for four or five people. Use the research to present a seminar on investments. The seminar is intended to last about 30 minutes and should result in an interesting and informative presentation to the entire class. The seminar should include investment considerations, how to read the bond section of the newspaper, how to read the mutual fund section, and higher-risk investments.

53. Group members have inherited $1 million. However, the group cannot spend any of the money for ten years. As a group, determine how to invest this money in order to maximize the money you will make over ten years. The money can be invested in as many ways as the group decides. Explain each investment decision. What are the risks involved in each investment plan?

SECTION 8.5 • INSTALLMENT BUYING

OBJECTIVES

1. Determine the amount financed, the installment price, and the finance charge for a fixed loan.

2. Determine the APR.

3. Compute unearned interest and the payoff amount for a loan paid off early.

4. Find the interest, the balance due, and the minimum monthly payment for credit card loans.

5. Calculate interest on credit cards using three methods.

Do you buy products with a credit card? Although your card lets you use a product while paying for it, the costs associated with such cards, including their high interest rates, fees, and penalties, stack the odds in favor of your getting hurt by them. In 2004, the average credit-card debt per U.S. household was $9312. If you use a credit card, you are engaging in **installment buying**, in which you repay a loan for the cost of a product on a monthly basis. A loan that you pay off with weekly or monthly payments, or payments in some other time period, is called an **installment loan**. The advantage of an installment loan is that the consumer gets to use a product immediately. In this section, we will see that the disadvantage is that it can add a substantial amount to the cost of a purchase. When it comes to installment buying, consumer beware!

1 | Determine the amount financed, the installment price, and the finance charge for a fixed loan.

Fixed Installment Loans

You decide to purchase a used pick-up truck that costs $9345. You can finance the truck by paying $300 at the time of purchase, called the **down payment**, and $194.38 per month for 60 months. A loan like this that has a schedule for paying a fixed amount each period is called a **fixed installment loan**. We begin with three terms associated with such loans.

> **THE VOCABULARY OF FIXED INSTALLMENT LOANS**
>
> The **amount financed** is what the consumer borrows:
>
> $$\text{Amount financed} = \text{Cash price} - \text{Down payment.}$$
>
> The **total installment price** is the sum of all monthly payments plus the down payment:
>
> $$\text{Total installment price} = \text{Total of all monthly payments} + \text{Down payment.}$$
>
> The **finance charge** is the interest on the installment loan:
>
> $$\text{Finance charge} = \text{Total installment price} - \text{Cash price.}$$

EXAMPLE 1	BUYING A PICK-UP TRUCK USING A FIXED INSTALLMENT LOAN

The cost of a used pick-up truck is $9345. We can finance the truck by paying $300 down and $194.38 per month for 60 months.

a. Determine the amount financed.

b. Determine the total installment price.

c. Determine the finance charge.

SOLUTION

a. Amount financed = Cash price − Down payment

$$= \$9345 - \$300$$
$$= \$9045$$

The amount financed is $9045.

b. The total installment price is obtained by adding the total of all monthly payments and the down payment. Because we are paying $194.38 per month for 60 months, the total of all monthly payments is

$$\frac{\$194.38}{\text{month}} \times 60 \text{ months} = \$194.38 \times 60.$$

Total installment price = Total of all monthly payments + Down payment

$$= \$194.38 \times 60 + \$300$$
$$= \$11{,}662.80 + \$300$$
$$= \$11{,}962.80$$

The total installment price is $11,962.80.

c. Finance charge = Total installment price − Cash price

$$= \$11{,}962.80 - \$9345$$
$$= \$2617.80$$

The finance charge for the loan is $2617.80.

 The cost of a new car is $14,000. You can finance the car by paying $280 down and $315 per month for 60 months.

a. Determine the amount financed.

b. Determine the total installment price.

c. Determine the finance charge.

You will be using these figures in Check Points 2, 3, and 4, so keep track of your answers.

2 | Determine the APR.

In Example 1, the finance charge for the loan, $2617.80, is the **interest** paid to finance the truck. What interest rate are we paying when we pay $2617.80 interest over 60 months? The interest rate per year is called the **annual percentage rate**, abbreviated **APR**. In 1969, the Federal Reserve Board established the **Truth-in-Lending Act**. It requires lending institutions to inform borrowers in writing of a loan's APR. **When comparing two or more loans with different terms, the loan with the lowest APR is the one that charges the least interest**. For many people, an important factor in deciding on a fixed installment loan is the cash down payment that is required. If you do not have a lot of cash at the time of purchase, you might select a loan with a smaller down payment even though it has a not-so-desirable APR.

The APR for a fixed installment loan can be determined using a table similar to the abbreviated version shown in Table 8.5. Here are the steps involved in using an APR table. These steps are illustrated in Example 2.

STEPS IN USING AN APR TABLE

1. Compute the finance charge per $100 financed:

$$\frac{\text{Finance charge}}{\text{Amount financed}} \times \$100.$$

2. Look in the row corresponding to the number of payments to be made and find the entry closest to the value in step 1.

3. Find the APR at the top of the column in which the entry from step 2 is found. (This is the APR rounded to the nearest $\frac{1}{2}\%$.)

TABLE 8.5 ANNUAL PERCENTAGE RATE (APR) FOR MONTHLY PAYMENT LOANS

Number of Monthly Payments	Annual Percentage Rate (APR)												
	10.0%	10.5%	11.0%	11.5%	12.0%	12.5%	13.0%	13.5%	14.0%	14.5%	15.0%	15.5%	16.0%
	(Finance charge per $100 of amount financed)												
6	$2.94	$3.08	$3.23	$3.38	$3.53	$3.68	$3.83	$3.97	$4.12	$4.27	$4.42	$4.57	$4.72
12	5.50	5.78	6.06	6.34	6.62	6.90	7.18	7.46	7.74	8.03	8.31	8.59	8.88
18	8.10	8.52	8.93	9.35	9.77	10.19	10.61	11.03	11.45	11.87	12.29	12.72	13.14
24	10.75	11.30	11.86	12.42	12.98	13.54	14.10	14.66	15.23	15.80	16.37	16.94	17.51
30	13.43	14.13	14.83	15.54	16.24	16.95	17.66	18.38	19.10	19.81	20.54	21.26	21.99
36	16.16	17.01	17.86	18.71	19.57	20.43	21.30	22.17	23.04	23.92	24.80	25.68	26.57
48	21.74	22.90	24.06	25.23	26.40	27.58	28.77	29.97	31.17	32.37	33.59	34.81	36.03
60	27.48	(28.96)	30.45	31.96	33.47	34.99	36.52	38.06	39.61	41.17	42.74	44.32	45.91

EXAMPLE 2   DETERMINING THE APR

In Example 1, we found that the amount financed for the truck was $9045 and the finance charge was $2617.80. The borrower financed the truck with 60 monthly payments. Use Table 8.5 to determine the APR.

SOLUTION

Step 1. Find the finance charge per $100 of the amount financed.

$$\text{Finance charge per \$100 financed} = \frac{\text{Finance charge}}{\text{Amount financed}} \times \$100$$

$$= \frac{\$2617.80}{\$9045.00} \times \$100$$

$$\approx \$28.94$$

This means that the borrower pays $28.94 interest for each $100 being financed.

Step 2. Look in the row corresponding to the number of payments to be made (60) and find the entry closest to the value in step 1 ($28.94). Table 8.5 presents three types of information: the number of monthly payments, the APR, and the finance charge per $100 financed. There are 60 monthly payments, so look for 60 in the left column. Then move across to the right until you find the amount closest to the finance charge per $100 financed, namely $28.94. This amount, $28.96, is circled in the table.

Step 3. Find the APR at the top of the column in which the entry from step 2 is found. Take a second look at the circled entry, $28.96. At the top of this column is 10.5%. Thus, the APR for the fixed installment truck loan is approximately 10.5%.

○

 Use Table 8.5 to determine the APR for the car loan described in Check Point 1.

⬤

A fixed installment loan can be paid off early so that a borrower need not pay the entire finance charge. The amount by which the finance charge is reduced is called the **unearned interest**. The interest saved by paying off the loan early can be calculated by one of two methods, the **actuarial method** or the **rule of 78**. The actuarial method uses the APR table and the rule of 78 does not. The Truth-in-Lending Act requires that the method for calculating the reduction of the finance charge be disclosed at the time the loan is signed.

Here are two formulas for computing unearned interest:

3 | Compute unearned interest and the payoff amount for a loan paid off early.

METHODS FOR COMPUTING UNEARNED INTEREST

Unearned interest is the amount by which a loan's finance charge is reduced when the loan is paid off early.

Actuarial Method

$$u = \frac{kRV}{100 + V}$$

u = unearned interest

k = remaining number of scheduled payments (excluding current payment)

R = regular monthly payment

V = finance charge per $100 (from the APR table) for a loan with the same APR and k monthly payments

Rule of 78

$$u = \frac{k(k + 1)}{n(n + 1)} \times F$$

u = unearned interest

k = remaining number of scheduled payments (excluding current payment)

n = original number of payments

F = original finance charge

The total amount due on the day that a loan is paid off early is called the **payoff amount**. Unearned interest is subtracted in computing the payoff amount. Examples 3 and 4 illustrate how the payoff amount is computed using the actuarial method in Example 3 and the rule of 78 in Example 4. Both examples refer back to the pick-up truck in Example 1. Shown in the margin is a summary of given and computed amounts for the truck.

Pick-up truck
cost: $9345
Financing: $300 + $194.38 per month for 60 months
Amount financed: $9045
Total installment price: $11,962.80
Finance charge (interest): $2617.80
Finance charge per $100 financed: $28.94
APR: 10.5%

EXAMPLE 3   EARLY PAYOFF: THE ACTUARIAL METHOD

You got a big bonus at work—and a raise. Instead of making the thirty-sixth payment on your truck, you decide to pay the remaining balance and terminate the loan.

a. Use the actuarial method to determine how much interest will be saved (the unearned interest, u) by repaying the loan early.

b. Find the payoff amount.

Pick-up truck
cost: $9345
Financing: $300 + $194.38 per month for 60 months
Amount financed: $9045
Total installment price: $11,962.80
Finance charge (interest): $2617.80
Finance charge per $100 financed: $28.94
APR: 10.5%

Given and computed amounts for the truck (repeated)

SOLUTION

a. We will use the formula $u = \dfrac{kRV}{100 + V}$ to find u, the unearned interest. We need values for k, R, and V. The current payment is payment number 36. There are 60 payments total. We subtract the number of the current payment from the total number of payments to find the number of remaining payments, k: $k = 60 - 36 = 24$. The value of R, the regular monthly payment, is given: $R = \$194.38$. To find the value for the finance charge per $100, V, use the APR table (Table 8.5 on page 482). In the Number of Monthly Payments Column, find the number of remaining payments, 24, and then look to the right until you reach the column headed by 10.5%, the APR. This row and column intersect at 11.30. Thus, $V = 11.30$. This is the finance charge per $100 for a loan with the same APR and k ($k = 24$) monthly payments. We substitute these values into the actuarial method formula.

$$u = \frac{kRV}{100 + V} = \frac{24 \times 194.38 \times 11.30}{100 + 11.30} \approx 473.64$$

Approximately $473.64 will be saved in interest by terminating the loan early using the actuarial method.

b. The payoff amount, the amount due on the day of the loan's termination, is determined as follows:

Payoff amount	=	payment number 36	plus	total of remaining payments after payment 36	minus	interest saved (unearned interest).
	=	$194.38	+	24 × $194.38	−	$473.64
	=	$4385.86.				

The payment needed to terminate the loan at the end of 36 months is $4385.86.

○

CHECK POINT 3 Instead of making the twenty-fourth payment on the car loan described in Check Points 1 and 2, you decide to pay the remaining balance and terminate the loan.

a. Use the actuarial method to determine how much interest will be saved (the unearned interest, u) by repaying the loan early.

b. Find the payoff amount.

EXAMPLE 4   EARLY PAYOFF: THE RULE OF 78

The loan in Example 3 is paid off at the time of the thirty-sixth monthly payment. Use the rule of 78 to find

a. the unearned interest.

b. the payoff amount.

SOLUTION

a. We will use the formula

$$u = \frac{k(k + 1)}{n(n + 1)} \times F$$

to find u, the unearned interest. We need values for k, n, and F. From Example 3, k, the number of remaining payments, is 24: $k = 24$. The original number of payments, n, is 60: $n = 60$. The summary of figures for the pick-up truck shown in the margin lists the finance charge: $F = \$2617.80$. We substitute these values into the rule of 78 formula.

$$u = \frac{k(k + 1)}{n(n + 1)} \times F = \frac{24(24 + 1)}{60(60 + 1)} \times \$2617.80 \approx \$429.15$$

By the rule of 78, the borrower will save $429.15 in interest.

b. Next, we determine the payoff amount.

Payoff amount	=	payment number 36	plus	total of remaining payments after payment 36	minus	interest saved (unearned interest).
	=	$194.38	+	24 × $194.38	−	$429.15
	=	$4430.35				

The payoff amount is $4430.35.

In Example 3, we found that $473.64 is saved in interest using the actuarial method, while in Example 4, we found that $429.15 is saved in interest using the rule of 78. These examples illustrate that the actuarial method is more beneficial to the borrower than the rule of 78 because it results in greater savings in interest at the loan's termination. For loans of 61 months or longer, only the actuarial method is allowed. Also, some states have shorter loan periods that do not allow the rule of 78.

The loan in Check Point 3 is paid off at the time of the twenty-fourth monthly payment. Use the rule of 78 to find

    a. the unearned interest.

    b. the payoff amount.

---

4 Find the interest, the balance due, and the minimum monthly payment for credit card loans.

Open-End Installment Loans

Using a credit card is an example of an open-end installment loan, commonly called **revolving credit**. Open-end loans differ from fixed installment loans in that there is no schedule for paying a fixed amount each period. Credit card loans require users to make only a minimum monthly payment that depends on the unpaid balance and the interest rate. Credit cards have high interest rates compared to other kinds of loans. The interest on credit cards is computed using the simple interest formula $I = Prt$. However, r represents the *monthly* interest rate and t is time in months rather than in years. A typical interest rate is 1.57% monthly. This is equivalent to a yearly rate of 12 × 1.57%, or 18.84%. With such a high APR, credit card balances should be paid off as quickly as possible.

Most credit card customers are billed every month. A typical billing period is May 1 through May 31, but it can also run from, say, May 5 through June 4. Customers receive a statement, called an **itemized billing**, that contains the unpaid balance on the first day of the billing period, the total balance owed on the last day of the billing period, a list of purchases and cash advances made during the billing period, the date of the last day of the billing period, the payment due date, and the minimum payment required.

Customers who make a purchase during the billing period and pay the entire amount of the purchase by the payment due date are not charged interest. By contrast, customers who make cash advances using their credit cards must pay interest from the day the money is advanced until the day it is repaid.

One method for calculating interest on credit cards is the **unpaid balance method**. Interest is calculated on the unpaid balance on the first day of the billing period less payments and credits.

EXAMPLE 5   BALANCE DUE ON A CREDIT CARD

A particular VISA card calculates interest using the unpaid balance method. The monthly interest rate is 1.3% on the unpaid balance on the first day of the billing period less payments and credits. Here are some of the details in the May 1–May 31 itemized billing:

May 1 Unpaid Balance: $1350

Payment Received May 8: $250

Purchases Charged to the VISA Account: Airline tickets: $375, Books: $57, Meals: $65

Last Day of the Billing Period: May 31

Payment Due Date: June 9

a. Find the interest due on the payment due date.

b. Find the total balance owed on the last day of the billing period.

c. This credit card requires a $10 minimum monthly payment if the total balance owed on the last day of the billing period is less than $360. Otherwise, the minimum monthly payment is $\frac{1}{36}$ of the balance owed on the last day of the billing period, rounded to the nearest whole dollar. What is the minimum monthly payment due by June 9?

SOLUTION

a. The monthly interest rate is 1.3% on the unpaid balance on the first day of the billing period, $1350, less payments and credits, $250. The interest due is computed using $I = Prt$.

$$I = Prt = (\$1350 - \$250) \times 0.013 \times 1 = \$1100 \times 0.013 \times 1 = \$14.30$$

> Time, t, is measured in months, and $t = 1$ month.

The interest due on the payment due date is $14.30.

b. The total balance owed on the last day of the billing period is determined as follows:

$$\begin{array}{ccccccc} \text{Balance} \\ \text{owed} \end{array} = \begin{array}{c} \text{unpaid balance} \\ \text{on the first day} \\ \text{of the billing period} \\ \text{minus payments} \end{array} \text{ plus } \text{interest} \text{ plus } \begin{array}{c} \text{charges for three items} \\ \text{during billing period.} \end{array}$$

$$= \$1100 + \$14.30 + \$375 + \$57 + \$65$$

$$= \$1611.30.$$

The total balance owed on the last day of the billing period is $1611.30.

c. Because the balance owed on the last day of the billing period, $1611.30, exceeds $360, the customer must pay a minimum of $\frac{1}{36}$ of the balance owed.

$$\text{Minimum monthly payment} = \frac{\text{balance owed}}{36} = \frac{\$1611.30}{36} \approx \$45$$

Rounded to the nearest whole dollar, the minimum monthly payment due by June 9 is $45.

○

CHECK POINT 5 A credit card calculates interest using the unpaid balance method. The monthly interest rate is 1.6% on the unpaid balance on the first day of the billing period less payments and credits. Here are some of the details in the May 1–May 31 itemized billing:

May 1 Unpaid Balance: $4720

Payment Received May 8: $1000

Purchases Charged to the Account: Computer: $1025, Meals: $45

Last Day of the Billing Period: May 31

Payment Due Date: June 9

Answer parts (a) through (c) in Example 5 using this information.

---

5 Calculate interest on credit cards using three methods.

Methods for calculating interest on credit cards vary and the interest can differ on credit cards that show the same APR. The three methods for calculating interest are summarized in the following box:

> ### METHODS FOR CALCULATING INTEREST ON CREDIT CARDS
>
> For all three methods, $I = Prt$, where r is the monthly rate and t is one month.
>
> **Unpaid balance method:**
>
> The principal, P, is the balance on the first day of the billing period less payments and credits.
>
> **Previous balance method:**
>
> The principal, P, is the unpaid balance on the first day of the billing period.
>
> **Average daily balance method:**
>
> The principal, P, is the **average daily balance**. This is determined by adding the unpaid balances for each day in the billing period and dividing by the number of days in the billing period.

BLITZER BONUS

Credit Cards and College

When College Students with Credit Cards Obtained a Card

Senior Year **2%**

Before College **24%**

Freshman Year **43%**

Sophomore Year **22%**

Junior Year **9%**

Source: Nellie Mae

EXAMPLE 6   COMPARING METHODS FOR CALCULATING INTEREST

A credit card has a monthly rate of 1.75%. (The APR is 21%.) In the January 1–January 31 itemized billing, the January 1 unpaid balance is $2500. A payment of $1000 was received on January 8. There are no purchases or cash advances in this billing period. The payment due date is February 9. Find the interest due on this date using each of the three methods for calculating credit card interest.

SOLUTION Because the monthly rate is 1.75%, for all three methods $I = Prt = P \times 0.0175 \times 1$ month. The principal, P, is different for each method.

a. The Unpaid Balance Method

The principal, P, is the unpaid balance on the first day of the billing period, $2500, less payments and credits, $1000. The interest is

$$I = Prt = (\$2500 - \$1000) \times 0.0175 \times 1 = \$1500 \times 0.0175 \times 1 = \$26.25.$$

The interest due on the payment due date is $26.25.

b. The Previous Balance Method

The principal, P, is the unpaid balance on the first day of the billing period, $2500. The interest is

$$I = Prt = \$2500 \times 0.0175 \times 1 = \$43.75.$$

The interest due on the payment due date is $43.75.

c. The Average Daily Balance Method

The principal, P, is the average daily balance. Add the unpaid balances for each day in the billing period and divide by the number of days in the billing period, 31. The unpaid balance on the first day of the billing period is $2500 and a $1000 payment is recorded on January 8. The sum of the balances owed for each day of

Comparing Credit Cards

With features such as miles toward air travel, insurance on rental cars, and special introductory rates, shopping for a credit card can be a daunting task. You can search the Internet for the most current information regarding annual fees and interest rates. Compare credit cards at Web sites such as Bankrate.com and CardWeb.com. Also check *Consumer Reports'* site, www.consumerreports.org, for the "ten most consumer-friendly credit cards."

the billing period is $2500 added for each of the first 7 days, expressed as $2500 × 7, plus $1500 added for each of the remaining 24 days, expressed as $1500 × 24.

Average daily balance

$$= \frac{\text{Sum of the unpaid balances for each day in the billing period}}{\text{Number of days in the billing period}}$$

$$= \frac{\$2500(7) + \$1500(24)}{31} \approx \$1725.81$$

The average daily balance serves as the principal. The interest is

$$I = Prt = \$1725.81 \times 0.0175 \times 1 \approx \$30.20.$$

The interest due on the payment due date is $30.20.

Most credit cards use the average daily balance method to determine interest due. Calculating the average daily balance by hand can be quite tedious when there are numerous transactions during a billing period. Credit card customers who are charged interest by the average daily balance method will find the average daily balance provided on monthly statements.

CHECK POINT 6 A credit card has a monthly rate of 1.8%. In the January 1–January 31 itemized billing, the January 1 unpaid balance is $6800. A payment of $500 was received on January 8. There are no purchases or cash advances in this billing period. The payment due date is February 9. Find the interest due on this date using each of the three methods for calculating credit card interest.

EXERCISE SET 8.5 ●●●●●●

• Practice and Application Exercises

1. The cost of a sports utility vehicle is $27,000. We can finance this by paying $5000 down and $410 per month for 60 months. Determine **a.** the amount financed; **b.** the total installment price; **c.** the finance charge.

2. The cost of a computer is $2450. We can finance this by paying $550 down and $94.50 per month for 24 months. Determine **a.** the amount financed; **b.** the total installment price; **c.** the finance charge.

3. The cost of a washer-dryer is $1100. We can finance this by paying $100 down and $110 per month for 12 months. Determine **a.** the amount financed; **b.** the total installment price; **c.** the finance charge.

4. The cost of a used car is $5675. We can finance this by paying $1223 down and $125 per month for 48 months. Determine **a.** the amount financed; **b.** the total installment price; **c.** the finance charge.

5. You plan to pay for a computer in 12 equal monthly payments. The finance charge per $100 financed is $6.90. Use Table 8.5 on page 482 to find the APR for this loan.

6. You plan to pay for a refrigerator in 18 equal monthly payments. The finance charge per $100 financed is $12.72. Use Table 8.5 on page 482 to find the APR for this loan.

7. The finance charge per $100 financed for a computer that is paid off in 24 equal monthly payments is $15.80. Use Table 8.5 on page 482 to find the APR for this loan.

8. The finance charge per $100 financed for a refrigerator that is paid off in 12 monthly payments is $8.59. Use Table 8.5 on page 482 to find the APR for this loan.

9. A used car is financed for $4450 over 48 months. If the total finance charge is $1279, find the APR for this loan.

10. A desk is financed for $1200 over 30 months. If the total finance charge is $264, find the APR for this loan.

11. The cash price for furniture for all rooms of a three-bedroom house is $17,500. The furniture can be financed by paying $500 down and $360.55 per month for 60 months.
    a. Determine the amount financed.
    b. Determine the total installment price.
    c. Determine the finance charge.
    d. What is the APR for this loan?

12. The cost of a Blazer is $18,000, which can be financed by paying $600 down and $385 per month for 60 months.

   a. Determine the amount financed.

   b. Determine the total installment price.

   c. Determine the finance charge.

   d. What is the APR for this loan?

13. In Exercise 11, instead of making the twenty-fourth payment, the borrower decides to pay the remaining balance and terminate the loan for the furniture.

   a. Use the actuarial method to determine how much interest will be saved by repaying the loan early.

   b. By the actuarial method, what is the total amount due on the day of the loan's termination?

   c. Use the rule of 78 to determine how much interest will be saved by repaying the loan early.

   d. By the rule of 78, what is the total amount due on the day of the loan's termination?

14. In Exercise 12, instead of making the twenty-fourth payment, the borrower decides to pay the remaining balance and terminate the loan for the Blazer.

   a. Use the actuarial method to determine how much interest will be saved by repaying the loan early.

   b. By the actuarial method, what is the total amount due on the day of the loan's termination?

   c. Use the rule of 78 to determine how much interest will be saved by repaying the loan early.

   d. By the rule of 78, what is the total amount due on the day of the loan's termination?

15. A particular VISA card calculates interest using the unpaid balance method. The monthly interest rate is 1.3% on the unpaid balance on the first day of the billing period less payments and credits. Here are some of the details in the May 1–May 31 itemized billing:

   May 1 Unpaid Balance: $950
   Payment Received May 8: $100
   Purchases Charged to the VISA Account: clothing, $85 and car repair, $67
   Last Day of the Billing Period: May 31
   Payment Due Date: June 9

   a. Find the interest due on the payment due date.

   b. Find the total balance owed on the last day of the billing period.

   c. This credit card requires a $10 minimum monthly payment if the total balance owed on the last day of the billing period is less than $360. Otherwise, the minimum monthly payment is $\frac{1}{36}$ of the balance owed on the last day of the billing period, rounded to the nearest whole dollar. What is the minimum monthly payment due by June 9?

16. A particular credit card calculates interest using the unpaid balance method. The monthly interest rate is 1.75% on the unpaid balance on the first day of the billing period less payments and credits. Here are some of the details in the September 1–September 30 itemized billing:

   September 1 Unpaid Balance: $425
   Payment Received September 6: $75
   Purchases Charged to the Account: groceries, $45 and clothing, $77
   Last Day of the Billing Period: September 30
   Payment Due Date: October 9

   a. Find the interest due on the payment due date.

   b. Find the total balance owed on the last day of the billing period.

   c. Terms for this credit card are shown in the following table. What is the minimum monthly payment due by October 9?

New Balance	Minimum Payment
$0.01 to $10.00	No payment due
10.01 to 200.00	$10.00
200.01 to 250.00	15.00
250.01 to 300.00	20.00
300.01 to 350.00	25.00
350.01 to 400.00	30.00
400.01 to 450.00	35.00
450.01 to 500.00	40.00
Over $500.00	$\frac{1}{10}$ of new balance

17. A credit card has a monthly rate of 1.5% and uses the average daily balance method for calculating interest. Here are some of the details in the April 1–April 30 itemized billing:

   April 1 Unpaid Balance: $445.59
   Payment Received April 5: $110
   Purchases Charged to the Account: $278.06
   Average Daily Balance: $330.90
   Last Day of the Billing Period: April 30
   Payment Due Date: May 9

   a. Find the interest due on the payment due date.

   b. Find the total balance owed on the last day of the billing period.

   c. Terms for this credit card are given in Exercise 16. What is the minimum monthly payment due by May 9?

18. A credit card has a monthly rate of 1.8% and uses the average daily balance method for calculating interest. Here are some of the details in the December 1–December 31 itemized billing:

   December 1 Unpaid Balance: $220
   Payment Received December 7: $60
   Purchases Charged to the Account: $90
   Average Daily Balance: $205.60
   Last Day of the Billing Period: December 31
   Payment Due Date: January 9

   a. Find the interest due on the payment due date.

   b. Find the total balance owed on the last day of the billing period.

   c. Terms for this credit card are given in Exercise 16. What is the minimum monthly payment due on January 9?

19. A credit card has a monthly rate of 1.5%. In the September 1–September 30 itemized billing, the September 1 unpaid balance is $3000. A payment of $2500 was received on September 6. There are no purchases or cash advances in this billing period. The payment due date is October 9. Find the interest due on this date using

   a. the unpaid balance method.

   b. the previous balance method.

   c. the average daily balance method.

20. A credit card has a monthly rate of 2.2%. In the October 1–October 31 itemized billing, the October 1 unpaid balance is $2000. A payment of $400 was received on October 6. There are no purchases or cash advances in this billing period. The payment due date is November 9. Find the interest due on this date using

a. the unpaid balance method.

b. the previous balance method.

c. the average daily balance method.

• Writing in Mathematics

21. Describe the difference between a fixed installment loan and an open-end installment loan.

22. For a fixed installment loan, what is the total installment price?

23. For a fixed installment loan, how is the total finance charge determined?

24. What is the APR?

25. What are the two methods for computing unearned interest when a loan is paid off early? Describe how the payoff amount is determined regardless of which method is used in the computation.

26. Name and describe each of the three methods for calculating interest on credit cards.

27. For a credit card billing period, describe how the average daily balance is determined. Why is this computation somewhat tedious when done by hand?

28. Which method for calculating interest on credit cards is most beneficial to the borrower and which is least benefical? Explain why this is so.

29. A Sears Revolving Charge Card has a monthly rate of 1.75%. The interest is a minimum of 50¢ if the average daily balance is $28.50 or less. Explain how this policy is beneficial to Sears.

• Critical Thinking Exercise

30. Which one of the following is true?

a. The finance charge on a fixed installment loan is the cash price minus the total installment price.

b. It is to a borrower's advantage to have unearned interest computed by the rule of 78 rather than by the actuarial method.

c. It is not necessary to know the number of days in a credit card billing period to determine the average daily balance.

d. If a credit card has a 2.2% monthly interest rate, the annual rate exceeds 25%.

Use estimation and not calculation to select the most reasonable value in Exercises 31–32.

31. If you purchase a $1400 item, put $200 down, and pay the balance in 30 monthly installments, what is a reasonable estimate of the monthly payment?

a. $35   **b.** $47   **c.** $70   **d.** $100

32. A reasonable estimate of the monthly interest on an average daily balance of $359.58 at a 1.3% monthly rate is

a. $50   **b.** $10   **c.** $5   **d.** $2

33. A bank bills its credit card holders on the first of each month for each itemized billing. The card provides a 20-day period in which to pay the bill before charging interest. If the card holder wants to buy an expensive gift for a September 30 wedding but can't pay for it until November 5, explain how this can be done without adding an interest charge.

34. A $1500 computer can be purchased using a credit card that charges a monthly rate of 1.5% using the unpaid balance method. The borrower is considering one of the following options:

Option A: Make a credit card payment of $300 at the end of each month for five months and pay off the balance at the end of the sixth month.

Option B: Make a credit card payment of $300 plus the month's interest at the end of each month for five months.

How much is saved in interest using option B?

• Technology Exercises

35. Set up a spreadsheet with one column each for the balance, number of days at that balance, payments, charges, and the product of each balance and the number of days at that balance. The balance on John and Jane Doe's credit card on July 5, their billing date, was $375.80. For the period ending August 4, they had the following transactions:

July 13, Payment: $150.00
July 15, Charge: Computer Store, $74.35
July 23, Charge: Clothing, $123.50
July 29, Charge: Restaurant, $42.50

a. Use the summation capabilities of the spreadsheet to determine the number of days in the billing period and the average daily balance.

b. Find the finance charge (the interest) that is owed on August 4. Assume the monthly rate is 1.3%.

c. Find the balance that is owed on August 4.

36. Set up a spreadsheet with one column each for the balance, number of days at that balance, payments, charges, and the product of each balance and the number of days at that balance. The balance on the Does' credit card on May 12, their billing date, was $378.50. For the period ending June 11, they had the following transactions:

May 13, Charge: Toys, $129.79

May 15, Payment: $50.00

May 18, Charge: Clothing, $135.85

May 29, Charge: Housewares, $37.63

a. Use the summation capabilities of the spreadsheet to determine the number of days in the billing period and the average daily balance.

b. Find the finance charge (the interest) that is owed on June 11. Assume the monthly rate is 0.75%.

c. Find the balance that is owed on June 11.

SECTION 8.6 • AMORTIZATION AND THE COST OF HOME OWNERSHIP

OBJECTIVES

1. Understand mortgage options.

2. Compute the monthly payment and interest costs for a mortgage.

3. Prepare a partial loan amortization schedule.

4. Compute payments and interest for other kinds of installment loans.

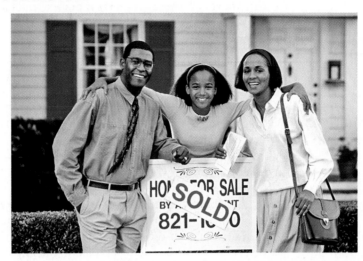

In 2006, the median U.S. home price jumped to $206,000, up a stunning 15% in a year and 55% over five years. (*Source*: National Association of Realtors) Americans now brag about having bought their home in the 1990s the way they used to boast about having bought Microsoft stock in the 1980s. The deeper implication of this real estate boom is the notion that a house is no longer just a home: Real estate has become as much about nest feathering as it is about nesting. And when love and money collide, things can get a little crazy. In this section, we focus on the cost of home ownership and the mathematics underlying America's raucous house party.

1 | Understand mortgage options.

Mortgages

A **mortgage** is a long-term loan (perhaps up to 30, 40, or even 50 years) for the purpose of buying a home, and for which the property is pledged as security for payment. If payments are not made on the loan, the lender gets to take possession of the property. The **down payment** is the portion of the sale price of the home that the buyer initially pays to the seller. The minimum required down payment is computed as a percentage of the sale price. For example, suppose you decide to buy a $220,000 home that requires you to pay the seller 10% of the sale price. You must pay 10% of $220,000, which is $0.10 \times \$220,000$, or $22,000, to the seller. Thus, $22,000 is the down payment. The **amount of the mortgage** is the difference between the sale price and the down payment. For your $220,000 home, the amount of the mortgage is $220,000 − $22,000, or $198,000.

There are many types of lenders and types of mortgages to choose from. Many banks, savings associations, mortgage companies, and credit unions provide mortgage loans. Some companies, called **mortgage brokers**, offer to find you a mortgage lender willing to make you a loan. Computer loan origination systems, or CLOs, are computer terminals sometimes available in real estate offices to help buyers sort through the various types of loans offered by different lenders.

Monthly payments for a mortgage depend on the amount of the mortgage, or the principal, the interest rate, and the time of the mortgage. Mortgages can have a fixed interest rate or a variable interest rate. **Fixed-rate mortgages** have the same monthly payment during the entire time of the loan. **Variable-rate mortgages**, also known as **adjustable-rate mortgages** (ARMs), have payment amounts that change from time to time depending on changes in the interest rate. ARMS are less predictable than fixed-rate mortgages. They start out at lower rates than fixed-rate mortgages. Caps limit how high rates can go over the term of the loan.

There are many other mortgage options. One option involves a short-term loan in which only the interest is paid, followed by a final payment (called a "balloon payment") for the entire loan amount. This kind of mortgage might appeal to a buyer who plans to sell the house in a short period of time. Some buyers are eligible for a mortgage insured through the Federal Housing Administration (FHA) or guaranteed by the Department of Veteran Affairs or similar programs operated by cities or states. These programs require a smaller down payment than standard loans.

2 | Compute the monthly payment and interest costs for a mortgage.

Computation Involved with Buying a Home

Although monthly payments for a mortgage depend on the amount of the mortgage, the time of the loan, and the interest rate, the rate is not the only cost of a mortgage. Most lending institutions require the buyer to pay one or more **points** at the time of closing—that is, the time at which the mortgage begins. A point is a one-time charge that equals 1% of the loan amount. For example, two points means that the buyer must pay 2% of the loan amount at closing. Often, a buyer can pay fewer points in exchange for a higher interest rate or more points for a lower rate. A document, called the **Truth-in-Lending Disclosure Statement**, shows the buyer the APR for the mortgage. The APR takes into account the interest rate and points.

A monthly mortgage payment is used to repay the principal plus interest. In addition, lending institutions can require that part of the monthly payment be deposited into an **escrow account**, an account used by the lender to pay real estate taxes and insurance. Interest is paid to the buyer on the amount in an escrow account.

We can use formulas for compound interest and the value of an annuity to determine the amount of mortgage payments for fixed-rate mortgages. Suppose that you borrow P dollars at interest rate r over t years.

> The lender expects A dollars at the end of t years.

> You save the A dollars in an annuity by paying PMT dollars n times per year.

$$A = P\left(1 + \frac{r}{n}\right)^{nt} \qquad A = \frac{PMT\left[\left(1 + \frac{r}{n}\right)^{nt} - 1\right]}{\frac{r}{n}}$$

To find your regular payment amount, PMT, we set the amount the lender expects to receive equal to the amount you will save in the annuity:

$$P\left(1 + \frac{r}{n}\right)^{nt} = \frac{PMT\left[\left(1 + \frac{r}{n}\right)^{nt} - 1\right]}{\frac{r}{n}}.$$

Solving this equation for PMT, we obtain a formula for the loan payment for any installment loan, including payments on fixed-rate mortgages.

STUDY TIP

Because the formula in the box assumes the same number of yearly payments and yearly compounding periods, the actual payments may differ slightly from those calculated using the formula.

LOAN PAYMENT FORMULA FOR INSTALLMENT LOANS

The regular payment amount, PMT, required to repay a loan of P dollars paid n times per year over t years at an annual rate r is given by

$$PMT = \frac{P\left(\frac{r}{n}\right)}{1 - \left(1 + \frac{r}{n}\right)^{-nt}}.$$

EXAMPLE 1   COMPUTING THE MONTHLY PAYMENT AND INTEREST COSTS FOR A MORTGAGE

The price of a home is $195,000. The bank requires a 10% down payment and two points at the time of closing. The cost of the home is financed with a 30-year fixed-rate mortgage at 7.5%.

a. Find the required down payment.

b. Find the amount of the mortgage.

c. How much must be paid for the two points at closing?

d. Find the monthly payment (excluding escrowed taxes and insurance).

e. Find the total interest paid over 30 years.

SOLUTION

a. The required down payment is 10% of $195,000 or

$$0.10 \times \$195,000 = \$19,500.$$

b. The amount of the mortgage is the difference between the price of the home and the down payment.

Amount of the mortgage	=	sale price	−	down payment

$$= \$195,000 - \$19,500$$

$$= \$175,500$$

c. To find the cost of two points on a mortgage of $175,500, find 2% of $175,500.

$$0.02 \times \$175,500 = \$3510$$

The down payment ($19,500) is paid to the seller and the cost of two points ($3510) is paid to the lending institution.

d. We are interested in finding the monthly payment for a $175,500 mortgage at 7.5% for 30 years. We use the loan payment formula for installment loans.

P, the mortgage amount, is $175,500.   Fixed rate, r, is 7.5%.   12 payments per year

$$PMT = \frac{P\left(\frac{r}{n}\right)}{1 - \left(1 + \frac{r}{n}\right)^{-nt}} = \frac{175{,}500\left(\frac{0.075}{12}\right)}{1 - \left(1 + \frac{0.075}{12}\right)^{-12(30)}}$$

The mortgage time, t, is 30 years.

$$= \frac{1096.875}{1 - (1.00625)^{-360}} \approx 1227$$

The monthly mortgage payment for principal and interest is approximately $1227.00. (Keep in mind that this payment does not include escrowed taxes and insurance.)

e. The total cost of interest over 30 years is equal to the difference between the total of all monthly payments and the amount of the mortgage. The total of all monthly payments is equal to the amount of the monthly payment multiplied by the number of payments. We found the amount of each monthly payment in (d): $1227. The number of payments is equal to the number of months in a year, 12, multiplied by the number of years in the mortgage, 30: $12 \times 30 = 360$. Thus, the total of all montlhly payments $= \$1227 \times 360$.

Now we can calculate the interest over 30 years.

Total interest paid	=	total of all monthly payments	minus	amount of the mortgage.

$$= \$1227 \times 360 - \$175{,}500$$

$$= \$441{,}720 - \$175{,}500 = \$266{,}220$$

The total interest paid over 30 years is approximately $266,220.

CHECK POINT 1 In Example 1, the $175,500 mortgage was financed with a 30-year fixed rate at 7.5%. The total interest paid over 30 years was approximately $266,220.

a. Use the loan payment formula for installment loans to find the monthly payment if the time of the mortgage is reduced to 15 years. Round to the nearest dollar.

b. Find the total interest paid over 15 years.

c. How much interest is saved by reducing the mortgage from 30 to 15 years?

3 Prepare a partial loan amortization schedule.

Loan Amortization Schedules

When a loan is paid off through a series of regular payments, it is said to be **amortized**, which literally means "killed off." In working Check Point 1(c), were you surprised that nearly $150,000 was saved when the mortgage was amortized over 15 years rather than over 30 years? What adds to the interest cost is the long period over which the loan is financed. **Although each payment is the same, with each successive payment the interest portion decreases and the principal portion increases.** The interest is computed using the simple interest formula $I = Prt$. The principal, P, is equal to the balance of the loan, which changes each month. The rate, r, is the annual interest rate of the mortgage loan. Because a payment is made each month, the time, t, is

$$\frac{1 \text{ month}}{12 \text{ months}} = \frac{1 \text{ month}}{12 \text{ months}}$$

or $\frac{1}{12}$ of a year.

A document showing important information about the status of the mortgage is called a **loan amortization schedule**. Typically, this document includes the number of the most recent payment and those of any previous monthly payments, the interest for each monthly payment, the principal payment for each monthly payment, and the balance of the loan.

EXAMPLE 2   PREPARING A LOAN AMORTIZATION SCHEDULE

Prepare a loan amortization schedule for the first two months of the mortgage loan shown in the following table:

LOAN AMORTIZATION SCHEDULE

Annual % rate: 9.5%			
Amount of Mortgage: $130,000		Monthly payment: $1357.50	
Number of Monthly Payments: 180		Term: Years 15, Months 0	
Payment Number	**Interest Payment**	**Principal Payment**	**Balance of Loan**
1			
2			

SOLUTION We begin with payment number 1.

$$\text{Interest for the month} = Prt = \$130{,}000 \times 0.095 \times \frac{1}{12} \approx \$1029.17$$

$$\text{Principal payment} = \text{Monthly payment} - \text{Interest payment}$$

$$= \$1357.50 - \$1029.17 = \$328.33$$

$$\text{Balance of loan} = \text{Principal balance} - \text{Principal payment}$$

$$= \$130{,}000 - \$328.33 = \$129{,}671.67$$

Early mortgage payments illustrate that it can be discouraging to realize how much goes toward interest and how little goes toward paying off the principal. Although you get socked with tons of interest in the early years of a loan, the one bright side to the staggering cost of a mortgage is the **mortgage interest tax deduction**. To make the cost of owning a home more affordable, the tax code permits deducting all the mortgage interest (but not the principal) that you pay per year on the loan. Table 8.7 illustrates how this tax loophole reduces the cost of the mortgage.

TABLE 8.7 TAX DEDUCTIONS FOR A $100,000 MORTGAGE AT 7% FOR A TAXPAYER IN THE 28% TAX BRACKET

Year	Interest	Tax Savings	Net Cost of Mortgage
1	$6968	$1951	$5017
2	$6895	$1931	$4964
3	$6816	$1908	$4908
4	$6732	$1885	$4847
5	$6641	$1859	$4782

Now, starting with a loan balance of $129,671.67, we repeat these computations for the second month.

$$\text{Interest for the month} = Prt = \$129{,}671.67 \times 0.095 \times \frac{1}{12} = \$1026.57$$

$$\text{Principal payment} = \text{Monthly payment} - \text{Interest payment}$$
$$= \$1357.50 - \$1026.57 = \$330.93$$

$$\text{Balance of loan} = \text{Principal balance} - \text{Principal payment}$$
$$= \$129{,}671.67 - \$330.93 = \$129{,}340.74$$

The results of these computations are included in Table 8.6, a partial loan amortization schedule. By using the simple interest formula month-to-month on the loan's balance, a complete loan amortization schedule for all 180 payments can be calculated.

TABLE 8.6 LOAN AMORTIZATION SCHEDULE

Annual % rate: 9.5%
Amount of Mortgage: $130,000   Monthly payment: $1357.50
Number of Monthly Payments: 180   Term: Years 15, Months 0

Payment Number	Interest Payment	Principal Payment	Balance of Loan
1	$1029.17	$328.33	$129,671.67
2	1026.57	330.93	129,340.74
3	1023.96	333.54	129,007.22
4	1021.32	336.18	128,671.04
30	944.82	412.68	118,931.35
31	941.55	415.95	118,515.52
125	484.62	872.88	60,340.84
126	477.71	879.79	59,461.05
179	21.26	1336.24	1347.74
180	9.76	1347.74	

Many lenders supply a loan amortization schedule like the one in Example 2. Such a schedule shows how the buyer pays slightly less in interest and more in principal for each payment over the entire life of the loan.

 Prepare a loan amortization schedule for the first two months of the mortgage loan shown in the following table:

Annual % rate: 7.0%
Amount of Mortgage: $200,000   Monthly payment: $1550.00
Number of Monthly Payments: 240   Term: Years 20, Months 0

Payment Number	Interest Payment	Principal Payment	Balance of Loan
1			
2			

4 | Compute payments and interest for other kinds of installment loans.

Monthly Payments and Interest Costs for Other Kinds of Installment Loans

The loan payment formula can be used to determine how much your regular payments will be on installment loans other than mortgages, including car loans and student loans. The portions of each payment going toward the principal and toward the interest will vary as the loan balance declines. Near the beginning of the loan term, the portion going toward the interest will be relatively high and the portion going toward the principal will be relatively low. As the loan term continues, the principal portion will gradually increase and the interest portion will gradually decrease.

EXAMPLE 3   COMPARING CAR LOANS

You decide to take a $20,000 loan for a new car. You can select one of the following loans, each requiring regular monthly payments:

Installment Loan A: 3-year loan at 7%
Installment Loan B: 5-year loan at 9%.

a. Find the monthly payments and the total interest for Loan A.
b. Find the monthly payments and the total interest for Loan B.
c. Compare the monthly payments and total interest for the two loans.

SOLUTION For each loan, we use the loan payment formula to compute the monthly payments.

a. We first determine monthly payments and total interest for Loan A.

P, the loan amount, is $20,000. / Rate, r, is 7%. / 12 payments per year / The loan is for 3 years.

$$PMT = \frac{P\left(\frac{r}{n}\right)}{1 - \left(1 + \frac{r}{n}\right)^{-nt}} = \frac{20{,}000\left(\frac{0.07}{12}\right)}{1 - \left(1 + \frac{0.07}{12}\right)^{-12(3)}} \approx 618$$

The monthly payments are approximately $618.
Now we calculate the interest over 3 years, or 36 months.

Total interest over 3 years $=$ Total of all monthly payments minus amount of the loan.

$$= \quad \$618 \quad \times \quad 36 \quad - \quad \$20{,}000$$
$$= \quad \$2248$$

The total interest paid over 3 years is approximately $2248.

b. Next, we determine monthly payments and total interest for Loan B.

P, the loan amount, is $20,000. / Rate, r, is 9%. / 12 payments per year / The loan is for 5 years.

$$PMT = \frac{P\left(\frac{r}{n}\right)}{1 - \left(1 + \frac{r}{n}\right)^{-nt}} = \frac{20{,}000\left(\frac{0.09}{12}\right)}{1 - \left(1 + \frac{0.09}{12}\right)^{-12(5)}} \approx 415$$

The monthly payments are approximately $415.

Now we calculate the interest over 5 years, or 60 months.

Total interest over 5 years	=	Total of all monthly payments	minus	amount of the loan.

$$= \quad \$415 \quad \times \quad 60 \quad - \quad \$20,000$$

$$= \quad \$4900$$

The total interest paid over 5 years is approximately $4900.

c. Table 8.8 compares the monthly payments and total interest for the two loans.

TABLE 8.8 COMPARING CAR LOANS

$20,000 loan	Monthly Payment	Total Interest
3-year loan at 7%	$618	$2248
5-year loan at 9%	$415	$4900

Monthly payments are less with the longer-term loan.   Interest is more with the longer-term loan.

 CHECK POINT 3 You decide to take a $15,000 loan for a new car. You can select one of the following loans, each requiring regular monthly payments:

Installment Loan A: 4-year loan at 8%

Installment Loan B: 6-year loan at 10%

a. Find the monthly payments and the total interest for Loan A.

b. Find the monthly payments and the total interest for Loan B.

c. Compare the monthly payments and total interest for the two loans.

EXERCISE SET 8.6 ●●●●●●

• Practice and Application Exercises

In all exercises, use

$$PMT = \frac{P\left(\dfrac{r}{n}\right)}{1 - \left(1 + \dfrac{r}{n}\right)^{-nt}}$$

to determine the regular payment amount, rounded to the nearest dollar.

Exercises 1–8 involve home mortgages.

1. The price of a home is $220,000. The bank requires a 20% down payment and three points at the time of closing. The cost of the home is financed with a 30-year fixed-rate mortgage at 7%.

a. Find the required down payment.

b. Find the amount of the mortgage.

c. How much must be paid for the three points at closing?

d. Find the monthly payment (excluding escrowed taxes and insurance).

e. Find the total cost of interest over 30 years.

2. The price of a condominium is $180,000. The bank requires a 5% down payment and one point at the time of closing. The cost of the condominium is financed with a 30-year fixed-rate mortgage at 8%.

a. Find the required down payment.

b. Find the amount of the mortgage.

c. How much must be paid for the one point at closing?

d. Find the monthly payment (excluding escrowed taxes and insurance).

e. Find the total cost of interest over 30 years.

3. The price of a small cabin is $100,000. The bank requires a 5% down payment. The buyer is offered two mortgage options: 20-year fixed at 8% or 30-year fixed at 8%. Calculate the amount of interest paid for each option. How much does the buyer save in interest with the 20-year option?

4. The price of a home is $160,000. The bank requires a 15% down payment. The buyer is offered two mortgage options: 15-year fixed at 8% or 30-year fixed at 8%. Calculate the amount of interest paid for each option. How much does the buyer save in interest with the 15-year option?

5. In terms of paying less in interest, which is more economical for a $150,000 mortgage: a 30-year fixed-rate at 8% or a 20-year fixed-rate at 7.5%? How much is saved in interest?

6. In terms of paying less in interest, which is more economical for a $90,000 mortgage: a 30-year fixed-rate at 8% or a 15-year fixed-rate at 7.5%? How much is saved in interest?

In Exercises 7–8, which mortgage loan has the greater total cost (closing costs + the amount paid for points + total cost of interest)? By how much?

7. A $120,000 mortgage with two loan options:

   Mortgage A: 30-year fixed at 7% with closing costs of $2000 and one point

   Mortgage B: 30-year fixed at 6.5% with closing costs of $1500 and four points

8. A $250,000 mortgage with two loan options:

   Mortgage A: 30-year fixed at 7.25% with closing costs of $2000 and one point

   Mortgage B: 30-year fixed at 6.25% with closing costs of $350 and four points

Exercises 9–18 involve installment loans other than mortgages.

9. Your credit card has a balance of $4200 and an annual interest rate of 18%. You decide to pay off the balance over two years. If there are no further purchases charged to the card,

   a. How much must you pay each month?

   b. How much total interest will you pay?

10. Your credit card has a balance of $3600 and an annual interest rate of 16.5%. You decide to pay off the balance over two years. If there are no further purchases charged to the card,

   a. How much must you pay each month?

   b. How much total interest will you pay?

11. To pay off the $4200 credit-card balance in Exercise 9, you can get a bank loan at 10.5% with a term of three years.

   a. How much will you pay each month? How does this compare with your credit-card payment in Exercise 9?

   b. How much total interest will you pay? How does this compare with your total credit-card interest in Exercise 9?

12. To pay off the $3600 credit-card balance in Exercise 10, you can get a bank loan at 9.5% with a term of three years.

   a. How much will you pay each month? How does this compare with your credit-card payment in Exercise 10?

   b. How much total interest will you pay? How does this compare with your total credit-card interest in Exercise 10?

13. Rework Exercise 9 if you decide to pay off the balance over one year, rather than two. How much more must you pay each month and how much less will you pay in total interest?

14. Rework Exercise 10 if you decide to pay off the balance over one year rather than two. How much more must you pay each month and how much less will you pay in total interest?

15. You borrow $10,000 for four years at 8% toward the purchase of a car.

   a. Find the monthly payments and the total interest for the loan.

b. Prepare a loan amortization schedule for the first three months of the car loan. Round entries to the nearest cent.

Payment Number	Interest	Principal	Loan Balance
1			
2			
3			

16. You borrow $30,000 for four years at 8% toward the purchase of a car.

   a. Find the monthly payments and the total interest for the loan.

   b. Prepare a loan amortization schedule for the first three months of the car loan. Use the table in Exercise 15(b) and round entries to the nearest cent.

17. A student graduates from college with a loan of $40,000. The interest rate is 8.5% and the loan term is 20 years.

   a. Find the monthly payments and the total interest for the loan.

   b. Prepare a loan amortization schedule for the first three months of the student loan. Use the table in Exercise 15(b) and round entries to the nearest cent.

   c. If the interest rate remains at 8.5% and the loan term is reduced to ten years, how much more must the student pay each month and how much less will be paid in total interest?

18. A student graduates from college with a loan of $50,000. The interest rate is 7.5% and the loan term is 20 years.

   a. Find the monthly payments and the total interest for the loan.

   b. Prepare a loan amortization schedule for the first three months of the student loan. Use the table in Exercise 15(b) and round entries to the nearest cent.

   c. If the interest rate remains at 7.5% and the loan term is reduced to ten years, how much more must the student pay each month and how much less will be paid in total interest?

• Writing in Mathematics

19. What is a mortgage?

20. What is a down payment?

21. How is the amount of a mortgage determined?

22. Describe why a buyer would select a 30-year fixed-rate mortgage instead of a 15-year fixed-rate mortgage if interest rates are $\frac{1}{4}$% to $\frac{1}{2}$% lower on a 15-year mortgage.

23. Describe one advantage and one disadvantage of an adjustable-rate mortgage over a fixed-rate mortgage.

24. What is a loan amortization schedule?

25. Describe what happens to the portions of payments going to principal and interest over the life of an installment loan.

26. Describe one advantage and one disadvantage of home ownership over renting.

• Critical Thinking Exercises

27. Use the discussion that precedes the box on page 492 to prove the loan payment formula shown in the box. Work with the equation in which the amount the lender expects to receive is equal to the amount saved in the annuity. Multiply both sides of this equation by $\frac{r}{n}$ and then solve for PMT by dividing both sides by the appropriate expression. Finally, divide the numerator and the denominator of the resulting formula for PMT by $\left(1 + \frac{r}{n}\right)^{nt}$ to obtain the form of the loan payment formula shown in the box.

28. The unpaid balance of an installment loan is equal to the present value of the remaining payments. The unpaid balance, P, is given by

$$P = PMT \frac{1 - \left(1 + \frac{r}{n}\right)^{-nt}}{\frac{r}{n}},$$

where PMT is the regular payment amount, r is the annual interest rate, n is the number of payments per year, and t is the number of years remaining in the mortgage.

  a. Use the loan payment formula to derive the unpaid balance formula.

  b. The price of a home is $180,000. The bank requires a 10% down payment. After the down payment, the balance is financed with a 30-year fixed-rate mortgage at 6.3%. Determine the unpaid balance after ten years.

• Group Exercise

29. Group members should go to the Internet and select a car that they might like to buy. Price the car and its options. Then find two loans with the best rates, but with different terms. For each loan, calculate the monthly payments and total interest. Select one of the loans and prepare a partial or complete amortization schedule.

•••••• CHAPTER SUMMARY, REVIEW, AND TEST

• S U M M A R Y DEFINITIONS AND CONCEPTS	EXAMPLES
8.1 Percent, Sales Tax, and Income Tax	
a. Percent means per hundred. Thus, $97\% = \frac{97}{100}$.	
b. To express a fraction as a percent, divide the numerator by the denominator, move the decimal point in the quotient two places to the right, and add a percent sign.	Ex. 1, p. 444
c. To express a decimal number as a percent, move the decimal point two places to the right and add a percent sign.	Ex. 2, p. 445
d. To express a percent as a decimal number, move the decimal point two places to the left and remove the percent sign.	Ex. 3, p. 445
e. The percent formula, $A = PB$, means A is P percent of B.	
f. Sales tax amount = tax rate $\times$ item's cost	Ex. 4, p. 446
g. Discount amount = discount rate $\times$ original price	Ex. 5, p. 446
h. Calculating Income Tax	Ex. 6, p. 448

    1. Determine adjusted gross income:

$$\text{Adjusted gross income} = \text{Gross income} - \text{Adjustments}.$$

    2. Determine taxable income:

$$\text{Taxable income} = \text{Adjusted gross income} - (\text{Exemptions} + \text{Deductions}).$$

    3. Determine the income tax:

$$\text{Income tax} = \text{Tax computation} - \text{Tax credits}.$$

See details in the box on page 447.

i. The fraction for percent increase (or decrease) is

$$\frac{\text{amount of increase (or decrease)}}{\text{original amount}}.$$

Ex. 7, p. 450;
Ex. 8, p. 451;
Ex. 9, p. 451;
Ex. 10, p. 451

Find the percent increase (or decrease) by expressing this fraction as a percent.

8.2 Simple Interest

a. Interest is the price we are paid for lending money or pay for borrowing money. The amount deposited or borrowed is the principal. The charge for interest, given as a percent, is the rate, assumed to be per year.

b. Simple interest involves interest calculated only on the principal and is computed using $I = Prt$.

Ex. 1, p. 455;
Ex. 2, p. 455

c. The future value, A, of P dollars at simple interest rate r for t years is $A = P(1 + rt)$.

Ex. 3, p. 456;
Ex. 4, p. 457;
Ex. 5, p. 457

d. Discounted loans deduct the interest, called the discount, from the loan amount at the time the loan is made.

Ex. 6, p. 458

8.3 Compound Interest

a. Compound interest involves interest computed on the original principal as well as on any accumulated interest. The amount in an account for one compounding period per year is $A = P(1 + r)^t$. For n compoundings per year, the amount is $A = P\left(1 + \frac{r}{n}\right)^{nt}$. For continuous compounding, the amount is $A = Pe^{rt}$, where $e \approx 2.72$.

Ex. 1, p. 461;
Ex. 2, p. 461;
Ex. 3, p. 462

b. Calculating Present Value
   If A dollars are to be accumulated in t years in an account that pays rate r compounded n times per year, then the present value, P, that needs to be invested now is given by

$$P = \frac{A}{\left(1 + \dfrac{r}{n}\right)^{nt}}.$$

Ex. 4, p. 463

c. Effective Annual Yield
   Effective annual yield is defined in the box on page 464. The effective annual yield, Y, for an account that pays rate r compounded n times per year is given by

$$Y = \left(1 + \frac{r}{n}\right)^{n} - 1.$$

Ex. 5, p. 464;
Ex. 6, p. 465

8.4 Annuities, Stocks, and Bonds

a. An annuity is a sequence of equal payments made at equal time periods. The value of an annuity is the sum of all deposits plus all interest paid.

Ex. 1, p. 468

b. The value of an annuity after t years is

$$A = \frac{P[(1 + r)^t - 1]}{r} \quad \text{or} \quad A = \frac{P\left[\left(1 + \dfrac{r}{n}\right)^{nt} - 1\right]}{\dfrac{r}{n}},$$

Ex. 2, p. 469;
Ex. 3, p. 470

depending on whether interest is compounded once a year or n times per year. See the box on page 469 and the box on page 470.

c. The formula

Ex. 4, p. 472

$$P = \frac{A\left(\dfrac{r}{n}\right)}{\left[\left(1 + \dfrac{r}{n}\right)^{nt} - 1\right]}$$

gives the deposit, P, into an annuity at the end of each compounding period needed to achieve a value of A dollars after t years. See the box on page 471.

d. The return on an investment is the percent increase in the investment.

e. Investors purchase stock, shares of ownership in a company. The shares indicate the percent of ownership. Trading refers to buying and selling stock. Investors make money by selling a stock for more money than they paid for it. They can also make money while they own stock if a company distributes all or part of its profits as dividends. Each share of stock is paid the same dividend.

f. Investors purchase a bond, lending money to the company from which they purchase the bond. The company commits itself to pay the price an investor pays for the bond at the time it was purchased, called its face value, along with interest payments at a given rate.

g. Reading stock tables is explained on pages 474–475.

Ex. 5, p. 475

8.5 Installment Buying

a. A fixed installment loan is paid off with a series of equal periodic payments. An open-end installment loan is paid off with variable monthly payments. Credit card loans are open-end installment loans.

b. The terms of fixed installment loans—the amount financed, the total installment price, and the finance charge—are explained in the box on page 481.

Ex. 1, p. 481

c. The interest rate per year on a loan is called the annual percentage rate (APR). The box on page 482 shows how to find the APR for a fixed installment loan.

Ex. 2, p. 482

d. Unearned interest is the amount by which the original finance charge is reduced when a fixed installment loan is paid off early. The two methods for computing unearned interest—the actuarial method and the rule of 78—are explained in the box on page 483.

Ex. 3, p. 483;
Ex. 4, p. 484

e. Open-end installment loans, such as credit cards, calculate interest using the simple interest formula $I = Prt$. The methods for determining the interest, the unpaid balance method, the previous balance method, and the average daily balance method, are described in the box on page 487.

Ex. 5, p. 486;
Ex. 6, p. 487

8.6 Amortization and the Cost of Home Ownership

a. A mortgage is a long-term loan for the purpose of buying a home, and for which the property is pledged as security for payment. The term of the mortgage is the number of years until final payoff. The down payment is the portion of the sale price of the home that the buyer initially pays. The amount of the mortgage is the difference between the sale price and the down payment.

b. Fixed-rate mortgages have the same monthly payment during the entire time of the loan. Variable-rate mortgages, or adjustable-rate mortgages, have payment amounts that change from time to time depending on changes in the interest rate.

c. A point is a one-time charge that equals 1% of the amount of a mortgage loan.

d. Loan Payment Formula for Installment Loans

Ex. 1, p. 492;
Ex. 3, p. 496

$$PMT = \frac{P\left(\dfrac{r}{n}\right)}{1 - \left(1 + \dfrac{r}{n}\right)^{-nt}}$$

PMT is the regular payment amount required to repay a loan of P dollars paid n times per year over t years at an annual interest rate r.

e. Amortizing a loan is the process of making regular payments on the principal and interest until the loan is paid off. A document containing the payment number, payment toward the interest, payment toward the principal, and balance of the loan is called a loan amortization schedule. Such a schedule shows how the buyer pays slightly less in interest and more in principal for each payment over the entire life of the loan.

Ex. 2, p. 494

REVIEW EXERCISES

8.1

In Exercises 1–3, express each fraction as a percent.

1. $\frac{4}{5}$ **2.** $\frac{1}{8}$ **3.** $\frac{3}{4}$

In Exercises 4–6, express each decimal as a percent.

4. 0.72   **5.** 0.0035   **6.** 4.756

In Exercises 7–12, express each percent as a decimal.

7. 65%   **8.** 99.7%   **9.** 150%

10. 3%   **11.** 0.65%   **12.** $\frac{1}{4}$%

13. What is 8% of 120?

14. Suppose that the local sales tax rate is 6% and you purchase a backpack for $24.

    a. How much tax is paid?

    b. What is the backpack's total cost?

15. A television with an original price of $850 is on sale at 35% off.

    a. What is the discount amount?

    b. What is the television's sale price?

16. Use the 2005 marginal tax rates in Table 8.1 on page 448 to calculate the income tax owed by the following person:

- Single, no dependents
- Gross income: $40,000
- $2500 paid to a tax-deferred IRA
- $6500 mortgage interest
- $1800 property taxes
- No tax credits

17. A college that had 40 students for each lecture course increased the number to 45 students. What is the percent increase in the number of students in a lecture course?

18. A dictionary regularly sells for $56.00. The sale price is $36.40. Find the percent decrease of the sale price from the regular price.

19. Consider the following statement:

My portfolio fell 10% last year, but then it rose 10% this year, so at least I recouped my losses.

Is this statement true? In particular, suppose you invested $10,000 in the stock market last year. How much money would be left in your portfolio with a 10% fall and then a 10% rise? If there is a loss, what is the percent decrease, to the nearest tenth of a percent, in your portfolio?

8.2

In Exercises 20–23, find the simple interest. (Assume 360 days in a year.)

Principal	Rate	Time
20. $6000	3%	1 year
21. $8400	5%	6 years
22. $20,000	8%	9 months
23. $36,000	15%	60 days

24. In order to pay for tuition and books, a student borrows $3500 for four months at 10.5% interest.

    a. How much interest must the student pay?

    b. Find the future value of the loan.

In Exercises 25–29, use the formula for future value at simple interest, $A = P(1 + rt)$, to find the missing quantity. Round dollar amounts to the nearest cent and rates to the nearest tenth of a percent.

25. $A = ?, P = \$12,000, r = 8.2\%, t = 9$ months

26. $A = \$5750, P = \$5000, r = ?, t = 2$ years

27. $A = \$16,000, P = ?, r = 6.5\%, t = 3$ years

28. You plan to buy a $12,000 sailboat in four years. How much should you invest now, at 7.3% simple interest, to have enough for the boat in four years? (Round up to the nearest cent.)

29. You borrow $1500 from a friend and promise to pay back $1800 in six months. What simple interest rate will you pay?

30. You borrow $1800 on a 7% discounted loan for a period of 9 months.

    a. What is the loan's discount?

    b. Determine the net amount of money you will receive.

    c. What is the loan's actual interest rate, to the nearest tenth of a percent?

8.3

In Exercises 31–33, the principal represents an amount of money deposited in a savings account that provides the lender compound interest at the given rate.

    a. Use the formula $A = P(1 + r)^t$ for one compounding period per year or $A = P\left(1 + \frac{r}{n}\right)^{nt}$ for n compounding periods per year to find how much money, to the nearest cent, there will be in the account after the given number of years.

    b. Find the interest earned.

Principal	Rate	Compoundings per Year	Time
31. $7000	3%	1	5 years
32. $30,000	2.5%	4	10 years
33. $2500	4%	12	20 years

34. Use $A = P\left(1 + \frac{r}{n}\right)^{nt}$ and $A = Pe^{rt}$ to solve this exercise. Suppose that you have $14,000 to invest. Which investment yields the greater return over 10 years: 7% compounded monthly or 6.85% compounded continuously? How much more (to the nearest dollar) is yielded by the better investment?

Solve Exercises 35–36 using the present value formula

$$P = \frac{A}{\left(1 + \frac{r}{n}\right)^{nt}}.$$

Round answers to the nearest cent.

35. How much money should parents deposit today in an account that earns 10% compounded monthly so that it will accumulate to $100,000 in 18 years for their child's college education?

36. How much money should be deposited today in an account that earns 5% compounded quarterly so that it will accumulate to $75,000 in 35 years for retirement?

37. You deposit $2000 in an account that pays 6% interest compounded quarterly.

a. Find the future value, to the nearest cent, after one year.

b. Use the future value formula for simple interest to determine the effective annual yield. Round to the nearest tenth of a percent.

Use the effective annual yield formula

$$Y = \left(1 + \frac{r}{n}\right)^n - 1$$

to solve Exercises 38–39.

38. What is the effective annual yield, to the nearest hundredth of a percent, of an account paying 5.5% compounded quarterly? What does your answer mean?

39. Which investment is the better choice: 6.25% compounded monthly or 6.3% compounded annually?

8.4

In Exercises 40–41, use the formula

$$A = \frac{P[(1 + r)^t - 1]}{r} \quad \text{or} \quad A = \frac{P\left[\left(1 + \frac{r}{n}\right)^{nt} - 1\right]}{\frac{r}{n}}$$

to find the value of each annuity. Round to the nearest dollar.

40. You spend $10 per week on lottery tickets, averaging $520 per year. Instead of buying tickets, if you deposited the $520 at the end of each year in an annuity paying 6% compounded annually,

a. How much would you have after 20 years?

b. Find the interest.

41. To save for retirement, you decide to deposit $100 at the end of each month in an IRA that pays 5.5% compounded monthly.

a. How much will you have from the IRA after 30 years?

b. Find the interest.

42. You would like to have $25,000 to use as a down payment for a home in five years by making regular deposits at the end of every three months in an annuity that pays 7.25% compounded quarterly.

a. Use the formula

$$P = \frac{A\left(\frac{r}{n}\right)}{\left[\left(1 + \frac{r}{n}\right)^{nt} - 1\right]}$$

to determine the amount of each deposit. Round up to the nearest dollar.

b. How much of the $25,000 comes from deposits and how much comes from interest?

Exercises 43–50, refer to the stock table for Harley Davidson (the motorcycle company). Where necessary, round dollar amounts to the nearest cent.

| 52-Week | | | | | Yld | |
High	Low	Stock	SYM	Div	%	PE
64.06	26.13	Harley Dav	HDI	.16	.3	41

| Vol | | | | Net |
100s	Hi	Lo	Close	Chg
5458	61.25	59.25	61	+1.75

43. What were the high and low prices for a share for the past 52 weeks?

44. If you owned 900 shares of this stock last year, what dividend did you receive?

45. What is the annual return for the dividends alone?

46. How many shares of this company's stock were traded yesterday?

47. What were the high and low prices for a share yesterday?

48. What was the price at which a share traded when the stock exchange closed yesterday?

49. What was the change in price for a share of stock from the market close two days ago to yesterday's market close?

50. Compute the company's annual earnings per share using

$$\text{Annual earnings per share} = \frac{\text{Yesterday's closing price per share}}{\text{PE ratio}}.$$

51. Explain the difference between investing in a stock and investing in a bond.

8.5

52. The cost of a new car is $16,500. You can finance the purchase by paying $500 down and $350 per month for 60 months.

a. Determine the amount financed.

b. Determine the total installment price.

c. Determine the finance charge.

d. Use Table 8.5 on page 482 to find the APR for this loan.

53. Use the actuarial method formula

$$u = \frac{kRV}{100 + V}$$

to solve this problem. In Exercise 52, instead of making the forty-eighth payment, the borrower decides to pay the remaining balance and terminate the loan for the car.

a. How much interest is saved by repaying the loan early?

b. What is the total amount due on the day of the loan's termination?

54. Use the rule of 78 formula

$$u = \frac{k(k + 1)}{n(n + 1)} \times F$$

to solve this problem. In Exercise 52, instead of making the forty-eighth payment, the borrower decides to pay the remaining balance and terminate the loan for the car.

a. How much interest is saved by repaying the loan early?

b. What is the total amount due on the day of the loan's termination?

55. Describe the difference between the answers in Exercises 53 and 54. Which method saves the borrower more money?

56. The terms of a particular credit card are based on the unpaid balance method. The monthly interest rate is 1.5% on the unpaid balance on the first day of the billing period less payments and credits. Here are some of the details in the June 1–June 30 itemized billing:

June 1 Unpaid Balance: $1300

Payment Received June 4: $200

Purchases Charged to the Account: airline ticket, $380; car repair, $120; groceries, $140

Last Day of the Billing Period: June 30

Due Date: July 9

a. Find the interest due on the payment due date.

b. Find the total balance owed on the last day of the billing period.

c. Terms for the credit card require a $10 minimum monthly payment if the balance due is less than $360. Otherwise, the minimum monthly payment is $\frac{1}{36}$ of the balance due, rounded to the nearest whole dollar. What is the minimum monthly payment due by July 9?

57. A credit card has a monthly rate of 1.8%. In the March 1–March 31 itemized billing, the March 1 unpaid balance is $3600. A payment of $2000 was received on March 6. There are no purchases or cash advances in this billing period. The payment due date is April 9. Find the interest due on this date using

a. the unpaid balance method.

b. the previous balance method.

c. the average daily balance method.

8.6

In Exercises 58–62, use

$$PMT = \frac{P\left(\dfrac{r}{n}\right)}{1 - \left(1 + \dfrac{r}{n}\right)^{-nt}}$$

to determine the regular payment amount, rounded to the nearest dollar.

58. The price of a home is $240,000. The bank requires a 20% down payment and two points at the time of closing. The cost of the home is financed with a 30-year fixed-rate mortgage at 7%.

a. Find the required down payment.

b. Find the amount of the mortgage.

c. How much must be paid for the two points at closing?

d. Find the monthly payment (excluding escrowed taxes and insurance).

e. Find the total cost of interest over 30 years.

59. In terms of paying less in interest, which is more economical for a $70,000 mortgage: a 30-year fixed-rate at 8.5% or a 20-year fixed-rate at 8%? How much is saved in interest? Discuss one advantage and one disadvantage for each mortgage option.

60. You need a loan of $100,000 to buy a home. Here are your options:

Option A: 30-year fixed-rate at 8.5% with no closing costs and no points

Option B: 30-year fixed-rate at 7.5% with closing costs of $1300 and three points.

a. Determine your monthly payments for each option and discuss how you would decide between the two options.

b. Which mortgage loan has the greater total cost (closing costs + the amount paid for points + total cost of interest)? By how much?

61. You decide to take a $15,000 loan for a new car. You can select one of the following loans, each requiring regular monthly payments:

Loan A: 3-year loan at 7.2%

Loan B: 5-year loan at 8.1%.

a. Find the monthly payments and the total interest for Loan A.

b. Find the monthly payments and the total interest for Loan B.

c. Compare the monthly payments and interest for the longer-term loan to the monthly payments and interest for the shorter-term loan.

62. The bar graph shows credit-card debt per U.S. household from 1995 through 2004.

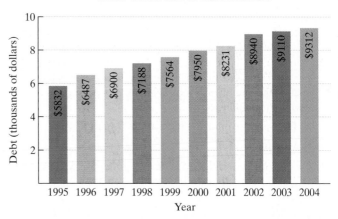

Credit-Card Debt Per U.S. Household

Source: CardWeb.com

In 2004, the average credit-card debt was $9312. Suppose your card has this balance and an annual interest rate of 18%. You decide to pay off the balance over two years. If there are no further purchases charged to the card,

a. How much must you pay each month?

b. How much total interest will you pay?

c. Prepare an amortization schedule for the first three months of payments. Round entries to the nearest cent.

Payment Number	Interest	Principal	Balance
1			
2			
3			

SUMMARY OF FINANCIAL MANAGEMENT FORMULAS

Simple Interest

$$I = Prt$$

$$A = P(1 + rt)$$

Compound Interest

$$A = P(1 + r)^t$$

$$A = P\left(1 + \frac{r}{n}\right)^{nt}$$

$$P = \frac{A}{\left(1 + \dfrac{r}{n}\right)^{nt}}$$

$$Y = \left(1 + \frac{r}{n}\right)^n - 1$$

Annuities

$$A = \frac{P[(1 + r)^t - 1]}{r}$$

$$A = \frac{P\left[\left(1 + \dfrac{r}{n}\right)^{nt} - 1\right]}{\dfrac{r}{n}}$$

$$P = \frac{A\left(\dfrac{r}{n}\right)}{\left[\left(1 + \dfrac{r}{n}\right)^{nt} - 1\right]}$$

Amortization

$$PMT = \frac{P\left(\dfrac{r}{n}\right)}{1 - \left(1 + \dfrac{r}{n}\right)^{-nt}}$$

●●●●●● CHAPTER 8 TEST

The box summarizes the financial management formulas you have worked with throughout the chapter. Where applicable, use the appropriate formula to solve an exercise in this test. Unless otherwise stated, round dollar amounts to the nearest cent and rates to the nearest tenth of a percent.

1. A CD player with an original price of $120 is on sale at 15% off.

   a. What is the amount of the discount?

   b. What is the sale price of the CD player?

2. Use the 2005 marginal tax rates in Table 8.1 on page 448 to calculate the income tax owed by the following person:

   • Single, no dependents

   • Gross income: $36,500

   • $2000 paid to a tax-deferred IRA

   • $4700 mortgage interest

   • $1300 property taxes

   • No tax credits

3. You purchased shares of stock for $2000 and sold them for $3500. Find the percent increase, or your return, on this investment.

4. You borrow $2400 for three months at 12% simple interest. Find the amount of interest paid and the future value of the loan.

5. You borrow $2000 from a friend and promise to pay back $3000 in two years. What simple interest rate will you pay?

6. In six months, you want to have $7000 worth of remodeling done to your home. How much should you invest now, at 9% simple interest, to have enough money for the project? (Round up to the nearest cent.)

7. Find the effective annual yield, to the nearest hundredth of a percent, of an account paying 4.5% compounded quarterly. What does your answer mean?

8. To save money to use as a down payment for a home in five years, you deposit $6000 in an account that pays 6.5% compounded monthly.

   a. How much, to the nearest dollar, will you have as a down payment after five years?

   b. Find the interest.

9. Instead of making the lump-sum deposit of $6000 described in Exercise 8, you decide to deposit $100 at the end of each month in an annuity that pays 6.5% compounded monthly.

   a. How much, to the nearest dollar, will you have as a down payment after five years?

   b. Find the interest.

   c. Why is less interest earned from this annuity than from the lump-sum deposit in Exercise 8? With less interest earned, why would one select the annuity rather than the lump-sum deposit?

10. You would like to have $3000 in four years for a special vacation by making a lump-sum investment in an account that pays 9.5% compounded semiannually. How much should you deposit now? Round up to the nearest dollar.

11. How much should you deposit at the end of each month in an IRA that pays 6.25% compounded monthly to have $1,500,000 when you retire in 40 years? How much of the $1.5 million comes from interest?

Use the stock table for AT&T to solve Exercises 12–14.

52-Week					Yld	
High	Low	Stock	SYM	Div	%	PE
26.50	24.25	AT & T	PNS	2.03	7.9	18

Vol				Net
100s	Hi	Lo	Close	Chg
961	25.75	25.50	25.75	+0.13

12. What were the high and low prices for a share yesterday?

13. If you owned 1000 shares of this stock last year, what dividend did you receive?

14. Suppose that you bought 600 shares of AT&T, paying the price per share at which a share traded when the stock exchange closed yesterday. If the broker charges 2.5% of the price paid for all 600 shares, find the broker's commission.

In Exercises 15–20, the cost of a new car is $16,000, which can be financed by paying $3000 down and $300 per month for 60 months.

15. Determine the amount financed.

16. Determine the total installment price.

17. Determine the finance charge.

18. Use Table 8.5 on page 482 to find the APR for this loan.

19. Use the rule of 78 formula

$$u = \frac{k(k + 1)}{n(n + 1)} \times F$$

to solve this problem. Instead of making the thirty-sixth payment, the borrower decides to pay the remaining balance and terminate the loan for the car. How much interest is saved by repaying the loan early?

20. Use the answer from Exercise 19 to find the total amount due on the day of the loan's termination.

Use the information at the top of the next column to solve Exercises 21–23. The terms of a particular credit card are based on the unpaid balance method. The monthly interest rate is 2% on the unpaid balance on the first day of the billing period less payments and credits. Here are some of the details in the November 1–November 30 itemized billing:

November 1 Unpaid Balance: $880
Payment Received November 5: $100
Purchases Charged to the Account: clothing, $350; gasoline, $70; groceries, $120
Last Day of the Billing Period: November 30
Due Date: December 8

21. Find the interest due on the payment due date.

22. Find the total balance owed on the last day of the billing period.

23. Terms for the credit card require a $10 minimum monthly payment if the balance due is less than $360. Otherwise, the minimum monthly payment is $\frac{1}{36}$ of the balance due, rounded to the nearest whole dollar. What is the minimum monthly payment due by December 8?

24. A credit card has a monthly rate of 1.6%. In the September 1–September 30 itemized billing, the September 1 unpaid balance is $2400. A payment of $1500 was received on September 4. There are no purchases or cash advances in this billing period. The payment due date is October 10. Find the interest due on this date using the average daily balance method.

Use this information to solve Exercises 25–29. The price of a home is $120,000. The bank requires a 10% down payment and two points at the time of closing. The cost of the home is financed with a 30-year fixed-rate mortgage at 8.5%.

25. Find the required down payment. Round to the nearest dollar.

26. Find the amount of the mortgage.

27. How much must be paid for the two points at closing?

28. Find the monthly payment (excluding escrowed taxes and insurance).

29. Find the total cost of interest over 30 years.

30. A student graduates from college with a loan of $20,000. The interest rate is 6.8% and the loan term is ten years.

    a. Find the monthly payments, rounded to the nearest dollar, and the total interest for the loan.

    b. Prepare a loan amortization schedule for the first two months of the student loan. Round entries to the nearest cent.

Payment Number	Interest	Principal	Balance
1			
2			

9

Measurement

Y ou are feeling crowded in. Perhaps it would be a good time to move to a state with more elbow room. But which state? You can look up the population of each state, but that does not take into account the amount of land the population occupies. How is this land measured and how can you use this measure to select a place where wildlife outnumber humans?

In this chapter, we explore ways of measuring things in our English system, as well as in the metric system. We return to finding a state with lots of room to spread out in Example 2 of Section 9.2. Knowing how units of measure are used to describe your world can help you make decisions on issues ranging from where to live to alcohol consumption (see the Blitzer Bonus on page 528).

SECTION 9.1 • MEASURING LENGTH; THE METRIC SYSTEM

OBJECTIVES

1. Use dimensional analysis to change units of measurement.
2. Understand and use metric prefixes.
3. Convert units within the metric system.
4. Use dimensional analysis to change to and from the metric system.

Linear units of measure were originally based on parts of the body. The Egyptians used the palm (equal to four fingers), the span (a handspan), and the cubit (length of forearm).

Have you seen either of the *Jurassic Park* films? The popularity of these movies reflects our fascination with dinosaurs and their incredible size. From end to end, the largest dinosaur from the Jurassic period, which lasted from 208 to 146 million years ago, was about 88 feet. To **measure** an object such as a dinosaur is to assign a number to its size. The number representing its measure from end to end is called its **length**. Measurements are used to describe properties of length, area, volume, weight, and temperature. Over the centuries, people have developed systems of measurement that are now accepted in most of the world.

Length

Every measurement consists of two parts: a number and a unit of measure. For example, if the length of a dinosaur is 88 feet, the number is 88 and the unit of measure is the foot. Many different units are commonly used in measuring length. The foot is from a system of measurement called the **English system**, which is generally used in the United States. In this system of measurement, length is expressed in such units as inches, feet, yards, and miles.

The result obtained from measuring length is called a **linear measurement** and is stated in **linear units**.

> ### LINEAR UNITS OF MEASURE: THE ENGLISH SYSTEM
>
> 12 inches (in.) = 1 foot (ft)
>
> 3 feet = 1 yard (yd)
>
> 36 inches = 1 yard
>
> 5280 feet = 1 mile (mi)

Because many of us are familiar with the measures in the box, we find it simple to change from one measure to another, say from feet to inches. We know that there are 12 inches in a foot. To convert from 5 feet to a measure in inches, we multiply by 12. Thus, 5 feet = 5 × 12 inches = 60 inches.

Another procedure to convert from one unit of measurement to another is called **dimensional analysis**. Dimensional analysis uses **unit fractions**. A unit fraction has two properties: The numerator and denominator contain different units and the value of the unit fraction is 1. Here are some examples of unit fractions:

$$\frac{12\text{ in.}}{1\text{ ft}}, \quad \frac{1\text{ ft}}{12\text{ in.}}, \quad \frac{3\text{ ft}}{1\text{ yd}}, \quad \frac{1\text{ yd}}{3\text{ ft}}, \quad \frac{5280\text{ ft}}{1\text{ mi}}, \quad \frac{1\text{ mi}}{5280\text{ ft}}.$$

In each unit fraction, the numerator and denominator are equal, making the value of the fraction 1.

1 | Use dimensional analysis to change units of measurement.

Let's see how to convert 5 feet to inches using a unit fraction.

$$5 \text{ ft} = ? \text{ in.}$$

We need to eliminate feet and introduce inches. The unit we need to introduce, inches, must appear in the numerator of the fraction. The unit we need to eliminate, feet, must appear in the denominator. Therefore, we choose the unit fraction with inches in the numerator and feet in the denominator. The units divide out as follows:

$$5 \text{ ft} = \frac{5 \cancel{\text{ft}}}{1} \cdot \frac{12 \text{ in.}}{1 \cancel{\text{ft}}} = 5 \cdot 12 \text{ in.} = 60 \text{ in.}$$

unit fraction

> ### DIMENSIONAL ANALYSIS
> To convert a measurement to a different unit, multiply by a unit fraction (or by unit fractions). The given unit of measurement should appear in the denominator of the unit fraction so that this unit cancels upon multiplication. The unit of measurement that needs to be introduced should appear in the numerator of the fraction so that this unit will be retained upon multiplication.

EXAMPLE 1   USING DIMENSIONAL ANALYSIS TO CHANGE UNITS OF MEASUREMENT

Convert:

a. 40 inches to feet

b. 13,200 feet to miles

c. 9 inches to yards.

SOLUTION

a. Because we want to convert 40 inches to feet, feet should appear in the numerator and inches in the denominator. We use the unit fraction

$$\frac{1 \text{ ft}}{12 \text{ in.}}$$

This period ends the sentence and is not part of the abbreviated unit.

and proceed as follows:

$$40 \text{ in.} = \frac{40 \cancel{\text{in.}}}{1} \cdot \frac{1 \text{ ft}}{12 \cancel{\text{in.}}} = \frac{40}{12} \text{ft} = 3\tfrac{1}{3} \text{ft or } 3.\overline{3} \text{ ft.}$$

b. To convert 13,200 feet to miles, miles should appear in the numerator and feet in the denominator. We use the unit fraction

$$\frac{1 \text{ mi}}{5280 \text{ ft}}$$

and proceed as follows:

$$13,200 \text{ ft} = \frac{13,200 \cancel{\text{ft}}}{1} \cdot \frac{1 \text{ mi}}{5280 \cancel{\text{ft}}} = \frac{13,200}{5280} \text{mi} = 2.5 \text{ mi.}$$

c. To convert 9 inches to yards, yards should appear in the numerator and inches in the denominator. We use the unit fraction

$$\frac{1 \text{ yd}}{36 \text{ in.}}$$

and proceed as follows:

$$9 \text{ in.} = \frac{9 \cancel{\text{in.}}}{1} \cdot \frac{1 \text{ yd}}{36 \cancel{\text{in.}}} = \frac{9}{36} \text{yd} = \frac{1}{4} \text{yd or } 0.25 \text{ yd.}$$

kilodollar

hectodollar

dekadollar

dollar

decidollar   centidollar

CHECK POINT 1 Convert:

a. 78 inches to feet

b. 17,160 feet to miles

c. 3 inches to yards.

2 | Understand and use metric prefixes.

Length and the Metric System

Although the English system of measurement is most commonly used in the United States, most industrialized countries use the metric system of measurement. One of the advantages of the metric system is that units are based on powers of ten, making it much easier than the English system to change from one unit of measure to another.

The basic unit for linear measure in the metric system is the meter (m). A meter is slightly longer than a yard, approximately 39.37 inches. Prefixes are used to denote a multiple or part of a meter. Table 9.1 summarizes the more commonly used metric prefixes and their meanings.

TABLE 9.1 COMMONLY USED METRIC PREFIXES

Prefix	Symbol	Meaning
kilo	k	$1000 \times$ base unit
hecto	h	$100 \times$ base unit
deka	da	$10 \times$ base unit
deci	d	$\frac{1}{10}$ of base unit
centi	c	$\frac{1}{100}$ of base unit
milli	m	$\frac{1}{1000}$ of base unit

STUDY TIP

Prefixes containing an "i" (deci, centi, milli) are all fractional parts of one unit.

The prefixes kilo, centi, and milli are used more frequently than hecto, deka, and deci. Table 9.2 applies all six prefixes to the meter. The first part of the symbol indicates the prefix and the second part (m) indicates meter.

TABLE 9.2 COMMONLY USED UNITS OF LINEAR MEASURE IN THE METRIC SYSTEM

Symbol	Unit	Meaning
km	kilometer	1000 meters
hm	hectometer	100 meters
dam	dekameter	10 meters
m	meter	1 meter
dm	decimeter	0.1 meter
cm	centimeter	0.01 meter
mm	millimeter	0.001 meter

Kilometer is pronounced kil'-oh-met-er with the accent on the **FIRST** syllable. If pronounced correctly, kilometers should sound something like "kill all meters."

In the metric system, the kilometer is used to measure distances comparable to those measured in miles in the English system. One kilometer is approximately 0.6 mile, and one mile is approximately 1.6 kilometers.

Metric units of centimeters and millimeters are used to measure what the English system measures in inches. Figure 9.1 shows that a centimeter is less than half an inch; there are 2.54 centimeters in an inch. The smaller markings on the bottom scale are millimeters. A millimeter is approximately the thickness of a dime. The length of a bee or a fly may be measured in millimeters.

FIGURE 9.1

Those of us born in the United States have a good sense of what a length in the English system tells us about an object. An 88-foot dinosaur is huge, about 15 times the length of a 6-foot man. But what sense can we make of knowing that a whale is 25 meters long? The following lengths and the given approximations can help give you a feel for metric units of linear measure.

$$(1 \text{ meter} \approx 39 \text{ inches} \quad 1 \text{ kilometer} \approx 0.62 \text{ mile})$$

Item	Approximate Length
Width of lead in pencil	2 mm or 0.08 in.
Width of an adult's thumb	2 cm or 0.8 in.
Height of adult male	1.8 m or 6 ft
Typical room height	2.5 m or 8.3 ft
Length of medium-size car	5 m or 16.7 ft
Height of Empire State Building	381 m or 1270 ft
Average depth of ocean	4 km or 2.5 mi
Length of Manhattan Island	18 km or 11.25 mi
Distance from New York City to San Francisco	4800 km or 3000 mi
Radius of Earth	6378 km or 3986 mi
Distance from Earth to the moon	384,401 km or 240,251 mi

Convert units within the metric system.

Although dimensional analysis can be used to convert from one unit to another within the metric system, there is an easier, faster way to accomplish this conversion. The procedure is based on the observation that successively smaller units involve division by 10 and successively larger units involve multiplication by 10.

> **CHANGING UNITS WITHIN THE METRIC SYSTEM**
> Use the following chart to find equivalent measures of length:
>
> Multiply by 10 for each step to the right.
>
> $\times 10$
> km hm dam m dm cm mm
> $\div 10$
>
> Divide by 10 for each step to the left.
>
> **1.** To change from a larger unit to a smaller unit (moving to the right in the diagram), multiply by 10 for each step to the right. Thus, move the decimal point in the given quantity one place to the right for each smaller unit until the desired unit is reached.
>
> **2.** To change from a smaller unit to a larger unit (moving to the left in the diagram), divide by 10 for each step to the left. Thus, move the decimal point in the given quantity one place to the left for each larger unit until the desired unit is reached.

The First Meter

The French first defined the meter in 1791, calculating its length as a romantic one ten-millionth of a line running from the Equator through Paris to the North Pole. Today's meter, officially accepted in 1983, is equal to the length of the path traveled by light in a vacuum during the time interval of 1/299,794,458 of a second.

1 meter = 1/10,000,000 of the distance from the North Pole to the Equator on the meridian through Paris.

STUDY TIP

The following question provides a way to remember the metric units for length from largest to smallest.

| Kitty , | how | does | my | dog | catch | mice | ? |

km   hm   dam   m   dm   cm   mm

EXAMPLE 2   CHANGING UNITS WITHIN THE METRIC SYSTEM

a. Convert 504.7 meters to kilometers.

b. Convert 27 meters to centimeters.

c. Convert 704 mm to hm.

d. Convert 9.71 dam to dm.

SOLUTION

a. To convert from meters to kilometers, we start at meters and move three steps to the left to obtain kilometers:

$$\text{km hm dam m dm cm mm.}$$

Hence, we move the decimal point three places to the left:

$$504.7 \text{ m} = 0.5047 \text{ km.}$$

Thus, 504.7 meters converts to 0.5047 kilometer. Changing from a smaller unit of measurement (meter) to a larger unit of measurement (kilometer) results in an answer with a smaller number of units.

b. To convert from meters to centimeters, we start at meters and move two steps to the right to obtain centimeters:

$$\text{km hm dam m dm cm mm.}$$

Hence, we move the decimal point two places to the right:

$$27 \text{ m} = 2700 \text{ cm.}$$

Thus, 27 meters converts to 2700 centimeters. Changing from a larger unit of measurement (meter) to a smaller unit of measurement (centimeter) results in an answer with a larger number of units.

c. To convert from mm (millimeters) to hm (hectometers), we start at mm and move five steps to the left to obtain hm:

$$\text{km hm dam m dm cm mm.}$$

Hence, we move the decimal point five places to the left:

$$704 \text{ mm} = 0.00704 \text{ hm.}$$

d. To convert from dam (dekameters) to dm (decimeters), we start at dam and move two places to the right to obtain dm:

$$\text{km hm dam m dm cm mm.}$$

Hence, we move the decimal point two places to the right:

$$9.71 \text{ dam} = 971 \text{ dm}.$$

In Example 2(b), we showed that 27 meters converts to 2700 centimeters. This is the average length of the California blue whale, the longest of the great whales. Blue whales can have lengths that exceed 30 meters, making them over 100 feet long.

Blue whale

a. Convert 8000 meters to kilometers.

b. Convert 53 meters to millimeters.

c. Convert 604 cm to hm.

d. Convert 6.72 dam to cm.

BLITZER BONUS

Viruses and Metric Prefixes

Viruses are measured in attometers. An attometer is one quintillionth of a meter, or 10^{-18} meter, symbolized am. If a virus measures 1 am, you can place 10^{15} of them across a penciled 1 millimeter dot. If you were to enlarge each of these viruses to the size of the dot, they would stretch far into space, almost reaching Saturn.

Here is a list of all twenty metric prefixes. When applied to the meter, they range from the yottameter (10^{24} meters) to the yoctometer (10^{-24} meters).

LARGER THAN THE BASIC UNIT

Prefix	Symbol	Power of Ten	English Name
yotta-	Y	+24	septillion
zetta-	Z	+21	sextillion
exa-	E	+18	quintillion
peta-	P	+15	quadrillion
tera-	T	+12	trillion
giga-	G	+9	billion
mega-	M	+6	million
kilo-	k	+3	thousand
hecto-	h	+2	hundred
deca-	da	+1	ten

SMALLER THAN THE BASIC UNIT

Prefix	Symbol	Power of Ten	English Name
deci-	d	−1	tenth
centi-	c	−2	hundredth
milli-	m	−3	thousandth
micro-	μ	−6	millionth
nano-	n	−9	billionth
pico-	p	−12	trillionth
femto-	f	−15	quadrillionth
atto-	a	−18	quintillionth
zepto-	z	−21	sextillionth
yocto-	y	−24	septillionth

4 | Use dimensional analysis to change to and from the metric system.

1 m
1 yd

1 yd = 0.9 m

Although dimensional analysis is not necessary when changing units within the metric system, it is a useful tool when converting to and from the metric system. Some approximate conversions are given in Table 9.3.

TABLE 9.3 APPROXIMATE ENGLISH AND METRIC EQUIVALENTS	
1 inch (in.) = 2.54 centimeters (cm)	These conversions are exact.
1 foot (ft) = 30.48 centimeters (cm)	
1 yard (yd) = 0.9 meter (m)	These conversions are approximate.
1 mile (mi) = 1.6 kilometers (km)	

EXAMPLE 3   USING DIMENSIONAL ANALYSIS TO CHANGE TO AND FROM THE METRIC SYSTEM

a. Convert 8 inches to centimeters.

b. Convert 125 miles to kilometers.

c. Convert 26,800 millimeters to inches.

SOLUTION

a. To convert 8 inches to centimeters, we use a unit fraction with centimeters in the numerator and inches in the denominator:

$$\frac{2.54 \text{ cm}}{1 \text{ in.}}.$$ Table 9.3 shows that 1 in. = 2.54 cm.

We proceed as follows.

$$8 \text{ in.} = \frac{8 \text{ in.}}{1} \cdot \frac{2.54 \text{ cm}}{1 \text{ in.}} = 8(2.54) \text{ cm} = 20.32 \text{ cm}$$

b. To convert 125 miles to kilometers, we use a unit fraction with kilometers in the numerator and miles in the denominator:

$$\frac{1.6 \text{ km}}{1 \text{ mi}}.$$ Table 9.3 shows that 1 mi = 1.6 km.

Thus,

$$125 \text{ mi} = \frac{125 \text{ mi}}{1} \cdot \frac{1.6 \text{ km}}{1 \text{ mi}} = 125(1.6) \text{ km} = 200 \text{ km}.$$

STUDY TIP

Keep in mind that the conversions shown here are *approximate*. More accurately,

$$1 \text{ mi} \approx 1.61 \text{ km}.$$

Thus,

$$125 \text{ mi} \approx 125(1.61) \text{ km}$$
$$\approx 201.25 \text{ km}.$$

c. To convert 26,800 millimeters to inches, we observe that Table 9.3 has only a conversion factor between inches and centimeters. We begin by changing millimeters to centimeters:

$$26,800 \text{ mm} = 2680.0 \text{ cm}$$

Now we need to convert 2680 centimeters to inches. We use a unit fraction with inches in the numerator and centimeters in the denominator:

$$\frac{1 \text{ in.}}{2.54 \text{ cm}}.$$

Thus,

$$26{,}800 \text{ mm} = 2680 \text{ cm} = \frac{2680 \text{ cm}}{1} \cdot \frac{1 \text{ in.}}{2.54 \text{ cm}} = \frac{2680}{2.54} \text{in.} \approx 1055 \text{ in.}$$

This measure is equivalent to about 88 feet, the length of the largest dinosaur from the Jurassic period. The diplodocus, a plant eater, was 26.8 meters, approximately 88 feet, long.

a. Convert 8 feet to centimeters.

b. Convert 20 meters to yards.

c. Convert 30 meters to inches.

So far, we have used dimensional analysis to change units of length. Dimensional analysis may also be used to convert other kinds of measures, such as speed.

EXAMPLE 4   USING DIMENSIONAL ANALYSIS

a. The speed limit on many highways in the United States is 55 miles per hour (mi/hr). How many kilometers per hour (km/hr) is this?

b. If a high-speed train in Japan is capable of traveling at 200 kilometers per hour, how many miles per hour is this?

SOLUTION

a. To change miles per hour to kilometers per hour, we need to concentrate on changing miles to kilometers, so we need a unit fraction with kilometers in the numerator and miles in the denominator:

$$\frac{1.6 \text{ km}}{1 \text{ mi}}.$$

Thus,

$$\frac{55 \text{ mi}}{\text{hr}} = \frac{55 \text{ mi}}{\text{hr}} \cdot \frac{1.6 \text{ km}}{1 \text{ mi}} = 55(1.6) \frac{\text{km}}{\text{hr}} = 88 \text{ km/hr}.$$

This shows that 55 miles per hour is equivalent to 88 kilometers per hour.

b. To change 200 kilometers per hour to miles per hour, we must convert kilometers to miles. We need a unit fraction with miles in the numerator and kilometers in the denominator:

$$\frac{1 \text{ mi}}{1.6 \text{ km}}.$$

Thus,

$$\frac{200 \text{ km}}{\text{hr}} = \frac{200 \text{ km}}{\text{hr}} \cdot \frac{1 \text{ mi}}{1.6 \text{ km}} = \frac{200}{1.6} \frac{\text{mi}}{\text{hr}} = 125 \text{ mi/hr}.$$

A train capable of traveling at 200 kilometers per hour can therefore travel at 125 miles per hour.

A road in Europe has a speed limit of 60 kilometers per hour. How many miles per hour is this?

The Mars Climate Orbiter

If you think that using dimensional analysis to change to and from the metric system is no big deal, consider this: The Mars Climate Orbiter, launched on December 11, 1998, was lost when it crashed into Mars about a year later due to failure to properly convert English units into metric units. The price tag: $125 million!

EXERCISE SET 9.1 ●●●●●●

• Practice Exercises

In Exercises 1–16, use dimensional analysis to convert the quantity to the indicated unit. If necessary, round the answer to two decimal places.

1. 30 in. to ft
2. 100 in. to ft
3. 30 ft to in.
4. 100 ft to in.
5. 6 in. to yd
6. 21 in. to yd
7. 6 yd to in.
8. 21 yd to in.
9. 6 yd to ft
10. 12 yd to ft
11. 6 ft to yd
12. 12 ft to yd
13. 23,760 ft to mi
14. 19,800 ft to mi
15. 0.75 mi to ft
16. 0.25 mi to ft

In Exercises 17–26, use the diagram in the box on page 511 to convert the given measurement to the unit indicated.

17. 5 m to cm
18. 8 dam to m
19. 16.3 hm to m
20. 0.37 hm to m
21. 317.8 cm to hm
22. 8.64 hm to cm
23. 0.023 mm to m
24. 0.00037 km to cm
25. 2196 mm to dm
26. 71 dm to km

In Exercises 27–44, use the following English and metric equivalents, along with dimensional analysis, to convert the given measurement to the unit indicated.

Approximate English and Metric Equivalents

$$1 \text{ in.} = 2.54 \text{ cm}$$
$$1 \text{ ft} = 30.48 \text{ cm}$$
$$1 \text{ yd} = 0.9 \text{ m}$$
$$1 \text{ mi} = 1.6 \text{ km}$$

27. 14 in. to cm
28. 26 in. to cm
29. 14 cm to in.
30. 26 cm to in.
31. 265 mi to km
32. 776 mi to km
33. 265 km to mi
34. 776 km to mi
35. 12 m to yd
36. 20 m to yd
37. 14 dm to in.
38. 1.2 dam to in.
39. 160 in. to dam
40. 180 in. to hm
41. 5 ft to m
42. 8 ft to m
43. 5 m to ft
44. 8 m to ft

Use 1 mi = 1.6 km to solve Exercises 45–48.

45. Express 96 kilometers per hour in miles per hour.
46. Express 104 kilometers per hour in miles per hour.
47. Express 45 miles per hour in kilometers per hour.
48. Express 50 miles per hour in kilometers per hour.

• Practice Plus

In Exercises 49–52, use the unit fractions

$$\frac{36 \text{ in.}}{1 \text{ yd}} \quad \text{and} \quad \frac{2.54 \text{ cm}}{1 \text{ in.}}.$$

49. Convert 5 yd to cm.
50. Convert 8 yd to cm.
51. Convert 762 cm to yd.
52. Convert 1016 cm to yd.

In Exercises 53–54, use the unit fractions

$$\frac{5280 \text{ ft}}{1 \text{ mi}}, \quad \frac{12 \text{ in.}}{1 \text{ ft}}, \quad \text{and} \quad \frac{2.54 \text{ cm}}{1 \text{ in.}}.$$

53. Convert 30 mi to km.
54. Convert 50 mi to km.
55. Use unit fractions to express 120 miles per hour in feet per second.
56. Use unit fractions to express 100 miles per hour in feet per second.

• Application Exercises

In Exercises 57–66, selecting from millimeter, meter, and kilometer, determine the best unit of measure to express the given length.

57. A person's height
58. The length of a football field
59. The length of a bee
60. The distance from New York City to Washington, D.C.
61. The distance around a one-acre lot
62. The length of a car
63. The width of a book
64. The altitude of an airplane
65. The diameter of a screw
66. The width of a human foot

In Exercises 67–74, select the best estimate for the measure of the given item.

67. The length of a pen
    a. 30 cm   **b.** 19 cm   **c.** 19 mm
68. The length of this page
    a. 2.5 mm   **b.** 25 mm   **c.** 250 mm
69. The height of a skyscraper
    a. 325 m   **b.** 32.5 km   **c.** 325 km   **d.** 3250 km
70. The length of a pair of pants
    a. 700 cm   **b.** 70 cm   **c.** 7 cm
71. The height of a room
    a. 4 mm   **b.** 4 cm   **c.** 4 m   **d.** 4 dm
72. The length of a rowboat
    a. 4 cm   **b.** 4 dm   **c.** 4 m   **d.** 4 dam
73. The width of an electric cord
    a. 4 mm   **b.** 4 cm   **c.** 4 dm   **d.** 4 m
74. The dimensions of a piece of typing paper
    a. 22 mm by 28 mm   **b.** 22 cm by 28 cm
    c. 22 dm by 28 dm   **d.** 22 m by 28 m
75. A baseball diamond measures 27 meters along each side. If a batter scored two home runs in a game, how many kilometers did the batter run?
76. If you jog six times around a track that is 700 meters long, how many kilometers have you covered?
77. The distance from the Earth to the sun is about 93 million miles. What is this distance in kilometers?
78. The distance from New York City to Los Angeles is 4690 kilometers. What is the distance in miles?

• Writing in Mathematics

79. Describe the two parts of a measurement.

80. Describe how to use dimensional analysis to convert 20 inches to feet.

81. Describe advantages of the metric system over the English system.

82. Explain how to change units within the metric system.

83. You jog 500 meters in a given period of time. The next day, you jog 500 yards over the same time period. On which day was your speed faster? Explain your answer.

84. What kind of difficulties might arise if the United States immediately eliminated all units of measure in the English system and replaced the system by the metric system?

85. The United States is the only Westernized country that does not use the metric system as its primary system of measurement. What reasons might be given for continuing to use the English system?

• Critical Thinking Exercises

In Exercises 86–90, convert to an appropriate metric unit so that the numerical expression in the given measure does not contain any zeros.

86. 6000 cm   **87.** 900 m   **88.** 7000 dm

89. 11,000 mm   **90.** 0.0002 km

SECTION 9.2 • MEASURING AREA AND VOLUME

O B J E C T I V E S

1. Use square units to measure area.

2. Use dimensional analysis to change units for area.

3. Use cubic units to measure volume.

4. Use English and metric units to measure capacity.

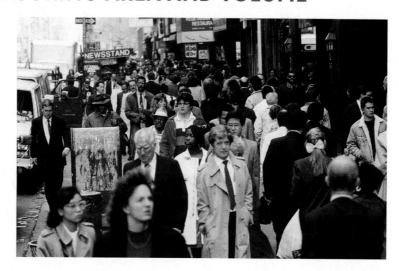

Are you feeling a bit crowded in? Although there are more people on the East coast of the United States than there are bears, there are places in the Northwest where bears outnumber humans. The most densely populated state is New Jersey, averaging 1134.5 people per square mile. The least densely populated state is Alaska, averaging 1.1 persons per square mile.

A square mile is one way of measuring the **area** of a state. A state's area is the region within its boundaries. Its **population density** is its population divided by its area. In this section, we discuss methods for measuring both area and volume.

1 | Use square units to measure area.

1 unit

1 unit

FIGURE 9.2 One square unit

Measuring Area

In order to measure a region that is enclosed by boundaries, we begin by selecting a **square unit**. A square unit is a square, each of whose sides is one unit in length, illustrated in Figure 9.2. The region in Figure 9.2 is said to have an area of **one square unit**. The side of the square can be 1 inch, 1 centimeter, 1 meter, 1 foot, or 1 of any linear unit of measure. The corresponding units of area are the square inch ($in.^2$), the square centimeter (cm^2), the square meter (m^2), the square foot (ft^2), and so on. Figure 9.3 illustrates 1 square inch and 1 square centimeter, drawn to actual size.

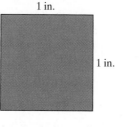

1 in.

1 in.

1 square inch, symbolized 1 $in.^2$

1 cm

1 cm

1 square centimeter, symbolized 1 cm^2

FIGURE 9.3 Common units of measurement for area, drawn to actual size

Square Unit

FIGURE 9.4

EXAMPLE 1 MEASURING AREA

What is the area of the region shown in Figure 9.4?

SOLUTION We can determine the area of the region by counting the number of square units contained within the region. There are 12 such units. Therefore, the area of the region is 12 square units.

CHECK POINT 1 What is the area of the region represented by the first two rows in Figure 9.4?

Although there are 12 inches in one foot and 3 feet in one yard, these numerical relationships are not the same for square units.

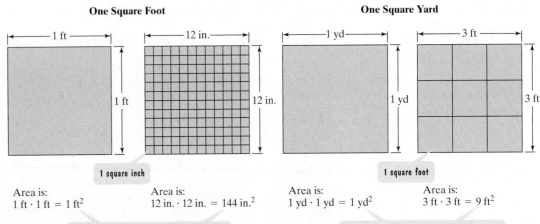

One Square Foot

Area is:
1 ft · 1 ft = 1 ft²

Area is:
12 in. · 12 in. = 144 in.²

Because the two figures have the same area,
1 ft² = 144 in.²

One Square Yard

Area is:
1 yd · 1 yd = 1 yd²

Area is:
3 ft · 3 ft = 9 ft²

Because the two figures have the same area,
1 yd² = 9 ft².

STUDY TIP

A small plot of land is usually measured in square feet, rather than a small fraction of an acre. Curiously, square yards are rarely used. However, square yards are commonly used for carpet and flooring measures.

SQUARE UNITS OF MEASURE: THE ENGLISH SYSTEM

$$1 \text{ square foot (ft}^2) = 144 \text{ square inches (in.}^2)$$
$$1 \text{ square yard (yd}^2) = 9 \text{ square feet (ft}^2)$$
$$1 \text{ acre (a)} = 43{,}560 \text{ ft}^2 \text{ or } 4840 \text{ yd}^2$$
$$1 \text{ square mile (mi}^2) = 640 \text{ acres}$$

EXAMPLE 2 USING SQUARE UNITS TO COMPUTE POPULATION DENSITY

After Alaska, Wyoming is the least densely populated state. The population of Wyoming is 506,529 and its area is 97,814 square miles. What is Wyoming's population density?

SOLUTION We compute the population density by dividing Wyoming's population by its area.

$$\text{population density} = \frac{\text{population}}{\text{area}} = \frac{506{,}529 \text{ people}}{97{,}814 \text{ square miles}}$$

Using a calculator and rounding to the nearest tenth, we obtain a population density of 5.2 people per square mile. This means that there is an average of only 5.2 people for each square mile of area.

CHECK POINT 2 The population of California is 35,893,799 and its area is 163,696 square miles. What is California's population density?

---

2 Use dimensional analysis to change units for area.

One theory is that using square units to measure area has its origin in the weaving of fabric.

In Section 9.1, we saw that in most other countries, the system of measurement that is used is the metric system. In the metric system, the square centimeter is used instead of the square inch. The square meter replaces the square foot and the square yard.

The English system uses the acre and the square mile to measure large land areas. The metric system uses the hectare (symbolized ha and pronounced "hectair"). A hectare is about the area of two football fields placed side by side, approximately 2.5 acres. One square mile of land consists of approximately 260 hectares. Just as the hectare replaces the acre, the square kilometer is used instead of the square mile. One square kilometer is approximately 0.38 square mile.

Some basic approximate conversions for units of area are given in Table 9.4.

TABLE 9.4 ENGLISH AND METRIC EQUIVALENTS FOR AREA	
1 square inch (in.^{2})	= 6.5 square centimeters (cm^2)
1 square foot (ft^2)	= 0.09 square meter (m^2)
1 square yard (yd^2)	= 0.8 square meter (m^2)
1 square mile (mi^2)	= 2.6 square kilometers (km^2)
1 acre	= 0.4 hectare (ha)

EXAMPLE 3 USING DIMENSIONAL ANALYSIS ON UNITS OF AREA

A property in Italy is advertised at $545,000 for 6.8 hectares.

a. Find the area of the property in acres.

b. What is the price per acre?

SOLUTION

a. Using Table 9.4, we see that 1 acre = 0.4 hectare. To convert 6.8 hectares to acres, we use a unit fraction with acres in the numerator and hectares in the denominator.

$$6.8 \text{ ha} = \frac{6.8 \text{ ha}}{1} \cdot \frac{1 \text{ acre}}{0.4 \text{ ha}} = \frac{6.8}{0.4} \text{ acres} = 17 \text{ acres}$$

The area of the property is 17 acres.

b. The price per acre is the total price, $545,000, divided by the number of acres, 17.

$$\text{price per acre} = \frac{\$545,000}{17 \text{ acres}} \approx \$32,059/\text{acre}$$

The price is approximately $32,059 per acre.

CHECK POINT 3 A property in Northern California is on the market at $415,000 for 1.8 acres.

a. Find the area of the property in hectares.

b. What is the price per hectare?

3 | Use cubic units to measure volume.

Measuring Volume

A shoe box and a basketball are examples of three-dimensional figures. **Volume** refers to the amount of space occupied by such figures. In order to measure this space, we begin by selecting a *cubic unit*. Two such cubic units are shown in Figure 9.5.

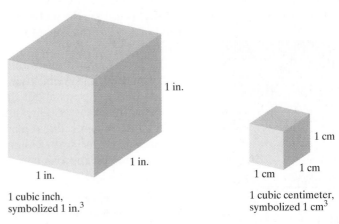

1 in.
1 in.
1 in.
1 cubic inch, symbolized 1 in.³

1 cm
1 cm
1 cm
1 cubic centimeter, symbolized 1 cm³

FIGURE 9.5 Common units of measurement for volume

The edges of a cube all have the same length. Other cubic units used to measure volume include 1 cubic foot (1 ft³) and 1 cubic meter (1 m³). One way to measure the volume of a solid is to calculate the number of cubic units contained in its interior.

Cubic unit　　Volume = ?

FIGURE 9.6

EXAMPLE 4　MEASURING VOLUME

What is the volume of the solid shown in Figure 9.6?

SOLUTION We can determine the volume of the solid by counting the number of cubic units contained within the region. Because we have drawn a solid three-dimensional figure on a flat two-dimensional page, some of the small cubic units in the back, right are hidden. The figures below show how the cubic units are used to fill the inside of the solid.

Do these figures help you to see that there are 18 cubic units inside the solid? The volume of the solid is 18 cubic units.

 What is the volume of the region represented by the bottom row of blocks in Figure 9.6?

We have seen that there are 3 feet in a yard, but 9 square feet in a square yard. Neither of these relationships holds for cubic units. Figure 9.7 illustrates that there are 27 cubic feet in a cubic yard. Furthermore, there are 1728 cubic inches in a cubic foot.

$$3 \text{ ft} = 1 \text{ yd}$$
$$(3 \text{ ft})^3 = (1 \text{ yd})^3$$
$$3 \cdot 3 \cdot 3 \text{ ft}^3 = 1 \cdot 1 \cdot 1 \text{ yd}^3.$$

Conclusion: $27 \text{ ft}^3 = 1 \text{ yd}^3$

$$12 \text{ in.} = 1 \text{ ft}$$
$$(12 \text{ in.})^3 = (1 \text{ ft})^3$$
$$12 \cdot 12 \cdot 12 \text{ in.}^3 = 1 \cdot 1 \cdot 1 \text{ ft}^3$$

Conclusion: $1728 \text{ in.}^3 = 1 \text{ ft}^3$

4 Use English and metric units to measure capacity.

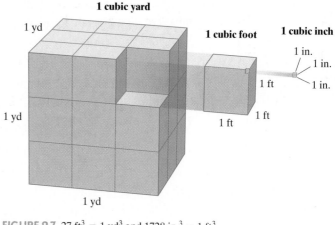

FIGURE 9.7 $27 \text{ ft}^3 = 1 \text{ yd}^3$ and $1728 \text{ in.}^3 = 1 \text{ ft}^3$

The measure of volume also includes the amount of fluid that a three-dimensional object can hold. This is often called the object's **capacity.** For example, we often refer to the capacity, in gallons, of a gas tank. A cubic yard has a capacity of about 200 gallons and a cubic foot has a capacity of about 7.48 gallons.

Table 9.5 contains information about standard units of capacity in the English system.

TABLE 9.5 ENGLISH UNITS FOR CAPACITY

2 pints (pt)	= 1 quart (qt)
4 quarts	= 1 gallon (gal)
1 gallon	= 128 ounces (oz)
1 cup (c)	= 8 ounces

Volume in Cubic Units	Capacity
1 cubic yard	about 200 gallons
1 cubic foot	about 7.48 gallons
231 cubic inches	about 1 gallon

EXAMPLE 5   VOLUME AND CAPACITY IN THE ENGLISH SYSTEM

A swimming pool has a volume of 22,500 cubic feet. How many gallons of water does the pool hold?

SOLUTION We use the fact that 1 cubic foot has a capacity of about 7.48 gallons to set up our unit fraction:

$$\frac{7.48 \text{ gal}}{1 \text{ ft}^3}.$$

We use this unit fraction to find the capacity of the 22,500 cubic feet.

$$22,500 \text{ ft}^3 = \frac{22,500 \text{ ft}^3}{1} \cdot \frac{7.48 \text{ gal}}{1 \text{ ft}^3} = 22,500(7.48) \text{ gal} = 168,300 \text{ gal}$$

The pool holds approximately 168,300 gallons of water.

 A pool has a volume of 10,000 cubic feet. How many gallons of water does the pool hold?

1 liter   1 quart

As we have come to expect, things are simpler when the metric system is used to measure capacity. The basic unit is the **liter,** symbolized by L. A liter is slightly larger than a quart.

$$1 \text{ liter} \approx 1.0567 \text{ quarts}$$

The standard metric prefixes are used to denote a multiple or part of a liter. Table 9.6 applies these prefixes to the liter.

TABLE 9.6 UNITS OF CAPACITY IN THE METRIC SYSTEM		
Symbol	**Unit**	**Meaning**
kL	kiloliter	1000 liters
hL	hectoliter	100 liters
daL	dekaliter	10 liters
L	liter	1 liter $\approx$ 1.06 quarts
dL	deciliter	0.1 liter
cL	centiliter	0.01 liter
mL	milliliter	0.001 liter

The following list should help give you a feel for capacity in the metric system.

Item	Capacity
Average cup of coffee	250 mL
12-ounce can of soda	355 mL
One quart of fruit juice	0.95 L
One gallon of milk	3.78 L
Average gas capacity of a car (about 18.5 gallons)	70 L

Figure 9.8 shows a 1-liter container filled with water. The water in the liter container will fit exactly into the box shown to its right. The volume of this box is 1000 cubic centimeters, or equivalently, 1 cubic decimeter. Thus,

$$1000 \text{ cm}^3 = 1 \text{ dm}^3 = 1 \text{ L}.$$

Table 9.7 expands on this relationship between volume and capacity in the metric system.

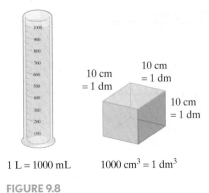

10 cm = 1 dm

10 cm = 1 dm

10 cm = 1 dm

1 L = 1000 mL   1000 cm³ = 1 dm³

FIGURE 9.8

TABLE 9.7 VOLUME AND CAPACITY IN THE METRIC SYSTEM		
Volume in Cubic Units		**Capacity**
1 cm³	=	1 mL
1 dm³ = 1000 cm³	=	1 L
1 m³	=	1 kL

EXAMPLE 6   VOLUME AND CAPACITY IN THE METRIC SYSTEM

An aquarium has a volume of 36,000 cubic centimeters. How many liters of water does the aquarium hold?

SOLUTION We use the fact that 1000 cubic centimeters corresponds to a capacity of 1 liter to set up our unit fraction:

$$\frac{1 \text{ L}}{1000 \text{ cm}^3}.$$

We use this unit fraction to find the capacity of the 36,000 cubic centimeters.

$$36,000 \text{ cm}^3 = \frac{36,000 \text{ cm}^3}{1} \cdot \frac{1 \text{ L}}{1000 \text{ cm}^3} = \frac{36,000}{1000} \text{L} = 36 \text{ L}$$

The aquarium holds 36 liters of water.

CHECK POINT 6 A fish pond has a volume of 220,000 cubic centimeters. How many liters of water does the pond hold?

EXERCISE SET 9.2 ●●●●●●

Practice Exercises

In Exercises 1–4, use the given figure to find its area in square units.

1.

2.

3.

4.

In Exercises 5–12, use Table 9.4 on page 519, along with dimensional analysis, to convert the given square unit to the square unit indicated. Where necessary, round answers to two decimal places.

5. 14 cm² to in.²
6. 20 m² to ft²
7. 30 m² to yd²
8. 14 mi² to km²
9. 10.2 ha to acres
10. 20.6 ha to acres
11. 14 in.² to cm²
12. 20 in.² to cm²

In Exercises 13–14, use the given figure to find its volume in cubic units.

13.

14.

In Exercises 15–22, use Table 9.5 on page 521, along with dimensional analysis, to convert the given unit to the unit indicated. Where necessary, round answers to two decimal places.

15. 10,000 ft³ to gal
16. 25,000 ft³ to gal
17. 8 yd³ to gal
18. 35 yd³ to gal
19. 2079 in.³ to gal
20. 6237 in.³ to gal
21. 2700 gal to yd³
22. 1496 gal to ft³

In Exercises 23–32, use Table 9.7 on page 522, along with dimensional analysis, to convert the given unit to the unit indicated.

23. 45,000 cm³ to L
24. 75,000 cm³ to L
25. 17 cm³ to mL
26. 19 cm³ to mL
27. 1.5 L to cm³
28. 4.5 L to cm³
29. 150 mL to cm³
30. 250 mL to cm³
31. 12 kL to dm³
32. 16 kL to dm³

• Practice Plus

The bar graph shows the resident population and the land area of the United States for selected years from 1800 through 2000. Use the information shown by the graph to solve Exercises 33–36.

U.S. Resident Population and Land Area

Source: U.S. Bureau of the Census

33. a. Find the population density of the United States, to the nearest tenth, in 1900 and in 2000.

 b. Find the percent increase in population density, to the nearest tenth of a percent, from 1900 to 2000.

34. a. Find the population density of the United States, to the nearest tenth, in 1800 and in 2000.

 b. Find the percent increase in population density, to the nearest tenth of a percent, from 1800 to 2000.

35. Find the population density of the United States, to the nearest tenth, expressed in people per square kilometer, in 1940.

36. Find the population density of the United States, to the nearest tenth, expressed in people per square kilometer, in 1980.

• Application Exercises

37. A property that measures 8 hectares is for sale.

   a. How large is the property in acres?

   b. If the property is selling for $250,000, what is the price per acre?

38. A property that measures 100 hectares is for sale.

   a. How large is the property in acres?

   b. If the property is selling for $350,000, what is the price per acre?

In Exercises 39–42, selecting from square centimeters, square meters, or square kilometers, determine the best unit of measure to express the area of the object described.

39. The top of a desk   **40.** A dollar bill

41. A national park   **42.** The wall of a room

In Exercises 43–46, select the best estimate for the measure of the area of the object described.

43. The area of the floor of a room

   a. 25 cm^2 **b.** 25 m^2 **c.** 25 km^2

44. The area of a television screen

   a. 2050 mm^2 **b.** 2050 cm^2 **c.** 2050 dm^2

45. The area of the face of a small coin

   a. 6 mm^2 **b.** 6 cm^2 **c.** 6 dm^2

46. The area of a parcel of land in a large metropolitan area on which a house can be built

   a. 900 cm^2 **b.** 900 m^2 **c.** 900 ha

47. A swimming pool has a volume of 45,000 cubic feet. How many gallons of water does the pool hold?

48. A swimming pool has a volume of 66,000 cubic feet. How many gallons of water does the pool hold?

49. A container of grapefruit juice has a volume of 4000 cubic centimeters. How many liters of juice does the container hold?

50. An aquarium has a volume of 17,500 cubic centimeters. How many liters of water does the aquarium hold?

• Writing in Mathematics

51. Describe how area is measured. Explain why linear units cannot be used.

52. New Mexico has a population density of 15 people per square mile. Describe what this means. Use an almanac or the Internet to compare this population density to that of the state in which you are now living.

53. Describe the difference between the following problems: How much fencing is needed to enclose a garden? How much fertilizer is needed for the garden?

54. Describe how volume is measured. Explain why linear or square units cannot be used.

55. For a swimming pool, what is the difference between the following units of measure: cubic feet and gallons? For each unit, write a sentence about the pool that makes the use of the unit appropriate.

56. If there are 10 decimeters in a meter, explain why there are not 10 cubic decimeters in a cubic meter.

• Critical Thinking Exercises

57. Singapore has the highest population density of any country: 46,690 people per 1000 hectares. How many people are there per square mile?

58. Nebraska has a population density of 22.3 people per square mile and a population of 1,747,214. What is the area of Nebraska?

59. A high population density is a condition common to extremely poor and extremely rich locales. Explain why this is so.

60. Although Alaska is the least densely populated state, over 90% of its land is protected federal property that is off-limits to settlement. A resident of Anchorage, Alaska, might feel hemmed in. In terms of "elbow room," what other important factor must be considered when calculating a state's population density?

61. Does an adult's body contain approximately 6.5 liters, kiloliters, or milliliters of blood? Explain your answer.

62. Is the volume of a coin approximately 1 cubic centimeter, 1 cubic millimeter, or 1 cubic decimeter? Explain your answer.

• Group Exercise

63. If you could select any place in the world, where would you like to live? Look up the population and area of your ideal place, and compute its population density. Group members should share places to live and population densities. What trend, if any, does the group observe?

SECTION 9.3 • MEASURING WEIGHT AND TEMPERATURE

You are watching CNN International on cable television. The temperature in Honolulu, Hawaii, is reported as 30°C. Are Honolulu's tourists running around in winter jackets? In this section, we will make sense of Celsius temperature readings, as we discuss methods for measuring temperature and weight.

Measuring Weight

You step on the scale at the doctor's office to check your weight, discovering that you are 150 pounds. Compare this to your weight on the moon: 25 pounds. Why the difference? **Weight** is the measure of the gravitational pull on an object. The gravitational pull on the moon is only about one-sixth the gravitational pull on Earth. Although your weight varies depending on the force of gravity, your mass is exactly the same in all locations. **Mass** is a measure of the quantity of matter in an object, determined by its molecular structure. On Earth, as your weight increases, so does your mass. In this section, we will treat weight and mass as equivalent and refer strictly to weight.

> ### UNITS OF WEIGHT: THE ENGLISH SYSTEM
>
> 16 ounces (oz) = 1 pound (lb)
>
> 2000 pounds (lb) = 1 ton (T)

1 Apply metric prefixes to units of weight.

The basic metric unit of weight is the **gram** (g), used for very small objects such as a coin, a candy bar, or a teaspoon of salt. A nickel has a weight of about 5 grams.

As with meters, prefixes are used to denote a multiple or part of a gram. Table 9.8 applies the common metric prefixes to the gram. The first part of the symbol indicates the prefix and the second part (g) indicates gram.

Symbol	Unit	Meaning
TABLE 9.8 COMMONLY USED UNITS OF WEIGHT IN THE METRIC SYSTEM		
kg	kilogram	1000 grams
hg	hectogram	100 grams
dag	dekagram	10 grams
g	gram	1 gram
dg	decigram	0.1 gram
cg	centigram	0.01 gram
mg	milligram	0.001 gram

Weight of paper clip is 1 g.

1 mm thick

1 cm wide

In the metric system, the kilogram is the comparable unit to the pound in the English system. **A weight of 1 kilogram is approximately 2.2 pounds.** Thus, an average man has a weight of about 75 kilograms. Objects that we measure in pounds are measured in kilograms in most countries.

A milligram, equivalent to 0.001 gram, is an extremely small unit of weight and is used extensively in the pharmaceutical industry. If you look at the label on a bottle of tablets, you will see that the amounts of different substances in each tablet are expressed in milligrams.

The weight of a very heavy object is expressed in terms of the metric tonne (t), which is equivalent to 1000 kilograms, or about 2200 pounds. This is 10 percent more than the English ton (T) of 2000 pounds.

We change units of weight within the metric system exactly the same way that we changed units of length.

2 Convert units of weight within the metric system.

CHANGING UNITS OF WEIGHT WITHIN THE METRIC SYSTEM

Use the following diagram to find equivalent measures of weight:

Multiply by 10 for each step to the right.

kg hg dag g dg cg mg.

Divide by 10 for each step to the left.

EXAMPLE 1   CHANGING UNITS WITHIN THE METRIC SYSTEM

a. Convert 8.7 dg to mg.

b. Convert 950 mg to g.

SOLUTION

a. To convert from dg (decigrams) to mg (milligrams), we start at dg and move two steps to the right:

$$\text{kg hg dag g dg cg mg.}$$

Hence, we move the decimal point two places to the right:

$$8.7 \text{ dg} = 870 \text{ mg.}$$

b. To convert from mg (milligrams) to g (grams), we start at mg and move three steps to the left:

$$\text{kg hg dag g dg cg mg.}$$

Hence, we move the decimal point three places to the left:

$$950 \text{ mg} = 0.950 \text{ g.}$$

a. Convert 4.2 dg to mg.

b. Convert 620 cg to g.

---

3 Use relationships between volume and weight within the metric system.

We have seen a convenient relationship in the metric system between volume and capacity:

$$1000 \text{ cm}^3 = 1 \text{ dm}^3 = 1 \text{ L.}$$

This relationship can be extended to include weight based on the following:

One kilogram of water has a volume of 1 liter.

Thus,

$$1000 \text{ cm}^3 = 1 \text{ dm}^3 = 1 \text{ L} = 1 \text{ kg.}$$

Table 9.9 shows the relationships between volume and weight of water in the metric system.

TABLE 9.9 VOLUME AND WEIGHT OF WATER IN THE METRIC SYSTEM

Volume		Capacity		Weight
1 cm^3	=	1 mL	= 1 g	
$1 \text{ dm}^3 = 1000 \text{ cm}^3$	=	1 L	= 1 kg	
1 m^3	=	1 kL	= 1000 kg = 1 t	

EXAMPLE 2 VOLUME AND WEIGHT IN THE METRIC SYSTEM

An aquarium holds 0.25 m^3 of water. How much does the water weigh?

SOLUTION We use the fact that 1 m^3 of water $= 1000$ kg of water to set up our unit fraction:

$$\frac{1000 \text{ kg}}{1 \text{ m}^3}.$$

Thus,

$$0.25 \text{ m}^3 = \frac{0.25 \text{ m}^3}{1} \cdot \frac{1000 \text{ kg}}{1 \text{ m}^3} = 250 \text{ kg}.$$

The water weighs 250 kilograms.

 An aquarium holds 0.145 m^3 of water. How much does the water weigh?

A problem like Example 2 involves more awkward computation in the English system. For example, if you know the aquarium's volume in cubic feet, you must also know that 1 cubic foot of water weighs about 62.5 pounds to determine the water's weight.

Dimensional analysis is a useful tool when converting units of weight between the English and metric systems. Some basic conversions are given in Table 9.10.

4 Use dimensional analysis to change units of weight to and from the metric system.

TABLE 9.10 WEIGHT: ENGLISH AND METRIC EQUIVALENTS

1 ounce (oz) = 28 grams (g)
1 pound (lb) = 0.45 kilogram (kg)
1 ton (T)   = 0.9 tonne (t)

EXAMPLE 3 USING DIMENSIONAL ANALYSIS

a. Convert 160 pounds to kilograms.

b. Convert 300 grams to ounces.

SOLUTION

a. To convert 160 pounds to kilograms, we use a unit fraction with kilograms in the numerator and pounds in the denominator:

$$\frac{0.45 \text{ kg}}{1 \text{ lb}}. \qquad \text{Table 9.10 shows that 1 lb} = 0.45 \text{ kg.}$$

Thus,

$$160 \text{ lb} = \frac{160 \text{ lb}}{1} \cdot \frac{0.45 \text{ kg}}{1 \text{ lb}} = 160(0.45) \text{ kg} = 72 \text{ kg}.$$

b. To convert 300 grams to ounces, we use a unit fraction with ounces in the numerator and grams in the denominator:

$$\frac{1 \text{ oz}}{28 \text{ g}}.$$ Table 9.10 shows that 1 oz = 28 g.

Thus,

$$300 \text{ g} = \frac{300 \text{ g}}{1} \cdot \frac{1 \text{ oz}}{28 \text{ g}} = \frac{300}{28} \text{ oz} \approx 10.7 \text{ oz}.$$

CHECK POINT 3

a. A man weighs 186 pounds. Convert his weight to kilograms.

b. For each kilogram of weight, 1.2 milligrams of a drug is to be given. What dosage should a 186-pound man be given?

BLITZER BONUS

Using the Metric System to Measure Blood Alcohol Concentration

Blood alcohol concentration (BAC) is measured in grams of alcohol per 100 milliliters of blood. To put this measurement into perspective, a 175-pound man has approximately 5 liters (5000 milliliters) of blood and a 12-ounce can of 6%-alcohol-by-volume beer contains about 15 grams of alcohol. Based on the time it takes for alcohol to be absorbed into the bloodstream, as well as its elimination at a rate of 10–15 grams per hour, Figure 9.9 shows the effect on BAC of a number of drinks on individuals within weight classes. It is illegal to drive with a BAC at 0.08 g/100 mL, or 0.8 gram of alcohol per 100 milliliters of blood, or greater.

Blood Alcohol Concentration by Number of Drinks and Weight

BAC: 0.01–0.04
Brain function impaired at 0.04 according to the American Medical Association

BAC: 0.05–0.07
Likely
DUI

BAC: ≥ 0.08
Definite DUI (coma, possibly death, ≥ 0.4)

Weight (pounds): 90—149, 150—169, 170—189, 190 or more

Number of Drinks Over Two Hours
(12-oz can of beer or 4-oz wine
or 1.25-oz 80-proof liquor)

FIGURE 9.9
Source: Patrick McSharry, *Everyday Numbers*, Random House, 2002

---

5 Understand temperature scales.

Measuring Temperature

You'll be leaving the cold of winter for a vacation to Hawaii. CNN International reports a temperature in Hawaii of 30°C. Should you pack a winter coat?

The idea of changing from Celsius readings—or is it Centigrade?—to familiar Fahrenheit readings can be disorienting. Reporting a temperature of 30°C doesn't have the same impact as the Fahrenheit equivalent of 86 degrees (don't pack the coat). Why these annoying temperature scales?

The **Fahrenheit temperature scale**, the one we are accustomed to, was established in 1714 by the German physicist Gabriel Daniel Fahrenheit. He took a mixture of salt and ice, then thought to be the coldest possible temperature, and called it 0 degrees. He called the temperature of the human body 96 degrees, dividing the space between 0 and 96 into 96 parts. Fahrenheit was wrong about body temperature. It was later found to be 98.6 degrees. On his scale, water froze (without salt) at 32 degrees and boiled at 212 degrees. The symbol ° was used to replace the word *degree*.

Twenty years later, the Swedish scientist Anders Celsius introduced another temperature scale. He set the freezing point of water at 0° and its boiling point at 100°, dividing the space into 100 parts. Degrees were called centigrade until 1948, when the name was officially changed to honor its inventor. However, *centigrade* is still commonly used in the United States.

FIGURE 9.10 The Celsius scale is on the left and the Fahrenheit scale is on the right.

Figure 9.10 shows a thermometer that measures temperatures in both degrees Celsius (°C is the scale on the left) and degrees Fahrenheit (°F is the scale on the right). The thermometer should help orient you if you need to know what a temperature in °C means. For example, if it is 40°C, find the horizontal line representing this temperature on the left. Now read across to the °F scale on the right. The reading is above 100°, indicating heat wave conditions.

The following formulas can be used to convert from one temperature scale to the other:

FROM CELSIUS TO FAHRENHEIT

$$F = \frac{9}{5}C + 32$$

FROM FAHRENHEIT TO CELSIUS

$$C = \frac{5}{9}(F - 32)$$

EXAMPLE 4   CONVERTING FROM CELSIUS TO FAHRENHEIT

The bills from your European vacation have you feeling a bit feverish, so you decide to take your temperature. The thermometer reads 37°C. Should you panic?

SOLUTION Use the formula

$$F = \frac{9}{5}C + 32$$

to convert 37°C from °C to °F. Substitute 37 for C in the formula and find the value of F.

$$F = \frac{9}{5}(37) + 32 = 66.6 + 32 = 98.6$$

No need to panic! Your temperature is 98.6°F, which is perfectly normal.

 Convert 50°C from °C to °F.

EXAMPLE 5   CONVERTING FROM FAHRENHEIT TO CELSIUS

The temperature on a warm spring day is 77°F. Find the equivalent temperature on the Celsius scale.

SOLUTION Use the formula

$$C = \frac{5}{9}(F - 32)$$

to convert 77°F from °F to °C. Substitute 77 for F in the formula and find the value of C.

$$C = \frac{5}{9}(77 - 32) = \frac{5}{9}(45) = 25$$

Thus, 77°F is equivalent to 25°C.

 Convert 59°F from °F to °C.

Lake Baikal, Siberia, is one of the coldest places on Earth, reaching −76°F (−60°C) in winter. The lowest temperature possible is absolute zero. Scientists have cooled atoms to a few millionths of a degree above absolute zero.

Because temperature is a measure of heat, scientists do not find negative temperatures meaningful in their work. In 1948, the British physicist Lord Kelvin introduced a third temperature scale. He put 0 degrees at absolute zero, the coldest possible temperature, at which there is no heat and molecules stop moving. Figure 9.11 illustrates the three temperature scales.

	Kelvin	Celsius	Fahrenheit	
	373.15 K	100° C	212° F	Water boils
	273.15 K	0° C	32° F	Water freezes
	0 K	−273.15° C	−459.67° F	Absolute zero

FIGURE 9.11 The three temperature scales

Figure 9.11 shows that water freezes at 273.15 K (read "K" or "Kelvins," not "degrees Kelvin") and boils at 373.15 K. The Kelvin scale is the same as the Celsius scale, except in its starting (zero) point. This makes it easy to go back and forth from Celsius to Kelvin.

FROM CELSIUS TO KELVIN
$$K = C + 273.15$$

FROM KELVIN TO CELSIUS
$$C = K - 273.15$$

Kelvin's scale was embraced by the scientific community. Today, it is the final authority, as scientists define Celsius and Fahrenheit in terms of Kelvins.

EXERCISE SET 9.3 ●●●●●●

• Practice Exercises

In Exercises 1–10, convert the given unit of weight to the unit indicated.

1. 7.4 dg to mg
2. 6.9 dg to mg
3. 870 mg to g
4. 640 mg to g
5. 8 g to cg
6. 7 g to cg
7. 18.6 kg to g
8. 0.37 kg to g
9. 0.018 mg to g
10. 0.029 mg to g

In Exercises 11–18, use Table 9.9 on page 527 to convert the given measurement of water to the unit indicated.

11. 0.05 m³ to kg
12. 0.02 m³ to kg
13. 4.2 kg to cm³
14. 5.8 kg to cm³
15. 1100 m³ to t
16. 1500 t to m³
17. 0.04 kL to g
18. 0.03 kL to g

In Exercises 19–30, use the following equivalents, along with dimensional analysis, to convert the given unit to the unit indicated. When necessary, round answers to two decimal places.

$$16 \text{ oz} = 1 \text{ lb}$$
$$2000 \text{ lb} = 1 \text{ T}$$
$$1 \text{ oz} = 28 \text{ g}$$
$$1 \text{ lb} = 0.45 \text{ kg}$$
$$1 \text{ T} = 0.9 \text{ t}$$

19. 36 oz to lb
20. 26 oz to lb
21. 36 oz to g
22. 26 oz to g

23. 540 lb to kg

24. 220 lb to kg

25. 80 lb to g

26. 150 lb to g

27. 540 kg to lb

28. 220 kg to lb

29. 200 t to T

30. 100 t to T

In Exercises 31–38, convert the given Celsius temperature to its equivalent temperature on the Fahrenheit scale. Where appropriate, round to the nearest tenth of a degree.

31. 10°C

32. 20°C

33. 35°C

34. 45°C

35. 57°C

36. 98°C

37. −5°C

38. −10°C

In Exercises 39–50, convert the given Fahrenheit temperature to its equivalent temperature on the Celsius scale. Where appropriate, round to the nearest tenth of a degree.

39. 68°F

40. 86°F

41. 41°F

42. 50°F

43. 72°F

44. 90°F

45. 23°F

46. 14°F

47. 350°F

48. 475°F

49. −22°F

50. −31°F

• Practice Plus

51. The nine points shown below represent Celsius temperatures and their equivalent Fahrenheit temperatures. Also shown is a line that passes through the points.

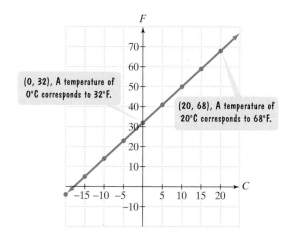

a. Use the coordinates of the two points identified by the voice balloons to compute the line's slope. Express the answer as a fraction reduced to lowest terms. What does this mean about the change in Fahrenheit temperature for each degree change in Celsius temperature?

b. Use the slope-intercept form of the equation of a line, $y = mx + b$, the slope from part (a), and the y-intercept shown by the graph to derive the formula used to convert from Celsius to Fahrenheit.

52. Solve the formula used to convert from Celsius to Fahrenheit for C and derive the other temperature conversion formula.

In Exercises 53–58, determine whether each compound statement is true or false.

53. −40°C = −40°F and 20°C is a reasonable classroom temperature.

54. −85°C = −121°F and 180°C is a reasonable oven temperature for roasting a turkey.

55. This textbook weights approximately 2 mg or the temperature of freezing rain is 0 K.

56. This textbook weighs approximately 6 mg or a good temperature for skiing is 20°C.

57. $(-85°C = -121°F \land -103°F = -75°C) \rightarrow$ normal body temperature is 40°C.

58. Normal body temperature is 40°C $\rightarrow$ $(-85°C = -121°F \land -103°F = -75°C)$.

• Application Exercises

In Exercises 59–65, selecting from milligram, gram, kilogram, and tonne, determine the best unit of measure to express the given item's weight.

59. A bee

60. This book

61. A tablespoon of salt

62. A Boeing 747

63. A stacked washer-dryer

64. A pen

65. An adult male

In Exercises 66–72, select the best estimate for the weight of the given item.

66. A newborn infant's weight

a. 3000 kg   **b.** 300 kg   **c.** 30 kg   **d.** 3 kg

67. The weight of a nickel

a. 5 kg   **b.** 5 g   **c.** 5 mg

68. A person's weight

a. 60 kg   **b.** 60 g   **c.** 60 dag

69. The weight of a box of cereal

a. 0.5 kg   **b.** 0.5 g   **c.** 0.5 t

70. The weight of a glass of water

a. 400 dg   **b.** 400 g   **c.** 400 dag   **d.** 400 hg

71. The weight of a regular-size car

a. 1500 dag   **b.** 1500 hg   **c.** 1500 kg   **d.** 15,000 kg

72. The weight of a bicycle

a. 140 kg   **b.** 140 hg   **c.** 140 dag   **d.** 140 g

73. Six items purchased at a grocery store weigh 14 kilograms. One of the items is detergent weighing 720 grams. What is the total weight, in kilograms, of the other five items?

74. If a nickel weighs 5 grams, how many nickels are there in 4 kilograms of nickels?

75. If the cost to mail a letter is 39 cents for mail weighing up to one ounce and 24 cents for each additional ounce or fraction of an ounce, find the cost of mailing a letter that weighs 85 grams.

76. Using the information given below the pictured finback whale, estimate the weight, in tons and kilograms, of the killer whale.

Killer whale

Weight: 50 T or 45,360 kg

Finback whale

77. Which is more economical: purchasing the economy size of a detergent at 3 kilograms for $3.15 or purchasing the regular size at 720 grams for 60¢?

Exercises 78–79 ask you to determine drug dosage by a patient's weight. Use the fact that 1 lb = 0.45 kg.

78. For each kilogram of a person's weight, 20 milligrams of a drug is to be given. What dosage should be given to a person who weighs 200 pounds?

79. For each kilogram of a person's weight, 2.5 milligrams of a drug is to be given. What dosage should be given to a child who weighs 80 pounds?

The label on a bottle of Emetrol ("for food or drink indiscretions") reads

> *Each 5 mL teaspoonful contains glucose, 1.87 g; levulose, 1.87 g; and phosphoric acid, 21.5 mg.*

Use this information to solve Exercises 80–81.

80. a. Find the amount of glucose in the recommended dosage of two teaspoons.

  b. If the bottle contains 4 ounces, find the quantity of glucose in the bottle. (1 oz = 30 mL)

81. a. Find the amount of phosphoric acid in the recommended dosage of two teaspoons.

  b. If the bottle contains 4 ounces, find the quantity of phosphoric acid in the bottle. (1 oz = 30 mL)

In Exercises 82–85, select the best estimate of the Celsius temperature of

82. A very hot day.
  a. 85°C   **b.** 65°C   **c.** 35°C   **d.** 20°C

83. A warm winter day in Washington, D.C.
  a. 10°C   **b.** 30°C   **c.** 50°C   **d.** 70°C

84. A setting for a home thermostat.
  a. 20°C   **b.** 40°C   **c.** 60°C   **d.** 80°C

85. The oven temperature for cooking a roast.
  a. 80°C   **b.** 100°C   **c.** 175°C   **d.** 350°C

86. Key West, Florida, has the highest average yearly temperature of any city in the United States: 25.7°C. What is this temperature, in °F, to the nearest tenth of a degree?

87. Plateau Station, Antarctica, has the lowest average yearly temperature of any place on Earth: −7°C. What is this temperature, in °F, to the nearest tenth of a degree?

• Writing in Mathematics

88. Describe the difference between weight and mass.

89. Explain how to use dimensional analysis to convert 200 pounds to kilograms.

90. Why do you think that countries using the metric system prefer the Celsius scale over the Fahrenheit scale?

91. Describe in words how to convert from Celsius to Fahrenheit.

92. Describe in words how to convert from Fahrenheit to Celsius.

93. If you decide to travel outside the United States, which one of the two temperature conversion formulas should you take? Explain your answer.

• Critical Thinking Exercises

94. Which one of the following is true?

  a. A 4-pound object weighs more than a 2000-gram object.

  b. A 100-milligram object weighs more than a 2-ounce object.

  c. A 50-gram object weighs more than a 2-ounce object.

  d. A 10-pound object weighs more than a 4-kilogram object.

95. Which one of the following is true?

  a. Flour selling at 3¢ per gram is a better buy than flour selling at 55¢ per pound.

  b. The measures

$$32,600 \text{ g}, \quad 32.1 \text{ kg}, \quad 4 \text{ lb}, \quad 36 \text{ oz}$$

  are arranged in order, from greatest to least weight.

  c. If you are taking aspirin to relieve cold symptoms, a reasonable dose is 2 kilograms four times a day.

  d. A large dog weighs about 350 kilograms.

• Group Exercise

96. Present a group report on the current status of the metric system in the United States. At present, does it appear that the United States will convert to the metric system? Who supports the conversion and who opposes it? Summarize each side's position. Give examples of how our current system of weights and measures is an economic liability. What are the current obstacles to metric conversion?

•••••• CHAPTER SUMMARY, REVIEW, AND TEST

• SUMMARY DEFINITIONS AND CONCEPTS EXAMPLES

9.1 Measuring Length; The Metric System

a. The result obtained from measuring length is called a linear measurement, stated in linear units.

b. Linear Units: The English System

$$12 \text{ in.} = 1 \text{ ft}, 3 \text{ ft} = 1 \text{ yd}, 36 \text{ in.} = 1 \text{ yd}, 5280 \text{ ft} = 1 \text{ mi}$$

c. Dimensional Analysis
Multiply the given measurement by a unit fraction with the unit of measurement that needs to be introduced in the numerator and the unit of measurement that needs to be eliminated in the denominator.

Ex. 1, p. 509

d. Linear Units: The Metric System
The basic unit is the meter (m), approximately 39 inches.

$$1 \text{ km} = 1000 \text{ m}, 1 \text{ hm} = 100 \text{ m}, 1 \text{ dam} = 10 \text{ m},$$

$$1 \text{ dm} = 0.1 \text{ m}, 1 \text{ cm} = 0.01 \text{ m}, 1 \text{ mm} = 0.001 \text{ m}$$

e. Changing Linear Units within the Metric System

Ex. 2, p. 512

$$\times 10$$

km hm dam m dm cm mm

$$\div 10$$

f. English and metric equivalents for length are given in Table 9.3 on page 514.

Ex. 3, p. 514;
Ex. 4, p. 515

9.2 Measuring Area and Volume

a. The area measure of a plane region is the number of square units contained in the given region.

Ex. 1, p. 518

b. English and metric equivalents for area are given in Table 9.4 on page 519.

Ex. 3, p. 519

c. The volume measure of a three-dimensional figure is the number of cubic units contained in its interior.

Ex. 4, p. 520

d. Capacity refers to the amount of fluid that a three-dimensional object can hold. English units for capacity include pints, quarts, and gallons: 2 pt = 1 qt; 4 qt = 1 gal; one cubic yard has a capacity of about 200 gallons. See Table 9.5 on page 521.

Ex. 5, p. 521

e. The basic unit for capacity in the metric system is the liter (L). One liter is about 1.06 quarts. Prefixes for the liter are the same as throughout the metric system.

f. Table 9.7 on page 522 shows relationships between volume and capacity in the metric system.

Ex. 6, p. 522

$$1 \text{ dm}^3 = 1000 \text{ cm}^3 = 1 \text{ L}$$

9.3 Measuring Weight and Temperature

a. Weight: The English System

$$16 \text{ oz} = 1 \text{ lb}, 2000 \text{ lb} = 1 \text{ T}$$

b. Units of Weight: The Metric System
The basic unit is the gram (g).

$$1000 \text{ grams (1 kg)} \approx 2.2 \text{ lb,}$$
$$1 \text{ kg} = 1000 \text{ g, } 1 \text{ hg} = 100 \text{ g, } 1 \text{ dag} = 10 \text{ g,}$$
$$1 \text{ dg} = 0.1 \text{ g, } 1 \text{ cg} = 0.01 \text{ g, } 1 \text{ mg} = 0.001 \text{ g}$$

c. Changing Units of Weight within the Metric System

Ex. 1, p. 526

$\times 10$

kg hg dag g dg cg mg

$\div 10$

d. One kilogram of water has a volume of 1 liter. Table 9.9 on page 527 shows relationships between volume and weight of water in the metric system.

Ex. 2, p. 527

e. English and metric equivalents for weight are given in Table 9.10 on page 527.

Ex. 3, p. 527

f. Temperature Scales: Celsius to Fahrenheit: $F = \frac{9}{5}C + 32$

Ex. 4, p. 529

g. Temperature Scales: Fahrenheit to Celsius: $C = \frac{5}{9}(F - 32)$

Ex. 5, p. 529

REVIEW EXERCISES

9.1

In Exercises 1–4, use dimensional analysis to convert the quantity to the indicated unit.

1. 69 in. to ft

2. 9 in. to yd

3. 21 ft to yd

4. 13,200 ft to mi

In Exercises 5–10, convert the given linear measurement to the metric unit indicated.

5. 22.8 m to cm

6. 7 dam to m

7. 19.2 hm to m

8. 144 cm to hm

9. 0.5 mm to m

10. 18 cm to mm

In Exercises 11–16, use the given English and metric equivalents, along with dimensional analysis, to convert the given measurement to the unit indicated. Where necessary, round answers to two decimal places.

11. 23 in. to cm

12. 19 cm to in.

13. 330 mi to km

14. 600 km to mi

15. 14 m to yd

16. 12 m to ft

1 in.	= 2.54 cm
1 ft	= 30.48 cm
1 yd	= 0.9 m
1 mi	= 1.6 km

17. Express 45 kilometers per hour in miles per hour.

18. Express 60 miles per hour in kilometers per hour.

19. Arrange from smallest to largest: 0.024 km, 2400 m, 24,000 cm.

20. If you jog six times around a track that is 800 meters long, how many kilometers have you covered?

9.2

21. Use the given figure to find its area in square units.

22. In April 2006, the United States, with an area of 3,537,441 square miles, had a population of 298,923,319. Find the population density, to the nearest tenth, at that time. Describe what this means.

23. Given 1 acre = 0.4 hectare, use dimensional analysis to find the size of a property in acres measured at 7.2 hectares.

24. Using 1 ft^2 = 0.09 m^2, convert 30 m^2 to ft^2.

25. Using 1 mi^2 = 2.6 km^2, convert 12 mi^2 to km^2.

26. Which one of the following is a reasonable measure for the area of a flower garden in a person's yard?

   a. 100 m^2 **b.** 0.4 ha   **c.** 0.01 km^2

27. Use the given figure to find its volume in cubic units.

28. A swimming pool has a volume of 33,600 cubic feet. Given that 1 cubic foot has a capacity of about 7.48 gallons, how many gallons of water does the pool hold?

29. An aquarium has a volume of 76,000 cubic centimeters. How many liters of water does the aquarium hold?

30. The capacity of a one-quart container of juice is approximately

    a. 0.1 kL   **b.** 0.5 L   **c.** 1 L   **d.** 1 mL

31. There are 3 feet in a yard. Explain why there are not 3 square feet in a square yard. If helpful, illustrate your explanation with a diagram.

32. Explain why the area of Texas could not be measured in cubic miles.

9.3

In Exercises 33–36, convert the given unit of weight to the unit indicated.

33. 12.4 dg to mg   **34.** 12 g to cg

35. 0.012 mg to g   **36.** 450 mg to kg

In Exercises 37–38, use Table 9.9 on page 527 to convert the given measurement of water to the unit or units indicated.

37. 50 kg to cm^3 **38.** 4 kL to dm^3 to g

39. Using 1 lb = 0.45 kg, convert 210 pounds to kilograms.

40. Using 1 oz = 28 g, convert 392 grams to ounces.

41. If you are interested in your weight in the metric system, would it be best to report it in milligrams, grams, or kilograms? Explain why the unit you selected would be most appropriate. Explain why each of the other two units is not the best choice for reporting your weight.

42. Given 16 oz = 1 lb, use dimensional analysis to convert 36 ounces to pounds.

In Exercises 43–44, select the best estimate for the weight of the given item.

43. A dollar bill:

    a. 1 g   **b.** 10 g   **c.** 1 kg   **d.** 4 kg

44. A hamburger:

    a. 3 kg   **b.** 1 kg   **c.** 200 g   **d.** 5 g

In Exercises 45–49, convert the given Celsius temperature to its equivalent temperature on the Fahrenheit scale.

45. 15°C   **46.** 100°C   **47.** 5°C

48. 0°C   **49.** −25°C

In Exercises 50–55, convert the given Fahrenheit temperature to its equivalent temperature on the Celsius scale.

50. 59°F   **51.** 41°F   **52.** 212°F

53. 98.6°F   **54.** 0°F   **55.** 14°F

56. Is a decrease of 15° Celsius more or less than a decrease of 15° Fahrenheit? Explain your answer.

●●●●●● CHAPTER 9 TEST

1. Change 807 mm to hm.

2. Given 1 inch = 2.54 centimeters, use dimensional analysis to change 635 centimeters to inches.

3. If you jog eight times around a track that is 600 meters long, how many kilometers have you covered?

In Exercises 4–6, write the most reasonable metric unit for length in each blank. Select from mm, cm, m, and km.

4. A human thumb is 20_____ wide.

5. The height of the table is 45_____.

6. The towns are 60_____ apart.

7. If 1 mile = 1.6 kilometers, express 80 miles per hour in kilometers per hour.

8. How many times greater is a square yard than a square foot?

9. Spain has a population of 39,133,966 and an area of 194,896 square miles. Find Spain's population density to the nearest tenth. Describe what this means.

10. Given 1 acre = 0.4 hectare, use dimensional analysis to find the area of a property measured at 18 hectares.

11. The area of a dollar bill is approximately

    a. 10 cm^2 **b.** 100 cm^2 **c.** 1000 cm^2 **d.** 1 m^2

12. There are 10 decimeters in a meter. Explain why there are not 10 cubic decimeters in a cubic meter. How many times greater is a cubic meter than a cubic decimeter?

13. A swimming pool has a volume of 10,000 cubic feet. Given that 1 cubic foot has a capacity of about 7.48 gallons, how many gallons of water does the pool hold?

14. The capacity of a pail used to wash floors is approximately

    a. 3 L   **b.** 12 L   **c.** 80 L   **d.** 2 kL

15. Change 137 g to kg.

16. Using 1 lb = 0.45 kg, convert 90 pounds to kilograms.

In Exercises 17–18, write the most reasonable metric unit for weight in each blank. Select from mg, g, and kg.

17. My suitcase weighs 20_____.

18. I took a 350_____ aspirin.

19. Convert 30°C to Fahrenheit.

20. Convert 176°F to Celsius.

21. Comfortable room temperature is approximately

    a. 70°C   **b.** 50°C   **c.** 30°C   **d.** 20°C

10

Geometry

Geometry is the study of the space you live in and the shapes that surround you. You're even made of it! The human lung consists of nearly 300 spherical air sacs, geometrically designed to provide the greatest surface area within the limited volume of our bodies. Viewed in this way, geometry becomes an intimate experience.

For thousands of years, people have studied geometry in some form to obtain a better understanding of the world in which they live. A study of the shape of your world will provide you with many practical applications and perhaps help to increase your appreciation of its beauty.

SECTION 10.1 • POINTS, LINES, PLANES, AND ANGLES

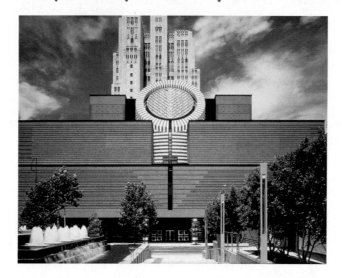

The San Francisco Museum of Modern Art was constructed in 1995 to illustrate how art and architecture can enrich one another. The exterior involves geometric shapes, symmetry, and unusual facades. Although there are no windows, natural light streams in through a truncated cylindrical skylight that crowns the building. The architect worked with a scale model of the museum at the site and observed how light hit it during different times of the day. These observations were used to cut the cylindrical skylight at an angle that maximizes sunlight entering the interior.

Angles play a critical role in creating modern architecture. They are also fundamental in the study of geometry. The word "geometry" means "earth measure." Because it involves the mathematics of shapes, geometry connects mathematics to art and architecture. It also has many practical applications. You can use geometry at home when you buy a carpet, build a fence, tile a floor, or determine whether a piece of furniture will fit through your doorway. In this chapter, we look at the shapes that surround us and their applications.

Understand points, lines, and planes as the basis of geometry.

Point *A*

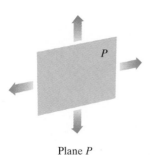

Line *AB*

Plane *P*

FIGURE 10.1 Representing a point, a line, and a plane

Points, Lines, and Planes

Points, lines, and planes make up the basis of all geometry. Stars in the night sky look like points of light. Long stretches of overhead power lines that appear to extend endlessly look like lines. The top of a flat table resembles part of a plane. However, stars, power lines, and table tops only approximate points, lines, and planes. Points, lines, and planes do not exist in the physical world. Representations of these forms are shown in Figure 10.1. A **point**, represented as a small dot, has no length, width, or thickness. No object in the real world has zero size. A **line**, connecting two points along the shortest possible path, has no thickness and extends infinitely in both directions. However, no familiar everyday object is infinite in length. A **plane** is a flat surface with no thickness and no boundaries. This page resembles a plane, although it does not extend indefinitely and it does have thickness.

A line may be named using any two of its points. In Figure 10.2(a), shown at the top of the next page, line *AB* can be symbolized $\overleftrightarrow{AB}$ or $\overleftrightarrow{BA}$. Any point on the line divides the line into three parts—the point and two **half-lines**. Figure 10.2(b) illustrates half-line *AB*, symbolized $(\overrightarrow{AB})$. The open circle above the *A* in the symbol and below the *A* in the diagram indicates that point *A* is not included in the half-line. A **ray** is a half-line with its endpoint included. Figure 10.2(c) illustrates ray *AB*, symbolized $\overrightarrow{AB}$. The closed dot below the *A* in the diagram shows that point *A* is included in the ray. A portion of a line joining two points and including the endpoints is called a **line segment**. Figure 10.2(d) illustrates line segment AB, symbolized $\overline{AB}$ or $\overline{BA}$.

(a) Line AB (b) Half line AB (c) Ray AB (d) Line Segment AB
$\overleftrightarrow{AB}$ or $\overleftrightarrow{BA}$ $\overset{\circ}{\longrightarrow}AB$ $\overrightarrow{AB}$ $\overline{AB}$ or $\overline{BA}$

FIGURE 10.2 Lines, half-lines, rays, and line segments

Angles

An **angle**, symbolized ⊿, is formed by the union of two rays that have a common endpoint. One ray is called the **initial side** and the other the **terminal side**.

A rotating ray is often a useful way to think about angles. The ray in Figure 10.3 rotates from 12 to 2. The ray pointing to 12 is the initial side and the ray pointing to 2 is the terminal side. The common endpoint of an angle's initial side and terminal side is the **vertex** of the angle.

Figure 10.4 shows an angle. The common endpoint of the two rays, B, is the vertex. The two rays that form the angle, $\overrightarrow{BA}$ and $\overrightarrow{BC}$, are the sides. The four ways of naming the angle are shown to the right of Figure 10.4.

FIGURE 10.3 Clock with hands forming an angle

Naming the Angle

⊿1   ⊿B ⊿ABC ⊿CBA

Vertex alone   Vertex letter in the middle

FIGURE 10.4 An angle: two rays with a common endpoint

2 | Solve problems involving angle measures.

Measuring Angles Using Degrees

Angles are measured by determining the amount of rotation from the initial side to the terminal side. One way to measure angles is in **degrees**, symbolized by a small, raised circle °. Think of the hour hand of a clock. From 12 noon to 12 midnight, the hour hand moves around in a complete circle. By definition, the ray has rotated through 360 degrees, or 360°. Using 360° as the amount of rotation of a ray back onto itself, **a degree, 1°, is $\frac{1}{360}$ of a complete rotation**.

EXAMPLE 1   USING DEGREE MEASURE

The hand of a clock moves from 12 to 2 o'clock, shown in Figure 10.3. Through how many degrees does it move?

SOLUTION We know that one complete rotation is 360°. Moving from 12 to 2 o'clock is $\frac{2}{12}$, or $\frac{1}{6}$, of a complete revolution. Thus, the hour hand moves

$$\frac{1}{6} \times 360° = \frac{360°}{6} = 60°$$

in going from 12 to 2 o'clock.   ○

A complete 360° rotation

 The hand of a clock moves from 12 to 1 o'clock. Through how many degrees does it move?

Figure 10.5 shows angles classified by their degree measurement. An **acute angle** measures less than 90° [see Figure 10.5(a)]. A **right angle**, one-quarter of a complete rotation, measures 90° [Figure 10.5(b)]. Examine the right angle—do you see a small square at the vertex? This symbol is used to indicate a right angle. An **obtuse angle** measures more than 90°, but less than 180° [Figure 10.5(c)]. Finally, a **straight angle**, one-half a complete rotation, measures 180° [Figure 10.5(d)]. The two rays in a straight angle form a straight line.

(a) **Acute angle**	(b) **Right angle**	(c) **Obtuse angle**	(d) **Straight angle**
Less than 90°	90°	More than 90° but less than 180°	180°

FIGURE 10.5 Classifying angles by their degree measurements

Figure 10.6 illustrates a **protractor**, used for finding the degree measure of an angle. As shown in the figure, we measure an angle by placing the center point of the protractor on the vertex of the angle and the straight side of the protractor along one side of the angle. The measure of ∡*ABC* is then read as 50°. Observe that the measure is not 130° because the angle is obviously less than 90°. We indicate the angle's measure by writing *m*∡*ABC* = 50°, read "the measure of angle *ABC* is 50°."

FIGURE 10.6 Using a protractor to measure an angle: *m*∡*ABC* = 50°

Two angles whose measures have a sum of 90° are called **complementary angles**. For example, angles measuring 70° and 20° are complementary angles because 70° + 20° = 90°. For angles such as those measuring 70° and 20°, each angle is the **complement** of the other: The 70° angle is the complement of the 20° angle and the 20° angle is the complement of the 70° angle. **The measure of the complement can be found by subtracting the angle's measure from 90°.** For example, we can find the complement of a 25° angle by subtracting 25° from 90°: 90° − 25° = 65°. Thus, an angle measuring 65° is the complement of one measuring 25°.

FIGURE 10.7

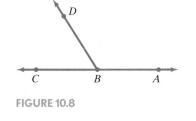

EXAMPLE 2 ANGLE MEASURES AND COMPLEMENTS

Use Figure 10.7 to find $m\angle DBC$.

SOLUTION The measure of $\angle DBC$ is not yet known. It is shown as ?° in Figure 10.7. The acute angles $\angle ABD$, which measures 62°, and $\angle DBC$ form a right angle, indicated by the square at the vertex. This means that the measures of the acute angles add up to 90°. Thus, $\angle DBC$ is the complement of the angle measuring 62°. The measure of $\angle DBC$ is found by subtracting 62° from 90°:

$$m\angle DBC = 90° - 62° = 28°.$$

The measure of $\angle DBC$ can also be found using an algebraic approach.

$m\angle ABD + m\angle DBC = 90°$	The sum of the measures of complementary angles is 90°.
$62° + m\angle DBC = 90°$	We are given $m\angle ABD = 62°$.
$m\angle DBC = 90° - 62° = 28°$	Subtract 62° from both sides of the equation.

○

2 In Figure 10.7, let $m\angle DBC = 19°$. Find $m\angle DBA$.

Two angles whose measures have a sum of 180° are called **supplementary angles**. For example, angles measuring 110° and 70° are supplementary angles because $110° + 70° = 180°$. For angles such as those measuring 110° and 70°, each angle is the **supplement** of the other: the 110° angle is the supplement of the 70° angle, and the 70° angle is the supplement of the 110° angle. **The measure of the supplement can be found by subtracting the angle's measure from 180°.** For example, we can find the supplement of a 25° angle by subtracting 25° from 180°: $180° - 25° = 155°$. Thus, an angle measuring 155° is the supplement of one measuring 25°.

FIGURE 10.8

EXAMPLE 3 ANGLE MEASURES AND SUPPLEMENTS

Figure 10.8 shows that $\angle ABD$ and $\angle DBC$ are supplementary angles. If $m\angle ABD$ is 66° greater than $m\angle DBC$, find the measure of each angle.

SOLUTION Let $m\angle DBC = x$. Because $m\angle ABD$ is 66° greater than $m\angle DBC$, then $m\angle ABD = x + 66°$. We are given that these angles are supplementary.

$m\angle DBC + m\angle ABD = 180°$	The sum of the measures of supplementary angles is 180°.
$x + (x + 66°) = 180°$	Substitute the variable expressions for the measures.
$2x + 66° = 180°$	Combine like terms: $x + x = 2x$.
$2x = 114°$	Subtract 66° from both sides.
$x = 57°$	Divide both sides by 2.

Thus, $m\angle DBC = 57°$ and $m\angle ABD = 57° + 66° = 123°$.

○

3 In Figure 10.8, if $m\angle ABD$ is 88° greater than $m\angle DBC$, find the measure of each angle.

FIGURE 10.9

FIGURE 10.11

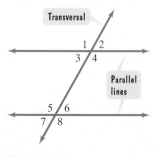

FIGURE 10.12

Figure 10.9 illustrates a highway sign that warns of a railroad crossing. When two lines intersect, the opposite angles formed are called **vertical angles**.

In Figure 10.10, there are two pairs of vertical angles. Angles 1 and 3 are vertical angles. Angles 2 and 4 are also vertical angles.

We can use Figure 10.10 to show that vertical angles have the same measure. Let's concentrate on angles 1 and 3, each denoted by one tick mark. Can you see that each of these angles is supplementary to angle 2?

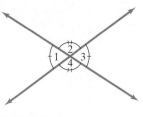

FIGURE 10.10

$$m\angle 1 + m\angle 2 = 180°$$ The sum of the measures of supplementary angles is 180°.

$$m\angle 2 + m\angle 3 = 180°$$

$$m\angle 1 + m\angle 2 = m\angle 2 + m\angle 3$$ Substitute $m\angle 2 + m\angle 3$ for 180° in the first equation.

$$m\angle 1 = m\angle 3$$ Subtract $m\angle 2$ from both sides.

Using a similar approach, we can show that $m\angle 2 = m\angle 4$, each denoted by two tick marks in Figure 10.10.

> Vertical angles have the same measure.

EXAMPLE 4   USING VERTICAL ANGLES

Figure 10.11 shows that the angle on the left measures 68°. Find the measures of the other three angles.

SOLUTION Angle 1 and the angle measuring 68° are vertical angles. Because vertical angles have the same measure,

$$m\angle 1 = 68°.$$

Angle 2 and the angle measuring 68° form a straight angle and are supplementary. Because their measures add up to 180°,

$$m\angle 2 = 180° - 68° = 112°.$$

Angle 2 and angle 3 are also vertical angles, so they have the same measure. Because the measure of angle 2 is 112°,

$$m\angle 3 = 112°.$$

○

 In Figure 10.11, assume that the angle on the left measures 57°. Find the measures of the other three angles.

Parallel Lines

Parallel lines are lines that lie in the same plane and have no points in common. If two different lines in the same plane are not parallel, they have a single point in common and are called **intersecting lines**. If the lines intersect at an angle of 90°, they are called **perpendicular lines**.

If we intersect a pair of parallel lines with a third line, called a **transversal**, eight angles are formed, as shown in Figure 10.12. Certain pairs of these angles have special names, as well as special properties. These names and properties are summarized in Table 10.1.

TABLE 10.1 NAMES OF ANGLE PAIRS FORMED BY A TRANSVERSAL INTERSECTING PARALLEL LINES

Name	Description	Sketch	Angle Pairs Described	Property
Alternate interior angles	Interior angles that do not have a common vertex on alternate sides of the transversal		$\angle 3$ and $\angle 6$ $\angle 4$ and $\angle 5$	Alternate interior angles have the same measure. $m\angle 3 = m\angle 6$ $m\angle 4 = m\angle 5$
Alternate exterior angles	Exterior angles that do not have a common vertex on alternate sides of the transversal		$\angle 1$ and $\angle 8$ $\angle 2$ and $\angle 7$	Alternate exterior angles have the same measure. $m\angle 1 = m\angle 8$ $m\angle 2 = m\angle 7$
Corresponding angles	One interior and one exterior angle on the same side of the transversal		$\angle 1$ and $\angle 5$ $\angle 2$ and $\angle 6$ $\angle 3$ and $\angle 7$ $\angle 4$ and $\angle 8$	Corresponding angles have the same measure. $m\angle 1 = m\angle 5$ $m\angle 2 = m\angle 6$ $m\angle 3 = m\angle 7$ $m\angle 4 = m\angle 8$

3 | Solve problems involving angles formed by parallel lines and transversals.

When two parallel lines are intersected by a transversal, the following relationships are true:

> **PARALLEL LINES AND ANGLE PAIRS**
> If parallel lines are intersected by a transversal,
>
> - alternate interior angles have the same measure,
> - alternate exterior angles have the same measure, and
> - corresponding angles have the same measure.
>
> Conversely, if two lines are intersected by a third line and an alternate interior angle pair or an alternate exterior angle pair or a pair of corresponding angles have the same measure, then the two lines are parallel.

EXAMPLE 5   FINDING ANGLE MEASURES WHEN PARALLEL LINES ARE INTERSECTED BY A TRANSVERSAL

In Figure 10.13, two parallel lines are intersected by a transversal. One of the angles ($\angle 8$) has a measure of 35°. Find the measure of each of the other seven angles.

SOLUTION Look carefully at Figure 10.13 and fill in the angle measures as you read each line in this solution.

$m\angle 1 = 35°$

$\angle 8$ and $\angle 1$ are vertical angles and vertical angles have the same measure.

$m\angle 6 = 180° - 35° = 145°$

$\angle 8$ and $\angle 6$ are supplementary.

$m\angle 7 = 145°$

$\angle 6$ and $\angle 7$ are vertical angles, so they have the same measure.

FIGURE 10.13

FIGURE 10.13 (repeated)

$m\angle 2 = 35°$

$\angle 8$ and $\angle 2$ are alternate interior angles, so they have the same measure.

$m\angle 3 = 145°$

$\angle 7$ and $\angle 3$ are alternate interior angles. Thus, they have the same measure.

$m\angle 5 = 35°$

$\angle 8$ and $\angle 5$ are corresponding angles. Thus, they have the same measure.

$m\angle 4 = 180° - 35° = 145°$

$\angle 4$ and $\angle 5$ are supplementary.

STUDY TIP

There is more than one way to solve Example 5. For example, once you know that $m\angle 2 = 35°$, $m\angle 5$ is also 35° because $\angle 2$ and $\angle 5$ are vertical angles.

CHECK POINT **5** In Figure 10.13, assume that $m\angle 8 = 29°$. Find the measure of each of the other seven angles.

EXERCISE SET 10.1 ●●●●●●

• Practice Exercises

1. The hour hand of a clock moves from 12 to 5 o'clock. Through how many degrees does it move?
2. The hour hand of a clock moves from 12 to 4 o'clock. Through how many degrees does it move?
3. The hour hand of a clock moves from 1 to 4 o'clock. Through how many degrees does it move?
4. The hour hand of a clock moves from 1 to 7 o'clock. Through how many degrees does it move?

In Exercises 5–10, use the protractor to find the measure of each angle. Then classify the angle as acute, right, straight, or obtuse.

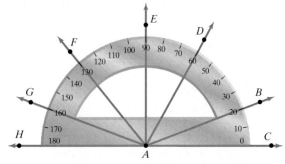

5. $\angle CAB$ 6. $\angle CAF$ 7. $\angle HAB$
8. $\angle HAF$ 9. $\angle CAH$ 10. $\angle HAE$

In Exercises 11–14, find the measure of the angle in which ?° appears.

11.   12.

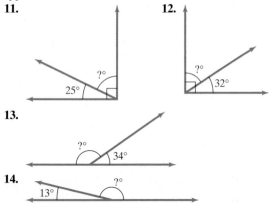

13.

14.

In Exercises 15–20, find the measure of the complement and the supplement of each angle.

15. 48°   **16.** 52°   **17.** 89°   **18.** 1°   **19.** 37.4°   **20.** $15\frac{1}{3}°$

In Exercises 21–24, use an algebraic equation to find the measures of the two angles described. Begin by letting x represent the degree measure of the angle's complement or its supplement.

21. The measure of the angle is 12° greater than its complement.
22. The measure of the angle is 56° greater than its complement.
23. The measure of the angle is three times greater than its supplement.
24. The measure of the angle is 81° more than twice that of its supplement.

In Exercises 25–28, find the measures of angles 1, 2, and 3.

25.   26.

27.   28.

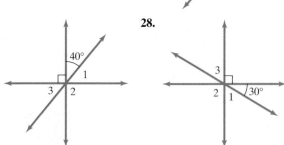

The figures for Exercises 29–30 show two parallel lines intersected by a transversal. One of the angle measures is given. Find the measure of each of the other seven angles.

29.   30.

The figures for Exercises 31–32 show two parallel lines intersected by more than one transversal. Two of the angle measures are given. Find the measures of angles 1, 2, and 3.

31.

32.

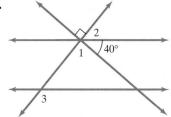

• Practice Plus

In Exercises 33–36, use an algebraic equation to find the measure of each angle that is represented in terms of x.

33.

$2x + 50°$
$4x + 10°$

34.

$3x + 134°$ $6x + 10°$

35.

$11x - 20°$
$7x + 28°$

36.

$12x - 3°$
Parallel lines
$10x + 15°$

Because geometric figures consist of sets of points, we can apply set operations to obtain the union, ∪, or the intersection, ∩, of such figures. The union of two geometric figures is the set of points that belong to either of the figures or to both figures. The intersection of two geometric figures is the set of points common to both figures. In Exercises 37–44, use the line shown to find each set of points.

37. $\overline{AC} \cap \overline{BD}$ **38.** $\overline{AB} \cap \overline{BC}$ **39.** $\overline{AC} \cup \overline{BD}$

40. $\overline{AB} \cup \overline{BC}$ **41.** $\overrightarrow{BA} \cup \overrightarrow{BC}$ **42.** $\overrightarrow{CB} \cup \overrightarrow{CD}$
43. $\overleftrightarrow{AD} \cap \overline{DB}$ **44.** $\overleftrightarrow{AC} \cap \overrightarrow{CB}$

• Application Exercises

45. The picture shows the top of an umbrella in which all the angles formed by the spokes have the same measure. Find the measure of each angle.

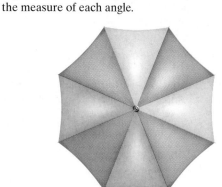

46. Use the definition of parallel lines to explain the joke in this B.C. cartoon.

Reproduced by permission of John L. Hart FLP and Creators Syndicate, Inc.

47. The picture shows a window with parallel framing in which snow has collected in the corners. What property of parallel lines is illustrated by where the snow has collected?

• Writing in Mathematics

48. Describe the differences among lines, half-lines, rays, and line segments.

49. What is an angle and what determines its size?

50. Describe each type of angle: acute, right, obtuse, and straight.

51. What are complementary angles? Describe how to find the measure of an angle's complement.

52. What are supplementary angles? Describe how to find the measure of an angle's supplement.

53. Describe the difference between perpendicular and parallel lines.

54. If two parallel lines are intersected by a transversal, describe the location of the alternate interior angles, the alternate exterior angles, and the corresponding angles.

55. Describe everyday objects that approximate points, lines, and planes.

56. If a transversal is perpendicular to one of two parallel lines, must it be perpendicular to the other parallel line as well? Explain your answer.

Critical Thinking Exercises

57. Use the figure shown at the top of the next column to select a pair of complementary angles from the following choices:

   a. ∡1 and ∡4   **b.** ∡3 and ∡6

   c. ∡2 and ∡5   **d.** ∡1 and ∡5.

58. If $m\angle AGB = m\angle BGC$, and $m\angle CGD = m\angle DGE$, find $m\angle BGD$.

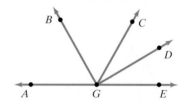

SECTION 10.2 • TRIANGLES

OBJECTIVES

1. Solve problems involving angle relationships in triangles.

2. Solve problems involving similar triangles.

3. Solve problems using the Pythagorean Theorem.

Jasper Johns *"0 Through 9,"* 1961. Oil on canvas, 137 × 105 cm.
The Saatchi Collection, courtesy of the Leo Castelli Gallery. (c) Jasper Johns/ Licensed by VAGA, New York, NY

In Chapter 1, we defined *deductive reasoning* as the process of proving a specific conclusion from one or more general statements. A conclusion that is proved to be true through deductive reasoning is called a **theorem**. The Greek mathematician Euclid, who lived more than 2000 years ago, used deductive reasoning. In his 13-volume book, the *Elements*, Euclid proved over 465 theorems about geometric figures. Euclid's work established deductive reasoning as a fundamental tool of mathematics.

A **triangle** is a geometric figure that has three sides, all of which lie on a flat surface or plane. If you start at any point along the triangle and trace along the entire figure exactly once, you will end at the same point at which you started. Because the beginning point and ending point are the same, the triangle is called a **closed** geometric figure. Euclid used parallel lines to prove one of the most important properties of triangles: The sum of the measures of the three angles of any triangle is 180°. Here is how he did it. He began with the following general statement:

EUCLID'S ASSUMPTION ABOUT PARALLEL LINES

Given a line and a point not on the line, one and only one line can be drawn through the given point parallel to the given line.

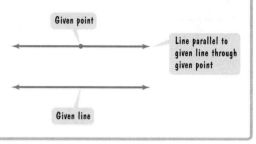

In Figure 10.14, triangle ABC represents any triangle. Using the general assumption given above, we draw a line through point B parallel to line AC.

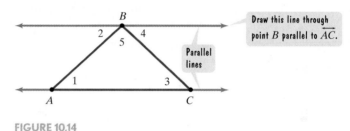

FIGURE 10.14

Because the lines are parallel, alternate interior angles have the same measure.

$$m\angle 1 = m\angle 2 \quad \text{and} \quad m\angle 3 = m\angle 4$$

Also observe that angles 2, 5, and 4 form a straight angle.

$$m\angle 2 + m\angle 5 + m\angle 4 = 180°$$

Because $m\angle 1 = m\angle 2$, replace $m\angle 2$ with $m\angle 1$.

Because $m\angle 3 = m\angle 4$, replace $m\angle 4$ with $m\angle 3$.

$$m\angle 1 + m\angle 5 + m\angle 3 = 180°$$

Because $\angle 1$, $\angle 5$, and $\angle 3$ are the three angles of the triangle, this last equation shows that the measures of the triangle's three angles have a 180° sum.

THE ANGLES OF A TRIANGLE

The sum of the measures of the three angles of any triangle is 180°.

---

1 Solve problems involving angle relationships in triangles.

EXAMPLE 1   USING ANGLE RELATIONSHIPS IN TRIANGLES

Find the measure of angle A for triangle ABC in Figure 10.15.

SOLUTION Because $m\angle A + m\angle B + m\angle C = 180°$, we obtain

$$m\angle A + 120° + 17° = 180°.$$

The sum of the measures of a triangle's three angles is 180°.

$$m\angle A + 137° = 180°$$

Simplify: $120° + 17° = 137°$.

$$m\angle A = 180° - 137°$$

Find the measure of A by subtracting 137° from both sides of the equation.

$$m\angle A = 43°$$

Simplify.

FIGURE 10.15

1 In Figure 10.15, suppose that $m\angle B = 116°$ and $m\angle C = 15°$. Find $m\angle A$.

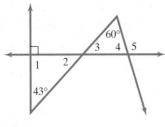

FIGURE 10.16

EXAMPLE 2   USING ANGLE RELATIONSHIPS IN TRIANGLES

Find the measures of angles 1 through 5 in Figure 10.16.

SOLUTION Because $\angle 1$ is supplementary to the right angle, $m\angle 1 = 90°$.

$m\angle 2$ can be found using the fact that the sum of the measures of the angles of a triangle is 180°.

$$m\angle 1 + m\angle 2 + 43° = 180°$$ The sum of the measures of a triangle's three angles is 180°.

$$90° + m\angle 2 + 43° = 180°$$ We previously found that $m\angle 1 = 90°$.

$$m\angle 2 + 133° = 180°$$ Simplify: $90° + 43° = 133°$.

$$m\angle 2 = 180° - 133°$$ Subtract 133° from both sides.

$$m\angle 2 = 47°$$ Simplify.

$m\angle 3$ can be found using the fact that vertical angles have equal measures. $m\angle 3 = m\angle 2$. Thus, $m\angle 3 = 47°$.

$m\angle 4$ can be found using the fact that the sum of the measures of the angles of a triangle is 180°. Refer to the triangle at the top of Figure 10.16.

$$m\angle 3 + m\angle 4 + 60° = 180°$$ The sum of the measures of a triangle's three angles is 180°.

$$47° + m\angle 4 + 60° = 180°$$ We previously found that $m\angle 3 = 47°$.

$$m\angle 4 + 107° = 180°$$ Simplify: $47° + 60° = 107°$.

$$m\angle 4 = 180° - 107°$$ Subtract 107° from both sides.

$$m\angle 4 = 73°$$ Simplify.

Finally, we can find $m\angle 5$ by observing that angles 4 and 5 form a straight angle.

$$m\angle 4 + m\angle 5 = 180°$$ A straight angle measures 180°.

$$73° + m\angle 5 = 180°$$ We previously found that $m\angle 4 = 73°$.

$$m\angle 5 = 180° - 73°$$ Subtract 73° from both sides.

$$m\angle 5 = 107°$$ Simplify.

CHECK POINT
2   In Figure 10.16, suppose that the angle shown to measure 43° measures, instead, 36°. Further suppose that the angle shown to measure 60° measures, instead, 58°. Under these new conditions, find the measures of angles 1 through 5 in the figure.

Triangles can be described using characteristics of their angles or their sides.

TRIANGLES AND THEIR CHARACTERISTICS

Classification by Angles

Acute Triangle	**Right Triangle**	**Obtuse Triangle**
All angles are acute.	One angle measures 90°.	One angle is obtuse.

Classification by Sides

Isosceles Triangle
Two sides have equal length.
(Angles opposite these sides have the same measure.)

Equilateral Triangle
All sides have equal length.
(Each angle measures 60°.)

Scalene Triangle
No two sides are equal in length.

2 | Solve problems involving similar triangles.

Similar Triangles

Shown in the margin is an international road sign. This sign is shaped just like the actual sign, although its size is smaller. Figures that have the same shape, but not the same size, are used in **scale drawings**. A scale drawing always pictures the exact shape of the object that the drawing represents. Architects, engineers, landscape gardeners, and interior decorators use scale drawings in planning their work.

Pedestrian crossing

Figures that have the same shape, but not necessarily the same size, are called **similar figures**. In Figure 10.17, triangles *ABC* and *DEF* are similar. Angles *A* and *D* measure the same number of degrees and are called **corresponding angles**. Angles *C* and *F* are corresponding angles, as are angles *B* and *E*. Angles with the same number of tick marks in Figure 10.17 are the corresponding angles.

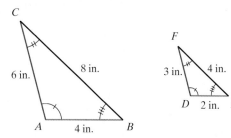

FIGURE 10.17

The sides opposite the corresponding angles are called **corresponding sides**. Thus, $\overline{CB}$ and $\overline{FE}$ are corresponding sides. $\overline{AB}$ and $\overline{DE}$ are also corresponding sides, as are $\overline{AC}$ and $\overline{DF}$. Corresponding angles measure the same number of degrees, but corresponding sides may or may not be the same length. For the triangles in Figure 10.17, each side in the smaller triangle is half the length of the corresponding side in the larger triangle.

The triangles in Figure 10.17 illustrate what it means to be **similar triangles**. **Corresponding angles have the same measure and the ratios of the lengths of the corresponding sides are equal.**

$$\frac{\text{length of } \overline{AC}}{\text{length of } \overline{DF}} = \frac{6 \text{ in.}}{3 \text{ in.}} = \frac{2}{1}; \quad \frac{\text{length of } \overline{CB}}{\text{length of } \overline{FE}} = \frac{8 \text{ in.}}{4 \text{ in.}} = \frac{2}{1}; \quad \frac{\text{length of } \overline{AB}}{\text{length of } \overline{DE}} = \frac{4 \text{ in.}}{2 \text{ in.}} = \frac{2}{1}$$

In similar triangles, the lengths of the corresponding sides are proportional. Thus,

AC represents the length of $\overline{AC}$, *DF* the length of $\overline{DF}$, and so on.

$$\frac{AC}{DF} = \frac{CB}{FE} = \frac{AB}{DE}.$$

If we know that two triangles are similar, we can set up a proportion to solve for the length of an unknown side.

BLITZER BONUS

Triangles in Construction Work

The triangle is used in most types of construction work, including bridges, radio towers, airplane wings, and pitched roofs. Its use in construction gives an object the quality of firmness, or stiffness, resulting in rigid, strong structures.

EXAMPLE 3   USING SIMILAR TRIANGLES

Triangles I and II in Figure 10.18 are similar. Find the missing length, *x*.

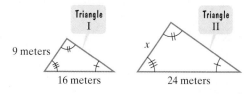

FIGURE 10.18

SOLUTION Because the triangles are similar, their corresponding sides are proportional.

Left side of △ I

Bottom side of △ I

$$\frac{9}{x} = \frac{16}{24}$$

Corresponding side on left of △ II

Corresponding side on bottom of △ II

FIGURE 10.18 (repeated)

We solve $\frac{9}{x} = \frac{16}{24}$ for x by applying the cross-products principle for proportions that we discussed in Section 6.4: If $\frac{a}{b} = \frac{c}{d}$, then $ad = bc$.

$16x = 9 \cdot 24$	Apply the cross-products principle.
$16x = 216$	Multiply: $9 \cdot 24 = 216$.
$\dfrac{16x}{16} = \dfrac{216}{16}$	Divide both sides by 16.
$x = 13.5$	Simplify.

The missing length, x, is 13.5 meters.

CHECK POINT 3 The similar triangles in the figure have the same orientation, positioned so that corresponding parts are in the same relative position. Find the missing length, x.

How can we quickly determine if two triangles are similar? **If the measures of two angles of one triangle are equal to those of two angles of a second triangle, then the two triangles are similar.** If the triangles are similar, then their corresponding sides are proportional.

EXAMPLE 4 PROBLEM SOLVING USING SIMILAR TRIANGLES

A man who is 6 feet tall is standing 10 feet from the base of a lamppost (see Figure 10.19). The man's shadow has a length of 4 feet. How tall is the lamppost?

SOLUTION The drawing in Figure 10.20 makes the similarity of the triangles easier to see. The large triangle with the lamppost on the left and the small triangle with the man on the left both contain 90° angles. They also share an angle. Thus, two angles of the large triangle are equal in measure to two angles of the small triangle. This means that the triangles are similar and their corresponding sides are proportional. We begin by letting x represent the height of the lamppost, in feet. Because corresponding sides of the two similar triangles are proportional,

$$\frac{x}{6} = \frac{14}{4}.$$

We solve for x by applying the cross-products principle.

$4x = 6 \cdot 14$	Apply the cross-products principle.
$4x = 84$	Multiply: $6 \cdot 14 = 84$.
$\dfrac{4x}{4} = \dfrac{84}{4}$	Divide both sides by 4.
$x = 21$	Simplify.

The lamppost is 21 feet tall.

FIGURE 10.19

FIGURE 10.20

CHECK POINT 4 Find the height of the lookout tower shown at the top of the next page using the figure that lines up the top of the tower with the top of a stick that is 2 yards long.

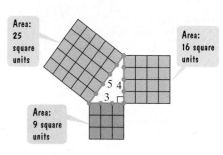

The Pythagorean Theorem

The ancient Greek philosopher and mathematician Pythagoras (approximately 582–500 B.C.) founded a school whose motto was "All is number." Pythagoras is best remembered for his work with the **right triangle**, a triangle with one angle measuring 90°. The side opposite the 90° angle is called the **hypotenuse**. The other sides are called **legs**. Pythagoras found that if he constructed squares on each of the legs, as well as a larger square on the hypotenuse, the sum of the areas of the smaller squares is equal to the area of the larger square. This is illustrated in Figure 10.21.

FIGURE 10.21 The area of the large square equals the sum of the areas of the smaller squares.

This relationship is usually stated in terms of the lengths of the three sides of a right triangle and is called the **Pythagorean Theorem**.

THE PYTHAGOREAN THEOREM

The sum of the squares of the lengths of the legs of a right triangle equals the square of the length of the hypotenuse.

If the legs have lengths a and b and the hypotenuse has length c, then

$$a^2 + b^2 = c^2.$$

EXAMPLE 5   USING THE PYTHAGOREAN THEOREM

Find the length of the hypotenuse c in the right triangle shown in Figure 10.22.

SOLUTION Let $a = 9$ and $b = 12$. Substituting these values into $c^2 = a^2 + b^2$ enables us to solve for c.

$$c^2 = a^2 + b^2$$ Use the symbolic statement of the Pythagorean Theorem.

$$c^2 = 9^2 + 12^2$$ Let $a = 9$ and $b = 12$.

$$c^2 = 81 + 144$$ $9^2 = 9 \cdot 9 = 81$ and $12^2 = 12 \cdot 12 = 144$.

$$c^2 = 225$$ Add.

$$c = \sqrt{225} = 15$$ Solve for c by taking the positive square root of 225.

The length of the hypotenuse is 15 feet.

FIGURE 10.22

 Find the length of the hypotenuse in a right triangle whose legs have lengths 7 feet and 24 feet.

EXAMPLE 6 USING THE PYTHAGOREAN THEOREM

a. A wheelchair ramp with a length of 122 inches has a horizontal distance of 120 inches. What is the ramp's vertical distance?

b. Construction laws are very specific when it comes to access ramps for the disabled. Every vertical rise of 1 inch requires a horizontal run of 12 inches. Does this ramp satisfy the requirement?

SOLUTION

a. Figure 10.23 shows the right triangle that is formed by the ramp, the wall, and the ground. We can find x, the ramp's vertical distance, using the Pythagorean Theorem.

$(leg)^2$	plus	$(leg)^2$	equals	$(hypotenuse)^2$
x^2	$+$	120^2	$=$	122^2

$$x^2 + 120^2 = 122^2$$ This is the equation resulting from the Pythagorean Theorem.

$$x^2 + 14{,}400 = 14{,}884$$ Square 120 and 122.

$$x^2 = 484$$ Isolate x^2 by subtracting 14,400 from both sides.

$$x = \sqrt{484} = 22$$ Solve for x by taking the positive square root of 484.

The ramp's vertical distance is 22 inches.

b. Every vertical rise of 1 inch requires a horizontal run of 12 inches. Because the ramp has a vertical distance of 22 inches, it requires a horizontal distance of 22(12) inches, or 264 inches. The horizontal distance is only 120 inches, so this ramp does not satisfy construction laws for access ramps for the disabled.

CHECK POINT 6 A radio tower is supported by two wires that are each 130 yards long and attached to the ground 50 yards from the base of the tower. How tall is the tower?

FIGURE 10.23

EXERCISE SET 10.2 ●●●●●●

• Practice Exercises

In Exercises 1–4, find the measure of angle A for the triangle shown.

1.

2.

3.

4.

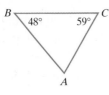

In Exercises 5–6, find the measures of angles 1 through 5 in the figure shown.

5.

6.

We have seen that isosceles triangles have two sides of equal length. The angles opposite these sides have the same measure. In Exercises 7–8, use this information to help find the measure of each numbered angle.

7.

8.

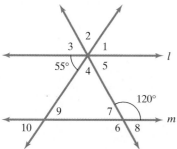

In Exercises 9–10, lines *l* and *m* are parallel. Find the measure of each numbered angle.

9.

10.

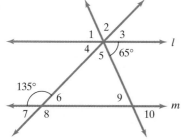

In Exercises 11–16, use similar triangles and the fact that corresponding sides are proportional to find the missing length, *x*.

11.

12.

13.

14.

15.

16.

In Exercises 17–19, △*ABC* and △*ADE* are similar. Find the length of the indicated side.

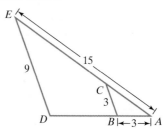

17. $\overline{CA}$ **18.** $\overline{DB}$ **19.** $\overline{DA}$

20. In the diagram for Exercises 17–19, suppose that you are not told that △*ABC* and △*ADE* are similar. Instead, you are given that $\overleftrightarrow{ED}$ and $\overleftrightarrow{CB}$ are parallel. Under these conditions, explain why the triangles must be similar.

In Exercises 21–26, use the Pythagorean Theorem to find the missing length in each right triangle. Use your calculator to find square roots, rounding, if necessary, to the nearest tenth.

21.   **22.**

23.

15 m / c / 36 m

24.

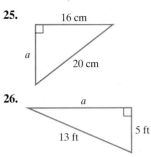

5 in. / c / 11 in.

25.

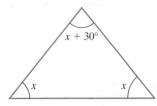

16 cm / a / 20 cm

26.

a / 5 ft / 13 ft

• Practice Plus

Use algebraic equations to solve Exercises 27–30.

27. Two angles of a triangle have the same measure and the third angle is 30° greater than the measure of the other two. Find the measure of each angle.

$x + 30°$ / x / x

28. One angle of a triangle is three times as large as another. The measure of the third angle is 40° more than that of the smallest angle. Find the measure of each angle.

$3x$ / x / $x + 40°$

29. One angle of a triangle is twice as large as another. The measure of the third angle is 20° more than that of the smallest angle. Find the measure of each angle.

30. One angle of a triangle is three times as large as another. The measure of the third angle is 30° greater than that of the smallest angle. Find the measure of each angle.

31. The Pythagorean Theorem tells us that if a triangle is a right triangle, then $a^2 + b^2 = c^2$. State the converse of the Pythagorean Theorem.

In Exercises 32–34, use the fact that the converse of the Pythagorean Theorem is a true statement to determine if each triangle with sides of the given lengths is a right triangle.

32. 10 cm, 24 cm, 26 cm

33. 4 m, 8 m, 9 m

34. $\sqrt{2}$ ft, $\sqrt{7}$ ft, 3 ft

• Application Exercises

Use similar triangles to solve Exercises 35–36.

35. A person who is 5 feet tall is standing 80 feet from the base of a tree, and the tree casts an 86-foot shadow. The person's shadow is 6 feet in length. What is the tree's height?

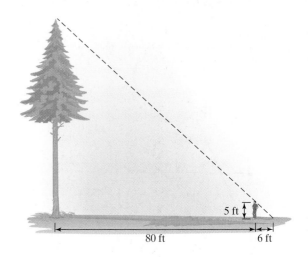

5 ft / 80 ft / 6 ft

36. A tree casts a shadow 12 feet long. At the same time, a vertical rod 8 feet high casts a shadow that is 6 feet long. How tall is the tree?

Sun's rays / 8 ft / 6 ft / Sun's rays / x / 12 ft

Use the Pythagorean Theorem to solve Exercises 37–45. Use your calculator to find square roots, rounding, if necessary, to the nearest tenth.

37. The doorway into a room is 4 feet wide and 8 feet high. What is the length of the longest rectangular panel that can be taken through this doorway diagonally?

4 ft / 8 ft

38. A baseball diamond is actually a square with 90-foot sides. What is the distance from home plate to second base?

39. A 20-foot ladder is 15 feet from the house. How far up the house does the ladder reach?

40. A supporting wire is to be attached to the top of a 50-foot antenna. If the wire must be anchored 50 feet from the base of the antenna, what length of wire is required?

41. A supporting wire is to be attached to the top of a 70-foot antenna. If the wire must be anchored 70 feet from the base of the antenna, what length of wire is required?

42. A rectangular park is 6 miles long and 3 miles wide. How long is a pedestrian route that runs diagonally across the park?

43. A rectangular park is 4 miles long and 2 miles wide. How long is a pedestrian route that runs diagonally across the park?

44. If construction costs are $150,000 per kilometer, find the cost of building the new road in the figure shown.

45. Picky, Picky, Picky This problem appeared on Arizona's high school exit exam:

Alex is building a ramp for a bike competition. He has two rectangular boards. One board is six meters and the other is five meters long. If the ramp has to form a right triangle, what should its height be?

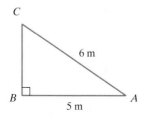

Students were asked to select the correct answer from the following options:

3 meters; 4 meters; 3.3 meters; 7.8 meters.

a. Among the available choices, which option best expresses the ramp's height? How many feet, to the nearest tenth of a foot, is this? Does a bike competition that requires riders to jump off these heights seem realistic? (ouch!)

b. Express the ramp's height to the nearest hundredth of a meter. By how many centimeters does this differ from the "correct" answer on the test? How many inches, to the nearest half inch, is this? Is it likely that a carpenter with a tape measure would make this error?

c. According to the problem, Alex has boards that measure 5 meters and 6 meters. A 6-meter board? How many feet, to the nearest tenth of a foot, is this? When was the last time you found a board of this length at Home Depot? (*Source: The New York Times*, April 24, 2005)

• Writing in Mathematics

46. If the measures of two angles of a triangle are known, explain how to find the measure of the third angle.

47. Can a triangle contain two right angles? Explain your answer.

48. What general assumption did Euclid make about a point and a line in order to prove that the sum of the measures of the angles of a triangle is 180°?

49. What are similar triangles?

50. If the ratio of the corresponding sides of two similar triangles is 1 to 1 $\left(\frac{1}{1}\right)$, what must be true about the triangles?

51. What are corresponding angles in similar triangles?

52. Describe how to identify the corresponding sides in similar triangles.

53. In your own words, state the Pythagorean Theorem.

54. In the 1939 movie *The Wizard of Oz*, upon being presented with a Th.D. (Doctor of Thinkology), the Scarecrow proudly exclaims, "The sum of the square roots of any two sides of an isosceles triangle is equal to the square root of the remaining side." Did the Scarecrow get the Pythagorean Theorem right? In particular, describe four errors in the Scarecrow's statement.

• Critical Thinking Exercises

55. Find the measure of angle R.

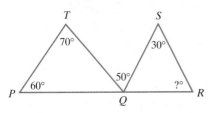

56. What is the length of $\overline{AB}$ in the accompanying figure?

57. Use a quadratic equation to solve this problem. The width of a rectangular carpet is 7 meters shorter than the length, and the diagonal is 1 meter longer than the length. What are the carpet's dimensions?

SECTION 10.3 • POLYGONS, PERIMETER, AND TESSELLATIONS

OBJECTIVES

1. Name certain polygons according to the number of sides.

2. Recognize the characteristics of certain quadrilaterals.

3. Solve problems involving a polygon's perimeter.

4. Find the sum of the measures of a polygon's angles.

5. Understand tessellations and their angle requirements.

You have just purchased a beautiful plot of land in the country, shown in Figure 10.24. In order to have more privacy, you decide to put fencing along each of its four sides. The cost of this project depends on the distance around the four outside edges of the plot, called its **perimeter**, as well as the cost for each foot of fencing.

FIGURE 10.24

1 | Name certain polygons according to the number of sides.

Your plot of land is a geometric figure: It has four straight sides that are line segments. The plot is on level ground, so that the four sides all lie on a flat surface, or plane. The plot is an example of a *polygon*. Any closed shape in the plane formed by three or more line segments is a **polygon**.

A polygon is named according to the number of sides it has. We know that a three-sided polygon is called a **triangle**. A four-sided polygon is called a **quadrilateral**.

A polygon whose sides are all the same length and whose angles all have the same measure is called a **regular polygon**. Table 10.2 provides the names of six polygons. Also shown are illustrations of regular polygons.

TABLE 10.2 ILLUSTRATIONS OF REGULAR POLYGONS

Name	Picture	Name	Picture
Triangle 3 sides		Hexagon 6 sides	
Quadrilateral 4 sides		Heptagon 7 sides	
Pentagon 5 sides		Octagon 8 sides	

2 Recognize the characteristics of certain quadrilaterals.

Bees and Regular Hexagons

Bees use honeycombs to store honey and house larvae. They construct honey storage cells from wax. Each cell has the shape of a regular hexagon. The cells fit together perfectly, preventing dirt or predators from entering. Squares or equilateral triangles would fit equally well, but regular hexagons provide the largest storage space for the amount of wax used.

Quadrilaterals

The plot of land in Figure 10.24 is a four-sided polygon, or a quadrilateral. However, when you first looked at the figure, perhaps you thought of the plot as a rectangular field. A **rectangle** is a special kind of quadrilateral in which both pairs of opposite sides are parallel, have the same measure, and whose angles are right angles. Table 10.3 presents some special quadrilaterals and their characteristics.

TABLE 10.3 TYPES OF QUADRILATERALS

Name	Characteristics	Representation
Parallelogram	Quadrilateral in which both pairs of opposite sides are parallel and have the same measure. Opposite angles have the same measure.	
Rhombus	Parallelogram with all sides having equal length.	
Rectangle	Parallelogram with four right angles. Because a rectangle is a parallelogram, opposite sides are parallel and have the same measure.	
Square	A rectangle with all sides having equal length. Each angle measures 90°, and the square is a regular quadrilateral.	
Trapezoid	A quadrilateral with exactly one pair of parallel sides.	

Perimeter

The **perimeter**, P, of a polygon is the sum of the lengths of its sides. Perimeter is measured in linear units, such as inches, feet, yards, meters, or kilometers.

Example 1 involves the perimeter of a rectangle. Because perimeter is the sum of the lengths of the sides, the perimeter of the rectangle shown in Figure 10.25 is $l + w + l + w$. This can be expressed as

$$P = 2l + 2w.$$

FIGURE 10.25 A rectangle with length l and width w

3 Solve problems involving a polygon's perimeter.

EXAMPLE 1   AN APPLICATION OF PERIMETER

The rectangular field we discussed at the beginning of this section (see Figure 10.24 on page 556) has a length of 42 yards and a width of 28 yards. If fencing costs $5.25 per foot, find the cost to enclose the field with fencing.

SOLUTION We begin by finding the perimeter of the rectangle in yards. Using 3 ft = 1 yd and dimensional analysis, we express the perimeter in feet. Finally, we multiply the perimeter, in feet, by $5.25 because the fencing costs $5.25 per foot.

The length, l, is 42 yards and the width, w, is 28 yards. The perimeter of the rectangle is determined using the formula $P = 2l + 2w$.

$$P = 2l + 2w = 2 \cdot 42 \text{ yd} + 2 \cdot 28 \text{ yd} = 84 \text{ yd} + 56 \text{ yd} = 140 \text{ yd}$$

Because 3 ft = 1 yd, we use the unit fraction $\frac{3\,ft}{1\,yd}$ to convert from yards to feet.

$$140\ \text{yd} = \frac{140\ \cancel{yd}}{1} \cdot \frac{3\ \text{ft}}{1\ \cancel{yd}} = 140 \cdot 3\ \text{ft} = 420\ \text{ft}$$

The perimeter of the rectangle is 420 feet. Now we are ready to find the cost of the fencing. We multiply 420 feet by $5.25, the cost per foot.

$$\text{Cost} = \frac{420\ \cancel{feet}}{1} \cdot \frac{\$5.25}{\cancel{foot}} = 420(\$5.25) = \$2205$$

The cost to enclose the rectangle with fencing is $2205.

1 A rectangular field has a length of 50 yards and a width of 30 yards. If fencing costs $6.50 per foot, find the cost to enclose the rectangle with fencing.

The Sum of the Measures of a Polygon's Angles

We know that the sum of the measures of the three angles of any triangle is 180°. We can use inductive reasoning to find the sum of the measures of the angles of any polygon. Start by drawing line segments from a single point where two sides meet so that nonoverlapping triangles are formed. This is done in Figure 10.26.

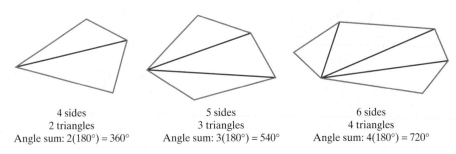

4 sides
2 triangles
Angle sum: 2(180°) = 360°

5 sides
3 triangles
Angle sum: 3(180°) = 540°

6 sides
4 triangles
Angle sum: 4(180°) = 720°

FIGURE 10.26

In each case, the number of triangles is two less than the number of sides of the polygon. Thus, for an *n*-sided polygon, there are $n - 2$ triangles. Because each triangle has an angle-measure sum of 180°, the sum of the measures for the angles in the $n - 2$ triangles is $(n - 2)180°$. Thus, the sum of the measures of the angles of an *n*-sided polygon is $(n - 2)180°$.

4 | Find the sum of the measures of a polygon's angles.

> ### THE ANGLES OF A POLYGON
> The sum of the measures of the angles of a polygon with *n* sides is
> $$(n - 2)180°.$$

EXAMPLE 2   USING THE FORMULA FOR THE ANGLES OF A POLYGON

a. Find the sum of the measures of the angles of an octagon.

b. Figure 10.27 shows a regular octagon. Find the measure of angle A.

c. Find the measure of exterior angle B.

SOLUTION

a. An octagon has eight sides. Using the formula $(n - 2)180°$ with $n = 8$, we can find the sum of the measures of its eight angles.

FIGURE 10.27 A regular octagon

The sum of the measures of an octagon's angles

$$= (n - 2)180°$$
$$= (8 - 2)180°$$
$$= 6 \cdot 180°$$
$$= 1080°.$$

b. Examine the regular octagon in Figure 10.27. Note that all eight sides have the same length. Likewise, all eight angles have the same degree measure. Angle A is one of these eight angles. We find its measure by taking the sum of the measures of all eight angles, 1080°, and dividing by 8.

$$m \angle A = \frac{1080°}{8} = 135°$$

c. Because $\angle B$ is the supplement of $\angle A$,

$$m \angle B = 180° - 135° = 45°.$$

a. Find the sum of the measures of the angles of a 12-sided polygon.

b. Find the measure of an angle of a regular 12-sided polygon.

Tessellations

5 Understand tessellations and their angle requirements.

A relationship between geometry and the visual arts is found in an art form called *tessellations*. A **tessellation**, or **tiling**, is a pattern consisting of the repeated use of the same geometric figures to completely cover a plane, leaving no gaps and no overlaps. Figure 10.28 shows eight tessellations, each consisting of the repeated use of two or more regular polygons.

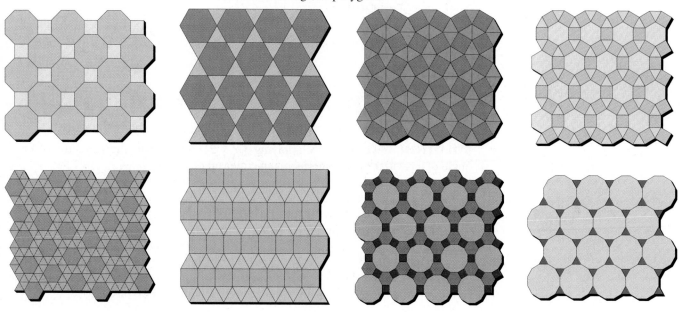

FIGURE 10.28 Eight tessellations formed by two or more regular polygons

FIGURE 10.29

In each tessellation in Figure 10.28, the same types of regular polygons surround every vertex (intersection point). Furthermore, **the sum of the measures of the angles that come together at each vertex is 360°, a requirement for the formation of a tessellation.** This is illustrated in the enlarged version of the tessellation in Figure 10.29. If you select any vertex and count the sides of the polygons that touch it, you'll see that vertices are surrounded by two regular octagons and a square. Can you see why the sum of the angle measures at every vertex is 360°?

$$135° + 135° + 90° = 360°$$

In Example 2, we found that each angle of a regular octagon measures 135°.

Each angle of a square measures 90°.

The most restrictive condition in creating tessellations is that just *one type of regular polygon* may be used. With this restriction, there are only three possible tessellations, made from equilateral triangles or squares or regular hexagons, as shown in Figure 10.30.

FIGURE 10.30 The three tessellations formed using one regular polygon

Each tessellation is possible because the angle sum at every vertex is 360°:

Six equilateral triangles at each vertex

$$60° + 60° + 60° + 60° + 60° + 60° = 360°$$

Four squares at each vertex

$$90° + 90° + 90° + 90° = 360°$$

Three regular hexagons at each vertex

$$120° + 120° + 120° = 360°.$$

Each angle measures $\dfrac{(n-2)180°}{n} = \dfrac{(6-2)180°}{6} = 120°.$

EXAMPLE 3   ANGLE REQUIREMENTS OF TESSELLATIONS

Explain why a tessellation cannot be created using only regular pentagons.

SOLUTION Let's begin by applying $(n - 2)180°$ to find the measure of each angle of a regular pentagon. Each angle measures

$$\frac{(5-2)180°}{5} = \frac{3(180°)}{5} = 108°.$$

A requirement for the formation of a tessellation is that the measures of the angles that come together at each vertex is 360°. With each angle of a regular pentagon measuring 108°, Figure 10.31 shows that three regular pentagons fill in $3 \cdot 108° = 324°$ and leave a $360° - 324°$, or a 36°, gap. Because the 360° angle requirement cannot be met, no tessellation by regular pentagons is possible. ○

FIGURE 10.31

Explain why a tessellation cannot be created using only regular octagons.

"Drawings showing how a surface can be regularly filled with similar-shaped figures which are contiguous to one another, without leaving any open spaces, are my richest source of inspiration."

—M. C. ESCHER

Tessellations that are not restricted to the repeated use of regular polygons are endless in number. They are prominent in Islamic art, Italian mosaics, quilts, and ceramics. The Dutch artist M. C. Escher (1898–1972) created a dazzling array of prints, drawings, and paintings using tessellations composed of stylized interlocking animals. Escher's art reflects the mathematics that underlies all things, while creating surreal manipulations of space and perspective that make gentle fun of consensus reality.

M.C. Escher, *Symmetry Drawing, E85* (*Lizard, Fish, Bat*), drawn at Baarn, April, 1952, ink, pencil, watercolor. ©2006 The M.C. Escher Company, Holland. All rights reserved.

EXERCISE SET 10.3 ●●●●●●

• Practice Exercises

In Exercises 1–4, use the number of sides to name the polygon.

1.

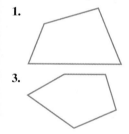

2.

3.

4.

Use these quadrilaterals to solve Exercises 5–10.

a.

b.

c.

d.

e.

5. Which of these quadrilaterals have opposite sides that are parallel? Name these quadrilaterals.

6. Which of these quadrilaterals have sides of equal length that meet at a vertex? Name these quadrilaterals.

7. Which of these quadrilaterals have right angles? Name these quadrilaterals.

8. Which of these quadrilaterals do not have four sides of equal length? Name these quadrilaterals.

9. Which of these quadrilaterals is not a parallelogram? Name this quadrilateral.

10. Which of these quadrilaterals is/are a regular polygon? Name this/these quadrilateral(s).

In Exercises 11–20, find the perimeter of the figure named and shown. Express the perimeter using the same unit of measure that appears on the given side or sides.

11. Rectangle

12 cm
3 cm   3 cm
12 cm

12. Parallelogram

14 cm
9 cm   9 cm
14 cm

13. Rectangle

14. Rectangle

6 yd
8 yd

7 in.
18 in.

15. Square

16. Square

250 in.

3.5 m

17. Triangle

9 ft   7 ft

11 ft

18. Triangle

16 yd

10 yd

8.5 yd

19. Equilateral triangle

6 yd

20. Regular hexagon

4 mm

In Exercises 21–24, find the perimeter of the figure shown. Express the perimeter using the same unit of measure that appears on the given side or sides.

21.

9 yd

9 yd

12 yd

21 yd

12 yd

21 yd

22.

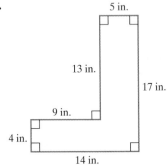

5 in.

13 in.

17 in.

9 in.

4 in.

14 in.

23.

3 ft

3 ft

6 ft

4 ft

24.

10 m

8 m

3 m

5 m

25. Find the sum of the measures of the angles of a five-sided polygon.

26. Find the sum of the measures of the angles of a six-sided polygon.

27. Find the sum of the measures of the angles of a quadrilateral.

28. Find the sum of the measures of the angles of a heptagon.

In Exercises 29–30, each figure shows a regular polygon. Find the measures of angle A and angle B.

29.

B A

30.

B A

*In Exercises 31–32, **a.** Find the sum of the measures of the angles for the figure given; **b.** Find the measures of angle A and angle B.*

31.

150°

70°

B   A

32.

A B

42°

In Exercises 33–36, tessellations formed by two or more regular polygons are shown.

a. *Name the types of regular polygons that surround each vertex.*

b. *Determine the number of angles that come together at each vertex, as well as the measures of these angles.*

c. *Use the angle measures from part (b) to explain why the tessellation is possible.*

33.

34.

35.

36.

37. Can a tessellation be created using only regular nine-sided polygons? Explain your answer.

38. Can a tessellation be created using only regular ten-sided polygons? Explain your answer.

• Practice Plus

In Exercises 39–42, use an algebraic equation to determine each rectangle's dimensions.

39. A rectangular field is four times as long as it is wide. If the perimeter of the field is 500 yards, what are the field's dimensions?

40. A rectangular field is five times as long as it is wide. If the perimeter of the field is 288 yards, what are the field's dimensions?

41. An American football field is a rectangle with a perimeter of 1040 feet. The length is 200 feet more than the width. Find the width and length of the rectangular field.

42. A basketball court is a rectangle with a perimeter of 86 meters. The length is 13 meters more than the width. Find the width and length of the basketball court.

In Exercises 43–44, use algebraic equations to find the measure of each angle that is represented in terms of x.

43.   **44.**

In the figure shown, the artist has cunningly distorted the "regular" polygons to create a fraudulent tessellation with discrepancies that are too subtle for the eye to notice. In Exercises 41–42, you will use mathematics, not your eyes, to observe the irregularities.

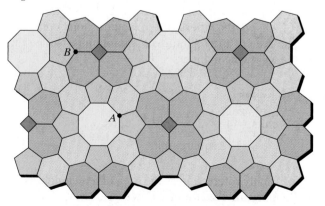

45. Find the sum of the angle measures at vertex *A*. Then explain why the tessellation is a fake.

46. Find the sum of the angle measures at vertex *B*. Then explain why the tessellation is a fake.

• Application Exercises

47. A school playground is in the shape of a rectangle 400 feet long and 200 feet wide. If fencing costs $14 per yard, what will it cost to place fencing around the playground?

48. A rectangular field is 70 feet long and 30 feet wide. If fencing costs $8 per yard, how much will it cost to enclose the field?

49. One side of a square flower bed is 8 feet long. How many plants are needed if they are to be spaced 8 inches apart around the outside of the bed?

50. What will it cost to place baseboard around the region shown if the baseboard costs $0.25 per foot? No baseboard is needed for the 2-foot doorway.

• Writing in Mathematics

51. What is a polygon?

52. Explain why rectangles and rhombuses are also parallelograms.

53. Explain why every square is a rectangle, a rhombus, a parallelogram, a quadrilateral, and a polygon.

54. Explain why a square is a regular polygon, but a rhombus is not.

55. Using words only, describe how to find the perimeter of a rectangle.

56. Describe a practical situation in which you needed to apply the concept of a geometric figure's perimeter.

57. Describe how to find the measure of an angle of a regular pentagon.

• Critical Thinking Exercises

In Exercises 58–59, write an algebraic expression that represents the perimeter of the figure shown.

58.

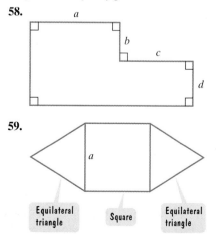

59.

60. Find $m\angle 1$ in the figure shown.

• Group Exercise

61. Group members should consult sites on the Internet devoted to tessellations, or tilings, and present a report that expands upon the information in this section. Include a discussion of cultures that have used tessellations on fabrics, wall coverings, baskets, rugs, and pottery, with examples. Include the Alhambra, a fourteenth-century palace in Granada, Spain, in the presentation, as well as works by the artist M. C. Escher. Discuss the various symmetries (translations, rotations, reflections) associated with tessellations. Demonstrate how to create unique tessellations, including Escher-type patterns. Other than creating beautiful works of art, are there any practical applications of tessellations?

SECTION 10.4 • AREA AND CIRCUMFERENCE

OBJECTIVES

1. Use area formulas to compute the areas of plane regions and solve applied problems.

2. Use formulas for a circle's circumference and area.

The size of a house is described in square feet. But how do you know from the real estate ad whether the 1200-square-foot home with the backyard pool is large enough to warrant a visit? Faced with hundreds of ads, you need some way to sort out the best bets. What does 1200 square feet mean and how is this area determined? In this section, we discuss how to compute the areas of plane regions.

| 1 | Use area formulas to compute the areas of plane regions and solve applied problems. |

FIGURE 10.32 The area of the region on the left is 12 square units.

Formulas for Area

In Section 9.2, we saw that the area of a two-dimensional figure is the number of square units, such as square inches or square miles, it takes to fill the interior of the figure. For example, Figure 10.32 shows that there are 12 square units contained within the rectangular region. The area of the region is 12 square units. Notice that the area can be determined in the following manner:

Distance across   Distance down

$$4 \text{ units} \times 3 \text{ units} = 4 \times 3 \times \text{units} \times \text{units}$$
$$= 12 \text{ square units.}$$

The area of a rectangular region, usually referred to as the area of a rectangle, is the product of the distance across (length) and the distance down (width).

AREA OF A RECTANGLE AND A SQUARE

The area, A, of a rectangle with length l and width w is given by the formula

$$A = lw.$$

The area, A, of a square with one side measuring s linear units is given by the formula

$$A = s^2.$$

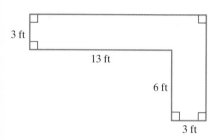

FIGURE 10.33

EXAMPLE 1   SOLVING AN AREA PROBLEM

You decide to cover the path shown in Figure 10.33 with bricks.

a. Find the area of the path.

b. If the path requires four bricks for every square foot, how many bricks are needed for the project?

SOLUTION

a. Because we have a formula for the area of a rectangle, we begin by drawing a dashed line that divides the path into two rectangles. One way of doing this is shown on the right. We then use the length and width of each rectangle to find its area. The computations for area are shown in the green and blue voice balloons.

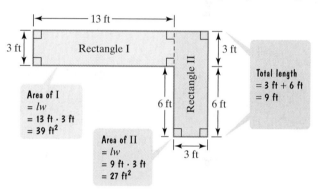

The area of the path is found by adding the areas of the two rectangles.

$$\text{Area of path} = 39 \text{ ft}^2 + 27 \text{ ft}^2 = 66 \text{ ft}^2$$

b. The path requires 4 bricks per square foot. The number of bricks needed for the project is the number of square feet in the path, its area, times 4.

$$\text{Number of bricks needed} = 66 \text{ ft}^2 \cdot \frac{4 \text{ bricks}}{\text{ft}^2} = 66 \cdot 4 \text{ bricks} = 264 \text{ bricks}$$

Thus, 264 bricks are needed for the project.

CHECK POINT 1 Find the area of the path described in Example 1, rendered on the right as a green region, by first measuring off a large rectangle as shown. The area of the path is the area of the large rectangle (the blue and green regions combined) minus the area of the blue rectangle. Do you get the same answer as we did in Example 1(a)?

In Section 9.2, we saw that although there are 3 linear feet in a linear yard, there are 9 square feet in a square yard. If a problem requires measurement of area in square yards and the linear measures are given in feet, to avoid errors, first convert feet to yards. Then apply the area formula. This idea is illustrated in Example 2.

EXAMPLE 2 | SOLVING AN AREA PROBLEM

What will it cost to carpet a rectangular floor measuring 12 feet by 15 feet if the carpet costs $18.50 per square yard?

SOLUTION We begin by converting the linear measures from feet to yards.

$$12 \text{ ft} = \frac{12 \text{ ft}}{1} \cdot \frac{1 \text{ yd}}{3 \text{ ft}} = \frac{12}{3} \text{yd} = 4 \text{ yd}$$

$$15 \text{ ft} = \frac{15 \text{ ft}}{1} \cdot \frac{1 \text{ yd}}{3 \text{ ft}} = \frac{15}{3} \text{yd} = 5 \text{ yd}$$

Next, we find the area of the rectangular floor in square yards.

$$A = lw = 5 \text{ yd} \cdot 4 \text{ yd} = 20 \text{ yd}^2$$

Finally, we find the cost of the carpet by multiplying the cost per square yard, $18.50, by the number of square yards in the floor, 20.

$$\text{Cost of carpet} = \frac{\$18.50}{\text{yd}^2} \cdot \frac{20 \text{ yd}^2}{1} = \$18.50(20) = \$370$$

It will cost $370 to carpet the floor.

 What will it cost to carpet a rectangular floor measuring 18 feet by 21 feet if the carpet costs $16 per square yard?

We can use the formula for the area of a rectangle to develop formulas for areas of other polygons. We begin with a parallelogram, a quadrilateral with opposite sides equal and parallel. The **height** of a parallelogram is the perpendicular distance between two of the parallel sides. Height is denoted by h in Figure 10.34. The **base**, denoted by b, is the length of either of these parallel sides.

FIGURE 10.34

FIGURE 10.35

In Figure 10.35, the red triangular region has been cut off from the right of the parallelogram and attached to the left. The resulting figure is a rectangle with length b and width h. Because bh is the area of the rectangle, it also represents the area of the parallelogram.

STUDY TIP

The height of a parallelogram is the perpendicular distance between two of the parallel sides. It is *not* the length of a side.

AREA OF A PARALLELOGRAM

The area, A, of a parallelogram with height h and base b is given by the formula

$$A = bh.$$

FIGURE 10.36

(a)

(b)

FIGURE 10.37

EXAMPLE 3	USING THE FORMULA FOR A PARALLELOGRAM'S AREA

Find the area of the parallelogram in Figure 10.36.

SOLUTION As shown in the figure, the base is 8 centimeters and the height is 4 centimeters. Thus, $b = 8$ and $h = 4$.

$$A = bh$$
$$A = 8 \text{ cm} \cdot 4 \text{ cm} = 32 \text{ cm}^2$$

The area is 32 cm².

 Find the area of a parallelogram with a base of 10 inches and a height of 6 inches.

Figure 10.37 demonstrates how we can use the formula for the area of a parallelogram to obtain a formula for the area of a triangle. The area of the parallelogram in Figure 10.37(a) is given by $A = bh$. The diagonal shown in the parallelogram divides it into two triangles with the same size and shape. This means that the area of each triangle is one-half that of the parallelogram. Thus, the area of the triangle in Figure 10.37(b) is given by $A = \frac{1}{2}bh$.

> **AREA OF A TRIANGLE**
>
> The area, A, of a triangle with height h and base b is given by the formula
>
> $$A = \frac{1}{2}bh.$$

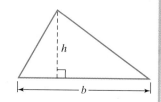

EXAMPLE 4	USING THE FORMULA FOR A TRIANGLE'S AREA

Find the area of each triangle in Figure 10.38.

SOLUTION

a. In Figure 10.38(a), the base is 16 meters and the height is 10 meters, so $b = 16$ and $h = 10$. We do not need the 10.5 meters or the 14 meters to find the area. The area of the triangle is

$$A = \frac{1}{2}bh = \frac{1}{2} \cdot 16 \text{ m} \cdot 10 \text{ m} = 80 \text{ m}^2.$$

The area is 80 square meters.

b. In Figure 10.38(b), the base is 12 inches. The base line needs to be extended to draw the height. However, we still use 12 inches for b in the area formula. The height, h, is given to be 9 inches. The area of the triangle is

$$A = \frac{1}{2}bh = \frac{1}{2} \cdot 12 \text{ in.} \cdot 9 \text{ in.} = 54 \text{ in.}^2.$$

The area of the triangle is 54 square inches.

(a)

(b)

FIGURE 10.38

 A sailboat has a triangular sail with a base of 12 feet and a height of 5 feet. Find the area of the sail.

FIGURE 10.39

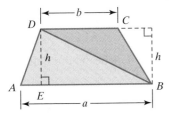

FIGURE 10.40

The formula for the area of a triangle can be used to obtain a formula for the area of a trapezoid. Consider the trapezoid shown in Figure 10.39. The lengths of the two parallel sides, called the **bases**, are represented by a (the lower base) and b (the upper base). The trapezoid's height, denoted by h, is the perpendicular distance between the two parallel sides.

In Figure 10.40, we have drawn line segment BD, dividing the trapezoid into two triangles, shown in yellow and red. The area of the trapezoid is the sum of the areas of these triangles.

Area of trapezoid	=	Area of yellow △	plus	Area of red △

$$A = \frac{1}{2}ah + \frac{1}{2}bh$$

$$= \frac{1}{2}h(a + b) \quad \text{Factor out } \frac{1}{2}h.$$

AREA OF A TRAPEZOID

The area, A, of a trapezoid with parallel bases a and b and height h is given by the formula

$$A = \frac{1}{2}h(a + b).$$

EXAMPLE 5   FINDING THE AREA OF A TRAPEZOID

Find the area of the trapezoid in Figure 10.41.

SOLUTION The height, h, is 13 feet. The lower base, a, is 46 feet, and the upper base, b, is 32 feet. We do not use the 17-foot and 19-foot sides in finding the trapezoid's area.

$$A = \frac{1}{2}h(a + b) = \frac{1}{2} \cdot 13 \text{ ft} \cdot (46 \text{ ft} + 32 \text{ ft})$$

$$= \frac{1}{2} \cdot 13 \text{ ft} \cdot 78 \text{ ft} = 507 \text{ ft}^2$$

The area of the trapezoid is 507 square feet.

FIGURE 10.41

CHECK POINT 5 Find the area of a trapezoid with bases of length 20 feet and 10 feet and height 7 feet.

2 | Use formulas for a circle's circumference and area.

The point at which a pebble hits a flat surface of water becomes the center of a number of circular ripples.

Circles

It's a good idea to know your way around a circle. Clocks, angles, maps, and compasses are based on circles. Circles occur everywhere in nature: in ripples on water, patterns on a butterfly's wings, and cross sections of trees. Some consider the circle to be the most pleasing of all shapes.

A **circle** is a set of points in the plane equally distant from a given point, its **center**. Figure 10.42 shows two circles. The **radius** (plural: radii), r, is a line segment from the center to any point on the circle. For a given circle, all radii have the same length. The **diameter**, d, is a line segment through the center whose endpoints both lie on the circle. For a given circle, all diameters have the same length. In any circle, the **length of the diameter is twice the length of the radius**.

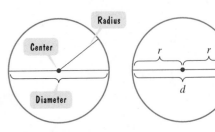

FIGURE 10.42

The words *radius* and *diameter* refer to both the line segments in Figure 10.42 as well as to their linear measures. The distance around a circle (its perimeter) is called its **circumference**, C. For all circles, if you divide the circumference by the diameter, or by twice the radius, you will get the same number. This ratio is the irrational number π and is approximately equal to 3.14:

$$\frac{C}{d} = \pi \quad \text{or} \quad \frac{C}{2r} = \pi.$$

Thus,

$$C = \pi d \quad \text{or} \quad C = 2\pi r.$$

> **FINDING THE DISTANCE AROUND A CIRCLE**
> The circumference, C, of a circle with diameter d and radius r is
> $$C = \pi d \quad \text{or} \quad C = 2\pi r.$$

When computing a circle's circumference by hand, round π to 3.14. When using a calculator, use the $\boxed{\pi}$ key, which gives the value of π rounded to approximately 11 decimal places. In either case, calculations involving π give approximate answers. These answers can vary slightly depending on how π is rounded. The symbol $\approx$ (is approximately equal to) will be written in these calculations.

EXAMPLE 6   FINDING A CIRCLE'S CIRCUMFERENCE

Find the circumference of the circle in Figure 10.43.

SOLUTION The diameter is 40 yards, so we use the formula for circumference with d in it.

$$C = \pi d = \pi(40 \text{ yd}) = 40\pi \text{ yd} \approx 125.7 \text{ yd}$$

The distance around the circle is approximately 125.7 yards.

40 yd

FIGURE 10.43

CHECK POINT **6** Find the circumference of a circle whose diameter measures 10 inches. Express the answer in terms of π and then round to the nearest tenth of an inch.

EXAMPLE 7   USING THE CIRCUMFERENCE FORMULA

How much trim, to the nearest tenth of a foot, is needed to go around the window shown in Figure 10.44?

SOLUTION The trim covers the 6-foot bottom of the window, the two 8-foot sides, and the half-circle (called a semicircle) on top. The length needed is

$$6 \text{ ft} + 8 \text{ ft} + 8 \text{ ft} + \text{circumference of the semicircle}.$$

The circumference of the semicircle is half the circumference of a circle whose diameter is 6 feet.

8 ft

6 ft

FIGURE 10.44

Circumference of semicircle

$\longleftarrow d = 6 \text{ ft} \longrightarrow$

$$\text{Circumference of semicircle} = \frac{1}{2}\pi d$$
$$= \frac{1}{2}\pi(6 \text{ ft}) = 3\pi \text{ ft} \approx 9.4 \text{ ft}$$

Rounding the circumference to the nearest tenth (9.4 feet), the length of trim that is needed is approximately

$$6 \text{ ft} + 8 \text{ ft} + 8 \text{ ft} + 9.4 \text{ ft,}$$

or 31.4 feet.

○

CHECK POINT 7   In Figure 10.44 on page 569, suppose that the dimensions are 10 feet and 12 feet for the window's bottom and side, respectively. How much trim, to the nearest tenth of a foot, is needed to go around the window?

●

We also use π to find the area of a circle in square units.

> **FINDING THE AREA OF A CIRCLE**
> The area, A, of a circle with radius r is
> $$A = \pi r^2.$$

EXAMPLE 8   PROBLEM SOLVING USING THE FORMULA FOR A CIRCLE'S AREA

Which one of the following is the better buy: a large pizza with a 16-inch diameter for $15.00 or a medium pizza with an 8-inch diameter for $7.50?

SOLUTION   The better buy is the pizza with the lower price per square inch. The radius of the large pizza is $\frac{1}{2} \cdot 16$ inches, or 8 inches, and the radius of the medium pizza is $\frac{1}{2} \cdot 8$ inches, or 4 inches. The area of the surface of each circular pizza is determined using the formula for the area of a circle.

Large pizza: $A = \pi r^2 = \pi(8 \text{ in.})^2 = 64\pi \text{ in.}^2 \approx 201 \text{ in.}^2$

Medium pizza: $A = \pi r^2 = \pi(4 \text{ in.})^2 = 16\pi \text{ in.}^2 \approx 50 \text{ in.}^2$

For each pizza, the price per square inch is found by dividing the price by the area:

Price per square inch for large pizza $= \dfrac{\$15.00}{64\pi \text{ in.}^2} \approx \dfrac{\$15.00}{201 \text{ in.}^2} \approx \dfrac{\$0.07}{\text{in.}^2}$

Price per square inch for medium pizza $= \dfrac{\$7.50}{16\pi \text{ in.}^2} \approx \dfrac{\$7.50}{50 \text{ in.}^2} = \dfrac{\$0.15}{\text{in.}^2}.$

The large pizza is the better buy.

○

In Example 8, did you at first think that the price per square inch would be the same for the large and the medium pizzas? After all, the radius of the large pizza is twice that of the medium pizza, and the cost of the large is twice that of the medium. However, the large pizza's area, 64π square inches, is *four times the area* of the medium pizza's, 16π square inches. Doubling the radius of a circle increases its area by a factor of 2^2, or 4. In general, if the radius of a circle is increased by k times its original linear measure, the area is multiplied by k^2. The same principle is true for any two-dimensional figure: If the shape of the figure is kept the same while linear dimensions are increased k times, the area of the larger, similar, figure is k^2 times greater than the area of the original figure.

CHECK POINT 8   Which one of the following is the better buy: a large pizza with an 18-inch diameter for $20.00 or a medium pizza with a 14-inch diameter for $14.00?

●

TECHNOLOGY

You can use your calculator to obtain the price per square inch for each pizza in Example 8. The price per square inch for the large pizza, $\dfrac{15}{64\pi}$, is approximated by one of the following sequences of keystrokes:

MANY SCIENTIFIC CALCULATORS

15 ÷ (64 × π) =

MANY GRAPHING CALCULATORS

15 ÷ (64 π) ENTER.

EXERCISE SET 10.4 ●●●●●●

• Practice Exercises

In Exercises 1–14, use the formulas developed in this section to find the area of each figure.

1.

3 m
6 m

2.

3 ft
4 ft

3.

4 in.
4 in.

4.

3 cm
3 cm

5.

50 cm
44 cm 42 cm 44 cm
50 cm

6.

58 ft
46 ft 43 ft 46 ft
58 ft

7.

9 in. 12 in.
8 in.
14 in.

8.
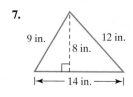
36 m 36 m
33 m
30 m

9.
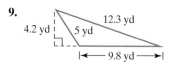
4.2 yd 12.3 yd
5 yd
9.8 yd

10.
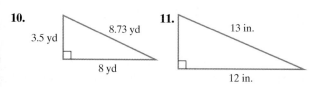
3.5 yd 8.73 yd
8 yd

11.
13 in.
12 in.

12.

10 m
8 m

13.

10 m
9.2 m 7 m 8.5 m
16 m

14.
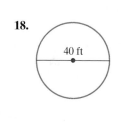
26 m
18 m 18 m 21.1 m
37 m

In Exercises 15–18, find the circumference and area of each circle. Express answers in terms of π and then round to the nearest tenth.

15.

4 cm

16.

9 m

17.
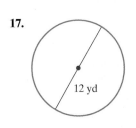
12 yd

18.
40 ft

Find the area of each figure in Exercises 19–24. Where necessary, express answers in terms of π and then round to the nearest tenth.

19.

4 m
9 m
8 m
3 m

20.
3 ft
5 ft
9 ft
2 ft

21.

13 m 13 m
10 m 15 m 10 m
24 m

22.

6 cm
3 cm
10 cm
9 cm

23.

10 cm

Square

24.

15 in.

9 in.

• Practice Plus

In Exercises 25–26, find the area of each shaded region.

25.

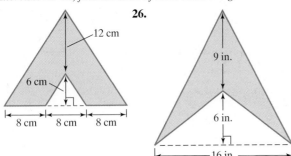

12 cm

6 cm

8 cm   8 cm   8 cm

26.

9 in.

6 in.

16 in.

In Exercises 27–28, find the perimeter and the area of each figure. Where necessary, express answers in terms of π and round to the nearest tenth.

27.

8 ft

15 ft   6 ft

8 ft

28.

40 m   40 m

80 m

In Exercises 29–32, use a quadratic equation to solve each problem.

29. The length of a rectangular garden is 5 feet greater than the width. The area of the rectangle is 300 square feet. Find the length and the width.

x

$x + 5$

30. The length of a rectangular sign is 3 feet longer than the width. If the sign has space for 40 square feet of advertising, find its length and its width.

31. Great white sharks have triangular teeth with a height that is 1 centimeter longer than the base. If the area of one tooth is 15 square centimeters, find its base and height.

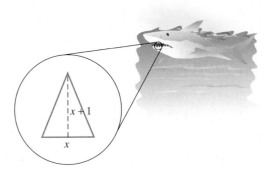

$x + 1$

x

32. Each end of a glass prism is a triangle with a height that is 1 inch shorter than twice the base. If the area of the triangle is 60 square inches, how long are the base and height?

x

• Application Exercises

33. What will it cost to carpet a rectangular floor measuring 9 feet by 21 feet if the carpet costs $26.50 per square yard?

34. A plastering contractor charges $18 per square yard. What is the cost of plastering 60 feet of wall in a house with a 9-foot ceiling?

35. A rectangular kitchen floor measures 12 feet by 15 feet. A stove on the floor has a rectangular base measuring 3 feet by 4 feet, and a refrigerator covers a rectangular area of the floor measuring 4 feet by 5 feet. How many square feet of tile will be needed to cover the kitchen floor not counting the area used by the stove and the refrigerator?

36. A rectangular room measures 12 feet by 15 feet. The entire room is to be covered with rectangular tiles that measure 3 inches by 2 inches. If the tiles are sold at ten for 30¢, what will it cost to tile the room?

37. The lot in the figure shown at the top of the next page, except for the house, shed, and driveway, is lawn. One bag of lawn fertilizer costs $25.00 and covers 4000 square feet.

  a. Determine the minimum number of bags of fertilizer needed for the lawn.

  b. Find the total cost of the fertilizer.

38. Taxpayers with an office in their home may deduct a percentage of their home-related expenses. This percentage is based on the ratio of the office's area to the area of the home. A taxpayer with an office in a 2200-square-foot home maintains a 20 foot by 16 foot office. If the yearly electric bills for the home come to $4800, how much of this is deductible?

39. You are planning to paint the house whose dimensions are shown in the figure.

a. How many square feet will you need to paint? (There are four windows, each 8 ft by 5 ft; two windows, each 30 ft by 2 ft; and two doors, each 80 in. by 36 in., that do not require paint.)

b. The paint that you have chosen is available in gallon cans only. Each can covers 500 square feet. If you want to use two coats of paint, how many cans will you need for the project?

c. If the paint you have chosen sells for $26.95 per gallon, what will it cost to paint the house?

The diagram shows the floor plan for a one-story home. Use the given measurements to solve Exercises 40–42. (A calculator will be helpful in performing the necessary computations.)

40. If construction costs $95 per square foot, find the cost of building the home.

41. If carpet costs $17.95 per square yard and is available in whole square yards only, find the cost of carpeting the three bedroom floors.

42. If ceramic tile costs $26.95 per square yard and is available in whole square yards only, find the cost of installing ceramic tile on the kitchen and dining room floors.

In Exercises 43–44, express the required calculation in terms of π and then round to the nearest tenth.

43. How much fencing is required to enclose a circular garden whose radius is 20 meters?

44. A circular rug is 6 feet in diameter. How many feet of fringe is required to edge this rug?

45. How many plants spaced every 6 inches are needed to surround a circular garden with a 30-foot radius?

46. A stained glass window is to be placed in a house. The window consists of a rectangle, 6 feet high by 3 feet wide, with a semicircle at the top. Approximately how many feet of stripping, to the nearest tenth of a foot, will be needed to frame the window?

47. Which one of the following is a better buy: a large pizza with a 14-inch diameter for $12.00 or a medium pizza with a 7-inch diameter for $5.00?

48. Which one of the following is a better buy: a large pizza with a 16-inch diameter for $12.00 or two small pizzas, each with a 10-inch diameter, for $12.00?

• Writing in Mathematics

49. Using the formula for the area of a rectangle, explain how the formula for the area of a parallelogram $(A = bh)$ is obtained.

50. Using the formula for the area of a parallelogram $(A = bh)$, explain how the formula for the area of a triangle $\left(A = \frac{1}{2}bh\right)$ is obtained.

51. Using the formula for the area of a triangle, explain how the formula for the area of a trapezoid is obtained.

52. Explain why a circle is not a polygon.

53. Describe the difference between the following problems: How much fencing is needed to enclose a circular garden? How much fertilizer is needed for a circular garden?

• Critical Thinking Exercises

54. You need to enclose a rectangular region with 200 feet of fencing. Experiment with different lengths and widths to determine the maximum area you can enclose. Which quadrilateral encloses the most area?

55. Suppose you know the cost for building a rectangular deck measuring 8 feet by 10 feet. If you decide to increase the dimensions to 12 feet by 15 feet, by how much will the cost increase?

56. A rectangular swimming pool measures 14 feet by 30 feet. The pool is surrounded on all four sides by a path that is 3 feet wide. If the cost to resurface the path is $2 per square foot, what is the total cost of resurfacing the path?

57. A proposed oil pipeline will cross 16.8 miles of national forest. The width of the land needed for the pipeline is 200 feet. If the U.S. Forest Service charges the oil company $32 per acre, calculate the total cost. (1 mile = 5280 feet and 1 acre = 43,560 square feet.)

58. Find the area of the shaded region in terms of π.

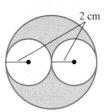

2 cm

SECTION 10.5 • VOLUME

OBJECTIVES

1. Use volume formulas to compute the volumes of three-dimensional figures and solve applied problems.

2. Compute the surface area of a three-dimensional figure.

---

1 | Use volume formulas to compute the volumes of three-dimensional figures and solve applied problems.

You are considering going to Judge Judy's Web site and filling out a case submission form to appear on her TV show. The case involves your contractor, who promised to install a water tank that holds 500 gallons of water. Upon delivery, you noticed that capacity was not printed anywhere, so you decided to do some measuring. The tank is shaped like a giant tuna can, with a circular top and bottom. You measured the radius of each circle to be 3 feet and you measured the tank's height to be 2 feet 4 inches. You know that 500 gallons is the capacity of a solid figure with a volume of about 67 cubic feet. Now you need some sort of method to compute the volume of the water tank. In this section, we discuss how to compute the volumes of various solid, three-dimensional figures. Using a formula you will learn in the section, you can determine whether the evidence indicates you can win a case against the contractor if you appear on *Judge Judy*. Or do you risk joining a cast of bozos who entertain television viewers by being loudly castigated by the judge? (Before a possible ear-piercing "Baloney, sir, you're a geometric idiot!", we suggest working Exercise 41 in Exercise Set 10.5.)

Formulas for Volume

In Section 9.2, we saw that **volume** refers to the amount of space occupied by a solid object, determined by the number of cubic units it takes to fill the interior of that object. For example, Figure 10.45 shows that there are 18 cubic units contained within the box. The volume of the box, called a **rectangular solid**, is 18 cubic units. The box has a length of 3 units, a width of 3 units, and a height of 2 units. The volume, 18 cubic units, may be determined by finding the product of the length, the width, and the height:

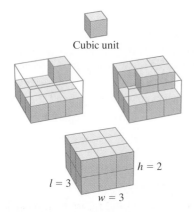

Cubic unit

$h = 2$
$l = 3$
$w = 3$

FIGURE 10.45
Volume = 18 cubic units

$$\text{Volume} = 3 \text{ units} \cdot 3 \text{ units} \cdot 2 \text{ units} = 18 \text{ units}^3.$$

In general, the volume, V, of a rectangular solid is the product of its length, l, its width, w, and its height, h:

$$V = lwh.$$

If the length, width, and height are the same, the rectangular solid is called a **cube**. Formulas for these boxlike shapes are given below.

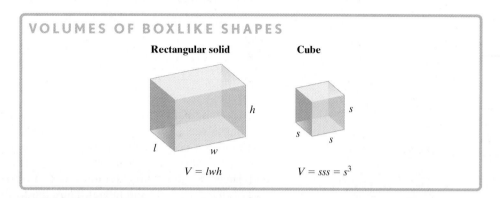

VOLUMES OF BOXLIKE SHAPES

Rectangular solid   Cube

$V = lwh$ $V = sss = s^3$

EXAMPLE 1   FINDING THE VOLUME OF A RECTANGULAR SOLID

Find the volume of the rectangular solid in Figure 10.46.

SOLUTION As shown in the figure, the length is 6 meters, the width is 2 meters, and the height is 4 meters. Thus, $l = 6$, $w = 2$, and $h = 4$.

$$V = lwh = 6\,\text{m} \cdot 2\,\text{m} \cdot 4\,\text{m} = 48\,\text{m}^3$$

The volume of the rectangular solid is 48 cubic meters.

 Find the volume of a rectangular solid with length 5 feet, width 3 feet, and height 7 feet.

FIGURE 10.46

2 m   6 m   4 m

In Section 9.2, we saw that although there are 3 feet in a yard, there are 27 cubic feet in a cubic yard. If a problem requires measurement of volume in cubic yards and the linear measures are given in feet, to avoid errors, first convert feet to yards. Then apply the volume formula. This idea is illustrated in Example 2.

EXAMPLE 2   SOLVING A VOLUME PROBLEM

You are about to begin work on a swimming pool in your yard. The first step is to have a hole dug that is 90 feet long, 60 feet wide, and 6 feet deep. You will use a truck that can carry 10 cubic yards of dirt and charges $12 per load. How much will it cost you to have all the dirt hauled away?

SOLUTION We begin by converting feet to yards:

$$90\,\text{ft} = \frac{90\,\text{ft}}{1} \cdot \frac{1\,\text{yd}}{3\,\text{ft}} = \frac{90}{3}\text{yd} = 30\,\text{yd}.$$

Similarly, 60 ft = 20 yd and 6 ft = 2 yd. Next, we find the volume of dirt that needs to be dug out and hauled off.

$$V = lwh = 30\,\text{yd} \cdot 20\,\text{yd} \cdot 2\,\text{yd} = 1200\,\text{yd}^3$$

Now, we find the number of loads that the truck needs to haul off all the dirt. Because the truck carries 10 cubic yards, divide the number of cubic yards of dirt by 10.

$$\text{Number of truckloads} = \frac{1200\,\text{yd}^3}{\dfrac{10\,\text{yd}^3}{\text{trip}}} = \frac{1200\,\text{yd}^3}{1} \cdot \frac{\text{trip}}{10\,\text{yd}^3} = \frac{1200}{10}\text{trips} = 120\,\text{trips}$$

Because the truck charges $12 per trip, the cost to have all the dirt hauled away is the number of trips, 120, times the cost per trip, $12.

$$\text{Cost to haul all dirt away} = \frac{120 \text{ trips}}{1} \cdot \frac{\$12}{\text{trip}} = 120(\$12) = \$1440$$

The dirt-hauling phase of the pool project will cost you $1440.

 2 Find the volume, in cubic yards, of a cube whose edges each measure 6 feet.

A rectangular solid is an example of a **polyhedron**, a solid figure bounded by polygons. A rectangular solid is bounded by six rectangles, called faces. By contrast, a **pyramid** is a polyhedron whose base is a polygon and whose sides are triangles. Figure 10.47 shows a pyramid with a rectangular base drawn inside a rectangular solid. The contents of three pyramids with rectangular bases exactly fill a rectangular solid of the same base and height. Thus, the formula for the volume of the pyramid is $\frac{1}{3}$ that of the rectangular solid.

FIGURE 10.47 The volume of a pyramid is $\frac{1}{3}$ the volume of a rectangular solid having the same base and the same height.

VOLUME OF A PYRAMID

The volume, V, of a pyramid is given by the formula

$$V = \frac{1}{3}Bh,$$

where B is the area of the base and h is the height (the perpendicular distance from the top to the base).

Pyramid

EXAMPLE 3   USING THE FORMULA FOR A PYRAMID'S VOLUME

Capped with a pointed spire on top of its 48 stories, the Transamerica Tower in San Francisco is a pyramid with a square base. The pyramid is 256 meters (853 feet) tall. Each side of the square base has a length of 52 meters. Although San Franciscans disliked it when it opened in 1972, they have since accepted it as part of the skyline. Find the volume of the building.

SOLUTION   First find the area of the square base, represented as B in the volume formula. Because each side of the square base is 52 meters, the area of the square base is

$$B = 52 \text{ m} \cdot 52 \text{ m} = 2704 \text{ m}^2.$$

The area of the square base is 2704 square meters. Because the pyramid is 256 meters tall, its height, h, is 256 meters. Now we apply the formula for the volume of a pyramid:

$$V = \frac{1}{3}Bh = \frac{1}{3} \cdot \frac{2704 \text{ m}^2}{1} \cdot \frac{256 \text{ m}}{1} = \frac{2704 \cdot 256}{3} \text{ m}^3 \approx 230{,}741 \text{ m}^3.$$

The volume of the building is approximately 230,741 cubic meters.

The San Francisco pyramid is relatively small compared to the Great Pyramid outside Cairo, Egypt. Built about 2550 B.C. by a labor force of 100,000, the Great Pyramid is approximately 11 times the volume of San Francisco's pyramid.

 3 A pyramid is 4 feet tall. Each side of the square base has a length of 6 feet. Find the pyramid's volume.

The Transamerica Tower's 3678 windows take cleaners one month to wash. Its foundation is sunk 15.5 m (52 ft) into the ground and is designed to move with earth tremors.

FIGURE 10.48

Not every three-dimensional figure is a polyhedron. Take, for example, the right circular cylinder shown in Figure 10.48. Its shape should remind you of a soup can or a stack of coins. The right circular cylinder is so named because the top and bottom are circles, and the side forms a right angle with the top and bottom. The formula for the volume of a right circular cylinder is given as follows:

VOLUME OF A RIGHT CIRCULAR CYLINDER

The volume, V, of a right circular cylinder is given by the formula

$$V = \pi r^2 h,$$

where r is the radius of the circle at either end and h is the height.

Right circular cylinder

EXAMPLE 4   FINDING THE VOLUME OF A CYLINDER

Find the volume of the cylinder in Figure 10.49.

SOLUTION In order to find the cylinder's volume, we need both its radius and its height. Because the diameter is 20 yards, the radius is half this length, or 10 yards. The height of the cylinder is given to be 9 yards. Thus, $r = 10$ and $h = 9$. Now we apply the formula for the volume of a cylinder.

$$V = \pi r^2 h = \pi (10 \text{ yd})^2 \cdot 9 \text{ yd} = 900\pi \text{ yd}^3 \approx 2827 \text{ yd}^3$$

The volume of the cylinder is approximately 2827 cubic yards.

FIGURE 10.49

CHECK POINT **4** Find the volume, to the nearest cubic inch, of a cylinder with a diameter of 8 inches and a height of 6 inches.

Figure 10.50 shows a **right circular cone** inside a cylinder, sharing the same circular base as the cylinder. The height of the cone, the perpendicular distance from the top to the circular base, is the same as that of the cylinder. Three such cones can occupy the same amount of space as the cylinder. Therefore, the formula for the volume of the cone is $\frac{1}{3}$ the volume of the cylinder.

FIGURE 10.50

VOLUME OF A CONE

The volume, V, of a right circular cone that has height h and radius r is given by the formula

$$V = \frac{1}{3}\pi r^2 h.$$

Cone

EXAMPLE 5   FINDING THE VOLUME OF A CONE

Find the volume of the cone in Figure 10.51.

SOLUTION The radius of the cone is 7 meters and the height is 10 meters. Thus, $r = 7$ and $h = 10$. Now we apply the formula for the volume of a cone.

$$V = \frac{1}{3}\pi r^2 h = \frac{1}{3}\pi (7 \text{ m})^2 \cdot 10 \text{ m} = \frac{490\pi}{3}\text{m}^3 \approx 513 \text{ m}^3$$

The volume of the cone is approximately 513 cubic meters.

FIGURE 10.51

FIGURE 10.52

Find the volume, to the nearest cubic inch, of a cone with a radius of 4 inches and a height of 6 inches.

Figure 10.52 shows a *sphere*. Its shape may remind you of a basketball. The Earth is not a perfect sphere, but it's close. A **sphere** is the set of points in space equally distant from a given point, its **center**. The **radius** is the line segment from the center to any point on the sphere. The word *radius* is also used to refer to the length of this line segment. A sphere's volume can be found by using π and its radius.

> **VOLUME OF A SPHERE**
>
> The volume, V, of a sphere of radius r is given by the formula
>
> $$V = \frac{4}{3}\pi r^3.$$
>
> **Sphere**
>
>

EXAMPLE 6   APPLYING VOLUME FORMULAS

An ice cream cone is 5 inches deep and has a radius of 1 inch. A spherical scoop of ice cream also has a radius of 1 inch. (See Figure 10.53.) If the ice cream melts into the cone, will it overflow?

SOLUTION The ice cream will overflow if the volume of the ice cream, a sphere, is greater than the volume of the cone. Find the volume of each.

$$V_{\text{cone}} = \frac{1}{3}\pi r^2 h = \frac{1}{3}\pi (1\text{ in.})^2 \cdot 5 \text{ in.} = \frac{5\pi}{3}\text{in.}^3 \approx 5 \text{ in.}^3$$

$$V_{\text{sphere}} = \frac{4}{3}\pi r^3 = \frac{4}{3}\pi (1\text{ in.})^3 = \frac{4\pi}{3}\text{in.}^3 \approx 4 \text{ in.}^3$$

FIGURE 10.53

The volume of the spherical scoop of ice cream is less than the volume of the cone, so there will be no overflow.

A basketball has a radius of 4.5 inches. If the ball is filled with 350 cubic inches of air, is this enough air to fill it completely?

2 | Compute the surface area of a three-dimensional figure.

Surface Area

In addition to volume, we can also measure the area of the outer surface of a three-dimensional object, called its **surface area**. Like area, surface area is measured in square units. For example, the surface area of the rectangular solid in Figure 10.54 is the sum of the areas of the six outside rectangles of the solid.

FIGURE 10.54

Surface Area $= lw + lw + lh + lh + wh + wh$

Areas of top and bottom rectangles   Areas of front and back rectangles   Areas of rectangles on left and right sides

$$= \quad 2lw \quad + \quad 2lh \quad + \quad 2wh$$

Formulas for the surface area, abbreviated *SA*, of three-dimensional figures are given in Table 10.4.

TABLE 10.4 COMMON FORMULAS FOR SURFACE AREA

Cube	Rectangular Solid	Circular Cylinder
$SA = 6s^2$	$SA = 2lw + 2lh + 2wh$	$SA = 2\pi r^2 + 2\pi rh$

EXAMPLE 7   FINDING THE SURFACE AREA OF A SOLID

Find the surface area of the rectangular solid in Figure 10.55.

SOLUTION As shown in the figure, the length is 8 yards, the width is 5 yards, and the height is 3 yards. Thus, $l = 8$, $w = 5$, and $h = 3$.

$$SA = 2lw + 2lh + 2wh$$
$$= 2 \cdot 8 \text{ yd} \cdot 5 \text{ yd} + 2 \cdot 8 \text{ yd} \cdot 3 \text{ yd} + 2 \cdot 5 \text{ yd} \cdot 3 \text{ yd}$$
$$= 80 \text{ yd}^2 + 48 \text{ yd}^2 + 30 \text{ yd}^2 = 158 \text{ yd}^2$$

The surface area is 158 square yards.

3 yd

5 yd   8 yd

FIGURE 10.55

CHECK POINT 7 If the length, width, and height shown in Figure 10.55 are each doubled, find the surface area of the resulting rectangular solid.

EXERCISE SET 10.5 ●●●●●●

• Practice Exercises

In Exercises 1–20, find the volume of each figure. If necessary, express answers in terms of π and then round to the nearest whole number.

1.

4 in.

3 in.
3 in.

2.

3 cm
3 cm
5 cm

3.

4 cm
4 cm
4 cm

4.
5 in.
5 in.
5 in.

5.

$h = 15$ yd

5 yd   7 yd

6.

$h = 20$ yd

8 yd   15 yd

7.

$h = 6$ in.

4 in.   7 in.

8.

$h = 12$ m

10 m   10 m

9.

5 cm

6 cm

10.
6 cm

8 cm

11.
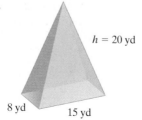
24 in.   21 in.

12.

14 cm   12 cm

13.

9 m
4 m

14.

16 m
5 m

15.

6 yd
5 yd

16.

6 yd
7 yd

17.

6 m

18.

15 m

19.

18 cm

20.

24 in.

In Exercises 21–24, find the surface area of each figure.

21.

3 m
2 m
5 m

22.

3 m
4 m
6 m

23.

4 ft
4 ft
4 ft

24.

6 ft
6 ft
6 ft

In Exercises 25–26, use two formulas for volume to find the volume of each figure. Express answers in terms of π and then round to the nearest whole number.

25.

12 cm
15 cm

26.

14 in.
11 in.
12 in.

• Practice Plus

27. Find the surface area and the volume of the figure shown.

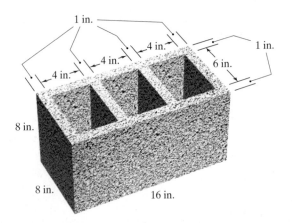
5 yd
2 yd
4 yd
5 yd
3 yd
9 yd
4 yd

28. Find the surface area and the volume of the cement block in the figure shown.

1 in.
4 in.
4 in.
1 in.
4 in.
4 in.
6 in.
8 in.
8 in.
16 in.

29. Find the surface area of the figure shown.

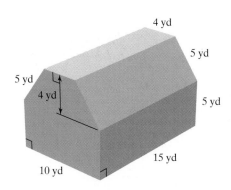

4 yd

5 yd

5 yd

4 yd

5 yd

5 yd

15 yd

10 yd

30. A machine produces open boxes using square sheets of metal measuring 12 inches on each side. The machine cuts equal-sized squares whose sides measure 2 inches from each corner. Then it shapes the metal into an open box by turning up the sides. Find the volume of the box.

31. Find the ratio, reduced to lowest terms, of the volume of a sphere with a radius of 3 inches to the volume of a sphere with a radius of 6 inches.

32. Find the ratio, reduced to lowest terms, of the volume of a sphere with a radius of 3 inches to the volume of a sphere with a radius of 9 inches.

33. A cylinder with radius 3 inches and height 4 inches has its radius tripled. How many times greater is the volume of the larger cylinder than the smaller cylinder?

34. A cylinder with radius 2 inches and height 3 inches has its radius quadrupled. How many times greater is the volume of the larger cylinder than the smaller cylinder?

• Application Exercises

35. A building contractor is to dig a foundation 12 feet long, 9 feet wide, and 6 feet deep for a toll booth. The contractor pays $10 per load for trucks to remove the dirt. Each truck holds 6 cubic yards. What is the cost to the contractor to have all the dirt hauled away?

36. What is the cost of concrete for a walkway that is 15 feet long, 8 feet wide, and 9 inches deep if the concrete costs $30 per cubic yard?

37. A furnace is designed to heat 10,000 cubic feet. Will this furnace be adequate for a 1400-square-foot house with a 9-foot ceiling?

38. A water reservoir is shaped like a rectangular solid with a base that is 50 yards by 30 yards, and a vertical height of 20 yards. At the start of a three-month period of no rain, the reservoir was completely full. At the end of this period, the height of the water was down to 6 yards. How much water was used in the three-month period?

39. The Great Pyramid outside Cairo, Egypt, has a square base measuring 756 feet on a side and a height of 480 feet.

　a. What is the volume of the Great Pyramid, in cubic yards?

　b. The stones used to build the Great Pyramid were limestone blocks with an average volume of 1.5 cubic yards. How many of these blocks were needed to construct the Great Pyramid?

40. Although the Eiffel Tower in Paris is not a solid pyramid, its shape approximates that of a pyramid with a square base measuring 120 feet on a side and a height of 980 feet. If it were a solid pyramid, what would be the Eiffel Tower's volume, in cubic yards?

41. You are about to sue your contractor who promised to install a water tank that holds 500 gallons of water. You know that 500 gallons is the capacity of a tank that holds 67 cubic feet. The cylindrical tank has a radius of 3 feet and a height of 2 feet 4 inches. Does the evidence indicate you can win the case against the contractor if it goes to court?

42. Two cylindrical cans of soup sell for the same price. One can has a diameter of 6 inches and a height of 5 inches. The other has a diameter of 5 inches and a height of 6 inches. Which can contains more soup and, therefore, is the better buy?

43. A circular backyard pool has a diameter of 24 feet and is 4 feet deep. One cubic foot of water has a capacity of approximately 7.48 gallons. If water costs $2 per thousand gallons, how much, to the nearest dollar, will it cost to fill the pool?

44. The tunnel under the English Channel that connects England and France is the world's longest tunnel. There are actually three separate tunnels built side by side. Each is a half-cylinder that is 50,000 meters long and 4 meters high. How many cubic meters of dirt had to be removed to build the tunnel?

• Writing in Mathematics

45. Explain the following analogy:

In terms of formulas used to compute volume, a pyramid is to a rectangular solid just as a cone is to a cylinder.

46. Explain why a cylinder is not a polyhedron.

• Critical Thinking Exercises

47. What happens to the volume of a sphere if its radius is doubled?

48. A scale model of a car is constructed so that its length, width, and height are each $\frac{1}{10}$ the length, width, and height of the actual car. By how many times does the volume of the car exceed its scale model?

In Exercises 49–50, find the volume of the darkly shaded region. If necessary, round to the nearest whole number.

49.

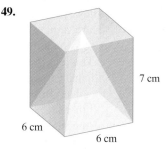

7 cm

6 cm

6 cm

50.

Dimensions shown: 2 in., 10 in., 6 in.

51. Find the surface area of the figure shown.

Dimensions shown: 3 cm, 4 cm, 6 cm

SECTION 10.6 • RIGHT TRIANGLE TRIGONOMETRY

OBJECTIVES

1. Use the lengths of the sides of a right triangle to find trigonometric ratios.

2. Use trigonometric ratios to find missing parts of right triangles.

3. Use trigonometric ratios to solve applied problems.

In the last century, Ang Rita Sherpa climbed Mount Everest ten times, all without the use of bottled oxygen.

Mountain climbers have forever been fascinated by reaching the top of Mount Everest, sometimes with tragic results. The mountain, on Asia's Tibet-Nepal border, is Earth's highest, peaking at an incredible 29,035 feet. The heights of mountains can be found using **trigonometry**. The word *trigonometry* means *measurement of triangles*. Trigonometry is used in navigation, building, and engineering. For centuries, Muslims used trigonometry and the stars to navigate across the Arabian desert to Mecca, the birthplace of the prophet Muhammad, the founder of Islam. The ancient Greeks used trigonometry to record the locations of thousands of stars and worked out the motion of the Moon relative to Earth. Today, trigonometry is used to study the structure of DNA, the master molecule that determines how we grow from a single cell to a complex, fully developed adult.

Ratios in Right Triangles

The right triangle forms the basis of trigonometry. If either acute angle of a right triangle stays the same size, the shape of the triangle does not change even if it is made larger or smaller. Because of properties of similar triangles, this means that the ratios of certain lengths stay the same regardless of the right triangle's size. These ratios have special names and are defined in terms of the **side opposite** an acute angle, the **side adjacent** to the acute angle, and the **hypotenuse**. In Figure 10.56, the length of the hypotenuse, the side opposite the $90°$ angle, is represented by c. The length of the side opposite angle A is represented by a. The length of the side adjacent to angle A is represented by b.

The three fundamental trigonometric ratios, **sine** (abbreviated sin), **cosine** (abbreviated cos), and **tangent** (abbreviated tan), are defined as ratios of the lengths of the sides of a right triangle. In the box that follows on the next page, when a side of a triangle is mentioned, we are referring to the *length* of that side.

Length of the hypotenuse

B

c

a

A

b

C

Length of the side opposite angle A

Length of the side adjacent to angle A

FIGURE 10.56 Naming a right triangle's sides from the point of view of an acute angle

1 | Use the lengths of the sides of a right triangle to find trigonometric ratios.

TRIGONOMETRIC RATIOS

Let A represent an acute angle of a right triangle, with right angle C, shown in Figure 10.56. For angle A, the trigonometric ratios are defined as follows:

sine of A
$$\sin A = \frac{\text{side opposite angle } A}{\text{hypotenuse}} = \frac{a}{c}$$

cosine of A
$$\cos A = \frac{\text{side adjacent to angle } A}{\text{hypotenuse}} = \frac{b}{c}$$

tangent of A
$$\tan A = \frac{\text{side opposite angle } A}{\text{side adjacent to angle } A} = \frac{a}{b}.$$

STUDY TIP

The word

SOHCAHTOA (pronounced: so-cah-tow-ah)

is a way to remember the definitions of the three trigonometric ratios.

$$\begin{array}{ccc} \text{S} \quad \overbrace{\text{O H}} & \text{C} \quad \overbrace{\text{A H}} & \text{T} \quad \overbrace{\text{O A}} \\ \uparrow \quad \dfrac{\text{opp}}{\text{hyp}} & \uparrow \quad \dfrac{\text{adj}}{\text{hyp}} & \uparrow \quad \dfrac{\text{opp}}{\text{adj}} \\ \text{Sine} & \text{Cosine} & \text{Tangent} \end{array}$$

"<u>S</u>ome <u>O</u>ld <u>H</u>og <u>C</u>ame <u>A</u>round <u>H</u>ere and <u>T</u>ook <u>O</u>ur <u>A</u>pples."

EXAMPLE 1 BECOMING FAMILIAR WITH THE TRIGONOMETRIC RATIOS

Find the sine, cosine, and tangent of A in Figure 10.57.

SOLUTION We begin by finding the measure of the hypotenuse c using the Pythagorean Theorem.

$$c^2 = a^2 + b^2 = 5^2 + 12^2 = 25 + 144 = 169$$
$$c = \sqrt{169} = 13$$

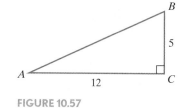

FIGURE 10.57

Now, we apply the definitions of the trigonometric ratios.

$$\sin A = \frac{\text{side opposite angle } A}{\text{hypotenuse}} = \frac{5}{13}$$

$$\cos A = \frac{\text{side adjacent to angle } A}{\text{hypotenuse}} = \frac{12}{13}$$

$$\tan A = \frac{\text{side opposite angle } A}{\text{side adjacent to angle } A} = \frac{5}{12}$$

○

CHECK POINT **1** Find the sine, cosine, and tangent of A in the figure shown.

2 | Use trigonometric ratios to find missing parts of right triangles.

A scientific or graphing calculator in the degree mode will give you decimal approximations for the trigonometric ratios of any angle. For example, to find an approximation for tan 37°, the tangent of 37°, a keystroke sequence similar to one of the following can be used:

Many Scientific Calculators: 37 [TAN]

Many Graphing Calculators: [TAN] 37 [ENTER].

The tangent of 37°, rounded to four decimal places, is 0.7536.

If we are given the length of one side and the measure of an acute angle of a right triangle, we can use trigonometry to solve for the length of either of the other two sides. Example 2 illustrates how this is done.

EXAMPLE 2 FINDING A MISSING LEG OF A RIGHT TRIANGLE

Find a in the right triangle in Figure 10.58.

SOLUTION We need to identify a trigonometric ratio that will make it possible to find a. Because we have a known angle, 40°, an unknown opposite side, a, and a known adjacent side, 150 cm, we use the tangent ratio.

$$\tan 40° = \frac{a}{150}$$

Side opposite the 40° angle
Side adjacent to the 40° angle

Now we solve for a by multiplying both sides by 150.

$$a = 150 \tan 40° \approx 126$$

The tangent ratio reveals that a is approximately 126 centimeters.

FIGURE 10.58

 In Figure 10.58, let $m\angle A = 62°$ and $b = 140$ cm. Find a to the nearest centimeter.

EXAMPLE 3 FINDING A MISSING HYPOTENUSE OF A RIGHT TRIANGLE

Find c in the right triangle in Figure 10.58.

SOLUTION In Example 2, we found a: $a \approx 126$. Because we are given that $b = 150$, it is possible to find c using the Pythagorean Theorem: $c^2 = a^2 + b^2$. However, if we made an error in computing a, we will perpetuate our mistake using this approach.

Instead, we will use the quantities given and identify a trigonometric ratio that will make it possible to find c. Refer to Figure 10.58. Because we have a known angle, 40°, a known adjacent side, 150 cm, and an unknown hypotenuse, c, we use the cosine ratio.

$$\cos 40° = \frac{150}{c}$$

Side adjacent to the 40° angle
Hypotenuse

$$c \cos 40° = 150 \quad \text{Multiply both sides by } c.$$
$$c = \frac{150}{\cos 40°} \quad \text{Divide both sides by } \cos 40°.$$
$$c \approx 196 \quad \text{Use a calculator.}$$

The cosine ratio reveals that the hypotenuse is approximately 196 centimeters.

 In Figure 10.58, let $m\angle A = 62°$ and $b = 140$ cm. Find c to the nearest centimeter.

TECHNOLOGY

Here is the keystroke sequence for 150 tan 40°:

MANY SCIENTIFIC CALCULATORS

150 [×] 40 [TAN] [=]

MANY GRAPHING CALCULATORS

150 [TAN] 40 [ENTER].

TECHNOLOGY

Here is the keystroke sequence for $\frac{150}{\cos 40°}$:

MANY SCIENTIFIC CALCULATORS

150 [÷] 40 [COS] [=]

MANY GRAPHING CALCULATORS

150 [÷] [COS] 40 [ENTER].

Applications of the Trigonometric Ratios

Trigonometry was first developed to measure heights and distances that are inconvenient or impossible to measure. These applications often involve the angle made with an imaginary horizontal line. As shown in Figure 10.59, an angle formed by a horizontal line and the line of sight to an object that is above the horizontal line is called the **angle of elevation**. The angle formed by a horizontal line and the line of sight to an object that is below the horizontal line is called the **angle of depression**. Transits and sextants are instruments used to measure such angles.

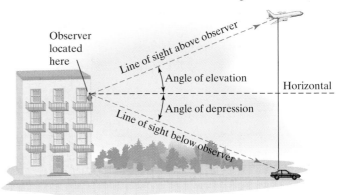

FIGURE 10.59

| EXAMPLE 4 | PROBLEM SOLVING USING AN ANGLE OF ELEVATION |

From a point on level ground 125 feet from the base of a tower, the angle of elevation to the top of the tower is 57.2°. Approximate the height of the tower to the nearest foot.

SOLUTION A sketch is shown in Figure 10.60, where a represents the height of the tower. In the right triangle, we have a known angle, an unknown opposite side, and a known adjacent side. Therefore, we use the tangent ratio.

$$\tan 57.2° = \frac{a}{125}$$

Side opposite the 57.2° angle

Side adjacent to the 57.2° angle

We solve for a by multiplying both sides of this equation by 125:

$$a = 125 \tan 57.2° \approx 194.$$

The tower is approximately 194 feet high.

 From a point on level ground 80 feet from the base of the Eiffel Tower, the angle of elevation is 85.4°. Approximate the height of the Eiffel Tower to the nearest foot.

If the measures of two sides of a right triangle are known, the measures of the two acute angles can be found using the **inverse trigonometric keys** on a calculator. For example, suppose that $\sin A = 0.866$. We can find the measure of angle A by using the *inverse sine* key, usually labeled $\boxed{\text{SIN}^{-1}}$. The key $\boxed{\text{SIN}^{-1}}$ is not a button you will actually press; it is the secondary function for the button labeled $\boxed{\text{SIN}}$.

Many Scientific Calculators:

.866 $\boxed{\text{2nd}}$ $\boxed{\text{SIN}}$

Pressing $\boxed{\text{2nd}}$ $\boxed{\text{SIN}}$ accesses the inverse sine key, $\boxed{\text{SIN}^{-1}}$.

Many Graphing Calculators:

$\boxed{\text{2nd}}$ $\boxed{\text{SIN}}$ .866 $\boxed{\text{ENTER}}$

The display should show approximately 59.99°, which can be rounded to 60°. Thus, if $\sin A = 0.866$, then $m \angle A \approx 60°$.

FIGURE 10.60 Determining height without using direct measurement

3 | Use trigonometric ratios to solve applied problems.

EXAMPLE 5   DETERMINING THE ANGLE OF ELEVATION

A building that is 21 meters tall casts a shadow 25 meters long. Find the angle of elevation of the sun.

SOLUTION The situation is illustrated in Figure 10.61. We are asked to find $m \angle A$. We begin with the tangent ratio.

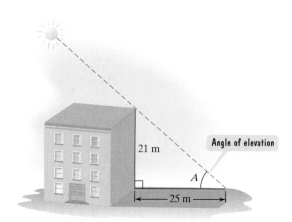

$$\tan A = \frac{21}{25}$$

Side opposite A

Side adjacent to A

FIGURE 10.61

We use the **inverse tangent** key, $\boxed{\text{TAN}^{-1}}$, to find A.

Pressing $\boxed{\text{2nd}}$ $\boxed{\text{TAN}}$ accesses the inverse tangent key, $\boxed{\text{TAN}^{-1}}$.

Many Scientific Calculators:

$\boxed{(}$ $\boxed{21}$ $\boxed{\div}$ $\boxed{25}$ $\boxed{)}$ $\boxed{\text{2nd}}$ $\boxed{\text{TAN}}$

Many Graphing Calculators:

$\boxed{\text{2nd}}$ $\boxed{\text{TAN}}$ $\boxed{(}$ $\boxed{21}$ $\boxed{\div}$ $\boxed{25}$ $\boxed{)}$ $\boxed{\text{ENTER}}$

The display should show approximately 40. Thus, the angle of elevation of the sun is approximately 40°.

CHECK POINT 5 A flagpole that is 14 meters tall casts a shadow 10 meters long. Find the angle of elevation of the sun to the nearest degree.

The Mountain Man

In the 1930s, a *National Geographic* team headed by Brad Washburn used trigonometry to create a map of the 5000-square-mile region of the Yukon, near the Canadian border. The team started with aerial photography. By drawing a network of angles on the photographs, the approximate locations of the major mountains and their rough heights were determined. The expedition then spent three months on foot to find the exact heights. Team members established two base points a known distance apart, one directly under the mountain's peak. By measuring the angle of elevation from one of the base points to the peak, the tangent ratio was used to determine the peak's height. The Yukon expedition was a major advance in the way maps are made.

EXERCISE SET 10.6 ●●●●●○

• Practice Exercises

In Exercises 1–8, use the given right triangles to find ratios, in reduced form, for sin A, cos A, and tan A.

1.

2.

3.

4.

5.

6.

7.

8.

In Exercises 9–18, find the measure of the side of the right triangle whose length is designated by a lowercase letter. Round answers to the nearest whole number.

9.

10.

11.

12.

13.

14.

15.

16.

17.

18.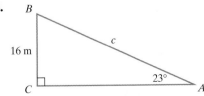

In Exercises 19–22, find the measures of the parts of the right triangle that are not given. Round all answers to the nearest whole number.

19.

20.

21.

22.

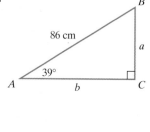

In Exercises 23–26, use the inverse trigonometric keys on a calculator to find the measure of angle A, rounded to the nearest whole degree.

23.

24.

25.

26.

• Practice Plus

In Exercises 27–34, find the length x to the nearest whole number.

27.

28.

29.

30.

31.

32.

33.

34.

• Application Exercises

35. To find the distance across a lake, a surveyor took the measurements in the figure shown at the top of the next page. Use these measurements to determine how far it is across the lake. Round to the nearest yard.

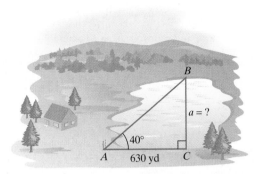

36. At a certain time of day, the angle of elevation of the sun is 40°. To the nearest foot, find the height of a tree whose shadow is 35 feet long.

37. A plane rises from take-off and flies at an angle of 10° with the horizontal runway. When it has gained 500 feet in altitude, find the distance, to the nearest foot, the plane has flown.

38. A road is inclined at an angle of 5°. After driving 5000 feet along this road, find the driver's increase in altitude. Round to the nearest foot.

39. The tallest television transmitting tower in the world is in North Dakota. From a point on level ground 5280 feet (one mile) from the base of the tower, the angle of elevation to the top of the tower is 21.3°. Approximate the height of the tower to the nearest foot.

40. From a point on level ground 30 yards from the base of a building, the angle of elevation to the top of the building is 38.7°. Approximate the height of the building to the nearest foot.

41. The Statue of Liberty is approximately 305 feet tall. If the angle of elevation of a ship to the top of the statue is 23.7°, how far, to the nearest foot, is the ship from the statue's base?

42. A 200-foot cliff drops vertically into the ocean. If the angle of elevation of a ship to the top of the cliff is 22.3°, how far off shore, to the nearest foot, is the ship?

43. A tower that is 125 feet tall casts a shadow 172 feet long. Find the angle of elevation of the sun to the nearest degree.

44. The Washington Monument is 555 feet high. If you stand one quarter of a mile, or 1320 feet, from the base of the monument and look to the top, find the angle of elevation to the nearest degree.

45. A helicopter hovers 1000 feet above a small island. The figure shows that the angle of depression from the helicopter to point P is 36°. How far off the coast, to the nearest foot, is the island?

46. A police helicopter is flying at 800 feet. A stolen car is sighted at an angle of depression of 72°. Find the distance of the stolen car, to the nearest foot, from a point directly below the helicopter.

47. A wheelchair ramp is to be built beside the steps to the campus library. Find the angle of elevation of the 23-foot ramp, to the nearest tenth of a degree, if its final height is 6 feet.

48. A kite flies at a height of 30 feet when 65 feet of string is out. If the string is in a straight line, find the angle that it makes with the ground. Round to the nearest tenth of a degree.

• Writing in Mathematics

49. If you are given the lengths of the sides of a right triangle, describe how to find the sine of either acute angle.

50. Describe one similarity and one difference between the sine ratio and the cosine ratio in terms of the sides of a right triangle.

51. If one of the acute angles of a right triangle is 37°, explain why the sine ratio does not increase as the size of the triangle increases.

52. If the measure of one of the acute angles and the hypotenuse of a right triangle are known, describe how to find the measure of the remaining parts of the triangle.

53. Describe what is meant by an angle of elevation and an angle of depression.

54. Give an example of an applied problem that can be solved using one or more trigonometric ratios. Be as specific as possible.

55. Use a calculator to find each of the following: sin 32° and cos 58°; sin 17° and cos 73°; sin 50° and cos 40°; sin 88° and cos 2°. Describe what you observe. Based on your observations, what do you think the *co* in *cosine* stands for?

56. Stonehenge, the famous "stone circle" in England, was built between 2750 B.C. and 1300 B.C. using solid stone blocks weighing over 99,000 pounds each. It required 550 people to pull a single stone up a ramp inclined at a 9°

angle. Describe how right triangle trigonometry can be used to determine the distance the 550 workers had to drag a stone in order to raise it to a height of 30 feet.

• Critical Thinking Exercises

57. Explain why the sine or cosine of an acute angle cannot be greater than or equal to 1.

58. Describe what happens to the tangent of an angle as the measure of the angle gets close to 90°. What happens at 90°?

59. From the top of a 250-foot lighthouse, a plane is sighted overhead and a ship is observed directly below the plane. The angle of elevation of the plane is 22° and the angle of depression of the ship is 35°. Find **a.** the distance of the ship from the lighthouse; **b.** the plane's height above the water. Round to the nearest foot.

60. Sighting the top of a building, a surveyor measured the angle of elevation to be 22°. The transit is 5 feet above the ground and 300 feet from the building. Find the building's height. Round to the nearest foot.

SECTION 10.7 • BEYOND EUCLIDEAN GEOMETRY

O B J E C T I V E

1. Gain an understanding of some of the general ideas of other kinds of geometries.

Think of your favorite natural setting. During the last quarter of the twentieth century, mathematicians developed a new kind of geometry that uses the computer to produce the diverse forms of nature that we see around us. These forms are not polygons, polyhedrons, circles, or cylinders. In this section, we move beyond Euclidean geometry to explore ideas which have extended geometry beyond the boundaries first laid down by the ancient Greek scholars.

The Geometry of Graphs

In the early 1700s, the city of Königsberg, Germany, was connected by seven bridges, shown in Figure 10.62. Many people in the city were interested in finding if it were possible to walk through the city so as to cross each bridge exactly once. After a few trials, you may be convinced that the answer is no. However, it is not easy to prove your answer by trial and error because there are a large number of ways of taking such a walk.

STUDY TIP

A more detailed presentation on the geometry of graphs, called *graph theory*, can be found in Chapter 15.

FIGURE 10.62

Ethane

Graph theory is used to show how atoms are linked to form molecules.

The problem was taken to the Swiss mathematician Leonhard Euler (1707–1783). In the year 1736, Euler proved that it is not possible to stroll through the city and cross each bridge exactly once. His solution of the problem opened up a new kind of geometry called **graph theory**. Graph theory is now used to design city streets, analyze traffic patterns, and find the most efficient routes for public transportation.

Euler solved the problem by introducing the following definitions:

A **vertex** is a point. An **edge** is a line segment or curve that starts and ends at a vertex.

Vertices and edges form a **graph**. A vertex with an odd number of attached edges is an **odd vertex**. A vertex with an even number of attached edges is an **even vertex**.

Using these definitions, Figure 10.63 shows that the graph in the Königsberg bridge problem has four odd vertices.

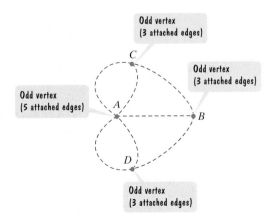

FIGURE 10.63

A graph is **traversable** if it can be traced without lifting the pencil from the paper and without tracing an edge more than once. Euler proved the following rules of traversability in solving the problem:

Because the graph in the Königsberg bridge problem has four odd vertices, it cannot be traversed.

EXAMPLE 1   TO TRAVERSE OR NOT TO TRAVERSE?

Consider the graph in Figure 10.64.

a. Is this graph traversable?

b. If it is, describe a path that will traverse it.

SOLUTION

a. Begin by determining if each vertex is even or odd.

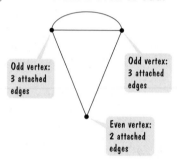

Because this graph has two odd vertices, by Euler's second rule, it is traversable.

b. In order to find a path that traverses this graph, we again use Euler's second rule. It states that we must start at either of the odd vertices and finish at the other. One of two possible paths is shown in Figure 10.65.

FIGURE 10.64

FIGURE 10.65

 Create a graph with two even and two odd vertices. Then describe a path that will traverse it.

Graph theory is used to solve many kinds of practical problems. The first step is to create a graph that represents, or models, the problem. For example, consider a UPS driver trying to find the best way to deliver packages around town. By modeling the delivery locations as vertices and roads between locations as edges, graph theory reveals the driver's most efficient path. Graphs are powerful tools because they illustrate the important aspects of a problem and leave out unnecessary detail.

Topology

A branch of modern geometry called **topology** looks at shapes in a completely new way. In Euclidean geometry, shapes are rigid and unchanging. In topology, shapes can be twisted, stretched, bent, and shrunk. Total flexibility is the rule.

A topologist does not know the difference between a doughnut and a coffee cup! This is because, topologically speaking, there is no difference. They both have one hole, and in this strange geometry of transformations, a doughnut can be flattened, pulled, and pushed to form a coffee cup.

In topology, objects are classified according to the number of holes in them, called their **genus**. The genus gives the largest number of complete cuts that can be made in the object without cutting the object into two pieces. Objects with the same genus are **topologically equivalent**.

The three shapes shown below (sphere, cube, irregular blob) have the same genus: 0. No complete cuts can be made without cutting these objects into two pieces.

STUDY TIP

The genus of an object is the same as the number of holes in the object.

How can a doughnut be transformed into a coffee cup? It can be stretched and deformed to make a bowl part of the surface. Both the doughnut and the coffee cup have genus 1. One complete cut can be made without cutting these objects into two pieces.

To a topologist, a lump with two holes in it is no different than a sugar bowl with two handles. Both have genus 2. Two complete cuts can be made without cutting these objects into two pieces.

Shown below is a transformation that results in a most unusual topological figure.

Start with a flexible glass tube.

Base

Neck

Pass the neck through a hole.

Join the neck to the base.

A Klein bottle

The figure that results is called a **Klein bottle**. You couldn't use one to carry water on a long hike. Because the inside surface loops back on itself to merge with the outside, it has neither an outside nor an inside and cannot hold water. A Klein bottle passes through itself without the existence of a hole, which is impossible in three-dimensional space. A true Klein bottle is visible only when generated on a computer.

A Klein bottle generated on a computer

Topology is more than an excursion in geometric fantasy. Topologists study knots and ways in which they are topologically equivalent. Knot theory is used to identify viruses and understand the ways in which they invade our cells. Such an understanding is a first step in finding vaccines for viruses ranging from the common cold to HIV.

Non-Euclidean Geometries

Imagine this: Earth is squeezed and compressed to the size of a golf ball. It becomes a **black hole**, a region in space where everything seems to disappear. Its pull of gravity is now so strong that the space near the golf ball can be thought of as a funnel with the black hole sitting at the bottom. Any object that comes near the funnel will be pulled into it by the immense gravity of the golf-ball-sized Earth. Then the object disappears! Although this sounds like science fiction, some physicists believe that there are billions of black holes in space.

Is there a geometry that describes this unusual phenomenon? Yes, although it's not the geometry of Euclid. Euclidean geometry is based on the assumption that given a point not on a line, there is one line that can be drawn through the point parallel to the given line, shown as the thinner white line in Figure 10.66. We used this assumption to prove that the sum of the measures of the three angles of any triangle is 180°.

Hyperbolic geometry was developed independently by the Russian mathematician Nikolay Lobachevsky (1792–1856) and the Hungarian mathematician Janos Bolyai (1802–1860). It is based on the assumption that given a point not on a line, there are an infinite number of lines that can be drawn through the point parallel to the given line. The shapes in this non-Euclidean geometry are not represented on a plane. Instead, they are drawn on a funnel-like surface, called a *pseudosphere*, shown in Figure 10.67. On such a surface, the shortest distance between two points is a curved line. A triangle's sides are composed of arcs, and the sum of the measures of its angles is less than 180°. The shape of the pseudosphere looks like the distorted space near a black hole.

Once the ice had been broken by Lobachevsky and Bolyai, mathematicians were stimulated to set up other non-Euclidean geometries. The best known of these was **elliptic geometry**, proposed by the German mathematician Bernhard Riemann (1826–1866). Riemann began his geometry with the assumption that there are no

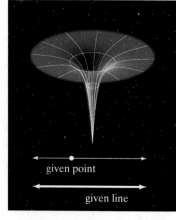

given point

given line

FIGURE 10.66

A   *B*

FIGURE 10.67

parallel lines. As shown in Figure 10.68, elliptic geometry is on a sphere, and the sum of the measures of the angles of a triangle is greater than 180°.

Riemann's elliptic geometry was used by Albert Einstein in his theory of the universe. One aspect of the theory states that if you set off on a journey through space and keep going in the same direction, you will eventually come back to your starting point. The same thing happens on the surface of a sphere. This means that space itself is "curved," although the idea is difficult to visualize. It is interesting that Einstein used ideas of non-Euclidean geometry more than 50 years after the system was logically developed. Mathematics often moves ahead of our understanding of the physical world.

FIGURE 10.68

BLITZER BONUS

Colorful Puzzles

How many different colors are needed to color a plane map so that any two regions that share a common border are colored differently? Even though no map could be found that required more than four colors, a proof that four colors would work for every map remained elusive to mathematicians for over 100 years. The conjecture that at most four colors are needed, stated in 1852, was proved by American mathematicians Kenneth Appel and Wolfgang Haken of the University of Illinois in 1976. Their proof translated maps into graphs that represented each region as a vertex and each shared common border as an edge between corresponding vertices. The proof relied heavily on computer computations that checked approximately 1500 special cases, requiring 1200 hours of computer time. Although there are recent rumors about a flaw in the proof, no one has found a proof that does not enlist the use of computer calculations.

If you take a strip of paper, give it a single half-twist, and paste the ends together, the result is a one-sided surface called a Möbius strip. A map on a Möbius strip requires six colors to make sure that no adjacent areas are the same color.

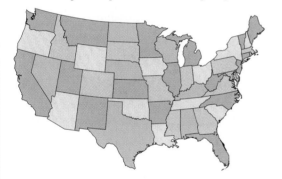

At most four colors are needed on a plane map.

At most six colors are needed on a map drawn on a Möbius strip.

We have seen that Dutch artist M. C. Escher is known for combining art and geometry. Many of his images are based on non-Euclidean geometry. In the woodcut shown on the right, things enlarge as they approach the center and shrink proportionally as they approach the boundary. The shortest distance between two points is a curved line, and the triangles that are formed look like those from hyperbolic geometry.

Table 10.5 on the next page compares Euclidean geometry with hyperbolic and elliptic geometry.

M. C. Escher, *Circle Limit III* © 2004 The M.C. Escher Company, The Netherlands, Baarn, Holland. All rights reserved.

TABLE 10.5 COMPARING THREE SYSTEMS OF GEOMETRY

Euclidean Geometry Euclid (300 B.C.)	Hyperbolic Geometry Lobachevsky, Bolyai (1830)	Elliptic Geometry Riemann (1850)
Given a point not on a line, there is one and only one line through the point parallel to the given line.	Given a point not on a line, there are an infinite number of lines through the point that do not intersect the given line.	There are no parallel lines.
Geometry is on a plane:	Geometry is on a pseudosphere:	Geometry is on a sphere:
The sum of the measures of the angles of a triangle is 180°.	The sum of the measures of the angles of a triangle is less than 180°.	The sum of the measures of the angles of a triangle is greater than 180°.

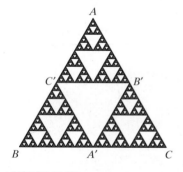

FIGURE 10.69

> "I love Euclidean geometry, but it is quite clear that it does not give a reasonable presentation of the world. Mountains are not cones, clouds are not spheres, trees are not cylinders, neither does lightning travel in a straight line. Almost everything around us is non-Euclidean."
>
> Benoit Mandelbrot

Fractal Geometry

How can geometry describe nature's complexity in objects such as ferns, coastlines, or the human circulatory system? Any magnified portion of a fern repeats much of the pattern of the whole fern, as well as new and unexpected patterns. This property is called **self-similarity**.

Magnified portion

Through the use of computers, a new geometry of natural shapes, called **fractal geometry**, has arrived. The word *fractal* is from the Latin word *fractus*, meaning "broken up," or "fragmented." The fractal shape shown in Figure 10.69 is, indeed, broken up. This shape was obtained by repeatedly subtracting triangles from within triangles. From the midpoints of the sides of triangle ABC, remove triangle $A'B'C'$.

FIGURE 10.70 Daryl H. Hepting and Allan N. Snider, "Desktop Tetrahedron" 1990. Computer generated at the University of Regina in Canada

Repeat the process for the three remaining triangles, then with each of the triangles left after that, and so on ad infinitum.

The process of repeating a rule again and again to create a self-similar fractal like the broken-up triangle is called **iteration**. The self-similar fractal shape in Figure 10.70 was generated on a computer by iteration that involved subtracting pyramids within pyramids. Computers can generate fractal shapes by carrying out thousands or millions of iterations.

In 1975, Benoit Mandelbrot (1924–), the mathematician who developed fractal geometry, published *The Fractal Geometry of Nature*. This book of beautiful computer graphics shows images that look like actual mountains, coastlines, underwater coral gardens, and flowers, all imitating nature's forms. Many of the realistic-looking landscapes that you see in movies are actually computer-generated fractal images.

These images are computer-generated fractals.

EXERCISE SET 10.7 ●●●●●●

• Practice and Application Exercises

For each graph in Exercises 1–6, **a.** *Is the graph traversable?* **b.** *If it is, describe a path that will traverse it.*

1.

2.

3.

4.

5.

6.

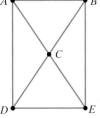

The model shows the way that carbon atoms (red) and hydrogen atoms (blue) link together to form a propane molecule. Use the model to answer Exercises 7–9.

Propane

7. Using each of the three red carbon atoms as a vertex and each of the eight black hydrogen atoms as a vertex, draw a graph for the propane molecule.

8. Determine if each vertex of the network is even or odd.

9. Is the network traversable?

The figure on the left shows the floor plan of a four-room house. By representing rooms as vertices, the outside, E, as a vertex, and doors as edges, the figure on the right is a graph that models the floor plan. Use these figures to solve Exercises 10–13.

 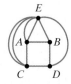

10. Use the floor plan to determine how many doors connect the outside, *E*, to room *A*. How is this shown in the graph?

11. Use the floor plan to determine how many doors connect the outside, *E*, to room *C*. How is this shown in the graph?

12. Is the graph traversable? Explain your answer.

13. If the graph is traversable, determine a path to walk through every room, using each door only once.

In Exercises 14–17, give the genus of each object.

14.

Pretzel

15.

Pitcher

16.

Wrench

17.

Button

18. In Exercises 14–17, which objects are topologically equivalent?

19. Draw (or find and describe) an object of genus 4 or more.

20. What does the figure shown illustrate about angles in a triangle when the triangle is drawn on a sphere?

21. The figure shows a quadrilateral that was drawn on the surface of a sphere. Angles *C* and *D* are obtuse angles. What does the figure illustrate about the sum of the measures of the four angles in a quadrilateral in elliptic geometry?

In Exercises 22–24, describe whether each figure shown exhibits self-similarity.

22.

23.

24.

25. Consult an Internet site devoted to fractals and download two fractal images that imitate nature's forms. How is self-similarity shown in each image?

• Writing in Mathematics

26. What is a graph?

27. What does it mean if a graph is traversable?

28. How do you determine whether or not a graph is traversable?

29. Describe one way in which topology is different than Euclidean geometry.

30. What is the genus of an object?

31. Describe how a rectangular solid and a sphere are topologically equivalent.

32. State the assumption that Euclid made about parallel lines that was altered in both hyperbolic and elliptic geometry.

33. How does hyperbolic geometry differ from Euclidean geometry?

34. How does elliptic geometry differ from Euclidean geometry?

35. What is self-similarity? Describe an object in nature that has this characteristic.

36. Some suggest that nature produces its many forms through a combination of both iteration and a touch of randomness. Describe what this means.

37. Find an Internet site devoted to fractals. Use the site to write a paper on a specific use of fractals.

38. Did you know that laid end to end, the veins, arteries, and capillaries of your body would reach over 40,000 miles? However, your vascular system occupies a very small fraction of your body's volume. Describe a self-similar object in nature, such as your vascular system, with enormous length but relatively small volume.

39. Describe a difference between the shapes of man-made objects and objects that occur in nature.

40. Explain what this short poem by Jonathan Swift has to do with fractal images:

So Nat'ralists observe, A Flea
Hath Smaller Fleas that on him prey
and these have smaller Fleas to bite'em
And so proceed, ad infinitum

41. In Tom Stoppard's play *Arcadia*, the characters talk about mathematics, including ideas from fractal geometry. Read the play and write a paper on one of the ideas that the characters discuss that is related to something presented in this section.

• Group Exercises

42. This activity is suggested for two or three people. Research some of the practical applications of topology. Present the results of your research in a seminar to the entire class. You may also want to include a discussion of some of topology's more unusual figures, such as the Klein bottle and the Möbius strip.

43. Research non-Euclidean geometry and plan a seminar based on your group's research. Each group member should research one of the following five areas:

a. Present an overview of the history of the people who developed non-Euclidean geometry. Who first used the term and why did he never publish his work?

b. Present an overview of the connection between Saccheri quadrilaterals and non-Euclidean geometry. Describe the work of Girolamo Saccheri.

c. Describe how Albert Einstein applied the ideas of Gauss and Riemann. Discuss the notion of curved space and a fourth dimension.

d. Present examples of the work of M. C. Escher that provide ways of visualizing hyperbolic and elliptic geometry.

e. Describe how non-Euclidean geometry changed the direction of subsequent research in mathematics.

After all research has been completed, the group should plan the order in which each group member will speak. Each person should plan on taking about five minutes for his or her portion of the presentation.

44. Albert Einstein's theory of general relativity is concerned with the structure, or the geometry, of the universe. In order to describe the universe, Einstein discovered that he needed four variables: three variables to locate an object in space and a fourth variable describing time. This system is known as space-time.

Because we are three-dimensional beings, how can we imagine four dimensions? One interesting approach to visualizing four dimensions is to consider an analogy of a two-dimensional being struggling to understand three dimensions. This approach first appeared in a book called *Flatland* by Edwin Abbott, written around 1884.

Flatland describes an entire race of beings who are two dimensional, living on a flat plane, unaware of the existence of anything outside their universe. A house in Flatland would look like a blueprint or a line drawing to us. If we were to draw a closed circle around Flatlanders, they would be imprisoned in a cell with no way to see out or escape because there is no way to move up and over the circle. For a two-dimensional being moving only on a plane, the idea of up would be incomprehensible. We could explain that up means moving in a new direction, perpendicular to the two dimensions they know, but it would be similar to telling us we can move in the fourth dimension by traveling perpendicular to our three dimensions.

Group members should obtain copies of or excerpts from Edwin Abbott's *Flatland*. We especially recommend *The Annotated Flatland*, Perseus Publishing, 2002, with fascinating commentary by mathematician and author Ian Stewart. Once all group members have read the story, the following questions are offered for group discussion.

a. How does the sphere, the visitor from the third dimension, reflect the same narrow perspective as the Flatlanders?

b. What are some of the sociological problems raised in the story?

c. What happens when we have a certain way of seeing the world that is challenged by coming into contact with something quite different? Be as specific as possible, citing either personal examples or historical examples.

d. How are A. Square's difficulties in visualizing three dimensions similar to those of a three-dimensional dweller trying to visualize four dimensions?

e. How does the author reflect the overt sexism of his time?

f. What "upward not northward" ideas do you hold that, if shared, would result in criticism, rejection, or a fate similar to that of the narrator of *Flatland*?

●●●●●● CHAPTER SUMMARY, REVIEW, AND TEST

● SUMMARY   DEFINITIONS AND CONCEPTS   EXAMPLES

10.1 Points, Lines, Planes, and Angles

a. Line AB ($\overleftrightarrow{AB}$ or $\overleftrightarrow{BA}$), half-line AB ($\overrightarrow{AB}$), ray AB ($\overrightarrow{AB}$), and line segment AB ($\overline{AB}$ or $\overline{BA}$) are represented in Figure 10.2 on page 539.

b. Angles are measured in degrees. A degree, $1°$, is $\frac{1}{360}$ of a complete rotation. Acute angles measure less than $90°$, right angles $90°$, obtuse angles more than $90°$ but less than $180°$, and straight angles $180°$.   Ex. 1, p. 539

c. Complementary angles are two angles whose measures have a sum of $90°$. Supplementary angles are two angles whose measures have a sum of $180°$.   Ex. 2, p. 541; Ex. 3, p. 541

d. Vertical angles have the same measure.   Ex. 4, p. 542

e. If parallel lines are intersected by a transversal, alternate interior angles, alternate exterior angles, and corresponding angles have the same measure.   Ex. 5, p. 543

10.2 Triangles

a. The sum of the measures of the three angles of any triangle is $180°$.   Ex. 1, p. 547; Ex. 2, p. 548

b. Triangles can be classified by angles (acute, right, obtuse) or by sides (isosceles, equilateral, scalene). See the box on page 548.

c. Similar triangles have the same shape, but not necessarily the same size. Corresponding angles have the same measure and corresponding sides are proportional. If the measures of two angles of one triangle are equal to those of two angles of a second triangle, then the two triangles are similar.   Ex. 3, p. 549; Ex. 4, p. 550

d. The Pythagorean Theorem: The sum of the squares of the lengths of the legs of a right triangle equals the square of the length of the hypotenuse.   Ex. 5, p. 551; Ex. 6, p. 552

10.3 Polygons, Perimeter, and Tessellations

a. A polygon is a closed geometric figure in a plane formed by three or more line segments. Names of some polygons, given in Table 10.2 on page 556, include triangles (three sides), quadrilaterals (four sides), pentagons (five sides), hexagons (six sides), heptagons (seven sides), and octagons (eight sides). A regular polygon is one whose sides are all the same length and whose angles all have the same measure. The perimeter of a polygon is the sum of the lengths of its sides.   Ex. 1, p. 557

b. Types of quadrilaterals, including the parallelogram, rhombus, rectangle, square, and trapezoid, and their characteristics, are given in Table 10.3 on page 557.

c. The sum of the measures of the angles of an n-sided polygon is $(n - 2)180°$. If the n-sided polygon is a regular polygon, then each angle measures $\dfrac{(n - 2)180°}{n}$.   Ex. 2 p. 558

d. A tessellation is a pattern consisting of the repeated use of the same geometric figures to completely cover a plane, leaving no gaps and having no overlaps. The angle requirement for the formation of a tessellation is that the sum of the measures of the angles at each vertex must be $360°$.   Ex. 3, p. 560

10.4 Area and Circumference

a. Formulas for Area
Rectangle: $A = lw$; Square: $A = s^2$; Parallelogram: $A = bh$;
Triangle: $A = \frac{1}{2}bh$; Trapezoid: $A = \frac{1}{2}h(a + b)$ Ex. 1, p. 565; Ex. 2, p. 566; Ex. 3, p. 567; Ex. 4, p. 567; Ex. 5, p. 568

b. Circles
Circumference: $C = 2\pi r$ or $C = \pi d$
Area: $A = \pi r^2$ Ex. 6, p. 569; Ex. 7, p. 569; Ex. 8, p. 570

10.5 Volume

a. Formulas for Volume
Rectangular Solid: $V = lwh$; Cube: $V = s^3$; Pyramid: $V = \frac{1}{3}Bh$;
Cylinder: $V = \pi r^2 h$; Cone: $V = \frac{1}{3}\pi r^2 h$;
Sphere: $V = \frac{4}{3}\pi r^3$

Ex. 1, p. 575;
Ex. 2, p. 575;
Ex. 3, p. 576;
Ex. 4, p. 577;
Ex. 5, p. 577;
Ex. 6, p. 578

b. Formulas for surface area are given in Table 10.4 on page 579.

Ex. 7, p. 579

10.6 Right Triangle Trigonometry

a. Trigonometric ratios, sin A, cos A, and tan A, are defined in the box on page 583.

Ex. 1, p. 583

b. Given one side and the measure of an acute angle of a right triangle, the trigonometric ratios can be used to find the measures of the other parts of the right triangle.

Ex. 2, p. 584;
Ex. 3, p. 584;
Ex. 4, p. 585

c. Given the measures of two sides of a right triangle, the measures of the acute angles can be found using the inverse trigonometric ratio keys $\boxed{\text{SIN}^{-1}}$, $\boxed{\text{COS}^{-1}}$, and $\boxed{\text{TAN}^{-1}}$, on a calculator.

Ex. 5, p. 586

10.7 Beyond Euclidean Geometry

a. A vertex is a point. An edge is a line segment or curve that starts and ends at a vertex. Vertices and edges form a graph. A vertex with an odd number of edges is odd; one with an even number of edges is even. A traversable graph is one that can be traced without removing the pencil from the paper and without tracing an edge more than once. A graph with all even vertices or one with two odd vertices is traversable. With more than two odd vertices, the graph cannot be traversed.

Ex. 1, p. 592

b. In topology, shapes are twisted, stretched, bent, and shrunk. The genus of an object refers to the number of holes in the object. Objects with the same genus are topologically equivalent.

c. Non-Euclidean geometries, including hyperbolic geometry and elliptic geometry, are outlined in Table 10.5 on page 596.

d. Fractal geometry includes self-similar forms; magnified portions of such forms repeat much of the pattern of the whole form.

REVIEW EXERCISES

10.1

In the figure shown, lines l and m are parallel. In Exercises 1–7, match each term with the numbered angle or angles in the figure.

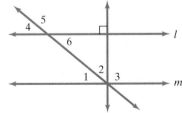

1. right angle
2. obtuse angle
3. vertical angles
4. alternate interior angles
5. corresponding angles
6. the complement of ∡1
7. the supplement of ∡6

In Exercises 8–9, find the measure of the angle in which ?° appears.

8.

9.

10. If an angle measures 73°, find the measure of its complement.

11. If an angle measures $46°$, find the measure of its supplement.

12. In the figure shown, find the measures of angles 1, 2, and 3.

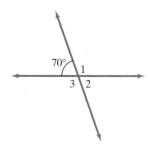

13. In the figure shown, two parallel lines are intersected by a transversal. One of the angle measures is given. Find the measure of each of the other seven angles.

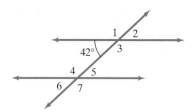

10.2

In Exercises 14–15, find the measure of angle A for the triangle shown.

14.

15.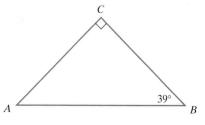

16. Find the measures of angles 1 through 5 in the figure shown.

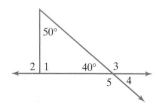

17. In the figure shown, lines *l* and *m* are parallel. Find the measure of each numbered angle.

In Exercises 18–19, use similar triangles and the fact that corresponding sides are proportional to find the length of each side marked with an x.

18.

19.

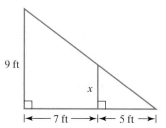

In Exercises 20–22, use the Pythagorean Theorem to find the missing length in each right triangle. Round, if necessary, to the nearest tenth.

20.   **21.**

22.

23. Find the height of the lamppost in the figure.

24. How far away from the building in the figure shown is the bottom of the ladder?

25. A vertical pole is to be supported by three wires. Each wire is 13 yards long and is anchored 5 yards from the base of the pole. How far up the pole will the wires be attached?

 10.3

26. Write the names of all quadrilaterals that always have four right angles.

27. Write the names of all quadrilaterals with four sides always having the same measure.

28. Write the names of all quadrilaterals that do not always have four angles with the same measure.

In Exercises 29–31, find the perimeter of the figure shown. Express the perimeter using the same unit of measure that appears in the figure.

29.

9 cm

6 cm

30.

|← 1240 yd →|

1000 yd   930 yd   1000 yd

1240 yd

31.

12 m

2 m

10 m

7 m

32. Find the sum of the measures of the angles of a 12-sided polygon.

33. Find the sum of the measures of the angles of an octagon.

34. The figure shown is a regular polygon. Find the measures of angle 1 and angle 2.

2   1

35. A carpenter is installing a baseboard around a room that has a length of 35 feet and a width of 15 feet. The room has four doorways and each doorway is 3 feet wide. If no baseboard is to be put across the doorways and the cost of the baseboard is $1.50 per foot, what is the cost of installing the baseboard around the room?

36. Use the following tessellation to solve this exercise.

  a. Name the types of regular polygons that surround each vertex.

  b. Determine the number of angles that come together at each vertex, as well as the measures of these angles.

  c. Use the angle measures from part (b) to explain why the tessellation is possible.

37. Can a tessellation be created using only regular hexagons? Explain your answer.

10.4

In Exercises 38–41, find the area of each figure.

38.

6.5 ft

5 ft

39.

5 m

6 m   4 m   6 m

5 m

40.

12 cm   10 cm

5 cm

|← 20 cm →|

41.

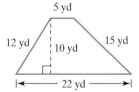

5 yd

12 yd   10 yd   15 yd

|← 22 yd →|

42. Find the circumference and the area of a circle with a diameter of 20 meters. Express answers in terms of π and then round to the nearest tenth.

In Exercises 43–44, find the area of each figure.

43.

8 in.

12 in.

12 in.

44.

45. What will it cost to carpet a rectangular floor measuring 15 feet by 21 feet if the carpet costs $22.50 per square yard?

46. What will it cost to cover a rectangular floor measuring 40 feet by 50 feet with square tiles that measure 2 feet on each side if a package of 10 tiles costs $13 per package?

47. How much fencing, to the nearest whole yard, is needed to enclose a circular garden that measures 10 yards across?

10.5

In Exercises 48–52, find the volume of each figure. Where necessary, express answers in terms of π and then round to the nearest whole number.

48.

49.

50.

51.

52.

53. Find the surface area of the figure shown.

54. A train is being loaded with shipping boxes. Each box is 8 meters long, 4 meters wide, and 3 meters high. If there are 50 shipping boxes, how much space is needed?

55. An Egyptian pyramid has a square base measuring 145 meters on each side. If the height of the pyramid is 93 meters, find its volume.

56. What is the cost of concrete for a walkway that is 27 feet long, 4 feet wide, and 6 inches deep if the concrete is $40 per cubic yard?

10.6

57. Use the right triangle shown to find ratios, in reduced form, for sin A, cos A, and tan A.

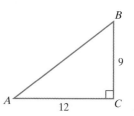

In Exercises 58–60, find the measure of the side of the right triangle whose length is designated by a lowercase letter. Round answers to the nearest whole number.

58.

59.   **60.**

61. Find the measure of angle A in the right triangle shown. Round to the nearest whole degree.

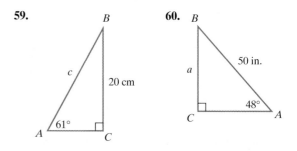

62. A hiker climbs for a half mile (2640 feet) up a slope whose inclination is 17°. How many feet of altitude, to the nearest foot, does the hiker gain?

63. To find the distance across a lake, a surveyor took the measurements in the figure shown. What is the distance across the lake? Round to the nearest meter.

50 m / 32°

64. When a six-foot pole casts a four-foot shadow, what is the angle of elevation of the sun? Round to the nearest whole degree.

10.7

For each graph in Exercises 65–66, determine whether it is traversable. If it is, describe a path that will traverse it.

65.

66.

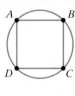

In Exercises 67–70, give the genus of each object. Which objects are topologically equivalent?

67.

68.

69.

70.

71. State Euclid's assumption about parallel lines that no longer applies in hyperbolic and elliptic geometry.

72. What is self-similarity? Describe an object in nature that has this characteristic.

●●●●●● CHAPTER 10 TEST

1. If an angle measures 54°, find the measure of its complement and supplement.

In Exercises 2–4, use the figure shown to find the measure of angle 1.

2.

133°
parallel lines
1

3.

1 / 40° / 70°

4.

100° / 1 / 65°

5. The triangles in the figure are similar. Find the length of the side marked with an x.

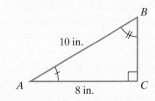

B / 10 in. / E / 4 in. / A / 8 in. / C / D / x / F

6. A vertical pole is to be supported by three wires. Each wire is 26 feet long and is anchored 24 feet from the base of the pole. How far up the pole should the wires be attached?

7. Find the sum of the measures of the angles of a ten-sided polygon.

8. Find the perimeter of the figure shown.

9. Which one of the following names a quadrilateral in which the sides that meet at each vertex have the same measure?

   a. rectangle   **b.** parallelogram

   c. trapezoid   **d.** rhombus

10. Use the following tessellation to solve this exercise.

   a. Name the types of regular polygons that surround each vertex.

   b. Determine the number of angles that come together at each vertex, as well as the measures of these angles.

   c. Use the angle measures from part (b) to explain why the tessellation is possible.

In Exercises 11–12, find the area of each figure.

11.

12.

13. The right triangle shown has one leg of length 5 centimeters and a hypotenuse of length 13 centimeters.

a. Find the length of the other leg.

b. What is the perimeter of the triangle?

c. What is the area of the triangle?

14. Find the circumference and area of a circle with a diameter of 40 meters. Express answers in terms of π and then round to the nearest tenth.

15. A rectangular floor measuring 8 feet by 6 feet is to be completely covered with square tiles measuring 8 inches on each side. How many tiles are needed to completely cover the floor?

In Exercises 16–18, find the volume of each figure. If necessary, express the answer in terms of π and then round to the nearest whole number.

16.

17.

18.

19. Find the measure, to the nearest whole number, of the side of the right triangle whose length is designated by c.

20. At a certain time of day, the angle of elevation of the sun is 34°. If a building casts a shadow measuring 104 feet, find the height of the building to the nearest foot.

21. Determine if the graph shown is traversable. If it is, describe a path that will traverse it.

22. Describe a difference between the shapes of fractal geometry and those of Euclidean geometry.

11

Counting Methods and Probability Theory

Two of America's best-loved presidents, Abraham Lincoln and John F. Kennedy, are linked by a bizarre series of coincidences:

- Lincoln was elected president in 1860. Kennedy was elected president in 1960.
- Lincoln's assassin, John Wilkes Booth, was born in 1839. Kennedy's assassin, Lee Harvey Oswald, was born in 1939.
- Lincoln's secretary, named Kennedy, warned him not to go to the theater on the night he was shot. Kennedy's secretary, named Lincoln, warned him not to go to Dallas on the day he was shot.
- Booth shot Lincoln in a theater and ran into a warehouse. Oswald shot Kennedy from a warehouse and ran into a theater.
- Both Lincoln and Kennedy were shot from behind, with their wives present.
- Andrew Johnson, who succeeded Lincoln, was born in 1808. Lyndon Johnson, who succeeded Kennedy, was born in 1908.

Source: Edward Burger and Michael Starbird, *Coincidences, Chaos, and All That Math Jazz*, W. W. Norton and Company, 2005.

Amazing coincidences? A cosmic conspiracy? Not really. In this chapter, you will see how the mathematics of uncertainty and risk, called probability theory, numerically describes situations in which to expect the unexpected. By assigning numbers to things that are extraordinarily unlikely, we can logically analyze coincidences without erroneous beliefs that strange and mystical events are occurring. We'll even see how wildly inaccurate our intuition can be about the likelihood of an event by examining an "amazing" coincidence that is nearly certain.

Coincidences are discussed in the Blitzer Bonus on page 658. Coincidences that are nearly certain are developed in Exercise 83 of Exercise Set 11.7.

SECTION 11.1 • THE FUNDAMENTAL COUNTING PRINCIPLE

OBJECTIVE

1. Use the Fundamental Counting Principle to determine the number of possible outcomes in a given situation.

Have you ever imagined what your life would be like if you won the lottery? What changes would you make? Before you fantasize about becoming a person of leisure with a staff of obedient elves, think about this: The probability of winning top prize in the lottery is about the same as the probability of being struck by lightning. There are millions of possible number combinations in lottery games, and only one way of winning the grand prize. Determining the probability of winning involves calculating the chance of getting the winning combination from all possible outcomes. In this section, we begin preparing for the surprising world of probability by looking at methods for counting possible outcomes.

1 | Use the Fundamental Counting Principle to determine the number of possible outcomes in a given situation.

The Fundamental Counting Principle with Two Groups of Items

It's early morning, you're groggy, and you have to select something to wear for your 8 A.M. class. (What *were* you thinking when you signed up for a class at that hour?!) Fortunately, your "lecture wardrobe" is rather limited—just two pairs of jeans to choose from (one blue, one black) and three T-shirts to choose from (one beige, one yellow, and one blue). Your early-morning dilemma is illustrated in Figure 11.1.

FIGURE 11.1 Selecting a wardrobe

The **tree diagram**, so named because of its branches, shows that you can form six different outfits from your two pairs of jeans and three T-shirts. Each pair of jeans can be combined with one of three T-shirts. Notice that the total number of outfits can be obtained by multiplying the number of choices for the jeans, 2, by the number of choices for the T-shirts, 3:

$$2 \cdot 3 = 6.$$

We can generalize this idea to any two groups of items—not just jeans and T-shirts—with the **Fundamental Counting Principle**.

> THE FUNDAMENTAL COUNTING PRINCIPLE
> If you can choose one item from a group of M items and a second item from a group of N items, then the total number of two-item choices is $M \cdot N$.

EXAMPLE 1	APPLYING THE FUNDAMENTAL COUNTING PRINCIPLE

The Greasy Spoon Restaurant offers 6 appetizers and 14 main courses. In how many ways can a person order a two-course meal?

SOLUTION Choosing from one of 6 appetizers and one of 14 main courses, the total number of two-course meals is

$$6 \cdot 14 = 84.$$

A person can order a two-course meal in 84 different ways.

A restaurant offers 10 appetizers and 15 main courses. In how many ways can you order a two-course meal?

EXAMPLE 2	APPLYING THE FUNDAMENTAL COUNTING PRINCIPLE

This is the semester that you will take your required psychology and social science courses. Because you decide to register early, there are 15 sections of psychology from which you can choose. Furthermore, there are 9 sections of social science that are available at times that do not conflict with those for psychology. In how many ways can you create two-course schedules that satisfy the psychology-social science requirement?

SOLUTION The number of ways that you can satisfy the requirement is found by multiplying the number of choices for each course. You can choose your psychology course from 15 sections and your social science course from 9 sections. For both courses you have

$$15 \cdot 9, \text{ or } 135$$

choices. Thus, you can satisfy the psychology-social science requirement in 135 ways.

Rework Example 2 given that the number of sections of psychology and nonconflicting sections of social science each decrease by 5.

The Fundamental Counting Principle with More Than Two Groups of Items

Whoops! You forgot something in choosing your lecture wardrobe—shoes! You have two pairs of sneakers to choose from—one black and one red, for that extra fashion flair! Your possible outfits, including sneakers, are shown in Figure 11.2.

FIGURE 11.2 Increasing wardrobe selections

The number of possible ways of playing the first four moves on each side in a game of chess is 318,979,564,000.

FIGURE 11.2 (repeated)

The tree diagram shows that you can form 12 outfits from your two pairs of jeans, three T-shirts, and two pairs of sneakers. Notice that the number of outfits can be obtained by multiplying the number of choices for jeans, 2, the number of choices for T-shirts, 3, and the number of choices for sneakers, 2:

$$2 \cdot 3 \cdot 2 = 12.$$

Unlike your earlier dilemma, you are now dealing with *three* groups of items. The Fundamental Counting Principle can be extended to determine the number of possible outcomes in situations in which there are three or more groups of items.

> **THE FUNDAMENTAL COUNTING PRINCIPLE**
> The number of ways in which a series of successive things can occur is found by multiplying the number of ways in which each thing can occur.

For example, if you own 30 pairs of jeans, 20 T-shirts, and 12 pairs of sneakers, you have

$$30 \cdot 20 \cdot 12 = 7200$$

choices for your wardrobe.

EXAMPLE 3   OPTIONS IN PLANNING A COURSE SCHEDULE

Next semester you are planning to take three courses—math, English, and humanities. Based on time blocks and highly recommended professors, there are 8 sections of math, 5 of English, and 4 of humanities that you find suitable. Assuming no scheduling conflicts, how many different three-course schedules are possible?

SOLUTION This situation involves making choices with three groups of items.

Math	English	Humanities
8 choices	5 choices	4 choices

We use the Fundamental Counting Principle to find the number of three-course schedules. Multiply the number of choices for each of the three groups.

$$8 \cdot 5 \cdot 4 = 160$$

Thus, there are 160 different three-course schedules. ○

CHECK POINT 3 A pizza can be ordered with two choices of size (medium or large), three choices of crust (thin, thick, or regular), and five choices of toppings (ground beef, sausage, pepperoni, bacon, or mushrooms). How many different one-topping pizzas can be ordered?

EXAMPLE 4   CAR OF THE FUTURE

Car manufacturers are now experimenting with lightweight three-wheel cars, designed for one person, and considered ideal for city driving. Intrigued? Suppose you could order such a car with a choice of 9 possible colors, with or without air conditioning, electric or gas powered, and with or without an onboard computer. In how many ways can this car be ordered with regard to these options?

SOLUTION This situation involves making choices with four groups of items.

Source: Corbin Motors
(www.Corbinmotors.com)

Color	Air conditioning	Power	Computer
9 choices	2 choices: with or without	2 choices: electric or gas	2 choices: with or without

We use the Fundamental Counting Principle to find the number of ordering options. Multiply the number of choices for each of the four groups.

$$9 \cdot 2 \cdot 2 \cdot 2 = 72$$

Thus, the car can be ordered in 72 different ways.

CHECK POINT 4 The car in Example 4 is now available in 10 possible colors. The options involving air conditioning, power, and an onboard computer still apply. Furthermore, the car is available with or without a global positioning system (for pinpointing your location at every moment). In how many ways can this car be ordered in terms of these options?

EXAMPLE 5   A MULTIPLE-CHOICE TEST

You are taking a multiple-choice test that has ten questions. Each of the questions has four answer choices, with one correct answer per question. If you select one of these four choices for each question and leave nothing blank, in how many ways can you answer the questions?

SOLUTION This situation involves making choices with ten questions.

| Question 1 | Question 2 | Question 3 | $\cdots$ | Question 9 | Question 10 |
| 4 choices | 4 choices | 4 choices | | 4 choices | 4 choices |

We use the Fundamental Counting Principle to determine the number of ways that you can answer the questions on the test. Multiply the number of choices, 4, for each of the ten questions.

$$4 \cdot 4 \cdot 4 \cdot 4 \cdot 4 \cdot 4 \cdot 4 \cdot 4 \cdot 4 \cdot 4 = 4^{10} = 1{,}048{,}576 \qquad \text{Use a calculator: } 4 \boxed{y^x} 10 \boxed{=}.$$

Thus, you can answer the questions in 1,048,576 different ways.

Are you surprised that there are over one million ways of answering a ten-question multiple-choice test? Of course, there is only one way to answer the test and receive a perfect score. The probability of guessing your way into a perfect score involves calculating the chance of getting a perfect score, just one way, from all 1,048,576 possible outcomes. In short, prepare for the test and do not rely on guessing!

CHECK POINT 5 You are taking a multiple-choice test that has six questions. Each of the questions has three answer choices, with one correct answer per question. If you select one of these three choices for each question and leave nothing blank, in how many ways can you answer the questions?

EXAMPLE 6   TELEPHONE NUMBERS IN THE UNITED STATES

Telephone numbers in the United States begin with three-digit area codes followed by seven-digit local telephone numbers. Area codes and local telephone numbers cannot begin with 0 or 1. How many different telephone numbers are possible?

SOLUTION This situation involves making choices with ten groups of items.

Area Code   Local Telephone Number

You cannot use 0 or 1 in these groups. There are only 8 choices: 2, 3, 4, 5, 6, 7, 8, or 9.

You can use 0, 1, 2, 3, 4, 5, 6, 7, 8, or 9 in these groups. There are 10 choices per group.

BLITZER BONUS

Running Out of Telephone Numbers

By the year 2020, portable telephones used for business and pleasure will all be videophones. At that time, U.S. population is expected to be 323 million. Faxes, beepers, cell phones, computer phone lines, and business lines may result in certain areas running out of phone numbers. Solution: Add more digits!

With or without extra digits, we expect that the 2020 videophone greeting will still be "hello," a word created by Thomas Edison in 1877. Phone inventor Alexander Graham Bell preferred "ahoy," but "hello" won out, appearing in the *Oxford English Dictionary* in 1883. (*Source: New York Times*)

Here are the choices for each of the ten groups of items:

Area Code	Local Telephone Number
8 10 10	8 10 10 10 10 10 10 .

We use the Fundamental Counting Principle to determine the number of different telephone numbers that are possible. The total number of telephone numbers possible is

$$8 \cdot 10 \cdot 10 \cdot 8 \cdot 10 \cdot 10 \cdot 10 \cdot 10 \cdot 10 \cdot 10 = 6{,}400{,}000{,}000.$$

There are six billion four hundred million different telephone numbers that are possible.

CHECK POINT 6 An electronic gate can be opened by entering five digits on a keypad containing the digits $0, 1, 2, 3, \ldots, 8, 9$. How many different keypad sequences are possible if the digit 0 cannot be used as the first digit?

EXERCISE SET 11.1 ●●●●●●

• Practice and Application Exercises

Solve Exercises 1–6 using the Fundamental Counting Principle with two groups of items.

1. A restaurant offers 8 appetizers and 10 main courses. In how many ways can a person order a two-course meal?

2. The model of the car you are thinking of buying is available in nine different colors and three different styles (hatchback, sedan, or station wagon). In how many ways can you order the car?

3. A popular brand of pen is available in three colors (red, green, or blue) and four writing tips (bold, medium, fine, or micro). How many different choices of pens do you have with this brand?

4. In how many ways can a casting director choose a female lead and a male lead from five female actors and six male actors?

5. A student is planning a two-part trip. The first leg of the trip is from San Francisco to New York, and the second leg is from New York to Paris. From San Francisco to New York, travel options include airplane, train, or bus. From New York to Paris, the options are limited to airplane or ship. In how many ways can the two-part trip be made?

6. For a temporary job between semesters, you are painting the parking spaces for a new shopping mall with a letter of the alphabet and a single digit from 1 to 9. The first parking space is A1 and the last parking space is Z9. How many parking spaces can you paint with distinct labels?

Solve Exercises 7–22 using the Fundamental Counting Principle with three or more groups of items.

7. An ice cream store sells two drinks (sodas or milk shakes), in four sizes (small, medium, large, or jumbo), and five flavors (vanilla, strawberry, chocolate, coffee, or pistachio). In how many ways can a customer order a drink?

8. A pizza can be ordered with three choices of size (small, medium, or large), four choices of crust (thin, thick, crispy, or regular), and six choices of toppings (ground beef, sausage, pepperoni, bacon, mushrooms, or onions). How many one-topping pizzas can be ordered?

9. A restaurant offers the following limited lunch menu.

Main Course	Vegetables	Beverages	Desserts
Ham	Potatoes	Coffee	Cake
Chicken	Peas	Tea	Pie
Fish	Green beans	Milk	Ice cream
Beef		Soda	

If one item is selected from each of the four groups, in how many ways can a meal be ordered? Describe two such orders.

10. An apartment complex offers apartments with four different options, designated by A through D.

A	B	C	D
one bedroom	one bathroom	first floor	lake view
two bedrooms	two bathrooms	second floor	golf course view
three bedrooms			no special view

How many apartment options are available? Describe two such options.

11. Shoppers in a large shopping mall are categorized as male or female, over 30 or 30 and under, and cash or credit card shoppers. In how many ways can the shoppers be categorized?

12. There are three highways from city A to city B, two highways from city B to city C, and four highways from city C to city D. How many different highway routes are there from city A to city D?

13. A person can order a new car with a choice of six possible colors, with or without air conditioning, with or without automatic transmission, with or without power windows, and with or without a CD player. In how many different ways can a new car be ordered with regard to these options?

14. A car model comes in nine colors, with or without air conditioning, with or without a sun roof, with or without automatic transmission, and with or without antilock brakes. In how many ways can the car be ordered with regard to these options?

15. You are taking a multiple-choice test that has five questions. Each of the questions has three answer choices, with one correct answer per question. If you select one of these three choices for each question and leave nothing blank, in how many ways can you answer the questions?

16. You are taking a multiple-choice test that has eight questions. Each of the questions has three answer choices, with one correct answer per question. If you select one of these three choices for each question and leave nothing blank, in how many ways can you answer the questions?

17. In the original plan for area codes in 1945, the first digit could be any number from 2 through 9, the second digit was either 0 or 1, and the third digit could be any number except 0. With this plan, how many different area codes are possible?

18. The local seven-digit telephone numbers in Inverness, California, have 669 as the first three digits. How many different telephone numbers are possible in Inverness?

19. License plates in a particular state display two letters followed by three numbers, such as AT-887 or BB-013. How many different license plates can be manufactured for this state?

20. How many different four-letter radio station call letters can be formed if the first letter must be W or K?

21. A stock can go up, go down, or stay unchanged. How many possibilities are there if you own seven stocks?

22. A social security number contains nine digits, such as 074-66-7795. How many different social security numbers can be formed?

• Writing in Mathematics

23. Explain the Fundamental Counting Principle.

24. Figure 11.2 on page 609 shows that a tree diagram can be used to find the total number of outfits. Describe one advantage of using the Fundamental Counting Principle rather than a tree diagram.

25. Write an original problem that can be solved using the Fundamental Counting Principle. Then solve the problem.

• Critical Thinking Exercises

26. How many four-digit odd numbers are there? Assume that the digit on the left cannot be 0.

27. In order to develop a more appealing hamburger, a franchise used taste tests with 12 different buns, 30 sauces, 4 types of lettuce, and 3 types of tomatoes. If the taste test was done at one restaurant by one tester who took 10 minutes to eat each hamburger, approximately how long would it take the tester to eat all possible hamburgers?

• Group Exercise

28. The group should select real-world situations where the Fundamental Counting Principle can be applied. These can involve the number of possible student ID numbers on your campus, the number of possible phone numbers in your community, the number of meal options at a local restaurant, the number of ways a person in the group can select outfits for class, the number of ways a condominium can be purchased in a nearby community, and so on. Once situations have been selected, group members should determine in how many ways each part of the task can be done. Group members will need to obtain menus, find out about telephone-digit requirements in the community, count shirts, pants, shoes in closets, visit condominium sales offices, and so on. Once the group reassembles, apply the Fundamental Counting Principle to determine the number of available options in each situation. Because these numbers may be quite large, use a calculator.

SECTION 11.2 • PERMUTATIONS

OBJECTIVES

1. Use the Fundamental Counting Principle to count permutations.

2. Evaluate factorial expressions.

3. Use the permutations formula.

4. Find the number of permutations of duplicate items.

Ladies and gentlemen: Please give a huge round of applause for

U2!   Bruce Springsteen and the E Street Band!
Aerosmith!   The Rolling Stones!

You are in charge of planning one of the most anticipated concert tours of the decade. All four of these groups will appear in concert, which will be seen in a pay-per-view cable special by millions of people throughout the world. One of your jobs is to determine the order in which the groups will perform. Each group will perform once. How many different ways can you put together this four-group concert?

You are familiar with the work of all these musicians *and* you know the Fundamental Counting Principle! (Who could be better qualified for this job?) You can choose any of the four groups as the first performer. Once you've chosen the first

1 Use the Fundamental Counting Principle to count permutations.

group, you'll have three groups left to choose from for the second performer. You'll then have two groups left to choose from for the third performance. After the first three performers are determined, you'll have only one group left for the final appearance in the concert. This situation can be shown as follows:

We use the Fundamental Counting Principle to find the number of ways you can put together the concert. Multiply the choices:

$$4 \cdot 3 \cdot 2 \cdot 1 = 24.$$

Thus, there are 24 different ways to arrange the concert. One of the 24 possible arrangements is

Aerosmith–Bruce Springsteen–U2–The Rolling Stones.

Such an ordered arrangement is called a *permutation* of the four rock groups.
A **permutation** is an ordered arrangement of items that occurs when

- No item is used more than once. (Each rock group performs exactly once.)
- The order of arrangement makes a difference. (It will make a difference in terms of how the concert is received if the Rolling Stones are the first group or the last group to perform.)

EXAMPLE 1   COUNTING PERMUTATIONS

Based on their long-standing contribution to rock music, you decide that the Rolling Stones should be the last group to perform at the four-group U2, Bruce Springsteen, Aerosmith, Rolling Stones concert. Given this decision, in how many ways can you put together the concert?

SOLUTION You can now choose any one of the three groups, U2, Bruce Springsteen and the E Street Band, or Aerosmith, as the opening act. Once you've chosen the first group, you'll have two groups left to choose from for the second performance. You'll then have just one group left to choose for the third performance. There is also just one choice for the closing act—the Rolling Stones. This situation can be shown as follows:

We use the Fundamental Counting Principle to find the number of ways you can put together the concert. Multiply the choices:

$$3 \cdot 2 \cdot 1 \cdot 1 = 6.$$

Thus, there are six different ways to arrange the concert if the Rolling Stones are the final group to perform.   ○

The Rolling Stones

CHECK POINT 1   For the concert in Example 1, suppose that U2 is to be the opening act and the Rolling Stones are to be the last group to perform. In how many ways can you put together the concert?

First Shelf Position	Second Shelf Position	Third Shelf Position	Fourth Shelf Position	Fifth Shelf Position	Sixth Shelf Position	Seventh Shelf Position
7 choices	6 choices	5 choices	4 choices	3 choices	2 choices	1 choice

2 | Evaluate factorial expressions.

FACTORIALS FROM 0 THROUGH 20

0!	1
1!	1
2!	2
3!	6
4!	24
5!	120
6!	720
7!	5040
8!	40,320
9!	362,880
10!	3,628,800
11!	39,916,800
12!	479,001,600
13!	6,227,020,800
14!	87,178,291,200
15!	1,307,674,368,000
16!	20,922,789,888,000
17!	355,687,428,096,000
18!	6,402,373,705,728,000
19!	121,645,100,408,832,000
20!	2,432,902,008,176,640,000

As n increases, $n!$ grows very rapidly. Factorial growth is more explosive than exponential growth discussed in Chapter 7.

EXAMPLE 2   COUNTING PERMUTATIONS

You need to arrange seven of your favorite books along a small shelf. How many different ways can you arrange the books, assuming that the order of the books makes a difference to you?

SOLUTION You may choose any of the seven books for the first position on the shelf. This leaves six choices for second position. After the first two positions are filled, there are five books to choose from for third position, four choices left for the fourth position, three choices left for the fifth position, then two choices for the sixth position, and only one choice for the last position. This situation can be shown as follows:

We use the Fundamental Counting Principle to find the number of ways you can arrange the seven books along the shelf. Multiply the choices:

$$7 \cdot 6 \cdot 5 \cdot 4 \cdot 3 \cdot 2 \cdot 1 = 5040.$$

Thus, you can arrange the books in 5040 ways. There are 5040 different possible permutations.

In how many ways can you arrange five books along a shelf, assuming that the order of the books makes a difference?

Factorial Notation

The product in Example 2,

$$7 \cdot 6 \cdot 5 \cdot 4 \cdot 3 \cdot 2 \cdot 1$$

is given a special name and symbol. It is called 7 **factorial**, and written 7!. Thus,

$$7! = 7 \cdot 6 \cdot 5 \cdot 4 \cdot 3 \cdot 2 \cdot 1.$$

In general, if n is a positive integer, then $n!$ (*n factorial*) is the product of all positive integers from n down through 1. For example,

$$1! = 1$$
$$2! = 2 \cdot 1 = 2$$
$$3! = 3 \cdot 2 \cdot 1 = 6$$
$$4! = 4 \cdot 3 \cdot 2 \cdot 1 = 24$$
$$5! = 5 \cdot 4 \cdot 3 \cdot 2 \cdot 1 = 120$$
$$6! = 6 \cdot 5 \cdot 4 \cdot 3 \cdot 2 \cdot 1 = 720.$$

FACTORIAL NOTATION

If n is a positive integer, the notation $n!$ (read "n factorial") is the product of all positive integers from n down through 1.

$$n! = n(n - 1)(n - 2) \cdots (3)(2)(1)$$

0! (zero factorial), by definition, is 1.

$$0! = 1$$

EXAMPLE 3   USING FACTORIAL NOTATION

Evaluate the following factorial expressions without using the factorial key on your calculator:

a. $\dfrac{8!}{5!}$ **b.** $\dfrac{26!}{21!}$ **c.** $\dfrac{500!}{499!}$.

TECHNOLOGY

Most calculators have a key or menu item for calculating factorials. Here are the keystrokes for finding 9!:

MANY SCIENTIFIC CALCULATORS:

9 $\boxed{x!}$ $\boxed{=}$

MANY GRAPHING CALCULATORS:

9 $\boxed{!}$ $\boxed{\text{ENTER}}$.

Because $n!$ becomes quite large as n increases, your calculator will display these larger values in scientific notation.

SOLUTION

a. We can evaluate the numerator and the denominator of $\frac{8!}{5!}$. However, it is easier to use the following simplification:

$$\frac{8!}{5!} = \frac{8 \cdot 7 \cdot 6 \cdot \boxed{5 \cdot 4 \cdot 3 \cdot 2 \cdot 1}}{\boxed{5 \cdot 4 \cdot 3 \cdot 2 \cdot 1}} = \frac{8 \cdot 7 \cdot 6 \cdot \boxed{5!}}{\boxed{5!}} = \frac{8 \cdot 7 \cdot 6 \cdot \cancel{5!}}{\cancel{5!}} = 8 \cdot 7 \cdot 6 = 336.$$

b. Rather than write out 26!, the numerator of $\frac{26!}{21!}$, as the product of all integers from 26 down to 1, we can express 26! as

$$26! = 26 \cdot 25 \cdot 24 \cdot 23 \cdot 22 \cdot 21!.$$

In this way, we can cancel 21! in the numerator and the denominator of the given expression.

$$\frac{26!}{21!} = \frac{26 \cdot 25 \cdot 24 \cdot 23 \cdot 22 \cdot 21!}{21!} = \frac{26 \cdot 25 \cdot 24 \cdot 23 \cdot 22 \cdot \cancel{21!}}{\cancel{21!}}$$
$$= 26 \cdot 25 \cdot 24 \cdot 23 \cdot 22 = 7{,}893{,}600$$

c. In order to cancel identical factorials in the numerator and the denominator of $\frac{500!}{499!}$, we can express 500! as $500 \cdot 499!$.

$$\frac{500!}{499!} = \frac{500 \cdot 499!}{499!} = \frac{500 \cdot \cancel{499!}}{\cancel{499!}} = 500$$

○

 Evaluate without using a calculator's factorial key:

a. $\dfrac{9!}{6!}$ **b.** $\dfrac{16!}{11!}$ **c.** $\dfrac{100!}{99!}$.

───

3 | Use the permutations formula.

A Formula for Permutations

You are the coach of a little league baseball team. There are 13 players on the team (and lots of parents hovering in the background, dreaming of stardom for their little "Barry Bonds"). You need to choose a batting order having 9 players. The order makes a difference, because, for instance, if bases are loaded and "Little Barry" is fourth or fifth at bat, his possible home run will drive in three additional runs. How many batting orders can you form?

You can choose any of 13 players for the first person at bat. Then you will have 12 players from which to choose the second batter, then 11 from which to choose the third batter, and so on. The situation can be shown as follows:

Batter 1	Batter 2	Batter 3	Batter 4	Batter 5	Batter 6	Batter 7	Batter 8	Batter 9
13 choices	12 choices	11 choices	10 choices	9 choices	8 choices	7 choices	6 choices	5 choices

The total number of batting orders is

$$13 \cdot 12 \cdot 11 \cdot 10 \cdot 9 \cdot 8 \cdot 7 \cdot 6 \cdot 5 = 259{,}459{,}200.$$

Nearly 260 million batting orders are possible for your 13-player little league team. Each batting order is a permutation because the order of the batters makes a difference. The number of permutations of 13 players taken 9 at a time is 259,459,200.

We can obtain a formula for finding the number of permutations by rewriting our computation:

$$13 \cdot 12 \cdot 11 \cdot 10 \cdot 9 \cdot 8 \cdot 7 \cdot 6 \cdot 5$$

$$= \frac{13 \cdot 12 \cdot 11 \cdot 10 \cdot 9 \cdot 8 \cdot 7 \cdot 6 \cdot 5 \cdot \boxed{4 \cdot 3 \cdot 2 \cdot 1}}{\boxed{4 \cdot 3 \cdot 2 \cdot 1}} = \frac{13!}{4!} = \frac{13!}{(13 - 9)!}.$$

Thus, the number of permutations of 13 things taken 9 at a time is $\frac{13!}{(13-9)!}$. The special notation $_{13}P_9$ is used to replace the phrase "the number of permutations of 13 things taken 9 at a time." Using this new notation, we can write

$$_{13}P_9 = \frac{13!}{(13 - 9)!}.$$

The numerator of this expression is the factorial of the number of items, 13 team members: 13!. The denominator is also a factorial. It is the factorial of the difference between the number of items, 13, and the number of items in each permutation, 9 batters: $(13 - 9)!$.

The notation $_nP_r$ means the **number of permutations of n things taken r at a time**. We can generalize from the situation in which 9 batters were taken from 13 players. By generalizing, we obtain the following formula for the number of permutations if r items are taken from n items:

PERMUTATIONS OF n THINGS TAKEN r AT A TIME

The number of possible permutations if r items are taken from n items is

$$_nP_r = \frac{n!}{(n - r)!}.$$

EXAMPLE 4   USING THE FORMULA FOR PERMUTATIONS

You and 19 of your friends have decided to form an Internet marketing consulting firm. The group needs to choose three officers—a CEO, an operating manager, and a treasurer. In how many ways can those offices be filled?

SOLUTION Your group is choosing $r = 3$ officers from a group of $n = 20$ people (you and 19 friends). The order in which the officers are chosen matters because the CEO, the operating manager, and the treasurer each have different responsibilities. Thus, we are looking for the number of permutations of 20 things taken 3 at a time. We use the formula

$$_nP_r = \frac{n!}{(n - r)!}$$

with $n = 20$ and $r = 3$.

$$_{20}P_3 = \frac{20!}{(20 - 3)!} = \frac{20!}{17!} = \frac{20 \cdot 19 \cdot 18 \cdot 17!}{17!} = \frac{20 \cdot 19 \cdot 18 \cdot \cancel{17!}}{\cancel{17!}} = 20 \cdot 19 \cdot 18 = 6840$$

Thus, there are 6840 different ways of filling the three offices.

TECHNOLOGY

Graphing calculators have a menu item for calculating permutations, usually labeled $\boxed{_nP_r}$. For example, to find $_{20}P_3$, the keystrokes are

$$20 \;\boxed{_nP_r}\; 3 \;\boxed{\text{ENTER}}.$$

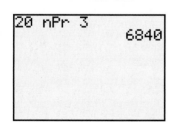

If you are using a scientific calculator, check your manual for the location of the menu item for calculating permutations and the required keystrokes.

A corporation has seven members on its board of directors. In how many different ways can it elect a president, vice-president, secretary, and treasurer?

EXAMPLE 5   USING THE FORMULA FOR PERMUTATIONS

You are working for The Sitcom Television Network. Your assignment is to help set up the television schedule for Monday evenings between 7 and 10 P.M. You need to schedule a show in each of six 30-minute time blocks, beginning with 7 to 7:30 and ending with 9:30 to 10:00. You can select from among the following situation comedies: *Home Improvement, Seinfeld, Mad About You, Cheers, Friends, Frasier, All in the Family, I Love Lucy, M*A*S*H, The Larry Sanders Show, The Jeffersons, Married with Children,* and *Happy Days.* How many different programming schedules can be arranged?

SOLUTION You are choosing $r = 6$ situation comedies from a collection of $n = 13$ classic sitcoms. The order in which the programs are aired matters. Family-oriented comedies have higher ratings when aired in earlier time blocks, such as 7 to 7:30. By contrast, comedies with adult themes do better in later time blocks. In short, we are looking for the number of permutations of 13 things taken 6 at a time. We use the formula

$$_nP_r = \frac{n!}{(n - r)!}$$

with $n = 13$ and $r = 6$.

$$_{13}P_6 = \frac{13!}{(13 - 6)!} = \frac{13!}{7!} = \frac{13 \cdot 12 \cdot 11 \cdot 10 \cdot 9 \cdot 8 \cdot \cancel{7!}}{\cancel{7!}} = 13 \cdot 12 \cdot 11 \cdot 10 \cdot 9 \cdot 8 = 1{,}235{,}520$$

There are 1,235,520 different programming schedules that can be arranged.

CHECK POINT 5 How many different programming schedules can be arranged by choosing 5 situation comedies from a collection of 9 classic sitcoms?

  Find the number of permutations of duplicate items.

Permutations of Duplicate Items

The number of permutations of the letters in the word SET is 3!, or 6. The six permutations are

> SET,   STE,   EST,   ETS,   TES,   TSE.

Are there also six permutations of the letters in the name ANA? The answer is no. Unlike SET, with three distinct letters, ANA contains three letters, of which the two As are duplicates. If we rearrange the letters just as we did with SET, we obtain

> ANA,   AAN,   NAA,   NAA,   ANA,   AAN.

Without the use of color to distinguish between the two As, there are only three distinct permutations: ANA, AAN, NAA.

There is a formula for finding the number of distinct permutations when duplicate items exist:

> **PERMUTATIONS OF DUPLICATE ITEMS**
>
> The number of permutations of n items, where p items are identical, q items are identical, r items are identical, and so on, is given by
>
> $$\frac{n!}{p!\, q!\, r! \ldots}.$$

For example, ANA contains three letters ($n = 3$), where two of the letters are identical ($p = 2$). The number of distinct permutations is

$$\frac{n!}{p!} = \frac{3!}{2!} = \frac{3 \cdot \cancel{2!}}{\cancel{2!}} = 3.$$

We saw that the three distinct permutations are ANA, AAN, and NAA.

TECHNOLOGY

Parentheses are necessary to enclose the factorials in the denominator when using a calculator to find

$$\frac{11!}{4!\,4!\,2!}.$$

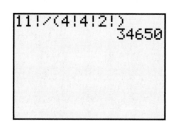

EXAMPLE 6   USING THE FORMULA FOR PERMUTATIONS OF DUPLICATE ITEMS

In how many distinct ways can the letters of the word MISSISSIPPI be arranged?

SOLUTION The word contains 11 letters ($n = 11$), where four Is are identical ($p = 4$), four Ss are identical ($q = 4$), and 2 Ps are identical ($r = 2$). The number of distinct permutations is

$$\frac{n!}{p!\,q!\,r!} = \frac{11!}{4!\,4!\,2!} = \frac{11 \cdot 10 \cdot 9 \cdot 8 \cdot 7 \cdot 6 \cdot 5 \cdot 4!}{4!\,4 \cdot 3 \cdot 2 \cdot 1 \cdot 2 \cdot 1} = 34{,}650$$

There are 34,650 distinct ways the letters in the word MISSISSIPPI can be arranged. ○

 In how many ways can the letters of the word OSMOSIS be arranged?

EXERCISE SET 11.2 ●●●●●●

• Practice and Application Exercises

Use the Fundamental Counting Principle to solve Exercises 1–12.

1. Six performers are to present their comedy acts on a weekend evening at a comedy club. How many different ways are there to schedule their appearances?

2. Five singers are to perform on a weekend evening at a night club. How many different ways are there to schedule their appearances?

3. In the *Cambridge Encyclopedia of Language* (Cambridge University Press, 1987), author David Crystal presents five sentences that make a reasonable paragraph regardless of their order. The sentences are as follows:

    Mark had told him about the foxes.
    John looked out of the window.
    Could it be a fox?
    However, nobody had seen one for months.
    He thought he saw a shape in the bushes.

    In how many different orders can the five sentences be arranged?

4. In how many different ways can a police department arrange eight suspects in a police lineup if each lineup contains all eight people?

5. As in Exercise 1, six performers are to present their comedy acts on a weekend evening at a comedy club. One of the performers insists on being the last stand-up comic of the evening. If this performer's request is granted, how many different ways are there to schedule the appearances?

6. As in Exercise 2, five singers are to perform at a night club. One of the singers insists on being the last performer of the evening. If this singer's request is granted, how many different ways are there to schedule the appearances?

7. You need to arrange nine of your favorite books along a small shelf. How many different ways can you arrange the books, assuming that the order of the books makes a difference to you?

8. You need to arrange ten of your favorite photographs on the mantel above a fireplace. How many ways can you arrange the photographs, assuming that the order of the pictures makes a difference to you?

In Exercises 9–10, use the five sentences that are given in Exercise 3.

9. How many different five-sentence paragraphs can be formed if the paragraph begins with "He thought he saw a shape in the bushes" and ends with "John looked out of the window"?

10. How many different five-sentence paragraphs can be formed if the paragraph begins with "He thought he saw a shape in the bushes" followed by "Mark had told him about the foxes"?

11. A television programmer is arranging the order that five movies will be seen between the hours of 6 P.M. and 4 A.M. Two of the movies have a G rating, and they are to be shown in the first two time blocks. One of the movies is rated NC-17, and it is to be shown in the last of the time blocks, from 2 A.M. until 4 A.M. Given these restrictions, in how many ways can the five movies be arranged during the indicated time blocks?

12. A camp counselor and six campers are to be seated along a picnic bench. In how many ways can this be done if the counselor must be seated in the middle and a camper who has a tendency to engage in food fights must sit to the counselor's immediate left?

In Exercises 13–32, evaluate each factorial expression.

13. $\dfrac{9!}{6!}$

14. $\dfrac{12!}{10!}$

15. $\dfrac{29!}{25!}$

16. $\dfrac{31!}{28!}$

17. $\dfrac{19!}{11!}$

18. $\dfrac{17!}{9!}$

19. $\dfrac{600!}{599!}$

20. $\dfrac{700!}{699!}$

21. $\dfrac{104!}{102!}$

22. $\dfrac{106!}{104!}$

23. $7! - 3!$

24. $6! - 3!$

25. $(7 - 3)!$

26. $(6 - 3)!$

27. $\left(\dfrac{12}{4}\right)!$

28. $\left(\dfrac{45}{9}\right)!$

29. $\dfrac{7!}{(7 - 2)!}$

30. $\dfrac{8!}{(8 - 5)!}$

31. $\dfrac{13!}{(13 - 3)!}$

32. $\dfrac{17!}{(17 - 3)!}$

In Exercises 33–40, use the formula for $_nP_r$ to evaluate each expression.

33. $_9P_4$ **34.** $_7P_3$ **35.** $_8P_5$

36. $_{10}P_4$ **37.** $_6P_6$ **38.** $_9P_9$

39. $_8P_0$ **40.** $_6P_0$

Use the formula for $_nP_r$ to solve Exercises 41–48.

41. A club with ten members is to choose three officers—president, vice-president, and secretary-treasurer. If each office is to be held by one person and no person can hold more than one office, in how many ways can those offices be filled?

42. A corporation has seven members on its board of directors. In how many different ways can it elect a president, vice-president, secretary, and treasurer?

43. For a segment of a radio show, a disc jockey can play 7 records. If there are 13 records to select from, in how many ways can the program for this segment be arranged?

44. Suppose you are asked to list, in order of preference, the three best movies you have seen this year. If you saw 20 movies during the year, in how many ways can the three best be chosen and ranked?

45. In a race in which six automobiles are entered and there are no ties, in how many ways can the first three finishers come in?

46. In a production of *West Side Story*, eight actors are considered for the male roles of Tony, Riff, and Bernardo. In how many ways can the director cast the male roles?

47. Nine bands have volunteered to perform at a benefit concert, but there is only enough time for five of the bands to play. How many lineups are possible?

48. How many arrangements can be made using four of the letters of the word COMBINE if no letter is to be used more than once?

Use the formula for the number of permutations of duplicate items to solve Exercises 49–56.

49. In how many distinct ways can the letters of the word DALLAS be arranged?

50. In how many distinct ways can the letters of the word SCIENCE be arranged?

51. How many distinct permutations can be formed using the letters of the word TALLAHASSEE?

52. How many distinct permutations can be formed using the letters of the word TENNESSEE?

53. In how many ways can the digits in the number 5,446,666 be arranged?

54. In how many ways can the digits in the number 5,432,435 be arranged?

In Exercises 55–56, a signal can be formed by running different colored flags up a pole, one above the other.

55. Find the number of different signals consisting of eight flags that can be made using three white flags, four red flags, and one blue flag.

56. Find the number of different signals consisting of nine flags that can be made using three white flags, five red flags, and one blue flag.

• Writing in Mathematics

57. What is a permutation?

58. Explain how to find $n!$, where n is a positive integer.

59. Explain the best way to evaluate $\frac{900!}{899!}$ without a calculator.

60. Describe what $_nP_r$ represents.

61. Write a word problem that can be solved by evaluating $5!$.

62. Write a word problem that can be solved by evaluating $_7P_3$.

63. If 24 permutations can be formed using the letters in the word BAKE, why can't 24 permutations also be formed using the letters in the word BABE? How is the number of permutations in BABE determined?

• Critical Thinking Exercises

64. Ten people board an airplane that has 12 aisle seats. In how many ways can they be seated if they all select aisle seats?

65. Six horses are entered in a race. If two horses are tied for first place, and there are no ties among the other four horses, in how many ways can the six horses cross the finish line?

66. Performing at a concert are eight rock bands and eight jazz groups. How many ways can the program be arranged if the first, third, and eighth performers are jazz groups?

67. Five men and five women line up at a checkout counter in a store. In how many ways can they line up if the first person in line is a woman, and the people in line alternate woman, man, woman, man, and so on?

68. How many four-digit odd numbers less than 6000 can be formed using the digits 2, 4, 6, 7, 8, and 9?

69. Express $_nP_{n-2}$ without using factorials.

SECTION 11.3 • COMBINATIONS

OBJECTIVES

1. Distinguish between permutation and combination problems.

2. Solve problems involving combinations using the combinations formula.

As the twentieth century drew to a close, *Time* magazine presented a series of special issues on the most influential people of the century. In its issue on heroes and icons (June 14, 1999), *Time* discussed a number of people whose careers became more profitable after their tragic deaths, including Marilyn Monroe, James Dean, Jim Morrison, Kurt Cobain, and Selena.

Imagine that you ask your friends the following question: "Of these five people, which three would you select to be included in a documentary featuring the best of their work?" You are not asking your friends to rank their three favorite artists in any kind of order—they should merely select the three to be included in the documentary.

One friend answers, "Jim Morrison, Kurt Cobain, and Selena." Another responds, "Selena, Kurt Cobain, and Jim Morrison." These two people have the same artists in their group of selections, even if they are named in a different order. We are interested *in which artists are named, not the order in which they are named* for the documentary. Because the items are taken without regard to order, this is not a permutation problem. No ranking of any sort is involved.

Later on, you ask your roommate which three artists she would select for the documentary. She names Marilyn Monroe, James Dean, and Selena. Her selection is different from those of your two other friends because different entertainers are cited.

Mathematicians describe the group of artists given by your roommate as a *combination*. A **combination** of items occurs when

- The items are selected from the same group (the five stars who died young and tragically).
- No item is used more than once. (You may adore Selena, but your three selections cannot be Selena, Selena, and Selena.)
- The order of items makes no difference. (Morrison, Cobain, Selena is the same group in the documentary as Selena, Cobain, Morrison.)

Do you see the difference between a permutation and a combination? A permutation is an ordered arrangement of a given group of items. A combination is a group of items taken without regard to their order. **Permutation** problems involve situations in which **order matters**. **Combination** problems involve situations in which the **order** of items **makes no difference**.

Marilyn Monroe, Actress (1927–1962)

James Dean, Actor (1931–1955)

Jim Morrison, Musician and Lead Singer of The Doors (1943–1971)

Kurt Cobain, Musician and Front Man for Nirvana (1967–1994)

Selena, Musician of Tejano Music (1971–1995)

1 Distinguish between permutation and combination problems.

EXAMPLE 1 DISTINGUISHING BETWEEN PERMUTATIONS AND COMBINATIONS

For each of the following problems, determine whether the problem is one involving permutations or combinations. (It is not necessary to solve the problem.)

a. Six students are running for student government president, vice-president, and treasurer. The student with the greatest number of votes becomes the president, the second highest vote-getter becomes vice-president, and the student who gets the third largest number of votes will be treasurer. How many different outcomes are possible for these three positions?

b. Six people are on the board of supervisors for your neighborhood park. A three-person committee is needed to study the possibility of expanding the park. How many different committees could be formed from the six people?

c. Baskin-Robbins offers 31 different flavors of ice cream. One of their items is a bowl consisting of three scoops of ice cream, each a different flavor. How many such bowls are possible?

SOLUTION

a. Students are choosing three student government officers from six candidates. The order in which the officers are chosen makes a difference because each of the offices (president, vice-president, treasurer) is different. Order matters. This is a problem involving permutations.

b. A three-person committee is to be formed from the six-person board of supervisors. The order in which the three people are selected does not matter because they are not filling different roles on the committee. Because order makes no difference, this is a problem involving combinations.

c. A three-scoop bowl of three different flavors is to be formed from Baskin-Robbin's 31 flavors. The order in which the three scoops of ice cream are put into the bowl is irrelevant. A bowl with chocolate, vanilla, and strawberry is exactly the same as a bowl with vanilla, strawberry, and chocolate. Different orderings do not change things, and so this is a problem involving combinations.

○

CHECK POINT 1 For each of the following problems, determine whether the problem is one involving permutations or combinations. (It is not necessary to solve the problem.)

a. How many ways can you select 6 free DVDs from a list of 200 DVDs?

b. In a race in which there are 50 runners and no ties, in how many ways can the first three finishers come in?

----

2 Solve problems involving combinations using the combinations formula.

A Formula for Combinations

We have seen that the notation $_nP_r$ means the number of permutations of n things taken r at a time. Similarly, the notation $_nC_r$ **means the number of combinations of n things taken r at a time**.

We can develop a formula for $_nC_r$ by comparing permutations and combinations. Consider the letters A, B, C, and D. The number of permutations of these four letters taken three at a time is

$$_4P_3 = \frac{4!}{(4-3)!} = \frac{4!}{1!} = \frac{4 \cdot 3 \cdot 2 \cdot 1}{1} = 24.$$

Here are the 24 permutations:

ABC,	ABD,	ACD,	BCD,
ACB,	ADB,	ADC,	BDC,
BAC,	BAD,	CAD,	CBD,
BCA,	BDA,	CDA,	CDB,
CAB,	DAB,	DAC,	DBC,
CBA,	DBA,	DCA,	DCB.

This column contains only one combination, ABC.   This column contains only one combination, ABD.   This column contains only one combination, ACD.   This column contains only one combination, BCD.

Because the order of items makes no difference in determining combinations, each column of six permutations represents one combination. There are a total of four combinations:

$$\text{ABC,} \quad \text{ABD,} \quad \text{ACD,} \quad \text{BCD.}$$

Thus, $_4C_3 = 4$: The number of combinations of 4 things taken 3 at a time is 4. With 24 permutations and only four combinations, there are 6, or 3!, times as many permutations as there are combinations.

In general, there are $r!$ times as many permutations of n things taken r at a time as there are combinations of n things taken r at a time. Thus, we find the number of combinations of n things taken r at a time by dividing the number of permutations of n things taken r at a time by $r!$.

$$_nC_r = \frac{_nP_r}{r!} = \frac{\dfrac{n!}{(n-r)!}}{r!} = \frac{n!}{(n-r)!\,r!}$$

STUDY TIP

The number of combinations if r items are taken from n items cannot be found using the Fundamental Counting Principle and requires the use of the formula shown on the right.

> **COMBINATIONS OF n THINGS TAKEN r AT A TIME**
> The number of possible combinations if r items are taken from n items is
> $$_nC_r = \frac{n!}{(n-r)!\,r!}.$$

EXAMPLE 2   USING THE FORMULA FOR COMBINATIONS

A three-person committee is needed to study ways of improving public transportation. How many committees could be formed from the eight people on the board of supervisors?

SOLUTION The order in which the three people are selected does not matter. This is a problem of selecting $r = 3$ people from a group of $n = 8$ people. We are looking for the number of combinations of eight things taken three at a time. We use the formula

$$_nC_r = \frac{n!}{(n-r)!\,r!}$$

with $n = 8$ and $r = 3$.

$$_8C_3 = \frac{8!}{(8-3)!\,3!} = \frac{8!}{5!\,3!} = \frac{8 \cdot 7 \cdot 6 \cdot 5!}{5! \cdot 3 \cdot 2 \cdot 1} = \frac{8 \cdot 7 \cdot 6 \cdot \cancel{5!}}{\cancel{5!} \cdot 3 \cdot 2 \cdot 1} = 56$$

Thus, 56 committees of three people each can be formed from the eight people on the board of supervisors.   ○

TECHNOLOGY

Graphing calculators have a menu item for calculating combinations, usually labeled $_nC_r$. For example, to find $_8C_3$, the keystrokes on most graphing calculators are

$\boxed{8}\ \boxed{_nC_r}\ \boxed{3}\ \boxed{\text{ENTER}}$.

If you are using a scientific calculator, check your manual to see whether there is a menu item for calculating combinations. If you use your calculator's factorial key to find $\frac{8!}{5!\,3!}$, be sure to enclose the factorials in the denominator with parentheses

$\boxed{8}\ \boxed{!}\ \boxed{\div}\ \boxed{(}\ \boxed{5}\ \boxed{!}\ \boxed{\times}\ \boxed{3}\ \boxed{!}\ \boxed{)}$

pressing $\boxed{=}$ or $\boxed{\text{ENTER}}$ to obtain the answer.

CHECK POINT 2 You volunteer to pet-sit for your friend who has seven different animals. How many different pet combinations are possible if you take three of the seven pets?

EXAMPLE 3   USING THE FORMULA FOR COMBINATIONS

In poker, a person is dealt 5 cards from a standard 52-card deck. The order in which you are dealt the 5 cards does not matter. How many different 5-card poker hands are possible?

SOLUTION Because the order in which the 5 cards are dealt does not matter, this is a problem involving combinations. We are looking for the number of combinations of $n = 52$ cards drawn $r = 5$ at a time. We use the formula

$$_nC_r = \frac{n!}{(n-r)!\,r!}$$

with $n = 52$ and $r = 5$.

$$_{52}C_5 = \frac{52!}{(52-5)!\,5!} = \frac{52!}{47!\,5!} = \frac{52 \cdot 51 \cdot 50 \cdot 49 \cdot 48 \cdot \cancel{47!}}{\cancel{47!} \cdot 5 \cdot 4 \cdot 3 \cdot 2 \cdot 1} = 2{,}598{,}960$$

Thus, there are 2,598,960 different 5-card poker hands possible. It surprises many people that more than 2.5 million 5-card hands can be dealt from a mere 52 cards.   ○

FIGURE 11.3 A royal flush

If you are a card player, it does not get any better than to be dealt the 5-card poker hand shown in Figure 11.3. This hand is called a *royal flush*. It consists of an ace, king, queen, jack, and 10, all of the same suit: all hearts, all diamonds, all clubs, or all spades. The probability of being dealt a royal flush involves calculating the number of ways of being dealt such a hand: just 4 of all 2,598,960 possible hands. In the next section, we move from counting possibilities to computing probabilities.

How many different 4-card hands can be dealt from a deck that has 16 different cards?

There are situations in which both the formula for combinations and the Fundamental Counting Principle are used together. Let's say that the U.S. Senate, with 100 members, consists of 54 Republicans and 46 Democrats. We want to form a committee of 3 Republicans and 2 Democrats.

100 Senate Members

54 Republicans   46 Democrats

Choose 3   Choose 2

There are $_{54}C_3$ There are $_{46}C_2$
choices.   choices.

By the Fundamental Counting Principle, the number of ways of choosing 3 Republicans and 2 Democrats is given by

$$_{54}C_3 \cdot {_{46}C_2}.$$

In Example 4, we develop these ideas in more detail.

EXAMPLE 4   USING THE FORMULA FOR COMBINATIONS AND THE FUNDAMENTAL COUNTING PRINCIPLE

The U.S. Senate of the 104th Congress consisted of 54 Republicans and 46 Democrats. How many committees can be formed if each committee must have 3 Republicans and 2 Democrats?

SOLUTION The order in which the members are selected does not matter. Thus, this is a problem involving combinations.

We begin with the number of ways of selecting 3 Republicans out of 54 Republicans without regard to order. We are looking for the number of combinations of $n = 54$ people taken $r = 3$ people at a time. We use the formula

$$_nC_r = \frac{n!}{(n-r)!\, r!}$$

with $n = 54$ and $r = 3$.

$$_{54}C_3 = \frac{54!}{(54-3)!\, 3!} = \frac{54!}{51!\, 3!} = \frac{54 \cdot 53 \cdot 52 \cdot \cancel{51!}}{\cancel{51!} \cdot 3 \cdot 2 \cdot 1} = \frac{54 \cdot 53 \cdot 52}{3 \cdot 2 \cdot 1} = 24,804$$

There are 24,804 choices for forming 3-member Republican committees.

Next, we find the number of ways of selecting 2 Democrats out of 46 Democrats without regard to order. We are looking for the number of combinations of $n = 46$ people taken $r = 2$ people at a time. Once again, we use the formula

$$_nC_r = \frac{n!}{(n-r)!\,r!}.$$

This time, $n = 46$ and $r = 2$.

$$_{46}C_2 = \frac{46!}{(46-2)!\,2!} = \frac{46!}{44!\,2!} = \frac{46 \cdot 45 \cdot 44!}{44! \cdot 2 \cdot 1} = 1035$$

There are 1035 choices for forming 2-member Democratic committees.

We use the Fundamental Counting Principle to find the number of committees that can be formed:

$$_{54}C_3 \cdot {}_{46}C_2 = 24{,}804 \cdot 1035 = 25{,}672{,}140.$$

Thus, 25,672,140 committees can be formed.

CHECK POINT 4 The U.S. Senate of the 107th Congress consisted of 50 Democrats, 49 Republicans, and one Independent. How many committees can be formed if each committee must have 3 Democrats and 2 Republicans?

EXERCISE SET 11.3 ●●●●●●

• Practice Exercises

In Exercises 1–4, does the problem involve permutations or combinations? Explain your answer. (It is not necessary to solve the problem.)

1. A medical researcher needs 6 people to test the effectiveness of an experimental drug. If 13 people have volunteered for the test, in how many ways can 6 people be selected?

2. Fifty people purchase raffle tickets. Three winning tickets are selected at random. If first prize is $1000, second prize is $500, and third prize is $100, in how many different ways can the prizes be awarded?

3. How many different four-letter passwords can be formed from the letters A, B, C, D, E, F, and G if no repetition of letters is allowed?

4. Fifty people purchase raffle tickets. Three winning tickets are selected at random. If each prize is $500, in how many different ways can the prizes be awarded?

In Exercises 5–20, use the formula for $_nC_r$ to evaluate each expression.

5. $_6C_5$ **6.** $_8C_7$ **7.** $_9C_5$ **8.** $_{10}C_6$

9. $_{11}C_4$ **10.** $_{12}C_5$ **11.** $_8C_1$ **12.** $_7C_1$

13. $_7C_7$ **14.** $_4C_4$ **15.** $_{30}C_3$ **16.** $_{25}C_4$

17. $_5C_0$ **18.** $_6C_0$ **19.** $\dfrac{_7C_3}{_5C_4}$ **20.** $\dfrac{_{10}C_3}{_6C_4}$

• Practice Plus

In Exercises 21–28, evaluate each expression.

21. $\dfrac{_7P_3}{3!} - {}_7C_3$ **22.** $\dfrac{_{20}P_2}{2!} - {}_{20}C_2$ **23.** $1 - \dfrac{_3P_2}{_4P_3}$

24. $1 - \dfrac{_5P_3}{_{10}P_4}$ **25.** $\dfrac{_7C_3}{_5C_4} - \dfrac{98!}{96!}$ **26.** $\dfrac{_{10}C_3}{_6C_4} - \dfrac{46!}{44!}$

27. $\dfrac{_4C_2 \cdot {}_6C_1}{_{18}C_3}$ **28.** $\dfrac{_5C_1 \cdot {}_7C_2}{_{12}C_3}$

• Application Exercises

Use the formula for $_nC_r$ to solve Exercises 29–36.

29. An election ballot asks voters to select three city commissioners from a group of six candidates. In how many ways can this be done?

30. A four-person committee is to be elected from an organization's membership of 11 people. How many different committees are possible?

31. Of 12 possible books, you plan to take 4 with you on vacation. How many different collections of 4 books can you take?

32. There are 14 standbys who hope to get seats on a flight, but only 6 seats are available on the plane. How many different ways can the 6 people be selected?

33. You volunteer to help drive children at a charity event to the zoo, but you can fit only 8 of the 17 children present in your van. How many different groups of 8 children can you drive?

34. Of the 100 people in the U.S. Senate, 18 serve on the Foreign Relations Committee. How many ways are there to select Senate members for this committee (assuming party affiliation is not a factor in the selection)?

35. To win at LOTTO in the state of Florida, one must correctly select 6 numbers from a collection of 53 numbers (1 through 53). The order in which the selection is made does not matter. How many different selections are possible?

36. To win in the New York State lottery, one must correctly select 6 numbers from 59 numbers. The order in which the selection is made does not matter. How many different selections are possible?

In Exercises 37–46, solve by the method of your choice.

37. In a race in which six automobiles are entered and there are no ties, in how many ways can the first four finishers come in?

38. A book club offers a choice of 8 books from a list of 40. In how many ways can a member make a selection?

39. A medical researcher needs 6 people to test the effectiveness of an experimental drug. If 13 people have volunteered for the test, in how many ways can 6 people be selected?

40. Fifty people purchase raffle tickets. Three winning tickets are selected at random. If first prize is $1000, second prize is $500, and third prize is $100, in how many different ways can the prizes be awarded?

41. From a club of 20 people, in how many ways can a group of three members be selected to attend a conference?

42. Fifty people purchase raffle tickets. Three winning tickets are selected at random. If each prize is $500, in how many different ways can the prizes be awarded?

43. How many different four-letter passwords can be formed from the letters A, B, C, D, E, F, and G if no repetition of letters is allowed?

44. Nine comedy acts will perform over two evenings. Five of the acts will perform on the first evening. How many ways can the schedule for the first evening be made?

45. Using 15 flavors of ice cream, how many cones with three different flavors can you create if it is important to you which flavor goes on the top, middle, and bottom?

46. Baskin-Robbins offers 31 different flavors of ice cream. One of its items is a bowl consisting of three scoops of ice cream, each a different flavor. How many such bowls are possible?

Use the formula for $_nC_r$ and the Fundamental Counting Principle to solve Exercises 47–50.

47. In how many ways can a committee of four men and five women be formed from a group of seven men and seven women?

48. How many different committees can be formed from 5 professors and 15 students if each committee is made up of 2 professors and 10 students?

49. The U.S. Senate of the 109th Congress consisted of 55 Republicans, 44 Democrats, and 1 Independent. How many committees can be formed if each committee must have 4 Republicans and 3 Democrats?

50. A mathematics exam consists of 10 multiple-choice questions and 5 open-ended problems in which all work must be shown. If an examinee must answer 8 of the multiple-choice questions and 3 of the open-ended problems, in how many ways can the questions and problems be chosen?

Thousands of jokes have been told about marriage and divorce. Exercises 51–58 are based on the following observations:

- *"By all means, marry; if you get a good wife, you'll be happy. If you get a bad one, you'll become a philosopher." - Socrates*

- *"My wife and I were happy for 20 years. Then we met." - Rodney Dangerfield*

- *"Whatever you may look like, marry a man your own age. As your beauty fades, so will his eyesight." - Phyllis Diller*

- *"Why do Jewish divorces cost so much? Because they're worth it." - Henny Youngman*

- *"I think men who have a pierced ear are better prepared for marriage. They've experienced pain and bought jewelry." - Rita Rudner*

- *"For a while we pondered whether to take a vacation or get a divorce. We decided that a trip to Bermuda is over in two weeks, but a divorce is something you always have." - Woody Allen*

51. In how many ways can these six jokes be ranked from best to worst?

52. If Socrates's thoughts about marriage are excluded, in how many ways can the remaining five jokes be ranked from best to worst?

53. In how many ways can people select their three favorite jokes from these thoughts about marriage and divorce?

54. In how many ways can people select their two favorite jokes from these thoughts about marriage and divorce?

55. If the order in which these jokes are told makes a difference in terms of how they are received, how many ways can they be delivered if Socrates's comments are scheduled first and Dangerfield's joke is told last?

56. If the order in which these jokes are told makes a difference in terms of how they are received, how many ways can they be delivered if a joke by a woman (Rudner or Diller) is told first?

57. In how many ways can people select their favorite joke told by a woman (Rudner or Diller) and their two favorite jokes told by a man?

58. In how many ways can people select their favorite joke told by a woman (Rudner or Diller) and their three favorite jokes told by a man?

• Writing in Mathematics

59. What is a combination?

60. Explain how to distinguish between permutation and combination problems.

61. Write a word problem that can be solved by evaluating $_7C_3$.

• Critical Thinking Exercises

62. Write a word problem that can be solved by evaluating $_{10}C_3 \cdot _7C_2$.

63. A 6/53 lottery involves choosing 6 of the numbers from 1 through 53 and a 5/36 lottery involves choosing 5 of the numbers from 1 through 36. The order in which the numbers are chosen does not matter. Which lottery is easier to win? Explain your answer.

64. If the number of permutations of n objects taken r at a time is six times the number of combinations of n objects taken r at a time, determine the value of r. Is there enough information to determine the value of n? Why or why not?

65. In a group of 20 people, how long will it take each person to shake hands with each of the other persons in the group, assuming that it takes three seconds for each shake and only 2 people can shake hands at a time? What if the group is increased to 40 people?

66. A sample of 4 telephones is selected from a shipment of 20 phones. There are 5 defective telephones in the shipment. How many of the samples of 4 phones do not include any of the defective ones?

SECTION 11.4 ● FUNDAMENTALS OF PROBABILITY

OBJECTIVES

1. Compute theoretical probability.
2. Compute empirical probability.

Hours of Sleep	**Number of Americans, in millions**
4 or less	12
5	27
6	75
7	90
8	81
9	9
10 or more	6

TABLE 11.1 THE HOURS OF SLEEP AMERICANS GET ON A TYPICAL NIGHT

Total: 300

Source: Discovery Health Media

100% or 1 — *Certain*

Likely

50% or $\frac{1}{2}$ — *50-50 Chance*

Unlikely

0% or 0 — *Impossible*

Possible Values for Probabilities

How many hours of sleep do you typically get each night? Table 11.1 indicates that 75 million out of 300 million Americans are getting six hours of sleep on a typical night. The *probability* of an American getting six hours of sleep on a typical night is $\frac{75}{300}$. This fraction can be reduced to $\frac{1}{4}$, or expressed as 0.25, or 25%. Thus, 25% of Americans get six hours of sleep each night.

We find a probability by dividing one number by another. Probabilities are assigned to an *event*, such as getting six hours of sleep on a typical night. Events that are certain to occur are assigned probabilities of 1, or 100%. For example, the probability that a given individual will eventually die is 1. Although Woody Allen whined, "I don't want to achieve immortality through my work. I want to achieve it through not dying," death (and taxes) are always certain. By contrast, if an event cannot occur, its probability is 0. Regrettably, the probability that Elvis will return and serenade us with one final reprise of "Don't Be Cruel" (and we hope we're not) is 0.

Probabilities of events are expressed as numbers ranging from 0 to 1, or 0% to 100%. The closer the probability of a given event is to 1, the more likely it is that the event will occur. The closer the probability of a given event is to 0, the less likely it is that the event will occur.

① Compute theoretical probability.

Theoretical Probability

You toss a coin. Although it is equally likely to land either heads up, denoted by *H*, or tails up, denoted by *T*, the actual outcome is uncertain. Any occurrence for which the outcome is uncertain is called an **experiment**. Thus, tossing a coin is an example of an experiment. The set of all possible outcomes of an experiment is the **sample space** of the experiment, denoted by *S*. The sample space for the coin-tossing experiment is

$$S = \{H, T\}.$$

Lands heads up   Lands tails up

An **event**, denoted by *E*, is any subset of a sample space. For example, the subset $E = \{T\}$ is the event of landing tails up when a coin is tossed.

Theoretical probability applies to situations like this, in which the sample space only contains equally likely outcomes, all of which are known. To calculate the theoretical probability of an event, we divide the number of outcomes resulting in the event by the total number of outcomes in the sample space.

> **COMPUTING THEORETICAL PROBABILITY**
>
> If an event E has $n(E)$ equally likely outcomes and its sample space S has $n(S)$ equally likely outcomes, the **theoretical probability** of event E, denoted by $P(E)$, is
>
> $$P(E) = \frac{\text{number of outcomes in event } E}{\text{total number of possible outcomes}} = \frac{n(E)}{n(S)}.$$

How can we use this formula to compute the probability of a coin landing tails up? We use the following sets:

$$E = \{T\} \qquad S = \{H, T\}.$$

This is the event of landing tails up.

This is the sample space with all equally likely outcomes.

The probability of a coin landing tails up is

$$P(E) = \frac{\text{number of outcomes that result in tails up}}{\text{total number of possible outcomes}} = \frac{n(E)}{n(S)} = \frac{1}{2}.$$

Theoretical probability applies to many games of chance, including dice rolling, lotteries, card games, and roulette. We begin with rolling a die. Figure 11.4 illustrates that when a die is rolled, there are six equally likely possible outcomes. The sample space can be shown as

$$S = \{1, 2, 3, 4, 5, 6\}.$$

FIGURE 11.4 Outcomes when a die is rolled

EXAMPLE 1   COMPUTING THEORETICAL PROBABILITY

A die is rolled once. Find the probability of rolling

a. a 3.   **b.** an even number.   **c.** a number less than 5.
d. a number less than 10.   **e.** a number greater than 6.

SOLUTION The sample space is $S = \{1, 2, 3, 4, 5, 6\}$ with $n(S) = 6$. We will use 6, the total number of possible outcomes, in the denominator of each probability fraction.

a. The phrase "rolling a 3" describes the event $E = \{3\}$. This event can occur in one way: $n(E) = 1$.

$$P(3) = \frac{\text{number of outcomes that result in 3}}{\text{total number of possible outcomes}} = \frac{n(E)}{n(S)} = \frac{1}{6}$$

The probability of rolling a 3 is $\frac{1}{6}$.

b. The phrase "rolling an even number" describes the event $E = \{2, 4, 6\}$. This event can occur in three ways: $n(E) = 3$.

$$P(\text{even number}) = \frac{\text{number of outcomes that result in an even number}}{\text{total number of possible outcomes}} = \frac{n(E)}{n(S)} = \frac{3}{6} = \frac{1}{2}$$

The probability of rolling an even number is $\frac{1}{2}$.

c. The phrase "rolling a number less than 5" describes the event $E = \{1, 2, 3, 4\}$. This event can occur in four ways: $n(E) = 4$.

$$P(\text{less than } 5) = \frac{\text{number of outcomes that are less than } 5}{\text{total number of possible outcomes}} = \frac{n(E)}{n(S)} = \frac{4}{6} = \frac{2}{3}$$

The probability of rolling a number less than 5 is $\frac{2}{3}$.

d. The phrase "rolling a number less than 10" describes the event $E = \{1, 2, 3, 4, 5, 6\}$. This event can occur in six ways: $n(E) = 6$. Can you see that all of the possible outcomes are less than 10? This event is certain to occur.

$$P(\text{less than } 10) = \frac{\text{number of outcomes that are less than } 10}{\text{total number of possible outcomes}} = \frac{n(E)}{n(S)} = \frac{6}{6} = 1$$

The probability of any certain event is 1.

e. The phrase "rolling a number greater than 6" describes an event that cannot occur, or the empty set. Thus, $E = \emptyset$ and $n(E) = 0$.

$$P(\text{greater than } 6) = \frac{\text{number of outcomes that are greater than } 6}{\text{total number of possible outcomes}} = \frac{n(E)}{n(S)} = \frac{0}{6} = 0$$

The probability of an event that cannot occur is 0.

In Example 1, there are six possible outcomes, each with a probability of $\frac{1}{6}$:

$$P(1) = \frac{1}{6} \quad P(2) = \frac{1}{6} \quad P(3) = \frac{1}{6} \quad P(4) = \frac{1}{6} \quad P(5) = \frac{1}{6} \quad P(6) = \frac{1}{6}.$$

The sum of these probabilities is 1: $\frac{1}{6} + \frac{1}{6} + \frac{1}{6} + \frac{1}{6} + \frac{1}{6} + \frac{1}{6} = 1$. In general, **the sum of the theoretical probabilities of all possible outcomes in the sample space is 1**.

CHECK POINT 1 A die is rolled once. Find the probability of rolling

    a. a 2.

    b. a number less than 4.

    c. a number greater than 7.

    d. a number less than 7.

Our next example involves a standard 52-card bridge deck, illustrated in Figure 11.5. The deck has four suits: Hearts and diamonds are red, and clubs and spades are black. Each suit has 13 different face values—A(ace), 2, 3, 4, 5, 6, 7, 8, 9, 10, J(jack), Q(queen), and K(king). Jacks, queens, and kings are called **picture cards** or **face cards**.

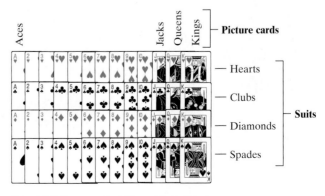

FIGURE 11.5 A standard 52-card bridge deck

FIGURE 11.5 (repeated)

EXAMPLE 2   PROBABILITY AND A DECK OF 52 CARDS

You are dealt one card from a standard 52-card deck. Find the probability of being dealt

a. a king.   **b.** a heart.   **c.** the king of hearts.

SOLUTION Because there are 52 cards in the deck, the total number of possible ways of being dealt a single card is 52. The number of outcomes in the sample space is 52: $n(S) = 52$. We use 52 as the denominator of each probability fraction.

a. Let E be the event of being dealt a king. Because there are four kings in the deck, this event can occur in four ways: $n(E) = 4$.

$$P(\text{king}) = \frac{\text{number of outcomes that result in a king}}{\text{total number of possible outcomes}} = \frac{n(E)}{n(S)} = \frac{4}{52} = \frac{1}{13}$$

The probability of being dealt a king is $\frac{1}{13}$.

b. Let E be the event of being dealt a heart. Because there are 13 hearts in the deck, this event can occur in 13 ways: $n(E) = 13$.

$$P(\text{heart}) = \frac{\text{number of outcomes that result in a heart}}{\text{total number of possible outcomes}} = \frac{n(E)}{n(S)} = \frac{13}{52} = \frac{1}{4}$$

The probability of being dealt a heart is $\frac{1}{4}$.

c. Let E be the event of being dealt the king of hearts. Because there is only one card in the deck that is the king of hearts, this event can occur in just one way: $n(E) = 1$.

$$P(\text{king of hearts}) = \frac{\text{number of outcomes that result in the king of hearts}}{\text{total number of possible outcomes}} = \frac{n(E)}{n(S)} = \frac{1}{52}$$

The probability of being dealt the king of hearts is $\frac{1}{52}$.

CHECK POINT 2 You are dealt one card from a standard 52-card deck. Find the probability of being dealt

a. an ace.   **b.** a red card.   **c.** a red king.

Probabilities play a valuable role in the science of genetics. Example 3 deals with cystic fibrosis, an inherited lung disease occurring in about 1 out of every 2000 births among Caucasians and in about 1 out of every 250,000 births among non-Caucasians.

EXAMPLE 3   PROBABILITIES IN GENETICS

Each person carries two genes that are related to the absence or presence of the disease cystic fibrosis. Most Americans have two normal genes for this trait and are unaffected by cystic fibrosis. However, 1 in 25 Americans carries one normal gene and one defective gene. If we use c to represent a defective gene and C a normal gene, such a carrier can be designated as Cc. Thus, CC is a person who neither carries nor has cystic fibrosis, Cc is a carrier who is not actually sick, and cc is a person sick with the disease. Table 11.2 shows the four equally likely outcomes for a child's genetic inheritance from two parents who are both carrying one cystic fibrosis gene. One copy of each gene is passed on to the child from the parents.

Genetic engineering offers some hope for cystic fibrosis patients. Geneticists can now isolate the c gene, the gene responsible for the disease. It is hoped that it will soon be possible to replace the defective c gene with a normal C gene.

TABLE 11.2 CYSTIC FIBROSIS AND GENETIC INHERITANCE

		Second Parent	
		C	**c**
First	**C**	CC	Cc
Parent	**c**	cC	cc

Shown in the table are the four possibilities for a child whose parents each carry one cystic fibrosis gene.

If each parent carries one cystic fibrosis gene, what is the probability that their child will have cystic fibrosis?

SOLUTION Table 11.2 shows that there are four equally likely outcomes. The sample space is $S = \{CC, Cc, cC, cc\}$ and $n(S) = 4$. The phrase "will have cystic fibrosis" describes only the cc child. Thus, $E = \{cc\}$ and $n(E) = 1$.

$$P(\text{cystic fibrosis}) = \frac{\text{number of outcomes that result in cystic fibrosis}}{\text{total number of possible outcomes}} = \frac{n(E)}{n(S)} = \frac{1}{4}$$

If each parent carries one cystic fibrosis gene, the probability that their child will have cystic fibrosis is $\frac{1}{4}$.

⊙

CHECK POINT 3 Use Table 11.2 in Example 3 to solve this exercise. If each parent carries one cystic fibrosis gene, find the probability that their child will be a carrier of the disease who is not actually sick.

2 Compute empirical probability.

Empirical Probability

Theoretical probability is based on a set of equally likely outcomes and the number of elements in the set. By contrast, *empirical probability* applies to situations in which we observe how frequently an event occurs. We use the following formula to compute the empirical probability of an event:

> **COMPUTING EMPIRICAL PROBABILITY**
> The empirical probability of event E is
> $$P(E) = \frac{\text{observed number of times } E \text{ occurs}}{\text{total number of observed occurrences}}.$$

EXAMPLE 4   COMPUTING EMPIRICAL PROBABILITY

Table 11.3 shows the distribution, by marital status and gender, of the 212.5 million Americans ages 18 or older.

TABLE 11.3 MARITAL STATUS OF THE U.S. POPULATION, AGES 18 OR OLDER, IN MILLIONS

	Never Married	Married	Widowed	Divorced	Total
Male	28.6	62.1	2.7	9.0	102.4
Female	23.3	62.8	11.3	12.7	110.1
Total	51.9	124.9	14.0	21.7	212.5

Total male:
28.6 + 62.1 + 2.7 + 9.0 = 102.4

Total female:
23.3 + 62.8 + 11.3 + 12.7 = 110.1

Total never married:
28.6 + 23.3 = 51.9

Total widowed:
2.7 + 11.3 = 14.0

Total adult population:
102.4 + 110.1 = 212.5

Total married:
62.1 + 62.8 = 124.9

Total divorced:
9.0 + 12.7 = 21.7

Source: U.S. Census Bureau

STUDY TIP

Our selection from the U.S. adult population is *random*. This means that every person in the population has an equal chance of being chosen. We'll have much more to say about random selections in Chapter 12, Statistics.

If one person is randomly selected from the population described in Table 11.3, find the probability, to the nearest hundreth, that the person

a. is divorced.   **b.** is female.

SOLUTION

a. The probability of selecting a divorced person is the observed number of divorced people, 21.7 (million), divided by the total number of U.S. adults, 212.5 (million).

P(selecting a divorced person from the U.S. adult population)

$$= \frac{\text{number of divorced people}}{\text{total number of U.S. adults}} = \frac{21.7}{212.5} \approx 0.10$$

The empirical probability of selecting a divorced person from the U.S. adult population is approximately 0.10.

b. Be sure to refer to Table 11.3 on the previous page. The probability of selecting a female is the observed number of females, 110.1 (million), divided by the total number of U.S. adults, 212.5 (million).

P(selecting a female from the U.S. adult population)

$$= \frac{\text{number of females}}{\text{total number of U.S. adults}} = \frac{110.1}{212.5} \approx 0.52$$

The empirical probability of selecting a female from the U.S. adult population is approximately 0.52.

CHECK POINT **4** If one person is randomly selected from the population described in Table 11.3 on page 631, find the probability, expressed as a decimal rounded to the nearest hundredth, that the person

a. has never been married.   **b.** is male.

In certain situations, we can establish a relationship between the two kinds of probability. Consider, for example, a coin that is equally likely to land heads or tails. Such a coin is called a **fair coin**. Empirical probability can be used to determine whether a coin is fair. Suppose we toss a coin 10, 50, 100, 1000, 10,000, and 100,000 times. We record the number of heads observed, shown in Table 11.4. For each of the six cases in the table, the empirical probability of heads is determined by dividing the number of heads observed by the number of tosses.

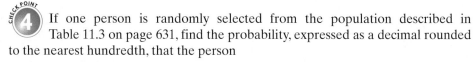

TABLE 11.4 EMPIRICAL PROBABILITIES OF HEADS AS THE NUMBER OF TOSSES INCREASES

Number of Tosses	Number of Heads Observed	Empirical Probability of Heads, or $P(H)$
10	4	$P(H) = \frac{4}{10} = 0.4$
50	27	$P(H) = \frac{27}{50} = 0.54$
100	44	$P(H) = \frac{44}{100} = 0.44$
1000	530	$P(H) = \frac{530}{1000} = 0.53$
10,000	4851	$P(H) = \frac{4851}{10,000} = 0.4851$
100,000	49,880	$P(H) = \frac{49,880}{100,000} = 0.4988$

A pattern is exhibited by the empirical probabilities in the right-hand column of Table 11.4. As the number of tosses increases, the empirical probabilities tend to get closer to 0.5, the theoretical probability. These results give us no reason to suspect that the coin is not fair.

Table 11.4 illustrates an important principle when observing uncertain outcomes such as the event of a coin landing on heads. As an experiment is repeated more and more times, the empirical probability of an event tends to get closer to the theoretical probability of that event. This principle is known as the **law of large numbers**.

EXERCISE SET 11.4 ●●●●●○

• Practice and Application Exercises

Exercises 1–54 involve theoretical probability. Use the theoretical probability formula to solve each exercise. Express each probability as a fraction reduced to lowest terms.

In Exercises 1–10, a die is rolled. The set of equally likely outcomes is $\{1, 2, 3, 4, 5, 6\}$. Find the probability of rolling

1. a 4.
2. a 5.
3. an odd number.
4. a number greater than 3.
5. a number less than 3.
6. a number greater than 4.
7. a number less than 7.
8. a number less than 8.
9. a number greater than 7.
10. a number greater than 8.

In Exercises 11–20, you are dealt one card from a standard 52-card deck. Find the probability of being dealt

11. a queen.
12. a jack.
13. a club.
14. a diamond.
15. a picture card.
16. a card greater than 3 and less than 7.
17. the queen of spades.
18. the ace of clubs.
19. a diamond and a spade.
20. a card with a green heart.

In Exercises 21–26, a fair coin is tossed two times in succession. The set of equally likely outcomes is $\{HH, HT, TH, TT\}$. Find the probability of getting

21. two heads.
22. two tails.
23. the same outcome on each toss.
24. different outcomes on each toss.
25. a head on the second toss.
26. at least one head.

In Exercises 27–34, you select a family with three children. If M represents a male child and F a female child, the set of equally likely outcomes for the children's genders is $\{MMM, MMF, MFM, MFF, FMM, FMF, FFM, FFF\}$. Find the probability of selecting a family with

27. exactly one female child.
28. exactly one male child.
29. exactly two male children.
30. exactly two female children.
31. at least one male child.
32. at least two female children.
33. four male children.
34. fewer than four female children.

In Exercises 35–40, a single die is rolled twice. The 36 equally likely outcomes are shown as follows:

		Second Roll					
		⚀	⚁	⚂	⚃	⚄	⚅
First Roll	⚀	(1,1)	(1,2)	(1,3)	(1,4)	(1,5)	(1,6)
	⚁	(2,1)	(2,2)	(2,3)	(2,4)	(2,5)	(2,6)
	⚂	(3,1)	(3,2)	(3,3)	(3,4)	(3,5)	(3,6)
	⚃	(4,1)	(4,2)	(4,3)	(4,4)	(4,5)	(4,6)
	⚄	(5,1)	(5,2)	(5,3)	(5,4)	(5,5)	(5,6)
	⚅	(6,1)	(6,2)	(6,3)	(6,4)	(6,5)	(6,6)

Find the probability of getting

35. two even numbers.
36. two odd numbers.
37. two numbers whose sum is 5.
38. two numbers whose sum is 6.
39. two numbers whose sum exceeds 12.
40. two numbers whose sum is less than 13.

Use the spinner shown to answer Exercises 41–48. Assume that it is equally probable that the pointer will land on any one of the ten colored regions. If the pointer lands on a borderline, spin again.

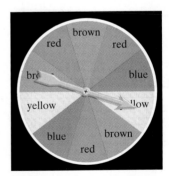

Find the probability that the spinner lands in

41. a red region.
42. a yellow region.
43. a blue region.
44. a brown region.
45. a region that is red or blue.
46. a region that is yellow or brown.
47. a region that is red and blue.
48. a region that is yellow and brown.

Exercises 49–54 deal with sickle cell anemia, an inherited disease in which red blood cells become distorted and deprived of oxygen. Approximately 1 in every 500 African-American infants is born with the disease; only 1 in 160,000 white infants has the disease. A person with two sickle cell genes will have the disease, but a person with only one sickle cell gene will have a mild, non-fatal anemia called sickle cell trait. (Approximately 8%–10% of the African-American population has this trait.)

		Second Parent	
		S	s
First	S	SS	Ss
Parent	s	sS	ss

If we use s to represent a sickle cell gene and S a healthy gene, the table shows the four possibilities for the children of two Ss parents. Each parent has only one sickle cell gene, so each has the relatively mild sickle cell trait. Find the probability that these parents give birth to a child who

49. has sickle cell anemia.   **50.** has sickle cell trait.

51. is healthy.

In Exercises 52–54, use the following table that shows the four possibilities for the children of one healthy, SS, parent, and one parent with sickle cell trait, Ss.

		Second Parent (with Sickle Cell Trait)	
		S	s
Healthy	S	SS	Ss
First Parent	S	SS	Ss

Find the probability that these parents give birth to a child who

52. has sickle cell anemia.   **53.** has sickle cell trait.
54. is healthy.

The table shows the distribution, by age and gender, of the 29.3 million Americans who live alone. Use the data in the table to solve Exercises 55–60.

NUMBER OF PEOPLE IN THE UNITED STATES LIVING ALONE, IN MILLIONS

	Ages 15–24	Ages 25–34	Ages 35–44	Ages 45–64	Ages 65–74	Ages ≥75	Total
Male	0.7	2.2	2.6	4.3	1.3	1.4	12.5
Female	0.8	1.6	1.6	5.0	2.9	4.9	16.8
Total	1.5	3.8	4.2	9.3	4.2	6.3	29.3

Source: U.S. Census Bureau

Find the probability, expressed as a decimal rounded to the nearest hundredth, that a randomly selected American living alone is

55. male.   **56.** female.

57. in the 25–34 age range.

58. in the 35–44 age range.

59. a woman in the 15–24 age range.

60. a man in the 45–64 age range.

The table shows the number of Americans who moved in 2004, categorized by where they moved and whether they were an owner or a renter. Use the data in the table, expressed in millions, to solve Exercises 61–66.

NUMBER OF PEOPLE IN THE UNITED STATES WHO MOVED IN 2004, IN MILLIONS

	Moved to Same State	Moved to Different State	Moved to Different Country
Owner	11.7	2.8	0.3
Renter	18.7	4.5	1.0

Source: U.S. Census Bureau

Find the probability, expressed as a decimal rounded to the nearest hundredth, that a randomly selected American who moved in 2004 was

61. an owner.

62. a renter.

63. a person who moved within the same state.

64. a person who moved to a different country.

65. a renter who moved to a different state.

66. an owner who moved to a different state.

• Writing in Mathematics

67. What is the sample space of an experiment? What is an event?

68. How is the theoretical probability of an event computed?

69. Describe the difference between theoretical probability and empirical probability.

70. Give an example of an event whose probability must be determined empirically rather than theoretically.

71. Use the definition of theoretical probability to explain why the probability of an event that cannot occur is 0.

72. Use the definition of theoretical probability to explain why the probability of an event that is certain to occur is 1.

73. Write a probability word problem whose answer is one of the following fractions: $\frac{1}{6}$ or $\frac{1}{4}$ or $\frac{1}{3}$.

74. The president of a large company with 10,000 employees is considering mandatory cocaine testing for every employee. The test that would be used is 90% accurate, meaning that it will detect 90% of the cocaine users who are tested, and that 90% of the nonusers will test negative. This also means that the test gives 10% false positive. Suppose that 1% of the employees actually use cocaine. Find the probability that someone who tests positive for cocaine use is, indeed, a user.

Hint: Find the following probability fraction:

the number of employees who test positive
and are cocaine users
the number of employes who test positive

This fraction is given by

$$\frac{90\% \text{ of } 1\% \text{ of } 10,000}{\text{the number who test positive who actually use}} .$$
the number who test positive who actually use
cocaine plus the number who test positive
who do not use cocaine

What does this probability indicate in terms of the percentage of employees who test positive who are not actually users? Discuss these numbers in terms of the issue of mandatory drug testing. Write a paper either in favor of or against mandatory drug testing, incorporating the actual percentage accuracy for such tests.

• Critical Thinking Exercises

75. The target in the figure shown in the next column contains four squares. If a dart thrown at random hits the target, find the probability that it will land in an orange region.

76. Some three-digit numbers, such as 101 and 313, read the same forward and backward. If you select a number from all three-digit numbers, find the probability that it will read the same forward and backward.

SECTION 11.5 • PROBABILITY WITH THE FUNDAMENTAL COUNTING PRINCIPLE, PERMUTATIONS, AND COMBINATIONS

O B J E C T I V E S

1. Compute probabilities with permutations.

2. Compute probabilities with combinations.

PROBABILITY OF DYING AT ANY GIVEN AGE

Age	Probability of Male Death	Probability of Female Death
10	0.00013	0.00010
20	0.00140	0.00050
30	0.00153	0.00050
40	0.00193	0.00095
50	0.00567	0.00305
60	0.01299	0.00792
70	0.03473	0.01764
80	0.07644	0.03966
90	0.15787	0.11250
100	0.26876	0.23969
110	0.39770	0.39043

Source: George Shaffner, *The Arithmetic of Life and Death*

George Tooker
(b. 1920) "*Mirror II*"
*1963, egg tempera on gesso
panel, 20 × 20 in., 1968.4.
Gift of R. H. Donnelley
Erdman (PA 1956). Addison
Gallery of American Art,
Phillips Academy, Andover,
Massachusetts. All Rights
Reserved.*

According to actuarial tables, there is no year in which death is as likely as continued life, at least until the age of 115. Until that age, the probability of dying in any one year ranges from a low of 0.00009 for a girl at age 11 to a high of 0.465 for either gender at age 114. For a healthy 30-year-old, how does the probability of dying this year compare to the probability of winning the top prize in a state lottery game? In this section, we provide the surprising answer to this question, as we study probability with the Fundamental Counting Principle, permutations, and combinations.

1 | Compute probabilities with permutations.

Probability with Permutations

We return to our concert tour with U2, Bruce Springsteen and the E Street Band, Aerosmith, and the Rolling Stones. Now, the two surviving members of the Beatles have agreed to join the tour! You really have your work cut out for you. In which order should the five groups in the concert perform? Because order makes a difference, this is a permutation situation. Example 1 is based on this scenario, and uses permutations to solve a probability problem.

EXAMPLE 1 PROBABILITY AND PERMUTATIONS

The five groups in the tour agree to determine the order of performance based on a random selection. Each band's name is written on one of five cards. The cards are placed in a hat and then five cards are drawn, one at a time. The order in which the cards are drawn determines the order in which the bands perform. What is the probability of the Rolling Stones performing fourth and the Beatles last?

SOLUTION We begin by applying the definition of probability to this situation.

P(Rolling Stones fourth, Beatles last)

$$= \frac{\text{number of permutations with Rolling Stones fourth, Beatles last}}{\text{total number of possible permutations}}$$

We can use the Fundamental Counting Principle to find the total number of possible permutations. This represents the number of ways you can put together the concert.

First Group to Perform	Second Group to Perform	Third Group to Perform	Fourth Group to Perform	Last Group to Perform
5 choices	4 choices	3 choices	2 choices	1 choice

There are $5 \cdot 4 \cdot 3 \cdot 2 \cdot 1$, or 120, possible permutations. Equivalently, the five groups can perform in 120 different orders.

We can also use the Fundamental Counting Principle to find the number of permutations with the Rolling Stones performing fourth and the Beatles performing last. You can choose any one of the three groups, U2, Bruce Springsteen and the E Street Band, or Aerosmith, as the opening act. This leaves two choices for the second group to perform, and only one choice for the third group to perform. There is only one choice for the fourth group—the Rolling Stones, and one choice for the closing act—the Beatles:

First Group to Perform	Second Group to Perform	Third Group to Perform	Fourth Group to Perform	Last Group to Perform
3 choices (U2, Springsteen, or Aerosmith)	2 choices	1 choice	1 choice: The Rolling Stones	1 choice: The Beatles

Thus, there are $3 \cdot 2 \cdot 1 \cdot 1 \cdot 1$, or 6 possible permutations. Equivalently, there are 6 lineups with the Rolling Stones performing fourth and the Beatles last.

Now we can return to our probability fraction.

P(Rolling Stones fourth, Beatles last)

$$= \frac{\text{number of permutations with Rolling Stones fourth, Beatles last}}{\text{total number of possible permutations}}$$

$$= \frac{6}{120} = \frac{1}{20}$$

The probability of the Rolling Stones performing fourth and the Beatles last is $\frac{1}{20}$.

 Use the information given in Example 1 to find the probability of U2 performing first, the Rolling Stones performing fourth, and the Beatles last.

In 2004, Americans spent $49.4 billion on lotteries set up by revenue-hungry states. Once prizes and administrative costs were paid, $15.1 billion was left in revenue for the states. Throughout the United States, 64% of lottery profits go to education funding.
Source: North American Association of State and Provincial Lotteries

2 | Compute probabilities with combinations.

Probability with Combinations

In 2006, 41 states and Washington, D.C., had lotteries, and several states were considering selling lottery tickets on the Internet. If your state has a lottery drawing each week, the probability that someone will win the top prize is relatively high. If there is no winner this week, it is virtually certain that eventually someone will be graced with millions of dollars. So, why are you so unlucky compared to this undisclosed someone? In Example 2, we provide an answer to this question.

| **EXAMPLE 2** | PROBABILITY AND COMBINATIONS: WINNING THE LOTTERY |

Florida's lottery game, LOTTO, is set up so that each player chooses six different numbers from 1 to 53. If the six numbers chosen match the six numbers drawn randomly, the player wins (or shares) the top cash prize. (As of this writing, the top cash prize has ranged from $7 million to $106.5 million.) With one LOTTO ticket, what is the probability of winning this prize?

SOLUTION Because the order of the six numbers does not matter, this is a situation involving combinations. We begin with the formula for probability.

$$P(\text{winning}) = \frac{\text{number of ways of winning}}{\text{total number of possible combinations}}$$

We can use the combinations formula

$$_nC_r = \frac{n!}{(n-r)!\, r!}$$

to find the total number of possible combinations. We are selecting $r = 6$ numbers from a collection of $n = 53$ numbers.

$$_{53}C_6 = \frac{53!}{(53-6)!\, 6!} = \frac{53!}{47!\, 6!} = \frac{53 \cdot 52 \cdot 51 \cdot 50 \cdot 49 \cdot 48 \cdot \cancel{47!}}{\cancel{47!} \cdot 6 \cdot 5 \cdot 4 \cdot 3 \cdot 2 \cdot 1} = 22{,}957{,}480$$

There are nearly 23 million number combinations possible in LOTTO. If a person buys one LOTTO ticket, that person has selected only one combination of the six numbers. With one LOTTO ticket, there is only one way of winning.

Now we can return to our probability fraction.

$$P(\text{winning}) = \frac{\text{number of ways of winning}}{\text{total number of possible combinations}} = \frac{1}{22{,}957{,}480} \approx 0.0000000436$$

The probability of winning the top prize with one LOTTO ticket is $\frac{1}{22{,}957{,}480}$, or about 1 in 23 million.

Suppose that a person buys 5000 different tickets in Florida's LOTTO. Because that person has selected 5000 different combinations of the six numbers, the probability of winning is

$$\frac{5000}{22{,}957{,}480} \approx 0.000218.$$

The chances of winning top prize are about 218 in a million. At $1 per LOTTO ticket, it is highly probable that our LOTTO player will be $5000 poorer. Knowing a little probability helps a lotto.

2 People lose interest when they do not win at games of chance, including Florida's LOTTO. With drawings twice weekly instead of once, the game described in Example 2 was brought in to bring back lost players and increase ticket sales. The original LOTTO was set up so that each player chose six different numbers from 1 to 49, rather than from 1 to 53, with a lottery drawing only once a week. With one LOTTO ticket, what was the probability of winning the top cash prize in Florida's original LOTTO? Express the answer as a fraction and as a decimal correct to ten places.

EXAMPLE 3   PROBABILITY AND COMBINATIONS

A club consists of five men and seven women. Three members are selected at random to attend a conference. Find the probability that the selected group consists of

a. three men.

b. one man and two women.

SOLUTION The order in which the three people are selected does not matter, so this is a problem involving combinations.

12 Club Members

5 Men   7 Women

↓

Select 3

a. We begin with the probability of selecting three men.

$$P(3 \text{ men}) = \frac{\text{number of ways of selecting 3 men}}{\text{total number of possible combinations}}$$

First, we consider the denominator of the probability fraction. We are selecting $r = 3$ people from a total group of $n = 12$ people (five men and seven women). The total number of possible combinations is

$$_{12}C_3 = \frac{12!}{(12-3)!\,3!} = \frac{12!}{9!\,3!} = \frac{12 \cdot 11 \cdot 10 \cdot \cancel{9!}}{\cancel{9!} \cdot 3 \cdot 2 \cdot 1} = 220.$$

Thus, there are 220 possible three-person selections.

Next, we consider the numerator of the probability fraction. We are interested in the number of ways of selecting three men from five men. We are selecting $r = 3$ men from a total group of $n = 5$ men. The number of possible combinations of three men is

$$_5C_3 = \frac{5!}{(5-3)!\,3!} = \frac{5!}{2!\,3!} = \frac{5 \cdot 4 \cdot \cancel{3!}}{2 \cdot 1 \cdot \cancel{3!}} = 10.$$

Thus, there are 10 ways of selecting three men from five men. Now we can fill in the numbers in the numerator and the denominator of our probability fraction.

$$P(3 \text{ men}) = \frac{\text{number of ways of selecting 3 men}}{\text{total number of possible combinations}} = \frac{10}{220} = \frac{1}{22}$$

The probability that the group selected to attend the conference consists of three men is $\frac{1}{22}$.

12 Club Members

5 Men   7 Women

↓   ↓

Select 1   Select 2

b. We set up the fraction for the probability that the selected group consists of one man and two women.

$$P(1 \text{ man, 2 women}) = \frac{\text{number of ways of selecting 1 man and 2 women}}{\text{total number of possible combinations}}$$

The denominator of this fraction is the same as the denominator in part (a). The total number of possible combinations is found by selecting $r = 3$ people from $n = 12$ people: $_{12}C_3 = 220$.

Next, we move to the numerator of the probability fraction. The number of ways of selecting $r = 1$ man from $n = 5$ men is

$$_5C_1 = \frac{5!}{(5-1)!\,1!} = \frac{5!}{4!\,1!} = \frac{5 \cdot \cancel{4!}}{\cancel{4!} \cdot 1} = 5.$$

The number of ways of selecting $r = 2$ women from $n = 7$ women is

$$_7C_2 = \frac{7!}{(7-2)!\,2!} = \frac{7!}{5!\,2!} = \frac{7 \cdot 6 \cdot \cancel{5!}}{\cancel{5!} \cdot 2 \cdot 1} = 21.$$

By the Fundamental Counting Principle, the number of ways of selecting 1 man and 2 women is

$$_5C_1 \cdot {_7C_2} = 5 \cdot 21 = 105.$$

Now we can fill in the numbers in the numerator and the denominator of our probability fraction.

$$P(1 \text{ man}, 2 \text{ women}) = \frac{\text{number of ways of selecting 1 man and 2 women}}{\text{total number of possible combinations}} = \frac{_5C_1 \cdot _7C_2}{_{12}C_3} = \frac{105}{220} = \frac{21}{44}$$

The probability that the group selected to attend the conference consists of one man and two women is $\frac{21}{44}$.

 A club consists of six men and four women. Three members are selected at random to attend a conference. Find the probability that the selected group consists of

a. three men.

b. two men and one woman.

E X E R C I S E   S E T   11.5 ●●●●●●

• Practice and Application Exercises

1. Martha, Lee, Nancy, Paul, and Armando have all been invited to a dinner party. They arrive randomly and each person arrives at a different time.

a. In how many ways can they arrive?

b. In how many ways can Martha arrive first and Armando last?

c. Find the probability that Martha will arrive first and Armando last.

2. Three men and three women line up at a checkout counter in a store.

a. In how many ways can they line up?

b. In how many ways can they line up if the first person in line is a woman, and then the line alternates by gender—that is a woman, a man, a woman, a man, and so on?

c. Find the probability that the first person in line is a woman and the line alternates by gender.

3. Six stand-up comics, A, B, C, D, E, and F, are to perform on a single evening at a comedy club. The order of performance is determined by random selection. Find the probability that

a. Comic E will perform first.

b. Comic C will perform fifth and comic B will perform last.

c. The comedians will perform in the following order: D, E, C, A, B, F.

d. Comic A or comic B will perform first.

4. Seven performers, A, B, C, D, E, F, and G, are to appear in a fund raiser. The order of performance is determined by random selection. Find the probability that

a. D will perform first.

b. E will perform sixth and B will perform last.

c. They will perform in the following order: C, D, B, A, G, F, E.

d. F or G will perform first.

5. A group consists of four men and five women. Three people are selected to attend a conference.

a. In how many ways can three people be selected from this group of nine?

b. In how many ways can three women be selected from the five women?

c. Find the probability that the selected group will consist of all women.

6. A political discussion group consists of five Democrats and six Republicans. Four people are selected to attend a conference.

a. In how many ways can four people be selected from this group of eleven?

b. In how many ways can four Republicans be selected from the six Republicans?

c. Find the probability that the selected group will consist of all Republicans.

7. To play the California lottery, a person has to correctly select 6 out of 51 numbers, paying $1 for each six-number selection. If the six numbers picked are the same as the ones drawn by the lottery, mountains of money are bestowed. What is the probability that a person with one combination of six numbers will win? What is the probability of winning if 100 different lottery tickets are purchased?

8. A state lottery is designed so that a player chooses five numbers from 1 to 30 on one lottery ticket. What is the probability that a player with one lottery ticket will win? What is the probability of winning if 100 different lottery tickets are purchased?

9. A box contains 25 transistors, 6 of which are defective. If 6 are selected at random, find the probability that

a. all are defective.

b. none are defective.

10. A committee of five people is to be formed from six lawyers and seven teachers. Find the probability that

a. all are lawyers.

b. none are lawyers.

11. A city council consists of six Democrats and four Republicans. If a committee of three people is selected, find the probability of selecting one Democrat and two Republicans.

12. A parent-teacher committee consisting of four people is to be selected from fifteen parents and five teachers. Find the probability of selecting two parents and two teachers.

Exercises 13–18 involve a deck of 52 cards. If necessary, refer to the picture of a deck of cards, Figure 11.5 on page 629.

13. A poker hand consists of five cards.
   a. Find the total number of possible five-card poker hands.
   b. A diamond flush is a five-card hand consisting of all diamonds. Find the number of possible diamond flushes.
   c. Find the probability of being dealt a diamond flush.

14. A poker hand consists of five cards.
   a. Find the total number of possible five-card poker hands.
   b. Find the number of ways in which four aces can be selected.
   c. Find the number of ways in which one king can be selected.
   d. Use the Fundamental Counting Principle and your answers from parts (b) and (c) to find the number of ways of getting four aces and one king.
   e. Find the probability of getting a poker hand consisting of four aces and one king.

15. If you are dealt 3 cards from a shuffled deck of 52 cards, find the probability that all 3 cards are picture cards.

16. If you are dealt 4 cards from a shuffled deck of 52 cards, find the probability that all 4 are hearts.

17. If you are dealt 4 cards from a shuffled deck of 52 cards, find the probability of getting two queens and two kings.

18. If you are dealt 4 cards from a shuffled deck of 52 cards, find the probability of getting three jacks and one queen.

• Writing in Mathematics

19. If people understood the mathematics involving probabilities and lotteries, as you now do, do you think they would continue to spend hundreds of dollars per year on lottery tickets? Explain your answer.

20. Write and solve an original problem involving probability and permutations.

21. Write and solve an original problem involving probability and combinations whose solution requires $\frac{_{14}C_{10}}{_{20}C_{10}}$.

• Critical Thinking Exercises

22. An apartment complex offers apartments with four different options, designated by A through D. There are an equal number of apartments with each combination of options.

A	B	C	D
one bedroom two bedrooms three bedrooms	one bathroom two bathrooms	first floor second floor	lake view golf course view no special view

If there is only one apartment left, what is the probability that it is precisely what a person is looking for, namely two bedrooms, two bathrooms, first floor, and a lake or golf course view?

23. Reread Exercise 7. How much must a person spend so that the probability of winning the California lottery is $\frac{1}{2}$?

24. Suppose that it is a week in which the cash prize in Florida's LOTTO is promised to exceed $50 million. If a person purchases 22,957,480 tickets in LOTTO at $1 per ticket (all possible combinations), isn't this a guarantee of winning the lottery? Because the probability in this situation is 1, what's wrong with doing this?

25. The digits 1, 2, 3, 4, and 5 are randomly arranged to form a three-digit number. (Digits are not repeated.) Find the probability that the number is even and greater than 500.

26. In a five-card poker hand, what is the probability of being dealt exactly one ace and no picture cards?

• Group Exercise

27. Research and present a group report on state lotteries. Include answers to some or all of the following questions. As always, make the report interesting and informative. Which states do not have lotteries? Why not? How much is spent per capita on lotteries? What are some of the lottery games? What is the probability of winning top prize in these games? What income groups spend the greatest amount of money on lotteries? If your state has a lottery, what does it do with the money it makes? Is the way the money is spent what was promised when the lottery first began?

SECTION 11.6 • EVENTS INVOLVING *NOT* AND *OR*; ODDS

OBJECTIVES

1. Find the probability that an event will not occur.

2. Find the probability of one event or a second event occurring.

3. Understand and use odds.

You take your first trip to London. You are surprised to learn that the British gamble on everything. Shops with bookmakers are available everywhere for placing bets. In such a shop, you overhear a conversation about turning up the king of hearts in a deck of cards. You are expecting to hear something about a probability of $\frac{1}{52}$. Instead, you hear the phrase "51 to 1 against." Are you having difficulty understanding the British accents or did you miss something in your liberal arts math course? Whatever happened to probability?

No, it's not the accent. There are several ways to express the likelihood of an event. For example, we can discuss the probability of an event. We can also discuss *odds against* an event and *odds in favor* of an event. In this section, we expand our knowledge of probability and explain the meaning of odds.

1 | Find the probability that an event will not occur.

Probability of an Event Not Occurring

If we know $P(E)$, the probability of an event E, we can determine the probability that the event will not occur, denoted by $P(\text{not } E)$. The event *not E* is the **complement** of E because it is the set of all outcomes in the sample space S that are not outcomes in the event E. In any experiment, an event must occur or its complement must occur. Thus, the sum of the probability that an event will occur and the probability that it will not occur is 1:

$$P(E) + P(\text{not } E) = 1.$$

Solving for $P(E)$ or for $P(\text{not } E)$, we obtain the following formulas:

COMPLEMENT RULES OF PROBABILITY

- The probability that an event E will not occur is equal to 1 minus the probability that it will occur.

$$P(\text{not } E) = 1 - P(E)$$

- The probability that an event E will occur is equal to 1 minus the probability that it will not occur.

$$P(E) = 1 - P(\text{not } E)$$

Using set notation, if E' is the complement of E, then $P(E') = 1 - P(E)$ and $P(E) = 1 - P(E')$.

| EXAMPLE 1 | THE PROBABILITY OF AN EVENT NOT OCCURRING |

If you are dealt one card from a standard 52-card deck, find the probability that you are not dealt a queen.

SOLUTION Because

$$P(\text{not } E) = 1 - P(E)$$

then

$$P(\text{not a queen}) = 1 - P(\text{queen}).$$

There are four queens in a deck of 52 cards. The probability of being dealt a queen is $\frac{4}{52} = \frac{1}{13}$. Thus,

$$P(\text{not a queen}) = 1 - P(\text{queen}) = 1 - \frac{1}{13} = \frac{13}{13} - \frac{1}{13} = \frac{12}{13}.$$

The probability that you are not dealt a queen is $\frac{12}{13}$.

 If you are dealt one card from a standard 52-card deck, find the probability that you are not dealt a diamond.

STUDY TIP

You can work Example 1 without using the formula for $P(\text{not } E)$. Here is how it's done:

$P(\text{not a queen})$

$= \dfrac{\text{number of ways a non-queen can occur}}{\text{total number of outcomes}}$

$= \dfrac{48}{52}$ *With 4 queens, $52 - 4 = 48$ cards are not queens.*

$= \dfrac{4 \cdot 12}{4 \cdot 13} = \dfrac{12}{13}.$

| EXAMPLE 2 | USING THE COMPLEMENT RULES |

The circle graph in Figure 11.6 shows the distribution, by age group, of the 191 million car drivers in the United States, with all numbers rounded to the nearest million. If one driver is randomly selected from this population, find the probability that the person

a. is not in the 20–29 age group.

b. is less than 80 years old.

Express probabilities as simplified fractions.

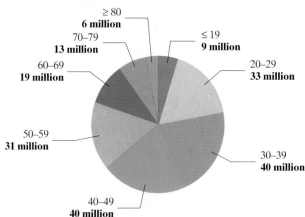

FIGURE 11.6
Source: U.S. Census Bureau

SOLUTION

a. We begin with the probability that a randomly selected driver is not in the 20–29 age group.

$P(\text{not in 20–29 age group})$

$$= 1 - P(\text{in 20–29 age group})$$

> The graph shows **33 million** drivers in the **20–29 age group.**

$$= 1 - \frac{33}{191}$$

> This number, **191 million drivers,** was given, but can be obtained by adding the numbers in the eight sectors.

$$= \frac{191}{191} - \frac{33}{191} = \frac{158}{191}$$

The probability that a randomly selected driver is not in the 20–29 age group is $\frac{158}{191}$.

b. We could compute the probability that a randomly selected driver is less than 80 years old by adding the numbers in each of the seven sectors representing drivers less than 80 and dividing this sum by 191 (million). However, it is easier to use complements. The complement of selecting a driver less than 80 years old is selecting a driver 80 or older.

$P(\text{less than 80 years old})$

$$= 1 - P(\text{80 or older})$$

$$= 1 - \frac{6}{191}$$

> The graph shows **6 million** drivers **80 or older.**

$$= \frac{191}{191} - \frac{6}{191} = \frac{185}{191}$$

The probability that a randomly selected driver is less than 80 years old is $\frac{185}{191}$.

If one driver is randomly selected from the population represented in Figure 11.6, find the probability, expressed as a simplified fraction, that the person

    a. is not in the 50–59 age group.

    b. is at least 20 years old.

2 | Find the probability of one event or a second event occurring.

Or **Probabilities with Mutually Exclusive Events**

Suppose that you randomly select one card from a deck of 52 cards. Let A be the event of selecting a king and B be the event of selecting a queen. Only one card is selected, so it is impossible to get both a king and a queen. The events of selecting a king and a queen cannot occur simultaneously. They are called *mutually exclusive events*.

> **MUTUALLY EXCLUSIVE EVENTS**
> If it is impossible for events A and B to occur simultaneously, the events are said to be **mutually exclusive**.

In general, if A and B are mutually exclusive events, the probability that either A or B will occur is determined by adding their individual probabilities.

> *OR* **PROBABILITIES WITH MUTUALLY EXCLUSIVE EVENTS**
> If A and B are mutually exclusive events, then
> $$P(A \text{ or } B) = P(A) + P(B).$$
> Using set notation, $P(A \cup B) = P(A) + P(B)$.

| EXAMPLE 3 | THE PROBABILITY OF EITHER OF TWO MUTUALLY EXCLUSIVE EVENTS OCCURRING |

If one card is randomly selected from a deck of cards, what is the probability of selecting a king or a queen?

SOLUTION We find the probability that either of these mutually exclusive events will occur by adding their individual probabilities.

$$P(\text{king or queen}) = P(\text{king}) + P(\text{queen}) = \frac{4}{52} + \frac{4}{52} = \frac{8}{52} = \frac{2}{13}$$

The probability of selecting a king or a queen is $\frac{2}{13}$.

 CHECK POINT 3 If you roll a single, six-sided die, what is the probability of getting either a 4 or a 5?

Or Probabilities with Events That Are Not Mutually Exclusive

Consider the deck of 52 cards shown in Figure 11.7. Suppose that these cards are shuffled and you randomly select one card from the deck. What is the probability of selecting a diamond or a picture card (jack, queen, king)? Begin by adding their individual probabilities.

$$P(\text{diamond}) + P(\text{picture card}) = \frac{13}{52} + \frac{12}{52}$$

There are 13 diamonds in the deck of 52 cards.   There are 12 picture cards in the deck of 52 cards.

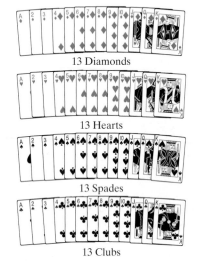

FIGURE 11.7 A deck of 52 cards

FIGURE 11.8 Three diamonds are picture cards.

However, this sum is not the probability of selecting a diamond or a picture card. The problem is that there are three cards that are *simultaneously* diamonds and picture cards, shown in Figure 11.8. The events of selecting a diamond and selecting a picture card are not mutually exclusive. It is possible to select a card that is both a diamond and a picture card.

The situation is illustrated in the Venn diagram in Figure 11.9. Why can't we find the probability of selecting a diamond or a picture card by adding their individual probabilities? The Venn diagram shows that three of the cards, the three diamonds that are picture cards, get counted twice when we add the individual probabilities. First the three cards get counted as diamonds, and then they get counted as picture cards. In order to avoid the error of counting the three cards twice, we need to subtract the probability of getting a diamond and a picture card, $\frac{3}{52}$, as follows:

$P(\text{diamond or picture card})$

$$= P(\text{diamond}) + P(\text{picture card}) - P(\text{diamond and picture card})$$

$$= \frac{13}{52} + \frac{12}{52} - \frac{3}{52} = \frac{13 + 12 - 3}{52} = \frac{22}{52} = \frac{11}{26}.$$

Thus, the probability of selecting a diamond or a picture card is $\frac{11}{26}$.

In general, if A and B are events that are not mutually exclusive, the probability that A or B will occur is determined by adding their individual probabilities and then subtracting the probability that A and B occur simultaneously.

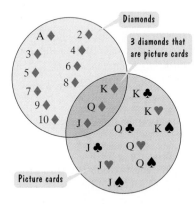

FIGURE 11.9

> **OR PROBABILITIES WITH EVENTS THAT ARE NOT MUTUALLY EXCLUSIVE**
>
> If A and B are not mutually exclusive events, then
> $$P(A \text{ or } B) = P(A) + P(B) - P(A \text{ and } B).$$
> Using set notation,
> $$P(A \cup B) = P(A) + P(B) - P(A \cap B).$$

| **EXAMPLE 4** | AN *OR* PROBABILITY WITH EVENTS THAT ARE NOT MUTUALLY EXCLUSIVE |

In a group of 25 baboons, 18 enjoy grooming their neighbors, 16 enjoy screeching wildly, while 10 enjoy grooming their neighbors and screeching wildly. If one baboon is selected at random from the group, find the probability that it enjoys grooming its neighbors or screeching wildly.

SOLUTION It is possible for a baboon in the group to enjoy both grooming its neighbors and screeching wildly. Ten of the brutes are given to engage in both activities. These events are not mutually exclusive.

$$P\left(\begin{array}{c}\text{grooming}\\\text{or screeching}\end{array}\right) = P(\text{grooming}) + P(\text{screeching}) - P\left(\begin{array}{c}\text{grooming}\\\text{and screeching}\end{array}\right)$$

$$= \frac{18}{25} + \frac{16}{25} - \frac{10}{25}$$

> 18 of the 25 baboons enjoy grooming.

> 16 of the 25 baboons enjoy screeching.

> 10 of the 25 baboons enjoy both.

$$= \frac{18 + 16 - 10}{25} = \frac{24}{25}$$

The probability that a baboon in the group enjoys grooming its neighbors or screeching wildly is $\frac{24}{25}$.

CHECK POINT 4 In a group of 50 students, 23 take math, 11 take psychology, and 7 take both math and psychology. If one student is selected at random, find the probability that the student takes math or psychology.

| **EXAMPLE 5** | AN *OR* PROBABILITY WITH EVENTS THAT ARE NOT MUTUALLY EXCLUSIVE |

Figure 11.10 illustrates a spinner. It is equally probable that the pointer will land on any one of the eight regions, numbered 1 through 8. If the pointer lands on a borderline, spin again. Find the probability that the pointer will stop on an even number or on a number greater than 5.

SOLUTION It is possible for the pointer to land on a number that is both even and greater than 5. Two of the numbers, 6 and 8, are even and greater than 5. These events are not mutually exclusive. The probability of landing on a number that is even or greater than 5 is calculated as follows:

$$P\left(\begin{array}{c}\text{even or}\\\text{greater than 5}\end{array}\right) = P(\text{even}) + P(\text{greater than 5}) - P\left(\begin{array}{c}\text{even and}\\\text{greater than 5}\end{array}\right)$$

$$= \frac{4}{8} + \frac{3}{8} - \frac{2}{8}$$

> Four of the eight numbers, 2, 4, 6, and 8, are even.

> Three of the eight numbers, 6, 7, and 8, are greater than 5.

> Two of the eight numbers, 6 and 8, are even and greater than 5.

$$= \frac{4 + 3 - 2}{8} = \frac{5}{8}.$$

The probability that the pointer will stop on an even number or a number greater than 5 is $\frac{5}{8}$.

FIGURE 11.10 It is equally probable that the pointer will land on any one of the eight regions.

CHECK POINT 5 Use Figure 11.10 to find the probability that the pointer will stop on an odd number or a number less than 5.

EXAMPLE 6   OR PROBABILITIES WITH REAL-WORLD DATA

Each year the Internal Revenue Service audits a sample of tax forms to verify their accuracy. Table 11.5 shows the number of tax returns filed and audited in 2003, by taxable income.

TABLE 11.5 TAX RETURNS FILED AND AUDITED, BY TAXABLE INCOME, 2003

	<$25,000	$25,000–$49,999	$50,000–$99,999	≥$100,000	Total
Audit	414,357	135,041	113,944	151,969	815,311
No audit	52,792,911	30,964,967	25,502,542	10,775,542	120,035,962
Total	53,207,268	31,100,008	25,616,486	10,927,511	120,851,273

Source: Internal Revenue Service

If one person is randomly selected from the population represented in Table 11.5, find the probability that

a. the taxpayer had a taxable income less than $25,000 or was audited.

b. the taxpayer had a taxable income less than $25,000 or at least $100,000.

Express probabilities as decimals rounded to the nearest hundredth.

SOLUTION

a. It is possible to select a taxpayer who both earned less than $25,000 and was audited. Thus, these events are not mutually exclusive.

P (less than $25,000 or audited)

$= P(\text{less than } \$25,000) + P(\text{audited}) - P(\text{less than } \$25,000 \text{ and audited})$

$$= \frac{53,207,268}{120,851,273} + \frac{815,311}{120,851,273} - \frac{414,357}{120,851,273}$$

Of the 120,851,273 taxpayers, 53,207,268 had taxable incomes less than $25,000.

Of the 120,851,273 taxpayers, 815,311 were audited.

Of the 120,851,273 taxpayers, 414,357 earned less than $25,000 and were audited.

$$= \frac{53,608,222}{120,851,273} \approx 0.44$$

The probability that a taxpayer had a taxable income less than $25,000 or was audited is approximately 0.44.

b. A taxable income of *at least* $100,000 means $100,000 or more. Thus, it is not possible to select a taxpayer with both a taxable income of less than $25,000 and at least $100,000. These events are mutually exclusive.

$P(\text{less than } \$25,000 \text{ or at least } \$100,000)$

$= P(\text{less than } \$25,000) + P(\text{at least } \$100,000)$

$$= \frac{53,207,268}{120,851,273} + \frac{10,927,511}{120,851,273}$$

Of the 120,851,273 taxpayers, 53,207,268 had taxable incomes less than $25,000.

Of the 120,851,273 taxpayers, 10,927,511 had taxable incomes of $100,000 or more.

$$= \frac{64,134,779}{120,851,273} \approx 0.53$$

The probability that a taxpayer had a taxable income less than $25,000 or at least $100,000 is approximately 0.53.

If one person is randomly selected from the population represented in Table 11.5, find the probability, expressed as a decimal rounded to the nearest hundredth, that

a. the taxpayer had a taxable income of at least $100,000 or was not audited.

b. the taxpayer had a taxable income less than $25,000 or between $50,000 and $99,999, inclusive.

---

3   Understand and use odds.

Odds

If we know the probability of an event E, we can also speak of the *odds in favor*, or the *odds against*, the event. The following definitions link together the concepts of odds and probabilities:

PROBABILITY TO ODDS

If $P(E)$ is the probability of an event E occurring, then

1. The **odds in favor of E** are found by taking the probability that E will occur and dividing by the probability that E will not occur.

$$\text{Odds in favor of } E = \frac{P(E)}{P(\text{not } E)}$$

2. The **odds against E** are found by taking the probability that E will not occur and dividing by the probability that E will occur.

$$\text{Odds against } E = \frac{P(\text{not } E)}{P(E)}$$

The odds against E can also be found by reversing the ratio representing the odds in favor of E.

EXAMPLE 7   FROM PROBABILITY TO ODDS

You roll a single, six-sided die.

a. Find the odds in favor of rolling a 2.

b. Find the odds against rolling a 2.

SOLUTION Let E represent the event of rolling a 2. In order to determine odds, we must first find the probability of E occurring and the probability of E not occurring. With $S = \{1, 2, 3, 4, 5, 6\}$ and $E = \{2\}$, we see that

$$P(E) = \frac{1}{6}$$

$$\text{and} \quad P(\text{not } E) = 1 - \frac{1}{6} = \frac{6}{6} - \frac{1}{6} = \frac{5}{6}.$$

Now we are ready to construct the ratios for the odds in favor of E and the odds against E.

STUDY TIP

When computing odds, the denominators of the two probabilities will always divide out.

a. $$\text{Odds in favor of } E \text{(rolling a 2)} = \frac{P(E)}{P(\text{not } E)} = \frac{\frac{1}{6}}{\frac{5}{6}} = \frac{1}{6} \cdot \frac{6}{5} = \frac{1}{5}$$

The odds in favor of rolling a 2 are $\frac{1}{5}$. The ratio $\frac{1}{5}$ is usually written 1:5 and is read "1 to 5." Thus, the odds in favor of rolling a 2 are 1 to 5.

b. Now that we have the odds in favor of rolling a 2, namely $\frac{1}{5}$ or 1:5, we can find the odds against rolling a 2 by reversing this ratio. Thus,

$$\text{Odds against } E(\text{rolling a 2}) = \frac{5}{1} \quad \text{or} \quad 5:1.$$

The odds against rolling a 2 are 5 to 1.

You are dealt one card from a 52-card deck.

a. Find the odds in favor of getting a red queen.

b. Find the odds against getting a red queen.

EXAMPLE 8   FROM PROBABILITY TO ODDS

The winner of a raffle will receive a new sports utility vehicle. If 500 raffle tickets were sold and you purchased ten tickets, what are the odds against your winning the car?

SOLUTION Let E represent the event of winning the SUV. Because you purchased ten tickets and 500 tickets were sold,

$$P(E) = \frac{10}{500} = \frac{1}{50} \quad \text{and} \quad P(\text{not } E) = 1 - \frac{1}{50} = \frac{50}{50} - \frac{1}{50} = \frac{49}{50}.$$

Now we are ready to construct the ratio for the odds against E (winning the SUV).

$$\text{Odds against } E = \frac{P(\text{not } E)}{P(E)} = \frac{\dfrac{49}{50}}{\dfrac{1}{50}} = \frac{49}{50} \cdot \frac{50}{1} = \frac{49}{1}$$

The odds against winning the SUV are 49 to 1, written 49:1.

The winner of a raffle will receive a two-year scholarship to the college of his or her choice. If 1000 raffle tickets were sold and you purchased five tickets, what are the odds against your winning the scholarship?

Odds enable us to play and bet fairly on games. For example, we have seen that the odds in favor of getting 2 when you roll a die are 1 to 5. Suppose this is a gaming situation and you bet $1 on a 2 turning up. In terms of your bet, there is one favorable outcome, rolling 2, and five unfavorable outcomes, rolling 1, 3, 4, 5, or 6. The odds in favor of getting 2, 1 to 5, compares the number of favorable outcomes, one, to the number of unfavorable outcomes, five.

Using odds in a gaming situation where money is waged, we can determine if the game is *fair*. If the odds in favor of an event E are a to b, the **game is fair** if a bet of a is lost if event E does not occur, but a win of b (as well as returning the bet of a) is realized if event E does occur. For example, the odds in favor of getting 2 on a die roll are 1 to 5. If you bet $1 on a 2 turning up and the game is fair, you should win $5 (and have your bet of $1 returned) if a 2 turns up.

Now that we know how to convert from probability to odds, let's see how to convert from odds to probability. Suppose that the odds in favor of event E occurring are a to b. This means that

$$\frac{P(E)}{P(\text{not } E)} = \frac{a}{b} \quad \text{or} \quad \frac{P(E)}{1 - P(E)} = \frac{a}{b}.$$

By solving the equation on the right for $P(E)$, we obtain the following formula for converting from odds to probability:

The odds given at horse races and at all games of chance are usually *odds against*. The horse in Example 9, with odds of winning at 2 to 5, has odds against winning at 5 to 2. At a horse race, the odds on this particular horse are given simply as 5 to 2. These **house odds** tell a gambler what the payoff is on a bet. For every $2 bet on the horse, the gambler would win $5 if the horse won, in addition to having the $2 bet returned.

ODDS TO PROBABILITY

If the odds in favor of event E are a to b, then the probability of the event is given by

$$P(E) = \frac{a}{a+b}.$$

EXAMPLE 9   FROM ODDS TO PROBABILITY

The odds in favor of a particular horse winning a race are 2 to 5. What is the probability that this horse will win the race?

SOLUTION   Because odds in favor, a to b, means a probability of $\frac{a}{a+b}$, then odds in favor, 2 to 5, means a probability of

$$\frac{2}{2+5} = \frac{2}{7}.$$

The probability that this horse will win the race is $\frac{2}{7}$.

CHECK POINT 9   The odds against a particular horse winning a race are 15 to 1. Find the odds in favor of the horse winning the race and the probability of the horse winning the race.

EXERCISE SET 11.6 ●●●●●●

• Practice and Application Exercises

In Exercises 1–6, you are dealt one card from a 52-card deck. Find the probability that you are not dealt

1. an ace.   **2.** a 3.   **3.** a heart.   **4.** a club.   **5.** a picture card.   **6.** a red picture card.

In 5-card poker, played with a standard 52-card deck, $_{52}C_5$, or 2,598,960, different hands are possible. The probability of being dealt various hands is the number of different ways they can occur divided by 2,598,960. Shown in Exercises 7–10 are various types of poker hands and their probabilities. In each exercise, find the probability of not being dealt this type of hand.

Type of Hand	Illustration	Number of Ways the Hand Can Occur	Probability
7. Straight flush: 5 cards with consecutive numbers, all in the same suit (excluding royal flush)		36	$\dfrac{36}{2,598,960}$
8. Four of a kind: 4 cards with the same number, plus 1 additional card		624	$\dfrac{624}{2,598,960}$
9. Full house: 3 cards of one number and 2 cards of a second number		3744	$\dfrac{3744}{2,598,960}$
10. Flush: 5 cards of the same suit (excluding royal flush and straight flush)		5108	$\dfrac{5108}{2,598,960}$

The graph shows the probability of cardiovascular disease, by age and gender. Use the information in the graph to solve Exercises 11–12. Express all probabilities as decimals, estimated to two decimal places.

Probability of Cardiovascular Disease, by Age and Gender

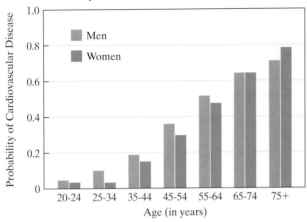

Source: American Heart Association

11. a. What is the probability that a randomly selected man between the ages of 25 and 34 has cardiovascular disease?

   b. What is the probability that a randomly selected man between the ages of 25 and 34 does not have cardiovascular disease?

12. a. What is the probability that a randomly selected woman, 75 or older, has cardiovascular disease?

   b. What is the probability that a randomly selected woman, 75 or older, does not have cardiovascular disease?

The table shows the distribution, by annual income, of the 112 million households in the United States in 2003, with all numbers rounded to the nearest million. Use this distribution to solve Exercises 13–16.

INCOME DISTRIBUTION OF U.S. HOUSEHOLDS, IN MILLIONS

Annual Income	Number	Annual Income	Number
Less than $10,000	10	$35,000–$49,999	17
$10,000–$14,999	8	$50,000–$74,999	20
$15,000–$24,999	15	$75,000–$99,999	12
$25,000–$34,999	13	$100,000 or more	17

Source: U.S. Census Bureau

If one household is randomly selected from this population, find the probability, expressed as a simplified fraction, that

13. the household income is not in the $50,000–$74,999 range.

14. the household income is not in the $15,000–$24,999 range.

15. the household income is less than $100,000.

16. the household income is at least $10,000.

In Exercises 17–22, you randomly select one card from a 52-card deck. Find the probability of selecting

17. a 2 or a 3.   **18.** a 7 or an 8.

19. a red 2 or a black 3.   **20.** a red 7 or a black 8.

21. the 2 of hearts or the 3 of spades.

22. the 7 of hearts or the 8 of spades.

23. The mathematics faculty at a college consists of 8 professors, 12 associate professors, 14 assistant professors, and 10 instructors. If one faculty member is randomly selected, find the probability of choosing a professor or an instructor.

24. A political discussion group consists of 30 Republicans, 25 Democrats, 8 Independents, and 4 members of the Green party. If one person is randomly selected from the group, find the probability of choosing an Independent or a Green.

In Exercises 25–26, a single die is rolled. Find the probability of rolling

25. an even number or a number less than 5.

26. an odd number or a number less than 4.

In Exercises 27–30, you are dealt one card from a 52-card deck. Find the probability that you are dealt

27. a 7 or a red card.

28. a 5 or a black card.

29. a heart or a picture card.

30. a card greater than 2 and less than 7, or a diamond.

In Exercises 31–34, it is equally probable that the pointer on the spinner shown will land on any one of the eight regions, numbered 1 through 8. If the pointer lands on a borderline, spin again.

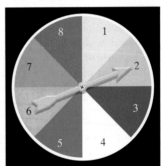

Find the probability that the pointer will stop on

31. an odd number or a number less than 6.

32. an odd number or a number greater than 3.

33. an even number or a number greater than 5.

34. an even number or a number less than 4.

Use this information to solve Exercises 35–38. The mathematics department of a college has 8 male professors, 11 female professors, 14 male teaching assistants, and 7 female teaching assistants. If a person is selected at random from the group, find the probability that the selected person is

35. a professor or a male.

36. a professor or a female.

37. a teaching assistant or a female.

38. a teaching assistant or a male.

39. In a class of 50 students, 29 are Democrats, 11 are business majors, and 5 of the business majors are Democrats. If one student is randomly selected from the class, find the probability of choosing a Democrat or a business major.

40. A student is selected at random from a group of 200 students in which 135 take math, 85 take English, and 65 take both math and English. Find the probability that the selected student takes math or English.

The table shows the educational attainment of the U.S. population, ages 25 and over, in 2004. Use the data in the table, expressed in millions, to solve Exercises 41–48.

EDUCATIONAL ATTAINMENT OF THE U.S. POPULATION, AGES 25 AND OVER, IN MILLIONS

	Less Than 4 Years High School	4 Years High School Only	Some College (Less than 4 years)	4 Years College (or More)	Total
Male	14	28	22	26	90
Female	14	32	26	25	97
Total	28	60	48	51	187

Source: U.S. Census Bureau

Find the probability, expressed as a simplified fraction, that a randomly selected American, aged 25 or over,

41. has not completed four years (or more) of college.

42. has not completed four years of high school.

43. has completed four years of high school only or less than four years of college.

44. has completed less than four years of high school or four years of high school only.

45. has completed four years of high school only or is a man.

46. has completed four years of high school only or is a woman.

Find the odds in favor and the odds against a randomly selected American, aged 25 and over, with

47. four years (or more) of college.

48. less than four years of high school.

The graph shows the distribution, by branch and gender, of the 1.43 million, or 1430 thousand, active-duty personnel in the U.S. military in 2003. Numbers are given in thousands and rounded to the nearest ten thousand. Use the data to solve Exercises 49–60.

Active Duty U.S. Military Personnel

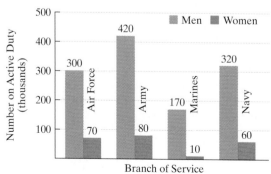

Source: U.S. Defense Department

If one person is randomly selected from the population represented in the bar graph in the previous column, find the probability, expressed as a simplified fraction, that the person

49. is not in the Army.

50. is not in the Marines.

51. is in the Navy or is a man.

52. is in the Army or is a woman.

53. is in the Air Force or the Marines.

54. is in the Army or the Navy.

Find the odds in favor and the odds against a randomly selected person from the population represented in the bar graph in the previous column being

55. in the Navy.

56. in the Army.

57. a woman in the Marines.

58. a woman in the Air Force.

59. a man.

60. a woman.

In Exercises 61–64, a single die is rolled. Find the odds

61. in favor of rolling a number greater than 2.

62. in favor of rolling a number less than 5.

63. against rolling a number greater than 2.

64. against rolling a number less than 5.

The circle graphs show the percentage of children in the United States whose parents are college graduates in one-parent households and two-parent households. Use the information shown to solve Exercises 65–66.

Percentage of U.S. Children Whose Parents Are College Graduates

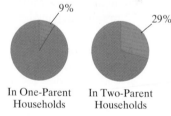

In One-Parent Households   In Two-Parent Households

Source: U.S. Census Bureau

65. a. What are the odds in favor of a child in a one-parent household having a parent who is a college graduate?

   b. What are the odds against a child in a one-parent household having a parent who is a college graduate?

66. a. What are the odds in favor of a child in a two-parent household having parents who are college graduates?

   b. What are the odds against a child in a two-parent household having parents who are college graduates?

In Exercises 67–76, one card is randomly selected from a deck of cards. Find the odds

67. in favor of drawing a heart.

68. in favor of drawing a picture card.

69. in favor of drawing a red card.

70. in favor of drawing a black card.

71. against drawing a 9.

72. against drawing a 5.

73. against drawing a black king.

74. against drawing a red jack.

75. against drawing a spade greater than 3 and less than 9.

76. against drawing a club greater than 4 and less than 10.

77. The winner of a raffle will receive a 21-foot outboard boat. If 1000 raffle tickets were sold and you purchased 20 tickets, what are the odds against your winning the boat?

78. The winner of a raffle will receive a 30-day all-expense-paid trip throughout Europe. If 5000 raffle tickets were sold and you purchased 30 tickets, what are the odds against your winning the trip?

Of the 38 plays attributed to Shakespeare, 18 are comedies, 10 are tragedies, and 10 are histories. In Exercises 79–86, one play is randomly selected from Shakespeare's 38 plays. Find the odds

79. in favor of selecting a comedy.

80. in favor of selecting a tragedy.

81. against selecting a history.

82. against selecting a comedy.

83. in favor of selecting a comedy or a tragedy.

84. in favor of selecting a tragedy or a history.

85. against selecting a tragedy or a history.

86. against selecting a comedy or a history.

87. If you are given odds of 3 to 4 in favor of winning a bet, what is the probability of winning the bet?

88. If you are given odds of 3 to 7 in favor of winning a bet, what is the probability of winning the bet?

89. Based on his skills in basketball, it was computed that when Michael Jordan shot a free throw, the odds in favor of his making it were 21 to 4. Find the probability that when Michael Jordan shot a free throw, he missed it. Out of every 100 free throws he attempted, on the average how many did he make?

90. The odds in favor of a person who is alive at age 20 still being alive at age 70 are 193 to 270. Find the probability that a person who is alive at age 20 will still be alive at age 70.

Exercises 91–92 give the odds against various flight risks. (Source: Men's Health, August 2005) Use these odds to determine the probability of the underlined event for those in flight.

91. odds against contracting an airborne disease: 999 to 1

92. odds against deep-vein thrombosis (blood clot in the leg): 28 to 1

• Writing in Mathematics

93. Explain how to find the probability of an event not occurring. Give an example.

94. What are mutually exclusive events? Give an example of two events that are mutually exclusive.

95. Explain how to find *or* probabilities with mutually exclusive events. Give an example.

96. Give an example of two events that are not mutually exclusive.

97. Explain how to find *or* probabilities with events that are not mutually exclusive. Give an example.

98. Explain how to find the odds in favor of an event if you know the probability that the event will occur.

99. Explain how to find the probability of an event if you know the odds in favor of that event.

• Critical Thinking Exercises

100. In Exercise 39, find the probability of choosing **a.** a Democrat who is not a business major; **b.** a student who is neither a Democrat nor a business major.

101. On New Year's Eve, the probability of a person driving while intoxicated or having a driving accident is 0.35. If the probability of driving while intoxicated is 0.32 and the probability of having a driving accident is 0.09, find the probability of a person having a driving accident while intoxicated.

102. The formula for converting from odds to probability is given in the box on page 649. Read the paragraph on the bottom of page 648 that precedes this box and derive the formula.

SECTION 11.7 • EVENTS INVOLVING *AND*; CONDITIONAL PROBABILITY

O B J E C T I V E S

1. Find the probability of one event and a second event occurring.

2. Compute conditional probabilities.

You are considering a job offer in South Florida. You were thrilled by images of Miami on MTV's *The Real World*. The job offer is just what you wanted and you are excited about living in the midst of Miami's tropical diversity. However, there is just one thing: the risk of hurricanes. If you expect to stay in Miami ten years and buy a home, what is the probability that South Florida will be hit by a hurricane at least once in the next ten years?

In this section, we look at the probability that an event occurs at least once by expanding our discussion of probability to events involving *and*.

1 | Find the probability of one event and a second event occurring.

And **Probabilities with Independent Events**

Consider tossing a fair coin two times in succession. The outcome of the first toss, heads or tails, does not affect what happens when you toss the coin a second time. For example, the occurrence of tails on the first toss does not make tails more likely or less likely to occur on the second toss. The repeated toss of a coin produces *independent events* because the outcome of one toss does not affect the outcome of others.

> **INDEPENDENT EVENTS**
> Two events are **independent events** if the occurrence of either of them has no effect on the probability of the other.

STUDY TIP

Do not confuse *independent events* and *mutually exclusive events*. Mutually exclusive events cannot occur at the same time. Independent events occur at different times, although they have no effect on each other.

When a fair coin is tossed two times in succession, the set of equally likely outcomes is

{heads heads, heads tails, tails heads, tails tails}.

We can use this set to find the probability of getting heads on the first toss and heads on the second toss:

$$P(\text{heads and heads}) = \frac{\text{number of ways two heads can occur}}{\text{total number of possible outcomes}} = \frac{1}{4}.$$

We can also determine the probability of two heads, $\frac{1}{4}$, without having to list all the equally likely outcomes. The probability of heads on the first toss is $\frac{1}{2}$. The probability of heads on the second toss is also $\frac{1}{2}$. The product of these probabilities, $\frac{1}{2} \cdot \frac{1}{2}$, results in the probability of two heads, namely $\frac{1}{4}$. Thus,

$$P(\text{heads and heads}) = P(\text{heads}) \cdot P(\text{heads}).$$

In general, if two events are independent, we can calculate the probability of the first occurring and the second occurring by multiplying their probabilities.

AND PROBABILITIES WITH INDEPENDENT EVENTS

If A and B are independent events, then

$$P(A \text{ and } B) = P(A) \cdot P(B).$$

EXAMPLE 1 | INDEPENDENT EVENTS ON A ROULETTE WHEEL

Figure 11.11 shows a U.S. roulette wheel that has 38 numbered slots (1 through 36, 0, and 00). Of the 38 compartments, 18 are black, 18 are red, and 2 are green. A play has the dealer spin the wheel and a small ball in opposite directions. As the ball slows to a stop, it can land with equal probability on any one of the 38 numbered slots. Find the probability of red occurring on two consecutive plays.

SOLUTION The wheel has 38 equally likely outcomes and 18 are red. Thus, the probability of red occurring on a play is $\frac{18}{38}$, or $\frac{9}{19}$. The result that occurs on each play is independent of all previous results. Thus,

$$P(\text{red and red}) = P(\text{red}) \cdot P(\text{red}) = \frac{9}{19} \cdot \frac{9}{19} = \frac{81}{361} \approx 0.224.$$

FIGURE 11.11 A U.S. roulette wheel

The probability of red occurring on two consecutive plays is $\frac{81}{361}$.

Some roulette players incorrectly believe that if red occurs on two consecutive plays, then another color is "due." Because the events are independent, the outcomes of previous spins have no effect on any other spins.

 Find the probability of green occurring on two consecutive plays on a roulette wheel.

The *and* rule for independent events can be extended to cover three or more events. Thus, if A, B, and C are independent events, then

$$P(A \text{ and } B \text{ and } C) = P(A) \cdot P(B) \cdot P(C).$$

EXAMPLE 2 | INDEPENDENT EVENTS IN A FAMILY

The picture in the margin shows a family that had nine girls in a row. Find the probability of this occurrence.

SOLUTION If two or more events are independent, we can find the probability of them all occurring by multiplying their probabilities. The probability of a baby girl is $\frac{1}{2}$, so the probability of nine girls in a row is $\frac{1}{2}$ used as a factor nine times.

$$P(\text{nine girls in a row}) = \frac{1}{2} \cdot \frac{1}{2} \cdot \frac{1}{2} \cdot \frac{1}{2} \cdot \frac{1}{2} \cdot \frac{1}{2} \cdot \frac{1}{2} \cdot \frac{1}{2} \cdot \frac{1}{2}$$

$$= \left(\frac{1}{2}\right)^9 = \frac{1}{512}$$

The probability of a run of nine girls in a row is $\frac{1}{512}$. (If another child is born into the family, this event is independent of the other nine and the probability of a girl is still $\frac{1}{2}$.)

 Find the probability of a family having four boys in a row.

TABLE 11.6 THE SAFFIR/SIMPSON HURRICANE SCALE	
Category	Winds (Miles per Hour)
1	74–95
2	96–110
3	111–130
4	131–155
5	>155

Now let us return to the hurricane problem that opened this section. The Saffir/Simpson scale assigns numbers 1 through 5 to measure the disaster potential of a hurricane's winds. Table 11.6 describes the scale. According to the National Hurricane Center, the probability that South Florida will be hit by a category 1 hurricane or higher in any single year is $\frac{5}{19}$, or approximately 0.26. In Example 3, we explore the risks of living in "Hurricane Alley."

EXAMPLE 3   HURRICANES AND PROBABILITIES

If the probability that South Florida will be hit by a hurricane in any single year is $\frac{5}{19}$,

a. What is the probability that South Florida will be hit by a hurricane in three consecutive years?

b. What is the probability that South Florida will not be hit by a hurricane in the next ten years?

SOLUTION

a. The probability that South Florida will be hit by a hurricane in three consecutive years is

$$P(\text{hurricane and hurricane and hurricane})$$

$$= P(\text{hurricane}) \cdot P(\text{hurricane}) \cdot P(\text{hurricane}) = \frac{5}{19} \cdot \frac{5}{19} \cdot \frac{5}{19} = \frac{125}{6859} \approx 0.018.$$

b. We will first find the probability that South Florida will not be hit by a hurricane in any single year.

$$P(\text{no hurricane}) = 1 - P(\text{hurricane}) = 1 - \frac{5}{19} = \frac{14}{19} \approx 0.737$$

The probability of not being hit by a hurricane in a single year is $\frac{14}{19}$. Therefore, the probability of not being hit by a hurricane ten years in a row is $\frac{14}{19}$ used as a factor ten times.

$P(\text{no hurricanes for ten years})$

$$= P\left(\begin{array}{c}\text{no hurricane}\\\text{for year 1}\end{array}\right) \cdot P\left(\begin{array}{c}\text{no hurricane}\\\text{for year 2}\end{array}\right) \cdot P\left(\begin{array}{c}\text{no hurricane}\\\text{for year 3}\end{array}\right) \cdot \ldots \cdot P\left(\begin{array}{c}\text{no hurricane}\\\text{for year 10}\end{array}\right)$$

$$= \frac{14}{19} \cdot \frac{14}{19} \cdot \frac{14}{19} \cdot \ldots \cdot \frac{14}{19}$$

$$= \left(\frac{14}{19}\right)^{10} \approx (0.737)^{10} \approx 0.047$$

The probability that South Florida will not be hit by a hurricane in the next ten years is approximately 0.047.

Now we are ready to answer your question:

What is the probability that South Florida will be hit by a hurricane at least once in the next ten years?

Because $P(\text{not } E) = 1 - P(E)$,

$P(\text{no hurricane for ten years}) = 1 - P(\text{at least one hurricane in ten years}).$

> In our logic chapter, we saw that the negation of "at least one" is "no."

Equivalently,

$P(\text{at least one hurricane in ten years}) = 1 - P(\text{no hurricane for ten years})$

$$= 1 - 0.047 = 0.953.$$

With a probability of 0.953, it is nearly certain that South Florida will be hit by a hurricane at least once in the next ten years.

STUDY TIP

When solving probability problems, begin by deciding whether to use the *or* formulas or the *and* formulas.

- *Or* problems usually have the word *or* in the statement of the problem. These problems involve only one selection.

Example:

If one person is selected, find the probability of selecting a man or a Canadian.

- *And* problems often do not have the word *and* in the statement of the problem. These problems involve more than one selection.

Example:

If two people are selected, find the probability that both are men.

> ### THE PROBABILITY OF AN EVENT HAPPENING AT LEAST ONCE
>
> $$P(\text{event happening at least once}) = 1 - P(\text{event does not happen})$$

3 If the probability that South Florida will be hit by a hurricane in any single year is $\frac{5}{19}$,

 a. What is the probability that South Florida will be hit by a hurricane in four consecutive years?

 b. What is the probability that South Florida will not be hit by a hurricane in the next four years?

 c. What is the probability that South Florida will be hit by a hurricane at least once in the next four years?

Express all probabilities as fractions and as decimals rounded to three places.

And Probabilities with Dependent Events

5 chocolate-covered cherries lie within the 20 pieces.

Chocolate lovers, please help yourselves! There are 20 mouth-watering tidbits to select from. What's that? You want 2? And you prefer chocolate-covered cherries? The problem is that there are only 5 chocolate-covered cherries, and it's impossible to tell what is inside each piece. They're all shaped exactly alike. At any rate, reach in, select a piece, enjoy, choose another piece, eat, and be well. There is nothing like savoring a good piece of chocolate in the midst of all this chit-chat about probability and hurricanes.

Another question? You want to know what your chances are of selecting 2 chocolate-covered cherries? Well, let's see. Five of the 20 pieces are chocolate-covered cherries, so the probability of getting one of them on your first selection is $\frac{5}{20}$, or $\frac{1}{4}$. Now, suppose that you did choose a chocolate-covered cherry on your first pick. Eat it slowly; there's no guarantee that you'll select your favorite on the second selection. There are now only 19 pieces of chocolate left. Only 4 are chocolate-covered cherries. The probability of getting a chocolate-covered cherry on your second try is 4 out of 19, or $\frac{4}{19}$. This is a different probability than the $\frac{1}{4}$ probability on your first selection. Selecting a chocolate-covered cherry the first time changes what is in the candy box. The probability of what you select the second time *is* affected by the outcome of the first event. For this reason, we say that these are *dependent events*.

> ### DEPENDENT EVENTS
> Two events are **dependent events** if the occurrence of one of them has an effect on the probability of the other.

Once a chocolate-covered cherry is selected, only 4 chocolate-covered cherries lie within the remaining 19 pieces.

The probability of selecting two chocolate-covered cherries in a row can be found by multiplying the $\frac{1}{4}$ probability on the first selection by the $\frac{4}{19}$ probability on the second selection:

$P(\text{chocolate-covered cherry and chocolate-covered cherry})$

$$= P(\text{chocolate-covered cherry}) \cdot P\left(\begin{array}{c}\text{chocolate-covered cherry} \\ \text{given that one was selected}\end{array}\right)$$

$$= \frac{1}{4} \cdot \frac{4}{19} = \frac{1}{19}.$$

The probability of selecting two chocolate-covered cherries in a row is $\frac{1}{19}$. This is a special case of finding the probability that each of two dependent events occurs.

> **AND PROBABILITIES WITH DEPENDENT EVENTS**
> If A and B are dependent events, then
> $$P(A \text{ and } B) = P(A) \cdot P(B \text{ given that } A \text{ has occurred}).$$

EXAMPLE 4   AN *AND* PROBABILITY WITH DEPENDENT EVENTS

Good news: You won a free trip to Madrid and can take two people with you, all expenses paid. Bad news: Ten of your cousins have appeared out of nowhere and are begging you to take them. You write each cousin's name on a card, place the cards in a hat, and select one name. Then you select a second name without replacing the first card. If three of your ten cousins speak Spanish, find the probability of selecting two Spanish-speaking cousins.

SOLUTION   Because $P(A \text{ and } B) = P(A) \cdot P(B \text{ given that } A \text{ has occurred})$, then
$P(\text{two Spanish-speaking cousins})$

$\quad = P(\text{speaks Spanish and speaks Spanish})$

$\quad = P(\text{speaks Spanish}) \cdot P\left(\begin{array}{c}\text{speaks Spanish given that a Spanish-speaking}\\ \text{cousin was selected first}\end{array}\right)$

$$\quad = \quad \frac{3}{10} \quad \cdot \quad \frac{2}{9}$$

> There are ten cousins, three of whom speak Spanish.

> After picking a Spanish-speaking cousin, there are nine cousins left, two of whom speak Spanish.

$$\quad = \frac{6}{90} = \frac{1}{15} \approx 0.067.$$

The probability of selecting two Spanish-speaking cousins is $\frac{1}{15}$.

4 You are dealt two cards from a 52-card deck. Find the probability of getting two kings.

The multiplication rule for dependent events can be extended to cover three or more dependent events. For example, in the case of three such events,

$P(A \text{ and } B \text{ and } C)$
$\quad = P(A) \cdot P(B \text{ given that } A \text{ occurred}) \cdot P(C \text{ given that } A \text{ and } B \text{ occurred}).$

EXAMPLE 5   AN *AND* PROBABILITY WITH THREE DEPENDENT EVENTS

Three people are randomly selected, one person at a time, from five freshmen, two sophomores, and four juniors. Find the probability that the first two people selected are freshmen and the third is a junior.

5 freshmen

2 sophomores

4 juniors

The given numbers (repeated)

SOLUTION

P(first two are freshmen and the third is a junior)

$$= P(\text{freshman}) \cdot P\binom{\text{freshman given that a}}{\text{freshman was selected first}} \cdot P\binom{\text{junior given that a freshman was}}{\text{selected first and a freshman was}}_{\text{selected second}}$$

$$= \frac{5}{11} \cdot \frac{4}{10} \cdot \frac{4}{9}$$

> There are 11 people, five of whom are freshmen.

> After picking a freshman, there are 10 people left, four of whom are freshmen.

> After the first two selections, 9 people are left, four of whom are juniors.

 Compute conditional probabilities.

$$= \frac{8}{99}$$

The probability that the first two people selected are freshmen and the third is a junior is $\frac{8}{99}$.

CHECK POINT 5 You are dealt three cards from a 52-card deck. Find the probability of getting three hearts.

Conditional Probability

We have seen that for any two dependent events A and B,

$$P(A \text{ and } B) = P(A) \cdot P(B \text{ given that } A \text{ occurs}).$$

The probability of B given that A occurs is called *conditional probability*, denoted by $P(B|A)$.

> **CONDITIONAL PROBABILITY**
> The probability of event B, assuming that the event A has already occurred, is called the **conditional probability** of B, given A. This probability is denoted by $P(B|A)$.

It is helpful to think of the conditional probability $P(B|A)$ as the **probability that event B occurs if the sample space is restricted to the outcomes associated with event A**.

EXAMPLE 6   FINDING CONDITIONAL PROBABILITY

A letter is randomly selected from the letters of the English alphabet. Find the probability of selecting a vowel, given that the outcome is a letter that precedes h.

SOLUTION We are looking for

$$P(\text{vowel}|\text{letter precedes h}).$$

This is the probability of a vowel if the sample space is restricted to the set of letters that precede h. Thus, the sample space is given by

$$S = \{a, b, c, d, e, f, g\}.$$

There are seven possible outcomes in the sample space. We can select a vowel from this set in one of two ways: a or e. Therefore, the probability of selecting a vowel, given that the outcome is a letter that precedes h, is $\frac{2}{7}$.

$$P(\text{vowel}|\text{letter precedes h}) = \frac{2}{7}$$

CHECK POINT 6 You are dealt one card from a 52-card deck. Find the probability of getting a heart, given that the card you were dealt is a red card.

EXAMPLE 7	CONDITIONAL PROBABILITIES WITH REAL-WORLD DATA

When women turn 40, their gynecologists typically remind them that it is time to undergo mammography screening for breast cancer. The data in Table 11.7 are based on 100,000 U.S. women, ages 40 to 50, who participated in mammography screening.

TABLE 11.7 MAMMOGRAPHY SCREENING ON 100,000 U.S. WOMEN, AGES 40 TO 50

	Breast Cancer	No Breast Cancer	Total
Positive Mammogram	720	6944	7664
Negative Mammogram	80	92,256	92,336
Total	800	99,200	100,000

Source: Gerd Gigerenzer, *Calculated Risks*. Simon and Schuster, 2002

Assuming that these numbers are representative of all U.S. women ages 40 to 50, find the probability that a woman in this age range

a. has a positive mammogram, given that she does not have breast cancer.

b. does not have breast cancer, given that she has a positive mammogram.

SOLUTION

a. We begin with the probability that a U.S. woman aged 40 to 50 has a positive mammogram, given that she does not have breast cancer:

$$P(\text{positive mammogram}|\text{no breast cancer}).$$

This is the probability of a positive mammogram if the data are restricted to women without breast cancer:

	No Breast Cancer
Positive Mammogram	6944
Negative Mammogram	92,256
Total	99,200

Within the restricted data, there are 6944 women with positive mammograms and 6944 + 92,256, or 99,200 women without breast cancer. Thus,

$$P(\text{positive mammogram}|\text{no breast cancer}) = \frac{6944}{99,200} = 0.07.$$

Among women without breast cancer, the probability of a positive mammogram is 0.07.

b. Now, we find the probability that a U.S. woman aged 40 to 50 does not have breast cancer, given that she has a positive mammogram:

$$P(\text{no breast cancer}|\text{positive mammogram}).$$

This is the probability of not having breast cancer if the data are restricted to women with positive mammograms:

	Breast Cancer	No Breast Cancer	Total
Positive Mammogram	720	6944	7664

Within the restricted data, there are 6944 women without breast cancer and 720 + 6944, or 7664 women with positive mammograms. Thus,

$$P(\text{no breast cancer}|\text{positive mammogram}) = \frac{6944}{7664} \approx 0.906.$$

Among women with positive mammograms, the probability of not having breast cancer is $\frac{6944}{7664}$, or approximately 0.906.

STUDY TIP

Example 7 shows that the probability of a positive mammogram among women without breast cancer, 0.07, is not the same as the probability of not having breast cancer among women with positive mammograms, approximately 0.9. In general, the conditional probability of B, given A, is not the same as the conditional probability of A, given B:

$$P(B|A) \neq P(A|B).$$

7 Use the data in Table 11.7 at the top of the previous page to find the probability that a U.S. woman aged 40 to 50

    a. has a positive mammogram, given that she has breast cancer.

    b. has breast cancer, given that she has a positive mammogram.

Express probabilities as decimals and, if necessary, round to three decimal places.

We have seen that $P(B|A)$ is the probability that event B occurs if the sample space is restricted to event A. Thus,

$$P(B|A) = \frac{\text{number of outcomes of } B \text{ that are in the restricted sample space } A}{\text{number of outcomes in the restricted sample space } A}.$$

This can be stated in terms of the following formula:

A FORMULA FOR CONDITIONAL PROBABILITY

$$P(B|A) = \frac{n(B \cap A)}{n(A)} = \frac{\text{number of outcomes common to } B \text{ and } A}{\text{number of outcomes in } A}$$

EXERCISE SET 11.7 ●●●●●●

• Practice and Application Exercises

Exercises 1–26 involve probabilities with independent events.

Use the spinner shown to solve Exercises 1–10. It is equally probable that the pointer will land on any one of the six regions. If the pointer lands on a borderline, spin again. If the pointer is spun twice, find the probability it will land on

1. green and then red.

2. yellow and then green.

3. yellow and then yellow.

4. red and then red.

5. a color other than red each time.

6. a color other than green each time.

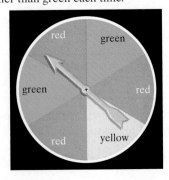

If the pointer is spun three times, find the probability it will land on

7. green and then red and then yellow.

8. red and then red and then green.

9. red every time.

10. green every time.

In Exercises 11–14, a single die is rolled twice. Find the probability of rolling

11. a 2 the first time and a 3 the second time.

12. a 5 the first time and a 1 the second time.

13. an even number the first time and a number greater than 2 the second time.

14. an odd number the first time and a number less than 3 the second time.

In Exercises 15–20, you draw one card from a 52-card deck. Then the card is replaced in the deck, the deck is shuffled, and you draw again. Find the probability of drawing

15. a picture card the first time and a heart the second time.

16. a jack the first time and a club the second time.

17. a king each time.

18. a 3 each time.

19. a red card each time.

20. a black card each time.

21. If you toss a fair coin six times, what is the probability of getting all heads?

22. If you toss a fair coin seven times, what is the probability of getting all tails?

In Exercises 23–24, a coin is tossed and a die is rolled. Find the probability of getting

23. a head and a number greater than 4.

24. a tail and a number less than 5.

25. The probability that South Florida will be hit by a major hurricane (category 4 or 5) in any single year is $\frac{1}{16}$.
(*Source:* National Hurricane Center)

   a. What is the probability that South Florida will be hit by a major hurricane two years in a row?

   b. What is the probability that South Florida will be hit by a major hurricane in three consecutive years?

   c. What is the probability that South Florida will not be hit by a major hurricane in the next ten years?

   d. What is the probability that South Florida will be hit by a major hurricane at least once in the next ten years?

26. The probability that a region prone to flooding will flood in any single year is $\frac{1}{10}$.

   a. What is the probability of a flood two years in a row?

   b. What is the probability of flooding in three consecutive years?

   c. What is the probability of no flooding for ten consecutive years?

   d. What is the probability of flooding at least once in the next ten years?

The graph shows that U.S. adults dependent on tobacco have a greater probability of suffering from some ailments than the general adult population. When making two or more selections from populations with large numbers, such as the U.S. adult population or the population dependent on tobacco, we assume that each selection is independent of every other selection. In Exercises 27–32, assume that the selections are independent events.

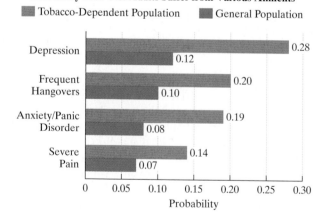

Probability That U.S. Adults Suffer from Various Ailments

Source: MARS 2005 OTC/DTC

27. If two adults are randomly selected from the general population, what is the probability that they both suffer from depression?

28. If two adults are randomly selected from the population of cigarette smokers, what is the probability that they both suffer from depression?

29. If three adults are randomly selected from the population of cigarette smokers, what is the probability that they all suffer from frequent hangovers?

30. If three adults are randomly selected from the general population, what is the probability that they all suffer from frequent hangovers?

31. If three adults are randomly selected from the population of cigarette smokers, what is the probability, expressed as a decimal correct to four places, that at least one person suffers from anxiety/panic disorder?

32. If three adults are randomly selected from the population of cigarette smokers, what is the probability, expressed as a decimal correct to four places, that at least one person suffers from severe pain?

Exercises 33–48 involve probabilities with dependent events.

In Exercises 33–36, we return to our box of chocolates. There are 30 chocolates in the box, all identically shaped. Five are filled with coconut, 10 with caramel, and 15 are solid chocolate. You randomly select one piece, eat it, and then select a second piece. Find the probability of selecting

33. two solid chocolates in a row.

34. two caramel-filled chocolates in a row.

35. a coconut-filled chocolate followed by a caramel-filled chocolate.

36. a coconut-filled chocolate followed by a solid chocolate.

In Exercises 37–42, consider a political discussion group consisting of 5 Democrats, 6 Republicans, and 4 Independents. Suppose that two group members are randomly selected, in succession, to attend a political convention. Find the probability of selecting

37. two Democrats.

38. two Republicans.

39. an Independent and then a Republican.

40. an Independent and then a Democrat.

41. no Independents.

42. no Democrats.

In Exercises 43–48, an ice chest contains six cans of apple juice, eight cans of grape juice, four cans of orange juice, and two cans of mango juice. Suppose that you reach into the container and randomly select three cans in succession. Find the probability of selecting

43. three cans of apple juice.

44. three cans of grape juice.

45. a can of grape juice, then a can of orange juice, then a can of mango juice.

46. a can of apple juice, then a can of grape juice, then a can of orange juice.

47. no grape juice.

48. no apple juice.

In Exercises 49–56, the numbered disks shown are placed in a box and one disk is selected at random.

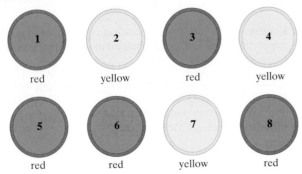

| red | yellow | red | yellow |

| red | red | yellow | red |

Find the probability of selecting

49. a 3, given that a red disk is selected.

50. a 7, given that a yellow disk is selected.

51. an even number, given that a yellow disk is selected.

52. an odd number, given that a red disk is selected.

53. a red disk, given that an odd number is selected.

54. a yellow disk, given that an odd number is selected.

55. a red disk, given that the number selected is at least 5.

56. a yellow disk, given that the number selected is at most 3.

The table shows the outcome of car accidents in Florida for a recent year by whether or not the driver wore a seat belt. Use the data to solve Exercises 57–60. Express probabilities as fractions and as decimals rounded to three places.

CAR ACCIDENTS IN FLORIDA

	Wore Seat Belt	**No Seat Belt**	**Total**
Driver Survived	412,368	162,527	574,895
Driver Died	510	1601	2111
Total	412,878	164,128	577,006

Source: Alan Agresti and Christine Franklin, *Statistics*, Prentice Hall, 2007

57. Find the probability of surviving a car accident, given that the driver wore a seat belt.

58. Find the probability of not surviving a car accident, given that the driver did not wear a seat belt.

59. Find the probability of wearing a seat belt, given that a driver survived a car accident.

60. Find the probability of not wearing a seat belt, given that a driver did not survive a car accident.

In Exercises 61–72, we return to the table showing the distribution, by marital status and gender, of the 212.5 million Americans ages 18 or older.

MARITAL STATUS OF THE U.S. POPULATION, AGES 18 OR OLDER, IN MILLIONS

	Never Married	**Married**	**Widowed**	**Divorced**	**Total**
Male	28.6	62.1	2.7	9.0	102.4
Female	23.3	62.8	11.3	12.7	110.1
Total	51.9	124.9	14.0	21.7	212.5

Source: U.S. Census Bureau

If one person is selected from the population described in the table at the bottom of the previous column, find the probability, expressed as a decimal rounded to three places, that the person

61. is not divorced.

62. is not widowed.

63. is widowed or divorced.

64. had never been married or is divorced.

65. is male or divorced.

66. is female or divorced.

67. is male, given that this person is divorced.

68. is female, given that this person is divorced.

69. is widowed, given that this person is a woman.

70. is divorced, given that this person is a man.

71. had never been married or is married, given that this person is a man.

72. had never been married or is married, given that this person is a woman.

• Writing in Mathematics

73. Explain how to find *and* probabilities with independent events. Give an example.

74. Explain how to find *and* probabilities with dependent events. Give an example.

75. What does $P(B|A)$ mean? Give an example.

In Exercises 76–80, write a probability problem involving the word "and" whose solution results in the probability fractions shown.

76. $\frac{1}{2} \cdot \frac{1}{2}$

77. $\frac{1}{6} \cdot \frac{1}{6} \cdot \frac{1}{6}$

78. $\frac{1}{2} \cdot \frac{1}{6}$

79. $\frac{13}{52} \cdot \frac{12}{51}$

80. $\frac{1}{4} \cdot \frac{3}{5}$

• Critical Thinking Exercises

81. If the probability of being hospitalized during a year is 0.1, find the probability that no one in a family of five will be hospitalized in a year.

82. If a single die is rolled five times, what is the probability it lands on 2 on the first, third, and fourth rolls, but not on any of the other rolls?

83. Probabilities and Coincidence of Shared Birthdays

   a. If two people are selected at random, the probability that they do not have the same birthday (day and month) is $\frac{365}{365} \cdot \frac{364}{365}$. Explain why this is so. (Ignore leap years and assume 365 days in a year.)

   b. If three people are selected at random, find the probability that they all have different birthdays.

   c. If three people are selected at random, find the probability that at least two of them have the same birthday.

   d. If 20 people are selected at random, find the probability that at least 2 of them have the same birthday.

   e. How large a group is needed to give a 0.5 chance of at least two people having the same birthday?

84. Nine cards numbered from 1 through 9 are placed into a box and two cards are selected without replacement. Find the probability that both numbers selected are odd, given that their sum is even.

• Group Exercises

85. Do you live in an area prone to catastrophes, such as earthquakes, fires, tornados, hurricanes, or floods? If so, research the probability of this catastrophe occurring in a single year. Group members should then use this probability to write and solve a problem similar to Exercise 25 in this exercise set.

86. Group members should use the table for Exercises 61–72 to write and solve four probability problems different than those in the exercises. Two should involve *or* (one with events that are mutually exclusive and one with events that are not), one should involve *and*—that is, events in succession—and one should involve conditional probability.

SECTION 11.8 • EXPECTED VALUE

O B J E C T I V E S

1. Compute expected value.

2. Use expected value to solve applied problems.

3. Use expected value to determine the average payoff or loss in a game of chance.

1	Compute expected value.

Would you be willing to spend $50 a year for an insurance policy that pays $200,000 if you become too ill to continue your education? It is unlikely that this will occur. Insurance companies make money by compensating us for events that have a low probability. If one in every 5000 students needs to quit college due to serious illness, the probability of this event is $\frac{1}{5000}$. Multiplying the amount of the claim, $200,000, by its probability, $\frac{1}{5000}$, tells the insurance company what to expect on average for each policy:

$$\$200,000 \times \frac{1}{5000} = \$40.$$

Amount of the claim   Probability of paying the claim

Over the long run, the insurance company can expect to pay $40 for each policy it sells. By selling the policy for $50, the expected profit is $10 per policy. If 400,000 students choose to take out this insurance, the company can expect to make 400,000 × $10, or $4,000,000.

Expected value is a mathematical way to use probabilities to determine what to expect in various situations over the long run. Expected value is used to determine premiums on insurance policies, weigh the risks versus the benefits of alternatives in business ventures, and indicate to a player of any game of chance what will happen if the game is played repeatedly.

The standard way to find expected value is to multiply each possible outcome by its probability, and then add these products. We use the letter E to represent expected value.

EXAMPLE 1 COMPUTING EXPECTED VALUE

Find the expected value for the outcome of the roll of a fair die.

SOLUTION The outcomes are 1, 2, 3, 4, 5, and 6, each with a probability of $\frac{1}{6}$. The expected value, E, is computed by multiplying each outcome by its probability and then adding these products.

$$E = 1 \cdot \frac{1}{6} + 2 \cdot \frac{1}{6} + 3 \cdot \frac{1}{6} + 4 \cdot \frac{1}{6} + 5 \cdot \frac{1}{6} + 6 \cdot \frac{1}{6}$$

$$= \frac{1 + 2 + 3 + 4 + 5 + 6}{6} = \frac{21}{6} = 3.5$$

The expected value of the roll of a fair die is 3.5. This means that if the die is rolled repeatedly, there are an average of 3.5 dots per roll over the long run. This expected value cannot occur on a single roll of the die. However, it is a long-run average of the various outcomes that can occur when a fair die is rolled.

CHECK POINT 1 It is equally probable that a pointer will land on any one of four regions, numbered 1 through 4. Find the expected value for where the pointer will stop.

TABLE 11.8 OUTCOMES AND PROBABILITIES FOR THE NUMBER OF GIRLS IN A THREE-CHILD FAMILY

Outcome: Number of Girls	Probability
0	$\frac{1}{8}$
1	$\frac{3}{8}$
2	$\frac{3}{8}$
3	$\frac{1}{8}$

EXAMPLE 2 COMPUTING EXPECTED VALUE

Find the expected value for the number of girls for a family with three children.

SOLUTION A family with three children can have 0, 1, 2, or 3 girls. There are eight ways these outcomes can occur.

No girls : Boy Boy Boy — *One way*
One girl : Girl Boy Boy, Boy Girl Boy, Boy Boy Girl — *Three ways*
Two girls : Girl Girl Boy, Girl Boy Girl, Boy Girl Girl — *Three ways*
Three girls : Girl Girl Girl — *One way*

Table 11.8 shows the probabilities for 0, 1, 2, and 3 girls.

The expected value, E, is computed by multiplying each outcome by its probability and then adding these products.

$$E = 0 \cdot \frac{1}{8} + 1 \cdot \frac{3}{8} + 2 \cdot \frac{3}{8} + 3 \cdot \frac{1}{8} = \frac{0 + 3 + 6 + 3}{8} = \frac{12}{8} = \frac{3}{2} = 1.5$$

The expected value is 1.5. This means that if we record the number of girls in many different three-child families, the average number of girls for all these families will be 1.5. In a three-child family, half the children are expected to be girls, so the expected value of 1.5 is consistent with this observation.

TABLE 11.9

Number of Heads	Probability
0	$\frac{1}{16}$
1	$\frac{4}{16}$
2	$\frac{6}{16}$
3	$\frac{4}{16}$
4	$\frac{1}{16}$

CHECK POINT 2 A fair coin is tossed four times in succession. Table 11.9 shows the probabilities for the different number of heads that can arise. Find the expected value for the number of heads.

2 Use expected value to solve applied problems.

Applications of Expected Value

Empirical probabilities can be determined in many situations by examining what has occurred in the past. For example, an insurance company can tally various claim amounts over many years. If 15% of these amounts are for a $2000 claim, then the probability of this claim amount is 0.15. By studying sales of similar houses in a particular area, a realtor can determine the probability that he or she will sell a listed house, another agent will sell the house, or the listed house will remain unsold. Once probabilities have been assigned to all possible outcomes, expected value can indicate what is expected to happen in the long run. These ideas are illustrated in Examples 3 and 4.

TABLE 11.10 PROBABILITIES FOR AUTO-CLAIMS

Amount of Claim (to the nearest $2000)	Probability
$0	0.70
$2000	0.15
$4000	0.08
$6000	0.05
$8000	0.01
$10,000	0.01

EXAMPLE 3   DETERMINING AN INSURANCE PREMIUM

An automobile insurance company has determined the probabilities for various claim amounts for drivers ages 16 through 21, shown in Table 11.10.

a. Calculate the expected value and describe what this means in practical terms.

b. How much should the company charge as an average premium so that it does not lose or gain money on its claim costs?

SOLUTION

a. The expected value, E, is computed by multiplying each outcome by its probability, and then adding these products.

$$E = \$0(0.70) + \$2000(0.15) + \$4000(0.08) + \$6000(0.05)$$
$$+ \$8000(0.01) + \$10{,}000(0.01)$$
$$= \$0 + \$300 + \$320 + \$300 + \$80 + \$100$$
$$= \$1100$$

The expected value is $1100. This means that in the long run the average cost of a claim is $1100. The insurance company should expect to pay $1100 per car insured to people in the 16–21 age group.

b. At the very least, the amount that the company should charge as an average premium for each person in the 16–21 group is $1100. In this way, it will not lose or gain money on its claims costs. It's quite probable that the company will charge more, moving from break-even to profit.

CHECK POINT 3 Work Example 3 again if the probabilities for claims of $0 and $10,000 are reversed. Thus, the probability of a $0 claim is 0.01 and the probability of a $10,000 claim is 0.70.

Business decisions are interpreted in terms of dollars and cents. In these situations, **expected value is calculated by multiplying the gain or loss for each possible outcome by its probability. The sum of these products is the expected value.**

THE REALTOR'S SUMMARY SHEET

My Cost:	$5000
My Possible Income:	
I sell house:	$30,000
Another agent sells house:	$15,000
House unsold after 4 months:	$0
The Probabilities:	
I sell house:	0.3
Another agent sells house:	0.2
House unsold after 4 months:	0.5
My Bottom Line:	
I take the listing only if I anticipate earning at least $6000.	

EXAMPLE 4   EXPECTATION IN A BUSINESS DECISION

You are a realtor considering listing a $500,000 house. The cost of advertising and providing food for other realtors during open showings is anticipated to cost you $5000. The house is quite unusual, and you are given a four-month listing. If the house is unsold after four months, you lose the listing and receive nothing. You anticipate that the probability you sell your own listed house is 0.3, the probability that another agent sells your listing is 0.2, and the probability that the house is unsold after 4 months is 0.5. If you sell your own listed house, the commission is a hefty $30,000. If another realtor sells your listing, the commission is $15,000. The bottom line: You will not take the listing unless you anticipate earning at least $6000. Should you list the house?

SOLUTION Shown in the margin is a summary of the amounts of money and probabilities that will determine your decision. The expected value in this situation is the sum of each income possibility times its probability. The expected value represents the amount you can anticipate earning if you take the listing. If the expected value is not at least $6000, you should not list the house.

THE REALTOR'S SUMMARY
SHEET(repeated)

My Cost:	$5000
My Possible Income:	
I sell house:	$30,000
Another agent sells house:	$15,000
House unsold after 4 months:	$0
The Probabilities:	
I sell house:	0.3
Another agent sells house:	0.2
House unsold after 4 months:	0.5
My Bottom Line:	
I take the listing only if I anticipate earning at least $6000.	

The possible incomes listed in the margin, $30,000, $15,000, and $0, do not take into account your $5000 costs. Because of these costs, each amount needs to be reduced by $5000. Thus, you can gain $30,000 − $5000, or $25,000, or you can gain $15,000 − $5000, or $10,000. Because $0 − $5000 = −$5000, you can also lose $5000. Table 11.11 summarizes possible outcomes if you take the listing, and their respective probabilities.

TABLE 11.11 GAINS, LOSSES, AND PROBABILITIES FOR LISTING A $500,000 HOUSE

Outcome	Gain or Loss	Probability
Sells house	$25,000	0.3
Another agent sells house	$10,000	0.2
House doesn't sell	−$5000	0.5

The expected value, E, is computed by multiplying each gain or loss in Table 11.11 by its probability, and then adding these results.

$$E = \$25,000(0.3) + \$10,000(0.2) + (-\$5000)(0.5)$$
$$= \$7500 + \$2000 + (-\$2500) = \$7000$$

You can expect to earn $7000 by listing the house. Because the expected value exceeds $6000, you should list the house.

CHECK POINT 4 The SAT is a multiple-choice test. Each question has five possible answers. The test taker must select one answer for each question or not answer the question. One point is awarded for each correct response and $\frac{1}{4}$ point is subtracted for each wrong answer. No points are added or subtracted for answers left blank. Table 11.12 summarizes the information for the outcomes of a random guess on an SAT question. Find the expected point value of a random guess. Is there anything to gain or lose on average by guessing? Explain your answer.

TABLE 11.12 GAINS AND LOSSES FOR GUESSING ON THE SAT

Outcome	Gain or Loss	Probability
Guess correctly	1	$\frac{1}{5}$
Guess incorrectly	$-\frac{1}{4}$	$\frac{4}{5}$

3 Use expected value to determine the average payoff or loss in a game of chance.

Expected Value and Games of Chance

Expected value can be interpreted as the average payoff in a contest or game when either is played a large number of times. **To find the expected value of a game, multiply the gain or loss for each possible outcome by its probability. Then add the products.**

EXAMPLE 5   EXPECTED VALUE AS AVERAGE PAYOFF

A game is played using one die. If the die is rolled and shows 1, 2, or 3, the player wins nothing. If the die shows 4 or 5, the player wins $3. If the die shows 6, the player wins $9. If there is a charge of $1 to play the game, what is the game's expected value? Describe what this means in practical terms.

SOLUTION Because there is a charge of $1 to play the game, a player who wins $9 gains $9 − $1, or $8. A player who wins $3 gains $3 − $1, or $2. If the player gets $0, there is a loss of $1 because $0 − $1 = −$1. The outcomes for the die, with their respective gains, losses, and probabilities, are summarized in Table 11.13.

Gambling It Away

Games in gambling casinos have probabilities and payoffs that result in negative expected values. This means that players will lose money in the long run. With no clocks on the walls or windows to look out of, casinos bet that players will forget about time and play longer. This brings casino owners closer to what they can expect to earn, while negative expected values sneak up on losing patrons. (No wonder they provide free beverages!)

A Potpourri of Gambling-Related Data

- Population of Las Vegas: 535,000

- Slot Machines in Las Vegas: 150,000

- Average Earnings per Slot Machine per Year: $100,000

- Average Amount Lost per Hour in Las Vegas Casinos: $696,000

- Average Amount an American Adult Loses Gambling per Year: $350

- Average Amount a Nevada Resident Loses Gambling per Year: $1000

Source: Paul Grobman, *Vital Statistics*, Plume, 2005

TABLE 11.13 GAINS, LOSSES, AND PROBABILITIES IN A GAME OF CHANCE		
Outcome	**Gain or Loss**	**Probability**
1, 2, or 3	−$1	$\frac{3}{6}$
4 or 5	$2	$\frac{2}{6}$
6	$8	$\frac{1}{6}$

Expected value, E, is computed by multiplying each gain or loss in Table 11.13 by its probability and then adding these results.

$$E = (-\$1)\left(\frac{3}{6}\right) + \$2\left(\frac{2}{6}\right) + \$8\left(\frac{1}{6}\right)$$

$$= \frac{-\$3 + \$4 + \$8}{6} = \frac{\$9}{6} = \$1.50$$

The expected value is $1.50. This means that in the long run, a player can expect to win an average of $1.50 for each game played. However, this does not mean that the player will win $1.50 on any single game. It does mean that if the game is played repeatedly, then, in the long run, the player should expect to win about $1.50 per play on the average. If 1000 games are played, one could expect to win $1500. However, if only three games are played, one's net winnings can range between −$3 and $24, even though the expected winnings are $1.50(3), or $4.50.

CHECK POINT 5 A charity is holding a raffle and sells 1000 raffle tickets for $2 each. One of the tickets will be selected to win a grand prize of $1000. Two other tickets will be selected to win consolation prizes of $50 each. Fill in the missing column in Table 11.14. Then find the expected value if you buy one raffle ticket. Describe what this means in practical terms. What can you expect to happen if you purchase five tickets?

TABLE 11.14 GAINS, LOSSES, AND PROBABILITIES IN A RAFFLE		
Outcome	**Gain or Loss**	**Probability**
Win Grand Prize		$\frac{1}{1000}$
Win Consolation Prize		$\frac{2}{1000}$
Win Nothing		$\frac{997}{1000}$

Unlike the game in Example 5, games in gambling casinos are set up so that players will lose in the long run. These games have negative expected values. Such a game is roulette, French for "little wheel." We first saw the roulette wheel in Section 11.7. It is shown again in Figure 11.12. Recall that the wheel has 38 numbered slots (1 through 36, 0, and 00). In each play of the game, the dealer spins the wheel and a small ball in opposite directions. The ball is equally likely to come to rest in any one of the slots, which are colored black, red, or green. Gamblers can place a number of different bets in roulette. Example 6 illustrates one gambling option.

FIGURE 11.12 A U.S. roulette wheel

How to Win at Roulette

A player may win or lose at roulette, but in the long run the casino always wins. Casinos make an average of three cents on every dollar spent by gamblers. There *is* a way to win at roulette in the long run: Own the casino.

EXAMPLE 6   EXPECTED VALUE AND ROULETTE

One way to bet in roulette is to place $1 on a single number. If the ball lands on that number, you are awarded $35 and get to keep the $1 that you paid to play the game. If the ball lands on any one of the other 37 slots, you are awarded nothing and the $1 that you bet is collected. Find the expected value for playing roulette if you bet $1 on number 20. Describe what this means.

SOLUTION Table 11.15 contains the two outcomes of interest: the ball landing on your number, 20, and the ball landing elsewhere (in any one of the other 37 slots). The outcomes, their respective gains, losses, and probabilities, are summarized in the table.

TABLE 11.15 PLAYING ONE NUMBER WITH A 35 TO 1 PAYOFF IN ROULETTE

Outcome	Gain or Loss	Probability
Ball lands on 20	$35	$\frac{1}{38}$
Ball does not land on 20	−$1	$\frac{37}{38}$

Expected value, E, is computed by multiplying each gain or loss in Table 11.15 by its probability and then adding these results.

$$E = \$35\left(\frac{1}{38}\right) + (-\$1)\left(\frac{37}{38}\right) = \frac{\$35 - \$37}{38} = \frac{-\$2}{38} \approx -\$0.05$$

The expected value is approximately −$0.05. This means that in the long run, a player can expect to lose about 5¢ for each game played. If 2000 games are played, one could expect to lose $100.

CHECK POINT 6 In the game of one-spot keno, a card is purchased for $1. It allows a player to choose one number from 1 to 80. A dealer then chooses twenty numbers at random. If the player's number is among those chosen, the player is paid $3.20, but does not get to keep the $1 paid to play the game. Find the expected value of a $1 bet. Describe what this means.

EXERCISE SET 11.8 ●●●●●●

• Practice and Application Exercises

In Exercises 1–2, the numbers that each pointer can land on and their respective probabilities are shown. Compute the expected value for the number on which each pointer lands.

1.

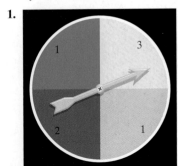

Outcome	Probability
1	$\frac{1}{2}$
2	$\frac{1}{4}$
3	$\frac{1}{4}$

2.

Outcome	Probability
1	$\frac{1}{8}$
2	$\frac{1}{8}$
3	$\frac{1}{2}$
4	$\frac{1}{4}$

The tables in Exercises 3–4 show claims and their probabilities for an insurance company.

a. *Calculate the expected value and describe what this means in practical terms.*

b. *How much should the company charge as an average premium so that it breaks even on its claim costs?*

c. *How much should the company charge to make a profit of $50 per policy?*

3. PROBABILITIES FOR HOMEOWNERS' INSURANCE CLAIMS

Amount of Claim (to the nearest $50,000)	Probability
$0	0.65
$50,000	0.20
$100,000	0.10
$150,000	0.03
$200,000	0.01
$250,000	0.01

4. PROBABILITIES FOR MEDICAL INSURANCE CLAIMS

Amount of Claim (to the nearest $20,000)	Probability
$0	0.70
$20,000	0.20
$40,000	0.06
$60,000	0.02
$80,000	0.01
$100,000	0.01

5. An architect is considering bidding for the design of a new museum. The cost of drawing plans and submitting a model is $10,000. The probability of being awarded the bid is 0.1, and anticipated profits are $100,000, resulting in a possible gain of this amount minus the $10,000 cost for plans and a model. What is the expected value in this situation? Describe what this value means.

6. A construction company is planning to bid on a building contract. The bid costs the company $1500. The probability that the bid is accepted is $\frac{1}{5}$. If the bid is accepted, the company will make $40,000 minus the cost of the bid. Find the expected value in this situation. Describe what this value means.

7. It is estimated that there are 27 deaths for every 10 million people who use airplanes. A company that sells flight insurance provides $100,000 in case of death in a plane crash. A policy can be purchased for $1. Calculate the expected value and thereby determine how much the insurance company can make over the long run for each policy that it sells.

8. A 25-year-old can purchase a one-year life insurance policy for $10,000 at a cost of $100. Past history indicates that the probability of a person dying at age 25 is 0.002. Determine the company's expected gain per policy.

Exercises 9–10 are related to the SAT, described in Check Point 4 on page 666.

9. Suppose that you can eliminate one of the possible five answers. Modify the two probabilities shown in the final column in Table 11.12 on page 666 by finding the probabilities of guessing correctly and guessing incorrectly under these circumstances. What is the expected point value of a random guess? Is it advantageous to guess under these circumstances?

10. Suppose that you can eliminate two of the possible five answers. Modify the two probabilities shown in the final column in Table 11.12 on page 666 by finding the probabilities of guessing correctly and guessing incorrectly under these circumstances. What is the expected point value of a random guess? Is it advantageous to guess under these circumstances?

11. A store specializing in mountain bikes is to open in one of two malls. If the first mall is selected, the store anticipates a yearly profit of $300,000 if successful and a yearly loss of $100,000 otherwise. The probability of success is $\frac{1}{2}$. If the second mall is selected, it is estimated that the yearly profit will be $200,000 if successful; otherwise, the annual loss will be $60,000. The probability of success at the second mall is $\frac{3}{4}$. Which mall should be chosen in order to maximize the expected profit?

12. An oil company is considering two sites on which to drill, described as follows:

Site A: Profit if oil is found: $80 million
Loss if no oil is found: $10 million
Probability of finding oil: 0.2
Site B: Profit if oil is found: $120 million
Loss if no oil is found: $18 million
Probability of finding oil: 0.1

Which site has the larger expected profit? By how much?

13. In a product liability case, a company can settle out of court for a loss of $350,000, or go to trial, losing $700,000 if found guilty and nothing if found not guilty. Lawyers for the company estimate the probability of a not-guilty verdict to be 0.8.

a. Find the expected value of the amount the company can lose by taking the case to court.

b. Should the company settle out of court?

14. A service that repairs air conditioners sells maintenance agreements for $80 a year. The average cost for repairing an air conditioner is $350 and 1 in every 100 people who purchase maintenance agreements have air conditioners that require repair. Find the service's expected profit per maintenance agreement.

Exercises 15–19 involve computing expected values in games of chance.

15. A game is played using one die. If the die is rolled and shows 1, the player wins $5. If the die shows any number other than 1, the player wins nothing. If there is a charge of $1 to play the game, what is the game's expected value? What does this value mean?

16. A game is played using one die. If the die is rolled and shows 1, the player wins $1; if 2, the player wins $2; if 3, the player wins $3. If the die shows 4, 5, or 6, the player wins nothing. If there is a charge of $1.25 to play the game, what is the game's expected value? What does this value mean?

17. Another option in a roulette game (see Example 6 on page 668) is to bet $1 on red. (There are 18 red compartments, 18 black compartments, and 2 compartments that are neither red nor black.) If the ball lands on red, you get to keep the $1 that you paid to play the game and you are awarded $1. If the ball lands elsewhere, you are awarded nothing and the $1 that you bet is collected. Find the expected value for playing roulette if you bet $1 on red. Describe what this number means.

18. The spinner on a wheel of fortune can land with an equal chance on any one of ten regions. Three regions are red, four are blue, two are yellow, and one is green. A player wins $4 if the spinner stops on red and $2 if it stops on green. The player loses $2 if it stops on blue and $3 if it stops on yellow. What is the expected value? What does this mean if the game is played ten times?

19. For many years, organized crime ran a numbers game that is now run legally by many state governments. The player selects a three-digit number from 000 to 999. There are 1000 such numbers. A bet of $1 is placed on a number, say number 115. If the number is selected, the player wins $500. If any other number is selected, the player wins nothing. Find the expected value for this game and describe what this means.

• Writing in Mathematics

20. What does the expected value for the outcome of the roll of a fair die represent?

21. Explain how to find the expected value for the number of girls for a family with two children. What is the expected value?

22. How do insurance companies use expected value to determine what to charge for a policy?

23. Describe a situation in which a business can use expected value.

24. If the expected value of a game is negative, what does this mean? Also describe the meaning of a positive and a zero expected value.

25. The expected value for purchasing a ticket in a raffle is −$0.75. Describe what this means. Will a person who purchases a ticket lose $0.75?

• Critical Thinking Exercises

26. A popular state lottery is the 5/35 lottery, played in Arizona, Connecticut, Illinois, Iowa, Kentucky, Maine, Massachusetts, New Hampshire, South Dakota, and Vermont. In Arizona's version of the game, prizes are set: First prize is $50,000, second prize is $500, and third prize is $5. To win first prize, you must select all five of the winning numbers, numbered from 1 to 35. Second prize is awarded to players who select any four of the five winning numbers, and third prize is awarded to players who select any three of the winning numbers. The cost to purchase a lottery ticket is $1. Find the expected value of Arizona's "Fantasy Five" game, and describe what this means in terms of buying a lottery ticket over the long run.

27. Refer to the probabilities of dying at any given age on page 635 to solve this exercise. A 20-year-old woman wants to purchase a $200,000 one-year life insurance policy. What should the insurance company charge the woman for the policy if it wants an expected profit of $60?

• Group Exercise

28. This activity is a group research project intended for people interested in games of chance at casinos. The research should culminate in a seminar on games of chance and their expected values. The seminar is intended to last about 30 minutes and should result in an interesting and informative presentation made to the entire class.

Each member of the group should research a game available at a typical casino. Describe the game to the class and compute its expected value. After each member has done this, so that class members now have an idea of those games with the greatest and smallest house advantages, a final group member might want to research and present ways for currently treating people whose addiction to these games has caused their lives to swirl out of control.

●●●●●● CHAPTER SUMMARY, REVIEW, AND TEST

● **SUMMARY**   DEFINITIONS AND CONCEPTS   EXAMPLES

11.1   The Fundamental Counting Principle

The number of ways in which a series of successive things can occur is found by multiplying the number of ways in which each thing can occur.

Ex. 1, p. 609;
Ex. 2, p. 609;
Ex. 3, p. 610;
Ex. 4, p. 610;
Ex. 5, p. 611;
Ex. 6, p. 611

11.2   Permutations

a. A permutation from a group of items occurs when no item is used more than once and the order of arrangement makes a difference. The Fundamental Counting Principle can be used to determine the number of permutations possible.

Ex. 1, p. 614;
Ex. 2, p. 615

b. Factorial Notation

Ex. 3, p. 616

$$n! = n(n-1)(n-2)\cdots(3)(2)(1) \text{ and } 0! = 1$$

c. Permutations Formula

Ex. 4, p. 617;
Ex. 5, p. 618

The number of permutations possible if r items are taken from n items is $_nP_r = \dfrac{n!}{(n-r)!}$.

d. Permutations of Duplicate Items

Ex. 6, p. 619

The number of permutations of n items, where p items are identical, q items are identical, r items are identical, and so on, is

$$\frac{n!}{p!\,q!\,r!\ldots}.$$

11.3 Combinations

a. A combination from a group of items occurs when no item is used more than once and the order of items makes no difference.

Ex. 1, p. 621

b. Combinations Formula

Ex. 2, p. 623;
Ex. 3, p. 623;
Ex. 4, p. 624

The number of combinations possible if r items are taken from n items is $_nC_r = \dfrac{n!}{(n-r)!\,r!}$.

11.4 Fundamentals of Probability

a. Theoretical probability applies to experiments in which the set of all equally likely outcomes, called the sample space, is known. An event is any subset of the sample space.

b. The theoretical probability of event E with sample space S is

Ex. 1, p. 628;
Ex. 2, p. 630;
Ex. 3, p. 630

$$P(E) = \frac{\text{number of outcomes in } E}{\text{total number of possible outcomes}} = \frac{n(E)}{n(S)}.$$

c. Empirical probability applies to situations in which we observe the frequency of the occurrence of an event.

d. The empirical probability of event E is

Ex. 4, p. 631

$$P(E) = \frac{\text{observed number of times } E \text{ occurs}}{\text{total number of observed occurrences}}.$$

11.5 Probability with the Fundamental Counting Principle, Permutations, and Combinations

a. Probability of a permutation

Ex. 1, p. 636

$$= \frac{\text{the number of ways the permutation can occur}}{\text{total number of possible permutations}}.$$

b. Probability of a combination

Ex. 2, p. 637;
Ex. 3, p. 638

$$= \frac{\text{the number of ways the combination can occur}}{\text{total number of possible combinations}}.$$

11.6 Events Involving Not and Or; Odds

a. Complement Rules of Probability

Ex. 1, p. 642;
Ex. 2, p. 642

$$P(\text{not } E) = 1 - P(E) \quad \text{and} \quad P(E) = 1 - P(\text{not } E)$$

b. If it is impossible for events A and B to occur simultaneously, the events are mutually exclusive.

c. If A and B are mutually exclusive events, then $P(A \text{ or } B) = P(A) + P(B)$.

Ex. 3, p. 644;
Ex. 6(b), p. 646

d. If A and B are not mutually exclusive events, then

$$P(A \text{ or } B) = P(A) + P(B) - P(A \text{ and } B).$$

Ex. 4, p. 645;
Ex. 5, p. 645;
Ex. 6(a), p. 646

e. Probability to Odds

Ex. 7, p. 647;
Ex. 8, p. 648

1. Odds in favor of $E = \dfrac{P(E)}{P(\text{not } E)}$ **2.** Odds against $E = \dfrac{P(\text{not } E)}{P(E)}$

f. Odds to Probability

Ex. 9. p. 649

If odds in favor of E are a to b, then $P(E) = \dfrac{a}{a + b}$.

11.7 Events Involving *And*; Conditional Probability

a. Two events are independent if the occurrence of either of them has no effect on the probability of the other.

b. If A and B are independent events,

Ex. 1, p. 654

$$P(A \text{ and } B) = P(A) \cdot P(B).$$

c. The probability of a succession of independent events is the product of each of their probabilities.

Ex. 2, p. 654;
Ex. 3, p. 655

d. Two events are dependent if the occurrence of one of them has an effect on the probability of the other.

e. If A and B are dependent events,

Ex. 4, p. 657

$$P(A \text{ and } B) = P(A) \cdot P(B \text{ given that } A \text{ has occurred}).$$

f. The multiplication rule for dependent events can be extended to cover three or more dependent events. In the case of three such events,

Ex. 5, p. 657

$$P(A \text{ and } B \text{ and } C)$$
$$= P(A) \cdot P(B \text{ given } A \text{ occurred}) \cdot P(C \text{ given } A \text{ and } B \text{ occurred}).$$

g. The conditional probability of B, given A, written $P(B|A)$, is the probability of B if the sample space is restricted to A.

Ex. 6, p. 658;
Ex. 7, p. 659

$$P(B|A) = \frac{n(B \cap A)}{n(A)} = \frac{\text{number of outcomes common to } B \text{ and } A}{\text{number of outcomes in } A}$$

11.8 Expected Value

a. Expected value, E, is found by multiplying every possible outcome by its probability and then adding these products.

Ex. 1, p. 664;
Ex. 2, p. 664;
Ex. 3, p. 665

b. In situations involving business decisions, expected value is calculated by multiplying the gain or loss for each possible outcome by its probability. The sum of these products is the expected value.

Ex. 4, p. 665

c. In a game of chance, expected value is the average payoff when the game is played a large number of times. To find the expected value of a game, multiply the gain or loss for each possible outcome by its probability. Then add the products.

Ex. 5, p. 666;
Ex. 6, p. 668

REVIEW EXERCISES

11.1

1. A restaurant offers 20 appetizers and 40 main courses. In how many ways can a person order a two-course meal?

2. A popular brand of pen comes in red, green, blue, or black ink. The writing tip can be chosen from extra bold, bold, regular, fine, or micro. How many different choices of pens do you have with this brand?

3. In how many ways can first and second prize be awarded in a contest with 100 people, assuming that each prize is awarded to a different person?

4. You are answering three multiple-choice questions. Each question has five answer choices, with one correct answer per question. If you select one of these five choices for each question and leave nothing blank, in how many ways can you answer the questions?

5. A stock can go up, go down, or stay unchanged. How many possibilities are there if you own five stocks?

6. A person can purchase a condominium with a choice of five kinds of carpeting, with or without a pool, with or without a porch, and with one, two, or three bedrooms. How many different options are there for the condominium?

11.2

7. Six acts are scheduled to perform in a variety show. How many different ways are there to schedule their appearances?

8. In how many ways can five airplanes line up for departure on a runway?

9. You need to arrange seven of your favorite books along a small shelf. Although you are not arranging the books by height, the tallest of the books is to be placed at the left end and the shortest of the books at the right end. How many different ways can you arrange the books?

In Exercises 10–13, evaluate each factorial expression.

10. $\dfrac{16!}{14!}$

11. $\dfrac{800!}{799!}$

12. $5! - 3!$

13. $\dfrac{11!}{(11 - 3)!}$

In Exercises 14–15, use the formula for $_nP_r$ to evaluate each expression.

14. $_{10}P_6$

15. $_{100}P_2$

Use the formula for $_nP_r$ to solve Exercises 16–17.

16. A club with 15 members is to choose four officers—president, vice-president, secretary, and treasurer. In how many ways can these offices be filled?

17. Suppose you are asked to list, in order of preference, the five favorite CDs you purchased in the past 12 months. If you bought 20 CDs over this time period, in how many ways can the five favorite be ranked?

Use the formula for the number of permutations with duplicate items to solve Exercises 18–19.

18. In how many distinct ways can the letters of the word TORONTO be arranged?

19. In how many ways can the digits in the number 335,557 be arranged?

11.3

In Exercises 20–22, does the problem involve permutations or combinations? Explain your answer. (It is not necessary to solve the problem.)

20. How many different 4-card hands can be dealt from a 52-card deck?

21. How many different ways can a director select from 20 male actors to cast the roles of Mark, Roger, Angel, and Collins in the musical *Rent*?

22. How many different ways can a director select 4 actors from a group of 20 actors to attend a workshop on performing in rock musicals?

In Exercises 23–24, use the formula for $_nC_r$ to evaluate each expression.

23. $_{11}C_7$

24. $_{14}C_5$

Use the formula for $_nC_r$ to solve Exercises 25–28.

25. An election ballot asks voters to select four city commissioners from a group of ten candidates. In how many ways can this be done?

26. How many different 5-card hands can be dealt from a deck that has only hearts (13 different cards)?

27. From the 20 CDs that you've bought during the past year, you plan to take 3 with you on vacation. How many different sets of three CDs can you take?

28. A political discussion group consists of 12 Republicans and 8 Democrats. In how many ways can 5 Republicans and 4 Democrats be selected to attend a conference on politics and social issues?

11.4

In Exercises 29–32, a die is rolled. Find the probability of rolling

29. a 6.

30. a number less than 5.

31. a number less than 7.

32. a number greater than 6.

In Exercises 33–37, you are dealt one card from a 52-card deck. Find the probability of being dealt

33. a 5.

34. a picture card.

35. a card greater than 4 and less than 8.

36. a 4 of diamonds.

37. a red ace.

In Exercises 38–40, suppose that you reach into a bag and randomly select one piece of candy from 15 chocolates, 10 caramels, and 5 peppermints. Find the probability of selecting

38. a chocolate.

39. a caramel.

40. a peppermint.

41. Tay-Sachs disease occurs in 1 of every 3600 births among Jews from central and eastern Europe, and in 1 in 600,000 births in other populations. The disease causes abnormal accumulation of certain fat compounds in the spinal cord and brain, resulting in paralysis, blindness, and mental impairment. Death generally occurs before the age of five. If we use t to represent a Tay-Sachs gene and T a healthy gene, the table below shows the four possibilities for the children of one healthy, TT, parent, and one parent who carries the disease, Tt, but is not sick.

a. Find the probability that a child of these parents will be a carrier without the disease.

b. Find the probability that a child of these parents will have the disease.

		Second Parent	
		T	t
First	T	TT	Tt
Parent	T	TT	Tt

The table shows the employment status of the U.S. civilian labor force in 2004, by gender. Use the data in the table, expressed in millions, to solve Exercises 42–44.

EMPLOYMENT STATUS OF THE U.S. LABOR FORCE, IN MILLIONS, IN 2004

	Employed	**Unemployed**	**Total**
Male	74.5	33.2	107.7
Female	64.7	51.0	115.7
Total	139.2	84.2	223.4

Source: U.S. Bureau of Labor Statistics

Find the probability, expressed as a decimal rounded to three places, that a randomly selected person from the civilian labor force represented in the table

42. is employed.

43. is female.

44. is an unemployed male.

11.5

45. If cities A, B, C, and D are visited in random order, each city visited once, find the probability that city D will be visited first, city B second, city A third, and city C last.

In Exercises 46–49, suppose that six singers are being lined up to perform at a charity. Call the singers A, B, C, D, E, and F. The order of performance is determined by writing each singer's name on one of six cards, placing the cards in a hat, and then drawing one card at a time. The order in which the cards are drawn determines the order in which the singers perform. Find the probability that

46. singer C will perform last.

47. singer B will perform first and singer A will perform last.

48. the singers will perform in the following order: F, E, A, D, C, B.

49. the performance will begin with singer A or C.

50. A lottery game is set up so that each player chooses five different numbers from 1 to 20. If the five numbers match the five numbers drawn in the lottery, the player wins (or shares) the top cash prize. What is the probability of winning the prize

a. with one lottery ticket?

b. with 100 different lottery tickets?

51. A committee of four people is to be selected from six Democrats and four Republicans. Find the probability that

a. all are Democrats.

b. two are Democrats and two are Republicans.

52. If you are dealt 3 cards from a shuffled deck of red cards (26 different cards), find the probability of getting exactly 2 picture cards.

11.6

In Exercises 53–57, a die is rolled. Find the probability of

53. not rolling a 5.

54. not rolling a number less than 4.

55. rolling a 3 or a 5.

56. rolling a number less than 3 or greater than 4.

57. rolling a number less than 5 or greater than 2.

In Exercises 58–63, you draw one card from a 52-card deck. Find the probability of

58. not drawing a picture card.

59. not drawing a diamond.

60. drawing an ace or a king.

61. drawing a black 6 or a red 7.

62. drawing a queen or a red card.

63. drawing a club or a picture card.

In Exercises 64–69, it is equally probable that the pointer on the spinner shown will land on any one of the six regions, numbered 1 through 6, and colored as shown. If the pointer lands on a borderline, spin again. Find the probability of

64. not stopping on 4.

65. not stopping on yellow.

66. not stopping on red.

67. stopping on red or yellow.

68. stopping on red or an even number.

69. stopping on red or a number greater than 3.

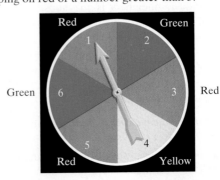

Use this information to solve Exercises 70–71. At a workshop on police work and the African-American community, there are 50 African-American male police officers, 20 African-American female police officers, 90 white male police officers, and 40 white female police officers. If one police officer is selected at random from the people at the workshop, find the probability that the selected person is

70. African American or male.

71. female or white.

Suppose that a survey of 350 college students is taken. Each student is asked the type of college attended (public or private) and the family's income level (low, middle, high). Use the data in the table to solve Exercises 72–75. Express probabilities as simplified fractions.

	Public	Private	Total
Low	120	20	140
Middle	110	50	160
High	22	28	50
Total	252	98	350

Find the probability that a randomly selected student in the survey

72. attends a public college.

73. is not from a high-income family.

74. is from a middle-income or a high-income family.

75. attends a private college or is from a high-income family.

76. One card is randomly selected from a deck of 52 cards. Find the odds in favor and the odds against getting a queen.

77. The winner of a raffle will receive a two-year scholarship to any college of the winner's choice. If 2000 raffle tickets were sold and you purchased 20 tickets, what are the odds against your winning the scholarship?

78. The odds in favor of a candidate winning an election are given at 3 to 1. What is the probability that this candidate will win the election?

11.7

Use the spinner shown to solve Exercises 79–83. It is equally likely that the pointer will land on any one of the six regions, numbered 1 through 6, and colored as shown. If the pointer lands on a borderline, spin again. If the pointer is spun twice, find the probability it will land on

79. yellow and then red.

80. 1 and then 3.

81. yellow both times.

If the pointer is spun three times, find the probability it will land on

82. yellow and then 4 and then an odd number.

83. red every time.

84. What is the probability of a family having five boys born in a row?

85. The probability of a flood in any given year in a region prone to flooding is 0.2.

   a. What is the probability of a flood two years in a row?

   b. What is the probability of a flood for three consecutive years?

   c. What is the probability of no flooding for four consecutive years?

   d. What is the probability of a flood at least once in the next four years?

In Exercises 86–87, two students are selected from a group of four psychology majors, three business majors, and two music majors. The two students are to meet with the campus cafeteria manager to voice the group's concerns about food prices and quality. One student is randomly selected and leaves for the cafeteria manager's office. Then, a second student is selected. Find the probability of selecting

86. a music major and then a psychology major.

87. two business majors.

88. A final visit to the box of chocolates: It's now grown to a box of 50, of which 30 are solid chocolate, 15 are filled with jelly, and 5 are filled with cherries. The story is still the same: They all look alike. You select a piece, eat it, select a second piece, eat it, and help yourself to a final sugar rush. Find the probability of selecting a solid chocolate followed by two cherry-filled chocolates.

89. A single die is tossed. Find the probability that the tossed die shows 5, given that the outcome is an odd number.

90. A letter is randomly selected from the letters of the English alphabet. Find the probability of selecting a vowel, given that the outcome is a letter that precedes k.

91. The numbers shown below are each written on a colored chip. The chips are placed into a bag and one chip is selected at random. Find the probability of selecting

   a. an odd number, given that a red chip is selected.

   b. a yellow chip, given that the number selected is at least 3.

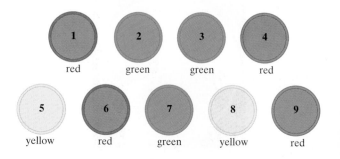

The data in the table are based on 145 Americans tested for tuberculosis. Use the data to solve Exercises 92–99. Express probabilities as simplified fractions.

	TB	No TB
Positive Screening Test	9	11
Negative Screening Test	1	124

Source: Deborah J. Bennett, *Randomness*, Harvard University Press, 1998

11.4 and 11.6–11.7

Find the probability that a randomly selected person from this group

92. does not have TB.

93. tests positive.

94. does not have TB or tests positive.

95. does not have TB, given a positive test.

96. has a positive test, given no TB.

97. has TB, given a negative test.

Suppose that two people are randomly selected, in succession, from this group. Find the probability of selecting

98. two people with TB.

99. two people with positive screening tests.

The table shows the distribution, by age and gender, of the 30,242 deaths in the United States involving firearms in 2002.

DEATHS IN THE UNITED STATES INVOLVING FIREARMS, 2002

	Under Age 5	Ages 5–14	Ages 15–19	Ages 20–24	Ages 25–44	Ages 45–64	Ages 65–74	Age ≥75	Total
Male	42	242	2209	3887	9850	5875	1768	2225	26,098
Female	29	106	265	419	1736	1165	225	199	4144
Total	71	348	2474	4306	11,586	7040	1993	2424	30,242

Source: National Safety Council

In Exercises 100–106, use the data in the table to find the probability, expressed as a fraction and as a decimal rounded to three places, that a firearm death in the United States

100. involved a male.

101. involved a person in the 25–44 age range.

102. involved a person less than 75 years old.

103. involved a person in the 20–24 age range or in the 25–44 age range.

104. involved a female or a person younger than 5.

105. involved a person in the 20–24 age range, given that this person was a male.

106. involved a male, given that this person was at least 75.

11.8

107. The numbers that the pointer can land on and their respective probabilities are shown below and in the next column.

Outcome	Probability
1	$\frac{1}{4}$
2	$\frac{1}{8}$
3	$\frac{1}{8}$
4	$\frac{1}{4}$
5	$\frac{1}{4}$

Compute the expected value for the number on which the pointer lands.

108. The table shows claims and their probabilities for an insurance company.

LIFE INSURANCE FOR AN AIRLINE FLIGHT

Amount of Claim	Probability
$0	0.9999995
$1,000,000	0.0000005

a. Calculate the expected value and describe what this value means.

b. How much should the company charge to make a profit of $9.50 per policy?

109. A construction company is planning to bid on a building contract. The bid costs the company $3000. The probability that the bid is accepted is $\frac{1}{4}$. If the bid is accepted, the company will make $30,000 minus the cost of the bid. Find the expected value in this situation. Describe what this value means.

110. A game is played using a fair coin that is tossed twice. The sample space is $\{HH, HT, TH, TT\}$. If exactly one head occurs, the player wins $5, and if exactly two tails occur, the player also wins $5. For any other outcome, the player receives nothing. There is a $4 charge to play the game. What is the expected value? What does this value mean?

•••••• • CHAPTER 11 TEST

1. A person can purchase a particular model of a new car with a choice of ten colors, with or without automatic transmission, with or without four-wheel drive, with or without air conditioning, and with two, three, or four radio-CD speakers. How many different options are there for this model of the car?

2. Four acts are scheduled to perform in a variety show. How many different ways are there to schedule their appearances?

3. In how many ways can seven airplanes line up for a departure on a runway if the plane with the greatest number of passengers must depart first?

4. A human resource manager has 11 applicants to fill three different positions. Assuming that all applicants are equally qualified for any of the three positions, in how many ways can this be done?

5. From the ten books that you've recently bought but not read, you plan to take four with you on vacation. How many different sets of four books can you take?

6. In how many distinct ways can the letters of the word ATLANTA be arranged?

In Exercises 7–9, one student is selected at random from a group of 12 freshmen, 16 sophomores, 20 juniors, and 2 seniors. Find the probability that the person selected is

7. a freshman.   8. not a sophomore.

9. a junior or a senior.

10. If you are dealt one card from a 52-card deck, find the probability of being dealt a card greater than 4 and less than 10.

11. Seven movies (A, B, C, D, E, F, and G) are being scheduled for showing. The order of showing is determined by random selection. Find the probability that film C will be shown first, film A next-to-last, and film E last.

12. A lottery game is set up so that each player chooses six different numbers from 1 to 15. If the six numbers match the six numbers drawn in the lottery, the player wins (or shares) the top cash prize. What is the probability of winning the prize with 50 different lottery tickets?

In Exercises 13–14, it is equally probable that the pointer on the spinner shown will land on any one of the eight colored regions. If the pointer lands on a borderline, spin again.

13. If the spinner is spun once, find the probability that the pointer will land on red or blue.

14. If the spinner is spun twice, find the probability that the pointer lands on red on the first spin and blue on the second spin.

15. A region is prone to flooding once every 20 years. The probability of flooding in any one year is $\frac{1}{20}$. What is the probability of flooding for three consecutive years?

16. One card is randomly selected from a deck of 52 cards. Find the probability of selecting a black card or a picture card.

17. A group of students consists of 10 male freshmen, 15 female freshmen, 20 male sophomores, and 5 female sophomores. If one person is randomly selected from the group, find the probability of selecting a freshman or a female.

18. A box contains five red balls, six green balls, and nine yellow balls. Suppose you select one ball at random from the box and do not replace it. Then you randomly select a second ball. Find the probability that both balls selected are red.

19. A quiz consisting of four multiple-choice questions has four available options (a, b, c, or d) for each question. If a person guesses at every question, what is the probability of answering *all* questions correctly?

20. A group is comprised of 20 men and 15 women. If one person is randomly selected from the group, find the odds against the person being a man.

21. The odds against a candidate winning an election are given at 1 to 4.

    a. What are the odds in favor of the candidate winning?

    b. What is the probability that the candidate will win the election?

A class is collecting data on eye color and gender. They organize the data they collected into the table shown. Numbers in the table represent the number of students from the class that belong to each of the categories. Use the data to solve Exercises 22–26. Express probabilities as simplified fractions.

	Brown	Blue	Green
Male	22	18	10
Female	18	20	12

Find the probability that a randomly selected student from this class

22. does not have brown eyes.

23. has brown eyes or blue eyes.

24. is female or has green eyes.

25. is male, given the student has blue eyes.

26. If two people are randomly selected, in succession, from the students in this class, find the probability that they both have green eyes.

27. An architect is considering bidding for the design of a new theater. The cost of drawing plans and submitting a model is $15,000. The probability of being awarded the bid is 0.2, and anticipated profits are $80,000, resulting in a possible gain of this amount minus the $15,000 cost for plans and models. What is the expected value if the architect decides to bid for the design? Describe what this value means.

28. A game is played by selecting one bill at random from a bag that contains ten $1 bills, five $2 bills, three $5 bills, one $10 bill, and one $100 bill. The player gets to keep the selected bill. There is a $20 charge to play the game. What is the expected value? What does this value mean?

12

Statistics

I n a 1996 study, researchers found that employees described as plain had salaries below the median level and those described as attractive had salaries above the median level.

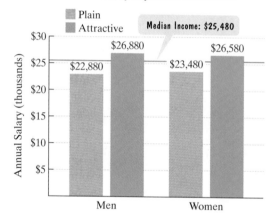

Annual Salaries of American Men and Women, by Physical Attractiveness

■ Plain
■ Attractive

Median Income: **$25,480**

Source: Jeff Biddle and Daniel Hamermesh, CompPsych Survey

Statisticians collect numerical data from subgroups of populations to find out everything imaginable about the population as a whole, including whom they favor in an election, what they watch on TV, how much money they make, what worries them, and even how being attractive pays off. Comedians and statisticians joke that 62.38% of all statistics are made up on the spot. Because statisticians both record and influence our behavior, it is important to distinguish between good and bad methods for collecting, presenting, and interpreting data. In this chapter, you will gain an understanding of where data come from and how these numbers are used to make decisions.

SECTION 12.1 • SAMPLING, FREQUENCY DISTRIBUTIONS, AND GRAPHS

O B J E C T I V E S

1. Describe the population whose properties are to be analyzed.

2. Select an appropriate sampling technique.

3. Organize and present data.

4. Identify deceptions in visual displays of data.

M*A*S*H took place in the early 1950s, during the Korean War. By the final episode, the show had lasted four times as long as the Korean War.

At the end of the twentieth century, there were 94 million households in the United States with television sets. The television program viewed by the greatest percentage of such households in that century was the final episode of *M*A*S*H*. Over 50 million American households watched this program.

Numerical information, such as the information about the top three TV shows of the twentieth century, shown in Table 12.1, is called **data**. The word **statistics** is often used when referring to data. However, statistics has a second meaning: Statistics is also a method for collecting, organizing, analyzing, and interpreting data, as well as drawing conclusions based on the data. This methodology divides statistics into two main areas. **Descriptive statistics** is concerned with collecting, organizing, summarizing, and presenting data. **Inferential statistics** has to do with making generalizations about and drawing conclusions from the data collected.

TABLE 12.1 TV PROGRAMS WITH THE GREATEST U.S. AUDIENCE VIEWING PERCENTAGE OF THE TWENTIETH CENTURY

Program	Total Households	Viewing Percentage
1. *M*A*S*H* Feb. 28, 1983	50,150,000	60.2%
2. *Dallas* Nov. 21, 1980	41,470,000	53.3%
3. *Roots Part 8* Jan. 30, 1977	36,380,000	51.1%

Source: Nielsen Media Research

1 | Describe the population whose properties are to be analyzed.

Populations and Samples

Consider the set of all American TV households. Such a set is called the *population*. In general, a **population** is the set containing all the people or objects whose properties are to be described and analyzed by the data collector.

The population of American TV households is huge. At the time of the *M*A*S*H* conclusion, there were nearly 84 million such households. Did over 50 million American TV households really watch the final episode of *M*A*S*H*? A friendly phone call to each household ("So, how are you? What's new? Watch any good television last night? If so, what?") is, of course, absurd. A **sample**, which is a subset or subgroup of the population, is needed. In this case, it would be appropriate to have a sample of a few thousand TV households to draw conclusions about the population of all TV households.

EXAMPLE 1   POPULATIONS AND SAMPLES

A group of hotel owners in a large city decide to conduct a survey among citizens of the city to discover their opinions about casino gambling.

a. Describe the population.

b. One of the hotel owners suggests obtaining a sample by surveying all the people at six of the largest nightclubs in the city on a Saturday night. Each person will be asked to express his or her opinion on casino gambling. Does this seem like a good idea?

SOLUTION

a. The population is the set containing all the citizens of the city.

b. Questioning people at six of the city's largest nightclubs is a terrible idea. The nightclub subset is probably more likely to have a positive attitude toward casino gambling than the population of all the city's citizens.

CHECK POINT
1   A city government wants to conduct a survey among the city's homeless to discover their opinions about required residence in city shelters from midnight until 6 A.M.

a. Describe the population.

b. A city commissioner suggests obtaining a sample by surveying all the homeless people at the city's largest shelter on a Sunday night. Does this seem like a good idea? Explain your answer.

Random Sampling

There is a way to use a small sample to make generalizations about a large population: Guarantee that every member of the population has an equal chance to be selected for the sample. Surveying people at six of the city's largest nightclubs does not provide this guarantee. Unless it can be established that all citizens of the city frequent these clubs, which seems unlikely, this sampling scheme does not permit each citizen an equal chance of selection.

> **RANDOM SAMPLES**
> A **random sample** is a sample obtained in such a way that every element in the population has an equal chance of being selected for the sample.

Suppose that you are elated with the quality of one of your courses. Although it's an auditorium section with 120 students, you feel that the professor is lecturing right to you. During a wonderful lecture, you look around the auditorium to see if any of the other students are sharing your enthusiasm. Based on body language, it's hard to tell. You really want to know the opinion of the population of 120 students taking this course. You think about asking students to grade the course on an A to F scale, anticipating a unanimous A. You cannot survey everyone. Eureka! Suddenly you have an idea on how to take a sample. Place cards numbered from 1 through 120, one number per card, in a box. Because the course has assigned seating by number, each numbered card corresponds to a student in the class. Reach in and randomly select six cards. Each card, and therefore each student, has an equal chance of being selected. Then use the opinions about the course from the six randomly selected students to generalize about the course opinion for the entire 120-student population.

Your idea is precisely how random samples are obtained. In random sampling, each element in the population must be identified and assigned a number. The numbers are generally assigned in order. The way to sample from the larger numbered population is to generate random numbers using a computer or calculator.

Each numbered element from the population that corresponds to one of the generated random numbers is selected for the sample.

Call-in polls on radio and television are not reliable because those polled do not represent the larger population. A person who calls in is likely to have feelings about an issue that are consistent with the politics of the show's host. For a poll to be accurate, the sample must be chosen randomly from the larger population. The A. C. Nielsen Company uses a random sample of approximately 5000 TV households to measure the percentage of households tuned in to a television program.

2 | Select an appropriate sampling technique.

EXAMPLE 2 SELECTING AN APPROPRIATE SAMPLING TECHNIQUE

We return to the hotel owners in the large city who are interested in how the city's citizens feel about casino gambling. Which of the following would be the most appropriate way to select a random sample?

a. Randomly survey people who live in the oceanfront condominiums in the city.

b. Survey the first 200 people whose names appear in the city's telephone directory.

c. Randomly select neighborhoods of the city and then randomly survey people within the selected neighborhoods.

SOLUTION Keep in mind that the population is the set containing all the city's citizens. A random sample must give each citizen an equal chance of being selected.

a. Randomly selecting people who live in the city's oceanfront condominiums is not a good idea. Many hotels lie along the oceanfront, and the oceanfront property owners might object to the traffic and noise as a result of casino gambling. Furthermore, this sample does not give each citizen of the city an equal chance of being selected.

b. If the hotel owners survey the first 200 names in the city's telephone directory, all citizens do not have an equal chance of selection. For example, individuals whose last name begins with a letter toward the end of the alphabet have no chance of being selected.

c. Randomly selecting neighborhoods of the city and then randomly surveying people within the selected neighborhoods is an appropriate technique. Using this method, each citizen has an equal chance of being selected.

In summary, given the three options, the sampling technique in part (c) is the most appropriate.

Surveys and polls involve data from a sample of some population. Regardless of the sampling technique used, the sample should exhibit characteristics typical of those possessed by the target population. This type of sample is called a **representative sample**.

CHECK POINT 2 Explain why the sampling technique described in Check Point 1(b) on page 681 is not a random sample. Then describe an appropriate way to select a random sample of the city's homeless.

3 | Organize and present data.

Frequency Distributions

After data have been collected from a sample of the population, the next task facing the statistician is to present the data in a condensed and manageable form. In this way, the data can be more easily interpreted.

Suppose, for example, that researchers are interested in determining the age at which adolescent males show the greatest rate of physical growth. A random sample of 35 ten-year-old boys is measured for height and then remeasured each year until they reach 18. The age of maximum yearly growth for each subject is as follows:

12, 14, 13, 14, 16, 14, 14, 17, 13, 10, 13, 18, 12, 15, 14, 15, 15, 14, 14, 13, 15, 16, 15, 12, 13, 16, 11, 15, 12, 13, 12, 11, 13, 14, 14.

A piece of data is called a **data item**. This list of data has 35 data items. Some of the data items are identical. Two of the data items are 11 and 11. Thus, we can say that the **data value** 11 occurs twice. Similarly, because five of the data items are 12, 12, 12, 12, and 12, the data value 12 occurs five times.

Collected data can be presented using a **frequency distribution**. Such a distribution consists of two columns. The data values are listed in one column. Numerical data are generally listed from smallest to largest. The adjacent column is labeled **frequency** and indicates the number of times each value occurs.

TABLE 12.2 A FREQUENCY DISTRIBUTION FOR A BOY'S AGE OF MAXIMUM YEARLY GROWTH

Age of Maximum Growth	Number of Boys (Frequency)
10	1
11	2
12	5
13	7
14	9
15	6
16	3
17	1
18	1
Total:	$n = 35$

35 is the sum of the frequencies.

EXAMPLE 3   CONSTRUCTING A FREQUENCY DISTRIBUTION

Construct a frequency distribution for the data of the age of maximum yearly growth for 35 boys:

12, 14, 13, 14, 16, 14, 14, 17, 13, 10, 13, 18, 12, 15, 14, 15, 15, 14, 14, 13, 15, 16, 15, 12, 13, 16, 11, 15, 12, 13, 12, 11, 13, 14, 14.

SOLUTION It is difficult to determine trends in the data above in its current format. Perhaps we can make sense of the data by organizing it into a frequency distribution. Let us create two columns. One lists all possible data values, from smallest (10) to largest (18). The other column indicates the number of times the value occurs in the sample. The frequency distribution is shown in Table 12.2.

The frequency distribution indicates that one subject had maximum growth at age 10, two at age 11, five at age 12, seven at age 13, and so on. The maximum growth for most of the subjects occurred between the ages of 12 and 15. Nine boys experienced maximum growth at age 14, more than at any other age within the sample. The sum of the frequencies, 35, is equal to the original number of data items.

The trend shown by the frequency distribution in Table 12.2 indicates that the number of boys who attain their maximum yearly growth at a given age increases until age 14 and decreases after that. This trend is not evident in the data in its original format.

○

CHECK POINT 3   Construct a frequency distribution for the data showing final course grades for students in a precalculus course, listed alphabetically by student name in a grade book:

F, A, B, B, C, C, B, C, A, A, C, C, D, C, B, D, C, C, B, C.

A frequency distribution that lists all possible data items can be quite cumbersome when there are many such items. For example, consider the following data items. These are statistics test scores for a class of 40 students.

82	47	75	64	57	82	63	93
76	68	84	54	88	77	79	80
94	92	94	80	94	66	81	67
75	73	66	87	76	45	43	56
57	74	50	78	71	84	59	76

It's difficult to determine how well the group did when the grades are displayed like this. Because there are so many data items, one way to organize these data so that the results are more meaningful is to arrange the grades into groups, or **classes**, based on something that interests us. Many grading systems assign an A to grades in the 90–100 class, B to grades in the 80–89 class, C to grades in the 70–79 class, and so on. These classes provide one way to organize the data.

Looking at the 40 statistics test scores, we see that they range from a low of 43 to a high of 94. We can use classes that run from 40 through 49, 50 through 59, 60 through 69, and so on up to 90 through 99, to organize the scores. In Example 4, we go through the data and tally each item into the appropriate class. This method for organizing data is called a **grouped frequency distribution**.

| EXAMPLE 4 | CONSTRUCTING A GROUPED FREQUENCY DISTRIBUTION |

Use the classes 40–49, 50–59, 60–69, 70–79, 80–89, and 90–99 to construct a grouped frequency distribution for the 40 test scores on the previous page.

SOLUTION We use the 40 given scores and tally the number of scores in each class.

Test Scores (Class)	Tally	Number of Students (Frequency)
40–49	|||	3
50–59	⁜		6
60–69	⁜		6
70–79	⁜ ⁜		11
80–89	⁜ ||||	9
90–99	⁜	5

The second score in the list, 47, is shown as the first tally in this row.

The first score in the list, 82, is shown as the first tally in this row.

TABLE 12.3

Class	Frequency
40–49	3
50–59	6
60–69	6
70–79	11
80–89	9
90–99	5
Total:	$n = 40$

40, the sum of the frequencies, is the number of data items.

Omitting the tally column results in the grouped frequency distribution in Table 12.3. The distribution shows that the greatest frequency of students scored in the 70–79 class. The number of students decreases in classes that contain successively lower and higher scores. The sum of the frequencies, 40, is equal to the original number of data items.

The leftmost number in each class of a grouped frequency distribution is called the **lower class limit**. For example, in Table 12.3, the lower limit of the first class is 40 and the lower limit of the third class is 60. The rightmost number in each class is called the **upper class limit**. In Table 12.3, 49 and 69 are the upper limits for the first and third classes, respectively. Notice that if we take the difference between any two consecutive lower class limits, we get the same number:

$$50 - 40 = 10, \ 60 - 50 = 10, \ 70 - 60 = 10, \ 80 - 70 = 10, \ 90 - 80 = 10.$$

The number 10 is called the **class width**.

When setting up class limits, each class, with the possible exception of the first or last, should have the same width. Because each data item must fall into exactly one class, it is sometimes helpful to vary the width of the first or last class to allow for items that fall far above or below most of the data.

4 Use the classes in Table 12.3 to construct a grouped frequency distribution for the following 37 exam scores:

73	58	68	75	94	79	96	79
87	83	89	52	99	97	89	58
95	77	75	81	75	73	73	62
69	76	77	71	50	57	41	98
77	71	69	90	75.

TABLE 12.2 (repeated) A FREQUENCY DISTRIBUTION FOR A BOY'S AGE OF MAXIMUM YEARLY GROWTH

Age of Maximum Growth	Number of Boys (Frequency)
10	1
11	2
12	5
13	7
14	9
15	6
16	3
17	1
18	1
Total: $n = 35$	

Histograms and Frequency Polygons

Take a second look at the frequency distribution for the age of a boy's maximum yearly growth, repeated in Table 12.2. A bar graph with bars that touch can be used to visually display the data. Such a graph is called a **histogram**. Figure 12.1 illustrates a histogram that was constructed using the frequency distribution in Table 12.2. A series of rectangles whose heights represent the frequencies are placed next to each other. For example, the height of the bar for the data value 10, shown in Figure 12.1, is 1. This corresponds to the frequency for 10 given in Table 12.2. The higher the bar, the more frequent the age. The break along the horizontal axis, symbolized by ⌁, eliminates listing the ages 1 through 9.

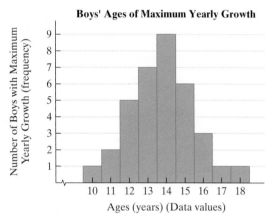

FIGURE 12.1 A histogram for a boy's age of maximum yearly growth

A line graph called a **frequency polygon** can also be used to visually convey the information shown in Figure 12.1. The axes are labeled just like those in a histogram. Thus, the horizontal axis shows data values and the vertical axis shows frequencies. Once a histogram has been constructed, it's fairly easy to draw a frequency polygon. Figure 12.2 shows a histogram with a dot at the top of each rectangle at its midpoint. Connect each of these midpoints with a straight line. To complete the frequency polygon at both ends, the lines should be drawn down to touch the horizontal axis. The completed frequency polygon is shown in Figure 12.3.

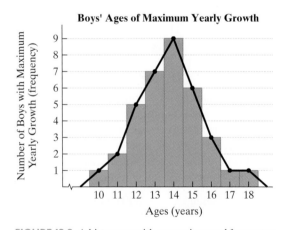

FIGURE 12.2 A histogram with a superimposed frequency polygon

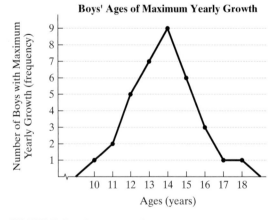

FIGURE 12.3 A frequency polygon

Stem-and-Leaf Plots

A unique way of displaying data uses a tool called a **stem-and-leaf plot**. Example 5 illustrates how we sort the data, revealing the same visual impression created by a histogram.

EXAMPLE 5　CONSTRUCTING A STEM-AND-LEAF PLOT

Use the data showing statistics test scores for 40 students to construct a stem-and-leaf plot:

82	47	75	64	57	82	63	93
76	68	84	54	88	77	79	80
94	92	94	80	94	66	81	67
75	73	66	87	76	45	43	56
57	74	50	78	71	84	59	76.

SOLUTION　The plot is constructed by separating each data item into two parts. The first part is the *stem*. The **stem** consists of the tens digit. For example, the stem for the score of 82 is 8. The second part is the *leaf*. The **leaf** consists of the units digit for a given value. For the score of 82, the leaf is 2. The possible stems for the 40 scores are 4, 5, 6, 7, 8, and 9, entered in the left column of the plot.

Begin by entering each data item in the first row:

82　　47　　75　　64　　57　　82　　63　　93.

Entering **8②:**		**Adding** **4⑦:**		**Adding** **7⑤:**		**Adding** **6④:**	
Stems	Leaves	Stems	Leaves	Stems	Leaves	Stems	Leaves
4		4	⑦	4	7	4	7
5		5		5		5	
6		6		6		6	④
7		7		7	5	7	5
8	②	8	2	8	2	8	2
9		9		9		9	

Adding **5⑦:**		**Adding** **8②:**		**Adding** **6③:**		**Adding** **9③:**	
Stems	Leaves	Stems	Leaves	Stems	Leaves	Stems	Leaves
4	7	4	7	4	7	4	7
5	⑦	5	7	5	7	5	7
6	4	6	4	6	4③	6	4 3
7	5	7	5	7	5	7	5
8	2	8	2②	8	2 2	8	2 2
9		9		9		9	③

We continue in this manner and enter all the data items. Figure 12.4 shows the completed stem-and-leaf plot. If you turn the page so that the left margin is on the bottom and facing you, the visual impression created by the enclosed leaves is the same as that created by a histogram. An advantage over the histogram is that the stem-and-leaf plot preserves exact data items. The enclosed leaves extend farthest to the right when the stem is 7. This shows that the greatest frequency of students scored in the 70s. ○

Tens digit	Units digit

Stems	Leaves
4	7　5　3
5	7　4　6　7　0　9
6	4　3　8　6　7　6
7	5　6　7　9　5　3　6　4　8　1　6
8	2　2　4　8　0　0　1　7　4
9	3　4　2　4　4

FIGURE 12.4　A stem-and-leaf plot displaying 40 test scores

CHECK POINT 5 Construct a stem-and-leaf plot for the data in Check Point 4 on page 684.

4 Identify deceptions in visual displays of data.

Deceptions in Visual Displays of Data

Benjamin Disraeli, Queen Victoria's prime minister, stated that there are "lies, damned lies, and statistics." The problem is not that statistics lie, but rather that liars use statistics. Graphs can be used to distort the underlying data, making it difficult for the viewer to learn the truth. One potential source of misunderstanding is the scale on the vertical axis used to draw the graph. This scale is important because it lets a researcher "inflate" or "deflate" a trend. For example, both graphs in Figure 12.5 present identical data for the percentage of people in the United States living below the poverty level from 2000 through 2004. The graph on the left stretches the scale on the vertical axis to create an overall impression of a poverty rate increasing rapidly over time. The graph on the right compresses the scale on the vertical axis to create an impression of a poverty rate that is slowly increasing, and beginning to level off, over time.

Percentage of People in the United States Living below the Poverty Level, 2000-2004

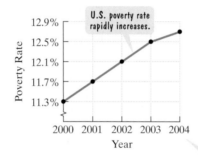

Year	Poverty Rate
2000	11.3%
2001	11.7%
2002	12.1%
2003	12.5%
2004	12.7%

The graph in both figures present this data.

FIGURE 12.5
Source: U.S. Census Bureau

THINGS TO WATCH FOR IN VISUAL DISPLAYS OF DATA

1. Is there a title that explains what is being displayed?
2. Are numbers lined up with tick marks on the vertical axis that clearly indicate the scale? Has the scale been varied to create a more or less dramatic impression than shown by the actual data?
3. Do too many design and cosmetic effects draw attention from or distort the data?
4. Has the wrong impression been created about how the data are changing because equally spaced time intervals are not used on the horizontal axis?
5. Are bar sizes scaled proportionately in terms of the data they represent?
6. Is there a source that indicates where the data in the display came from? Do the data come from an entire population or a sample? Was a random sample used and, if so, are there possible differences between what is displayed in the graph and what is occurring in the entire population? (We'll discuss these *margins of error* in Section 12.4.) Who is presenting the visual display, and does that person have a special case to make for or against the trend shown by the graph?

Table 12.4 on the next page contains two examples of misleading visual displays.

TABLE 12.4 EXAMPLES OF MISLEADING VISUAL DISPLAYS

Graphic Display	Presentation Problems
Purchasing Power of the Diminishing Dollar $1.00 — 1980 63¢ — 1990 54¢ — 1995 48¢ — 2000 43¢ — 2005 *Source:* Bureau of Labor Statistics	Although the length of each dollar bill is proportional to its spending power, the visual display varies both the length *and width* of the bills to show the diminishing power of the dollar over time. Because our eyes focus on the *areas* of the dollar-shaped bars, this creates the impression that the purchasing power of the dollar diminished even more than it really did. If the area of the dollar were drawn to reflect its purchasing power, the 2005 dollar would be approximately twice as large as the one shown in the graphic display.
Number of Square Feet in an Average U.S. Single-Family Home 1500 — 1970 2080 — 1990 2349 — 2004 *Source:* National Association of Home Builders	Cosmetic effects of homes with equal heights, but different frontal additions and shadow lengths, make it impossible to tell if they proportionately depict the given areas. Time intervals on the horizontal axis are not uniform in size, making it appear that dwelling swelling has been linear from 1970 through 2004. The data indicate that this is not the case. There was a greater increase in area from 1970 through 1980, averaging 29 square feet per year, than from 1990 through 2004, averaging approximately 19.2 square feet per year.

BLITZER BONUS

Creating an Inaccurate Picture by Leaving Something Out

On Monday, October 19, 1987, the Dow Jones Industrial Average plunged 508 points, losing 22.6% of its value. The graph shown on the left, which appeared in a major newspaper following "Black Monday" (as it was instantly dubbed), creates the impression that the Dow average had been "bullish" from 1972 through 1987, increasing throughout this period. The graph creates this inaccurate picture by leaving something out. The graph on the right illustrates that the stock market rose and fell sharply over these years. The impressively smooth curve on the left was obtained by plotting only three of the data points. By ignoring most of the data, increases and decreases are not accounted for and the actual behavior of the market over the 15 years leading to "Black Monday" is inaccurately conveyed.

The Dow Jones Industrial Average: 1972–1987

Growth Using Only Three Data Points

Growth and Decline Using All Data

Source: A. K. Dewdney, *200% of Nothing*, John Wiley and Sons, 1993

EXERCISE SET 12.1 ●●●●●●

• Practice and Application Exercises

1. "The Man Poll" of 1014 randomly selected American men ages 18 and older was taken by *Newsweek* June 2–4, 2003. The data shown below are from the poll.

IN GENERAL, HOW WOULD YOU DESCRIBE YOUR HEALTH?

	Age		
	18–34	**35–55**	**≥56**
Excellent	23%	19%	15%
Very good	37	39	32
Good	28	28	28
Fair	10	10	16
Poor	2	4	8
Don't know	0	0	1

a. Describe the population and the sample of this poll.

b. For each man, what variable is measured? Are the data quantitative (numerical) or qualitative (nonnumerical categories)?

2. The *American Association of Nurse Anesthetists Journal* (Feb. 2000) published the results of a study on the use of herbal medicines before surgery. Of 500 surgical patients who were randomly selected for the study, 51% used herbal or alternative medicines prior to surgery.

a. Describe the population and the sample of this study.

b. Is the sample representative of the population? Explain your answer.

c. For each patient, what variable is measured? Are the data quantitative (numerical) or qualitative (nonnumerical categories)?

3. The government of a large city needs to determine whether the city's residents will support the construction of a new jail. The government decides to conduct a survey of a sample of the city's residents. Which one of the following procedures would be most appropriate for obtaining a sample of the city's residents?

a. Survey a random sample of the employees and inmates at the old jail.

b. Survey every fifth person who walks into City Hall on a given day.

c. Survey a random sample of persons within each geographic region of the city.

d. Survey the first 200 people listed in the city's telephone directory.

4. The city council of a large city needs to know whether its residents will support the building of three new schools. The council decides to conduct a survey of a sample of the city's residents. Which procedure would be most appropriate for obtaining a sample of the city's residents?

a. Survey a random sample of teachers who live in the city.

b. Survey 100 individuals who are randomly selected from a list of all people living in the state in which the city in question is located.

c. Survey a random sample of persons within each neighborhood of the city.

d. Survey every tenth person who enters City Hall on a randomly selected day.

A questionnaire was given to students in an introductory statistics class during the first week of the course. One question asked, "How stressed have you been in the last $2\frac{1}{2}$ weeks, on a scale of 0 to 10, with 0 being not at all stressed and 10 being as stressed as possible?" The students' responses are shown in the frequency distribution. Use this frequency distribution to solve Exercises 5–8.

Stress Rating	**Frequency**
0	2
1	1
2	3
3	12
4	16
5	18
6	13
7	31
8	26
9	15
10	14

Source: Journal of Personality and Social Psychology, 69, 1102–1112

5. Which stress rating describes the greatest number of students? How many students responded with this rating?

6. Which stress rating describes the least number of students? How many responded with this rating?

7. How many students were involved in this study?

8. How many students had a stress rating of 8 or more?

9. A random sample of 30 college students is selected. Each student is asked how much time he or she spent on homework during the previous week. The following times (in hours) are obtained:

16, 24, 18, 21, 18, 16, 18, 17, 15, 21, 19, 17, 17, 16, 19, 18, 15, 15, 20, 17, 15, 17, 24, 19, 16, 20, 16, 19, 18, 17.

Construct a frequency distribution for the data.

10. A random sample of 30 male college students is selected. Each student is asked his height (to the nearest inch). The heights are as follows:

72, 70, 68, 72, 71, 71, 71, 69, 73, 71, 73, 75, 66, 67, 75, 74, 73, 71, 72, 67, 72, 68, 67, 71, 73, 71, 72, 70, 73, 70.

Construct a frequency distribution for the data.

A college professor had students keep a diary of their social interactions for a week. Excluding family and work situations, the number of social interactions of ten minutes or longer over the week is shown in the following grouped frequency distribution. Use this information to solve Exercises 11–18.

Number of Social Interactions	Frequency
0–4	12
5–9	16
10–14	16
15–19	16
20–24	10
25–29	11
30–34	4
35–39	3
40–44	3
45–49	3

Source: Society for Personality and Social Psychology

11. Identify the lower class limit for each class.
12. Identify the upper class limit for each class.
13. What is the class width?
14. How many students were involved in this study?
15. How many students had at least 30 social interactions for the week?
16. How many students had at most 14 social interactions for the week?
17. Among the classes with the greatest frequency, which class has the least number of social interactions?
18. Among the classes with the smallest frequency, which class has the least number of social interactions?
19. As of 2007, the following are the ages, in chronological order, at which U.S. presidents were inaugurated:

57, 61, 57, 57, 58, 57, 61, 54, 68, 51, 49, 64, 50, 48, 65, 52, 56, 46, 54, 49, 50, 47, 55, 55, 54, 42, 51, 56, 55, 51, 54, 51, 60, 62, 43, 55, 56, 61, 52, 69, 64, 46, 54.

Source: Time Almanac

Construct a grouped frequency distribution for the data. Use 41–45 for the first class and use the same width for each subsequent class.

20. The IQ scores of 70 students enrolled in a liberal arts course at a college are as follows:

102, 100, 103, 86, 120, 117, 111, 101, 93, 97, 99, 95, 95, 104, 104, 105, 106, 109, 109, 89, 94, 95, 99, 99, 103, 104, 105, 109, 110, 114, 124, 123, 118, 117, 116, 110, 114, 114, 96, 99, 103, 103, 104, 107, 107, 110, 111, 112, 113, 117, 115, 116, 100, 104, 102, 94, 93, 93, 96, 96, 111, 116, 107, 109, 105, 106, 97, 106, 107, 108.

Construct a grouped frequency distribution for the data. Use 85–89 for the first class and use the same width for each subsequent class.

21. Construct a histogram and a frequency polygon for the data involving stress ratings in Exercises 5–8.
22. Construct a histogram and a frequency polygon for the data in Exercise 9.

23. Construct a histogram and a frequency polygon for the data in Exercise 10.
24. The histogram shows the distribution of starting salaries (rounded to the nearest thousand dollars) for college graduates based on a random sample of recent graduates.

Starting Salaries of Recent College Graduates

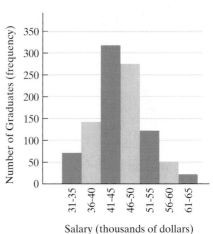

Which one of the following is true according to the graph?

a. The graph is based on a sample of approximately 500 recent college graduates.
b. More college graduates had starting salaries in the $51,000–$55,000 range than in the $36,000–$40,000 range.
c. If the sample is truly representative, then for a group of 400 college graduates, we can expect about 28 of them to have starting salaries in the $31,000–$35,000 range.
d. The percentage of starting salaries falling above those shown by any rectangular bar is equal to the percentage of starting salaries falling below that bar.

25. The frequency polygon shows a distribution of IQ scores. Which one of the following is true based upon the graph?

a. The graph is based on a sample of approximately 50 people.
b. More people had an IQ score of 100 than any other IQ score, and as the deviation from 100 increases or decreases, the scores fall off in a symmetrical manner.
c. More people had an IQ score of 110 than a score of 90.
d. The percentage of scores above any IQ score is equal to the percentage of scores below that score.

Distribution of IQ Scores

26. Construct a stem-and-leaf plot for the data in Exercise 19 showing the ages at which U.S. presidents were inaugurated.

27. A random sample of 40 college professors is selected from all professors at a university. The following list gives their ages:

63, 48, 42, 42, 38, 59, 41, 44, 45, 28, 54, 62, 51, 44, 63, 66, 59,
46, 51, 28, 37, 66, 42, 40, 30, 31, 48, 32, 29, 42, 63, 37, 36, 47,
25, 34, 49, 30, 35, 50.

Construct a stem-and-leaf plot for the data. What does the shape of the display reveal about the ages of the professors?

28. In "Ages of Oscar-Winning Best Actors and Actresses" (*Mathematics Teacher* magazine) by Richard Brown and Gretchen Davis, the stem-and-leaf plots shown compare the ages of actors and actresses for 30 winners of the Oscar at the time they won the award.

Actors	Stems	Actresses
	2	146667
98753221	3	00113344455778
88776543322100	4	11129
6651	5	
210	6	011
6	7	4
	8	0

a. What is the age of the youngest actor to win an Oscar?

b. What is the age difference between the oldest and the youngest actress to win an Oscar?

c. What is the oldest age shared by two actors to win an Oscar?

d. What differences do you observe between the two stem-and-leaf plots? What explanations can you offer for these differences?

In Exercises 29–33, describe what is misleading in each visual display of data.

29.

World Population, in Billions

Source: U.S. Census Bureau

30.

Book Title Output in the United States

Source: R. R. Bowker

31.

Percentage of the World's Computers in Use, by Country

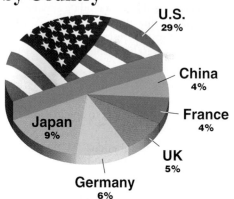

Source: Computer Industry Almanac

32.

Enrollment at the University of Georgia

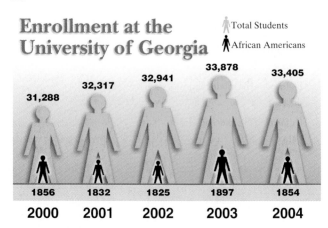

Source: University of Georgia Office of Institutional Research

33.

Student Loans on the Rise:
Percentage of Bachelor's Degree Recipients with
Federal Student Loans and Median Loan Amount

1992–93	36.8% $10,008
1995–96	50.1% $13,327
1999–00	60.3% $16,958
2003–04	63.0% $16,432

Source: American Council on Education

• Writing in Mathematics

34. What is a population? What is a sample?

35. Describe what is meant by a random sample.

36. Suppose you are interested in whether or not the students at your college would favor a grading system in which students may receive final grades of A+, A, A−, B+, B, B−, C+, C, C−, and so on. Describe how you might obtain a random sample of 100 students from the entire student population.

37. For Exercise 36, would questioning every fifth student as he or she is leaving the campus library until 100 students are interviewed be a good way to obtain a random sample? Explain your answer.

38. What is a frequency distribution?

39. What is a histogram?

40. What is a frequency polygon?

41. Describe how to construct a frequency polygon from a histogram.

42. Describe how to construct a stem-and-leaf plot from a set of data.

43. Describe two ways that graphs can be misleading.

• Critical Thinking Exercises

44. Construct a grouped frequency distribution for the following data, showing the length, in miles, of the 25 longest rivers in the United States. Use five classes that have the same width.

2540	2340	1980	1900	1900
1460	1450	1420	1310	1290
1280	1240	1040	990	926
906	886	862	800	774
743	724	692	659	649

Source: U.S. Department of the Interior

45. Use two line graphs drawn in the same coordinate system that show a better way to portray the enrollment information for 2000 through 2004 in Exercise 32.

• Group Exercises

46. The classic book on distortion using statistics is *How to Lie with Statistics* by Darrell Huff. This activity is designed for five people. Each person should select two chapters from Huff's book and then present to the class the common methods of statistical manipulation and distortion that Huff discusses.

47. Each group member should find one example of a graph that presents data with integrity and one example of a graph that is misleading. Use newspapers, magazines, the Internet, books, and so forth. Once graphs have been collected, each member should share his or her graphs with the entire group. Be sure to explain why one graph depicts data in a forthright manner and how the other graph misleads the viewer.

SECTION 12.2 • MEASURES OF CENTRAL TENDENCY

OBJECTIVES

1. Determine the mean for a data set.
2. Determine the median for a data set.
3. Determine the mode for a data set.
4. Determine the midrange for a data set.

© NAS. Reprinted with permission of North America Syndicate.

According to researchers, "Robert," the average American guy, is 31 years old, 5 feet 10 inches, 172 pounds, works 6.1 hours daily, and sleeps 7.7 hours. These numbers represent what is "average" or "typical" of American men. In statistics, such values are known as **measures of central tendency** because they are generally located toward the center of a distribution. Four such measures are discussed in this section:

the mean, the median, the mode, and the midrange. Each measure of central tendency is calculated in a different way. Thus, it is better to use a specific term (mean, median, mode, or midrange) than to use the generic descriptive term "average."

1 | Determine the mean for a data set.

The Mean

By far the most commonly used measure of central tendency is the *mean*. The **mean** is obtained by adding all the data items and then dividing the sum by the number of items. The Greek letter sigma, Σ, called a **symbol of summation**, is used to indicate the sum of data items. The notation Σx, read "the sum of x," means to add all the data items in a given data set. We can use this symbol to give a formula for calculating the mean.

> ### THE MEAN
> The **mean** is the sum of the data items divided by the number of items.
>
> $$\text{Mean} = \frac{\Sigma x}{n},$$
>
> where Σx represents the sum of all the data items and n represents the number of items.

EXAMPLE 1   CALCULATING THE MEAN

Table 12.5 shows the ten youngest male singers in the United States to have a number 1 single. Find the mean age of these male singers at the time of their number 1 single.

TABLE 12.5 YOUNGEST U.S. MALE SINGERS TO HAVE A NUMBER 1 SINGLE		
Artist/Year	**Title**	**Age**
Stevie Wonder, 1963	"Fingertips"	13
Donny Osmond, 1971	"Go Away Little Girl"	13
Michael Jackson, 1972	"Ben"	14
Laurie London, 1958	"He's Got the Whole World in His Hands"	14
Paul Anka, 1957	"Diana"	16
Brian Hyland, 1960	"Itsy Bitsy Teenie Weenie Yellow Polkadot Bikini"	16
Shaun Cassidy, 1977	"Da Doo Ron Ron"	17
Bobby Vee, 1961	"Take Good Care of My Baby"	18
Usher, 1998	"Nice & Slow"	19
Andy Gibb, 1977	"I Just Want to Be Your Everything"	19

Source: Russell Ash, *The Top 10 of Everything*

SOLUTION We find the mean by adding the ages and dividing this sum by 10, the number of data items.

$$\text{Mean} = \frac{\Sigma x}{n} = \frac{13 + 13 + 14 + 14 + 16 + 16 + 17 + 18 + 19 + 19}{10} = \frac{159}{10} = 15.9$$

The mean age of the ten youngest singers to have a number 1 single is 15.9.

One and only one mean can be calculated for any group of numerical data. The mean may or may not be one of the actual data items. In Example 1, the mean was 15.9, although no data item is 15.9.

Find the mean for each group of data items:

    a. 10, 20, 30, 40, 50   **b.** 3, 10, 10, 10, 117.

In Example 1, some of the data items were identical. We can use multiplication when computing the mean for these identical items:

$$\text{Mean} = \frac{13 + 13 + 14 + 14 + 16 + 16 + 17 + 18 + 19 + 19}{10}$$

$$= \frac{13 \cdot 2 + 14 \cdot 2 + 16 \cdot 2 + 17 \cdot 1 + 18 \cdot 1 + 19 \cdot 2}{10}$$

> The data values 13, 14, 16, and 19 each have a frequency of 2.

When many data values occur more than once and a frequency distribution is used to organize the data, we can use the following formula to calculate the mean:

CALCULATING THE MEAN FOR A FREQUENCY DISTRIBUTION

$$\text{Mean} = \frac{\Sigma xf}{n},$$

where

x represents a data value.

f represents the frequency of that data value.

Σxf represents the sum of all the products obtained by multiplying each data value by its frequency.

n represents the *total frequency* of the distribution.

TABLE 12.6 STUDENTS' STRESS-LEVEL RATINGS

Stress Rating x	Frequency f
0	2
1	1
2	3
3	12
4	16
5	18
6	13
7	31
8	26
9	15
10	14

Source: Journal of Personality and Social Psychology, 69, 1102–1112

EXAMPLE 2   CALCULATING THE MEAN FOR A FREQUENCY DISTRIBUTION

In the previous exercise set, we mentioned a questionnaire given to students in an introductory statistics class during the first week of the course. One question asked, "How stressed have you been in the last $2\frac{1}{2}$ weeks, on a scale of 0 to 10, with 0 being not at all stressed and 10 being as stressed as possible?" Table 12.6 shows the students' responses. Use this frequency distribution to find the mean of the stress-level ratings.

SOLUTION We use the formula

$$\text{Mean} = \frac{\Sigma xf}{n}.$$

First, we must find xf, obtained by multiplying each data value, x, by its frequency, f. Then, we need to find the sum of these products, Σxf. We can use the frequency distribution to organize these computations. Add a third column in which each data value is multiplied by its frequency. This column, shown on the right, is headed xf. Then, find the sum of the values, Σxf, in this column.

x	f	xf
0	2	$0 \cdot 2 = 0$
1	1	$1 \cdot 1 = 1$
2	3	$2 \cdot 3 = 6$
3	12	$3 \cdot 12 = 36$
4	16	$4 \cdot 16 = 64$
5	18	$5 \cdot 18 = 90$
6	13	$6 \cdot 13 = 78$
7	31	$7 \cdot 31 = 217$
8	26	$8 \cdot 26 = 208$
9	15	$9 \cdot 15 = 135$
10	14	$10 \cdot 14 = 140$

Totals: $n = 151$ $\Sigma xf = 975$

> Σxf is the sum of the numbers in the third column.

> This value, the sum of the numbers in the second column, is the total frequency of the distribution.

Now, substitute these values into the formula for the mean. Remember that n is the *total frequency* of the distribution, or 151.

$$\text{Mean} = \frac{\Sigma xf}{n} = \frac{975}{151} \approx 6.46$$

The mean of the 0 to 10 stress-level ratings is approximately 6.46. Notice that the mean is greater than 5, the middle of the 0 to 10 scale.

 Find the mean for the data items in the frequency distribution. (In order to save space, we've written the frequency distribution horizontally.)

Score, x	30	33	40	50
Frequency, f	3	4	4	1

2 Determine the median for a data set.

The Median

The *median* age in the United States is 35.3. The oldest state by median age is Florida (38.7) and the youngest state is Utah (27.1). To find these values, researchers begin with appropriate random samples. The data items—that is, the ages—are arranged from youngest to oldest. The median age is the data item in the middle of each set of ranked, or ordered, data.

> **THE MEDIAN**
> To find the **median** of a group of data items,
>
> 1. Arrange the data items in order, from smallest to largest.
> 2. If the number of data items is odd, the median is the data item in the middle of the list.
> 3. If the number of data items is even, the median is the mean of the two middle data items.

EXAMPLE 3   FINDING THE MEDIAN

Find the median for each of the following groups of data:

a. 84, 90, 98, 95, 88

b. 68, 74, 7, 13, 15, 25, 28, 59, 34, 47.

SOLUTION

a. Arrange the data items in order, from smallest to largest. The number of data items in the list, five, is odd. Thus, the median is the middle number.

84, 88, 90, 95, 98

Middle data item

The median is 90. Notice that two data items lie above 90 and two data items lie below 90.

b. Arrange the data items in order, from smallest to largest. The number of data items in the list, ten, is even. Thus, the median is the mean of the two middle data items.

7, 13, 15, 25, 28, 34, 47, 59, 68, 74

Middle data items are 28 and 34.

$$\text{Median} = \frac{28 + 34}{2} = \frac{62}{2} = 31$$

The median is 31. Five data items lie above 31 and five data items lie below 31.

7 13 15 25 28 │ 34 47 59 68 74

Five data items lie below 31.

Five data items lie above 31.

Median is 31.

 Find the median for each of the following groups of data:

   a. 28, 42, 40, 25, 35

   b. 72, 61, 85, 93, 79, 87.

If a relatively long list of data items is arranged in order, it may be difficult to identify the item or items in the middle. In cases like this, the median can be found by determining its position in the list of items.

POSITION OF THE MEDIAN

If n data items are arranged in order, from smallest to largest, the median is the value in the

$$\frac{n+1}{2}$$

position.

STUDY TIP

The formula

$$\frac{n+1}{2}$$

gives the *position* of the median, and not the actual value of the median. When finding the median, be sure to first arrange the data items in order from smallest to largest.

EXAMPLE 4   FINDING THE MEDIAN USING THE POSITION FORMULA

Listed below are the points scored per season by the 13 top point scorers in the National Football League. Find the median points scored per season for the top 13 scorers.

144, 144, 145, 145, 145, 146, 147, 149, 150, 155, 161, 164, 176

SOLUTION The data items are arranged from smallest to largest. There are 13 data items, so $n = 13$. The median is the value in the

$$\frac{n+1}{2} \text{ position} = \frac{13+1}{2} \text{ position} = \frac{14}{2} \text{ position} = \text{seventh position.}$$

We find the median by selecting the data item in the seventh position.

Position 3   Position 4   Position 7

144, 144, 145, 145, 145, 146, 147, 149, 150, 155, 161, 164, 176

Position 1   Position 2   Position 5   Position 6

The median is 147. Notice that six data items lie above 147 and six data items lie below it. The median points scored per season for the top 13 scorers in the National Football League is 147.

 Find the median for the following group of data items:

1, 2, 2, 2, 3, 3, 3, 3, 3, 5, 6, 7, 7, 10, 11, 13, 19, 24, 26.

TABLE 12.7 NUMBER OF HOME RUNS BY BASEBALL TEAMS IN THE NATIONAL LEAGUE, 2005

Team	Home Runs
Washington Nationals	117
Florida Marlins	128
San Francisco Giants	128
San Diego Padres	130
Pittsburgh Pirates	139
Los Angeles Dodgers	149
Colorado Rockies	150
Houston Astros	161
Philadelphia Phillies	167
St. Louis Cardinals	170
Milwaukee Brewers	175
New York Mets	175
Atlanta Braves	184
Arizona Diamondbacks	191
Chicago Cubs	194
Cincinnati Reds	222

Source: The World Almanac

EXAMPLE 5 FINDING THE MEDIAN USING THE POSITION FORMULA

Table 12.7 gives the number of home runs for the 16 baseball teams in the National League in 2005. Find the median number of home runs for these teams.

SOLUTION The data items are arranged from smallest to largest. There are 16 data items, so $n = 16$. The median is the value in the

$$\frac{n + 1}{2} \text{ position} = \frac{16 + 1}{2} \text{ position} = \frac{17}{2} \text{ position} = 8.5 \text{ position}.$$

This means that the median is the mean of the data items in positions 8 and 9.

117, 128, 128, 130, 139, 149, 150, 161, 167, 170, 175, 175, 184, 191, 194, 222

$$\text{Median} = \frac{161 + 167}{2} = \frac{328}{2} = 164$$

The median number of home runs for the teams in the National League in 2005 was 164.

CHECK POINT 5 Listed below are the number of home runs for each of the 14 baseball teams in the American League in 2005. Find the median number of home runs for these teams.

126, 130, 134, 136, 147, 155, 157, 168, 189, 199, 200, 207, 229, 260

When individual data items are listed from smallest to largest, you can find the median by identifying the item or items in the middle or by using the $\frac{n + 1}{2}$ formula for its position. However, the formula for the position of the median is useful when data items are organized in a frequency distribution.

EXAMPLE 6 FINDING THE MEDIAN FOR A FREQUENCY DISTRIBUTION

The frequency distribution for the stress-level ratings of 151 students is repeated below using a horizontal format. Find the median stress-level rating.

Stress rating x	0	1	2	3	4	5	6	7	8	9	10
Number of college students f	2	1	3	12	16	18	13	31	26	15	14

Total: $n = 151$

SOLUTION There are 151 data items, so $n = 151$. The median is the value in the

$$\frac{n + 1}{2} \text{ position} = \frac{151 + 1}{2} \text{ position} = \frac{152}{2} \text{ position} = 76\text{th position}.$$

We find the median by selecting the data item in the 76th position. The frequency distribution indicates that the data items begin with

$$0, 0, 1, 2, 2, 2, \ldots.$$

We can write the data items all out and then select the median, the 76th data item. A more efficient way to proceed is to count down the frequency column in the distribution until we identify the 76th data item:

x	f
0	2
1	1
2	3
3	12
4	16
5	18
6	13
7	31
8	26
9	15
10	14

We count down the frequency column.

1, 2

3

4, 5, 6

7, 8, 9, 10, 11, 12, 13, 14, 15, 16, 17, 18

19, 20, 21, 22, 23, 24, 25, 26, 27, 28, 29, 30, 31, 32, 33, 34

35, 36, 37, 38, 39, 40, 41, 42, 43, 44, 45, 46, 47, 48, 49, 50, 51, 52,

53, 54, 55, 56, 57, 58, 59, 60, 61, 62, 63, 64, 65

66, 67, 68, 69, 70, 71, 72, 73, 74, 75, 76

Stop counting. We've reached the 76th data item.

The 76th data item is 7. The median stress-level rating is 7.

6 Find the median for the following frequency distribution.

Age at presidential inauguration

Number of U.S. presidents assuming office in the 20th century with the given age

x	42	43	46	51	52	54	55	56	60	61	64	69
f	1	1	1	3	1	2	2	2	1	2	1	1

Statisticians generally use the median, rather than the mean, when reporting income. Why? Our next example will help to answer this question.

EXAMPLE 7　COMPARING THE MEDIAN AND THE MEAN

Five employees in the assembly section of a television manufacturing company earn salaries of $19,700, $20,400, $21,500, $22,600, and $23,000 annually. The section manager has an annual salary of $95,000.

a. Find the median annual salary for the six people.

b. Find the mean annual salary for the six people.

SOLUTION

a. To compute the median, first arrange the salaries in order:

$$\$19,700, \quad \$20,400, \quad \$21,500, \quad \$22,600, \quad \$23,000, \quad \$95,000.$$

Because the list contains an even number of data items, six, the median is the mean of the two middle items.

$$\text{Median} = \frac{\$21,500 + \$22,600}{2} = \frac{\$44,100}{2} = \$22,050$$

The median annual salary is $22,050.

b. We find the mean annual salary by adding the six annual salaries and dividing by 6.

$$\text{Mean} = \frac{\$19,700 + \$20,400 + \$21,500 + \$22,600 + \$23,000 + \$95,000}{6}$$

$$= \frac{\$202,200}{6} = \$33,700$$

The mean annual salary is $33,700.

In Example 7, the median annual salary is $22,050 and the mean annual salary is $33,700. Why such a big difference between these two measures of central tendency? The relatively high annual salary of the section manager, $95,000, pulls the mean salary to a value considerably higher than the median salary. When one or more data items are much greater than the other items, these extreme values can greatly influence the mean. In cases like this, the median is often more representative of the data.

This is why the median, rather than the mean, is used to summarize the incomes, by gender and race, shown in Figure 12.6. Because no one can earn less than $0, the distribution of income must come to an end at $0 for each of these eight groups. By contrast, there is no upper limit on income on the high side. In the United States, the wealthiest 5% of the population earn about 21% of the total income. The relatively few people with very high annual incomes tend to pull the mean income to a value considerably greater than the median income. Reporting mean incomes in Figure 12.6 would inflate the numbers shown, making them nonrepresentative of the millions of workers in each of the eight groups.

U.S. Median Income in 2003, by Gender and Race

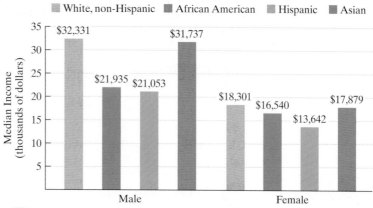

FIGURE 12.6
Source: U.S. Census Bureau

CHECK POINT 7 The ten countries in Table 12.8 accounted for 75% of the nearly $900 billion spent in 2003 on defense worldwide.

TABLE 12.8 TOP TEN MILITARY SPENDERS, 2003

Country	National Expenditure (billions of dollars)	Dollars Spent per Resident	Percentage of Global Military Spending
United States	$417.4	$1419	47%
Japan	$ 46.9	$ 367	5%
UK	$ 37.1	$ 627	4%
France	$ 35.0	$ 583	4%
China	$ 32.8	$ 25	4%
Germany	$ 27.2	$ 329	3%
Italy	$ 20.8	$ 362	2%
Iran	$ 19.2	$ 279	2%
Saudi Arabia	$ 19.1	$ 789	2%
South Korea	$ 13.9	$ 292	2%

Source: SIPRI, "The Major Spenders in 2003"

a. Find the mean national expenditure on defense, in billions of dollars, for the ten countries.

b. Find the median national expenditure on defense, in billions of dollars, for the ten countries.

c. Describe why one of the measures of central tendency is so much greater than the other.

3 | Determine the mode for a data set.

The Mode

Let's take one final look at the frequency distribution for the stress-level ratings of 151 college students.

Stress rating

Number of college students

x	0	1	2	3	4	5	6	7	8	9	10
f	2	1	3	12	16	18	13	31	26	15	14

7 is the stress rating with the greatest frequency.

The data value that occurs most often in this distribution is 7, the stress rating for 31 of the 151 students. We call 7 the *mode* of this distribution.

> **THE MODE**
> The **mode** is the data value that occurs most often in a data set. If no data items are repeated, then the data set has no mode. If more than one data value has the highest frequency, then each of these data values is a mode.

EXAMPLE 8   FINDING THE MODE

Find the mode for the following group of data:

$$7, 2, 4, 7, 8, 10.$$

SOLUTION The number 7 occurs more often than any other. Therefore, 7 is the mode.

 Find the mode for the following group of data:

$$8, 6, 2, 4, 6, 8, 10, 8.$$

Be aware that a data set might not have a mode. For example, no data item in 2, 1, 4, 5, 3 is repeated, so this data group has no mode. By contrast, 3, 3, 4, 5, 6, 6 has two data values with the highest frequency, namely 3 and 6. Each of these data values is a mode and the data set is said to be **bimodal**.

4 | Determine the midrange for a data set.

The Midrange

Table 12.9 shows the ten hottest cities in the United States. Because temperature is constantly changing, you might wonder how the mean temperatures shown in the table are obtained.

First, we need to find a representative daily temperature. This is obtained by adding the lowest and highest temperatures for the day and then dividing this sum by 2. Next, we take the representative daily temperatures for all 365 days, add them, and divide the sum by 365. These are the mean temperatures that appear in Table 12.9.

Representative daily temperature,

$$\frac{\text{lowest daily temperature} + \text{highest daily temperature}}{2},$$

is an example of a measure of central tendency called the *midrange*.

> **THE MIDRANGE**
> The **midrange** is found by adding the lowest and highest data values and dividing the sum by 2.
>
> $$\text{Midrange} = \frac{\text{lowest data value} + \text{highest data value}}{2}$$

TABLE 12.9 TEN HOTTEST U.S. CITIES

City	Mean Temperature
Key West, FL	77.8°
Miami, FL	75.9°
West Palm Beach, FL	74.7°
Fort Myers, FL	74.4°
Yuma, AZ	74.2°
Brownsville, TX	73.8°
Phoenix, AZ	72.6°
Vero Beach, FL	72.4°
Orlando, FL	72.3°
Tampa, FL	72.3°

Source: National Oceanic and Atmospheric Administration

EXAMPLE 9   FINDING THE MIDRANGE

One criticism of major league baseball is that the discrepancy between team payrolls hampers fair competition. In 2006, the New York Yankees had the greatest payroll, a record $194,663,100 (median salary: $2,925,000). The Florida Marlins were the worst paid team, with a payroll of $14,998,500 (median salary: $327,000). Find the midrange for the annual payroll of major league baseball teams in 2006. (*Source*: usatoday.com)

SOLUTION

$$\text{Midrange} = \frac{\text{lowest annual payroll} + \text{highest annual payroll}}{2}$$

$$= \frac{\$14,998,500 + \$194,663,100}{2} = \frac{\$209,661,600}{2} = \$104,830,800$$

The midrange for the annual payroll of major league baseball teams in 2006 was $104,830,800.

We can find the mean annual payroll of the 30 professional baseball teams in 2006 by adding up the payrolls of all 30 teams and then dividing the sum by 30. It is much faster to calculate the midrange, which is often used as an estimate for the mean.

CHECK POINT 9 The best paid state governor is in New York, earning $179,000 annually. The worst paid is the governor of Maine, earning $70,000 annually. Find the midrange for annual salaries of U.S. governors.

EXAMPLE 10   FINDING THE FOUR MEASURES OF CENTRAL TENDENCY

Suppose your six exam grades in a course are

52, 69, 75, 86, 86, and 92.

Compute your final course grade ($90-100 = A$, $80-89 = B$, $70-79 = C$, $60-69 = D$, below $60 = F$) using the

a. mean.   **b.** median.   **c.** mode.   **d.** midrange.

SOLUTION

a. The mean is the sum of the data items divided by the number of items, 6.

$$\text{Mean} = \frac{52 + 69 + 75 + 86 + 86 + 92}{6} = \frac{460}{6} \approx 76.67$$

Using the mean, your final course grade is C.

b. The six data items, 52, 69, 75, 86, 86, and 92, are arranged in order. Because the number of data items is even, the median is the mean of the two middle items.

$$\text{Median} = \frac{75 + 86}{2} = \frac{161}{2} = 80.5$$

Using the median, your final course grade is B.

c. The mode is the data value that occurs most frequently. Because 86 occurs most often, the mode is 86. Using the mode, your final course grade is B.

d. The midrange is the mean of the lowest and highest data values.

$$\text{Midrange} = \frac{52 + 92}{2} = \frac{144}{2} = 72$$

Using the midrange, your final course grade is C.

Consumer Reports magazine gave the following data for the number of calories in a meat hot dog for each of 17 brands:

173, 191, 182, 190, 172, 147, 146, 138, 175, 136, 179, 153, 107, 195, 135, 140, 138.

Find the mean, median, mode, and midrange for the number of calories in a meat hot dog for the 17 brands. If necessary, round answers to the nearest tenth of a calorie.

EXERCISE SET 12.2 ●●●●●●

• Practice Exercises

In Exercises 1–8, find the mean for each group of data items.

1. 7, 4, 3, 2, 8, 5, 1, 3

2. 11, 6, 4, 0, 2, 1, 12, 0, 0

3. 91, 95, 99, 97, 93, 95

4. 100, 100, 90, 30, 70, 100

5. 100, 40, 70, 40, 60

6. 1, 3, 5, 10, 8, 5, 6, 8

7. 1.6, 3.8, 5.0, 2.7, 4.2, 4.2, 3.2, 4.7, 3.6, 2.5, 2.5

8. 1.4, 2.1, 1.6, 3.0, 1.4, 2.2, 1.4, 9.0, 9.0, 1.8

In Exercises 9–12, find the mean for the data items in the given frequency distribution.

9.

Score x	Frequency f
1	1
2	3
3	4
4	4
5	6
6	5
7	3
8	2

10.

Score x	Frequency f
1	2
2	4
3	5
4	7
5	6
6	4
7	3

11.

Score x	Frequency f
1	1
2	1
3	2
4	5
5	7
6	9
7	8
8	6
9	4
10	3

12.

Score x	Frequency f
1	3
2	4
3	6
4	8
5	9
6	7
7	5
8	2
9	1
10	1

In Exercises 13–20, find the median for each group of data items.

13. 7, 4, 3, 2, 8, 5, 1, 3

14. 11, 6, 4, 0, 2, 1, 12, 0, 0

15. 91, 95, 99, 97, 93, 95

16. 100, 100, 90, 30, 70, 100

17. 100, 40, 70, 40, 60

18. 1, 3, 5, 10, 8, 5, 6, 8

19. 1.6, 3.8, 5.0, 2.7, 4.2, 4.2, 3.2, 4.7, 3.6, 2.5, 2.5

20. 1.4, 2.1, 1.6, 3.0, 1.4, 2.2, 1.4, 9.0, 9.0, 1.8

Find the median for the data items in the frequency distribution in

21. Exercise 9.

22. Exercise 10.

23. Exercise 11.

24. Exercise 12.

In Exercises 25–32, find the mode for each group of data items. If there is no mode, so state.

25. 7, 4, 3, 2, 8, 5, 1, 3

26. 11, 6, 4, 0, 2, 1, 12, 0, 0

27. 91, 95, 99, 97, 93, 95

28. 100, 100, 90, 30, 70, 100

29. 100, 40, 70, 40, 60

30. 1, 3, 5, 10, 8, 5, 6, 8

31. 1.6, 3.8, 5.0, 2.7, 4.2, 4.2, 3.2, 4.7, 3.6, 2.5, 2.5

32. 1.4, 2.1, 1.6, 3.0, 1.4, 2.2, 1.4, 9.0, 9.0, 1.8

Find the mode for the data items in the frequency distribution in

33. Exercise 9.

34. Exercise 10.

35. Exercise 11.

36. Exercise 12.

In Exercises 37–44, find the midrange for each group of data items.

37. 7, 4, 3, 2, 8, 5, 1, 3

38. 11, 6, 4, 0, 2, 1, 12, 0, 0

39. 91, 95, 99, 97, 93, 95

40. 100, 100, 90, 30, 70, 100

41. 100, 40, 70, 40, 60

42. 1, 3, 5, 10, 8, 5, 6, 8

43. 1.6, 3.8, 5.0, 2.7, 4.2, 4.2, 3.2, 4.7, 3.6, 2.5, 2.5

44. 1.4, 2.1, 1.6, 3.0, 1.4, 2.2, 1.4, 9.0, 9.0, 1.8

Find the midrange for the data items in the frequency distribution in

45. Exercise 9.

46. Exercise 10.

47. Exercise 11.

48. Exercise 12.

• Practice Plus

In Exercises 49–54, use each display of data items to find the mean, median, mode, and midrange.

49.

50.

51.

52.

53.

Stems	Leaves			
2	1	4	5	
3	0	1	1	3
4	2	5		

54.

Stems	Leaves			
2	8			
3	2	4	4	9
4	0	1	5	7

• Application Exercises

Exercises 55–59 present data on a variety of topics. For each data set described in boldface, find the

a. *mean.*

b. *median.*

c. *mode (or state that there is no mode).*

d. *midrange.*

55. Ages of the Justices of the United States Supreme Court in 2007

Roberts (52), Stevens (87), Scalia (71), Kennedy (71), Souter (68), Thomas (59), Ginsburg (74), Breyer (69), Alito (56)

56. Number of Reported Violent Attacks against the Homeless in the United States for Various Years from 1995 through 2005

60, 63, 52, 36, 70, 105, 86

Source: National Coalition for the Homeless

57. Number of Home Runs Hit by Each of the 12 Batters for the New York Yankees in 2005

0, 4, 8, 12, 14, 17, 19, 19, 23, 32, 34, 48

Source: The World Almanac

58. Number of Home Runs Hit by Each of the Ten Batters for the Florida Marlins in 2005

2, 3, 4, 5, 6, 8, 9, 16, 33, 33

Source: The World Almanac

59. Number of Social Interactions of College Students In Exercise Set 12.1, we presented a grouped frequency distribution showing the number of social interactions of ten minutes or longer over a one-week period for a group of college students. (These interactions excluded family and work situations.) Use the frequency distribution shown to solve this exercise. (This distribution was obtained by replacing the classes in the grouped frequency distribution previously shown with the midpoints of the classes.)

Social interactions in a week →

Number of college students →

x	2	7	12	17	22	27	32	37	42	47
f	12	16	16	16	10	11	4	3	3	3

The weights (to the nearest five pounds) of 40 randomly selected male college students are organized in a histogram with a superimposed frequency polygon. Use the graph to answer Exercises 60–63.

60. Find the mean weight.   **61.** Find the median weight.

62. Find the modal weight.   **63.** Find the midrange weight.

Weights of 40 Male College Students

64. An advertisement for a speed-reading course claimed that the "average" reading speed for people completing the course was 1000 words per minute. Shown below are the actual data for the reading speeds per minute for a sample of 24 people who completed the course.

1000	900	800	1000	900	850
650	1000	1050	800	1000	850
700	750	800	850	900	950
600	1100	950	700	750	650

   a. Find the mean, median, mode, and midrange. (If you prefer, first organize the data in a frequency distribution.)

   b. Which measure of central tendency was given in the advertisement?

   c. Which measure of central tendency is the best indicator of the "average" reading speed in this situation? Explain your answer.

65. In one common system for finding a grade-point average, or GPA,

$$A = 4, B = 3, C = 2, D = 1, F = 0.$$

The GPA is calculated by multiplying the number of credit hours for a course and the number assigned to each grade, and then adding these products. Then divide this sum by the total number of credit hours. Because each course grade is weighted according to the number of credits of the course, GPA is called a *weighted mean*. Calculate the GPA for this transcript:

   Sociology: 3 cr. A; Biology: 3.5 cr. C; Music: 1 cr. B; Math: 4 cr. B; English: 3 cr. C.

• Writing in Mathematics

66. What is the mean and how is it obtained?

67. What is the median and how is it obtained?

68. What is the mode and how is it obtained?

69. What is the midrange and how is it obtained?

70. The "average" income in the United States can be given by the mean or the median.

   a. Which measure would be used in anti-U.S. propaganda? Explain your answer.

   b. Which measure would be used in pro-U.S. propaganda? Explain your answer.

71. In a class of 40 students, 21 have examination scores of 77%. Which measure or measures of central tendency can you immediately determine? Explain your answer.

72. You read an article that states, "Of the 411 players in the National Basketball Association, only 138 make more than the average salary of $3.12 million." Is $3.12 million the mean or the median salary? Explain your answer.

73. A student's parents promise to pay for next semester's tuition if an A average is earned in chemistry. With examination grades of 97%, 97%, 75%, 70%, and 55%, the student reports that an A average has been earned. Which measure of central tendency is the student reporting as the average? How is this student misrepresenting the course performance with statistics?

74. According to the National Oceanic and Atmospheric Administration, the coldest city in the United States is International Falls, Minnesota, with a mean Fahrenheit temperature of 36.8°. Explain how this mean is obtained.

75. Using Table 12.8 on page 699, explain why the mean amount spent on defense per resident is so much greater than the median amount spent on defense per resident for the ten countries.

• Critical Thinking Exercises

76. Give an example of a set of six examination grades (from 0 to 100) with each of the following characteristics:

   a. The mean and the median have the same value, but the mode has a different value.

   b. The mean and the mode have the same value, but the median has a different value.

   c. The mean is greater than the median.

   d. The mode is greater than the mean.

   e. The mean, median, and mode have the same value.

   f. The mean and mode have values of 72.

77. On an examination given to 30 students, no student scored below the mean. Describe how this occurred.

• Group Exercises

78. Select a characteristic, such as shoe size or height, for which each member of the group can provide a number. Choose a characteristic of genuine interest to the group. For this characteristic, organize the data collected into a frequency distribution and a graph. Compute the mean, median, mode, and midrange. Discuss any differences among these values. What happens if the group is divided (men and women, or people under a certain age and people over a certain age) and these measures of central tendency are computed for each of the subgroups? Attempt to use measures of central tendency to discover something interesting about the entire group or the subgroups.

79. A recent book on spotting bad statistics and learning to think critically about these influential numbers is *Damn Lies and Statistics* by Joel Best (University of California Press, 2001). This activity is designed for six people. Each person should select one chapter from Best's book. The group report should include examples of the use, misuse, and abuse of statistical information. Explain exactly how and why bad statistics emerge, spread, and come to shape policy debates. What specific ways does Best recommend to detect bad statistics?

SECTION 12.3 • MEASURES OF DISPERSION

OBJECTIVES

1. Determine the range for a data set.
2. Determine the standard deviation for a data set.

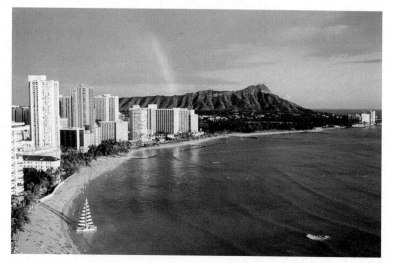

When you think of Houston, Texas and Honolulu, Hawaii, do balmy temperatures come to mind? Both cities have a mean temperature of 75°. However, the mean temperature does not tell the whole story. The temperature in Houston differs seasonally from a low of about 40° in January to a high of close to 100° in July and August. By contrast, Honolulu's temperature varies less throughout the year, usually ranging between 60° and 90°.

Measures of dispersion are used to describe the spread of data items in a data set. Two of the most common measures of dispersion, the *range* and the *standard deviation*, are discussed in this section.

1 | Determine the range for a data set.

The Range

A quick but rough measure of dispersion is the **range**, the difference between the highest and lowest data values in a data set. For example, if Houston's hottest annual temperature is 103° and its coldest annual temperature is 33°, the range in temperature is

$$103° − 33°, \quad \text{or} \quad 70°.$$

If Honolulu's hottest day is 89° and its coldest day 61°, the range in temperature is

$$89° − 61°, \quad \text{or} \quad 28°.$$

> ### THE RANGE
> The **range**, the difference between the highest and lowest data values in a data set, indicates the total spread of the data.
>
> Range = highest data value − lowest data value

EXAMPLE 1 COMPUTING THE RANGE

Figure 12.7 shows the number of workers, in millions, for the five countries with the largest labor forces. Find the range of workers, in millions, for these five countries.

SOLUTION

$$\text{Range} = \text{highest data value} − \text{lowest data value}$$
$$= 778 − 82 = 696$$

The range is 696 million workers.

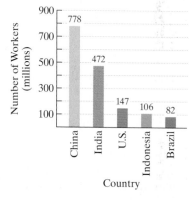

Countries with the Most Workers

Find the range for the following group of data items:

$$4, 2, 11, 7.$$

FIGURE 12.7
Source: Central Intelligence Agency

The Standard Deviation

A second measure of dispersion, and one that is dependent on *all* of the data items, is called the **standard deviation**. The standard deviation is found by determining how much each data item differs from the mean.

In order to compute the standard deviation, it is necessary to find by how much each data item deviates from the mean. First compute the mean. Then subtract the mean from each data item. Example 2 shows how this is done. In Example 3, we will use this skill to actually find the standard deviation.

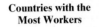

EXAMPLE 2   PREPARING TO FIND THE STANDARD DEVIATION; FINDING DEVIATIONS FROM THE MEAN

Find the deviations from the mean for the five data items 778, 472, 147, 106, and 82, shown in Figure 12.7.

SOLUTION First, calculate the mean.

$$\text{Mean} = \frac{\Sigma x}{n} = \frac{778 + 472 + 147 + 106 + 82}{5} = \frac{1585}{5} = 317$$

The mean for the five countries with the largest labor forces is 317 million workers. Now, let's find by how much each of the five data items in Figure 12.7 differs from 317, the mean. For China, with 778 million workers, the computation is shown as follows:

$$\text{Deviation from mean} = \text{data item} - \text{mean}$$
$$= 778 - 317 = 461.$$

This indicates that the labor force in China exceeds the mean by 461 million workers. The computation for the United States, with 147 million workers, is given by

$$\text{Deviation from mean} = \text{data item} - \text{mean}$$
$$= 147 - 317 = -170.$$

This indicates that the labor force in the United States is 170 million workers below the mean.

The deviations from the mean for each of the five given data items are shown in Table 12.10.

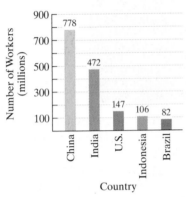

Countries with the Most Workers

Number of Workers (millions)

- China: 778
- India: 472
- U.S.: 147
- Indonesia: 106
- Brazil: 82

Country

FIGURE 12.7 (repeated)
Source: Central Intelligence Agency

TABLE 12.10 DEVIATIONS FROM THE MEAN

Data item	Deviation: data item − mean
778	778 − 317 = 461
472	472 − 317 = 155
147	147 − 317 = −170
106	106 − 317 = −211
82	82 − 317 = −235

 Compute the mean for the following group of data items:

$$2, 4, 7, 11.$$

Then find the deviations from the mean for the four data items. Organize your work in table form just like Table 12.10. Keep track of these computations. You will be using them in Check Point 3.

The sum of the deviations for a set of data is always zero. For the deviations shown in Table 12.10,

$$461 + 155 + (-170) + (-211) + (-235) = 616 + (-616) = 0.$$

This shows that we cannot find a measure of dispersion by finding the mean of the deviations, because this value is always zero. However, a kind of average of the deviations from the mean, called the **standard deviation**, can be computed. We do so by squaring each deviation and later introducing a square root in the computation. Here are the details on how to find the standard deviation for a set of data:

2 Determine the standard deviation for a data set.

> **COMPUTING THE STANDARD DEVIATION FOR A DATA SET**
>
> 1. Find the mean of the data items.
> 2. Find the deviation of each data item from the mean:
> $$\text{data item} - \text{mean}.$$
> 3. Square each deviation:
> $$(\text{data item} - \text{mean})^2.$$
> 4. Sum the squared deviations:
> $$\Sigma(\text{data item} - \text{mean})^2.$$
> 5. Divide the sum in step 4 by $n - 1$, where n represents the number of data items:
> $$\frac{\Sigma(\text{data item} - \text{mean})^2}{n - 1}.$$
> 6. Take the square root of the quotient in step 5. This value is the standard deviation for the data set.
> $$\text{Standard deviation} = \sqrt{\frac{\Sigma(\text{data item} - \text{mean})^2}{n - 1}}$$

The computation of the standard deviation can be organized using a table with three columns:

Data item	Deviation: Data item − mean	(Deviation)²: (Data item − mean)²

In Example 2, we worked out the first two columns of such a table. Let's continue working with the data for the countries with the most workers and compute the standard deviation.

EXAMPLE 3   COMPUTING THE STANDARD DEVIATION

Figure 12.7, showing the number of workers, in millions, for the five countries with the largest labor forces, appears in the margin on page 706. Find the standard deviation, in millions, for these five countries.

SOLUTION

Step 1. Find the mean. From our work in Example 2, the mean is 317.

Step 2. Find the deviation of each data item from the mean: data item − mean. This, too, was done in Example 2 for each of the five data items.

Step 3. Square each deviation: (data item − mean)². We square each of the numbers in the (data item − mean) column, shown in Table 12.11. Notice that squaring the difference always results in a positive number.

TABLE 12.11 COMPUTING THE STANDARD DEVIATION

Data item	Deviation: data item − mean	(Deviation)²: (data item − mean)²
778	$778 - 317 = 461$	$461^2 = 461 \cdot 461 = 212{,}521$
472	$472 - 317 = 155$	$155^2 = 155 \cdot 155 = 24{,}025$
147	$147 - 317 = -170$	$(-170)^2 = (-170)(-170) = 28{,}900$
106	$106 - 317 = -211$	$(-211)^2 = (-211)(-211) = 44{,}521$
82	$82 - 317 = -235$	$(-235)^2 = (-235)(-235) = 55{,}225$
Totals:	0	365,192

The sum of the deviations for a set of data is always zero.

Adding the five numbers in the third column gives the sum of the squared deviations:
$$\Sigma(\text{data item} - \text{mean})^2.$$

TECHNOLOGY

Almost all scientific and graphing calculators compute the standard deviation of a set of data. Using the data items in Example 3,

778, 472, 147, 106, 82,

the keystrokes for obtaining the standard deviation on many scientific calculators are as follows:

778 $\boxed{\Sigma+}$ 472 $\boxed{\Sigma+}$ 147 $\boxed{\Sigma+}$

106 $\boxed{\Sigma+}$ 82 $\boxed{\Sigma+}$ $\boxed{2nd}$ $\boxed{\sigma n-1}$.

Graphing calculators require that you specify if data items are from an entire population or a sample of the population.

Step 4. Sum the squared deviations: $\Sigma(\text{data item} - \text{mean})^2$. This step is shown in Table 12.11 on the previous page. The squares in the third column were added, resulting in a sum of 365,192.

Step 5. Divide the sum in step 4 by $n - 1$, where n represents the number of data items. The number of data items is 5 so we divide by 4.

$$\frac{\Sigma(\text{data item} - \text{mean})^2}{n - 1} = \frac{365{,}192}{5 - 1} = \frac{365{,}192}{4} = 91{,}298$$

Step 6. The standard deviation is the square root of the quotient in step 5.

$$\text{Standard deviation} = \sqrt{\frac{\Sigma(\text{data item} - \text{mean})^2}{n - 1}} = \sqrt{91{,}298} \approx 302.16$$

The standard deviation for the five countries with the largest labor forces is approximately 302.16 million workers.

 Find the standard deviation for the group of data items in Check Point 2 on page 706. Round to two decimal places.

Example 4 illustrates that as the spread of data items increases, the standard deviation gets larger.

EXAMPLE 4   COMPUTING THE STANDARD DEVIATION

Find the standard deviation of the data items in each of the samples shown below.

Sample A	Sample B
17, 18, 19, 20, 21, 22, 23	5, 10, 15, 20, 25, 30, 35

SOLUTION Begin by finding the mean for each sample.

Sample A:

$$\text{Mean} = \frac{17 + 18 + 19 + 20 + 21 + 22 + 23}{7} = \frac{140}{7} = 20$$

Sample B:

$$\text{Mean} = \frac{5 + 10 + 15 + 20 + 25 + 30 + 35}{7} = \frac{140}{7} = 20$$

Although both samples have the same mean, the data items in sample B are more spread out. Thus, we would expect sample B to have the greater standard deviation. The computation of the standard deviation requires that we find $\Sigma(\text{data item} - \text{mean})^2$, shown in Table 12.12.

TABLE 12.12 COMPUTING STANDARD DEVIATIONS FOR TWO SAMPLES

	Sample A			Sample B	
Data item	Deviation: data item − mean	(Deviation)²: (data item − mean)²	Data item	Deviation: data item − mean	(Deviation)²: (data item − mean)²
17	$17 - 20 = -3$	$(-3)^2 = 9$	5	$5 - 20 = -15$	$(-15)^2 = 225$
18	$18 - 20 = -2$	$(-2)^2 = 4$	10	$10 - 20 = -10$	$(-10)^2 = 100$
19	$19 - 20 = -1$	$(-1)^2 = 1$	15	$15 - 20 = -5$	$(-5)^2 = 25$
20	$20 - 20 = 0$	$0^2 = 0$	20	$20 - 20 = 0$	$0^2 = 0$
21	$21 - 20 = 1$	$1^2 = 1$	25	$25 - 20 = 5$	$5^2 = 25$
22	$22 - 20 = 2$	$2^2 = 4$	30	$30 - 20 = 10$	$10^2 = 100$
23	$23 - 20 = 3$	$3^2 = 9$	35	$35 - 20 = 15$	$15^2 = 225$
Totals:		$\Sigma(\text{data item} - \text{mean})^2 = 28$			$\Sigma(\text{data item} - \text{mean})^2 = 700$

Each sample contains seven data items, so we compute the standard deviation by dividing the sums in Table 12.12, 28 and 700, by 7 − 1, or 6. Then we take the square root of each quotient.

$$\text{Standard deviation} = \sqrt{\frac{\Sigma(\text{data item} - \text{mean})^2}{n - 1}}$$

Sample A:

$$\text{Standard deviation} = \sqrt{\frac{28}{6}} \approx 2.16$$

Sample B:

$$\text{Standard deviation} = \sqrt{\frac{700}{6}} \approx 10.80$$

Sample A has a standard deviation of approximately 2.16 and sample B has a standard deviation of approximately 10.80. The scores in sample B are more spread out than those in sample A.

 Find the standard deviation of the data items in each of the samples shown below. Round to two decimal places.

Sample A: 73, 75, 77, 79, 81, 83

Sample B: 40, 44, 92, 94, 98, 100

Figure 12.8 illustrates four sets of data items organized in histograms. From left to right, the data items are

Figure 12.8(a): 4, 4, 4, 4, 4, 4, 4
Figure 12.8(b): 3, 3, 4, 4, 4, 5, 5
Figure 12.8(c): 3, 3, 3, 4, 5, 5, 5
Figure 12.8(d): 1, 1, 1, 4, 7, 7, 7.

Each data set has a mean of 4. However, as the spread of data items increases, the standard deviation gets larger. Observe that when all the data items are the same, the standard deviation is 0.

FIGURE 12.8 The standard deviation gets larger with increased dispersion among data items. In each case, the mean is 4.

EXAMPLE 5   INTERPRETING STANDARD DEVIATION

Two fifth-grade classes have nearly identical mean scores on an aptitude test, but one class has a standard deviation three times that of the other. All other factors being equal, which class is easier to teach, and why?

SOLUTION The class with the smaller standard deviation is easier to teach because there is less variation among student aptitudes. Course work can be aimed at the average student without too much concern that the work will be too easy for some or too difficult for others. By contrast, the class with greater dispersion poses a greater challenge. By teaching to the average student, the students whose scores are significantly above the mean will be bored; students whose scores are significantly below the mean will be confused.

 Shown below are the means and standard deviations of the yearly returns on two investments from 1926 through 2004.

Investment	Mean Yearly Interest	Standard Deviation
Small-Company Stocks	17.5%	33.3%
Large-Company Stocks	12.4%	20.4%

Source: Summary Statistics of Annual Total Returns 1926 to 2004 Yearbook, Ibbotson Associates, Chicago

a. Use the means to determine which investment provided the greater yearly return.

b. Use the standard deviations to determine which investment had the greater risk. Explain your answer.

EXERCISE SET 12.3 ●●●●●●

• Practice Exercises

In Exercises 1–6, find the range for each group of data items.

1. 1, 2, 3, 4, 5
2. 16, 17, 18, 19, 20
3. 7, 9, 9, 15
4. 11, 13, 14, 15, 17
5. 3, 3, 4, 4, 5, 5
6. 3, 3, 3, 4, 5, 5, 5

In Exercises 7–10, a group of data items and their mean are given.

a. *Find the deviation from the mean for each of the data items.*

b. *Find the sum of the deviations in part (a).*

7. 3, 5, 7, 12, 18, 27; Mean = 12
8. 84, 88, 90, 95, 98; Mean = 91
9. 29, 38, 48, 49, 53, 77; Mean = 49
10. 60, 60, 62, 65, 65, 65, 66, 67, 70, 70; Mean = 65

In Exercises 11–16, find a. *the mean;* b. *the deviation from the mean for each data item; and* c. *the sum of the deviations in part (b).*

11. 85, 95, 90, 85, 100
12. 94, 62, 88, 85, 91
13. 146, 153, 155, 160, 161
14. 150, 132, 144, 122
15. 2.25, 3.50, 2.75, 3.10, 1.90
16. 0.35, 0.37, 0.41, 0.39, 0.43

In Exercises 17–26, find the standard deviation for each group of data items. Round answers to two decimal places.

17. 1, 2, 3, 4, 5
18. 16, 17, 18, 19, 20
19. 7, 9, 9, 15
20. 11, 13, 14, 15, 17
21. 3, 3, 4, 4, 5, 5
22. 3, 3, 3, 4, 5, 5, 5
23. 1, 1, 1, 4, 7, 7, 7
24. 6, 6, 6, 6, 7, 7, 7, 4, 8, 3
25. 9, 5, 9, 5, 9, 5, 9, 5
26. 6, 10, 6, 10, 6, 10, 6, 10

In Exercises 27–28, compute the mean, range, and standard deviation for the data items in each of the three samples. Then describe one way in which the samples are alike and one way in which they are different.

27. Sample A: 6, 8, 10, 12, 14, 16, 18
    Sample B: 6, 7, 8, 12, 16, 17, 18
    Sample C: 6, 6, 6, 12, 18, 18, 18

28. Sample A: 8, 10, 12, 14, 16, 18, 20
    Sample B: 8, 9, 10, 14, 18, 19, 20
    Sample C: 8, 8, 8, 14, 20, 20, 20

• Practice Plus

In Exercises 29–36, use each display of data items to find the standard deviation. Where necessary, round answers to two decimal places.

29.

30.

31.

32.

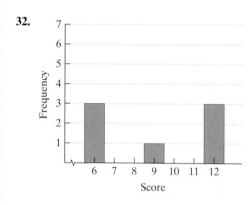

Year	Best Actress	Age
1999	Hilary Swank	25
2000	Julia Roberts	33
2001	Halle Berry	35
2002	Nicole Kidman	35
2003	Charlize Theron	28
2004	Hilary Swank	30
2005	Reese Witherspoon	29

Source: www.oscars.org

a. Without calculating, which data set has the greater mean age? Explain your answer.

b. Verify your conjecture from part (a) by calculating the mean age for each data set. Round answers to two decimal places.

c. Without calculating, which data set has the greater standard deviation? Explain your answer.

d. Verify your conjecture from part (c) by calculating the standard deviation for each data set. Round answers to two decimal places.

38. The data sets give the ages of the first six U.S. presidents and the last six U.S. presidents (through G. W. Bush).

AGE OF FIRST SIX U.S. PRESIDENTS AT INAUGURATION

President	Age
Washington	57
J. Adams	61
Jefferson	57
Madison	57
Monroe	58
J. Q. Adams	57

AGE OF LAST SIX U.S. PRESIDENTS AT INAUGURATION

President	Age
Ford	61
Carter	52
Reagan	69
G. H. W. Bush	64
Clinton	46
G. W. Bush	54

Source: Time Almanac

a. Without calculating, which set has the greater standard deviation? Explain your answer.

b. Verify your conjecture from part (b) by calculating the standard deviation for each data set. Round answers to two decimal places.

33.

Stems	Leaves
0	5
1	0 5
2	0 5

34.

Stems	Leaves
0	4 8
1	2 6
2	0

35.

Stems	Leaves
1	8 9 9 8 7 8
2	0 1 0 2

36.

Stems	Leaves
1	3 5 3 8 3 4
2	3 0 0 4

• Application Exercises

37. The data sets give the ages of Oscar winners from 1999 through 2005 at the time of the award.

Year	Best Actor	Age
1999	Kevin Spacey	40
2000	Russell Crowe	36
2001	Denzel Washington	47
2002	Adrien Brody	29
2003	Sean Penn	43
2004	Jamie Foxx	37
2005	Philip Seymour Hoffman	38

• Writing in Mathematics

39. Describe how to find the range of a data set.

40. Describe why the range might not be the best measure of dispersion.

41. Describe how the standard deviation is computed.

42. Describe what the standard deviation reveals about a data set.

43. If a set of test scores has a standard deviation of zero, what does this mean about the scores?

44. Two classes took a statistics test. Both classes had a mean score of 73. The scores of class A had a standard deviation of 5 and those of class B had a standard deviation of 10. Discuss the difference between the two classes' performance on the test.

45. A sample of cereals indicates a mean potassium content per serving of 93 milligrams and a standard deviation of 2 milligrams. Write a description of what this means for a person who knows nothing about statistics.

46. Over a one-month period, stock A had a mean daily closing price of 124.7 and a standard deviation of 12.5. By contrast, stock B had a mean daily closing price of 78.2 and a standard deviation of 6.1. Which stock was more volatile? Explain your answer.

• Critical Thinking Exercises

47. Which one of the following is true?

   a. If the same number is added to each data item in a set of data, the standard deviation does not change.

   b. If each number in a data set is multiplied by 4, the standard deviation is doubled.

   c. It is possible for a set of scores to have a negative standard deviation.

   d. Data sets with different means cannot have the same standard deviation.

48. Describe a situation in which a relatively large standard deviation is desirable.

49. If a set of test scores has a large range but a small standard deviation, describe what this means about students' performance on the test.

50. Use the data 1, 2, 3, 5, 6, 7. Without actually computing the standard deviation, which of the following best approximates the standard deviation?

   a. 2   **b.** 6   **c.** 10   **d.** 20

51. Use the data 0, 1, 3, 4, 4, 6. Add 2 to each of the numbers. How does this affect the mean? How does this affect the standard deviation?

• Group Exercises

52. As a follow-up to Group Exercise 78 on page 704, the group should reassemble and compute the standard deviation for each data set whose mean you previously determined. Does the standard deviation tell you anything new or interesting about the entire group or subgroups that you did not discover during the previous group activity?

53. Group members should consult a current almanac or the Internet and select intriguing data. The group's function is to use statistics to tell a story. Once "intriguing" data are identified, as a group

   a. Summarize the data. Use words, frequency distributions, and graphic displays.

   b. Compute measures of central tendency and dispersion, using these statistics to discuss the data.

SECTION 12.4 • THE NORMAL DISTRIBUTION

OBJECTIVES

1. Recognize characteristics of normal distributions.

2. Understand the 68-95-99.7 Rule.

3. Find scores at a specified standard deviation from the mean.

4. Use the 68-95-99.7 Rule.

5. Convert a data item to a z-score.

6. Understand percentiles and quartiles.

7. Solve applied problems involving normal distributions.

8. Use and interpret margins of error.

9. Recognize distributions that are not normal.

Mean Adult Heights

5'2" 5'7"   5'5" 5'10"   5'7" 6'0"

1900   2000   2050

Source: National Center for Health Statistics

Our heights are on the rise! In one million B.C., the mean height for men was 4 feet 6 inches. The mean height for women was 4 feet 2 inches. Because of improved diets and medical care, the mean height for men is now 5 feet 10 inches and for women it is 5 feet 5 inches. Mean adult heights are expected to plateau by 2050.

Suppose that a researcher selects a random sample of 100 adult men, measures their heights, and constructs a histogram. The graph is shown in Figure 12.9 at the top of the next page. Figure 12.9 illustrates what happens as the sample size increases. In Figure 12.9(c), if you were to fold the graph down the middle, the left side would fit the right side. As we move out from the middle, the heights of the bars are the same to the left and right. Such a histogram is called **symmetric**. As the sample size increases, so does the graph's symmetry. If it were possible to measure

1 | Recognize characteristics of normal distributions.

the heights of all adult males, the entire population, the histogram would approach what is called the **normal distribution**, shown in Figure 12.9(d). This distribution is also called the **bell curve** or the **Gaussian distribution**, named for the German mathematician Carl Friedrich Gauss (1777–1855).

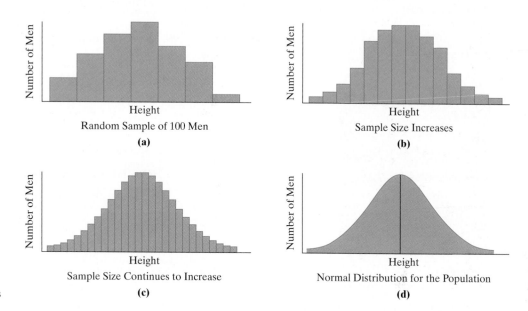

FIGURE 12.9 Heights of adult males

Figure 12.9(d) illustrates that the normal distribution is bell shaped and symmetric about a vertical line through its center. Furthermore, **the mean, median, and mode** of a normal distribution **are all equal** and located at the center of the distribution.

The shape of the normal distribution depends on the mean and the standard deviation. Figure 12.10 illustrates three normal distributions with the same mean, but different standard deviations. As the standard deviation increases, the distribution becomes more dispersed, or spread out, but retains its symmetric bell shape.

FIGURE 12.10

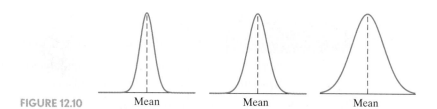

The normal distribution provides a wonderful model for all kinds of phenomena because many sets of data items closely resemble this population distribution. Examples include heights and weights of adult males, intelligence quotients, SAT scores, prices paid for a new car model, and life spans of light bulbs. In these distributions, the data items tend to cluster around the mean. The more an item differs from the mean, the less likely it is to occur.

The normal distribution is used to make predictions about an entire population using data from a sample. In this section, we focus on the characteristics and applications of the normal distribution.

2 | Understand the 68–95–99.7 Rule.

The Standard Deviation and z-Scores in Normal Distributions

The standard deviation plays a crucial role in the normal distribution, summarized by the **68–95–99.7 Rule**. This rule is illustrated in Figure 12.11 on the next page.

THE 68-95-99.7 RULE FOR THE NORMAL DISTRIBUTION

1. Approximately 68% of the data items fall within 1 standard deviation of the mean (in both directions).
2. Approximately 95% of the data items fall within 2 standard deviations of the mean.
3. Approximately 99.7% of the data items fall within 3 standard deviations of the mean.

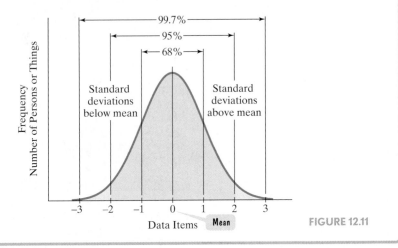

FIGURE 12.11

Figure 12.11 illustrates that a very small percentage of the data in a normal distribution lies more than 3 standard deviations above or below the mean. As we move from the mean, the curve falls rapidly, and then more and more gradually, toward the horizontal axis. The tails of the curve approach, but never touch, the horizontal axis, although they are quite close to the axis at 3 standard deviations from the mean. The range of the normal distribution is infinite. No matter how far out from the mean we move, there is always the probability (although very small) of a data item occurring even farther out.

3 Find scores at a specified standard deviation from the mean.

EXAMPLE 1   FINDING SCORES AT A SPECIFIED STANDARD DEVIATION FROM THE MEAN

Male adult heights in North America are approximately normally distributed with a mean of 70 inches and a standard deviation of 4 inches. Find the height that is

a. 2 standard deviations above the mean.

b. 3 standard deviations below the mean.

SOLUTION

a. First, let us find the height that is 2 standard deviations above the mean.

$$\text{Height} = \text{mean} + 2 \cdot \text{standard deviation}$$
$$= 70 + 2 \cdot 4 = 70 + 8 = 78$$

A height of 78 inches is 2 standard deviations above the mean.

b. Next, let us find the height that is 3 standard deviations below the mean.

$$\text{Height} = \text{mean} - 3 \cdot \text{standard deviation}$$
$$= 70 - 3 \cdot 4 = 70 - 12 = 58$$

A height of 58 inches is 3 standard deviations below the mean.

The distribution of male adult heights in North America is illustrated as a normal distribution in Figure 12.12.

Normal Distribution of Male Adult Heights

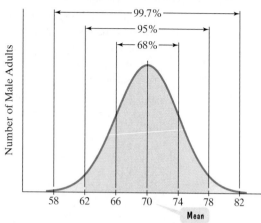

Male Adult Heights in North America

FIGURE 12.12

CHECK POINT 1 Female adult heights in North America are approximately normally distributed with a mean of 65 inches and a standard deviation of 3.5 inches. Find the height that is

a. 3 standard deviations above the mean.

b. 2 standard deviations below the mean.

4   Use the 68–95–99.7 Rule.

EXAMPLE 2   USING THE 68-95-99.7 RULE

Use the distribution of male adult heights in Figure 12.12 to find the percentage of men in North America with heights

a. between 66 inches and 74 inches.   **b.** between 70 inches and 74 inches.

c. above 78 inches.

SOLUTION

a. The 68–95–99.7 Rule states that approximately 68% of the data items fall within 1 standard deviation, 4, of the mean, 70.

$$\text{mean} - 1 \cdot \text{standard deviation} = 70 - 1 \cdot 4 = 70 - 4 = 66$$
$$\text{mean} + 1 \cdot \text{standard deviation} = 70 + 1 \cdot 4 = 70 + 4 = 74$$

Figure 12.12 shows that 68% of male adults have heights between 66 inches and 74 inches.

b. The percentage of men with heights between 70 inches and 74 inches is not given directly in Figure 12.12 or Figure 12.13. Because of the distribution's symmetry, the percentage with heights between 66 inches and 70 inches is the same as the percentage with heights between 70 and 74 inches. Figure 12.13 indicates that 68% have heights between 66 inches and 74 inches. Thus, half of 68%, or 34%, of men have heights between 70 inches and 74 inches.

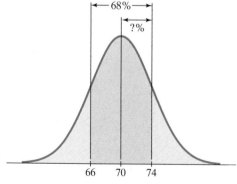

FIGURE 12.13 What percentage have heights between 70 inches and 74 inches?

c. The percentage of men with heights above 78 inches is not given directly in Figure 12.12 or Figure 12.14. A height of 78 inches is 2 standard deviations, $2 \cdot 4$, or 8 inches, above the mean, 70 inches. The 68–95–99.7 Rule states that approximately 95% of the data items fall within 2 standard deviations of the mean. Thus, approximately $100\% - 95\%$, or 5%, of the data items are farther than 2 standard deviations from the mean. The 5% of the data items are represented by the two shaded green regions in Figure 12.14. Because of the distribution's symmetry, half of 5%, or 2.5%, of the data items are more than 2 standard deviations above the mean. This means that 2.5% of men have heights above 78 inches.

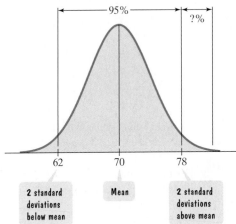

2 standard deviations below mean

Mean

2 standard deviations above mean

FIGURE 12.14 What percentage have heights above 78 inches?

 CHECK POINT 2 Use the distribution of male adult heights in North America in Figure 12.12 on page 715 to find the percentage of men with heights

a. between 62 inches and 78 inches.

b. between 70 inches and 78 inches.

c. above 74 inches.

Because the normal distribution of male adult heights in North America has a mean of 70 inches and a standard deviation of 4 inches, a height of 78 inches lies 2 standard deviations above the mean. In a normal distribution, a **z-score** describes how many standard deviations a particular data item lies above or below the mean. Thus, the z-score for the data item 78 is 2.

The following formula can be used to express a data item in a normal distribution as a z-score:

5 | Convert a data item to a z-score.

COMPUTING z-SCORES

A z-score describes how many standard deviations a data item in a normal distribution lies above or below the mean. The z-score can be obtained using

$$z\text{-score} = \frac{\text{data item} - \text{mean}}{\text{standard deviation}}.$$

Data items above the mean have positive z-scores. Data items below the mean have negative z-scores. The z-score for the mean is 0.

EXAMPLE 3   COMPUTING z-SCORES

The mean weight of newborn infants is 7 pounds and the standard deviation is 0.8 pound. The weights of newborn infants are normally distributed. Find the z-score for a weight of

a. 9 pounds.   **b.** 7 pounds.   **c.** 6 pounds.

SOLUTION We compute the z-score for each weight by using the z-score formula. The mean is 7 and the standard deviation is 0.8.

a. The z-score for a weight of 9 pounds, written z_9, is

$$z_9 = \frac{\text{data item} - \text{mean}}{\text{standard deviation}} = \frac{9 - 7}{0.8} = \frac{2}{0.8} = 2.5.$$

The z-score of a data item greater than the mean is always positive. A 9-pound infant is a chubby little tyke, with a weight that is 2.5 standard deviations above the mean.

b. The z-score for a weight of 7 pounds is

$$z_7 = \frac{\text{data item} - \text{mean}}{\text{standard deviation}} = \frac{7 - 7}{0.8} = \frac{0}{0.8} = 0.$$

The z-score for the mean is always 0. A 7-pound infant is right at the mean, deviating 0 pounds above or below it.

c. The z-score for a weight of 6 pounds is

$$z_6 = \frac{\text{data item} - \text{mean}}{\text{standard deviation}} = \frac{6 - 7}{0.8} = \frac{-1}{0.8} = -1.25.$$

The z-score of a data item less than the mean is always negative. A 6-pound infant's weight is 1.25 standard deviations below the mean.   ○

Figure 12.15 shows the normal distribution of weights of newborn infants. The horizontal axis is labeled in terms of weights and z-scores.

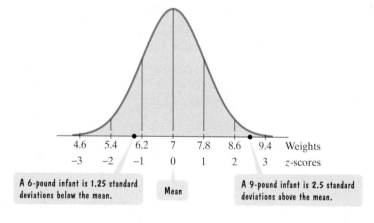

Normal Distribution of Weights of Newborn Infants

Weights	4.6	5.4	6.2	7	7.8	8.6	9.4
z-scores	−3	−2	−1	0	1	2	3

A 6-pound infant is 1.25 standard deviations below the mean.   Mean   A 9-pound infant is 2.5 standard deviations above the mean.

FIGURE 12.15 Infants' weights are normally distributed.

CHECK POINT 3 The length of horse pregnancies from conception to birth is normally distributed with a mean of 336 days and a standard deviation of 3 days. Find the z-score for a horse pregnancy of

a. 342 days.   **b.** 336 days.   **c.** 333 days.

In Example 4, we consider two normally distributed sets of test scores, in which a higher score generally indicates a better result. To compare scores on two different tests in relation to the mean on each test, we can use z-scores. The better score is the item with the greater z-score.

EXAMPLE 4 USING AND INTERPRETING z-SCORES

A student scores 70 on an arithmetic test and 66 on a vocabulary test. The scores for both tests are normally distributed. The arithmetic test has a mean of 60 and a standard deviation of 20. The vocabulary test has a mean of 60 and a standard deviation of 2. On which test did the student have the better score?

SOLUTION To answer the question, we need to find the student's z-score on each test, using

$$z = \frac{\text{data item} - \text{mean}}{\text{standard deviation}}.$$

The arithmetic test has a mean of 60 and a standard deviation of 20.

$$z\text{-score for } 70 = z_{70} = \frac{70 - 60}{20} = \frac{10}{20} = 0.5$$

The vocabulary test has a mean of 60 and a standard deviation of 2.

$$z\text{-score for } 66 = z_{66} = \frac{66 - 60}{2} = \frac{6}{2} = 3$$

The arithmetic score, 70, is half a standard deviation above the mean, whereas the vocabulary score, 66, is 3 standard deviations above the mean. The student did much better than the mean on the vocabulary test. ○

CHECK POINT 4 The SAT (Scholastic Aptitude Test) has a mean of 500 and a standard deviation of 100. The ACT (American College Test) has a mean of 18 and a standard deviation of 6. Both tests measure the same kind of ability, with scores that are normally distributed. Suppose that you score 550 on the SAT and 24 on the ACT. On which test did you have the better score?

EXAMPLE 5 UNDERSTANDING z-SCORES

Intelligence quotients (IQs) on the Stanford-Binet intelligence test are normally distributed with a mean of 100 and a standard deviation of 16.

a. What is the IQ corresponding to a z-score of -1.5?

b. Mensa is a group of people with high IQs whose members have z-scores of 2.05 or greater on the Stanford-Binet intelligence test. What is the IQ corresponding to a z-score of 2.05?

SOLUTION

a. We begin with the IQ corresponding to a z-score of -1.5. The negative sign in -1.5 tells us that the IQ is $1\frac{1}{2}$ standard deviations below the mean.

$$IQ = \text{mean} - 1.5 \cdot \text{standard deviation}$$
$$= 100 - 1.5(16) = 100 - 24 = 76$$

The IQ corresponding to a z-score of -1.5 is 76.

b. Next, we find the IQ corresponding to a z-score of 2.05. The positive sign implied in 2.05 tells us that the IQ is 2.05 standard deviations above the mean.

$$IQ = \text{mean} + 2.05 \cdot \text{standard deviation}$$
$$= 100 + 2.05(16) = 100 + 32.8 = 132.8$$

The IQ corresponding to a z-score of 2.05 is 132.8. (An IQ score of at least 133 is required to join Mensa.) ○

CHECK POINT 5 Use the information in Example 5 to find the IQ corresponding to a z-score of

a. -2.25.　　**b.** 1.75.

BLITZER BONUS

The IQ Controversy

Is intelligence something we are born with or is it a quality that can be manipulated through education? Can it be measured accurately and is IQ the way to measure it? There are no clear answers to these questions.

In a study by Carolyn Bird (*Pygmalion in the Classroom*), a group of third-grade teachers was told that they had classes of students with IQs well above the mean. These classes made incredible progress throughout the year. In reality, these were not gifted kids, but, rather, a random sample of all third-graders. It was the teachers' expectations, and not the IQs of the students, that resulted in increased performance.

6 Understand percentiles and quartiles.

Percentiles and Quartiles

A *z*-score measures a data item's position in a normal distribution. Another measure of a data item's position is its **percentile**. Percentiles are often associated with scores on standardized tests. If a score is in the 45th percentile, this means that 45% of the scores are less than this score. If a score is in the 95th percentile, this indicates that 95% of the scores are less than this score.

> **PERCENTILES**
>
> If *n*% of the items in a distribution are less than a particular data item, we say that the data item is in the ***n*th percentile** of the distribution.

STUDY TIP

A score in the 98th percentile does *not* mean that 98% of the answers are correct. Nor does it mean that the score was 98%.

EXAMPLE 6   INTERPRETING PERCENTILE

The cutoff IQ score for Mensa membership, 132.8, is in the 98th percentile. What does this mean?

SOLUTION Because 132.8 is in the 98th percentile, this means that 98% of IQ scores fall below 132.8.

 A student scored in the 75th percentile on the SAT. What does this mean?

Three commonly encountered percentiles are the *quartiles*. **Quartiles** divide data sets into four equal parts. The 25th percentile is the **first quartile**: 25% of the data fall below the first quartile. The 50th percentile is the **second quartile**: 50% of the data fall below the second quartile, so the second quartile is equivalent to the median. The 75th percentile is the **third quartile**: 75% of the data fall below the third quartile. Figure 12.16 illustrates the concept of quartiles for the normal distribution.

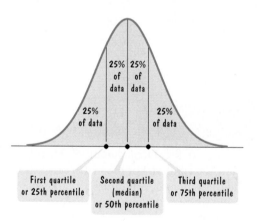

FIGURE 12.16 Quartiles

7 Solve applied problems involving normal distributions.

Two entries from Table 12.13. The complete table is on the next page.

z-Score	Percentile
2.0	97.72
0.0	50.00

Problem Solving Using *z*-Scores and Percentiles

Table 12.13 on the next page gives a percentile interpretation for *z*-scores. For example, the portion of the table in the margin indicates that the corresponding percentile for a data item with a *z*-score of 2 is 97.72. A student with this score on a test whose results are normally distributed outperformed 97.72% of those who took the test.

In a normal distribution, the mean, median, and mode all have a corresponding *z*-score of 0. Table 12.13 shows that the percentile for a *z*-score of 0 is 50.00. Thus, 50% of the data items in a normal distribution are less than the mean, median, and mode. Consequently, 50% of the data items are greater than or equal to the mean, median, and mode.

Table 12.13 can be used to find the percentage of data items that are less than any data item in a normal distribution. Begin by converting the data item to a z-score. Then, use the table to find the percentile for this z-score. This percentile is the percentage of data items that are less than the data item in question.

TABLE 12.13 z-SCORES AND PERCENTILES

z-Score	Percentile	z-Score	Percentile	z-Score	Percentile	z-Score	Percentile
−4.0	0.003	−1.0	15.87	0.0	50.00	1.1	86.43
−3.5	0.02	−0.95	17.11	0.05	51.99	1.2	88.49
−3.0	0.13	−0.90	18.41	0.10	53.98	1.3	90.32
−2.9	0.19	−0.85	19.77	0.15	55.96	1.4	91.92
−2.8	0.26	−0.80	21.19	0.20	57.93	1.5	93.32
−2.7	0.35	−0.75	22.66	0.25	59.87	1.6	94.52
−2.6	0.47	−0.70	24.20	0.30	61.79	1.7	95.54
−2.5	0.62	−0.65	25.78	0.35	63.68	1.8	96.41
−2.4	0.82	−0.60	27.43	0.40	65.54	1.9	97.13
−2.3	1.07	−0.55	29.12	0.45	67.36	2.0	97.72
−2.2	1.39	−0.50	30.85	0.50	69.15	2.1	98.21
−2.1	1.79	−0.45	32.64	0.55	70.88	2.2	98.61
−2.0	2.28	−0.40	34.46	0.60	72.57	2.3	98.93
−1.9	2.87	−0.35	36.32	0.65	74.22	2.4	99.18
−1.8	3.59	−0.30	38.21	0.70	75.80	2.5	99.38
−1.7	4.46	−0.25	40.13	0.75	77.34	2.6	99.53
−1.6	5.48	−0.20	42.07	0.80	78.81	2.7	99.65
−1.5	6.68	−0.15	44.04	0.85	80.23	2.8	99.74
−1.4	8.08	−0.10	46.02	0.90	81.59	2.9	99.81
−1.3	9.68	−0.05	48.01	0.95	82.89	3.0	99.87
−1.2	11.51	0.0	50.00	1.0	84.13	3.5	99.98
−1.1	13.57					4.0	99.997

EXAMPLE 7 FINDING THE PERCENTAGE OF DATA ITEMS LESS THAN A GIVEN DATA ITEM

According to the Department of Health and Education, cholesterol levels are normally distributed. For men between 18 and 24 years, the mean is 178.1 (measured in milligrams per 100 milliliters) and the standard deviation is 40.7. What percentage of men in this age range have a cholesterol level less than 239.15?

SOLUTION If you are familiar with your own cholesterol level, you probably recognize that a level of 239.15 is fairly high for a young man. Because of this, we would expect most young men to have a level less than 239.15. Let's see if this is so. Table 12.13 requires that we use z-scores. We compute the z-score for a 239.15 cholesterol level by using the z-score formula.

$$z_{239.15} = \frac{\text{data item} - \text{mean}}{\text{standard deviation}} = \frac{239.15 - 178.1}{40.7} = \frac{61.05}{40.7} = 1.5$$

A man between 18 and 24 with a 239.15 cholesterol level is 1.5 standard deviations above the mean, illustrated in Figure 12.17(a). The question mark indicates that we must find the percentage of men with a cholesterol level less than $z = 1.5$, the z-score for a 239.15 cholesterol level. Table 12.13 gives this percentage as a percentile.

Find 1.5 in the z-score column in the right portion of the table. The percentile given to the right of 1.5 is 93.32. Thus, 93.32% of men between 18 and 24 have a cholesterol level less than 239.15, shown in Figure 12.17(b).

A PORTION OF TABLE 12.13

z-Score	Percentile
1.4	91.92
1.5	93.32
1.6	94.52

FIGURE 12.17(a)

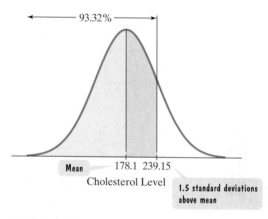

FIGURE 12.17(b)

CHECK POINT 7 The distribution of monthly charges for cellphone plans in the United States is approximately normal with a mean of $62 and a standard deviation of $18. What percentage of plans have charges that are less than $83.60?

The normal distribution accounts for all data items, meaning 100% of the scores. This means that Table 12.13 can also be used to find the percentage of data items that are greater than any data item in a normal distribution. Use the percentile in the table to determine the percentage of data items less than the data item in question. Then subtract this percentage from 100% to find the percentage of data items greater than the item in question. In using this technique, we will treat the phrases "greater than" and "greater than or equal to" as equivalent.

EXAMPLE 8   FINDING THE PERCENTAGE OF DATA ITEMS GREATER THAN A GIVEN DATA ITEM

Lengths of pregnancies of women are normally distributed with a mean of 266 days and a standard deviation of 16 days. What percentage of children are born from pregnancies lasting more than 274 days?

SOLUTION Table 12.13 requires that we use z-scores. We compute the z-score for a 274-day pregnancy by using the z-score formula.

$$z_{274} = \frac{\text{data item} - \text{mean}}{\text{standard deviation}} = \frac{274 - 266}{16} = \frac{8}{16} = 0.5$$

A 274-day pregnancy is 0.5 standard deviation above the mean. Table 12.13 gives the percentile corresponding to 0.50 as 69.15. This means that 69.15% of pregnancies last less than 274 days, illustrated in Figure 12.18. We must find the number of pregnancies lasting more than 274 days by subtracting 69.15% from 100%.

$$100\% - 69.15\% = 30.85\%$$

Thus, 30.85% of children are born from pregnancies lasting more than 274 days.

A Portion of Table 12.13

z-Score	Percentile
0.45	67.36
0.50	69.15
0.55	70.88

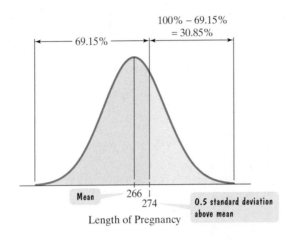

FIGURE 12.18

CHECK POINT **8** Female adult heights in North America are approximately normally distributed with a mean of 65 inches and a standard deviation of 3.5 inches. What percentage of North American women have heights that exceed 69.9 inches?

We have seen how Table 12.13 is used to find the percentage of data items that are less than or greater than any given item. The table can also be used to find the percentage of data items *between* two given items. Because the percentile for each item is the percentage of data items less than the given item, the percentage of data between the two given items is found by subtracting the lesser percent from the greater percent. This is illustrated in Figure 12.19.

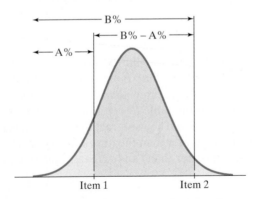

FIGURE 12.19 The percentile for data item 1 is A. The percentile for data item 2 is B. The percentage of data items between item 1 and item 2 is B% − A%.

FINDING THE PERCENTAGE OF DATA ITEMS BETWEEN TWO GIVEN ITEMS IN A NORMAL DISTRIBUTION

1. Convert each given data item to a z-score:

$$z = \frac{\text{data item} - \text{mean}}{\text{standard deviation}}.$$

2. Use Table 12.13 to find the percentile corresponding to each z-score in step 1.
3. Subtract the lesser percentile from the greater percentile and attach a % sign.

EXAMPLE 9	FINDING THE PERCENTAGE OF DATA ITEMS BETWEEN TWO GIVEN DATA ITEMS

The amount of time that self-employed Americans work each week is normally distributed with a mean of 44.6 hours and a standard deviation of 14.4 hours. What percentage of self-employed individuals in the United States work between 37.4 and 80.6 hours per week?

SOLUTION
Step 1. Convert each given data item to a z-score.

$$z_{37.4} = \frac{\text{data item} - \text{mean}}{\text{standard deviation}} = \frac{37.4 - 44.6}{14.4} = \frac{-7.2}{14.4} = -0.5$$

$$z_{80.6} = \frac{\text{data item} - \text{mean}}{\text{standard deviation}} = \frac{80.6 - 44.6}{14.4} = \frac{36}{14.4} = 2.5$$

A Portion of Table 12.13

z-Score	Percentile
−0.55	29.12
−0.50	30.85
−0.45	32.64

A Portion of Table 12.13

z-Score	Percentile
2.4	99.18
2.5	99.38
2.6	99.53

Step 2. Use Table 12.13 to find the percentile corresponding to these z-scores. The percentile given to the right of −0.50 is 30.85. This means that 30.85% of self-employed Americans work less than 37.4 hours per week.

Table 12.13 also gives the percentile corresponding to $z = 2.5$. Find 2.5 in the z-score column in the far-right portion of the table. The percentile given to the right of 2.5 is 99.38. This means that 99.38% of self-employed Americans work less than 80.6 hours per week.

Step 3. Subtract the lesser percentile from the greater percentile and attach a % sign. Subtracting percentiles, we obtain

$$99.38 - 30.85 = 68.53.$$

Thus, 68.53% of self-employed Americans work between 37.4 and 80.6 hours per week. The solution is illustrated in Figure 12.20.

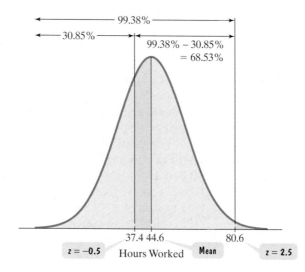

FIGURE 12.20

○

CHECK POINT 9 The distribution for the life of refrigerators is approximately normal with a mean of 14 years and a standard deviation of 2.5 years. What percentage of refrigerators have lives between 11 years and 18 years?

Our work in Examples 7 through 9 is summarized as follows:

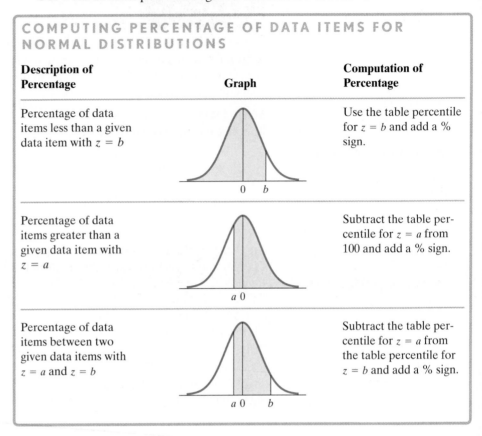

COMPUTING PERCENTAGE OF DATA ITEMS FOR NORMAL DISTRIBUTIONS

Description of Percentage	Graph	Computation of Percentage
Percentage of data items less than a given data item with $z = b$		Use the table percentile for $z = b$ and add a % sign.
Percentage of data items greater than a given data item with $z = a$		Subtract the table percentile for $z = a$ from 100 and add a % sign.
Percentage of data items between two given data items with $z = a$ and $z = b$		Subtract the table percentile for $z = a$ from the table percentile for $z = b$ and add a % sign.

8 | Use and interpret margins of error.

Polls and Margins of Error

When you were between the ages of 6 and 14, how would you have responded to this question:

What is bad about being a kid?

What Is Bad about Being a Kid?

Kids Say	
Getting bossed around	17%
School, homework	15%
Can't do everything I want	11%
Chores	9%
Being grounded	9%

Source: Penn, Schoen, and Berland using 1172 interviews with children ages 6 to 14 from May 14 to June 1, 1999, Margin of error: ±2.9%

Note the margin of error.

In a random sample of 1172 children ages 6 through 14, 17% of the children responded, "Getting bossed around." The problem is that this is a single random sample. Do 17% of kids in the entire population of children ages 6 through 14 think that getting bossed around is a bad thing?

Statisticians use properties of the normal distribution to estimate the probability that a result obtained from a single sample reflects what is truly happening in the population. If you look at the results of a poll like the one shown in the margin, you will observe that a *margin of error* is reported. Surveys and opinion polls often give a margin of error. Let's use our understanding of the normal distribution to see how to calculate and interpret margins of error.

Suppose that $p\%$ of the population of children ages 6 through 14 hold the opinion that getting bossed around is a bad thing about being a kid. Instead of taking only one random sample of 1172 children, we repeat the process of selecting a random sample of 1172 children hundreds of times. Then, we calculate the percentage of children for each sample who think being bossed around is bad. With random sampling, we expect to find the percentage in many of the samples close to $p\%$, with relatively few samples having percentages far from $p\%$. Figure 12.21 on the next page shows that the percentages of children from the hundreds of samples can be modeled by a normal distribution. The mean of this distribution is the actual population percent, $p\%$, and is the most frequent result from the samples.

Percentage of Children Who Feel
Being Bossed Around Is Bad

FIGURE 12.21 Percentage of children
who feel being bossed around is bad

Mathematicians have shown that the standard deviation of a normal distribution of samples like the one in Figure 12.21 is approximately $\frac{1}{2\sqrt{n}}$, where n is the sample size. Using the 68–95–99.7 Rule, approximately 95% of the samples have a percentage within 2 standard deviations of the true population percentage, $p\%$:

$$2 \text{ standard deviations} = 2 \cdot \frac{1}{2\sqrt{n}} = \frac{1}{\sqrt{n}}.$$

If we use a single random sample of size n, there is a 95% probability that the percent obtained will lie within two standard deviations, or $\frac{1}{\sqrt{n}}$, of the true population percent. We can be 95% confident that the true population percent lies between

$$\text{the sample percent} - \frac{1}{\sqrt{n}}$$

and

$$\text{the sample percent} + \frac{1}{\sqrt{n}}.$$

We call $\pm\frac{1}{\sqrt{n}}$ the **margin of error**.

MARGIN OF ERROR IN A SURVEY

If a statistic is obtained from a random sample of size n, there is a 95% probability that it lies within $\frac{1}{\sqrt{n}}$ of the true population statistic, where $\pm\frac{1}{\sqrt{n}}$ is called the **margin of error**.

EXAMPLE 10   USING AND INTERPRETING MARGIN OF ERROR

In a random sample of 1172 children ages 6 through 14, 17% of the children said getting bossed around is a bad thing about being a kid.

a. Verify the margin of error that was given for this survey.

b. Write a statement about the percentage of children in the population who feel that getting bossed around is a bad thing about being a kid.

SOLUTION

a. The sample size is $n = 1172$. The margin of error is

$$\pm\frac{1}{\sqrt{n}} = \pm\frac{1}{\sqrt{1172}} \approx \pm0.029 = \pm2.9\%.$$

b. There is a 95% probability that the true population percentage lies between

$$\text{the sample percent} - \frac{1}{\sqrt{n}} = 17\% - 2.9\% = 14.1\%$$

WHAT IS BAD ABOUT
BEING A KID?

Kids Say	
Getting bossed around	17%
School, homework	15%
Can't do everything I want	11%
Chores	9%
Being grounded	9%

Source: Penn, Schoen, and Berland using 1172
interviews with children ages 6 to 14 from May
14 to June 1, 1999, Margin of error: ±2.9%

9 | Recognize distributions that are not normal.

FIGURE 12.23 Histogram of the ages of females interviewed by Kinsey and his associates

and

$$\text{the sample percent} + \frac{1}{\sqrt{n}} = 17\% + 2.9\% = 19.9\%.$$

We can be 95% confident that between 14.1% and 19.9% of all children feel that getting bossed around is a bad thing about being a kid.

CHECK POINT 10 Figure 12.22 shows the question and results of a *USA Today,* CNN/Gallup poll of 485 randomly selected American adults on physician-assisted suicide.

a. Find the margin of error for this survey. Round to the nearest tenth of a percent.

b. Write a statement about the percentage of American adults in the population who support physician-assisted suicide.

c. Based on your answer to part (b), explain how the title given with the circle graph in Figure 12.22 is misleading.

Majority Supports Assisted Suicide

Should a doctor be allowed to help a terminally ill patient end his or her life with an overdose of medication if the patient is mentally competent and requests it?

Yes 54%

No 40%

No opinion 6%

FIGURE 12.22
Source: USA Today, CNN/Gallup Poll

Other Kinds of Distributions

The histogram in Figure 12.23 represents the frequencies of the ages of women interviewed by Kinsey and his colleagues in their study of female sexual behavior. This distribution is not symmetric. The greatest frequency of women interviewed was in the 16–20 age range. The bars get shorter and shorter after this. The shorter bars fall on the right, indicating that relatively few older women were included in Kinsey's interviews.

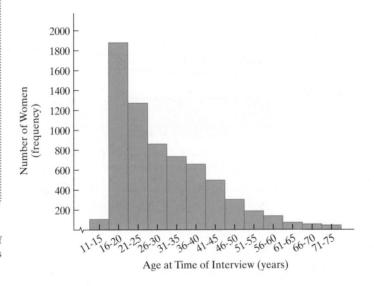

Although the normal distribution is the most important of all distributions in terms of analyzing data, not all data can be approximated by this symmetric distribution with its mean, median, and mode all having the same value.

In our discussion of measures of central tendency, we mentioned that the median, rather than the mean, is used to summarize income. Figure 12.24 at the top of the next page illustrates the population distribution of weekly earnings in the

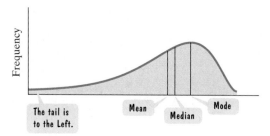

FIGURE 12.24 Skewed to the right

United States. There is no upper limit on weekly earnings. The relatively few people with very high weekly incomes tend to pull the mean income to a value greater than the median. The most frequent income, the mode, occurs toward the low end of the data items. The mean, median, and mode do not have the same value, and a normal distribution is not an appropriate model for describing weekly earnings in the United States.

The distribution in Figure 12.24 is called a *skewed distribution*. A distribution of data is **skewed** if a large number of data items are piled up at one end or the other, with a "tail" at the opposite end. In the distribution of weekly earnings in Figure 12.24, the tail is to the right. Such a distribution is said to be **skewed to the right**.

By contrast to the distribution of weekly earnings, the distribution in Figure 12.25 has more data items at the high end of the scale than at the low end. The tail of this distribution is to the left. The distribution is said to be **skewed to the left**. In many colleges, an example of a distribution skewed to the left is based on the student ratings of faculty teaching performance. Most professors are given rather high ratings, while only a few are rated terrible. These low ratings pull the value of the mean lower than the median.

FIGURE 12.25 Skewed to the left

EXERCISE SET 12.4 ●●●●●●

• Practice and Application Exercises

The scores on a test are normally distributed with a mean of 100 and a standard deviation of 20. In Exercises 1–10, find the score that is

1. 1 standard deviation above the mean.

2. 2 standard deviations above the mean.

3. 3 standard deviations above the mean.

4. $1\frac{1}{2}$ standard deviations above the mean.

5. $2\frac{1}{2}$ standard deviations above the mean.

6. 1 standard deviation below the mean.

7. 2 standard deviations below the mean.

8. 3 standard deviations below the mean.

9. one-half a standard deviation below the mean.

10. $2\frac{1}{2}$ standard deviations below the mean.

Not everyone pays the same price for the same model of a car. The figure illustrates a normal distribution for the prices paid for a particular model of a new car. The mean is $17,000 and the standard deviation is $500.

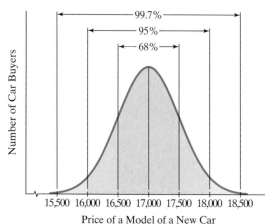

In Exercises 11–22, use the 68–95–99.7 Rule, illustrated in the figure at the bottom of the previous page, to find the percentage of buyers who paid

11. between $16,500 and $17,500.

12. between $16,000 and $18,000.

13. between $17,000 and $17,500.

14. between $17,000 and $18,000.

15. between $16,000 and $17,000.

16. between $16,500 and $17,000.

17. between $15,500 and $17,000.

18. between $17,000 and $18,500.

19. more than $17,500.

20. more than $18,000.

21. less than $16,000.

22. less than $16,500.

Intelligence quotients (IQs) on the Stanford-Binet intelligence test are normally distributed with a mean of 100 and a standard deviation of 16. In Exercises 23–32, use the 68–95–99.7 Rule to find the percentage of people with IQs

23. between 68 and 132.   24. between 84 and 116.

25. between 68 and 100.   26. between 84 and 100.

27. above 116.   28. above 132.

29. below 68.   30. below 84.

31. above 148.   32. below 52.

A set of data items is normally distributed with a mean of 60 and a standard deviation of 8. In Exercises 33–48, convert each data item to a z-score.

33. 68	34. 76	35. 84	36. 92
37. 64	38. 72	39. 74	40. 78
41. 60	42. 100	43. 52	44. 44
45. 48	46. 40	47. 34	48. 30

Yearly returns on large-company stocks are normally distributed with mean yearly interest at 12.4% and a standard deviation of 20.4%. In Exercises 49–56, find the z-score for an investment that

49. earns 43% annually.   50. earns 48.1% annually.

51. earns 58.3% annually.   52. earns 78.7% annually.

53. loses 13.1% annually.   54. loses 2.9% annually.

55. loses 18.2% annually.   56. loses 38.6% annually.

Intelligence quotients on the Stanford-Binet intelligence test are normally distributed with a mean of 100 and a standard deviation of 16. Intelligence quotients on the Wechsler intelligence test are normally distributed with a mean of 100 and a standard deviation of 15. Use this information to solve Exercises 57–58.

57. Use z-scores to determine which person has the higher IQ: an individual who scores 128 on the Stanford-Binet or an individual who scores 127 on the Wechsler.

58. Use z-scores to determine which person has the higher IQ: an individual who scores 150 on the Stanford-Binet or an individual who scores 148 on the Wechsler.

A set of data items is normally distributed with a mean of 400 and a standard deviation of 50. In Exercises 59–66, find the data item in this distribution that corresponds to the given z-score.

59. $z = 2$ 60. $z = 3$

61. $z = 1.5$ 62. $z = 2.5$

63. $z = -3$ 64. $z = -2$

65. $z = -2.5$ 66. $z = -1.5$

Use Table 12.13 on page 720 to solve Exercises 67–82.

*In Exercises 67–74, find the percentage of data items in a normal distribution that lie **a.** below and **b.** above the given z-score.*

67. $z = 0.6$ 68. $z = 0.8$

69. $z = 1.2$ 70. $z = 1.4$

71. $z = -0.7$ 72. $z = -0.4$

73. $z = -1.2$ 74. $z = -1.8$

In Exercises 75–82, find the percentage of data items in a normal distribution that lie between

75. $z = 0.2$ and $z = 1.4$.   76. $z = 0.3$ and $z = 2.1$.

77. $z = 1$ and $z = 3$.   78. $z = 2$ and $z = 3$.

79. $z = -1.5$ and $z = 1.5$.   80. $z = -1.2$ and $z = 1.2$.

81. $z = -2$ and $z = -0.5$.   82. $z = -2.2$ and $z = -0.3$.

Systolic blood pressure readings are normally distributed with a mean of 121 and a standard deviation of 15. (A reading above 140 is considered to be high blood pressure.) In Exercises 83–92, begin by converting any given blood pressure reading or readings into z-scores. Then use Table 12.13 on page 720 to find the percentage of people with blood pressure readings

83. below 142.   84. below 148.

85. above 130.   86. above 133.

87. above 103.   88. above 100.

89. between 142 and 154.   90. between 145 and 157.

91. between 112 and 130.   92. between 109 and 133.

The weights for 12-month-old baby boys are normally distributed with a mean of 22.5 pounds and a standard deviation of 2.2 pounds. In Exercises 93–96, use Table 12.13 on page 720 to find the percentage of 12-month-old baby boys who weigh

93. more than 25.8 pounds.

94. more than 23.6 pounds.

95. between 19.2 and 21.4 pounds.

96. between 18.1 and 19.2 pounds.

97. Using a random sample of 2272 American adults with children, a Harris survey asked respondents to name their dream job for their child or children. The top five responses and the percentage of parents who named each of these jobs are shown in the bar graph at the top of the next page.

What is Your Dream Job for Your Child/Children?
Top Responses

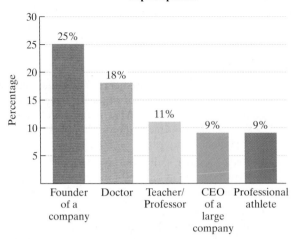

a. Find the margin of error, to the nearest tenth of a percent, for this survey.

b. Write a statement about the percentage of parents in the population who consider a doctor as the dream job for their child.

98. Using a random sample of 2297 American adults, an NBC *Today Show* poll asked respondents if they got enough sleep at night. The responses are shown in the circle graph.

Do You Get Enough
Sleep at Night?

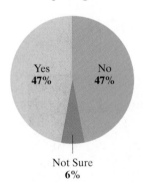

a. Find the margin of error, to the nearest tenth of a percent, for this survey.

b. Write a statement about the percentage of American adults in the population who do not get enough sleep at night.

99. Using a random sample of 4000 TV households, Nielsen Media Research found that 60.2% watched the final episode of $M*A*S*H$.

a. Find the margin of error in this percent.

b. Write a statement about the percentage of TV households in the population who tuned into the final episode of $M*A*S*H$.

100. Using a random sample of 4000 TV households, Nielsen Media Research found that 51.1% watched *Roots, Part 8*.

a. Find the margin of error in this percent.

b. Write a statement about the percentage of TV households in the population who tuned into *Roots, Part 8*.

101. In 1997, Nielsen Media Research increased its random sample to 5000 TV households. By how much, to the nearest tenth of a percent, did this improve the margin of error over that in Exercises 99 and 100?

102. If Nielsen Media Research were to increase its random sample from 5000 to 10,000 TV households, by how much, to the nearest tenth of a percent, would this improve the margin of error?

103. The histogram shows murder rates per 100,000 residents and the number of U.S. states that had these rates in 2003.

U.S. Murder Rates per 100,000 Residents,
by State and Washington, D.C.

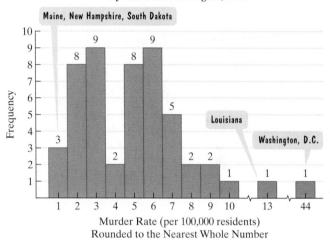

Murder Rate (per 100,000 residents)
Rounded to the Nearest Whole Number

Source: FBI, *Crime in the United States*

a. Is the shape of this distribution best classified as normal, skewed to the right, or skewed to the left?

b. Calculate the mean murder rate per 100,000 residents for the 50 states and Washington, D.C.

c. Find the median murder rate per 100,000 residents for the 50 states and Washington, D.C.

d. Are the mean and median murder rates consistent with the shape of the distribution that you described in part (a)? Explain your answer.

e. The standard deviation for the data is approximately 6.1. If the distribution were roughly normal, what would be the z-score, rounded to one decimal place, for Washington, D.C.? Does this seem unusually high? Explain your answer.

• **Writing in Mathematics**

104. What is a symmetric histogram?

105. Describe the normal distribution and discuss some of its properties.

106. Describe the 68–95–99.7 Rule.

107. Describe how to determine the z-score for a data item in a normal distribution.

108. What does a z-score measure?

109. Give an example of both a commonly occurring and an infrequently occurring z-score. Explain how you arrived at these examples.

110. Describe when a z-score is negative.

111. If you score in the 83rd percentile, what does this mean?

112. If your weight is in the third quartile, what does this mean?

113. Explain how to find the percentage of data items between the first quartile and the third quartile.

114. Two students have scores with the same percentile, but for different administrations of the SAT. Does this mean that the students have the same score on the SAT? Explain your answer.

115. Give an example of a phenomenon that is normally distributed. Explain why. (Try to be creative and not use one of the distributions discussed in this section.) Estimate what the mean and the standard deviation might be and describe how you determined these estimates.

116. Give an example of a phenomenon that is not normally distributed and explain why.

• Critical Thinking Exercises

117. Find two *z*-scores so that 40% of the data in the distribution lies between them. (More than one answer is possible.)

118. A woman insists that she will never marry a man as short or shorter than she, knowing that only one man in 400 falls into this category. Assuming a mean height of 69 inches for men with a standard deviation of 2.5 inches (and a normal distribution), approximately how tall is the woman?

119. The placement test for a college has scores that are normally distributed with a mean of 500 and a standard deviation of 100. If the college accepts only the top 10% of examinees, what is the cutoff score on the test for admission?

• Group Exercise

120. For this activity, group members will conduct interviews with a random sample of students on campus. Each student is to be asked. "What is the worst thing about being a student?" One response should be recorded for each student.

    a. Each member should interview enough students so that there are at least 50 randomly selected students in the sample.

    b. After all responses have been recorded, the group should organize the four most common answers. For each answer, compute the percentage of students in the sample who felt that this is the worst thing about being a student.

    c. Find the margin of error for your survey.

    d. For each of the four most common answers, write a statement about the percentage of all students on your campus who feel that this is the worst thing about being a student.

SECTION 12.5 • SCATTER PLOTS, CORRELATION, AND REGRESSION LINES

OBJECTIVES

1. Make a scatter plot for a table of data items.

2. Interpret information given in a scatter plot.

3. Compute the correlation coefficient.

4. Write the equation of the regression line.

5. Use a sample's correlation coefficient to determine whether there is a correlation in the population.

Surprised by the number of people smoking cigarettes in movies and television shows made in the 1940s and 1950s? At that time, there was little awareness of the relationship between tobacco use and numerous diseases. Cigarette smoking was seen as a healthy way to relax and help digest a hearty meal. Then, in 1964, an equation changed everything. To understand the mathematics behind this turning point in public health, we need to explore situations involving data collected on two variables.

Up to this point in the chapter, we have studied situations in which data sets involve a single variable, such as heights, weights, cholesterol levels, and lengths of pregnancies. By contrast, the 1964 study involved data collected on two variables from 11 countries—annual cigarette consumption for each adult male and deaths per million males from lung cancer. In this section, we consider situations in which there are two data items for each randomly selected person or thing. Our interest is in determining whether or not there is a relationship between the two variables and, if so, the strength of that relationship.

Scatter Plots and Correlation

Is there a relationship between education and prejudice? With increased education, does a person's level of prejudice tend to decrease? Notice that we are interested in two quantities—years of education and level of prejudice. For each person in our sample, we will record the number of years of school completed and the score on a test measuring prejudice. Higher scores on this 1-to-10 test indicate greater prejudice. Using x to represent years of education and y to represent scores on a test measuring prejudice, Table 12.14 shows these two quantities for a random sample of ten people.

1 | Make a scatter plot for a table of data items.

TABLE 12.14 RECORDING TWO QUANTITIES IN A SAMPLE OF TEN PEOPLE										
Respondent	**A**	**B**	**C**	**D**	**E**	**F**	**G**	**H**	**I**	**J**
Years of education (x)	12	5	14	13	8	10	16	11	12	4
Score on prejudice test (y)	1	7	2	3	5	4	1	2	3	10

When two data items are collected for every person or object in a sample, the data items can be visually displayed using a *scatter plot*. A **scatter plot** is a collection of data points, one data point per person or object. We can make a scatter plot of the data in Table 12.14 by drawing a horizontal axis to represent years of education and a vertical axis to represent scores on a test measuring prejudice. We then represent each of the ten respondents with a single point on the graph. For example, the dot for respondent A is located to represent 12 years of education on the horizontal axis and 1 on the prejudice test on the vertical axis. Plotting each of the ten pieces of data in a rectangular coordinate system results in the scatter plot shown in Figure 12.26.

A scatter plot like the one in Figure 12.26 can be used to determine whether two quantities are related. If there is a clear relationship, the quantities are said to be **correlated**. The scatter plot shows a downward trend among the data points, although there are a few exceptions. People with increased education tend to have a lower score on the test measuring prejudice. **Correlation** is used to determine if there is a relationship between two variables and, if so, the strength and direction of that relationship.

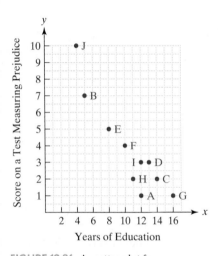

FIGURE 12.26 A scatter plot for education-prejudice data

Correlation and Causal Connections

Correlations can often be seen when data items are displayed on a scatter plot. Although the scatter plot in Figure 12.26 indicates a correlation between education and prejudice, we cannot conclude that increased education causes a person's level of prejudice to decrease. There are at least three possible explanations:

1. The correlation between increased education and decreased prejudice is simply a coincidence.
2. Education usually involves classrooms with a variety of different kinds of people. Increased exposure to diversity in the classroom setting, which accompanies increased levels of education, might be an underlying cause for decreased prejudice.
3. Education, the process of acquiring knowledge, requires people to look at new ideas and see things in different ways. Thus, education causes one to be more tolerant and less prejudiced.

STUDY TIP

The numbered list on the right represents three possibilities. Perhaps you can provide a better explanation about decreasing prejudice with increased education.

Establishing that one thing causes another is extremely difficult, even if there is a strong correlation between these things. For example, as the air temperature increases, there is an increase in the number of people stung by jellyfish at the beach. This does not mean that an increase in air temperature causes more people to be stung. It might mean that because it is hotter, more people go into the water. With an increased number of swimmers, more people are likely to be stung. In short, correlation is not necessarily causation.

Regression Lines and Correlation Coefficients

Figure 12.27 shows the scatter plot for the education-prejudice data. Also shown is a straight line that seems to approximately "fit" the data points. Most of the data points lie either near or on this line. A line that best fits the data points in a scatter plot is called a **regression line**. The regression line is the particular line in which the spread of the data points around it is as small as possible.

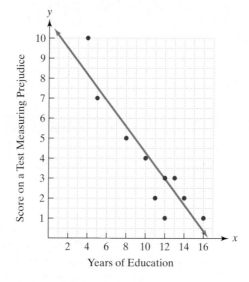

FIGURE 12.27 A scatter plot with a regression line

2 | Interpret information given in a scatter plot.

A measure that is used to describe the strength and direction of a relationship between variables whose data points lie on or near a line is called the **correlation coefficient**, designated by r. Figure 12.28 shows scatter plots and correlation coefficients. Variables are **positively correlated** if they tend to increase or decrease together, as in Figure 12.28 (a), (b), and (c). By contrast, variables are **negatively correlated** if one variable tends to decrease while the other increases, as in Figure 12.28 (e), (f), and (g). Figure 12.28 illustrates that a correlation coefficient, r, is a number between -1 and 1, inclusive. Figure 12.28(a) shows a value of 1. This indicates a **perfect positive correlation** in which all points in the scatter plot lie precisely on the regression line that rises from left to right. Figure 12.28(g) shows a value of -1. This indicates a **perfect negative correlation** in which all points in the scatter plot lie precisely on the regression line that falls from left to right.

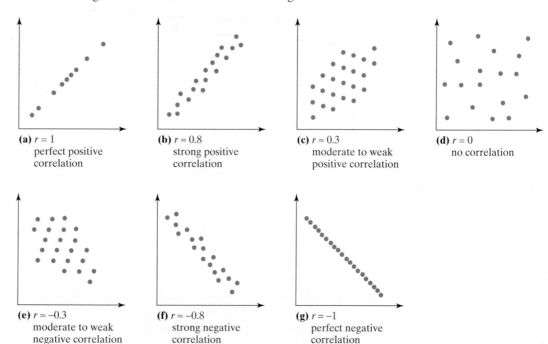

(a) $r = 1$
perfect positive
correlation

(b) $r \approx 0.8$
strong positive
correlation

(c) $r \approx 0.3$
moderate to weak
positive correlation

(d) $r = 0$
no correlation

(e) $r \approx -0.3$
moderate to weak
negative correlation

(f) $r \approx -0.8$
strong negative
correlation

(g) $r = -1$
perfect negative
correlation

FIGURE 12.28 Scatter plots and correlation coefficients

Take another look at Figure 12.28. If r is between 0 and 1, as in (b) and (c), the two variables are positively correlated, but not perfectly. Although all the data points will not lie on the regression line, as in (a), an increase in one variable tends to be accompanied by an increase in the other.

Negative correlations are also illustrated in Figure 12.28. If r is between 0 and -1, as in (e) and (f), the two variables are negatively correlated, but not perfectly. Although all the data points will not lie on the regression line, as in (g), an increase in one variable tends to be accompanied by a decrease in the other.

EXAMPLE 1   INTERPRETING A CORRELATION COEFFICIENT

In a 1971 study involving 232 subjects, researchers found a relationship between the subjects' level of stress and how often they became ill. The correlation coefficient in this study was 0.32. Does this indicate a strong relationship between stress and illness?

SOLUTION   The correlation coefficient $r = 0.32$ means that as stress increases, frequency of illness also tends to increase. However, 0.32 is only a moderate correlation, illustrated in Figure 12.28(c). There is not, based on this study, a strong relationship between stress and illness. In this study, the relationship is somewhat weak.

○

CHECK POINT 1   In a 1996 study involving obesity in mothers and daughters, researchers found a relationship between a high body-mass index for the girls and their mothers. (Body-mass index is a measure of weight relative to height. People with a high body-mass index are overweight or obese.) The correlation coefficient in this study was 0.51. Does this indicate a weak relationship between the body-mass index of daughters and the body-mass index of their mothers?

How to Obtain the Correlation Coefficient and the Equation of the Regression Line

The easiest way to find the correlation coefficient and the equation of the regression line is to use a graphing or statistical calculator. Graphing calculators have statistical menus that enable you to enter the x and y data items for the variables. Based on this information, you can instruct the calculator to display a scatter plot, the equation of the regression line, and the correlation coefficient.

We can also compute the correlation coefficient and the equation of the regression line by hand using formulas. First, we compute the correlation coefficient.

3 Compute the correlation coefficient.

COMPUTING THE CORRELATION COEFFICIENT BY HAND

The following formula is used to calculate the correlation coefficient, r:

$$r = \frac{n(\Sigma xy) - (\Sigma x)(\Sigma y)}{\sqrt{n(\Sigma x^2) - (\Sigma x)^2}\sqrt{n(\Sigma y^2) - (\Sigma y)^2}}.$$

In the formula,

$$n = \text{the number of data points, } (x, y)$$
$$\Sigma x = \text{the sum of the } x\text{-values}$$
$$\Sigma y = \text{the sum of the } y\text{-values}$$
$$\Sigma xy = \text{the sum of the product of } x \text{ and } y \text{ in each pair}$$
$$\Sigma x^2 = \text{the sum of the squares of the } x\text{-values}$$
$$\Sigma y^2 = \text{the sum of the squares of the } y\text{-values}$$
$$(\Sigma x)^2 = \text{the square of the sum of the } x\text{-values}$$
$$(\Sigma y)^2 = \text{the square of the sum of the } y\text{-values}$$

When computing the correlation coefficient by hand, organize your work in five columns:

x	y	xy	x^2	y^2

Find the sum of the numbers in each column. Then, substitute these values into the formula for r. Example 2 illustrates computing the correlation coefficient for the education-prejudice test data.

EXAMPLE 2 — COMPUTING THE CORRELATION COEFFICIENT

Shown below are the data involving the number of years of school, x, completed by ten randomly selected people and their scores on a test measuring prejudice, y. Recall that higher scores on the measure of prejudice (1 to 10) indicate greater levels of prejudice. Determine the correlation coefficient between years of education and scores on a prejudice test.

Respondent	A	B	C	D	E	F	G	H	I	J
Years of education (x)	12	5	14	13	8	10	16	11	12	4
Score on prejudice test (y)	1	7	2	3	5	4	1	2	3	10

SOLUTION As suggested, organize the work in five columns.

x	y	xy	x^2	y^2
12	1	12	144	1
5	7	35	25	49
14	2	28	196	4
13	3	39	169	9
8	5	40	64	25
10	4	40	100	16
16	1	16	256	1
11	2	22	121	4
12	3	36	144	9
4	10	40	16	100
$\Sigma x = 105$	$\Sigma y = 38$	$\Sigma xy = 308$	$\Sigma x^2 = 1235$	$\Sigma y^2 = 218$

Add all values in the x-column.
Add all values in the y-column.
Add all values in the xy-column.
Add all values in the x^2-column.
Add all values in the y^2-column.

We use these five sums to calculate the correlation coefficient.

Another value in the formula for r that we have not yet determined is n, the number of data points (x, y). Because there are ten items in the x-column and ten items in the y-column, the number of data points (x, y) is ten. Thus, $n = 10$.

In order to calculate r, we also need to find the square of the sum of the x-values and the y-values:

$$(\Sigma x)^2 = (105)^2 = 11{,}025 \quad \text{and} \quad (\Sigma y)^2 = (38)^2 = 1444.$$

We are ready to determine the value for r.

$$r = \frac{n(\Sigma xy) - (\Sigma x)(\Sigma y)}{\sqrt{n(\Sigma x^2) - (\Sigma x)^2}\sqrt{n(\Sigma y^2) - (\Sigma y)^2}}$$

$$= \frac{10(308) - 105(38)}{\sqrt{10(1235) - 11{,}025}\sqrt{10(218) - 1444}}$$

$$= \frac{-910}{\sqrt{1325}\sqrt{736}}$$

$$\approx -0.92$$

The value for r, approximately -0.92, is fairly close to -1 and indicates a strong negative correlation. This means that the more education a person has, the less prejudiced that person is (based on scores on the test measuring levels of prejudice). ○

CHECK POINT 2 Is there a relationship between alcohol from moderate wine consumption and heart disease death rate? The table gives data from 19 developed countries. Using a calculator, determine the correlation coefficient between these variables. Round to two decimal places.

France   U.S.

Country	A	B	C	D	E	F	G	H	I	J	K	L	M	N	O	P	Q	R	S
Liters of alcohol from drinking wine, per person per year (x)	2.5	3.9	2.9	2.4	2.9	0.8	9.1	0.8	0.7	7.9	1.8	1.9	0.8	6.5	1.6	5.8	1.3	1.2	2.7
Deaths from heart disease, per 100,000 people per year (y)	211	167	131	191	220	297	71	211	300	107	167	266	227	86	207	115	285	199	172

Source: New York Times, December 28, 1994

Once we have determined that two variables are related, we can use the equation of the regression line to determine the exact relationship. Here is the formula for writing the equation of the line that best fits the data:

4 Write the equation of the regression line.

WRITING THE EQUATION OF THE REGRESSION LINE BY HAND

The equation of the regression line is

$$y = mx + b,$$

where

$$m = \frac{n(\Sigma xy) - (\Sigma x)(\Sigma y)}{n(\Sigma x^2) - (\Sigma x)^2} \quad \text{and} \quad b = \frac{\Sigma y - m(\Sigma x)}{n}.$$

EXAMPLE 3 **WRITING THE EQUATION OF THE REGRESSION LINE**

a. Shown, again, in Figure 12.27 is the scatter plot and the regression line for the data in Example 2. Use the data to find the equation of the regression line that relates years of education and scores on a prejudice test.

b. Approximately what score on the test can be anticipated by a person with nine years of education?

SOLUTION

a. We use the sums obtained in Example 2. We begin by computing m.

$$m = \frac{n(\Sigma xy) - (\Sigma x)(\Sigma y)}{n(\Sigma x^2) - (\Sigma x)^2} = \frac{10(308) - 105(38)}{10(1235) - (105)^2} = \frac{-910}{1325} \approx -0.69$$

With a negative correlation coefficient, it makes sense that the slope of the regression line is negative. This line falls from left to right, indicating a negative correlation.

Now, we find the y-intercept, b.

$$b = \frac{\Sigma y - m(\Sigma x)}{n} = \frac{38 - (-0.69)(105)}{10} = \frac{110.45}{10} \approx 11.05$$

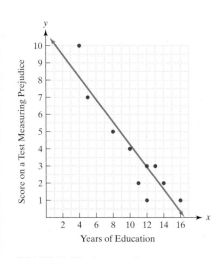

FIGURE 12.27 (repeated)

Using $m \approx -0.69$ and $b \approx 11.05$, the equation of the regression line, $y = mx + b$, is

$$y = -0.69x + 11.05,$$

where x represents the number of years of education and y represents the score on the prejudice test.

b. To anticipate the score on the prejudice test for a person with nine years of education, substitute 9 for x in the regression line's equation.

$$y = -0.69x + 11.05$$
$$y = -0.69(9) + 11.05 = 4.84$$

A person with nine years of education is anticipated to have a score close to 5 on the prejudice test.

○

CHECK POINT 3 Use the data in Check Point 2 on page 735 to find the equation of the regression line. Use the equation to predict the heart disease death rate in a country where adults average 10 liters of alcohol per person per year.

The Level of Significance of r

In Example 2, we found a strong negative correlation between education and prejudice, computing the correlation coefficient, r, to be -0.92. However, the sample size ($n = 10$) was relatively small. With such a small sample, can we truly conclude that a correlation exists in the population? Or could it be that education and prejudice are not related? Perhaps the results we obtained were simply due to sampling error and chance.

Mathematicians have identified values to determine whether r, the correlation coefficient for a sample, can be attributed to a relationship between variables in the population. These values are shown in the second and third columns of Table 12.15. They depend on the sample size, n, listed in the left column. If $|r|$, the absolute value of the correlation coefficient computed for the sample, is greater than the value given in the table, a correlation exists between the variables in the population. The column headed $\alpha = 0.05$ denotes a **significance level of 5%**, meaning that there is a 0.05 probability that, when the statistician says the variables are correlated, they are actually not related in the population. The column on the right, headed $\alpha = 0.01$, denotes a **significance level of 1%**, meaning that there is a 0.01 probability that, when the statistician says the variables are correlated, they are actually not related in the population. Values in the $\alpha = 0.01$ column are greater than those in the $\alpha = 0.05$ column. Because of the possibility of sampling error, there is always a probability that when we say the variables are related, there is actually not a correlation in the population from which the sample was randomly selected.

EXAMPLE 4   DETERMINING A CORRELATION IN THE POPULATION

In Example 2, we computed $r = -0.92$ for $n = 10$. Can we conclude that there is a negative correlation between education and prejudice in the population?

SOLUTION Begin by taking the absolute value of the calculated correlation coefficient.

$$|r| = |-0.92| = 0.92$$

Now, look to the right of $n = 10$ in Table 12.15. Because 0.92 is greater than both of these values (0.632 and 0.765), we may conclude that a correlation does exist between education and prejudice in the population. (There is a probability of at most 0.01 that the variables are not really correlated in the population and our results could be attributed to chance.)

○

Objective 5: Use a sample's correlation coefficient to determine whether there is a correlation in the population.

TABLE 12.15 VALUES FOR DETERMINING CORRELATIONS IN A POPULATION

n	$\alpha = 0.05$	$\alpha = 0.01$
4	0.950	0.990
5	0.878	0.959
6	0.811	0.917
7	0.754	0.875
8	0.707	0.834
9	0.666	0.798
10	0.632	0.765
11	0.602	0.735
12	0.576	0.708
13	0.553	0.684
14	0.532	0.661
15	0.514	0.641
16	0.497	0.623
17	0.482	0.606
18	0.468	0.590
19	0.456	0.575
20	0.444	0.561
22	0.423	0.537
27	0.381	0.487
32	0.349	0.449
37	0.325	0.418
42	0.304	0.393
47	0.288	0.372
52	0.273	0.354
62	0.250	0.325
72	0.232	0.302
82	0.217	0.283
92	0.205	0.267
102	0.195	0.254

The larger the sample size, n, the smaller is the value of r needed for a correlation in the population.

CHECK POINT 4 If you worked Check Point 2 correctly, you should have found that $r \approx -0.84$ for $n = 19$. Can you conclude that there is a negative correlation between moderate wine consumption and heart disease death rate?

BLITZER BONUS

Cigarettes and Lung Cancer

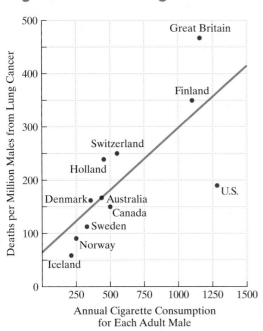

Source: Smoking and Health, Washington, D.C., 1964

This scatter plot shows a relationship between cigarette consumption among males and deaths due to lung cancer per million males. The data are from 11 countries and date back to a 1964 report by the U.S. Surgeon General. The scatter plot can be modeled by a line whose slope indicates an increasing death rate from lung cancer with increased cigarette consumption. At that time, the tobacco industry argued that in spite of this regression line, tobacco use is not the cause of cancer. Recent data do, indeed, show a causal effect between tobacco use and numerous diseases.

EXERCISE SET 12.5 ●●●●●●

• Practice and Application Exercises

In Exercises 1–8, make a scatter plot for the given data. Use the scatter plot to describe whether or not the variables appear to be related.

1.

x	1	6	4	3	7	2
y	2	5	3	3	4	1

2.

x	2	1	6	3	4
y	4	5	10	8	9

3.

x	8	6	1	5	4	10	3
y	2	4	10	5	6	2	9

4.

x	4	5	2	1
y	1	3	5	4

5.

Respondent	A	B	C	D	E	F	G
Years of education of parent (x)	13	9	7	12	12	10	11
Years of education of child (y)	13	11	7	16	17	8	17

6.

Respondent	A	B	C	D	E
IQ (x)	110	115	120	125	135
Annual income(y) (in thousands of dollars)	30	32	36	40	44

7. The data show the number of registered automatic weapons, in thousands, and the murder rate, in murders per 100,000, for eight randomly selected states.

Automatic weapons, x	11.6	8.3	6.9	3.6	2.6	2.5	2.4	0.6
Murder rate, y	13.1	10.6	11.5	10.1	5.3	6.6	3.6	4.4

Source: FBI and Bureau of Alcohol, Tobacco, and Firearms

8. The data show the number of employed and unemployed male workers, 20 years and older, in thousands, for six selected years in the United States.

Year	1995	1996	1997	1998	1999	2000
Employed, x	64,085	64,897	66,524	67,134	67,761	68,580
Unemployed, y	3239	3147	2826	2580	2433	2350

Source: Bureau of Labor Statistics

The scatter plot in the figure shows the relationship between the percentage of married women of child-bearing age using contraceptives and births per woman in selected countries. Use the scatter plot to determine whether each of the statements in Exercises 9–18 is true or false.

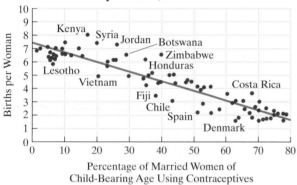

Source: Population Reference Bureau

9. There is a strong positive correlation between contraceptive use and births per woman.

10. There is no correlation between contraceptive use and births per woman.

11. There is a strong negative correlation between contraceptive use and births per woman.

12. There is a causal relationship between contraceptive use and births per woman.

13. With approximately 43% of women of child-bearing age using contraceptives, there are 3 births per woman in Chile.

14. With 20% of women of child-bearing age using contraceptives, there are 6 births per woman in Vietnam.

15. No two countries have a different number of births per woman with the same percentage of married women using contraceptives.

16. The country with the greatest number of births per woman also has the smallest percentage of women using contraceptives.

17. Most of the data points do not lie on the regression line.

18. The number of selected countries shown in the scatter plot is approximately 20.

Just as money doesn't buy happiness for individuals, the two don't necessarily go together for countries either. However, the scatter plot does show a relationship between a country's annual per capita income and the percentage of people in that country who call themselves "happy." Use the scatter plot to determine whether each of the statements in Exercises 19–26 is true or false.

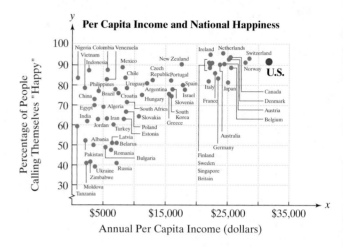

Source: Richard Layard, *Happiness: Lessons from a New Science*, Penguin, 2005

19. There is no correlation between per capita income and the percentage of people who call themselves "happy."

20. There is an almost-perfect positive correlation between per capita income and the percentage of people who call themselves "happy."

21. There is a positive correlation between per capita income and the percentage of people who call themselves "happy."

22. As per capita income decreases, the percentage of people who call themselves "happy" also tends to decrease.

23. The country with the lowest per capita income has the least percentage of people who call themselves "happy."

24. The country with the highest per capita income has the greatest percentage of people who call themselves "happy."

25. A reasonable estimate of the correlation coefficient for the data is 0.8.

26. A reasonable estimate of the correlation coefficient for the data is −0.3.

Use the scatter plots shown, labeled (a)–(f), to solve Exercises 27–30.

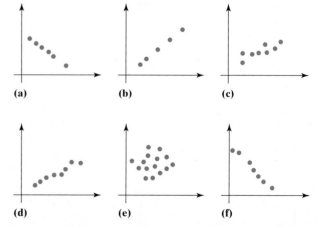

27. Which scatter plot indicates a perfect negative correlation?

28. Which scatter plot indicates a perfect positive correlation?

29. In which scatter plot is $r = 0.9$?

30. In which scatter plot is $r = 0.01$?

Compute r, the correlation coefficient, rounded to the nearest thousandth, for the data in

31. Exercise 1.   **32.** Exercise 2.

33. Exercise 3.   **34.** Exercise 4.

35. Use the data in Exercise 5 to solve this exercise.
  a. Determine the correlation coefficient between years of education of parent and child.
  b. Find the equation of the regression line for years of education of parent and child.
  c. Approximately how many years of education can we predict for a child with a parent who has 16 years of education?

36. Use the data in Exercise 6 to solve this exercise.
  a. Determine the correlation coefficient between IQ and income.
  b. Find the equation of the regression line for IQ and income.
  c. Approximately what annual income can be anticipated by a person whose IQ is 123?

37. Use the data in Exercise 7 to solve this exercise.
  a. Determine the correlation coefficient between the number of automatic weapons and the murder rate.
  b. Find the equation of the regression line.
  c. Approximately what murder rate can we anticipate in a state that has 14 thousand registered weapons?

38. Use the data in Exercise 8 to solve this exercise.
  a. Determine the correlation coefficient between the number of employed males and the number of unemployed males.
  b. Find the equation of the regression line.
  c. Approximately how many unemployed males can we anticipate for a year in which there are 70,000 thousand employed males?

In Exercises 39–45, the correlation coefficient, r, is given for a sample of n data points. Use the $\alpha = 0.05$ column in Table 12.15 on page 736 to determine whether or not we may conclude that a correlation does exist in the population. (Using the $\alpha = 0.05$ column, there is a probability of 0.05 that the variables are not really correlated in the population and our results could be attributed to chance. Ignore this possibility when concluding whether or not there is a correlation in the population.)

39. $n = 20, r = 0.5$ **40.** $n = 27, r = 0.4$

41. $n = 12, r = 0.5$ **42.** $n = 22, r = 0.04$

43. $n = 72, r = -0.351$ **44.** $n = 37, r = -0.37$

45. $n = 20, r = -0.37$

46. In the 1964 study on cigarette consumption and deaths due to lung cancer (see the Blitzer Bonus on page 737), $n = 11$ and $r = 0.73$. What can you conclude using the $\alpha = 0.05$ column in Table 12.15?

• Writing in Mathematics

47. What is a scatter plot?

48. How does a scatter plot indicate that two variables are correlated?

49. Give an example of two variables with a strong positive correlation and explain why this is so.

50. Give an example of two variables with a strong negative correlation and explain why this is so.

51. What is meant by a regression line?

52. When all points in a scatter plot fall on the regression line, what is the value of the correlation coefficient? Describe what this means.

For the pairs of quantities in Exercises 53–56, describe whether a scatter plot will show a positive correlation, a negative correlation, or no correlation. If there is a correlation, is it strong, moderate, or weak? Explain your answers.

53. Height and weight

54. Number of days absent and grade in a course

55. Height and grade in a course

56. Hours of television watched and grade in a course

57. Explain how to use the correlation coefficient for a sample to determine if there is a correlation in the population.

• Critical Thinking Exercises

58. Which one of the following is true?
  a. A scatter plot need not define y as a function of x.
  b. The correlation coefficient and the slope of the regression line for the same set of data can have opposite signs.
  c. When all points in a scatter plot fall on the regression line, the value of the correlation coefficient is 0.
  d. If the same number is subtracted from each x-item, but the y-item stays the same, the correlation coefficient for these new data points decreases.

59. Give an example of two variables with a strong correlation, where each variable is not the cause of the other.

• Technology Exercise

60. Use the linear regression feature of a graphing calculator to verify your work in any two exercises from Exercises 35–38, parts (a) and (b).

• Group Exercises

61. The group should select two variables related to people on your campus that it believes have a strong positive or negative correlation. Once these variables have been determined,
  a. Collect at least 30 ordered pairs of data (x, y) from a sample of people on your campus.
  b. Draw a scatter plot for the data collected.
  c. Does the scatter plot indicate a positive correlation, a negative correlation, or no relationship between the variables?
  d. Calculate r. Does the value of r reinforce the impression conveyed by the scatter plot?
  e. Find the equation of the regression line.
  f. Use the regression line's equation to make a prediction about a y-value given an x-value.
  g. Are the results of this project consistent with the group's original belief about the correlation between the variables, or are there some surprises in the data collected?

62. What is the opinion of students on your campus about ... ? Group members should begin by deciding on some aspect of college life around which student opinion can be polled. The poll should consist of the question, "What is your opinion of ... ?" Be sure to provide options such as excellent, good, average, poor, horrible, or a 1-to-10 scale, or possibly grades of A, B, C, D, F. Use a random sample of students on your campus and conduct the opinion survey. After collecting the data, present and interpret it using as many of the skills and techniques learned in this chapter as possible.

●●●●●○ CHAPTER SUMMARY, REVIEW, AND TEST

● SUMMARY   DEFINITIONS AND CONCEPTS   EXAMPLES

12.1 Sampling, Frequency Distributions, and Graphs

a. A population is the set containing all objects whose properties are to be described and analyzed. A sample is a subset of the population.
Ex. 1, p. 681

b. Random samples are obtained in such a way that each member of the population has an equal chance of being selected.
Ex. 2, p. 682

c. Data can be organized and presented in frequency distributions, grouped frequency distributions, histograms, frequency polygons, and stem-and-leaf plots.
Ex. 3, p. 683;
Ex. 4, p. 684;
Figures 12.2 and 12.3, p. 685;
Ex. 5, p. 686

d. The box on page 687 lists some things to watch for in visual displays of data.
Table 12.4, p. 688

12.2 Measures of Central Tendency

a. The mean is the sum of the data items divided by the number of items. Mean $= \dfrac{\Sigma x}{n}$.
Ex. 1, p. 693

b. The mean of a frequency distribution is computed using

$$\text{Mean} = \frac{\Sigma xf}{n},$$

where x is each data value, f is its frequency, and n is the total frequency of the distribution.
Ex. 2, p. 694

c. The median of ranked data is the item in the middle or the mean of the two middlemost items. The median is the value in the $\frac{n+1}{2}$ position in the list of ranked data.
Ex. 3, p. 695;
Ex. 4, p. 696;
Ex. 5, p. 697;
Ex. 6, p. 697

d. When one or more data items are much greater than or much less than the other items, these extreme values greatly influence the mean, often making the median more representative of the data.
Ex. 7, p. 698

e. The mode of a data set is the value that occurs most often. If there is no such value, there is no mode. If more than one data value has the highest frequency, then each of these data values is a mode.
Ex. 8, p. 700

f. The midrange is computed using

$$\frac{\text{lowest data value} + \text{highest data value}}{2}.$$
Ex. 9, p. 701;
Ex. 10, p. 701

12.3 Measures of Dispersion

a. Range = highest data value − lowest data value
Ex. 1, p. 705

b. Standard deviation $= \sqrt{\dfrac{\Sigma(\text{data item} - \text{mean})^2}{n-1}}$

Ex. 2, p. 706;
Ex. 3, p. 707;
Ex. 4, p. 708

c. As the spread of data items increases, the standard deviation gets larger.

Ex. 5, p. 709

12.4 The Normal Distribution

a. The normal distribution is a theoretical distribution for the entire population. The distribution is bell shaped and symmetric about a vertical line through its center, where the mean, median, and mode are located.

b. The 68–95–99.7 Rule

Ex. 1, p. 714;
Ex. 2, p. 715

Approximately 68% of the data items fall within 1 standard deviation of the mean,

95% of the data items fall within 2 standard deviations of the mean, and

99.7% of the data items fall within 3 standard deviations of the mean.

c. A z-score describes how many standard deviations a data item in a normal distribution lies above or below the mean.

Ex. 3, p. 716;
Ex. 4, p. 718;
Ex. 5, p. 718

$$z\text{-score} = \dfrac{\text{data item} - \text{mean}}{\text{standard deviation}}$$

d. If $n\%$ of the items in a distribution are less than a particular data item, that data item is in the nth percentile of the distribution. The 25th percentile is the first quartile, the 50th percentile, or the median, is the second quartile, and the 75th percentile is the third quartile.

Ex. 6, p. 719;
Figure 12.16, p. 719

e. A table showing z-scores and their percentiles can be used to find the percentage of data items less than or greater than a given data item in a normal distribution, as well as the percentage of data items between two given items. See the boxed summary on computing percentage of data items on page 724.

Ex. 7, p. 720;
Ex. 8, p. 721;
Ex. 9, p. 723

f. If a statistic is obtained from a random sample of size n, there is a 95% probability that it lies within $\dfrac{1}{\sqrt{n}}$ of the true population statistic. $\pm\dfrac{1}{\sqrt{n}}$ is called the margin of error.

Ex. 10, p. 725

g. A distribution of data is skewed if a large number of data items are piled up at one end or the other, with a "tail" at the opposite end.

Figure 12.24, p. 727;
Figure 12.25, p. 727

12.5 Scatter Plots, Correlation, and Regression Lines

a. A plot of data points is called a scatter plot. If the points lie approximately along a line, the line that best fits the data is called a regression line.

b. A correlation coefficient, r, measures the strength and direction of a possible relationship between variables. If $r = 1$, there is a perfect positive correlation, and if $r = -1$, there is a perfect negative correlation. If $r = 0$, there is no relationship between the variables. Table 12.15 on page 736 indicates whether r denotes a correlation in the population.

Ex. 1, p. 733;
Ex. 4, p. 736

c. The formula for computing the correlation coefficient, r, is given in the box on page 733. The equation of the regression line is given in the box on page 735.

Ex. 2, p. 734;
Ex. 3, p. 735

REVIEW EXERCISES

12.1

A survey of 1511 randomly selected American women ages 25 through 60 was taken by CyberPulse Advisory Panel. The data below are from the poll. Use this information to solve Exercises 1–2.

How Often Do You Entertain Guests for Dinner?

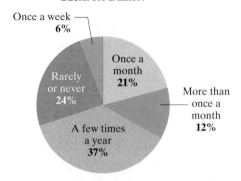

1. Describe the population and the sample of this poll.
2. For each woman polled, what variable is measured?
3. The government of a large city wants to know if its citizens will support a three-year tax increase to provide additional support to the city's community college system. The government decides to conduct a survey of the city's residents before placing a tax increase initiative on the ballot. Which one of the following is most appropriate for obtaining a sample of the city's residents?
   a. Survey a random sample of persons within each geographic region of the city.
   b. Survey a random sample of community college professors living in the city.
   c. Survey every tenth person who walks into the city's government center on two randomly selected days of the week.
   d. Survey a random sample of persons within each geographic region of the state in which the city is located.

A random sample of ten college students is selected and each student is asked how much time he or she spent on homework during the previous weekend. The following times, in hours, are obtained:

$$8, 10, 9, 7, 9, 8, 7, 6, 8, 7.$$

Use these data items to solve Exercises 4–6.

4. Construct a frequency distribution for the data.
5. Construct a histogram for the data.
6. Construct a frequency polygon for the data.

The 50 grades on a physiology test are shown. Use the data to solve Exercises 7–8.

44	24	54	81	18
34	39	63	67	60
72	36	91	47	75
57	74	87	49	86
59	14	26	41	90
13	29	13	31	68
63	35	29	70	22
95	17	50	42	27
73	11	42	31	69
56	40	31	45	51

7. Construct a grouped frequency distribution for the data. Use 0–39 for the first class, 40–49 for the second class, and make each subsequent class width the same as the second class.
8. Construct a stem-and-leaf plot for the data.
9. Describe what is misleading about the size of the barrels in the following visual display.

Average Daily Price per Barrel of Oil

Source: U.S. Department of Energy

12.2

In Exercises 10–11, find the mean for each group of data items.

10. 84, 90, 95, 89, 98
11. 33, 27, 9, 10, 6, 7, 11, 23, 27
12. Find the mean for the data items in the given frequency distribution.

Score x	Frequency f
1	2
2	4
3	3
4	1

In Exercises 13–14, find the median for each group of data items.

13. 33, 27, 9, 10, 6, 7, 11, 23, 27
14. 28, 16, 22, 28, 34
15. Find the median for the data items in the frequency distribution in Exercise 12.

In Exercises 16–17, find the mode for each group of data items. If there is no mode, so state.

16. 33, 27, 9, 10, 6, 7, 11, 23, 27
17. 582, 585, 583, 585, 587, 587, 589
18. Find the mode for the data items in the frequency distribution in Exercise 12.

In Exercises 19–20, find the midrange for each group of data items.

19. 84, 90, 95, 88, 98
20. 33, 27, 9, 10, 6, 7, 11, 23, 27
21. Find the midrange for the data items in the frequency distribution in Exercise 12.

22. Researchers at Emory University studied national health-care data from 14,000 Americans in 1987 and 2002. Explain how the research team obtained the mean annual health-care costs shown in the bar graph.

Mean Annual Health-Care Costs

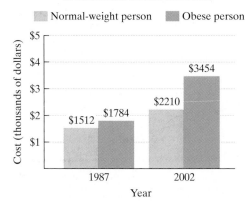

Source: Kenneth Thorpe, Emory University

23. A student took seven tests in a course, scoring between 90% and 95% on three of the tests, between 80% and 89% on three of the tests, and below 40% on one of the tests. In this distribution, is the mean or the median more representative of the student's overall performance in the course? Explain your answer.

24. The data items below are the ages of U.S. presidents at the time of their first inauguration.

```
57  61  57  57  58  57  61  54  68  51  49  64   50  48
65  52  56  46  54  49  51  47  55  55  54  42   51  56
55  51  54  51  60  62  43  55  56  61  52  69   64  46 54
```

  a. Organize the data in a frequency distribution.
  b. Use the frequency distribution to find the mean age, median age, modal age, and midrange age of the presidents when they were inaugurated.

12.3

In Exercises 25–26, find the range for each group of data items.

25. 28, 34, 16, 22, 28

26. 312, 783, 219, 312, 426, 219

27. The mean for the data items 29, 9, 8, 22, 46, 51, 48, 42, 53, 42 is 35. Find **a.** the deviation from the mean for each data item and **b.** the sum of the deviations in part (a).

28. Use the data items 36, 26, 24, 90, and 74 to find **a.** the mean, **b.** the deviation from the mean for each data item, and **c.** the sum of the deviations in part (b).

In Exercises 29–30, find the standard deviation for each group of data items.

29. 3, 3, 5, 8, 10, 13

30. 20, 27, 23, 26, 28, 32, 33, 35

31. A test measuring anxiety levels is administered to a sample of ten college students with the following results. (High scores indicate high anxiety.)

  10, 30, 37, 40, 43, 44, 45, 69, 86, 86

  Find the mean, range, and standard deviation for the data.

32. Compute the mean and the standard deviation for each of the following data sets. Then, write a brief description of similarities and differences between the two sets based on each of your computations.

  Set A: 80, 80, 80, 80   Set B: 70, 70, 90, 90

33. Describe how you would determine
  a. which of the two groups, men or women, at your college has a higher mean grade point average.
  b. which of the groups is more consistently close to its mean grade point average.

12.4

The scores on a test are normally distributed with a mean of 70 and a standard deviation of 8. In Exercises 34–36, find the score that is

34. 2 standard deviations above the mean.

35. $3\frac{1}{2}$ standard deviations above the mean.

36. $1\frac{1}{4}$ standard deviations below the mean.

The ages of people living in a retirement community are normally distributed with a mean age of 68 years and a standard deviation of 4 years. In Exercises 37–43, use the 68–95–99.7 Rule to find the percentage of people in the community whose ages

37. are between 64 and 72.   **38.** are between 60 and 76.

39. are between 68 and 72.   **40.** are between 56 and 80.

41. exceed 72.   **42.** are less than 72.

43. exceed 76.

A set of data items is normally distributed with a mean of 50 and a standard deviation of 5. In Exercises 44–48, convert each data item to a z-score.

44. 50   **45.** 60   **46.** 58

47. 35   **48.** 44

49. A student scores 60 on a vocabulary test and 80 on a grammar test. The data items for both tests are normally distributed. The vocabulary test has a mean of 50 and a standard deviation of 5. The grammar test has a mean of 72 and a standard deviation of 6. On which test did the student have the better score? Explain why this is so.

The number of miles that a particular brand of car tires lasts is normally distributed with a mean of 32,000 miles and a standard deviation of 4000 miles. In Exercises 50–52, find the data item in this distribution that corresponds to the given z-score.

50. $z = 1.5$ **51.** $z = 2.25$ **52.** $z = -2.5$

The mean cholesterol level for all men in the United States is 200 and the standard deviation is 15. In Exercises 53–56, use Table 12.13 on page 720 to find the percentage of U.S. men whose cholesterol level

53. is less than 221.   **54.** is greater than 173.

55. is between 173 and 221.   **56.** is between 164 and 182.

Use the percentiles for the weights of adult men over 40 to solve Exercises 57–59.

Weight	Percentile
235	86
227	third quartile
180	second quartile
173	first quartile

Find the percentage of men over 40 who weigh

57. less than 227 pounds.   **58.** more than 235 pounds.

59. between 227 and 235 pounds.

60. Using a random sample of 2041 executives of American companies, a Korn/Ferry survey asked respondents if their career was related to the area of their college degree. The poll indicated that 85% of the executives responded "yes" and 15% said "no."

a. Find the margin of error, to the nearest tenth of a percent, for this survey.

b. Write a statement about the percentage of American executives in the population whose career is not related to their college degree.

61. The histogram indicates the frequencies of the number of syllables per word for 100 randomly selected words in Japanese.

**Number of Syllables
in Japanese Words**

a. Is the shape of this distribution best classified as normal, skewed to the right, or skewed to the left?

b. Find the mean, median, and mode for the number of syllables in the sample of Japanese words.

c. Are the measures of central tendency from part (b) consistent with the shape of the distribution that you described in part (a)? Explain your answer.

12.5

In Exercises 62–63, make a scatter plot for the given data. Use the scatter plot to describe whether or not the variables appear to be related.

62.

x	1	3	4	6	8	9
y	1	2	3	3	5	5

63.

Country	Canada	U.S.	Mexico	Brazil	Costa Rica
Life expectancy in years, x	79	76	72	64	76
Infant deaths per 1000 births, y	5.6	6.4	25.9	40.0	13.1

Denmark	China	Egypt	Pakistan	Bangladesh	Australia	Japan	Russia
76	70	62	59	57	80	80	65
6.8	45.5	69.3	93.5	97.7	5.3	4.1	23.3

Source: U.S. Bureau of the Census International Database

The scatter plot in the figure shows the relationship between the percentage of adult females in a country who are literate and the mortality of children under five. Also shown is the regression line. Use this information to determine whether each of the statements in Exercises 64–70 is true or false.

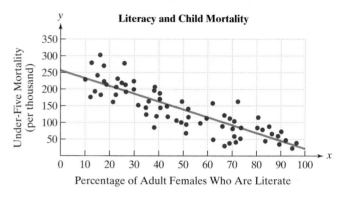

Source: United Nations

64. There is a perfect negative correlation between the percentage of adult females who are literate and under-five mortality.

65. As the percentage of adult females who are literate increases, under-five mortality tends to decrease.

66. The country with the least percentage of adult females who are literate has the greatest under-five mortality.

67. No two countries have the same percentage of adult females who are literate but different under-five mortalities.

68. There are more than 20 countries in this sample.

69. There is no correlation between the percentage of adult females who are literate and under-five mortality.

70. The country with the greatest percentage of adult females who are literate has an under-five mortality rate that is less than 50 children per thousand.

71. Which one of the following scatter plots indicates a correlation coefficient of approximately −0.9?

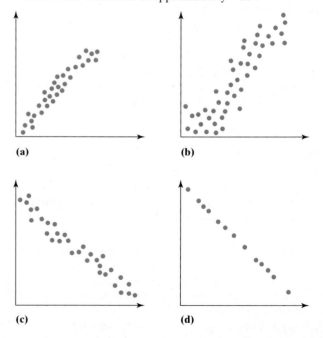

72. Use the data in Exercise 62 to solve the exercise.

    a. Compute r, the correlation coefficient, rounded to the nearest thousandth.

    b. Find the equation of the regression line.

73. The graph, based on Nielsen Media Research 2005 data taken from random samples of Americans at various ages, indicates that as we get older, we watch more television.

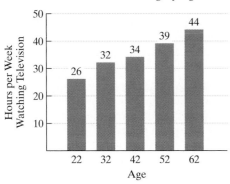

Source: Nielsen Media Research

a. Let x represent one's age and let y represent hours per week watching television. Calculate the correlation coefficient.

b. Using Table 12.15 on page 736 and the $\alpha = 0.05$ column, determine whether there is a correlation between age and time spent watching television in the American population.

●●●●●● CHAPTER 12 TEST

1. Politicians in the Florida Keys need to know if the residents of Key Largo think the amount of money charged for water is reasonable. The politicians decide to conduct a survey of a sample of Key Largo's residents. Which procedure would be most appropriate for a sample of Key Largo's residents?

    a. Survey all water customers who pay their water bills at Key Largo City Hall on the third day of the month.

    b. Survey a random sample of executives who work for the water company in Key Largo.

    c. Survey 5000 individuals who are randomly selected from a list of all people living in Georgia and Florida.

    d. Survey a random sample of persons within each neighborhood of Key Largo.

Use these scores on a ten-point quiz to solve Exercises 2–4.

8, 5, 3, 6, 5, 10, 6, 9, 4, 5, 7, 9, 7, 4, 8, 8

2. Construct a frequency distribution for the data.

3. Construct a histogram for the data.

4. Construct a frequency polygon for the data.

Use the 30 test scores listed below to solve Exercises 5–6.

79	51	67	50	78
62	89	83	73	80
88	48	60	71	79
89	63	55	93	71
41	81	46	50	61
59	50	90	75	61

5. Construct a grouped frequency distribution for the data. Use 40–49 for the first class and use the same width for each subsequent class.

6. Construct a stem-and-leaf display for the data.

7. The graph shows the percentage of students in the United States through grade 12 who were home-schooled in 1999 and 2003. What impression does the roofline in the visual display imply about what occurred in 2000 through 2002? How might this be misleading?

Source: National Center for Education Statistics

Use the six data items listed below to solve Exercises 8–11.

3, 6, 2, 1, 7, 3

8. Find the mean.

9. Find the median.

10. Find the midrange.

11. Find the standard deviation.

Use the frequency distribution shown to solve Exercises 12–14.

Score x	Frequency f
1	3
2	5
3	2
4	2

12. Find the mean.

13. Find the median.

14. Find the mode.

15. The annual salaries of four salespeople and the owner of a bookstore are

$17,500, $19,000, $22,000, $27,500, $98,500.

Is the mean or the median more representative of the five annual salaries? Briefly explain your answer.

According to the American Freshman, *the number of hours that college freshmen spend studying each week is normally distributed with a mean of 7 hours and a standard deviation of 5.3 hours. In Exercises 16–17, use the 68–95–99.7 Rule to find the percentage of college freshmen who study*

16. between 7 and 12.3 hours each week.

17. more than 17.6 hours each week.

18. IQ scores are normally distributed in the population. Who has a higher IQ: a student with a 120 IQ on a scale where 100 is the mean and 10 is the standard deviation, or a professor with a 128 IQ on a scale where 100 is the mean and 15 is the standard deviation? Briefly explain your answer.

19. Use the z-scores and the corresponding percentiles shown below to solve this exercise. Test scores are normally distributed with a mean of 74 and a standard deviation of 10. What percentage of the scores are above 88?

z-Score	Percentile
1.1	86.43
1.2	88.49
1.3	90.32
1.4	91.92
1.5	93.32

20. Use the percentiles in the table shown below to find the percentage of scores between 630 and 690.

Score	Percentile
780	99
750	87
720	72
690	49
660	26
630	8
600	1

21. Using a random sample of 100 students from a campus of approximately 12,000 students, 60% of the students in the sample said they were very satisfied with their professors.

  a. Find the margin of error in this percent.

  b. Write a statement about the percentage of the entire population of students from this campus who are very satisfied with their professors.

22. Make a scatter plot for the given data. Use the scatter plot to describe whether or not the variables appear to be related.

x	1	4	3	5	2
y	5	2	2	1	4

The scatter plot shows the number of minutes each of 16 people exercise per week and the number of headaches per month each person experiences. Use the scatter plot to determine whether each of the statements in Exercises 23–25 is true or false.

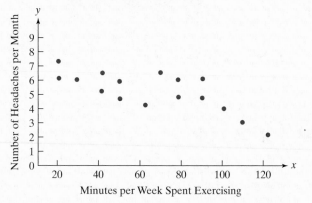

23. An increase in the number of minutes devoted to exercise causes a decrease in headaches.

24. There is a perfect negative correlation between time spent exercising and number of headaches.

25. The person who exercised most per week had the least number of headaches per month.

26. Is the relationship between the price of gas and the number of people visiting our national parks a positive correlation, a negative correlation, or is there no correlation? Explain your answer.

Mathematical Systems

I s beauty in the eye of the beholder? Or are there certain objects (or people) that are so well balanced and proportioned that they are universally pleasing to the eye? In this chapter, you will learn to use mathematics to describe the characteristics of forms such as the passion-flower that many people find alluring.

SECTION 13.1 • MATHEMATICAL SYSTEMS

OBJECTIVES

1. Understand what is meant by a mathematical system.

2. Understand properties of certain mathematical systems.

FIGURE 13.1 A three-way switch on the table lamp

Thanks for the gift. What, exactly, is it? Oh, a lamp. It's—uh—very nice. (What am I ever going to do with this hideous monument to bad taste?) What's that? You want to tell me about some of its special features? I'm all ears. We're going to start with the three-way switch. Looks pretty high-tech: Does it come with a manual? Only kidding. Do go on. So, if I turn the switch once to the right, I get low-intensity light. Another turn to the right gives medium-intensity light. Still another turn results in high-intensity light. Finally, one more right turn puts the switch in the off position, resulting in no light. You've even made me a diagram of the switch? (See Figure 13.1.) Nothing like capping off this fascinating tutorial with a visual aid. Life is good.

Despite the sarcasm of the lamp's recipient, there is something mathematical happening. We begin with the obvious: The amount of light that you get depends on the position of the three-way switch when you begin and the number of turns to the right you move the switch. Using $\oplus$ to represent turning the switch to the right (clockwise), here are some examples:

1 | Understand what is meant by a mathematical system.

$$0 \qquad \oplus \qquad 2 \qquad = \qquad 2$$

| The switch is in the off position. | Turn the switch clockwise **2** turns. | The final position of the switch is **2**, giving medium light. |

$$1 \qquad \oplus \qquad 2 \qquad = \qquad 3$$

| The switch is in the low position. | Turn the switch clockwise **2** turns. | The final position of the switch is 3, giving high-intensity light. |

$$3 \qquad \oplus \qquad 1 \qquad = \qquad 0.$$

| The switch is in the high position. | Turn the switch clockwise **1** turn. | The final position of the switch is 0, the off position with no light. |

TABLE 13.1

$\oplus$	0	1	2	3
0	0	1	2	3
1	1	2	3	0
2	2	3	0	1
3	3	0	1	2

Number of clockwise turns (column header)

Starting positions

We can use a table to show all possible starting and ending positions for the three-way switch. In Table 13.1, the starting positions are shown in the left column. The number of clockwise turns are shown across the top. The 16 entries in the table represent all possible final positions of the switch. For example, to find $2 \oplus 3$, find 2 in the left column and 3 across the top. Assuming a horizontal line through 2 and a vertical line through 3, as in Figure 13.2, the point of intersection of these lines is 1. Thus, $2 \oplus 3 = 1$. This means that if the switch starts in the 2, medium, position and is turned 3 positions clockwise, its final position is 1, the setting for low-intensity light.

Table 13.1 consists of a set of four elements, namely $\{0, 1, 2, 3\}$. The table provides a rule, designated by $\oplus$, that can be performed on two elements of the set at a time. Such a rule is called a *binary operation*. **A binary operation** is a rule that can be used to combine any two elements of a set, resulting in a single element. A **mathematical system** consists of a set of elements and at least one binary operation. Many mathematical systems are presented in the form of a table, such as Table 13.1.

$\oplus$	0	1	2	3
0	0	1	2	3
1	1	2	3	0
2	2	3	0	①
3	3	0	1	2

FIGURE 13.2 Using Table 13.1 to find $2 \oplus 3$; the intersecting lines show that $2 \oplus 3 = 1$.

If two even or two odd numbers are added, the sum is even. For example, $4 + 4 = 8$ (even + even = even). Likewise, $5 + 5 = 10$ (odd + odd = even). By contrast, if one number is even and the other odd, the sum is odd. For example, $4 + 3 = 7$ (even + odd = odd). Likewise, $7 + 6 = 13$ (odd + even = odd). If we let E represent any even number and O any odd number, these observations are summarized in Table 13.2.

a. What is the set of elements of this mathematical system?
b. What is the binary operation of this mathematical system?
c. Use Table 13.2 to find $E + O$. Explain what this means.

SOLUTION

a. The set of elements of this mathematical system is $\{E, O\}$.
b. The binary operation used to combine any two elements of $\{E, O\}$ is $+$.
c. We find $E + O$ by drawing a horizontal line through E in the left column and a vertical line through O in the top row. These lines intersect at O, shown in Figure 13.3. Thus, $E + O = O$. This means that the sum of an even number and an odd number is an odd number.

CHECK POINT 1 Use Table 13.2 to find $O + O$. Explain what this means.

TABLE 13.2

Now add an even or odd number.

+	E	O
E	E	O
O	O	E

Start with an even or odd number.

+	E	O
E	E	Ⓞ
O	O	E

FIGURE 13.3 Using Table 13.2 to find $E + O$

2 Understand properties of certain mathematical systems.

Properties of Some Mathematical Systems

We now look at five properties that apply to certain mathematical systems. You may recognize some of these properties from our work in Chapter 5, where we studied the set of real numbers with two binary operations: addition and multiplication.

The Closure Property

A mathematical system is **closed** under a binary operation if the answer to any possible combination of two elements of the set is an element that is in the set. For example, take a second look at Table 13.1, which shows all possible starting and ending positions for the three-way switch. The answers in the body of the table are all elements of the set $\{0, 1, 2, 3\}$. Thus, the system is closed under $\oplus$. If an element other than 0, 1, 2, or 3 had appeared in the body of the table, the system would not have been closed under the binary operation.

> **CLOSED SETS; SETS HAVING CLOSURE**
> Suppose a binary operation is performed on any two elements of a set. If the result is an element of the set, then that set is **closed** (or has **closure**) under the binary operation.

Is the set $\{0, 1, 2, 3\}$ closed under the operation of addition?

SOLUTION   Shown on the right is an addition table for $\{0, 1, 2, 3\}$. Is every entry in the table an element of $\{0, 1, 2, 3\}$? The answer is no. The numbers 4, 5, and 6 are not elements of $\{0, 1, 2, 3\}$. The set $\{0, 1, 2, 3\}$ is not closed under addition.

+	0	1	2	3
0	0	1	2	3
1	1	2	3	4
2	2	3	4	5
3	3	4	5	6

CHECK POINT 2 Is the set $\{0, 1, 2\}$ closed under the operation of addition?

EXAMPLE 3   UNDERSTANDING THE CLOSURE PROPERTY

Consider the set of integers

$$\{\ldots, -3, -2, -1, 0, 1, 2, 3, \ldots\}.$$

Is this set closed under the operation of multiplication?

SOLUTION If any two integers are multiplied, the product will be an integer. Thus, the set of integers is closed under multiplication.

 Is the set of natural numbers, $\{1, 2, 3, 4, \ldots\}$, closed under the operation of multiplication?

EXAMPLE 4   UNDERSTANDING THE CLOSURE PROPERTY

Is the set of integers closed under the operation of division?

SOLUTION If any two integers are divided, the quotient might not be an integer. For example,

$$\underbrace{\frac{-3}{9}}_{\text{-3 and 9 are integers.}} = -\frac{1}{3}. \quad \text{-}\tfrac{1}{3} \text{ is not an integer.}$$

Thus, the set of integers is not closed under division.

 Is the set of natural numbers, $\{1, 2, 3, 4, \ldots\}$, closed under the operation of division?

The Commutative Property

Suppose that ∘ represents a binary operation for the elements of a set. The set is **commutative** under the operation ∘ if for any two elements a and b of the set, $a \circ b = b \circ a$. The order of the two elements being combined in a commutative binary operation can be switched without changing the answer.

In Chapter 5, we saw that the integers are commutative under the operations of addition and multiplication. For example,

$$3 + 7 = 7 + 3 \quad \text{and} \quad 3 \cdot 7 = 7 \cdot 3.$$

By contrast, the integers are not commutative under the operations of subtraction and division. For example,

$$8 - 4 \neq 4 - 8 \quad \text{and} \quad 8 \div 4 \neq 4 \div 8.$$

In Figure 13.4, we use the table for the three-way lamp switch to show that $2 \oplus 3 = 3 \oplus 2$. Observe that $2 \oplus 3$ is found by first locating 2 on the left and 3 across the top. The green intersecting lines show that $2 \oplus 3 = 1$. We find $3 \oplus 2$ by locating 3 on the left and 2 across the top, again using intersecting lines. These yellow lines show that $3 \oplus 2 = 1$. Thus, $2 \oplus 3 = 3 \oplus 2$ because both binary operations give 1.

To verify that $\{0, 1, 2, 3\}$ is commutative under the operation $\oplus$, we need to verify all possibilities, not just $2 \oplus 3 = 3 \oplus 2$. This might take a while. Fortunately, there is a way to determine if a mathematical system given by a table is commutative under the operation shown in the table. Draw a diagonal line from the upper left corner to the lower right corner, as in Figure 13.5. Observe that for each number in the table, the same number is repeated the same number of times in the same configuration on each side of the green diagonal. For any mathematical system presented in the form of a table, if the part of the table above the diagonal is a mirror image of the part below the diagonal, the system is commutative under the operation given in the table.

$\oplus$	0	1	2	3
0	0	1	2	3
1	1	2	3	0
2	2	3	0	①
3	3	0	①	2

$2 \oplus 3 = 1$

$3 \oplus 2 = 1$

FIGURE 13.4 Showing that $2 \oplus 3 = 3 \oplus 2$

FIGURE 13.5 Showing that $\{0, 1, 2, 3\}$ is commutative under $\oplus$

The Associative Property

A set of elements is **associative** under a given operation ∘ if for any three elements a, b, and c of the set,

$$(a \circ b) \circ c = a \circ (b \circ c).$$

If a binary operation is associative, the answer does not change if we group the first two elements together or the last two elements together.

In Chapter 5, we saw that the integers are associative under the operations of addition and multiplication. For example,

$$(3 + 4) + 2 = 3 + (4 + 2) \qquad\qquad (3 \cdot 4) \cdot 2 = 3 \cdot (4 \cdot 2)$$
$$7 + 2 = 3 + 6 \qquad\qquad\qquad 12 \cdot 2 = 3 \cdot 8$$
$$9 = 9 \qquad\qquad\qquad\qquad 24 = 24.$$

By contrast, the integers are not associative under the operations of subtraction and division. For example,

$$(6 - 3) - 2 \neq 6 - (3 - 2) \qquad (6 \div 3) \div 2 \neq 6 \div (3 \div 2)$$
$$3 - 2 \neq 6 - 1 \qquad\qquad 2 \div 2 \neq 6 \div 1.5$$
$$1 \neq 5 \qquad\qquad\qquad 1 \neq 4.$$

EXAMPLE 5	VERIFYING ONE CASE FOR THE ASSOCIATIVE PROPERTY

Use Table 13.3, the table for the three-way lamp switch, to verify the associative property for $a = 3, b = 2$, and $c = 1$.

TABLE 13.3

⊕	0	1	2	3
0	0	1	2	3
1	1	2	3	0
2	2	3	0	1
3	3	0	1	2

SOLUTION We must show that $(3 \oplus 2) \oplus 1 = 3 \oplus (2 \oplus 1)$.

Locate 3 on the left and 2 on the top of Table 13.3. Intersecting lines show 3 ⊕ 2 = 1.

$$(3 \oplus 2) \oplus 1 = 3 \oplus (2 \oplus 1)$$
$$1 \oplus 1 = 3 \oplus 3$$
$$2 = 2$$

Locate 2 on the left and 1 across the top of Table 13.3. Intersecting lines show 2 ⊕ 1 = 3.

Changing the location of the parentheses does not change the answer, 2. ○

 Use Table 13.3 to verify the associative property for $a = 1, b = 3$, and $c = 2$.

If every choice of three elements from the set $\{0, 1, 2, 3\}$ were checked, it would show that the mathematical system in Table 13.3 is associative under the operation ⊕.

The Identity Property

I see your hand on my three-way lamp switch. Please do not turn it because I like the light intensity just the way that it is. If it's off, leave it off: $0 \oplus 0 = 0$. If it's in the low position, leave it there: $1 \oplus 0 = 1$. If it's in the medium position, don't change anything: $2 \oplus 0 = 2$. Finally, if the light intensity is high, on high it will remain: $3 \oplus 0 = 3$.

Does not changing anything remind you of the role that the number 0 plays in addition and the number 1 plays in multiplication? If a represents any real number,

$$a + 0 = a \quad \text{and} \quad 0 + a = a$$
$$a \cdot 1 = a \quad \text{and} \quad 1 \cdot a = a.$$

In each equation, the number a is unchanged when we add with 0 or multiply with 1. We call 0 the **identity element of addition** and 1 the **identity element of multiplication**.

In a mathematical system, the **identity element** (if there is one) is an element from the set such that when a binary operation is performed on any element in the set and the identity element, the result is the given element. If a represents any element in the set and the binary operation is represented by $\circ$:

$$a \circ \text{identity element} = a \quad \text{and} \quad \text{identity element} \circ a = a.$$

An element does not change when we perform an operation with an identity element.

EXAMPLE 6   IDENTIFYING THE IDENTITY ELEMENT

Consider the set $\{a, b, c\}$. A binary operation on this set is given in Table 13.4. What is the identity element for this mathematical system?

TABLE 13.4

$\circ$	a	b	c
a	c	a	b
b	a	b	c
c	b	c	a

SOLUTION Look for the element in $\{a, b, c\}$ that doesn't change anything when used in the binary operation $\circ$. Notice that the column under b is the same as the column with the boldface letters on the left.

$$a \circ b = a \quad b \circ b = b \quad c \circ b = c$$

Notice, too, that the row to the right of b is the same as the top row with the boldface letters.

$$b \circ a = a \quad b \circ b = b \quad b \circ c = c$$

When any element is combined with b under the operation $\circ$, the result is that element. The element b does not change anything. Thus, b is the identity element for the mathematical system.   ○

CHECK POINT 6 Consider the set $\{e, f, g\}$. A binary operation for this set is shown in the table on the right. What is the identity element for this mathematical system?

$\circ$	e	f	g
e	f	g	e
f	g	e	f
g	e	f	g

The Inverse Property

It's time to get this lamp with the three-way switch out of my life. Hope I don't get charged with design pollution while driving it to the dump. I'll start by turning it off. (See Figure 13.6.) If it's already off, I'll leave it there: $0 \oplus 0 = 0$. If it's on low, 1, I'll move it to the off position by 3 clockwise turns: $1 \oplus 3 = 0$. If it's on medium, 2, two turns to the right will quiet the beast: $2 \oplus 2 = 0$. Finally, if it's on high, 3, one right turn will slay the dragon: $3 \oplus 1 = 0$.

$0 \oplus 0 = 0$ $1 \oplus 3 = 0$ $2 \oplus 2 = 0$ $3 \oplus 1 = 0$

FIGURE 13.6 Slaying the dragon

Buried in this lamp rant is a property that applies to many, but not all, mathematical systems. Do you see that the answer to each of the four binary operations in Figure 13.6 is the identity element 0? For example,

identity element

$$1 \oplus 3 = 0.$$

In a situation like this, we say that 3 is the *inverse* of 1. Similarly, since $3 \oplus 1 = 0$, 1 is the *inverse* of 3. In general, suppose that a binary operation is performed on two elements in a set and the result is the identity element for the binary operation. Under these conditions, each element is called the **inverse** of the other. Inverses restore the identity.

Element	$\oplus$	Inverse	=	Identity
0	$\oplus$	0	=	0
1	$\oplus$	3	=	0
2	$\oplus$	2	=	0
3	$\oplus$	1	=	0

0 is its own inverse.
2 is its own inverse.

1 and 3 are inverses of each other.

EXAMPLE 7   IDENTIFYING AN INVERSE

Consider the set of integers

$$\{ \ldots, -3, -2, -1, 0, 1, 2, 3, \ldots \}.$$

What is the inverse of 17 under the operation of addition?

SOLUTION When an element operates on its inverse, the result is the identity element. Because the operation is addition, the identity element is 0. To find the inverse of 17, we answer the question: Which integer must be added to 17 to obtain a sum of 0?

$$17 + ? = 0$$

The required integer is -17: $17 + (-17) = 0$. Thus, the inverse of 17 under the operation of addition is -17.

 Consider the set of integers. What is the inverse of 12 under the operation of addition?

We can generalize from Example 7. If a is an integer, the inverse for the operation of addition is $-a$.

$$a + (-a) = 0$$

$-a$ is often called the **additive inverse** of a.

In Chapter 5, we defined the set of *rational numbers* as the set of all numbers in the form $\frac{a}{b}$, where a and b are integers and $b \neq 0$. Our next example involves a mathematical system with rational numbers.

EXAMPLE 8   IDENTIFYING AN INVERSE

Consider the set of rational numbers. What is the inverse of 17 under the operation of multiplication?

SOLUTION When an element operates on its inverse, the result is the identity element. Because the operation is multiplication, the identity element is 1. To find the inverse of 17, we answer the question: 17 times which rational number gives 1?

$$17 \cdot ? = 1$$

The required rational number is $\frac{1}{17}$: $17 \cdot \frac{1}{17} = 1$. Thus, the inverse of 17 under the operation of multiplication is $\frac{1}{17}$.

 Consider the set of rational numbers. What is the inverse of 12 under the operation of multiplication?

We can generalize from Example 8. If a is any rational number *other than zero*, the inverse for the operation of multiplication is $\frac{1}{a}$.

$$a \cdot \frac{1}{a} = 1$$

$\frac{1}{a}$ is often called the **multiplicative inverse** of a. Zero has no multiplicative inverse because no rational number can be multiplied by 0 to give 1.

EXAMPLE 9   IDENTITY ELEMENT AND INVERSE ELEMENTS

For the mathematical system defined by Table 13.5,

a. What is the identity element?

b. Find the inverse for each element in $\{S, L, A, R\}$.

TABLE 13.5

∘	**S**	**L**	**A**	**R**
S	S	L	A	R
L	L	A	R	S
A	A	R	S	L
R	R	S	L	A

∘	**S**	**L**	**A**	**R**
S	S	L	A	R
L	L	A	R	S
A	A	R	S	L
R	R	S	L	A

FIGURE 13.7 S does not change any element with which it is combined.

SOLUTION

a. The identity element is the element in $\{S, L, A, R\}$ that does not change any element with which it is combined in the binary operation ∘. Figure 13.7 shows that the column under S is the same as the column with the boldface letters on the left and the row next to S is the same as the row with the boldface letters on the top. The element S does not change anything. Thus, S is the identity element.

b. When an element operates on its inverse, the result is the identity element:

$$\text{element} \circ \text{inverse} = \text{identity element}.$$

Inverses restore the identity.

Because the identity element is S, we can find the inverse of each element in $\{S, L, A, R\}$ by replacing the question mark in

$$\text{element} \circ \text{?} = S.$$

How do we replace this question mark? Look at the entries on the left, find S in the body of the table in each row, and then locate the entry across the top that gives S. Figure 13.8 shows that

$$S \circ S = S, \text{ so } S \text{ is its own inverse.}$$

$$L \circ R = S, \text{ so } R \text{ is the inverse of } L.$$

$$A \circ A = S, \text{ so the inverse of } A \text{ is } A.$$

$$R \circ L = S, \text{ so } L \text{ is the inverse of } R.$$

∘	**S**	**L**	**A**	**R**
S	S	L	A	R
L	L	A	R	S
A	A	R	S	L
R	R	S	L	A

FIGURE 13.8 Locating inverses

CHECK POINT 9 For the mathematical system defined by the table on the right,

a. What is the identity element?

b. Find the inverse for each element in $\{j, k, l, m\}$.

∘	**j**	**k**	**l**	**m**
j	m	j	k	l
k	j	k	l	m
l	k	l	m	j
m	l	m	j	k

EXERCISE SET 13.1 ●●●●●●

• Practice Exercises

Use the mathematical system given by the table shown to solve Exercises 1–14.

∘	e	a	b	c
e	e	a	b	c
a	a	e	c	b
b	b	c	e	a
c	c	b	a	e

1. What is the set of elements of this mathematical system?
2. What is the binary operation of this mathematical system?

In Exercises 3–13, find each result.

3. $a \circ b$
4. $c \circ a$
5. $b \circ c$
6. $c \circ b$
7. $e \circ e$
8. $e \circ a$
9. $b \circ e$
10. $c \circ e$
11. $a \circ a$
12. $(b \circ b) \circ c$
13. $(c \circ c) \circ a$

14. Is the mathematical system closed under the binary operation? Explain your answer.
15. Is the set $\{0, 1, 2, 3, 4\}$ closed under the operation of addition? Explain your answer.
16. Is the set $\{0, 1, 2, 3, 4, 5\}$ closed under the operation of addition? Explain your answer.
17. Is the set of natural numbers $\{1, 2, 3, 4, 5, \ldots\}$ closed under the operation of addition? Explain your answer.
18. Is the set of natural numbers $\{1, 2, 3, 4, 5, \ldots\}$ closed under the operation of multiplication? Explain your answer.
19. Is the set of natural numbers closed under the operation of subtraction? Explain your answer.
20. Is the set of natural numbers closed under the operation of division? Explain your answer.

*In Exercises 21–22, use the table shown to explain whether or not the mathematical system is closed under the binary operation *.*

21.

*	a	b
a	a	b
b	c	a

22.

*	d	e	f
d	d	e	g
e	e	d	f
f	f	e	d

Use the mathematical system given by the table shown to solve Exercises 23–32.

⊕	0	1	2	3	4
0	0	1	2	3	4
1	1	2	3	4	0
2	2	3	4	0	1
3	3	4	0	1	2
4	4	0	1	2	3

In Exercises 23–36, show that

23. $2 \oplus 4 = 4 \oplus 2$.
24. $3 \oplus 4 = 4 \oplus 3$.
25. $4 \oplus 1 = 1 \oplus 4$.
26. $2 \oplus 3 = 3 \oplus 2$.

27. What property is illustrated in Exercises 23–26? Use the table to explain how to verify this property for all possible cases without having to consider one case at a time.

In Exercises 28–31, use the table to show that

28. $(3 \oplus 2) \oplus 4 = 3 \oplus (2 \oplus 4)$.
29. $(4 \oplus 3) \oplus 2 = 4 \oplus (3 \oplus 2)$.
30. $(2 \oplus 2) \oplus 3 = 2 \oplus (2 \oplus 3)$.
31. $(4 \oplus 4) \oplus 2 = 4 \oplus (4 \oplus 2)$.

32. What property is illustrated in Exercises 28–31?

33. Use the table shown below to find each result.
    a. $(b \circ c) \circ b$
    b. $b \circ (c \circ b)$
    c. Is the mathematical system associative under the operation $\circ$? Explain your answer.

∘	a	b	c
a	a	b	c
b	b	a	c
c	c	b	a

34. Use the table shown below to find each result.
    a. $(b \circ b) \circ c$
    b. $b \circ (b \circ c)$
    c. Is the mathematical system associative under the operation $\circ$? Explain your answer.

∘	a	b	c
a	a	b	c
b	b	b	a
c	c	a	c

35. Provide an original example to show that the integers are not associative under subtraction.
36. Provide an original example to show that the integers are not associative under division.

In Exercises 37–40, consider the set of rational numbers.

37. What is the inverse of 29 under the operation of addition?
38. What is the inverse of 43 under the operation of addition?
39. What is the inverse of 29 under the operation of multiplication?
40. What is the inverse of 43 under the operation of multiplication?

Use the mathematical system given by the table shown to solve Exercises 41–56.

∘	a	b	c	d	e
a	a	b	c	d	e
b	b	c	d	e	a
c	c	d	e	a	b
d	d	e	a	b	c
e	e	a	b	c	d

Find each result.

41. $a \circ a$ **42.** $a \circ b$ **43.** $a \circ c$

44. $a \circ d$ **45.** $a \circ e$ **46.** $b \circ a$

47. $c \circ a$ **48.** $d \circ a$ **49.** $e \circ a$

50. What can you conclude about the element a in this mathematical system?

Find the element represented by a question mark.

51. $a \circ ? = a$ **52.** $b \circ ? = a$

53. $c \circ ? = a$ **54.** $d \circ ? = a$

55. $e \circ ? = a$

56. What is true about the relationship between the elements on the left sides of the equations in Exercises 51–55?

Use the mathematical system given by the table shown to solve Exercises 57–62.

⊕	0	1	2	3	4
0	0	1	2	3	4
1	1	2	3	4	0
2	2	3	4	0	1
3	3	4	0	1	2
4	4	0	1	2	3

57. What is the identity element?

Find the inverse for each element.

58. 0   **59.** 1   **60.** 2   **61.** 3   **62.** 4

63. a. Use the table shown below to find the identity element for this mathematical system.

b. Find the inverse for each element of the set that has one. Which elements do not have inverses?

∘	a	b	c	d
a	a	a	a	a
b	a	b	b	b
c	a	b	c	c
d	a	b	c	d

64. a. Use the table shown at the top of the next column to find the identity element for this mathematical system.

b. Find the inverse for each element of the set that has one. Which elements do not have inverses?

∘	a	b	c	d	e
a	d	e	a	b	b
b	e	a	b	a	d
c	a	b	c	d	e
d	b	a	d	e	c
e	b	d	e	c	a

• **Practice Plus**

Use the mathematical systems given by the tables to solve Exercises 65–72.

□	a	b	c	d	e
a	a	b	c	d	e
b	b	c	d	e	a
c	c	d	e	a	b
d	d	e	a	b	c
e	e	a	b	c	d

△	a	b	c	d	e
a	a	a	a	a	a
b	a	b	c	d	e
c	a	c	e	b	d
d	a	d	b	e	c
e	a	e	d	c	b

65. a. Show that $e \triangle (c \square d) = (e \triangle c) \square (e \triangle d)$.

b. What property of the real numbers is illustrated in part (a)?

66. a. Show that $c \triangle (d \square e) = (c \triangle d) \square (c \triangle e)$.

b. What property of the real numbers is illustrated in part (a)?

67. Find $c \triangle [c \square (c \triangle c)]$.

68. Find $d \triangle [d \square (d \triangle d)]$.

In Exercises 69–72, replace x with a, b, c, d, or e to form a true statement.

69. $x \square d = e$ **70.** $x \square d = a$

71. $x \triangle (e \square c) = d$ **72.** $x \triangle (e \square d) = b$

• **Application Exercises**

73. Suppose that a lamp has a four-way switch. The positions of the switch are 0 : off, 1 : dim, 2 : low, 3 : medium, and 4 : high. Describe the relationship between this switch and the mathematical system given by the table shown for Exercises 57–62.

74. An army drill instructor gives you four different commands. They are S : stand still, L : left face (turn 90° to your left), A : about face (turn 180° to your right), and R : right face (turn 90° to your right). The operation ∘ represents two commands in succession. Describe the relationship between this situation and the mathematical system given by Table 13.5 on page 754.

Let E represent any even number, let O represent any odd number, and let × represent the operation of multiplication. In order to solve Exercises 75–80, begin by filling in the four missing entries in the table shown.

×	E	O
E	—	—
O	—	—

75. Is the set $\{E, O\}$ closed under the operation of multiplication? Explain your answer.

76. Verify one case of the commutative property.

77. Verify one case of the associative property.

78. What is the identity element?

79. Find the inverse of E.

80. Find the inverse of O.

• Writing in Mathematics

81. Describe what is meant by a mathematical system.

82. What is the closure property? Give an example.

83. What is the commutative property? Give an example.

84. What is the associative property? Give an example.

85. What is the identity property? Give an example.

86. What is the inverse property? Give an example.

87. Describe the difference between a nonzero number's additive inverse and its multiplicative inverse. Provide an example.

• Critical Thinking Exercises

88. Give an example of a mathematical system that is different than any seen in this section.

89. If $\begin{bmatrix} a & b \\ c & d \end{bmatrix} \times \begin{bmatrix} e & f \\ g & h \end{bmatrix} = \begin{bmatrix} ae + bg & af + bh \\ ce + dg & cf + dh \end{bmatrix}$, find

   a. $\begin{bmatrix} 2 & 3 \\ 4 & 7 \end{bmatrix} \times \begin{bmatrix} 0 & 1 \\ 5 & 6 \end{bmatrix}$.

   b. $\begin{bmatrix} 0 & 1 \\ 5 & 6 \end{bmatrix} \times \begin{bmatrix} 2 & 3 \\ 4 & 7 \end{bmatrix}$.

   c. Draw a conclusion about one of the properties discussed in this section in terms of these arrays of numbers under multiplication.

SECTION 13.2 • ROTATIONAL SYMMETRY, GROUPS, AND CLOCK ARITHMETIC

OBJECTIVES

1. Recognize rotational symmetry.

2. Determine if a mathematical system is a group.

3. Understand clock systems as groups.

4. Understand congruence in a modulo m system.

5. Perform additions in a modulo m system.

FIGURE 13.9

Mathematics is about the patterns that arise in the world about us. Mathematicians look at a snowflake in terms of its underlying structure. Notice that if the snowflake in Figure 13.9 is rotated by any multiple of 60° ($\frac{1}{6}$ of a rotation), it will always look about the same. A **symmetry** of an object is a motion that moves the object back onto itself. In a symmetry, you cannot tell, at the end of the motion, that the object has been moved.

$\boxed{1}$ Recognize rotational symmetry.

The snowflake in Figure 13.9 has **sixfold rotational symmetry**. After six 60° turns, the snowflake is back to its original position. If it takes m equal turns to restore an object to its original position and each of these turns is a figure that is identical to the original figure, the object has ***m*-fold rotational symmetry**. Consider, for example, a pinwheel. Figure 13.10 shows that as the pinwheel rotates, at each quarter turn it is in a new position, yet it looks exactly the same as it did at the start. If all its petals are the same color, we cannot distinguish the original position from the new position after one quarter turn, two quarter turns, or three quarter turns. After four quarters (that is, after a full rotation), we are back to the starting position. The pinwheel has **fourfold rotational symmetry**. If the blades are colored or numbered, it is possible to keep track of the pinwheel's rotation.

| Original position | 1/4 turn | 1/2 turn | 3/4 turn | Full rotation (back to original) |

FIGURE 13.10

A two-blade propeller with twofold rotational symmetry

The logo from a Korean bank with fivefold rotational symmetry

The seedpod of the autograph tree (*Clusia Rosea*) with eightfold rotational symmetry

2 | Determine if a mathematical system is a group.

Does the pinwheel remind you of anything? Its symmetry is exactly the same as that of the infamous light switch with its off, low, medium, and high positions. Special kinds of mathematical systems, called *groups*, are used to study the symmetries and hidden structure of our world. Objects that appear to be totally different, such as a pinwheel and a lamp switch, can be unified by the definition of a group. We begin with this definition.

Groups

I went to the movies with a *group* of friends. I bought an interesting *group* of paintings for my living room wall. We use the word *group* in everyday speech when referring to any collection of persons or things. However, in mathematics *group* means something entirely different. A group is a mathematical system meeting four requirements.

DEFINITION OF A GROUP

A mathematical system that meets the following four requirements is called a **group**:

1. The set of elements in the mathematical system is *closed* under the given binary operation, represented in this box by ∘ .

2. The set of elements is *associative* under the given binary operation. If a, b, and c are any three elements of the set,

$$(a \circ b) \circ c = a \circ (b \circ c).$$

3. The set of elements contains an *identity* element. When the binary operation ∘ is performed on the identity element and each element in the set, the result is the given element.

4. Each element of the set has an *inverse* that lies within the set. When an element operates on its inverse, the result is the identity element.

Do you notice anything missing from these four requirements? The commutative property does not need to hold for a mathematical system to be a group. If a group does satisfy the commutative property (that is, if $a \circ b = b \circ a$ for any two elements of the set), it is called a **commutative group**.

EXAMPLE 1 | SHOWING THAT A MATHEMATICAL SYSTEM IS A GROUP

Table 13.6 is a mathematical system for the set $\{-1, 1\}$ under the binary operation of multiplication.

a. Show that the mathematical system is a group.

b. Show that the group is commutative.

SOLUTION

a. We begin by checking the four requirements—closure, the associative property, the identity property, and the inverse property—for a mathematical system to qualify as a group.

1. **The Closure Property.** The set $\{-1, 1\}$ is closed under the binary operation of multiplication because the entries in the body of Table 13.6 are all elements of the set.

2. **The Associative Property.** Is $(a \cdot b) \cdot c = a \cdot (b \cdot c)$ for all elements a, b, and c of the set? Let us select some values for a, b, and c. Let $a = 1$, $b = -1$, and $c = -1$. Then

$$[1 \cdot (-1)] \cdot (-1) = -1 \cdot (-1) = 1$$

TABLE 13.6

·	−1	1
−1	1	−1
1	−1	1

and

$$1 \cdot [(-1) \cdot (-1)] = 1 \cdot 1 = 1.$$

The associative property holds for $a = 1$, $b = -1$, and $c = -1$. This particular case does not prove that the mathematical system is associative. However, we could check every possible choice of three elements from the set. Such a check would verify that the system does satisfy the associative property.

3. **The Identity Property.** Look for the element in $\{-1, 1\}$ that does not change anything when used in multiplication. The element 1 does not change anything:

$$-1 \cdot 1 = -1 \quad 1 \cdot (-1) = -1 \quad 1 \cdot 1 = 1$$

> An element does not change when we multiply with 1.

Thus, 1 is the identity element. The identity property is satisfied because 1 is contained in the set $\{-1, 1\}$.

4. **The Inverse Property.** When an element operates on its inverse, the result is the identity element. Because the identity element is 1, we can find the inverse of each element in $\{-1, 1\}$ by answering the question: What must each element be multiplied by to obtain 1?

$$\text{element} \cdot ? = 1$$

Figure 13.11 illustrates how we answer the question. If each element in $\{-1, 1\}$ has an inverse that restores the identity element 1, then a 1 will appear in every row and column of the table. This is, indeed, the case. Using 1 in each row, we see that

FIGURE 13.11

- $-1 \cdot -1 = 1$, so the inverse of -1 is -1.
- $1 \cdot 1 = 1$, so the inverse of 1 is 1.

Because each element in $\{-1, 1\}$ has an inverse within the set, the inverse property is satisfied.

In summary, the set $\{-1, 1\}$ satisfies the closure property, the associative property, the identity property, and the inverse property under the operation of multiplication. Thus, the mathematical system is a group.

b. To show that the group is commutative, we must show that the commutative property is satisfied. Is $a \cdot b = b \cdot a$ for all elements a and b of $\{-1, 1\}$? We need to examine only one case, the case where a and b have different values.

$$1 \cdot (-1) = -1 \quad \text{and} \quad -1 \cdot 1 = -1$$

The order of the factors in the multiplication does not matter. Thus, $\{-1, 1\}$ is a commutative group under multiplication.

○

 The table on the right is a mathematical system for $\{E, O\}$ under the binary operation $\circ$.

$\circ$	E	O
E	E	O
O	O	E

a. Show that the mathematical system is a group. Just verify two examples for the associative property.

b. Show that the group is commutative.

....

If a mathematical system fails to meet even one of the four requirements for a group, that system is not a group. For example, consider the set of integers $\{\ldots, -3, -2, -1, 0, 1, 2, 3, \ldots\}$ under the operation of multiplication. Although the

Sixfold rotational symmetry
Flowers with rotational symmetries

Fivefold rotational symmetry

closure property, the associative property, and the identity property are satisfied, the inverses of the integers are not contained within the set. For example, the multiplicative inverse of 3 is $\frac{1}{3}$ $\left(3 \cdot \frac{1}{3} = 1\right)$. However, $\frac{1}{3}$ is not an integer. Because there is at least one element, 3, in the set of integers that fails to have an inverse that lies within the set, the integers do not satisfy the inverse property under multiplication. The failure to meet one of a group's four requirements means that the integers are not a group under multiplication.

3 | Understand clock systems as groups.

FIGURE 13.12 A 12-hour clock

Clock Arithmetic and Groups

Figure 13.12 looks like the ordinary face of a clock, with two differences. The minute hand is left off, and 12 is replaced with 0. If we replace each number with a small tick-mark, we can observe 12-fold rotational symmetry. If the clock is rotated $\frac{1}{12}$ of a rotation, the tick-marks will fall in the same positions and you cannot tell that the clock's face has been moved. Because Figure 13.12 has numbers instead of tick-marks, it takes 12 turns to restore 0 to its original position.

Consider the mathematical system formed by the set of numbers on the 12-hour clock:

$$\{0, 1, 2, 3, 4, 5, 6, 7, 8, 9, 10, 11\}$$

and a binary operation called *clock addition*. **Clock addition** is defined as follows: Add by moving the hour hand in a clockwise direction. The symbol $+$ is used to designate clock addition. Using the definition of clock addition, Figure 13.13 illustrates that $5 + 2 = 7$, $8 + 9 = 5$, and $11 + 4 = 3$.

$5 + 2 = 7$ $8 + 9 = 5$ $11 + 4 = 3$

8 plus 9 hours   11 plus 4 hours

5 plus 2 hours

FIGURE 13.13 Addition in a 12-hour clock system

Friendship with Morocco 1787–1987

USA 22

Table 13.7 is the addition table for clock addition in a 12-hour clock system.

TABLE 13.7	TABLE FOR 12-HOUR CLOCK ADDITION										
+	**0**	**1**	**2**	**3**	**4**	**5**	**6**	**7**	**8**	**9**	**10**	**11**
0	0	1	2	3	4	5	6	7	8	9	10	11
1	1	2	3	4	5	6	7	8	9	10	11	0
2	2	3	4	5	6	7	8	9	10	11	0	1
3	3	4	5	6	7	8	9	10	11	0	1	2
4	4	5	6	7	8	9	10	11	0	1	2	3
5	5	6	7	8	9	10	11	0	1	2	3	4
6	6	7	8	9	10	11	0	1	2	3	4	5
7	7	8	9	10	11	0	1	2	3	4	5	6
8	8	9	10	11	0	1	2	3	4	5	6	7
9	9	10	11	0	1	2	3	4	5	6	7	8
10	10	11	0	1	2	3	4	5	6	7	8	9
11	11	0	1	2	3	4	5	6	7	8	9	10

EXAMPLE 2   THE 12-HOUR CLOCK SYSTEM AS A GROUP

Show that the mathematical system given by Table 13.7 is a commutative group.

SOLUTION We must check the five requirements—the closure property, the associative property, the identity property, the inverse property, and the commutative property—for a commutative group.

1. **The Closure Property.** The set $\{0, 1, 2, 3, 4, 5, 6, 7, 8, 9, 10, 11\}$ is closed under the operation of clock addition because the entries in the body of Table 13.7 are all elements of the set.

2. **The Associative Property.** Is $(a + b) + c = a + (b + c)$ for all elements a, b, and c of the set? Let us select some values for a, b, and c. Let $a = 4$, $b = 7$, and $c = 9$.

| Locate 4 on the left and 7 on the top of Table 13.7. Intersecting lines show 4 + 7 = 11. | $(4 + 7) + 9 = 4 + (7 + 9)$
 $11 + 9 = 4 + 4$
 $8 = 8$ | Locate 7 on the left and 9 across the top of Table 13.7. Intersecting lines show 7 + 9 = 4. |

The associative property holds for $a = 4$, $b = 7$, and $c = 9$. As always, this particular case does not prove that the mathematical system is associative under clock addition. However, we could check every possible choice of three elements from the set. Such a check would verify that the system does satisfy the associative property.

3. **The Identity Property.** Look for the element in Table 13.7 that does not change anything when used in clock addition. Table 13.7 shows that the column under 0 is the same as the column with boldface numbers on the left. Thus, $0 + 0 = 0, 1 + 0 = 1, 2 + 0 = 2, 3 + 0 = 3$, and so on, up through $11 + 0 = 11$. The table also shows that the row next to 0 is the same as the row with boldface numbers on top. Thus, $0 + 0 = 0, 0 + 1 = 1, 0 + 2 = 2$, up through $0 + 11 = 11$. Each element of the set does not change when we perform clock addition with 0. Thus, 0 is the identity element. The identity property is satisfied because 0 is contained in the given set.

4. **The Inverse Property.** When an element operates on its inverse, the result is the identity element. Because the identity element is 0, we can find the inverse of each element in $\{0, 1, 2, 3, 4, 5, 6, 7, 8, 9, 10, 11\}$ by answering the question: What must be added to each element to obtain 0?

$$\text{element} + ? = 0$$

Figure 13.14 illustrates how we answer the question. If each element in the set has an inverse that restores the identity element 0, then a 0 will appear in every row and column of the table. This is, indeed, the case. Use the 0 in each row. Because each element in $\{0, 1, 2, 3, 4, 5, 6, 7, 8, 9, 10, 11\}$ has an inverse within the set, the inverse property is satisfied.

+	0	1	2	3	4	5	6	7	8	9	10	11
0	0	1	2	3	4	5	6	7	8	9	10	11
1	1	2	3	4	5	6	7	8	9	10	11	0
2	2	3	4	5	6	7	8	9	10	11	0	1
3	3	4	5	6	7	8	9	10	11	0	1	2
4	4	5	6	7	8	9	10	11	0	1	2	3
5	5	6	7	8	9	10	11	0	1	2	3	4
6	6	7	8	9	10	11	0	1	2	3	4	5
7	7	8	9	10	11	0	1	2	3	4	5	6
8	8	9	10	11	0	1	2	3	4	5	6	7
9	9	10	11	0	1	2	3	4	5	6	7	8
10	10	11	0	1	2	3	4	5	6	7	8	9
11	11	0	1	2	3	4	5	6	7	8	9	10

0 + 0 = 0: The inverse of 0 is 0.

1 + 11 = 0: The inverse of 1 is 11.

2 + 10 = 0: The inverse of 2 is 10.

3 + 9 = 0: The inverse of 3 is 9.

4 + 8 = 0: The inverse of 4 is 8.

5 + 7 = 0: The inverse of 5 is 7.

6 + 6 = 0: The inverse of 6 is 6.

7 + 5 = 0: The inverse of 7 is 5.

8 + 4 = 0: The inverse of 8 is 4.

9 + 3 = 0: The inverse of 9 is 3.

10 + 2 = 0: The inverse of 10 is 2.

11 + 1 = 0: The inverse of 11 is 1.

FIGURE 13.14 Locating inverses. The arrows illustrate that $1 + 11 = 0$ and $8 + 4 = 0$.

5. The Commutative Property. Is $a + b = b + a$ for all elements a and b of $\{0, 1, 2, 3, 4, 5, 6, 7, 8, 9, 10, 11\}$? Let us check a few cases. $6 + 9$ and $9 + 6$ both yield 3. Also, $5 + 8$ and $8 + 5$ both yield 1. Order of clock addition does not matter for these cases.

We can use the method discussed in the previous section to avoid checking the commutative property one case at a time. Draw a diagonal line from upper left to lower right, as in Figure 13.15. The part of the table above the diagonal is a mirror image of the part below the diagonal. For each number in the table, the same number is repeated the same number of times on each side of the diagonal in an identical configuration. Thus, the system satisfies the commutative property.

+	0	1	2	3	4	5	6	7	8	9	10	11
0	0	1	2	3	4	5	6	7	8	9	10	11
1	1	2	3	4	5	6	7	8	9	10	11	0
2	2	3	4	5	6	7	8	9	10	11	0	1
3	3	4	5	6	7	8	9	10	11	0	1	2
4	4	5	6	7	8	9	10	11	0	1	2	3
5	5	6	7	8	9	10	11	0	1	2	3	4
6	6	7	8	9	10	11	0	1	2	3	4	5
7	7	8	9	10	11	0	1	2	3	4	5	6
8	8	9	10	11	0	1	2	3	4	5	6	7
9	9	10	11	0	1	2	3	4	5	6	7	8
10	10	11	0	1	2	3	4	5	6	7	8	9
11	11	0	1	2	3	4	5	6	7	8	9	10

FIGURE 13.15 Showing that a system is commutative by observing symmetry about the diagonal

Because the closure, associative, identity, inverse, and commutative properties are satisfied, the 12-hour clock system is a commutative group.

CHECK POINT **2**

a. Use Table 13.7 on page 760 to verify that $(a + b) + c = a + (b + c)$ for $a = 8$, $b = 5$, and $c = 11$.

b. Verify that $9 + 4 = 4 + 9$.

FIGURE 13.16 Symmetry in Native American design

FIGURE 13.17 Mod 7 $\{0, 1, 2, 3, 4, 5, 6\}$

Modular Systems

The 12-hour clock system and the operation of clock addition form what is called a **modulo 12** system, or a **mod 12** system. Although this system is ideal for illuminating the structure of 12-fold symmetry, it would not be a system used to describe the structure of the design in Figure 13.16. Native American pottery has decorations with a wide variety of different kinds of rotational symmetry. This design, similar to those found on Pueblo pottery, has sevenfold rotational symmetry. Its pattern can be studied with a modulo 7 system consisting of seven elements, 0 through 6, and the binary operation of clock addition. The seven-hour clock for the mod 7 system is shown in Figure 13.17.

We perform clock addition in the mod 7 system exactly as we did in the 12-hour clock system. For example, the figure on the right shows how we can find $6 + 3$. If we move the hour hand forward 6 hours from 0, and then forward another 3 hours, this puts the hour hand at 2. The traditional sum, $6 + 3 = 9$, suggests that 9 and 2 are, in a sense, equivalent. We express this by writing

$$9 \equiv 2 \ (\text{mod } 7).$$

6 plus 3 hours

$6 + 3 = 2$ in mod 7

FIGURE 13.18 Mod 5
{0, 1, 2, 3, 4}

4   Understand congruence in a modulo *m* system.

The symbol $\equiv$ is read "is congruent to." Thus, 9 is congruent to 2 in a modulo 7 system. Notice that if 9 is divided by 7, the remainder is 2. We can also say that the same remainder, 2, is obtained when 9 and 2 are divided by 7.

Generalizing from this situation, we describe *m*-fold rotational symmetry with a **modulo *m*** system. Such a system consists of *m* integers, starting with 0 and ending with $m - 1$. For example, a modulo 5 system (Figure 13.18) consists of five integers, starting with 0 and ending with $5 - 1$, or 4.

The concept of congruence can be applied to any modulo *m* system.

CONGRUENCE MODULO *m*

a* is congruent to *b* modulo *m, written

$$a \equiv b \ (\text{mod } m)$$

means that if *a* is divided by *m*, the remainder is *b*. Equivalently,

$$a \equiv b \ (\text{mod } m)$$

if and only if *a* and *b* have the same remainder when divided by *m*.

EXAMPLE 3   UNDERSTANDING CONGRUENCE

Label each statement as true or false:

a. $22 \equiv 4 \ (\text{mod } 6)$ **b.** $12 \equiv 2 \ (\text{mod } 3)$ **c.** $49 \equiv 5 \ (\text{mod } 11)$.

SOLUTION

a. Is $22 \equiv 4 \ (\text{mod } 6)$? If 22 is divided by 6, is the remainder 4? $22 \div 6 = 3$, remainder 4. Because the remainder is 4, the statement is true.

b. Is $12 \equiv 2 \ (\text{mod } 3)$? If 12 is divided by 3, is the remainder 2? $12 \div 3 = 4$, remainder 0. Because the remainder is not 2, the statement is false. A true statement is $12 \equiv 0 \ (\text{mod } 3)$.

c. Is $49 \equiv 5 \ (\text{mod } 11)$? If 49 is divided by 11, is the remainder 5? $49 \div 11 = 4$, remainder 5. Because the remainder is 5, the statement is true.

 Label each statement as true or false:

a. $61 \equiv 5 \ (\text{mod } 7)$ **b.** $36 \equiv 0 \ (\text{mod } 6)$ **c.** $57 \equiv 3 \ (\text{mod } 11)$.

---

5   Perform additions in a modulo *m* system.

Understanding congruence gives us a procedure for performing addition in any modulo system without having to draw a clock.

HOW TO ADD IN A MODULO *m* SYSTEM

1. Add the numbers using ordinary arithmetic.

2. If the sum is less than *m*, the answer is the sum obtained.

3. If the sum is greater than or equal to *m*, the answer is the remainder obtained upon dividing the sum in step 1 by *m*.

EXAMPLE 4   MODULAR ADDITIONS

Find each of the following sums:

a. $(2 + 4)(\text{mod } 7)$ **b.** $(4 + 4)(\text{mod } 5)$ **c.** $(9 + 10)(\text{mod } 12)$.

SOLUTION

a. To find $(2 + 4)(\text{mod } 7)$, first add $2 + 4$ to get 6. Because this sum is less than 7,

$$2 + 4 \equiv 6 \ (\text{mod } 7).$$

b. To find $(4 + 4)(\text{mod } 5)$, first add $4 + 4$ to get 8. Because 8 is greater than 5, divide 8 by 5.

$$8 \div 5 = 1, \text{ remainder } 3$$

The remainder, 3, is the desired sum.

$$4 + 4 \equiv 3 \ (\text{mod } 5)$$

c. To find $(9 + 10)(\text{mod } 12)$, first add $9 + 10$ to get 19. Because this sum is greater than 12, divide 19 by 12.

$$19 \div 12 = 1, \text{ remainder } 7$$

The remainder, 7, is the desired sum.

$$9 + 10 \equiv 7 \ (\text{mod } 12)$$

 CHECK POINT 4 Find each of the following sums:

    a. $(1 + 3)(\text{mod } 5)$ **b.** $(5 + 4)(\text{mod } 7)$ **c.** $(8 + 10)(\text{mod } 13)$.

Being able to add in a modular system without having to draw a clock means that we can construct an addition table for the system fairly quickly. All such tables represent mathematical systems that are commutative groups. We can show that any modular system is a commutative group under addition by verifying each of the five properties (closure, associative, identity, inverse, commutative) as we did for the modulo 12 system in Example 2.

Modulo systems are also used to solve problems involving cyclical changes, such as calendar problems. Because there are 7 days in a week, we can consider this as a modulo 7 system, in which Sunday is 0, Monday is 1, Tuesday 2, Wednesday 3, Thursday 4, Friday 5, and Saturday 6.

EXAMPLE 5   SOLVING A CALENDAR PROBLEM

Suppose today is Thursday, July 2. Which day of the week will it be 47 days from now?

SOLUTION Dates that differ by a multiple of 7 fall on the same day of the week. This means that we can divide 47 by 7 and keep the remainder: $47 \div 7 = 6$, remainder 5. Equivalently,

$$47 \equiv 5 \ (\text{mod } 7).$$

Thus, the desired day of the week is 5 days past Thursday, or Tuesday.

 CHECK POINT 5 Suppose today is Wednesday, May 4. Which day of the week will it be 97 days from now?

In the exercise set that follows, there is a problem in a modulo 27 system that illustrates how modular arithmetic is used in coding. Modular arithmetic is central to the security of the Internet, which utilizes calculations in systems whose clock faces contain more numbers than there are atoms in the observable universe.

EXERCISE SET 13.2 ●●●●●●

• Practice Exercises

Name the kind of rotational symmetry shown in Exercises 1–4.

1.

2.

3.

4.

In Exercises 5–19, use the mathematical system given by the table shown.

∘	*e*	*p*	*q*	*r*	*s*	*t*
e	*e*	*p*	*q*	*r*	*s*	*t*
p	*p*	*q*	*e*	*s*	*t*	*r*
q	*q*	*e*	*p*	*t*	*r*	*s*
r	*r*	*t*	*s*	*e*	*q*	*p*
s	*s*	*r*	*t*	*p*	*e*	*q*
t	*t*	*s*	*r*	*q*	*p*	*e*

5. Explain why the closure property is satisfied for the given binary operation.

6. Show that $(p \circ s) \circ t = p \circ (s \circ t)$.

7. Show that $(r \circ t) \circ q = r \circ (t \circ q)$.

8. As in Exercises 6–7, if every choice of three elements is checked, changing the location of the parentheses will not change the answer. What property is satisfied by the mathematical system?

9. What is the identity element?

Find the inverse of each element.

10. *e*   **11.** *p*   **12.** *q*   **13.** *r*   **14.** *s*   **15.** *t*

16. Based on Exercises 5–15, what can you conclude about this mathematical system?

17. Find $r \circ p$.   **18.** Find $p \circ r$.

19. Based on Exercises 17–18, what can you conclude about this mathematical system?

In Exercises 20–22, give a reason to support each statement.

20. The natural numbers $\{1, 2, 3, 4, 5, \ldots\}$ are not a group under addition.

21. The natural numbers $\{1, 2, 3, 4, 5, \ldots\}$ are not a group under multiplication.

22. The integers $\{\ldots, -3, -2, -1, 0, 1, 2, 3, \ldots\}$ are not a group under subtraction.

23. Consider the 6-hour, modulo 6, clock system under the operation of clock addition.

a. Complete the clock addition table.

+	0	1	2	3	4	5
0						
1						
2						
3						
4						
5						

b. Show that this mathematical system is a commutative group. Just verify two examples for the associative property.

24. Consider the 7-hour, modulo 7, clock system under the operation of clock addition.

a. Complete the clock addition table.

+	0	1	2	3	4	5	6
0							
1							
2							
3							
4							
5							
6							

b. Show that this mathematical system is a commutative group. Just verify two examples for the associative property.

In Exercises 25–34, determine if each statement is true or false. If the statement is false, change the first number on the right side of the congruence to make it true.

25. $7 \equiv 2 \pmod 5$ **26.** $8 \equiv 3 \pmod 5$

27. $41 \equiv 6 \pmod 7$ **28.** $77 \equiv 5 \pmod{12}$

29. $84 \equiv 1 \pmod 7$ **30.** $21 \equiv 5 \pmod 7$

31. $23 \equiv 2 \pmod 4$ **32.** $29 \equiv 3 \pmod 4$

33. $55 \equiv 0 \pmod{11}$ **34.** $75 \equiv 0 \pmod{25}$

In Exercise 35–42, find each sum.

35. $(3 + 2)\pmod 6$ **36.** $(3 + 4)\pmod 8$

37. $(4 + 5)\pmod 6$ **38.** $(5 + 6)\pmod 8$

39. $(6 + 5)\pmod 7$ **40.** $(8 + 7)\pmod 9$

41. $(49 + 49)\pmod{50}$ **42.** $(75 + 75)\pmod{100}$

• Practice Plus

Exercises 43–52 involve multiplication in modulo m systems. To multiply in such systems, find the product using ordinary arithmetic. If the product is less than m, the answer is the product obtained. If the product is greater than or equal to m, the answer is the remainder obtained upon dividing the product by m.

43. Find the product: $(5 \times 7)\pmod{12}$.

44. Find the product: $(6 \times 5)\pmod 8$.

45. a. Find $[3 \times (4 + 5)]\pmod 7$.

     b. Find $[(3 \times 4) + (3 \times 5)]\pmod 7$.

     c. What property of the real numbers is illustrated by parts (a) and (b)?

46. a. Find $[5 \times (3 + 7)]\pmod 9$.

     b. Find $[(5 \times 3) + (5 \times 7)]\pmod 9$.

     c. What property of the real numbers is illustrated by parts (a) and (b)?

In Exercises 47–52, use trial and error to find all replacements for x that are less than the modulus that make the statement true. If no such replacements exist, so state.

47. $3x \equiv 1 \pmod 5$ **48.** $3x \equiv 2 \pmod 7$

49. $3x \equiv 3 \pmod 6$ **50.** $2x \equiv 0 \pmod{12}$

51. $4x \equiv 5 \pmod 8$ **52.** $4x \equiv 1 \pmod 6$

• Application Exercises

To avoid A.M. and P.M. designations, the military uses a 24-hour clock. For example, 11 A.M. is designated 1100 hours, and 11 P.M. (12 noon + 11 hours) is designated 2300 hours. In this system, the first two digits represent hours and the last two digits represent minutes. In Exercises 53–56, find each sum in the 24-hour clock system.

53. $1200 + 0600$ **54.** $1300 + 1900$

55. $0830 + 1550$ **56.** $1315 + 0945$

57. Suppose today is Wednesday, July 8. Which day of the week will it be 67 days from now?

58. Suppose today is Tuesday, October 12. Which day of the week will it be 147 days from now?

59. The figure shows a modulo 27 system used for coding. Each number on the clock represents a letter of the alphabet and 0 represents a space between words. Add 20, mod 27, called the *code key*, to each of the following numbers and use the figure to decipher this code:

9   12   8   20   7   20   12   7   1   23.

*Each book published since 1968 is assigned a ten-digit number, called the **International Standard Book Number** (ISBN). The first nine digits identify the country of publication, the publisher, and the book itself. The tenth digit is a check digit to determine if the number is valid. If the digits of an ISBN are denoted by $a_1, a_2, a_3, a_4, \ldots, a_{10}$, with the first nine digits in the range 0–9, then a_{10} must be in the 0–10 range satisfying*

$$(a_1 + 2a_2 + 3a_3 + 4a_4 + 5a_5 + 6a_6 + 7a_7 + 8a_8 + 9a_9) \equiv a_{10} \pmod{11}.$$

If a_{10} is 10, it is recorded as an X. In Exercises 60–65, use this requirement for the tenth digit to determine whether or not each ten-digit number is a valid ISBN.

60. 0-13-143243-5   **61.** 0-13-219141-5

62. 3-41-610927-4   **63.** 2-41-971329-0

64. 3-49-216627-X   **65.** 0-13-225980-X

*Each product for sale in North America can be identified by a **universal product number**, represented as a series of black and white stripes of various thicknesses. If a 12-digit universal product number is valid, it must satisfy the equation*

$$[3(\text{sum of digits in odd positions}) + (\text{sum of digits in even positions})] \equiv 0 \pmod{10}.$$

In Exercises 66–69, use this requirement to determine whether or not each 12-digit number is a valid universal product number.

66. 0-12189-29109-4   **67.** 2-52998-17394-9

68. 0-12345-67890-1   **69.** 0-64200-11589-7

• Writing in Mathematics

70. Describe the three kinds of rotational symmetry exhibited by different parts of the passionflower shown in the introduction to this chapter (page 747).

71. Look around and find an object that exhibits rotational symmetry. Describe the object and the kind of rotational symmetry shown.

72. Under what conditions is a mathematical system a group?

73. Describe two ways of finding 8 + 7 in a modulo 12, 12-hour clock system.

74. Describe two ways of finding 4 + 4 in a modulo 5 system.

75. Describe the meaning of $a \equiv b \pmod{m}$ and give an example.

76. The days of the week can be considered a modulo 7 system. Describe another phenomenon that occurs in a cycle. What modulo system is appropriate for this phenomenon?

77. A fascinating collection of readings in mathematics can be found in the four-volume set *The World of Mathematics*, published by Simon and Schuster. Read the two pages in the selection "The Group Concept" by Cassius J. Keyser in volume 3 that begin with the header "A Question for Psychologists." In this part of the selection, the author presents a model in which the "mind" might be viewed within the framework of the group definition. After reading the article, describe an example of nonclosure within your own learning experiences.

• **Critical Thinking Exercises**

78. Consider the following operations on a conditional statement:

E: leaves the conditional unchanged

C: changes the conditional into its converse

I: changes the conditional into its inverse

CP: changes the conditional into its contrapositive.

The operation $\circ$ means "followed by."

a. Show that $C \circ CP = I$ and $C \circ I = CP$.

b. Fill in the following table.

$\circ$	E	C	I	CP
E				
C				
I				
CP				

c. Show that this mathematical system is a commutative group. Just verify two examples for the associative property.

79. A mathematical system consists of the set of integers and the operation $\circ$ defined by $a \circ b = a - b + ab$. Use an example involving the associative property and explain why the mathematical system is not a group.

80. Give an example of a mathematical system with just one element which is a group.

81. If it is now 5:00 P.M., what time will it be 99,999,999 hours from now?

82. Clock subtraction is defined by moving a clock's hour hand in a *counterclockwise direction*. Use this definition to find each difference.

a. $(3 - 6)(\mathrm{mod}\ 7)$

b. $(2 - 4)(\mathrm{mod}\ 5)$

• **Group Exercise**

83. One of the reasons that a passionflower is so visually appealing is that it has three parts with different kinds of rotational symmetry: three-, five-, and tenfold. The flower has three stigmas, five stamens, and ten petals. For this activity, each member of the group should find an object or picture of an object that exhibits rotational symmetry. Once each member has shared the object with the group, the group should

a. Construct a clock addition table for the object's symmetry.

b. Describe how each of the properties for a commutative group applies to or describes something about the object.

●●●●●● CHAPTER SUMMARY, REVIEW, AND TEST

• S U M M A R Y   DEFINITIONS AND CONCEPTS   EXAMPLES

13.1 Mathematical Systems

a. A mathematical system consists of a set of elements and at least one binary operation.

Ex. 1, p. 749

b. Certain mathematical systems satisfy the closure, associative, identity, inverse, and commutative properties. These properties are described in the box on page 758. The commutative property is described directly under the box.

Ex. 2, p. 749;
Ex. 3, p. 750;
Ex. 4, p. 750;
Ex. 5, p. 751;
Ex. 6, p. 752;
Ex. 7, p. 753;
Ex. 8, p. 753;
Ex. 9, p. 754

13.2 Rotational Symmetry, Groups, and Clock Arithmetic

a. If it takes m equal turns to restore an object to its original position and each of these turns is a figure that is identical to the original figure, the object has m-fold rotational symmetry. The object will look the same after each turn.

b. A group is a mathematical system meeting the requirements for the closure, associative, identity, and inverse properties. See the box on page 758.   Ex. 1, p. 758

c. A group that meets the requirements for the commutative property is called a commutative group.

d. Clock addition is defined by moving a clock's hour hand in a clockwise direction.

e. Our usual 12-hour clock system is a modulo 12 system. It is a commutative group under clock addition.   Ex. 2, p. 761

f. A modulo m system consists of m integers, starting with 0 and ending with $m - 1$. A modulo m system describes the properties of objects having m-fold rotational symmetry. All such systems are commutative groups under clock addition.

g. The integer a is congruent to b modulo m, denoted $a \equiv b \pmod{m}$, means that if a is divided by m, the remainder is b.   Ex. 3, p. 763

h. Addition in a modulo m system can be performed using a clock or the rule given in the box on page 763.   Ex. 4, p. 763

REVIEW EXERCISES

13.1

Use the mathematical system given by the table shown to solve Exercises 1–18.

∘	e	c	f	r
e	e	c	f	r
c	c	f	r	e
f	f	r	e	c
r	r	e	c	f

1. What is the set of elements of this mathematical system?

2. Is the mathematical system closed under the binary operation? Explain your answer.

Find each result.

3. $c \circ f$ **4.** $r \circ r$ **5.** $e \circ c$

6. $c \circ r$ and $r \circ c$ **7.** $f \circ r$ and $r \circ f$ **8.** $f \circ e$ and $e \circ f$

9. What property is illustrated in Exercises 6–8?

10. Use the table to explain how the property you named in Exercise 9 can be verified for all possible cases without having to consider one case at a time.

Find each result.

11. $(c \circ r) \circ f$ and $c \circ (r \circ f)$

12. $(r \circ e) \circ c$ and $r \circ (e \circ c)$

13. What property is illustrated in Exercises 11–12?

14. What is the identity element for the mathematical system?

Find the inverse for each element.

15. e **16.** c **17.** f **18.** r

19. Is the set $\{0, 1\}$ closed under the operation of ordinary addition? Explain your answer.

20. Is the set $\{0, 1\}$ closed under the operation of multiplication? Explain your answer.

21. Is the set $\{1, 2, 4\}$ closed under division? Explain your answer.

In Exercises 22–23, consider the set of rational numbers.

22. What is the additive inverse of 123?

23. What is the multiplicative inverse of 123?

24. Suppose that $a \circ b$ means to select the larger of the two numbers a and b, or if the numbers are the same, select either number.

a. Complete the following table.

∘	0	1	2	3	4
0					
1					
2					
3					
4					

b. What is the identity element?

c. Does 2 have an inverse? Explain your answer.

13.2

Name the kind of rotational symmetry shown in Exercises 25–26.

25.

Mercedes Benz symbol

26.

Based on the form of a sea urchin

+	0	1	2	3	4
0					
1					
2					
3					
4					

b. Show that this mathematical system is a commutative group. Just verify one example for the associative property.

In Exercises 28–30, determine if each statement is true or false. If the statement is false, change the first number on the right side of the congruence to make it true.

28. $17 \equiv 2 \pmod 8$ **29.** $37 \equiv 3 \pmod 5$

30. $60 \equiv 0 \pmod{10}$

27. Consider the 5-hour, modulo 5, clock system under the operation of clock addition.

a. Complete the clock addition table.

In Exercises 31–34, find each sum.

31. $(4 + 3)\pmod 6$ **32.** $(7 + 7)\pmod 8$

33. $(4 + 3)\pmod 9$ **34.** $(3 + 18)\pmod{20}$

● ● ● ● ● ● ●   CHAPTER 13 TEST

Use the mathematical system given by the table shown to solve Exercises 1–5.

∘	x	y	z
x	x	y	z
y	y	z	x
z	z	x	y

1. Is the mathematical system closed under the binary operation? Explain your answer.

2. Find $z \circ y$ and $y \circ z$. What property is illustrated?

3. Find $(x \circ z) \circ z$ and $x \circ (z \circ z)$. What property is illustrated?

4. What is the identity element for the mathematical system?

5. Give the inverse for each element in the mathematical system.

6. Is the set $\{-1, 0, 1\}$ closed under the operation of ordinary addition? Explain your answer.

7. In the set of rational numbers, what is the multiplicative inverse of 5? Explain your answer.

8. Name the kind of rotational symmetry shown in the design on the right. Describe why the design has this particular kind of rotational symmetry.

In Exercises 9–10, consider the 4-hour, modulo 4, clock system under the operation of clock addition.

9. Complete the clock addition table.

+	0	1	2	3
0				
1				
2				
3				

10. Show that this mathematical system is a commutative group. Present your work clearly, naming and explaining one property at a time. Just verify one example for the associative property.

In Exercises 11–12, determine if each statement is true or false. If the statement is false, change the first number on the right side of the congruence to make it true.

11. $39 \equiv 3 \pmod 6$

12. $14 \equiv 2 \pmod 7$

In Exercises 13–14, find each sum.

13. $(9 + 1)\pmod{11}$

14. $(9 + 6)\pmod{10}$

CHAPTER 14

Voting and Apportionment

As citizens of a free society, we have both a right and a duty to vote. The political, social, financial, and environmental choices we make in elections can affect every aspect of our lives. However, voting is only part of the story. The second part—methods for counting our votes—lies at the heart of the democratic process.

In this chapter, you will learn the role that mathematics plays in finding our collective voice when faced with more than two options in an election. You will see that determining the winning option may depend on the method used for counting votes, as well as on the issues and the preferences of the voters. Is there a method for counting votes that is always fair? In exploring voting theory, as well as the ideal of "one person, one vote," you will begin to understand some of the mathematical paradoxes of our democracy. This will increase your ability to function as a more fully aware citizen.

SECTION 14.1 • VOTING METHODS

Orson Welles (center), star and director of the highly innovative *Citizen Kane*

In the dramatic arts, ours is the era of the movies. As individuals and as a nation, we've grown up with them. Our images of love, war, family, country—even of things that terrify us—owe much to what we've seen on screen.

To celebrate one hundred years of movie making (1896–1996), more than 1500 ballots were sent to leaders in the industry to rank the top American films. The winner? *Citizen Kane* (1941). Controversial outcome? You bet. In this section, you will see how an outcome can be greatly influenced by the voting method used. We begin our discussion of voting theory with a group of students who love movies and are attempting to elect a president of their club. We will use this example throughout the section. Its importance is not in the example itself, but in its implications for conducting fair elections in a democracy.

1 | Understand and use preference tables.

Preference Tables

Four candidates are running for president of the Student Film Institute: Paul (P), Rita (R), Sarah (S), and Tim (T). Each of the club's 37 members submits a secret ballot indicating his or her first, second, third, and fourth choice for president. The 37 ballots are shown in Figure 14.1.

Ballot 1	Ballot 2	Ballot 3	Ballot 4	Ballot 5	Ballot 6	Ballot 7	Ballot 8	Ballot 9	Ballot 10	Ballot 11
1st P	1st S	1st R	1st P	1st R	1st S	1st S	1st S	1st P	1st S	1st P
2nd R	2nd R	2nd T	2nd R	2nd R	2nd R	2nd T	2nd R	2nd R	2nd R	2nd R
3rd S	3rd T	3rd S	3rd S	3rd S	3rd T	3rd S	3rd T	3rd S	3rd T	3rd S
4th T	4th P	4th P	4th T	4th P	4th P	4th P	4th P	4th T	4th P	4th T

Ballot 12	Ballot 13	Ballot 14	Ballot 15	Ballot 16	Ballot 17	Ballot 18	Ballot 19	Ballot 20	Ballot 21	Ballot 22	Ballot 23	Ballot 24
1st T	1st P	1st T	1st S	1st P	1st T	1st R	1st P	1st S	1st P	1st P	1st T	1st P
2nd S	2nd R	2nd S	2nd R	2nd R	2nd T	2nd T	2nd R	2nd R	2nd R	2nd R	2nd S	2nd R
3rd R	3rd S	3rd R	3rd T	3rd S	3rd R	3rd S	3rd S	3rd T	3rd S	3rd S	3rd R	3rd S
4th P	4th T	4th P	4th P	4th T	4th P	4th P	4th T	4th P	4th T	4th T	4th P	4th T

Ballot 25	Ballot 26	Ballot 27	Ballot 28	Ballot 29	Ballot 30	Ballot 31	Ballot 32	Ballot 33	Ballot 34	Ballot 35	Ballot 36	Ballot 37
1st T	1st P	1st P	1st S	1st P	1st S	1st T	1st S	1st P	1st T	1st T	1st S	1st S
2nd S	2nd R	2nd R	2nd R	2nd R	2nd R	2nd S	2nd R	2nd R	2nd S	2nd S	2nd R	2nd R
3rd R	3rd S	3rd S	3rd T	3rd S	3rd T	3rd R	3rd T	3rd S	3rd R	3rd R	3rd T	3rd T
4th P	4th T	4th T	4th P	4th T	4th P	4th P	4th P	4th T	4th P	4th P	4th P	4th P

FIGURE 14.1 The 37 ballots for the Student Film Institute election

Do you see that several club members had identical ballots? For example, ballots 3, 5, 7, and 18 ranked the candidates exactly the same way, namely RTSP. We can group together these identical ballots. Figure 14.2 shows the 37 ballots placed in identical stacks.

FIGURE 14.2 The 37 election ballots placed into identical stacks

Preference ballots are ballots in which a voter is asked to rank all the candidates in order of preference. Rather than placing the preference ballots in identical stacks, we can use a *preference table* to summarize the results of the election. A **preference table** shows how often each particular outcome occurred. Table 14.1 shows a preference table for the 37 ballots cast for president of the Student Film Institute.

There were 14 + 10 + 8 + 4 + 1, or 37 voters in the election.

TABLE 14.1 PREFERENCE TABLE FOR THE STUDENT FILM INSTITUTE ELECTION

Number of Votes	14	10	8	4	1
First Choice	P	S	T	R	S
Second Choice	R	R	S	T	T
Third Choice	S	T	R	S	R
Fourth Choice	T	P	P	P	P

14 ballots rank the candidates P, R, S, T.

10 ballots rank the candidates S, R, T, P.

8 ballots rank the candidates T, S, R, P.

4 ballots rank the candidates R, T, S, P.

1 ballot ranks the candidates S, T, R, P.

EXAMPLE 1 UNDERSTANDING A PREFERENCE TABLE

Four candidates are running for mayor of Smallville: Antonio (A), Bob (B), Carmen (C), and Donna (D). The voters were asked to rank all the candidates in order of preference. Table 14.2 shows the preference table for this election.

TABLE 14.2 PREFERENCE TABLE FOR THE SMALLVILLE MAYORAL ELECTION

Number of Votes	130	120	100	150
First Choice	A	D	D	C
Second Choice	B	B	B	B
Third Choice	C	C	A	A
Fourth Choice	D	A	C	D

a. How many people voted in the election?

b. How many people selected the candidates in this order: D, B, A, C?

c. How many people selected Donna (D) as their first choice for mayor?

SOLUTION

a. We find the number of people who voted in the election by adding the numbers in the row labeled *Number of Votes*:

$$130 + 120 + 100 + 150 = 500.$$

Thus, 500 people voted in the election.

b. We find the number of people selecting the candidates in the order D, B, A, C by referring to the third column of letters in the preference table. Above this column is the number 100. Thus, 100 people voted for the candidates in the order D, B, A, C.

TABLE 14.2 (REPEATED)

Number of Votes	130	120	100	150
First Choice	A	D	D	C
Second Choice	B	B	B	B
Third Choice	C	C	A	A
Fourth Choice	D	A	C	D

c. We find the number of people who voted for D as their first choice by reading across the row that says *First Choice*. When you see a D in this row, write the number above it. Then find the sum of the numbers:

$$120 + 100 = 220.$$

Thus, 220 voters selected Donna as their first choice for mayor.

CHECK POINT 1 Four candidates are running for student body president: Alan (A), Bonnie (B), Carlos (C), and Samir (S). The students were asked to rank all the candidates in order of preference. Table 14.3 shows the preference table for this election.

TABLE 14.3 PREFERENCE TABLE FOR THE ELECTION OF STUDENT BODY PRESIDENT

Number of Votes	2100	1305	765	40
First Choice	S	A	S	B
Second Choice	A	S	A	S
Third Choice	B	B	C	A
Fourth Choice	C	C	B	C

a. How many students voted in the election?

b. How many students selected the candidates in this order: B, S, A, C?

c. How many students selected Samir (S) as their first choice for student body president?

Now that you know how to summarize the results of an election using a preference table, it's time to decide the outcome of elections in general and the Student Film Institute election in particular. We will discuss four of the most popular voting methods:

1. the plurality method
2. the Borda count method
3. the plurality-with-elimination method
4. the pairwise comparison method.

2 Use the plurality method to determine an election's winner.

The Plurality Method

If there are three or more candidates in an election, it often happens that no single candidate receives a majority of first-place votes—that is, more than 50% of the votes. Using the **plurality method**, the candidate with the most first-place votes wins. The only information that we use from the preference ballots are the votes for first place.

> **THE PLURALITY METHOD**
> The candidate (or candidates, if there is more than one) with the most first-place votes is the winner.

EXAMPLE 2 USING THE PLURALITY METHOD

Table 14.1, repeated at the top of the next page, shows the preference table for the four candidates running for president of the Student Film Institute: Paul (P), Rita (R), Sarah (S), and Tim (T). Who is declared the winner using the plurality method?

SOLUTION The candidate with the most first-place votes is the winner. When using Table 14.1, we only need to look at the row indicating the number of first-choice votes.

TABLE 14.1 PREFERENCE TABLE FOR THE STUDENT FILM INSTITUTE ELECTION

Number of Votes	14	10	8	4	1
First Choice	P	S	T	R	S
Second Choice	R	R	S	T	T
Third Choice	S	T	R	S	R
Fourth Choice	T	P	P	P	P

The voice balloon to the left of the preference table indicates that P (Paul) is the winner and the new president of the Student Film Institute. Although Paul received the most first-place votes, he received only $\frac{14}{37}$, or approximately 38%, of the first-place votes, which is less than a majority.

○

CHECK POINT 2 Table 14.2 on page 773 shows the preference table for the four candidates running for mayor of Smallville: Antonio (A), Bob (B), Carmen (C), and Donna (D). Who is declared the winner using the plurality method?

⋯⋯⋯⋯⋯⋯⋯⋯⋯⋯⋯⋯⋯⋯⋯⋯⋯⋯⋯⋯⋯⋯⋯⋯⋯⋯⋯●

3 Use the Borda count method to determine an election's winner.

The Borda Count Method

The **Borda count method**, developed by the French mathematician and naval captain Jean-Charles de Borda (1733–1799), assigns points to each candidate based on how they are ranked by the voters.

> **THE BORDA COUNT METHOD**
> Each voter ranks the candidates from the most favorable to the least favorable. Each last-place vote is given 1 point, each next-to-last-place vote is given 2 points, each third-from-last-place vote is given 3 points, and so on. The points are totaled for each candidate separately. The candidate with the most points is the winner.

When using the plurality method, all the information in the preference table not related to first place is ignored. Example 3 illustrates that this is not the case when using the Borda count method. The Borda count method takes into account all the information provided by the voters' preferences.

EXAMPLE 3   USING THE BORDA COUNT METHOD

Table 14.1, repeated below, shows the preference table for the four candidates running for president of the Student Film Institute: Paul (P), Rita (R), Sarah (S), and Tim (T). Who is declared the winner using the Borda count method?

TABLE 14.1 PREFERENCE TABLE FOR THE STUDENT FILM INSTITUTE ELECTION

Number of Votes	14	10	8	4	1
First Choice	P	S	T	R	S
Second Choice	R	R	S	T	T
Third Choice	S	T	SR	S	R
Fourth Choice	T	P	P	P	P

SOLUTION Because there are four candidates, a first-place vote is worth 4 points, a second-place vote is worth 3 points, a third-place vote is worth 2 points, and a fourth-place vote is worth 1 point. Table 14.4 shows the points produced by the votes in the preference table.

TABLE 14.4 POINTS FOR THE STUDENT FILM INSTITUTE ELECTION

Number of Votes	14	10	8	4	1
First Choice: 4 points	P: $14 \times 4 = 56$ pts	S: $10 \times 4 = 40$ pts	T: $8 \times 4 = 32$ pts	R: $4 \times 4 = 16$ pts	S: $1 \times 4 = 4$ pts
Second Choice: 3 points	R: $14 \times 3 = 42$ pts	R: $10 \times 3 = 30$ pts	S: $8 \times 3 = 24$ pts	T: $4 \times 3 = 12$ pts	T: $1 \times 3 = 3$ pts
Third Choice: 2 points	S: $14 \times 2 = 28$ pts	T: $10 \times 2 = 20$ pts	R: $8 \times 2 = 16$ pts	S: $4 \times 2 = 8$ pts	R: $1 \times 2 = 2$ pts
Fourth Choice: 1 point	T: $14 \times 1 = 14$ pts	P: $10 \times 1 = 10$ pts	P: $8 \times 1 = 8$ pts	P: $4 \times 1 = 4$ pts	P: $1 \times 1 = 1$ pt

Now we read down each column and total the points for each candidate separately.

$$\text{P gets} \quad 56 + 10 + 8 + 4 + 1 = 79 \text{ points.}$$

$$\text{R gets} \quad 42 + 30 + 16 + 16 + 2 = 106 \text{ points.}$$

$$\text{S gets} \quad 28 + 40 + 24 + 8 + 4 = 104 \text{ points.}$$

$$\text{T gets} \quad 14 + 20 + 32 + 12 + 3 = 81 \text{ points.}$$

Because R (Rita) has received the most points, she is the winner and the new president of the Student Film Institute.

In Examples 2 and 3, the plurality method and the Borda count method produced different election winners. This illustrates the importance of choosing a voting system prior to an election.

CHECK POINT 3 Table 14.2 on page 773 shows the preference table for the four candidates running for mayor of Smallville: Antonio (A), Bob (B), Carmen (C), and Donna (D). Who is declared the winner using the Borda count method?

4 Use the plurality-with-elimination method to determine an election's winner.

The Plurality-with-Elimination Method

The **plurality-with-elimination method** is based on "survival of the fittest" and may involve a series of elections. If a candidate receives a majority of votes, that candidate is the "fittest" and is declared the winner. If no candidate receives a majority of votes, the candidate with the least number of votes is eliminated and a second election is held. The process is repeated until a candidate receives a majority.

Multiple elections are not necessary when using preference ballots. We remove the eliminated candidate from the preference table and assume that the relative preferences of a voter are not affected by the elimination of this candidate.

> **THE PLURALITY-WITH-ELIMINATION METHOD USING PREFERENCE BALLOTS**
>
> The candidate with the majority of first-place votes is the winner. If no candidate receives a majority of first-place votes, eliminate the candidate (or candidates if there is a tie) with the fewest first-place votes from the preference table. Move the candidates in each column below the eliminated candidate up one place. The candidate with the majority of first-place votes in the new preference table is the winner. If no candidate receives a majority of first-place votes, repeat this process until a candidate receives a majority.

EXAMPLE 4 USING THE PLURALITY-WITH-ELIMINATION METHOD

Table 14.1, repeated below, shows the preference table for the four candidates running for president of the Student Film Institute: Paul (P), Rita (R), Sarah (S), and Tim (T). Who is declared the winner using the plurality-with-elimination method?

TABLE 14.1 PREFERENCE TABLE FOR THE STUDENT FILM INSTITUTE ELECTION

Number of Votes	14	10	8	4	1
First Choice	P	S	T	R	S
Second Choice	R	R	S	T	T
Third Choice	S	T	R	S	R
Fourth Choice	T	P	P	P	P

SOLUTION Recall that there are $14 + 10 + 8 + 4 + 1$, or 37, people voting. In order to receive a majority, a candidate must receive more than 50% of the first-place votes, meaning 19 or more votes. The number of first-place votes for each candidate is

$$P(\text{Paul}) = 14 \qquad S(\text{Sarah}) = 10 + 1 = 11 \qquad T(\text{Tim}) = 8 \qquad R(\text{Rita}) = 4.$$

We see that no candidate received a majority of first-place votes. Because Rita received the fewest first-place votes, she is eliminated in the first round.

The new preference table with R eliminated is shown in Table 14.5. Compare this table with Table 14.1. For each column, each candidate below R moves up one place while the positions of candidates above R remain unchanged. Thus, once Rita is eliminated, the order of preference is preserved.

TABLE 14.5 PREFERENCE TABLE FOR THE STUDENT FILM INSTITUTE ELECTION WITH R ELIMINATED

Number of Votes	14	10	8	4	1
First Choice	P	S	T	T	S
Second Choice	S	T	S	S	T
Third Choice	T	P	P	P	P

Recall that to receive a majority, a candidate must get 19 or more first-place votes. The number of first-place votes for each candidate is now

$$P(\text{Paul}) = 14 \qquad S(\text{Sarah}) = 10 + 1 = 11 \qquad T(\text{Tim}) = 8 + 4 = 12.$$

Once again, no candidate receives a majority of first-place votes. Because Sarah received the fewest first-place votes, she is eliminated in the second round.

The new preference table with S eliminated is shown in Table 14.6. Compare this table with Table 14.5. For each column, each candidate below S moves up one place while the positions of candidates above S remain unchanged.

TABLE 14.6 PREFERENCE TABLE FOR THE STUDENT FILM INSTITUTE ELECTION WITH R AND S ELIMINATED

Number of Votes	14	10	8	4	1
First Choice	P	T	T	T	T
Second Choice	T	P	P	P	P

TABLE 14.6 (repeated)

Number of Votes	14	10	8	4	1
First Choice	P	T	T	T	T
Second Choice	T	P	P	P	P

Keep in mind that a candidate must get 19 or more first-place votes to receive a majority. The number of first-place votes for each candidate is now

$$P(\text{Paul}) = 14 \qquad T(\text{Tim}) = 10 + 8 + 4 + 1 = 23.$$

Because T (Tim) has received the majority of first-place votes, he is the winner and the new president of the Student Film Institute.

We have now used three different voting methods in the same election. Each method resulted in a different winner. Can you now see how important it is to choose a voting system before an election takes place?

CHECK POINT 4 Table 14.2 on page 773 shows the preference table for the four candidates running for mayor of Smallville: Antonio (A), Bob (B), Carmen (C), and Donna (D). Who is declared the winner using the plurality-with-elimination method?

BLITZER BONUS

Choosing a New Voting System in San Francisco

A little-noticed proposition approved in 2003 by San Francisco voters offers a glimpse of how we might vote in the future. Instead of casting their ballots for just one candidate, San Franciscans rank the candidates in most local races according to their first, second, and third choices. The election's winner is declared using the plurality-with-elimination method, also known as instant-runoff voting. San Francisco approved this new voting system after a runoff election for city attorney drew an abysmally low 16.6% of registered voters.

---

5 | Use the pairwise comparison method to determine an election's winner.

The Pairwise Comparison Method

Using the **pairwise comparison method**, every candidate is compared one-on-one with every other candidate. For example, the candidates running for president of the Student Film Institute are Paul, Rita, Sarah, and Tim. Thus, we make the following comparisons:

Paul vs. Rita	Paul vs. Sarah	Paul vs. Tim
Rita vs. Sarah	Rita vs. Tim	Sarah vs. Tim.

We must make 6 comparisons.

Is there a formula for how many comparisons are needed when there are n candidates? The answer is yes. We are basically counting the number of combinations possible if 2 candidates are taken from n candidates. In Section 11.3, we saw that the number of possible combinations if r items are taken from n items is

$$_nC_r = \frac{n!}{(n-r)!\,r!}.$$

The number of comparisons needed if 2 candidates are taken from n candidates is

$$_nC_2 = \frac{n!}{(n-2)!\,2!} = \frac{n(n-1)(n-2)!}{(n-2)!\,2 \cdot 1} = \frac{n(n-1)}{2}.$$

> **THE NUMBER OF COMPARISONS USING THE PAIRWISE COMPARISON METHOD**
>
> In an election with n candidates, the number of comparisons, C, that must be made is
>
> $$C = \frac{n(n-1)}{2}.$$

The Heisman Trophy

Heisman winner, Ricky Williams, 1998

The Heisman Trophy, given each year since 1935 to the best college football player in the country, is chosen using a variation of the Borda count method. Voting is done by approximately 950 sports journalists and former Heisman winners. Each preference ballot allows for 3 names (out of thousands of college football players). A player receives 3 points for each first-place vote, 2 points for each second-place vote, and 1 point for each third-place vote.

Heisman Winners with the Most Points

1968—O. J. Simpson, USC, 2853
1976—Tony Dorsett, Pittsburgh, 2357
1998—Ricky Williams, Texas, 2355
1993—Charlie Ward, FSU, 2350
1984—Doug Flutie, Boston College, 2240

Source: ESPN Sports Almanac

How do we make each of these comparisons? We use the preference table and award points, as described in the following box:

THE PAIRWISE COMPARISON METHOD

Voters rank all the candidates and the results are summarized in a preference table. The table is used to make a series of comparisons in which each candidate is compared to each of the other candidates. For each pair of candidates, X and Y, use the table to determine how many voters prefer X to Y and vice versa. If a majority prefer X to Y, then X receives 1 point. If a majority prefer Y to X, then Y receives 1 point. If the candidates tie, then each receives $\frac{1}{2}$ point. After all comparisons have been made, the candidate receiving the most points is the winner.

EXAMPLE 5   USING THE PAIRWISE COMPARISON METHOD

Table 14.1, repeated below, shows the preference table for the four candidates running for president of the Student Film Institute: Paul (P), Rita (R), Sarah (S), and Tim (T). Who is declared the winner using the pairwise comparison method?

TABLE 14.1 PREFERENCE TABLE FOR THE STUDENT FILM INSTITUTE ELECTION

Number of Votes	14	10	8	4	1
First Choice	P	S	T	R	S
Second Choice	R	R	S	T	T
Third Choice	S	T	R	S	R
Fourth Choice	T	P	P	P	P

STUDY TIP

You can list the comparisons by first listing all the candidates. Then pair each candidate with every other person whose name follows in the list.

SOLUTION Because there are 4 candidates, $n = 4$ and the number of comparisons we must make is

$$C = \frac{n(n-1)}{2} = \frac{4(4-1)}{2} = \frac{4 \cdot 3}{2} = \frac{12}{2} = 6.$$

Although you can make each of the 6 comparisons using Table 14.1, we will show the table 6 times to make certain you can follow the details behind each comparison. With P, R, S, and T, the comparisons are P vs. R, P vs. S, P vs. T, R vs. S, R vs. T, and S vs. T.

P vs. R

14	10	8	4	1
P	S	T	R	S
R	R	S	T	T
S	T	R	S	R
T	P	P	P	P

14 voters prefer P to R.

10 + 8 + 4 + 1, or 23, voters prefer R to P.

Conclusion: R wins this comparison and gets 1 point.

P vs. S

14	10	8	4	1
P	S	T	R	S
R	R	S	T	T
S	T	R	S	R
T	P	P	P	P

14 voters prefer P to S.

10 + 8 + 4 + 1, or 23, voters prefer S to P.

Conclusion: S wins this comparison and gets 1 point.

P vs. T

14	10	8	4	1
P	S	T	R	S
R	R	S	T	T
S	T	R	S	R
T	P	P	P	P

14 voters prefer P to T.

10 + 8 + 4 + 1, or 23, voters prefer T to P.

Conclusion: T wins this comparison and gets 1 point.

R vs. S

14	10	8	4	1
P	S	T	R	S
R	R	S	T	T
S	T	R	S	R
T	P	P	P	P

14 + 4, or 18, voters prefer R to S.

10 + 8 + 1, or 19, voters prefer S to R.

Conclusion: S wins this comparison and gets 1 point.

R vs. T

14	10	8	4	1
P	S	T	R	S
R	R	S	T	T
S	T	R	S	R
T	P	P	P	P

14 + 10 + 4, or 28, voters prefer R to T.

8 + 1, or 9, voters prefer T to R.

Conclusion: R wins this comparison and gets 1 point.

S vs. T

14	10	8	4	1
P	S	T	R	S
R	R	S	T	T
S	T	R	S	R
T	P	P	P	P

14 + 10 + 1, or 25, voters prefer S to T.

8 + 4, or 12, voters prefer T to S.

Conclusion: S wins this comparison and gets 1 point.

Now let's use each of the six conclusions and add points for the six comparisons.

R gets 1 + 1 = 2 points.

S gets 1 + 1 + 1 = 3 points.

T gets 1 point.

After all comparisons have been made, the candidate receiving the most points is S (Sarah). Sarah is the winner and the new president of the Student Film Institute.

CHECK POINT 5 Table 14.2 on page 773 shows the preference table for the four candidates running for mayor of Smallville: Antonio (A), Bob (B), Carmen (C), and Donna (D). Make 6 comparisons (A vs. B, A vs. C, A vs. D, B vs. C, B vs. D, and C vs. D) and determine the winner using the pairwise comparison method.

If an election results in a tie, a tie-breaking method should be determined before the election takes place. For example, prior to an election it can be announced that the plurality method will be used to determine the winner and the pairwise comparison method will decide the winner in the event that the plurality method leads to a tie.

In this section we have seen that the chosen voting method can affect the election results. Table 14.7 summarizes the four voting methods we discussed. Which of these methods is the best? Unfortunately, each method has serious flaws, as you will see in the next section.

TABLE 14.7 SUMMARY OF VOTING METHODS	
Voting Method	**How the Winning Candidate Is Determined**
Plurality Method	The candidate with the most first-place votes is the winner.
Borda Count Method	Voters rank all candidates from the most favorable to the least favorable. Each last-place vote receives 1 point, each next-to-last-place vote 2 points, and so on. The candidate with the most points is the winner.
Plurality-with-Elimination Method	The candidate with the majority (over 50%) of first-place votes is the winner. If no candidate receives a majority, eliminate the candidate with the fewest first-place votes. Either hold another election or adjust the preference table. Continue this process until a candidate receives a majority of first-place votes. That candidate is the winner.
Pairwise Comparison Method	Voters rank all the candidates. A series of comparisons is made in which each candidate is compared to each of the other candidates. The preferred candidate in each comparison receives 1 point; in case of a tie, each receives $\frac{1}{2}$ point. The candidate with the most points is the winner.

STUDY TIP

All candidates must be ranked by voters when using the Borda count and pairwise comparison methods. Ranking is not necessary with the plurality method, in which voters need only select one candidate. Ranking is optional in the plurality-with-elimination method. If voters do not rank all the candidates and simply vote for one candidate, multiple elections can result. If they do rank the candidates, multiple elections can be avoided.

EXERCISE SET 14.1 ●●●●●●

• Practice and Application Exercises

In Exercises 1–2, the preference ballots for three candidates (A, B, and C) are shown. Fill in the number of votes in the first row of the given preference table.

1.
ABC	BCA	BCA	CBA
CBA	ABC	ABC	BCA
BCA	CBA	ABC	ABC
BCA	ABC	ABC	CBA

Number of Votes			
First Choice	A	B	C
Second Choice	B	C	B
Third Choice	C	A	A

2.
ABC	CBA	BCA	BCA
ABC	BCA	BCA	ABC
ABC	ABC	BCA	CBA
BCA	ABC	ABC	ABC

Number of Votes			
First Choice	A	B	C
Second Choice	B	C	B
Third Choice	C	A	A

In Exercises 3–4, four students are running for president of the Let's-Talk-Politics Club: Ann (A), Barbara (B), Charlie (C), and Devon (D). The preference ballots for the four candidates are shown. Construct a preference table to illustrate the results of the election.

3.
ABCD	BDCA	CBDA	ABCD	CBDA	CBDA
ABCD	ABCD	CBAD	CBAD	ABCD	CBDA

4.
ABCD	CBAD	CBAD	ABCD	BDCA	CBAD
CBAD	ABCD	CBDA	CBAD	ABCD	CBDA

5. Your class is given the option of choosing a day for the final exam. The students in the class are asked to rank the three available days, Monday (M), Wednesday (W), and Friday (F). The results of the election are shown in the following preference table.

Number of Votes	14	8	3	1
First Choice	F	F	W	M
Second Choice	W	M	F	W
Third Choice	M	W	M	F

a. How many students voted in the election?

b. How many students selected the days in this order: F, M, W?

c. How many students selected Friday as their first choice for the final?

d. How many students selected Wednesday as their first choice for the final?

6. Students at your college are given the option of choosing a topic for which a speaker will be selected. Students are asked to rank three topics: Technology (T), Environmental Issues (E), and Terrorism in the Name of Religion (R). The results of the election are shown in the following preference table.

Number of Votes	70	30	10	5
First Choice	R	T	T	E
Second Choice	E	R	E	T
Third Choice	T	E	R	R

   a. How many students voted?

   b. How many students selected the topics in this order: T, E, R?

   c. How many students selected technology as their first choice for a speaker's topic?

   d. How many students selected environmental issues as their second choice for a speaker's topic?

7. The theater society members are voting for the kind of play they will perform next semester: a comedy (C), a drama (D), or a musical (M). Their votes are summarized in the following preference table.

Number of Votes	10	6	6	4	2	2
First Choice	M	C	D	C	D	M
Second Choice	C	M	C	D	M	D
Third Choice	D	D	M	M	C	C

Which type of play is selected using the plurality method?

8. The travel club members are voting for the American city they will visit next semester: New York (N), San Francisco (S), or Chicago (C). Their votes are summarized in the following preference table.

Number of Votes	16	8	6	4
First Choice	S	N	N	C
Second Choice	N	S	C	N
Third Choice	C	C	S	S

Which city is selected using the plurality method?

9. Four professors are running for chair of the Natural Science Division: Professors Darwin (D), Einstein (E), Freud (F), and Hawking (H). The votes of the professors in the natural science division are summarized in the following preference table.

Number of Votes	30	22	20	12	2
First Choice	D	E	F	H	H
Second Choice	H	F	E	E	F
Third Choice	F	H	H	F	D
Fourth Choice	E	D	D	D	E

Who is declared the new division chair using the plurality method?

10. Four professors are running for president of the League of Innovation: Professors Disney (D), Ford (F), Gates (G), and Sarnoff (S). The votes of the members in the League of Innovation are summarized in the following preference table.

Number of Votes	30	22	18	10	2
First Choice	F	G	S	D	G
Second Choice	D	D	G	S	S
Third Choice	G	S	D	G	D
Fourth Choice	S	F	F	F	F

Who is declared the new president using the plurality method?

11. Use the preference table shown in Exercise 7. Which type of play is selected using the Borda count method?

12. Use the preference table shown in Exercise 8. Which city is selected using the Borda count method?

13. Use the preference table shown in Exercise 9. Who is declared the new division chair using the Borda count method?

14. Use the preference table shown in Exercise 10. Who is declared the new president using the Borda count method?

15. Use the preference table shown in Exercise 7. Which type of play is selected using the plurality-with-elimination method?

16. Use the preference table shown in Exercise 8. Which city is selected using the plurality-with-elimination method?

17. Use the preference table shown in Exercise 9. Who is declared the new division chair using the plurality-with-elimination method?

18. Use the preference table shown in Exercise 10. Who is declared the new president using the plurality-with-elimination method?

In Exercises 19–22, suppose that the pairwise comparison method is used to determine the winner in an election.

19. If there are 5 candidates, how many comparisons must be made?

20. If there are 6 candidates, how many comparisons must be made?

21. If there are 8 candidates, how many comparisons must be made?

22. If there are 9 candidates, how many comparisons must be made?

23. Use the preference table shown in Exercise 7. Which type of play is selected using the pairwise comparison method?

24. Use the preference table shown in Exercise 8. Which city is selected using the pairwise comparison method?

25. Use the preference table shown in Exercise 9. Who is declared the new division chair using the pairwise comparison method?

26. Use the preference table shown in Exercise 10. Who is declared the new president using the pairwise comparison method?

In Exercises 27–30, 72 voters are asked to rank four brands of soup: A, B, C, and D. The votes are summarized in the following preference table.

Number of Votes	34	30	6	2
First Choice	A	B	C	D
Second Choice	B	C	D	B
Third Choice	C	D	B	C
Fourth Choice	D	A	A	A

27. Determine the winner using the plurality method.

28. Determine the winner using the Borda count method.

29. Determine the winner using the plurality-with-elimination method.

30. Determine the winner using the pairwise comparison method.

The programmers at the Theater Channel need to select a live musical to introduce their new network. The five choices are Cabaret (C), The Producers (P), Rent (R), Sweeney Todd (S), or West Side Story (W). The 22 programmers rank their choices, summarized in the following preference table. Use the table to solve Exercises 31–34.

Number of Votes	5	5	4	3	3	2
First Choice	C	S	C	W	W	P
Second Choice	R	R	P	P	R	S
Third Choice	P	W	R	R	S	C
Fourth Choice	W	P	S	S	C	R
Fifth Choice	S	C	W	C	P	W

31. Determine which musical is selected using the Borda count method.

32. Determine which musical is selected using the plurality method.

33. Determine which musical is selected using the pairwise comparison method.

34. Determine which musical is selected using the plurality-with-elimination method.

35. Five candidates, A, B, C, D, and E, are running for chair of the Psychology Department. The votes of the department members are summarized in the following preference table.

Number of Votes	5	5	3	3	3	2
First Choice	A	C	D	A	B	D
Second Choice	B	E	C	D	E	C
Third Choice	C	D	B	B	A	B
Fourth Choice	D	A	E	C	C	A
Fifth Choice	E	B	A	E	D	E

a. Who is declared the new department chair using the Borda count method?

b. Suppose that Professor E withdraws from the running before the votes are counted. Write the new preference table. Now who is declared the new department chair using the Borda count method?

36. Rework parts (a) and (b) of Exercise 35 using the pairwise comparison method.

37. Three candidates, A, B, and C, are running for mayor. Election rules stipulate that the plurality method will determine the winner. In the event that the plurality method leads to a tie, the Borda count method will decide the winner. The election results are summarized in the following preference table. Under these rules, which candidate becomes the new mayor?

Number of Votes	12,000	7500	4500
First Choice	C	A	A
Second Choice	B	B	C
Third Choice	A	C	B

38. Three candidates, A, B, and C, are running for mayor. Election rules stipulate that the pairwise comparison method will determine the winner. In the event that the pairwise comparison method leads to a tie, the Borda count method will decide the winner. The election results are summarized in the following preference table. Under these rules, which candidate becomes the new mayor?

Number of Votes	60,000	40,000	40,000	20,000	20,000
First Choice	A	C	B	A	C
Second Choice	B	A	C	C	B
Third Choice	C	B	A	B	A

• Writing in Mathematics

39. What is a preference ballot?

40. Describe what is contained in a preference table. What does the table show?

41. Describe the plurality method. Why is ranking not necessary when using this method?

42. Describe the Borda count method. Is it possible to use this method without ranking the candidates? Explain.

43. What is the plurality-with-elimination method? Why is it advantageous to rank the candidates when using this method?

44. What is the pairwise comparison method? Is it possible to use this method without ranking the candidates? Explain.

45. Describe the process used to determine how many comparisons must be made with the pairwise comparison method.

46. Why is it important to choose a voting system before an election takes place?

47. Playwright Tom Stoppard wrote, "It's not the voting that's democracy; it's the counting." Explain what he meant by this.

48. Based on the answers to Exercises 27–30, if you were at the market, which brand of soup, A, B, C, or D, would you select? Explain your choice.

• Critical Thinking Exercises

49. Select the false statement or statements from the following list. If all statements are true, so state.

   a. A candidate with the majority always wins under the plurality method.

   b. A candidate with the majority always wins under the Borda count method.

   c. A candidate with the majority always wins under the plurality-with-elimination method.

   d. A candidate with the majority always wins under the pairwise comparison method.

50. An election with 20 candidates is to be determined using the pairwise comparison method. If it takes two minutes to calculate a pairwise comparison, how long will it take to calculate the election results?

In Exercises 51–54, construct a preference table for an election with candidates A, B, and C satisfying the given condition.

51. A wins using the Borda count method.

52. B wins using the plurality-with-elimination method.

53. C wins using the pairwise comparison method.

54. B wins using all four methods discussed in this section.

• Group Exercises

55. Research and present a group report on how voting is conducted for the Academy Awards. Describe the single transferable voting method, a variation of the plurality-with-elimination method, in the nomination stage for best picture. (Members of the Irish Senate are also elected by this method.) Be sure to describe some of the more bizarre occurrences at the Oscar ceremonies.

56. Research and present a group report on how voting is conducted for one or more of the following awards: the Heisman Trophy, the Nobel Prize, the Grammy, the Tony, the Emmy, the Pulitzer Prize, or any event or award that the group finds intriguing. Be sure to discuss how the nominees are selected, who participates in the voting, the voting system or systems used, and who counts the results.

SECTION 14.2 • FLAWS OF VOTING METHODS

OBJECTIVES

1. Use the majority criterion to determine a voting system's fairness.

2. Use the head-to-head criterion to determine a voting system's fairness.

3. Use the monotonicity criterion to determine a voting system's fairness.

4. Use the irrelevant alternatives criterion to determine a voting system's fairness.

5. Understand Arrow's Impossibility Theorem.

It's not fair! The Olympic Games can generate $10 billion in spending for the host city. With all that money at stake, no wonder the selection process has a questionable past. In 1998, evidence surfaced to indicate what many Olympic insiders had been whispering for years: that bid cities had showered members of the International Olympic Committee (IOC) with gifts—fully paid shopping trips for spouses, college scholarships for children, and even cash in envelopes for members. A 2004 BBC documentary, *Buying the Games*, investigated the taking of bribes by IOC members in the bidding process for the 2012 Summer Olympics.

   The voting method used to select the winning Olympic host city is a variation of the plurality-with-elimination method. If the International Olympic Committee can eliminate the abuse and bribery that has plagued its selection process, can a winning city be fairly elected? Not necessarily. In the early 1950s, the mathematical economist Kenneth Arrow (1921–) proved that **a method for determining election results that is democratic and always fair is a mathematical impossibility**.

   What exactly is meant by "democratic" and "fair"? In this section, we will look at four criteria that mathematicians and political scientists have agreed a fair voting system should meet. These four **fairness criteria** include the *majority criterion*, the *head-to-head criterion*, the *monotonicity criterion*, and the *irrelevant alternatives criterion*.

| 1 | Use the majority criterion to determine a voting system's fairness. |

The Majority Criterion

Most people would agree that if a single candidate receives more than half of the first-place votes in an election, then that candidate should be declared the winner. This requirement for a fair and democratic election is called the **majority criterion**.

STUDY TIP

Remember that a *majority* refers to receiving more than half the first-place votes. A *plurality* refers to receiving the most first-place votes.

THE MAJORITY CRITERION
If a candidate receives a majority of first-place votes in an election, then that candidate should win the election.

Example 1 shows that the Borda count method may not satisfy the majority criterion.

EXAMPLE 1   THE BORDA COUNT METHOD VIOLATES THE MAJORITY CRITERION

The 11 members of the Board of Trustees of your college must hire a new college president. The four finalists for the job, E, F, G, and H, are ranked by the 11 members. The preference table is shown in Table 14.8. The board members agree to use the Borda count method to determine the winner.

a. Which candidate has a majority of first-place votes?

b. Which candidate is declared the new college president using the Borda count method?

TABLE 14.8 PREFERENCE TABLE FOR SELECTING A NEW COLLEGE PRESIDENT

Number of Votes	6	3	2
First Choice	E	G	F
Second Choice	F	H	G
Third Choice	G	F	H
Fourth Choice	H	E	E

SOLUTION

a. There are 11 first-place votes. Because a majority involves more than half of these votes, any candidate with 6 or more first-place votes receives a majority. The first-choice row in Table 14.8 shows that candidate E received 6 first-place votes. Thus, candidate E has a majority of first-place votes. By the majority criterion, candidate E should be the new college president.

b. Using the Borda count method with four candidates, a first-place vote is worth 4 points, a second-place vote 3 points, a third-place vote 2 points, and a fourth-place vote 1 point. Table 14.9 shows the points produced by the votes in the preference table.

TABLE 14.9 POINTS FOR THE COLLEGE PRESIDENT ELECTION

Number of Votes	6	3	2
First Choice: 4 points	E: $6 \times 4 = 24$ pts	G: $3 \times 4 = 12$ pts	F: $2 \times 4 = 8$ pts
Second Choice: 3 points	F: $6 \times 3 = 18$ pts	H: $3 \times 3 = 9$ pts	G: $2 \times 3 = 6$ pts
Third Choice: 2 points	G: $6 \times 2 = 12$ pts	F: $3 \times 2 = 6$ pts	H: $2 \times 2 = 4$ pts
Fourth Choice: 1 point	H: $6 \times 1 = 6$ pts	E: $3 \times 1 = 3$ pts	E: $2 \times 1 = 2$ pts

Now we read down the columns and total the points for each candidate.

E gets $24 + 3 + 2 = 29$ points.   F gets $18 + 6 + 8 = 32$ points.

G gets $12 + 12 + 6 = 30$ points.   H gets $6 + 9 + 4 = 19$ points.

Because candidate F has received the most points, candidate F is declared the new college president using the Borda count method.

In Example 1, although a majority of members of the Board of Trustees preferred candidate E, the Borda count method yielded a different choice, candidate F. In a situation like this, the Borda count method is said to *violate* the majority criterion.

CHECK POINT 1 The 14 members of the school board must hire a new principal. The four finalists for the job, A, B, C, and D, are ranked by the 14 members. The preference table is shown in Table 14.10. The board members agree to use the Borda count method to determine the winner.

TABLE 14.10 PREFERENCE TABLE FOR SELECTING A NEW PRINCIPAL				
Number of Votes	**6**	**4**	**2**	**2**
First Choice	A	B	B	A
Second Choice	B	C	D	B
Third Choice	C	D	C	D
Fourth Choice	D	A	A	C

a. Which candidate has a majority of first-place votes?

b. Which candidate is declared the new principal using the Borda count method?

We have seen that an advantage of the Borda count method is that it takes into account all the information about the voters' preferences in the preference table. However, a candidate who has a majority of first-place votes can lose an election with the Borda count method. The other three voting methods that we have discussed—the plurality method, the plurality-with-elimination method, and the pairwise comparison method—never violate the majority criterion. Unfortunately, there are other fairness criteria that are violated by each of these three systems.

2 Use the head-to-head criterion to determine a voting system's fairness.

The Head-to-Head Criterion

Most people would agree that if there is one candidate who is favored by the voters when compared, in turn, to each of the other candidates, then that candidate should win the election. This requirement of a fair and democratic election is called the **head-to-head criterion**.

> **THE HEAD-TO-HEAD CRITERION**
> If a candidate is favored when compared separately—that is, head-to-head—with every other candidate, then that candidate should win the election.

Example 2 shows that the plurality method may violate the head-to-head criterion.

EXAMPLE 2 THE PLURALITY METHOD VIOLATES THE HEAD-TO-HEAD CRITERION

Twenty-two people are asked to taste-test and rank three different brands, A, B, and C, of tuna fish. The results are summarized in the preference table in Table 14.11.

a. Which brand is favored over the other two using a head-to-head comparison?

b. Which brand wins the taste test using the plurality method?

TABLE 14.11 PREFERENCE TABLE FOR THREE BRANDS OF TUNA FISH

Number of Votes	8	6	4	4
First Choice	A	C	C	B
Second Choice	B	B	A	A
Third Choice	C	A	B	C

SOLUTION

a. We begin by comparing brands A and B using Table 14.11. A is favored over B in columns 1 and 3, giving A 8 + 4, or 12, votes. B is favored over A in columns 2 and 4, giving B 6 + 4, or 10, votes. Because A has 12 votes and B has 10 votes, A is favored when compared to B.

Now let's use Table 14.11 to compare brands A and C. A is favored over C in columns 1 and 4, giving A 8 + 4, or 12, votes. C is favored over A in columns 2 and 3, giving C 6 + 4, or 10, votes. Because A has 12 votes and C has 10 votes, A is favored when compared to C.

We see that A is favored over the other two brands using a head-to-head comparison.

b. Using the plurality method, the brand with the most first-place votes is the winner. Look at the row indicating the first choice. A received 8 votes, B received 4 votes, and C received 6 + 4, or 10, votes. Brand C wins the taste test using the plurality method.   ○

In Example 2, although brand A was favored over the other two brands using a head-to-head comparison, the plurality method yielded a different winner, brand C. Thus, in this situation, the plurality method violates the head-to-head criterion.

Is the plurality method the only voting method with the potential to violate the head-to-head criterion? The answer is no. The Borda count method and the plurality-with-elimination method both have the potential to violate the head-to-head criterion. Can this occur with the pairwise comparison method? No. A candidate who defeats each of the other candidates in a head-to-head vote wins every pairwise comparison and thus gets the greatest number of points under this method.

 Seven people are asked to listen to and rate three different pairs of stereo speakers, A, B, and C. The results are summarized in Table 14.12.

a. Which brand is favored over all others using a head-to-head comparison?

b. Which brand wins the listening test using the plurality method?

TABLE 14.12 PREFERENCE TABLE FOR THREE PAIRS OF STEREO SPEAKERS

Number of Votes	3	2	2
First Choice	A	B	C
Second Choice	B	A	B
Third Choice	C	C	A

3 Use the monotonicity criterion to determine a voting system's fairness.

The Monotonicity Criterion

Elections are generally preceded by a campaign and discussions of the candidates' strengths and weaknesses. In some situations, a preliminary election in which votes do not count, called a **straw vote**, is taken as a measure of voters' intentions. Most people would agree that if a candidate wins the straw poll, which we can consider the first election, and then gains additional support without losing any of the original support, then that candidate should win the second election. This requirement for a fair and democratic election is called the **monotonicity criterion**.

> ### THE MONOTONICITY CRITERION
> If a candidate wins an election and, in a reelection, the only changes are changes that favor the candidate, then that candidate should win the reelection.

Example 3 shows that the plurality-with-elimination method may not satisfy the monotonicity criterion.

EXAMPLE 3 THE PLURALITY-WITH-ELIMINATION METHOD VIOLATES THE MONOTONICITY CRITERION

The 58 members of the Student Activity Council are meeting to elect a keynote speaker to launch student involvement week. The choices are Bill Gates (G), Howard Stern (S), or Oprah Winfrey (W). A straw vote is taken and the results are given in Table 14.13. After a lengthy discussion, all but eight students vote in exactly the same way. The eight voters, shown in the last column of Table 14.13, all changed their ballots to make Oprah Winfrey (W) their first choice. The results of the second election are given in Table 14.14. Notice that the first column has increased by 8 votes.

TABLE 14.13 PREFERENCE TABLE FOR THE STRAW VOTE

Number of Votes	20	16	14	8
First Choice	W	S	G	G
Second Choice	G	W	S	W
Third Choice	S	G	W	S

TABLE 14.14 PREFERENCE TABLE FOR THE SECOND ELECTION

Number of Votes	28	16	14
First Choice	W	S	G
Second Choice	G	W	S
Third Choice	S	G	W

These 8 voters changed their ballots to make Oprah Winfrey (W) their first choice.

a. Using the plurality-with-elimination method, which speaker wins the first election?
b. Using the plurality-with-elimination method, which speaker wins the second election?
c. Does this violate the monotonicity criterion?

SOLUTION

a. There are 58 people voting. No speaker receives a majority of votes (30 or more votes) in Table 14.13, the first election (the straw vote). Using the plurality-with-elimination method, because S (Howard Stern) receives the fewest first-place votes, he is eliminated in the first round. The new preference table with S eliminated is shown in Table 14.15 at the top of the next page. Because W (Oprah Winfrey) has received a majority of first-place votes, she is the winner of the straw poll.

b. Now we focus on Table 14.14, the preference table for the second election. No speaker receives a majority of votes (30 or more votes) in this election. Using the plurality-with-elimination method, because G (Bill Gates) receives the fewest first-place votes, he is eliminated in the first round. The new preference table with G eliminated is shown in Table 14.16. Because S (Howard Stern) has received a majority of first-place votes, he is the winner of the second election.

TABLE 14.15 PREFERENCE TABLE FOR THE STRAW VOTE WITH S ELIMINATED				
Number of Votes	20	16	14	8
First Choice	W	W	G	G
Second Choice	G	G	W	W

TABLE 14.16 PREFERENCE TABLE FOR THE SECOND ELECTION WITH G ELIMINATED			
Number of Votes	28	16	14
First Choice	W	S	S
Second Choice	S	W	W

c. Oprah Winfrey (W) won the first election. She then gained additional support with the 8 voters who changed their ballots to make her their first choice. However, she lost the second election. This violates the monotonicity criterion.

Example 3 illustrates the bizarre possibility that you can actually do worse by doing better! Of the four voting methods we have studied, the only one that can violate the monotonicity criterion is the plurality-with-elimination method.

(3) An election with 120 voters and three candidates, A, B, and C, is to be decided using the plurality-with-elimination method. Table 14.17 shows the results of a straw poll. After the straw poll, 12 voters all changed their ballots to make candidate A their first choice. The results of the second election are given in Table 14.18.

TABLE 14.17 PREFERENCE TABLE FOR THE STRAW VOTE				
Number of Votes	42	34	28	16
First Choice	A	C	B	B
Second Choice	B	A	C	A
Third Choice	C	B	A	C

TABLE 14.18 PREFERENCE TABLE FOR THE SECOND ELECTION				
Number of Votes	54	34	28	4
First Choice	A	C	B	B
Second Choice	B	A	C	A
Third Choice	C	B	A	C

a. Using the plurality-with-elimination method, which candidate wins the first election?

b. Using the plurality-with-elimination method, which candidate wins the second election?

c. Does this violate the monotonicity criterion? Explain your answer.

4 Use the irrelevant alternatives criterion to determine a voting system's fairness.

The Irrelevant Alternatives Criterion

A candidate wins an election. Then one or more of the other candidates are removed from the ballot and a recount is done. Most people would agree that the previous winner should still be declared the winner. This requirement for a fair and democratic election is called the **irrelevant alternatives criterion**.

> **THE IRRELEVANT ALTERNATIVES CRITERION**
> If a candidate wins an election and, in a recount, the only changes are that one or more of the other candidates are removed from the ballot, then that candidate should still win the election.

Each of the four voting methods we have discussed may violate the irrelevant alternatives criterion. Example 4 shows that the pairwise comparison method may not satisfy the criterion.

| EXAMPLE 4 | THE PAIRWISE COMPARISON METHOD VIOLATES THE IRRELEVANT ALTERNATIVES CRITERION |

Four candidates, E, F, G, and H, are running for mayor of Bolinas. The election results are shown in Table 14.19.

TABLE 14.19 PREFERENCE TABLE FOR THE MAYOR OF BOLINAS

Number of Votes	160	100	80	20
First Choice	E	G	H	H
Second Choice	F	F	E	E
Third Choice	G	H	G	F
Fourth Choice	H	E	F	G

a. Using the pairwise comparison method, who wins this election?

b. Prior to the announcement of the election results, candidates F and G both withdraw from the running. Using the pairwise comparison method, which candidate is declared mayor of Bolinas with F and G eliminated from the preference table?

c. Does this violate the irrelevant alternatives criterion?

SOLUTION

a. Because there are 4 candidates, $n = 4$ and the number of comparisons we must make is

$$C = \frac{n(n-1)}{2} = \frac{4(4-1)}{2} = \frac{4 \cdot 3}{2} = \frac{12}{2} = 6.$$

The following table shows the results of these 6 comparisons. Use Table 14.19 to verify each of these results.

Comparison	Vote Results	Conclusion
E vs. F	260 voters prefer E to F. 100 voters prefer F to E.	E wins and gets 1 point.
E vs. G	260 voters prefer E to G. 100 voters prefer G to E.	E wins and gets 1 point.
E vs. H	160 voters prefer E to H. 200 voters prefer H to E.	H wins and gets 1 point.
F vs. G	180 voters prefer F to G. 180 voters prefer G to F.	It's a tie. F gets $\frac{1}{2}$ point. G gets $\frac{1}{2}$ point.
F vs. H	260 voters prefer F to H. 100 voters prefer H to F.	F wins and gets 1 point.
G vs. H	260 voters prefer G to H. 100 voters prefer H to G.	G wins and gets 1 point.

Thus, E gets 2 points, F and G each get $1\frac{1}{2}$ points, and H gets 1 point. Therefore, E is the winner when candidates F and G are included.

b. Once F and G both withdraw from the running, only two candidates, E and H, remain. Keep in mind that E was the winning candidate prior to this withdrawl. The new preference table is shown in Table 14.20. Using the pairwise comparison test, there are 2 candidates and the number of comparisons we must make is

$$C = \frac{n(n-1)}{2} = \frac{2(2-1)}{2} = \frac{2 \cdot 1}{2} = 1.$$

The one comparison we must make is E to H. The voice balloons below Table 14.20 show that H wins, defeating E by 200 votes to 160 votes. H gets 1 point, E gets 0 points, and candidate H is the new mayor of Bolinas.

c. The first election count produced E as the winner. Then, even though F and G were not the winning candidates, their removal from the ballots produced H, not E, as the winner. This violates the irrelevant alternatives criterion.

TABLE 14.20 PREFERENCE TABLE FOR THE MAYOR OF BOLINAS WITH F AND G REMOVED

Number of Votes	160	100	80	20
First choice	E	H	H	H
Second choice	H	E	E	E

160 voters prefer E to H.   200 voters prefer H to E.

TABLE 14.21 PREFERENCE TABLE FOR MAYOR

Number of Votes	150	90	90	30
First Choice	A	C	D	D
Second Choice	B	B	A	A
Third Choice	C	D	C	B
Fourth Choice	D	A	B	C

Four candidates, A, B, C, and D, are running for mayor. The election results are shown in Table 14.21.

a. Using the pairwise comparison method, who wins this election?

b. Prior to the announcement of the election results, candidates B and C both withdraw from the running. Using the pairwise comparison method, which candidate is declared mayor with B and C eliminated from the preference table?

c. Does this violate the irrelevant alternatives criterion? Explain your answer.

Table 14.22 summarizes the four fairness criteria we have discussed. Table 14.23 shows which voting methods satisfy the criteria.

TABLE 14.22 SUMMARY OF FAIRNESS CRITERIA

Criterion	Description
Majority Criterion	If a candidate receives a majority of first-place votes in an election, then that candidate should win the election.
Head-to-Head Criterion	If a candidate is favored when compared head-to-head with every other candidate, then that candidate should win the election.
Monotonicity Criterion	If a candidate wins an election and, in a reelection, the only changes are changes that favor the candidate, then that candidate should win the reelection.
Irrelevant Alternatives Criterion	If a candidate wins an election and, in a recount, the only changes are that one or more of the other candidates are removed from the ballot, then that candidate should still win the election.

TABLE 14.23 VOTING METHODS AND WHETHER THEY SATISFY THE FAIRNESS CRITERIA

Fairness Criteria	Voting Method			
	Plurality Method	Borda Count Method	Plurality-with-Elimination Method	Pairwise Comparison Method
Majority Criterion	Always satisfies	May not satisfy	Always satisfies	Always satisfies
Head-to-Head Criterion	May not satisfy	May not satisfy	May not satisfy	Always satisfies
Monotonicity Criterion	Always satisfies	Always satisfies	May not satisfy	Always satisfies
Irrelevant Alternatives Criterion	May not satisfy	May not satisfy	May not satisfy	May not satisfy

E-Voting

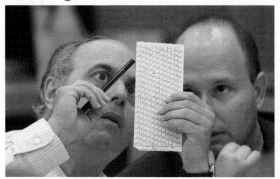

In 2006, electronic voting machines, adopted after the disputed Florida ballot count in the 2000 presidential election, were under legal attack. Lawsuits filed in at least six states argued that the machines were vulnerable to software tampering, did not keep an easily recountable printed record, and could miscount, switch, or not record votes, and even add phantom votes.

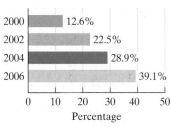

Percentage of U.S. Voters Using Electronic Voting Machines

2000   12.6%
2002   22.5%
2004   28.9%
2006   39.1%

Source: Election Data Services

Kenneth Arrow (1921–). Awarded 1972 Nobel Prize in Economics

5 | Understand Arrow's Impossibility Theorem.

The Search for a Fair Voting System

We have seen that none of the voting methods discussed in this chapter always satisfies each of the fairness criteria. Is there another democratic voting method that does satisfy all four criteria—a perfectly fair voting system? For elections involving more than two candidates, the answer is no. No perfectly fair voting method exists. How do we know? In 1951, economist Kenneth Arrow proved the now famous **Arrow's Impossibility Theorem**: There does not exist, and will never exist, any democratic voting system that satisfies all of the fairness criteria.

> ### ARROW'S IMPOSSIBILITY THEOREM
> It is mathematically impossible for any democratic voting system to satisfy each of the four fairness criteria.

In 1972, Arrow was awarded the Nobel Prize in Economics for his pioneering work. Arrow's discipline is now known as *social-choice theory*, a field that combines mathematics, economics, and political science.

EXERCISE SET 14.2 ●●●●●●

• Practice and Application Exercises

1. Voters in a small town are considering four proposals, A, B, C, and D, for the design of affordable housing. The winning design is to be determined by the Borda count method. The preference table for the election is shown.

   a. Which design has a majority of first-place votes?

   b. Using the Borda count method, which design will be used for the affordable housing?

   c. Is the majority criterion satisfied? Explain your answer.

Number of Votes	300	120	90	60
First Choice	D	C	C	A
Second Choice	A	A	A	D
Third Choice	B	B	D	B
Fourth Choice	C	D	B	C

2. Fifty-three people are asked to taste-test and rank three different brands of yogurt, A, B, and C. The preference table shows the rankings of the 53 voters.

   a. Which brand has a majority of first-place votes?

   b. Suppose that the Borda count method is used to determine the winner. Which brand wins the taste test?

   c. Is the majority criterion satisfied? Explain your answer.

Number of Votes	27	24	2
First Choice	A	B	C
Second Choice	C	C	B
Third Choice	B	A	A

3. MTV's *Real World* is considering three cities for its new season: Amsterdam (A), Rio de Janeiro (R), or Vancouver (V). Programming executives and the show's production

team vote to decide where the new season will be taped. The winning city is to be determined by the plurality method. The preference table for the election is shown.

   a. Which city is favored over all others using a head-to-head comparison?

   b. Which city wins the vote using the plurality method?

   c. Is the head-to-head criterion satisfied? Explain your answer.

Number of Votes	12	9	4	4
First Choice	A	V	V	R
Second Choice	R	R	A	A
Third Choice	V	A	R	V

4. A computer company is considering opening a new branch in Atlanta (A), Boston (B), or Chicago (C). Senior managers vote to decide where the new branch will be located. The winning city is to be determined by the plurality method. The preference table for the election is shown.

   a. Which city is favored over all others using a head-to-head comparison?

   b. Which city wins the vote using the plurality method?

   c. Is the head-to-head criterion satisfied? Explain your answer.

Number of Votes	20	19	5
First Choice	A	B	C
Second Choice	B	C	B
Third Choice	C	A	A

5. A town is voting on an ordinance dealing with smoking in public spaces. The options are (A) permit unrestricted smoking; (B) permit smoking in designated areas only;

and (C) ban all smoking in public places. The winner is to be determined by the Borda count method. The preference table for the election is shown.

a. Which option is favored over all others using a head-to-head comparison?

b. Which option wins the vote using the Borda count method?

c. Is the head-to-head criterion satisfied? Explain your answer.

Number of Votes	120	60	30	30	30
First Choice	A	C	B	C	B
Second Choice	C	B	A	A	C
Third Choice	B	A	C	B	A

6. A town is voting on an ordinance dealing with nudity at its public beaches. The options are (A) make clothing optional at all beaches; (B) permit nudity at designated beaches only; and (C) permit no nudity at public beaches. The winner is to be determined by the Borda count method. The preference table for the election is shown.

a. Which option is favored over all others using a head-to-head comparison?

b. Which option wins the vote using the Borda count method?

c. Is the head-to-head criterion satisfied? Explain your answer.

Number of Votes	200	80	80
First Choice	C	B	A
Second Choice	A	A	B
Third Choice	B	C	C

7. The preference table gives the results of a straw vote among three candidates, A, B, and C.

a. Using the plurality-with-elimination method, which candidate wins the straw vote?

b. In the actual election, the four voters in the last column who voted A, C, B, in that order, change their votes to C, A, B. Using the plurality-with-elimination method, which candidate wins the actual election?

c. Is the monotonicity criterion satisfied? Explain your answer.

Number of Votes	10	8	7	4
First Choice	C	B	A	A
Second Choice	A	C	B	C
Third Choice	B	A	C	B

8. The preference table at the top of the next column gives the results of a straw vote among three candidates, A, B, and C.

a. Using the plurality-with-elimination method, which candidate wins the straw vote?

b. In the actual election, the six voters in the last column who voted A, C, B, in that order, change their votes to

C, A, B. Using the plurality-with-elimination method, which candidate wins the actual election?

c. Is the monotonicity criterion satisfied? Explain your answer.

Number of Votes	14	12	10	6
First Choice	C	B	A	A
Second Choice	A	C	B	C
Third Choice	B	A	C	B

9. Members of the Student Activity Committee at a college are considering three film directors to speak at a campus arts festival: Ron Howard (H), Spike Lee (L), and Steven Spielberg (S). Committee members vote for their preferred speaker. The winner is to be selected by the pairwise comparison method. The preference table for the election is shown.

a. Using the pairwise comparison method, who is selected as the speaker?

b. Prior to the announcement of the speaker, Ron Howard informs the committee that he will not be able to participate due to other commitments. Construct a new preference table for the election with H eliminated. Using the new table and the pairwise comparison method, who is selected as the speaker?

c. Is the irrelevant alternatives criterion satisfied? Explain your answer.

Number of Votes	10	8	5
First Choice	H	L	S
Second Choice	S	S	L
Third Choice	L	H	H

10. Members of the student activity committee at a college are considering three actors to speak at a campus festival on women in the arts: Whoopi Goldberg (G), Julia Roberts (R), and Meryl Streep (S). Committee members vote for their preferred speaker. The winner is to be selected by the pairwise comparison method. The preference table for the election is shown.

a. Using the pairwise comparison method, who is selected as the speaker?

b. Prior to the announcement of the speaker, Meryl Streep informs the committee that she will not be able to participate due to other commitments. Construct a new preference table for the election with S eliminated. Using the new table and the pairwise comparison method, who is selected as the speaker?

c. Is the irrelevant alternatives criterion satisfied? Explain your answer.

Number of Votes	12	8	6
First Choice	S	R	G
Second Choice	G	G	R
Third Choice	R	S	S

In Exercises 11–18, the preference table for an election is given. Use the table to answer the questions that appear below it.

11.

Number of Votes	20	16	10	4
First Choice	D	C	C	A
Second Choice	A	A	B	B
Third Choice	B	B	D	D
Fourth Choice	C	D	A	C

a. Using the Borda count method, who is the winner?

b. Is the majority criterion satisfied? Explain your answer.

12.

Number of Votes	20	15	3	1
First Choice	A	B	C	D
Second Choice	B	C	D	B
Third Choice	C	D	B	C
Fourth Choice	D	A	A	A

a. Using the Borda count method, who is the winner?

b. Is the majority criterion satisfied? Explain your answer.

13.

Number of Votes	24	18	10	8	8	2
First Choice	D	C	A	A	C	B
Second Choice	A	A	D	B	B	C
Third Choice	B	B	B	C	D	A
Fourth Choice	C	D	C	D	A	D

a. Using the plurality-with-elimination method, who is the winner?

b. Is the head-to-head criterion satisfied? Explain your answer.

14.

Number of Votes	18	10	9	7	4	3
First Choice	A	C	C	B	D	D
Second Choice	D	B	D	D	B	C
Third Choice	C	D	B	C	A	A
Fourth Choice	B	A	A	A	C	B

a. Using the plurality-with-elimination method, who is the winner?

b. Is the head-to-head criterion satisfied? Explain your answer.

15.

Number of Votes	14	8	4
First Choice	A	B	D
Second Choice	B	D	A
Third Choice	C	C	C
Fourth Choice	D	A	B

a. Using the Borda count method, who is the winner?

b. Is the majority criterion satisfied? Explain your answer.

c. Is the head-to-head criterion satisfied? Explain your answer.

d. Suppose that candidate C drops out of the race. Using the Borda count method, who among the remaining candidates wins the election? Is the irrelevant alternatives criterion satisfied? Explain your answer.

16.

Number of Votes	14	12	10	6
First Choice	A	B	C	D
Second Choice	B	A	B	C
Third Choice	C	C	A	B
Fourth Choice	D	D	D	A

a. Using the plurality-with-elimination method, who is the winner?

b. The six voters on the right all move candidate A from last place on their preference lists to first place on their preference lists. Construct a new preference table for the election. Using this table and the plurality-with-elimination method, who is the winner? Is the monotonicity criterion satisfied? Explain your answer.

17.

Number of Votes	16	14	12	4	2
First Choice	A	D	D	C	E
Second Choice	B	B	B	A	A
Third Choice	C	A	E	B	D
Fourth Choice	D	C	C	D	B
Fifth Choice	E	E	A	E	C

a. Using the Borda count method, who is the winner?

b. Is the majority criterion satisfied? Explain your answer.

c. Is the head-to-head criterion satisfied? Explain your answer.

18.

Number of Votes	6	6	6	6	2	2	2	2
First Choice	A	B	A	B	C	C	E	B
Second Choice	D	A	C	A	E	B	D	A
Third Choice	E	D	D	C	B	A	A	E
Fourth Choice	C	E	E	D	D	D	C	C
Fifth Choice	B	C	B	E	A	E	B	D

a. Using the pairwise comparison method, who is the winner?

b. Suppose that candidate C drops out, but the winner is still chosen using the pairwise comparison method. Is the irrelevant alternatives criterion satisfied? Explain your answer.

19. The preference table shows the results of an election among three candidates, A, B, and C.

Number of Votes	7	3	2
First Choice	A	B	C
Second Choice	B	C	B
Third Choice	C	A	A

a. Using the plurality method, who is the winner?

b. Is the majority criterion satisfied? Explain your answer.

c. Is the head-to-head criterion satisfied? Explain your answer.

d. The two voters on the right both move candidate A from last place on their preference lists to first place on their preference lists. Construct a new preference table for the election. Using the table and the plurality method, who is the winner?

e. Suppose that candidate C drops out, but the winner is still chosen by the plurality method. Is the irrelevant alternatives criterion satisfied? Explain your answer.

f. Do your results from parts (b) through (e) contradict Arrow's Impossibility Theorem? Explain your answer.

• Writing in Mathematics

20. Describe the majority criterion.

21. Describe the head-to-head criterion.

22. Describe the monotonicity criterion.

23. Describe the irrelevant alternatives criterion.

24. In your own words, state Arrow's Impossibility Theorem.

25. Write a realistic voting problem similar to Exercise 5 or 6 that would be relevant to your college or the area of the country in which you live. Describe the voting method that you will use to determine the winning option. What problems might occur due to flaws in this method?

26. Is it possible to have election results using a particular voting method that satisfy all four fairness criteria? If so, does this contradict Arrow's Impossibility Theorem?

27. William Arrow wrote, "Well, okay, since we can't find perfection, let's at least try to find a method that works well most of the time." Explain what he meant by this.

• Critical Thinking Exercises

28. Why must the pairwise comparison method always satisfy the majority criterion?

In Exercises 29–32, construct a preference table for an election among three candidates, A, B, and C, with the given characteristics. Do not use any of the tables from this section.

29. The Borda count winner violates the majority criterion.

30. The winner by the plurality method violates the head-to-head criterion.

31. The winner by the plurality method violates the irrelevant alternatives criterion.

32. The winner by the plurality-with-elimination method violates the monotonicity criterion.

• Group Exercise

33. Citizen-initiated ballot measures often present voters with controversial issues over which they do not think alike. Here's one your author would like to initiate:

> Please rank each of the following options regarding permitting dogs on national park trails.

A. Unleashed dogs accompanied by their caregivers should be permitted on designated national park trails.

B. Leashed dogs accompanied by their caregivers should be permitted on designated national park trails.

C. No dogs should be permitted on any national park trails.

Your author was not happy with the fact that he could not take his dog running with him on the park trails at Point Reyes National Seashore. Of course, that is his issue. For this project, group members should write a ballot measure, perhaps controversial, like the sample above, but dealing with an issue of relevance to your campus and community. Rather than holding an election, use a random sample of students on your campus, administer the ballot, and have them rank their choices.

a. Use each of the four voting methods to determine the winning option for your ballot measure.

b. Check to see if any of the four fairness criteria are violated.

SECTION 14.3 • APPORTIONMENT METHODS

The Signing of the Constitution

The Senate of the United States shall be composed of two Senators from each state . . .

Article I. Section 3. Constitution of the United States

Representatives . . . shall be apportioned among the several states . . . according to their respective numbers . . .

Article I. Section 2. Constitution of the United States

It is the summer of 1787. Delegates from the 13 states are meeting in Philadelphia to draft a constitution for a new nation. The most heated debate concerns the makeup of the new legislature.

The smaller states, led by New Jersey, insist that all states have the same number of representatives. The larger states, led by Virginia, want some form of proportional representation based on population. The delegates compromise on this issue by creating a Senate, in which each state has two senators, and a House of Representatives, in which each state has a number of representatives based on its population.

According to the Constitution of the United States, "Representatives ... shall be apportioned among the several states ... according to their respective numbers...." But how are these calculations to be done, and what sorts of problems can arise? In this section, you will learn to divide, on an equitable basis, those things that are not individually divisible. By doing this, you will get to look at a unique role that mathematics played in United States history.

1 | Find standard divisors and standard quotas.

Standard Divisors and Standard Quotas

Our discussion in the first part of this section deals with the following simple, but important example: The Republic of Margaritaville is composed of four states, A, B, C, and D. According to the country's constitution, the congress will have 30 seats, divided among the four states according to their respective populations. Table 14.24 shows each state's population.

TABLE 14.24 POPULATION OF MARGARITAVILLE BY STATE					
State	A	B	C	D	Total
Population (in thousands)	275	383	465	767	1890

Before determining a method to allocate the 30 seats in a fair manner, we introduce two important definitions. The first quantity we define is called the *standard divisor*.

THE STANDARD DIVISOR

The **standard divisor** is found by dividing the total population under consideration by the number of items to be allocated.

$$\text{Standard divisor} = \frac{\text{total population}}{\text{number of allocated items}}$$

For the population of Margaritaville in Table 14.24, the standard divisor is found as follows:

$$\text{Standard divisor} = \frac{\text{total population}}{\text{number of allocated items}} = \frac{1890}{30} = 63.$$

> The congress will have 30 seats.

In situations dealing with allocating congressional seats to states based on their populations, the standard divisor gives the number of people per seat in congress on a national basis. Thus, in Margaritaville, there are 63 thousand people for each seat in congress.

The second quantity we define is called the *standard quota*.

THE STANDARD QUOTA

The **standard quota** for a particular group is found by dividing that group's population by the standard divisor.

$$\text{Standard quota} = \frac{\text{population of a particular group}}{\text{standard divisor}}$$

In computing standard divisors and standard quotas, we will round to the nearest hundredth—that is, to two decimal places.

EXAMPLE 1   FINDING STANDARD QUOTAS

Find the standard quotas for states A, B, C, and D in Margaritaville and complete Table 14.25.

TABLE 14.25 POPULATION OF MARGARITAVILLE BY STATE

State	A	B	C	D	Total
Population	275	383	465	767	1890
Standard Quota					

SOLUTION The standard quotas are obtained by dividing each state's population by the standard divisor. We previously computed the standard divisor and found it to be 63. Thus, we use 63 in the denominator for each of the four computations for the standard quota.

$$\text{Standard quota for state A} = \frac{\text{population of state A}}{\text{standard divisor}} = \frac{275}{63} \approx 4.37$$

$$\text{Standard quota for state B} = \frac{\text{population of state B}}{\text{standard divisor}} = \frac{383}{63} \approx 6.08$$

$$\text{Standard quota for state C} = \frac{\text{population of state C}}{\text{standard divisor}} = \frac{465}{63} \approx 7.38$$

$$\text{Standard quota for state D} = \frac{\text{population of state D}}{\text{standard divisor}} = \frac{767}{63} \approx 12.17$$

Table 14.26 shows the standard quotas for each state in the Republic of Margaritaville.

TABLE 14.26 STANDARD QUOTAS FOR EACH STATE IN MARGARITAVILLE

State	A	B	C	D	Total
Population	275	383	465	767	1890
Standard Quota	4.37	6.08	7.38	12.17	30

Notice that the sum of all the standard quotas is 30, the total number of seats in the congress.

CHECK POINT 1 The Republic of Amador is composed of five states, A, B, C, D, and E. According to the country's constitution, the congress will have 200 seats, divided among the five states according to their respective populations. Table 14.27 shows each state's population.

TABLE 14.27 POPULATION OF AMADOR BY STATE

State	A	B	C	D	E	Total
Population (in thousands)	1112	1118	1320	1515	4935	10,000
Standard Quota						

a. Find the standard divisor.

b. Find the standard quota for each state and complete Table 14.27.

2 | Understand the apportionment problem.

The Apportionment Problem

The standard quotas in Table 14.26 represent each state's exact fair share of the 30 seats for the congress of Margaritaville. However, what do we mean by saying that state A has 4.37 seats in congress? Seats have to be given out in whole numbers. The **apportionment problem** is to determine a method for rounding standard quotas into whole numbers so that the sum of the numbers is the total number of allocated items.

Can we possibly round standard quotas down to the nearest whole number or up to the nearest whole number and solve the apportionment problem? The **lower quota** is the standard quota rounded down to the nearest whole number. The **upper quota** is the standard quota rounded up to the nearest whole number. Table 14.28 shows the lower and upper quotas.

TABLE 14.28 STANDARD QUOTAS, LOWER QUOTAS, AND UPPER QUOTAS FOR EACH STATE IN MARGARITAVILLE

State	A	B	C	D	Total
Population	275	383	465	767	1890
Standard quota	4.37	6.08	7.38	12.17	30
Lower quota	4	6	7	12	29
Upper quota	5	7	8	13	33

These totals should be 30 because Margaritaville has 30 seats in congress.

3 | Use Hamilton's method.

BLITZER BONUS

Alexander Hamilton (1757–1804)

Alexander Hamilton was the nation's first Secretary of the Treasury in George Washington's administration. Hamilton and Thomas Jefferson were bitter political adversaries. In 1804, Hamilton was killed in a duel with Aaron Burr, who served as vice president under Jefferson.

The voice balloon shows that by rounding to lower or upper quotas, we have not solved the apportionment problem. We are giving out either 29 or 33 seats in congress. With 29 seats, where will the extra seat go? With 33 seats, where are those three extra seats going to come from?

We now discuss four different **apportionment methods**—that is, methods for solving the apportionment problem. The methods are called *Hamilton's method*, *Jefferson's method*, *Adams's method*, and *Webster's method*.

Hamilton's Method

Hamilton's method of apportionment proceeds in three steps.

> **HAMILTON'S METHOD**
>
> **1.** Calculate each group's standard quota.
> **2.** Round each standard quota down to the nearest whole number, thereby finding the lower quota. Initially, give to each group its lower quota.
> **3.** Give the surplus items, one at a time, to the groups with the largest decimal parts until there are no more surplus items.

For example, consider the lower quotas in the Margaritaville example. We initially give each state its lower quota, shown in Table 14.29. Because there are 30 seats in congress, can you see that there is one surplus seat?

TABLE 14.29 STANDARD QUOTAS, AND LOWER QUOTAS, FOR EACH STATE IN MARGARITAVILLE

State	A	B	C	D	Total
Population	275	383	465	767	1890
Standard quota	4.37	6.08	7.38	12.17	30
Lower quota	4	6	7	12	29

> There are 30 seats in congress. Who will get the extra seat?

The surplus seat goes to the state with the greatest decimal part. The greatest decimal part is 0.38, corresponding to state C. Thus, state C receives the additional seat, and is assigned 8 seats in congress.

Table 14.30 summarizes the congressional seat assignments for the states.

TABLE 14.30 SOLVING MARGARITAVILLE'S APPORTIONMENT PROBLEM: HAMILTON'S METHOD

State	A	B	C	D	Total
Lower Quota	4	6	7	12	29
Hamilton's Apportionment	4	6	8	12	30

EXAMPLE 2   USING HAMILTON'S METHOD

A rapid transit service operates 130 buses along six routes, A, B, C, D, E, and F. The number of buses assigned to each route is based on the average number of daily passengers per route, given in Table 14.31. Use Hamilton's method to apportion the buses.

TABLE 14.31

Route	A	B	C	D	E	F	Total
Average Number of Passengers	4360	5130	7080	10,245	15,535	22,650	65,000

SOLUTION Before applying Hamilton's method, we must compute the standard divisor.

$$\text{Standard divisor} = \frac{\text{total population}}{\text{number of allocated items}}$$

$$= \frac{\text{total number of passengers}}{\text{number of buses}} = \frac{65,000}{130} = 500$$

The standard divisor, 500, represents the average number of passengers per bus per day. Using this value, Table 14.32 shows the three steps in Hamilton's method.

TABLE 14.32 APPORTIONMENT OF BUSES USING HAMILTON'S METHOD

Route	Passengers	Standard Quota	Lower Quota	Decimal Part	Surplus Buses	Final Apportionment
A	4360	8.72	8	0.72 *largest*	1	9
B	5130	10.26	10	0.26		10
C	7080	14.16	14	0.16		14
D	10,245	20.49	20 *next largest*	0.49	1	21
E	15,535	31.07	31	0.07		31
F	22,650	45.30	45	0.30		45
Total	65,000	130	128			130

Step 1 Calculate each standard quota:
standard quota
$= \dfrac{\text{population of a group}}{\text{standard divisor}}$
$= \dfrac{\text{number of passengers}}{500}$

Step 2 Round down and find each lower quota. The sum, 128, indicates we must assign two extra buses.

Step 3 Give the two surplus buses, one at a time, to the routes with the largest decimal parts.

The apportionment of buses, shown in the final column of Table 14.32, is computed by giving each route its lower quota of buses plus any surplus buses.

 Refer to Check Point 1 on page 798. Use Hamilton's method to apportion the 200 congressional seats.

4 | Understand the quota rule.

Have you noticed that every apportionment in Hamilton's method is either the lower quota or the upper quota? This is an important criterion for fairness, called the **quota rule**.

> **THE QUOTA RULE**
> A group's apportionment should be either its upper quota or its lower quota. An apportionment method that guarantees that this will always occur is said to **satisfy the quota rule**.

5 | Use Jefferson's method.

Jefferson's Method

Congress approved Hamilton's method as the apportionment method to be used following the 1790 census. However, the method was vetoed by President Washington. The veto was sustained, and a method proposed by Thomas Jefferson was adopted. (In the 1850s, Congress resurrected Hamilton's method; it was used until 1900.)

What could possibly concern President Washington about Hamilton's method? Perhaps it was the fact that in allocating congressional seats, some states would be chosen over others for preferential treatment. These would be the states with the greatest fractional parts in their standard quotas. Ideally, we should be able to

Thomas Jefferson (1743-1826)

"Science is my passion, politics my duty."

Thomas Jefferson, third president of the United States (1801–1809), was the author of the Declaration of Independence at age 33 and Secretary of State under Washington. Although he suffered most of his life from migraine headaches, Jefferson was an outstanding politician, writer, philosopher, and inventor. Known as "long Tom," the $6'2\frac{1}{2}''$ Jefferson often scandalized visitors with his informal attire, a worn brown coat and carpet slippers. Under his presidency, the area of the country doubled through the Louisiana Purchase in 1803.

replace the standard divisor by some other divisor, called the *modified divisor*. After dividing every state's population by this divisor and then rounding the modified quotas down, we should be left with no surplus items. Thus, no group (or state) could receive preferential treatment.

JEFFERSON'S METHOD

1. Find a **modified divisor**, d, such that when each group's **modified quota** (group's population divided by d) is rounded down to the nearest whole number, the sum of the whole numbers for all the groups is the number of items to be apportioned. The modified quotients that are rounded down are called **modified lower quotas**.

2. Apportion to each group its modified lower quota.

How do we find the modified divisor, d, that makes Jefferson's method work? Before turning to this issue, let's illustrate the method using calculations based on a given value of the modified divisor.

EXAMPLE 3   USING JEFFERSON'S METHOD

As in Example 2, a rapid transit service operates 130 buses along six routes, A, B, C, D, E, and F. The number of buses assigned to each route is based on the average number of daily passengers per route, repeated in Table 14.31. Use Jefferson's method with $d = 486$ to apportion the buses.

TABLE 14.31 (REPEATED)

Route	A	B	C	D	E	F	Total
Average Number of Passengers	4360	5130	7080	10,245	15,535	22,650	65,000

SOLUTION Using $d = 486$, Table 14.33 illustrates Jefferson's method.

TABLE 14.33 APPORTIONMENT OF BUSES USING JEFFERSON'S METHOD WITH $d = 486$

Route	Passengers	Modified Quota	Modified Lower Quota	Final Apportionment
A	4360	8.97	8	8
B	5130	10.56	10	10
C	7080	14.57	14	14
D	10,245	21.08	21	21
E	15,535	31.97	31	31
F	22,650	46.60	46	46
Total	65,000		130	130

Modified quota $= \dfrac{\text{number of passengers}}{486}$

Round each modified quota down to the nearest whole number. The sum, 130, indicates there are no surplus buses to assign.

The apportionment of buses, shown in the final column of Table 14.33, is determined by giving each route a number of buses equal to its modified lower quota.

Refer to Check Point 1 on page 798. Use Jefferson's method with $d = 49.3$ to apportion the 200 congressional seats.

Unfortunately, there is no formula for the modified divisor, d. Furthermore, there is usually more than one modified divisor that will make Jefferson's method work. You can find one of these values using trial and error. Begin with the fact that **in Jefferson's method, a modified divisor is slightly less than the standard divisor.** Pick a number d that you think might work. Carry out the calculations required by Jefferson's method: Divide each group's population by d, round down to the nearest whole number, and find the sum of the whole numbers. With luck, the sum is the number of items to be apportioned. Otherwise, change the value of d (make it greater if the sum is too high and less if the sum is too low) and try again. In most cases, with two or three guesses, you will find a modified divisor, d, that works.

Jefferson's method was adopted in 1791. In the apportionment of 1832, New York, with a standard quota of 38.59, received 40 seats in the House of Representatives. Because 40 is neither the upper quota nor the lower quota of 38.59, it was discovered that Jefferson's method violated the quota rule. The apportionment of 1832 was the last time the House of Representatives was apportioned using Jefferson's method.

6 | Use Adams's method.

Adams's Method

At the same time that Jefferson's method was found to be problematic because of its violation of the quota rule, John Quincy Adams proposed a method that is the mirror image of it. Rather than using modified lower quotas as in Jefferson's method, Adams suggested using modified upper quotas.

In Example 4, we will use trial and error to find a modified divisor, d, that satisfies Adams's method. **When using Adams's method, begin with a modified divisor that is slightly greater than the standard divisor.**

ADAMS'S METHOD

1. Find a **modified divisor**, d, such that when each group's **modified quota** (group's population divided by d) is rounded up to the nearest whole number, the sum of the whole numbers for all the groups is the number of items to be apportioned. The modified quotas that are rounded up are called **modified upper quotas**.
2. Apportion to each group its modified upper quota.

EXAMPLE 4   USING ADAMS'S METHOD

Consider, again, the rapid transit service that operates 130 buses along six routes, A, B, C, D, E, and F. The number of buses assigned to each route is based on the average number of daily passengers per route, repeated in Table 14.31. Use Adams's method to apportion the buses.

TABLE 14.31 (REPEATED)

Route	A	B	C	D	E	F	Total
Average Number of Passengers	4360	5130	7080	10,245	15,535	22,650	65,000

SOLUTION In Example 2, we found that the standard divisor is 500. We begin by guessing at a possible modified divisor, d, that we hope will work. This value of d must be greater than 500 so that the modified quotas will be less than the standard quotas.

When rounded up, the sum of these whole numbers should be 130, the number of buses to be apportioned. Perhaps a good guess might be $d = 512$. Table 14.34 shows the calculations using Adams's method with $d = 512$.

TABLE 14.34 CALCULATIONS USING ADAMS'S METHOD WITH $d = 512$

Route	Passengers	Modified Quota	Modified Upper Quota
A	4360	8.52	9
B	5130	10.02	11
C	7080	13.83	14
D	10,245	20.01	21
E	15,535	30.34	31
F	22,650	44.24	45
Total	65,000		131

Modified quota
$= \dfrac{\text{number of passengers}}{512}$

The sum should be 130, not 131.

Because the sum of modified upper quotas is too high, we need to lower the modified quotas a bit. We tried a higher divisor, $d = 513$, and obtained 129 for the sum of modified upper quotas. Because this sum is too low, we increase the modified divisor from $d = 512$ a bit and try $d = 512.7$. Table 14.35 shows the calculations required by Adams's method using this value.

TABLE 14.35 CALCULATIONS USING ADAMS'S METHOD WITH $d = 512.7$

Route	Passengers	Modified Quota	Modified Upper Quota	Final Apportionment
A	4360	8.50	9	9
B	5130	10.01	11	11
C	7080	13.81	14	14
D	10,245	19.98	20	20
E	15,535	30.30	31	31
F	22,650	44.18	45	45
Total	65,000		130	130

Modified quota
$= \dfrac{\text{number of passengers}}{512.7}$

This sum is precisely the number of buses to be apportioned.

The apportionment of buses, shown in the final column of Table 14.35, is determined by giving each route a number of buses equal to its modified upper quota.

CHECK POINT 4 Refer to Check Point 1 on page 798. Use Adams's method to apportion the 200 congressional seats. In guessing at a value for d, begin with $d = 50.5$. If necessary, modify this value as we did in Example 4.

Recall that by Jefferson's method, a delighted New York, with a standard quota of 38.59, received 40 seats. This exceeds 39, the upper quota, and is called an

upper-quota violation. Adams thought he could avoid this violation, which he did. Unfortunately, his method can result in an assignment of seats in the House of Representatives that is below a state's lower quota. This flaw in Adams's method is called a **lower-quota violation**. With Adams's method, all violations of the quota rule are of this kind.

7 | Use Webster's method.

Webster's Method

In 1832, Daniel Webster suggested an apportionment method that sounds like a compromise between Jefferson's method, where modified quotas are rounded down, and Adams's method, where modified quotas are rounded up. Let's round the modified quotas in the usual way that we round decimals: If the fractional part is less than 0.5, round down to the nearest whole number. If the fractional part is greater than or equal to 0.5, round up to the nearest whole number. Webster believed that this was the only fair way to round numbers.

> **WEBSTER'S METHOD**
>
> 1. Find a **modified divisor**, d, such that when each group's **modified quota** (group's population divided by d) is rounded to the nearest whole number, the sum of the whole numbers for all the groups is the number of items to be apportioned. The modified quotas that are rounded are called **modified rounded quotas**.
>
> 2. Apportion to each group its modified rounded quota.

In many ways, Webster's method works in a manner that is similar to Jefferson's and Adams's methods. However, **when using Webster's method, the modified divisor, d, can be less than, greater than, or equal to the standard divisor**. Thus, it may take a bit longer to find a modified divisor that satisfies Webster's method.

EXAMPLE 5   USING WEBSTER'S METHOD

We return, for the last time, to the rapid transit service that operates 130 buses along six routes, A, B, C, D, E, and F. The number of buses assigned to each route is based on the average number of daily passengers per route, repeated in Table 14.31. Use Webster's method to apportion the buses.

TABLE 14.31 (REPEATED)

Route	A	B	C	D	E	F	Total
Average Number of Passengers	4360	5130	7080	10,245	15,535	22,650	65,000

SOLUTION From Example 2, we know that the standard divisor is 500. We begin by trying $d = 502$, using a modified divisor greater than the standard divisor. After rounding the modified quotients to the nearest integer and taking the resulting sum, we obtain 129, rather than the desired 130. Because 129 is too low, this suggests that the modified divisor is too large, so we should guess at a modified divisor less than 500, the standard divisor. We try $d = 498$. Table 14.36 at the top of the next page shows the calculations required by Webster's method using this value.

TABLE 14.36 CALCULATIONS USING WEBSTER'S METHOD WITH $d = 498$

Route	Passengers	Modified Quota	Modified Rounded Quotas	Find Apportionment
A	4360	8.76	9	9
B	5130	10.30	10	10
C	7080	14.22	14	14
D	10,245	20.57	21	21
E	15,535	31.19	31	31
F	22,650	45.48	45	45
Total	65,000		130	130

Modified quota $= \dfrac{\text{number of passengers}}{498}$

This sum is precisely the number of buses to be apportioned.

The apportionment of buses, shown in the final column of Table 14.36, is determined by giving each route a number of buses equal to its modified rounded quota.

CHECK POINT **5** Refer to Check Point 1 on page 798. Use Webster's method with $d = 49.8$ to apportion the 200 congressional seats.

In Examples 2–5, we apportioned the buses using four different methods. Although the final apportionment using Hamilton's method is the same as the one obtained using Webster's method, this is not always the case. Like voting methods, different apportionment methods applied to the same situation can produce different results.

Although Webster's method can violate the quota rule, such violations are rare. Many experts consider Webster's method the best overall apportionment method available. The method currently used to apportion the U.S. House of Representatives is known as the *Huntington-Hill method*. (See Exercise 46.) However, some experts believe that in our lifetimes Webster's method will make a comeback and replace Huntington-Hill.

Table 14.37 summarizes the four apportionment methods discussed in this section.

Montana vs. the U.S. Department of Commerce

In 1992, Montana challenged the constitutionality of the apportionment method being used. Based on the 1990 census, Montana was concerned that it would have to give up one of its two seats in the House of Representatives to the state of Washington. The Supreme Court ruled against Montana and upheld the Huntington-Hill method as constitutional.

TABLE 14.37 SUMMARY OF APPORTIONMENT METHODS

Method	Divisor	Apportionment
Hamilton's	Standard divisor $= \dfrac{\text{total population}}{\text{number of allocated items}}$	Round each standard quota down to the nearest whole number. Initially give each group its lower quota. Give surplus items, one at a time, to the groups with the largest decimal parts.
Jefferson's	The modified divisor is less than the standard divisor.	Round each group's modified quota down to the nearest whole number. Apportion to each group its modified lower quota.
Adams's	The modified divisor is greater than the standard divisor.	Round each group's modified quota up to the nearest whole number. Apportion to each group its modified upper quota.
Webster's	The modified divisor is less than, greater than, or equal to, the standard divisor.	Round each group's modified quota to the nearest whole number. Apportion to each group its modified rounded quota.

BLITZER BONUS

The Electoral College

The framers of the Constitution believed that the opinion of the majority sometimes had to be tempered by the wisdom of elected representatives. Consequently, the President and the Vice President are the only elected U.S. officials who are not chosen by a direct vote of the people, but rather by the Electoral College.

Here is an outline of how the Electoral College works.

- There are a total of 538 electoral votes.

- The votes are divided by the states and among the District of Columbia. The number of electoral votes for each state is equal to its total number of Congressional senators and representatives.

- The candidate who wins a majority of popular votes in a given state earns all the votes of that state's Electoral College members.

- The candidate who wins the majority, not merely a plurality, of the electoral votes is declared the winner. A presidential candidate needs at least 270 electoral votes to win. If no candidate wins, then the election is turned over to the House of Representatives, who vote for one of the top three contenders.

Electoral Votes for President

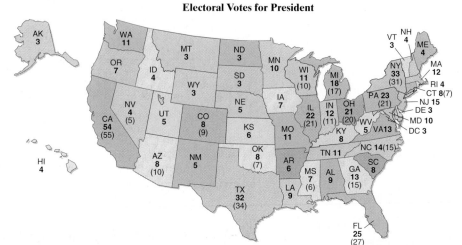

Figures in boldface, based on the 1990 census, were used in the 1992, 1996, and 2000 elections. Some of the electoral votes for the 2004 election, based on the 2000 census, were different. These are given in parentheses.

Source: Federal Election Commission

As we know from the 2000 election, it is possible for a presidential candidate who has not won the popular vote to win the election. If a candidate wins the popular vote in large states (ones with lots of electoral votes) by only a slim margin and loses the popular vote in smaller states by a wide margin, it is possible that the popular vote winner will actually lose the election. Is George W. Bush the only U.S. president who lost the popular vote but won the election? The answer is no. In 1888, Benjamin Harrison won the popular vote over Grover Cleveland, but Cleveland won the electoral vote and became president. Also, in our next section opener, we describe how the "flawed" electoral college system led to an election debacle in 1876 reminiscent of the bitter divisiveness that tainted the 2000 election.

EXERCISE SET 14.3 ●●●●●●

• Practice and Application Exercises

Throughout this exercise set, in computing standard divisors, standard quotas, and modified quotas, round to the nearest hundredth when necessary.

A small country is comprised of four states, A, B, C, and D. The population of each state, in thousands, is given in the following table. Use this information to solve Exercises 1–2.

State	A	B	C	D	Total
Population (in thousands)	138	266	534	662	1600

1. According to the country's constitution, the congress will have 80 seats, divided among the four states according to their respective populations.
   a. Find the standard divisor, in thousands. How many people are there for each seat in congress?
   b. Find each state's standard quota.
   c. Find each state's lower quota and upper quota.

2. According to the country's constitution, the congress will have 200 seats, divided among the four states according to their respective populations.
   a. Find the standard divisor, in thousands. How many people are there for each seat in congress?
   b. Find each state's standard quota.
   c. Find each state's lower quota and upper quota.

3. Use Hamilton's method to find each state's apportionment of congressional seats in Exercise 1.

4. Use Hamilton's method to find each state's apportionment of congressional seats in Exercise 2.

5. A university is composed of five schools. The enrollment in each school is given in the following table.

School	Humanities	Social Science	Engineering	Business	Education
Enrollment	1050	1410	1830	2540	3580

There are 300 new computers to be apportioned among the five schools according to their respective enrollments. Use Hamilton's method to find each school's apportionment of computers.

6. A university is composed of five schools. The enrollment in each school is given in the following table.

School	Liberal Arts	Education	Business	Engineering	Sciences
Enrollment	1180	1290	2140	2930	3320

There are 300 new computers to be apportioned among the five schools according to their respective enrollments. Use Hamilton's method to find each school's apportionment of computers.

7. A small country is composed of five states, A, B, C, D, and E. The population of each state is given in the following table. Congress will have 57 seats, divided among the five states according to their respective populations. Use Jefferson's method with $d = 32,920$ to apportion the 57 congressional seats.

State	A	B	C	D	E
Population	126,316	196,492	425,264	526,664	725,264

8. A small country is comprised of four states, A, B, C, and D. The population of each state, in thousands, is given in the following table. Congress will have 400 seats, divided among the four states according to their respective populations. Use Jefferson's method with $d = 7.82$ to apportion the 400 congressional seats.

State	A	B	C	D
Population (in thousands)	424	664	892	1162

9. An HMO has 150 doctors to be apportioned among four clinics. The HMO decides to apportion the doctors based on the average weekly patient load for each clinic, given in the following table. Use Jefferson's method to apportion the 150 doctors. (*Hint*: Find the standard divisor. A modified divisor that is less than this standard divisor will work.)

Clinic	A	B	C	D
Average Weekly Patient Load	1714	5460	2440	5386

10. An HMO has 70 doctors to be apportioned among six clinics. The HMO decides to apportion the doctors based on the average weekly patient load for each clinic, given in the following table. Use Jefferson's method to apportion the 70 doctors. (*Hint*: A modified divisor between 39 and 40 will work.)

Clinic	A	B	C	D	E	F
Average Weekly Patient Load	316	598	396	692	426	486

11. The police department in a large city has 180 new officers to be apportioned among six high-crime precincts. Crimes by precinct are shown in the following table. Use Adams's method with $d = 16$ to apportion the new officers among the precincts.

Precinct	A	B	C	D	E	F
Crimes	446	526	835	227	338	456

12. Four people pool their money to buy 60 shares of stock. The amount that each person contributes is shown in the following table. Use Adams's method with $d = 108$ to apportion the shares of stock.

Person	A	B	C	D
Contribution	$2013	$187	$290	$3862

13. Three people pool their money to buy 30 shares of stock. The amount that each person contributes is shown in the following table. Use Adams's method to apportion the shares of stock. (*Hint*: Find the standard divisor. A modified divisor that is greater than this standard divisor will work.)

Person	A	B	C
Amount	$795	$705	$525

14. Refer to Exercise 9. Use Adams's method to apportion the 150 doctors. (*Hint*: Find the standard divisor. A modified divisor that is greater than this standard divisor will work.)

15. Twenty sections of bilingual math courses, taught in both English and Spanish, are to be offered in introductory algebra, intermediate algebra, and liberal arts math. The preregistration figures for the number of students planning to enroll in these bilingual sections are given in the following table. Use Webster's method with $d = 29.6$ to determine how many bilingual sections of each course should be offered.

Course	Introductory Algebra	Intermediate Algebra	Liberal Arts Math
Enrollment	130	282	188

16. Refer to the populations of the four states in Exercise 8. Unlike Exercise 8, Congress now has 314 seats to divide among the states according to their respective populations. Use Webster's method with $d = 9.98$ to apportion the 314 congressional seats.

17. A rapid transit service operates 200 buses along five routes, A, B, C, D, and E. The number of buses assigned to each route is based on the average number of daily passengers per route, given in the following table. Use Webster's method to apportion the buses. (*Hint*: A modified divisor between 55 and 56 will work.)

Route	A	B	C	D	E
Average Number of Passengers	1087	1323	1592	1596	5462

18. Refer to Exercise 11. Use Webster's method to apportion the 180 new officers among the precincts. (*Hint:* A modified divisor between 15 and 16 will work.)

A hospital has a nursing staff of 250 nurses working in four shifts: A (7:00 A.M. to 1:00 P.M.), B (1:00 P.M. to 7:00 P.M.), C (7:00 P.M. to 1:00 A.M.), and D (1:00 A.M. to 7:00 A.M.). The number of nurses apportioned to each shift is based on the average number of patients per shift, given in the following table. Use this information to solve Exercises 19–22.

Shift	A	B	C	D
Average Number of Patients	453	650	547	350

19. Use Hamilton's method to apportion the 250 nurses among the shifts at the hospital.

20. Use Jefferson's method to apportion the 250 nurses among the shifts in the hospital. (*Hint:* A modified divisor that works should be less than the standard divisor in Exercise 19.)

21. Use Adams's method to apportion the 250 nurses among the shifts in the hospital. (*Hint:* A modified divisor that works should be greater than the standard divisor in Exercise 19.)

22. Use Webster's method to apportion the 250 nurses among the shifts in the hospital. (*Hint:* A modified divisor that works is equal to the standard divisor that you found in Exercise 19.)

The table shows the 1790 United States census. In 1793, at the direction of President George Washington, 105 seats in the House of Representatives were to be divided among the 15 states according to their 1790 populations. Use this information to solve Exercises 23–26.

1790 United States Census			
Connecticut	236,841	New York	331,589
Delaware	55,540	North Carolina	353,523
Georgia	70,835	Pennsylvania	432,879
Kentucky	68,705	Rhode Island	68,446
Maryland	278,514	South Carolina	206,236
Massachusetts	475,327	Vermont	85,533
New Hampshire	141,822	Virginia	630,560
New Jersey	179,570		

23. Use Hamilton's method to find each state's apportionment of congressional seats.

24. Use Jefferson's method with $d = 33,000$ to find each state's apportionment of congressional seats.

25. Use Adams's method with $d = 36,100$ to find each state's apportionment of congressional seats.

26. Use Webster's method with $d = 34,500$ to find each state's apportionment of congressional seats.

• Writing in Mathematics

27. Describe how to find a standard divisor.

28. Describe how to determine a standard quota for a particular group.

29. How is the lower quota found from a standard quota?

30. How is the upper quota found from a standard quota?

31. Describe the apportionment problem.

32. In your own words, describe Hamilton's method of apportionment.

33. What is the quota rule?

34. Explain why Hamilton's method satisfies the quota rule.

35. Describe the difference between how modified quotas are rounded using Jefferson's method and Adams's method.

36. Suppose that you guess at a modified divisor, d, using Jefferson's method. How do you determine if your guess satisfies the method?

37. Describe the difference between the modified divisor, d, in terms of the standard divisor using Jefferson's method and Adams's method.

38. In allocating congressional seats, how does Hamilton's method choose some states over others for preferential treatment? Explain how this is avoided in Jefferson's and Adams's methods.

39. How are modified quotas rounded using Webster's method?

40. Why might it take longer to guess at a modified divisor that works using Webster's method than using Jefferson's method or Adams's method?

41. In this exercise set, we have used apportionment methods to divide congressional seats, assign computers to schools, assign doctors to clinics, divide police officers among precincts, divide shares of stock, assign sections of bilingual math, assign buses to city routes, and assign nurses to hospital shifts. Describe another situation that requires the use of apportionment methods.

• Critical Thinking Exercises

42. In 1880, there were 300 congressional seats in the U.S. House of Representatives. The population of Alabama was 1,262,505, and its standard quota was 7.671. Find, to the nearest whole number, the U.S. population in 1880.

A small country is composed of three states, A, B, and C. The country's constitution specifies that congressional seats will be divided among the three states according to their respective populations. In Exercises 43–45, write an apportionment problem satisfying the given criterion.

43. Hamilton's method and Jefferson's method result in the same apportionment.

44. Hamilton's method and Adams's method result in the same apportionment.

45. Hamilton's method and Webster's method result in the same apportionment.

• Group Exercises

46. The method currently used to apportion the U.S. House of Representatives is known as the **Huntington-Hill method**, and more commonly as the **method of equal proportions**. Research and present a group report on this method. Include the history of how the method came into use and describe how the method works.

47. Research and present a group report on a brief history of apportionment in the United States.

SECTION 14.4 • FLAWS OF APPORTIONMENT METHODS

Posters from the controversial election of 1876. The candidates were Rutherford B. Hayes (Republican) and Samuel J. Tilden (Democrat).

The very mention of Florida outraged the Democrats. Florida's contested electoral votes helped elect a Republican president who had lost the popular vote.

No, we're not referring to the controversial election of 2000, but rather the 1876 election of Republican Rutherford B. Hayes over Democrat Samuel J. Tilden. Tilden won the popular vote with 4,300,590 votes, whereas Hayes received 4,036,298 votes. In 1872, a power grab among the states resulted in an illegal apportionment of the House of Representatives that was not based on Hamilton's method. Two seats that would have gone to New York and Illinois under Hamilton's method instead went to Florida and New Hampshire. Four years later, Rutherford B. Hayes became President of the United States based on this unconstitutional apportionment, winning the electoral vote by a margin of one vote, 185 to 184. If Hamilton's method had been used in the congressional apportionment, New York would have had one more vote, taking the Hayes votes away from Florida or New Hampshire. In short, if the 1872 apportionment of the House of Representatives had been carried out according to the legal Hamilton's method, Tilden would have won the electoral vote and, therefore, the presidency.

Hamilton's method may appear to be a fair and reasonable apportionment method. It is the only method that satisfies the quota rule—that is, a group's apportionment is always its upper quota or its lower quota. Unfortunately, it is also the only method that can produce some serious problems, called the *Alabama paradox*, the *population paradox*, and the *new-states paradox*. In this section, we discuss each of these flaws. We conclude by seeing if there is an ideal apportionment method that can guarantee the states their fair share of seats in the House of Representatives. At stake is equal representation, avoiding election debacles such as the one that occurred in 1876, and the reality that many government policies are based on the number of representatives for each state.

The Alabama Paradox

1 | Understand and illustrate the Alabama paradox.

After the 1880 census, two possible sizes for the House of Representatives were under consideration: 299 members or 300 members. The chief clerk of the U.S. Census Office used Hamilton's method to compute apportionments for both House sizes. He found that adding one more seat to the House in order to have 300 seats would actually decrease the number of seats for Alabama, from 8 seats to 7 seats. This was the first time this paradoxical behavior was observed in Congressional apportionment; as a result, it is called the **Alabama paradox**.

> "No invasions of the Constitution are fundamentally so dangerous as the tricks played on their own numbers."
>
> Thomas Jefferson

> **THE ALABAMA PARADOX**
> An increase in the total number of items to be apportioned results in the loss of an item for a group.

EXAMPLE 1 ILLUSTRATING THE ALABAMA PARADOX

A small country with a population of 10,000 is composed of three states. According to the country's constitution, the congress will have 200 seats, divided among the three states according to their respective populations. Table 14.38 shows each state's population. Use Hamilton's method to show that the Alabama paradox occurs if the number of seats is increased to 201.

TABLE 14.38

State	A	B	C	Total
Population	5015	4515	470	10,000

SOLUTION We begin with 200 seats in the congress. First we compute the standard divisor.

$$\text{Standard divisor} = \frac{\text{total population}}{\text{number of allocated items}} = \frac{10{,}000}{200} = 50$$

Using this value, Table 14.39 shows the apportionment for each state using Hamilton's method.

TABLE 14.39 APPORTIONMENT OF 200 CONGRESSIONAL SEATS USING HAMILTON'S METHOD

State	Population	Standard Quota	Lower Quota	Decimal Part	Surplus Seats	Final Apportionment
A	5015	100.3	100	0.3		100
B	4515	90.3	90	0.3		90
C	470	9.4	9	0.4	1	10
Total	10,000	200	199	largest		200

Standard quota $= \dfrac{\text{population}}{50}$

This sum indicates we must assign one extra seat.

Now let's see what happens with 201 seats in congress. First we compute the standard divisor.

$$\text{Standard divisor} = \frac{\text{total population}}{\text{number of allocated items}} = \frac{10{,}000}{201} \approx 49.75$$

Using this value, Table 14.40 shows the apportionment for each state using Hamilton's method.

TABLE 14.40 APPORTIONMENT OF 201 CONGRESSIONAL SEATS USING HAMILTON'S METHOD

State	Population	Standard Quota	Lower Quota	Decimal Part	Surplus Seats	Final Apportionment
A	5015	100.80	100	largest 0.80	1	101
B	4515	90.75	90	next largest 0.75	1	91
C	470	9.45	9	0.45		9
Total	10,000	201	199			201

Standard quota $= \dfrac{\text{population}}{49.75}$

This sum indicates we must assign two extra seats.

The final apportionments are summarized in Table 14.41. When the number of seats increased from 200 to 201, state C's apportionment actually decreased, from 10 to 9. This is an example of the Alabama paradox. In this situation, the larger states, A and B, benefit at the expense of the smaller state, C.

TABLE 14.41 ILLUSTRATING THE ALABAMA PARADOX		
State	**Apportionment with 200 Seats**	**Apportionment with 201 Seats**
A	100	101
B	90	91
C	10	9

State C's apportionment decreased from 10 to 9.

CHECK POINT 1 Table 14.42 shows the populations of the four states in a country with a population of 20,000. Use Hamilton's method to show that the Alabama paradox occurs if the number of seats in congress is increased from 99 to 100.

TABLE 14.42					
State	A	B	C	D	Total
Population	2060	2080	7730	8130	20,000

Understand and illustrate the population paradox.

The Population Paradox

The issue of power and representation among the states has been a serious concern since the drafting of the Constitution. In the early 1900s, Virginia was growing much faster than Maine—about 60% faster—yet Virginia lost a seat to Maine in the House of Representatives. This paradox, called the **population paradox**, illustrates another serious flaw of Hamilton's method.

> **THE POPULATION PARADOX**
> Group A loses items to group B, even though the population of group A grew at a faster rate than that of group B.

EXAMPLE 2   ILLUSTRATING THE POPULATION PARADOX

A small country with a population of 10,000 is composed of three states. There are 11 seats in the congress, divided among the three states according to their respective populations. Using Hamilton's method, Table 14.43 shows the apportionment of congressional seats for each state.

TABLE 14.43 APPORTIONMENT OF 11 CONGRESSIONAL SEATS USING HAMILTON'S METHOD				
State	**Population**	**Standard Quota**	**Lower Quota**	**Hamilton's Apportionment**
A	540	0.59	0	0
B	2430	2.67	2	3
C	7030	7.73	7	8
Total	10,000	10.99	9	11

The population of the country increases, shown in Table 14.44.

TABLE 14.44

State	A	B	C	Total
Original Population	540	2430	7030	10,000
New Population	560	2550	7890	11,000

a. Find the percent increase in the population of each state.

b. Use Hamilton's method to show that the population paradox occurs.

SOLUTION

a. Recall that the fraction for percent increase is the amount of increase divided by the original amount. The percent increase in the population of each state is determined as follows:

$$\text{State A:} \quad \frac{560 - 540}{540} = \frac{20}{540} \approx 0.037 = 3.7\%$$

increase in population   original population

$$\text{State B:} \quad \frac{2550 - 2430}{2430} = \frac{120}{2430} \approx 0.049 = 4.9\%$$

$$\text{State C:} \quad \frac{7890 - 7030}{7030} = \frac{860}{7030} \approx 0.122 = 12.2\%$$

All three states had an increase in their populations. State C is increasing at a faster rate than state B, while state B is increasing at a faster rate than state A.

b. We need to use Hamilton's method to find the apportionment for each state with its new population. First we compute the standard divisor.

$$\text{Standard divisor} = \frac{\text{total population}}{\text{number of allocated items}} = \frac{11,000}{11} = 1000$$

Using this value, Table 14.45 shows the apportionment for each state using Hamilton's method.

TABLE 14.45 APPORTIONMENT OF 11 CONGRESSIONAL SEATS FOR THE NEW POPULATIONS USING HAMILTON'S METHOD

State	Population	Standard Quota	Lower Quota	Decimal Part	Surplus Seats	Final Apportionment
A	560	0.56	0	0.56	1	1
B	2550	2.55	2	0.55		2
C	7890	7.89	7	0.89	1	8
Total	11,000	11	9			11

Standard quota
$$= \frac{\text{population}}{1000}$$

This sum indicates we must assign two extra seats.

The final apportionments are summarized in Table 14.46. The good news is that state A now has a congressional seat. The bad news is that state B has lost a seat to state A, even though state B's population grew at a faster rate than that of state A. This is an example of the population paradox.

TABLE 14.46 ILLUSTRATING THE POPULATION PARADOX

State	Growth Rate	Original Apportionment	New Apportionment
A	3.7%	0	1
B	4.9%	3	2
C	12.2%	8	8

State B lost a seat to state A.

CHECK POINT 2 A small country has 100 seats in the congress, divided among the three states according to their respective populations. Table 14.47 shows each state's population before and after the country's population increase.

TABLE 14.47

State	A	B	C	Total
Original Population	19,110	39,090	141,800	200,000
New Population	19,302	39,480	141,800	200,582

a. Use Hamilton's method to apportion the 100 congressional seats using the original population.

b. Find the percent increase in the populations of states A and B. (State C did not have any change in population.)

c. Use Hamilton's method to apportion the 100 congressional seats using the new population. Show that the population paradox occurs.

The New-States Paradox

Another flaw in Hamilton's method was discovered in 1907 when Oklahoma became a state. Previously, the House of Representatives had had 386 seats. Based on its population, it was determined that Oklahoma should have 5 seats. Thus, the House size was changed from 386 to 391. The intent was to leave the number of seats unchanged for the other states. However, when the apportionment was recalculated using Hamilton's method, Maine gained a seat (4 instead of 3) and New York lost a seat (from 38 to 37). The addition of Oklahoma, with its fair share of seats, forced New York to give a seat to Maine. The **new-states paradox** occurs when the addition of a new state affects the apportionments of other states.

3 Understand and illustrate the new-states paradox.

THE NEW-STATES PARADOX
The addition of a new group changes the apportionments of other groups.

EXAMPLE 3   ILLUSTRATING THE NEW-STATES PARADOX

A school district has two high schools: East High, with an enrollment of 1688 students, and West High, with an enrollment of 7912 students. The school district has a counseling staff of 48 counselors, who are apportioned to the schools using Hamilton's method. This apportionment results in 8 counselors assigned to East High and 40 counselors assigned to West High, shown in Table 14.48. The standard divisor is

$$\frac{\text{total population}}{\text{number of allocated items}} = \frac{9600}{48} = 200.$$

> There are **200** students per counselor.

TABLE 14.48 APPORTIONMENT OF 48 COUNSELORS USING HAMILTON'S METHOD

School	Population	Standard Quota	Lower Quota	Hamilton's Apportionment
East High	1688	8.44	8	8
West High	7912	39.56	39	40
Total	9600	48	47	48

Suppose that a new high school, North High, with a population of 1448 students, is added to the district. Using the standard divisor of 200 students per counselor, the school district decides to hire 7 new counselors for North High. Show that the new-states paradox occurs when the counselors are reapportioned.

SOLUTION   The new total population is the previous student population, 9600, plus the student population at North High, 1448: 9600 + 1448 = 11,048. The new number of counselors is the previous number, 48, plus the new counselors hired at North High, 7: 48 + 7 = 55. Thus, when North High is added, the new standard divisor is

$$\frac{\text{total population}}{\text{number of allocated items}} = \frac{11{,}048}{55} \approx 200.87.$$

The new standard quotas and Hamilton's apportionment are shown in Table 14.49.

TABLE 14.49 APPORTIONMENT OF 55 COUNSELORS USING HAMILTON'S METHOD

School	Population	Standard Quota	Lower Quota	Decimal Part	Surplus Counselors	Final Apportionment
East High	1688	8.40	8 *largest*	0.40	1	9
West High	7912	39.39	39	0.39		39
North High	1448	7.21	7	0.21		7
Total	11,048	55	54			55

> standard quota
> $= \dfrac{\text{school population}}{200.87}$

> This sum indicates we must assign one extra counselor.

Before North High was added to the district, East High was assigned 8 counselors and West High was assigned 40 counselors. After the addition of a new school and an increase in the total number of counselors to be apportioned, East High was assigned 9 counselors and West High was assigned 39 counselors. Thus, West High ended up losing a counselor to East High. The addition of a new high school changed the apportionments of the other two high schools. This is an example of the new-states paradox.

a. A school district has two high schools, East High, with an enrollment of 2574 students, and West High, with an enrollment of 9426 students. The school district has a counseling staff of 100 counselors. Use Hamilton's method to apportion the counselors to the two schools.

b. Suppose that a new high school, North High, with a population of 750 students, is added to the district. The school district decides to hire 6 new counselors for North High. Use Hamilton's method to show that the new-states paradox occurs when the counselors are reapportioned.

---

4   Understand Balinski and Young's Impossibility Theorem.

The Search for an Ideal Apportionment Method

We have seen that although Hamilton's method satisfies the quota rule, it can produce paradoxes. By contrast, Jefferson's, Adams's, and Webster's methods can all violate the quota rule, but do not produce paradoxes. Furthermore, Hamilton's and Jefferson's methods can favor large states, while Adams's and Webster's methods can favor small states. For many years, scholars inside and outside Congress hoped mathematicians would eventually devise an ideal apportionment method—one that satisfies the quota rule, does not produce any paradoxes, and treats large and small states without favoritism.

Is there an ideal apportionment method? The answer, unfortunately, is no. In 1980, mathematicians Michel L. Balinski and H. Peyton Young proved that there is no apportionment method that avoids all paradoxes and at the same time satisfies the quota rule. Their theorem is known as **Balinski and Young's Impossibility Theorem**.

> **BALINSKI AND YOUNG'S IMPOSSIBILITY THEOREM**
> There is no perfect apportionment method. Any apportionment method that does not violate the quota rule must produce paradoxes, and any apportionment method that does not produce paradoxes must violate the quota rule.

Because any apportionment method must be flawed, the politics of representation can play as large a role as mathematics when Congress discusses an apportionment method. The United States House of Representatives has been apportioned approximately 20 times, and the choice of an apportionment method can ultimately be a political decision.

Table 14.50 compares the four apportionment methods we discussed and serves as an example of Balinski and Young's Impossibility Theorem.

TABLE 14.50 FLAWS OF APPORTIONMENT METHODS

	Apportionment Method: Is It Flawed?			
Flaw	**Hamilton**	**Jefferson**	**Adams**	**Webster**
May not satisfy the quota rule (apportionment should always be the upper or lower quota)	No	Yes	Yes	Yes
May produce the Alabama paradox (an increase in total apportioned items results in the loss of an item for a group)	Yes	No	No	No
May produce the population paradox (group A loses items to group B, even though group A's population grew at a faster rate than group B's)	Yes	No	No	No
May produce the new-states paradox (the addition of a new group changes the apportionments of other groups)	Yes	No	No	No
In the House of Representatives, apportionment method favors large states	Yes	Yes	No	No
In the House of Representatives, apportionment method favors small states	No	No	Yes	Yes

BLITZER BONUS

Florida, Ohio, and the Presidential Elections of 2000 and 2004

Results of the 2000 Presidential Election				
Party	**Candidate**	**Popular Vote**	**Percent**	**Electoral Vote**
Republican	George W. Bush and Dick Cheney	50,455,156	47.87	271
Democrat	Al Gore and Joe Lieberman	50,992,335	48.38	266
	Total Vote	105,396,641		

Results of the 2004 Presidential Election				
Party	**Candidate**	**Popular Vote**	**Percent**	**Electoral Vote**
Republican	George W. Bush and Dick Cheney	62,028,285	50.72	286
Democrat	John Kerry and John Edwards	59,028,109	48.27	251
	Total Vote	122,294,978		

Source: Federal Election Commission

The 2000 presidential election was surely the most spectacular in any living person's memory. On November 7, 2000, Americans expected to end the day knowing who their new president would be. By early in the evening, most states were decided. Because of how the numbers were adding up, the winner of Florida's 25 electoral votes would win the majority of electoral votes and the election. By 8 P.M. in the East, most television networks announced that Al Gore had won Florida. Later that evening, Gore's lead dwindled and George W. Bush was announced as Florida's winner. Still later, Bush's lead shrank. People went to bed not knowing who the next president would be.

The next 36 days brought an unprecedented struggle over Florida's ballots. Bush led the state's popular vote by fewer than one thousand votes out of six million cast. Allegations of confusing ballots, illegal barring of voters, and defective voting machines threw the process of recounting votes into chaos. The race ended on December 12, when the U.S. Supreme Court, largely along party lines, voted 5 to 4 to suspend recounts in Florida. This gave Bush a majority of electoral votes and the White House. Although Gore won the popular vote by more than 500,000 votes, he conceded the election the next day.

The presidential election of 2004 was filled with high passion and intense emotion. The country avoided its second consecutive problematic election by having a clear popular vote and electoral vote victory for George W. Bush. The state of Ohio proved to be *the* consummate battleground state. Bush won Ohio's 20 electoral votes by a margin of 130,000 out of nearly 3.5 million votes cast, meaning a change of 65,000 votes in Ohio would have tipped it to Kerry. With 20 additional electoral votes, Kerry would have won the presidency, even though finishing more than three million popular votes behind Bush.

Although the country avoided the chaos that followed the 2000 election, the Internet buzzed with claims of a nasty array of tactics in the presidential election of 2004, ranging from manipulating the vote count to old-fashioned voter intimidation. The most definite thing that can be said now is that we will continue having presidential elections every four years, with different environments, interesting and notable outcomes, and with new sets of heroes and scapegoats.

EXERCISE SET 14.4 ●●●●●●

• Practice and Application Exercises

1. The mathematics department has 30 teaching assistants to be divided among three courses, according to their respective enrollments. The table shows the courses and the number of students enrolled in each course.

Course	College Algebra	Statistics	Liberal Arts Math	Total
Enrollment	978	500	322	1800

a. Apportion the teaching assistants using Hamilton's method.

b. Use Hamilton's method to determine if the Alabama paradox occurs if the number of teaching assistants is increased from 30 to 31. Explain your answer.

2. A school district has 57 new laptop computers to be divided among four schools, according to their respective enrollments. The table shows the number of students enrolled in each school.

School	A	B	C	D	Total
Enrollment	5040	4560	4040	610	14,250

a. Apportion the laptop computers using Hamilton's method.

b. Use Hamilton's method to determine if the Alabama paradox occurs if the number of laptop computers is increased from 57 to 58. Explain your answer.

3. The table shows the populations of three states in a country with a population of 20,000. Use Hamilton's method to show that the Alabama paradox occurs if the number of seats in congress is increased from 40 to 41.

State	A	B	C	Total
Population	680	9150	10,170	20,000

4. The table shows the populations, in thousands, of the three states in a country with a population of 3760 thousand. Use Hamilton's method to show that the Alabama paradox occurs if the number of seats in congress is increased from 24 to 25.

State	A	B	C	Total
Population (in thousands)	530	990	2240	3760

5. A small country has 24 seats in the congress, divided among the three states according to their respective populations. The table shows each state's population, in thousands, before and after the country's population increase.

State	A	B	C	Total
Original Population (in thousands)	530	990	2240	3760
New Population (in thousands)	680	1250	2570	4500

a. Use Hamilton's method to apportion the 24 congressional seats using the original population.

b. Find the percent increase, to the nearest tenth of a percent, in the population of each state.

c. Use Hamilton's method to apportion the 24 congressional seats using the new population. Does the population paradox occur? Explain your answer.

6. A country has 200 seats in the congress, divided among the five states according to their respective populations. The table shows each state's population, in thousands, before and after the country's population increase.

State	A	B	C	D	E	Total
Original Population (in thousands)	2224	2236	2640	3030	9870	20,000
New Population (in thousands)	2424	2436	2740	3130	10,070	20,800

a. Use Hamilton's method to apportion the 200 congressional seats using the original population.

b. Find the percent increase, to the nearest tenth of a percent, in the population of each state.

c. Use Hamilton's method to apportion the 200 congressional seats using the new population. What do you observe about the percent increases for states A and B and their respective changes in apportioned seats? Is this the population paradox?

7. A town has 40 mail trucks and four districts in which mail is distributed. The trucks are to be apportioned according

to each district's population. The table shows these populations before and after the town's population increase. Use Hamilton's method to show that the population paradox occurs.

District	A	B	C	D	Total
Original Population	1188	1424	2538	3730	8880
New Population	1188	1420	2544	3848	9000

8. A town has five districts in which mail is distributed and 50 mail trucks. The trucks are to be apportioned according to each district's population. The table shows these populations before and after the town's population increase. Use Hamilton's method to show that the population paradox occurs.

District	A	B	C	D	E	Total
Original Population	780	1500	1730	2040	2950	9000
New Population	780	1500	1810	2040	2960	9090

9. A corporation has two branches, A and B. Each year the company awards 100 promotions within its branches. The table shows the number of employees in each branch.

Branch	A	B	Total
Employees	1045	8955	10,000

a. Use Hamilton's method to apportion the promotions.

b. Suppose that a third branch, C, with the number of employees shown in the table, is added to the corporation. The company adds 5 new yearly promotions for branch C. Use Hamilton's method to determine if the new-states paradox occurs when the promotions are reapportioned.

Branch	A	B	C	Total
Employees	1045	8955	525	10,525

10. A corporation has three branches, A, B, and C. Each year the company awards 60 promotions within its branches. The table shows the number of employees in each branch.

Branch	A	B	C	Total
Employees	209	769	2022	3000

a. Use Hamilton's method to apportion the promotions.

b. Suppose that a fourth branch, D, with the number of employees shown in the table, is added to the corporation. The company adds 5 new yearly promotions for branch D. Use Hamilton's method to determine if the new-states paradox occurs when the promotions are reapportioned.

Branch	A	B	C	D	Total
Employees	209	769	2022	260	3260

11. a. A country has two states, state A, with a population of 9450, and state B, with a population of 90,550. The congress has 100 seats, divided between the two states according to their respective populations. Use Hamilton's method to apportion the congressional seats to the states.

b. Suppose that a third state, state C, with a population of 10,400, is added to the country. The country adds 10 new congressional seats for state C. Use Hamilton's method to show that the new-states paradox occurs when the congressional seats are reapportioned.

12. a. A country has three states, state A, with a population of 99,000, state B, with a population of 214,000, and state C, with a population of 487,000. The congress has 50 seats, divided among the three states according to their respective populations. Use Hamilton's method to apportion the congressional seats to the states.

b. Suppose that a fourth state, state D, with a population of 116,000, is added to the country. The country adds 7 new congressional seats for state D. Use Hamilton's method to show that the new-states paradox occurs when the congressional seats are reapportioned.

13. In Exercise 12, use Jefferson's method with $d = 15,500$ to solve parts (a) and (b). Does the new-states paradox occur? Explain your answer.

• Writing in Mathematics

14. What is the Alabama paradox?

15. What is the population paradox?

16. What is the new-states paradox?

17. According to Balinski and Young's Impossibility Theorem, can the democratic ideal of "one person, one vote" ever be perfectly achieved? Explain your answer.

• Critical Thinking Exercises

18. Which one of the following is true?

a. If a country has two states and congressional seats are apportioned by population using Hamilton's method, the Alabama paradox cannot occur if the number of seats increases.

b. Balinski and Young's Theorem shows that "one person, one vote" is mathematically possible.

c. In an apportionment for a country with two states, both Jefferson's and Adams's methods can violate the quota rule.

d. None of the above is true.

19. Give an example of a country with three states in which the Alabama paradox occurs using Hamilton's method when the number of seats in congress is increased from 3 to 4.

●●●●●● CHAPTER SUMMARY, REVIEW, AND TEST

• S U M M A R Y   DEFINITIONS AND CONCEPTS

EXAMPLES

14.1 Voting Methods

a. Preference ballots are ballots in which a voter is asked to rank all the candidates in order of preference. Preference tables show how often each particular outcome occurred.

Ex. 1, p. 773

b. The four voting methods—the plurality method, the Borda count method, the plurality-with-elimination method, and the pairwise comparison method—are summarized in Table 14.7 on page 781.

Ex. 2, p. 774;
Ex. 3, p. 775;
Ex. 4, p. 777;
Ex. 5, p. 779

14.2 Flaws of Voting Methods

a. The four fairness criteria for voting methods—the majority criterion, the head-to-head criterion, the monotonicity criterion, and the irrelevant alternatives criterion—are summarized in Table 14.22 on page 791. Table 14.23 on page 791 shows which voting methods satisfy which criteria.

Ex. 1, p. 785;
Ex. 2, p. 786;
Ex. 3, p. 788;
Ex. 4, p. 790

b. Arrow's Impossibility Theorem states that it is mathematically impossible for any democratic voting system to satisfy each of the four fairness criteria.

14.3 Apportionment Methods

a. Standard divisors and standard quotas are defined as follows:

$$\text{Standard divisor} = \frac{\text{total population}}{\text{number of allocated items}} \qquad \text{Standard quota} = \frac{\text{population of a particular group}}{\text{standard divisor}}.$$

Ex. 1, p. 797

b. The lower quota is the standard quota rounded down to the nearest whole number. The upper quota is the standard quota rounded up to the nearest whole number.

c. The apportionment problem is to determine a method for rounding standard or modified quotas into whole numbers so that the sum of the numbers is the total number of allocated items.

d. The four apportionment methods discussed in the text—Hamilton's method, Jefferson's method, Adams's method, and Webster's method—are summarized in Table 14.37 on page 805. The quota rule states that a group's apportionment should be either its upper quota or its lower quota.

Ex. 2, p. 799;
Ex. 3, p. 801;
Ex. 4, p. 802;
Ex. 5, p. 804

14.4 Flaws of Apportionment Methods

a. Although Hamilton's method satisfies the quota rule, it may produce paradoxes, including the Alabama paradox, the population paradox, and the new-states paradox. These paradoxes are summarized in Table 14.50 on page 815.

Ex. 1, p. 810;
Ex. 2, p. 811;
Ex. 3, p. 814

b. Although Jefferson's, Adams's, and Webster's methods do not produce paradoxes, they may not satisfy the quota rule.

c. Balinski and Young's Impossibility Theorem states that there is no perfect apportionment method. Any method that does not violate the quota rule must produce paradoxes, and any method that does not produce paradoxes must violate the quota rule.

REVIEW EXERCISES

14.1

1. The 12 preference ballots for four candidates (A, B, C, and D) are shown. Construct a preference table to illustrate the results of the election.

ABCD   BDCA   CBDA   ABCD   CBDA   ABCD
BDCA   BDCA   CBAD   CBAD   ABCD   CBDA

In Exercises 2–5, your class is given the option of choosing a day for the final exam. Students are asked to rank the four available days, Monday (M), Tuesday (T), Wednesday (W), and Friday (F). The results of the election are shown in the preference table.

Number of Votes	9	5	4	2	2	1
First Choice	T	T	M	T	W	W
Second Choice	W	W	T	M	F	M
Third Choice	F	M	F	W	T	F
Fourth Choice	M	F	W	F	M	T

2. How many students voted in the election?

3. How many students selected the days in this order: M, T, F, W?

4. How many students selected Tuesday as their first choice for the final?

5. How many students selected Wednesday as their second choice for the final?

In Exercises 6–9, the Theater Society members are voting for the kind of play they will perform next semester: a comedy (C), a drama (D), or a musical (M). Their votes are summarized in the following preference table.

Number of Votes	10	8	4	2
First Choice	C	M	M	D
Second Choice	D	C	D	M
Third Choice	M	D	C	C

6. Which type of play is selected using the plurality method?

7. Which type of play is selected using the Borda count method?

8. Which type of play is selected using the plurality-with-elimination method?

9. Which type of play is selected using the pairwise comparison method?

In Exercises 10–13, four candidates, A, B, C, and D, are running for chair of the Natural Science Division. The votes of the division members are summarized in the following preference table.

Number of Votes	40	30	6	2
First Choice	A	B	C	D
Second Choice	B	C	D	B
Third Choice	C	D	B	C
Fourth Choice	D	A	A	A

10. Determine the winner using the plurality method.

11. Determine the winner using the Borda count method.

12. Determine the winner using the plurality-with-elimination method.

13. Determine the winner using the pairwise comparison method.

14.2

In Exercises 14–16, voters in a small town are considering four proposals, A, B, C, and D, for the design of affordable housing. Their votes are summarized in the following preference table.

Number of Votes	1500	600	300
First Choice	A	B	C
Second Choice	B	D	B
Third Choice	C	C	D
Fourth Choice	D	A	A

14. Using the Borda count method, which design will be used for the affordable housing?

15. Which design has a majority of first-place votes? Based on your answer to Exercise 14, is the majority criterion satisfied?

16. Which design is favored over all others using a head-to-head comparison? Based on your answer to Exercise 14, is the head-to-head criterion satisfied?

Use the following preference table to solve Exercises 17–18.

Number of Votes	1500	700	300
First Choice	B	A	C
Second Choice	C	B	A
Third Choice	A	C	B

17. Using the plurality-with-elimination method, which candidate wins the election?

18. Which candidate is favored over all others using a head-to-head comparison? Based on your answer to Exercise 17, is the head-to-head criterion satisfied?

Use the following preference table to solve Exercises 19–23.

Number of Votes	180	100	40	30
First Choice	A	B	D	C
Second Choice	B	D	B	B
Third Choice	C	A	C	A
Fourth Choice	D	C	A	D

19. Using the plurality method, which candidate wins the election?

20. Using the Borda count method, which candidate wins the election?

21. Using the plurality-with-elimination method, which candidate wins the election?

22. Using the pairwise comparison method, which candidate wins the election?

23. Which candidate has a majority of first-place votes? Based on your answers to Exercises 19–22, which voting system(s) violate the majority criterion in this election?

Use the following preference table, which shows the results of a straw vote, to solve Exercises 24–25.

Number of Votes	500	400	350	200
First Choice	B	A	C	C
Second Choice	C	B	A	B
Third Choice	A	C	B	A

24. Using the plurality-with-elimination method, which candidate wins the straw vote?

25. In the actual election, the 200 voters in the last column who voted C, B, A, in that order, change their votes to B, C, A. Using the plurality-with-elimination method, which candidate wins the actual election? Based on your answer to Exercise 24, is the monotonicity criterion satisfied?

Use the following preference table to solve Exercises 26–29.

Number of Votes	400	250	200
First Choice	A	C	B
Second Choice	B	B	C
Third Choice	C	A	A

26. Using the plurality method, which candidate wins the election?

27. Suppose that candidate B drops out. Construct a new preference table for the election with B eliminated. Using the new table and the plurality method, which candidate wins the election? Based on your answer to Exercise 26, is the irrelevant alternatives criterion satisfied by the plurality method?

28. Using the Borda count method, which candidate wins the election?

29. If candidate C drops out, which candidate wins the election using the Borda count method? Based on your answer to Exercise 28, is the irrelevant alternatives criterion satisfied by the Borda count method?

14.3

In Exercises 30–36, an HMO has 40 doctors to be apportioned among four clinics. The HMO decides to apportion the doctors based on the average weekly patient load for each clinic, given in the following table.

Clinic	A	B	C	D
Average Weekly Patient Load	275	392	611	724

30. Find the standard divisor.

31. Find each clinic's standard quota.

32. Find each clinic's lower quota and upper quota.

33. Use Hamilton's method to apportion the doctors to the clinics.

34. Use Jefferson's method with $d = 48$ to apportion the doctors to the clinics.

35. Use Adams's method with $d = 52$ to apportion the doctors to the clinics.

36. Use Webster's method with $d = 49.95$ to apportion the doctors to the clinics.

In Exercises 37–40, a country is composed of four states, A, B, C, and D. The population of each state is given in the following table. Congress will have 200 seats, divided among the four states according to their respective populations.

State	A	B	C	D
Population	3320	10,060	15,020	19,600

37. Use Hamilton's method to apportion the congressional seats.

38. Use Jefferson's method to apportion the congressional seats. (*Hint:* A modified divisor that works should be less than the standard divisor in Exercise 37.)

39. Use Adams's method to apportion the congressional seats. (*Hint:* A modified divisor that works should be greater than the standard divisor in Exercise 37.)

40. Use Webster's method to apportion the congressional seats. (*Hint:* A modified divisor that works should lie between 240 and 241.)

14.4

41. A school district has 150 new laptop computers to be divided among three schools, according to their respective enrollments. The table shows the number of students enrolled in each school.

School	A	B	C	Total
Enrollment	370	3365	3765	7500

a. Apportion the laptop computers using Hamilton's method.

b. Use Hamilton's method to determine if the Alabama paradox occurs if the number of laptop computers is increased from 150 to 151.

42. A country has 100 seats in the congress, divided among the three states according to their respective populations. The table shows each state's population before and after the country's population increase.

State	A	B	C	Total
Original Population	143,796	41,090	15,114	200,000
New Population	143,796	41,420	15,304	200,520

a. Use Hamilton's method to apportion the 100 congressional seats using the original population.

b. Find the percent increase, to the nearest tenth of a percent, in the population of state B and state C.

c. Use Hamilton's method to apportion the 100 congressional seats using the new population. Does the population paradox occur?

43. A corporation has two branches, A and B. Each year the company awards 33 promotions within its branches. The table shows the number of employees in each branch.

Branch	A	B	Total
Employees	372	1278	1650

a. Use Hamilton's method to apportion the promotions.

b. Suppose that a third branch, C, with the number of employees shown in the table, is added to the corporation. The company adds 7 new yearly promotions for branch C. Use Hamilton's method to determine if the new-states paradox occurs when the promotions are reapportioned.

Branch	A	B	C	Total
Employees	372	1278	355	2005

44. Is the following statement true or false?

There are perfect voting methods, as well as perfect apportionment methods.

Explain your answer.

●●●●●● CHAPTER 14 TEST

In Exercises 1–8, three candidates, A, B, and C, are running for mayor of a small town. The results of the election are shown in the following preference table.

Number of Votes	1200	900	900	600
First Choice	A	C	B	B
Second Choice	B	A	C	A
Third Choice	C	B	A	C

1. How many people voted in the election?

2. How many people selected the candidates in this order: B, A, C?

3. How many people selected candidate B as their first choice?

4. How many people selected candidate A as their second choice?

5. Determine the winner using the plurality method.

6. Determine the winner using the Borda count method.

7. Determine the winner using the plurality-with-elimination method.

8. Determine the winner using the pairwise comparison method.

Use the following preference table to solve Exercises 9–10.

Number of Votes	240	160	60
First Choice	A	C	D
Second Choice	B	B	A
Third Choice	C	D	C
Fourth Choice	D	A	B

9. Determine the winner using the Borda count method.

10. Which candidate has a majority of first-place votes? Based on your answer to Exercise 9, is the majority criterion satisfied?

Use the following preference table to solve Exercises 11–12.

Number of Votes	1500	1000	1000
First Choice	A	B	C
Second Choice	B	A	B
Third Choice	C	C	A

11. Determine the winner using the plurality method.

12. Which candidate is favored over all others using a head-to-head comparison? Based on your answer to Exercise 11, is the head-to-head criterion satisfied?

Use the following preference table, which shows the results of a straw vote, to solve Exercises 13–14.

Number of Votes	70	60	50	30
First Choice	C	B	A	A
Second Choice	A	C	B	C
Third Choice	B	A	C	B

13. Determine the winner using the plurality-with-elimination method.

14. In the actual election, the 30 voters in the last column who voted A, C, B, in that order, change their votes to C, A, B. Using the plurality-with-elimination method, which candidate wins the election? Based on your answer to Exercise 13, is the monotonicity criterion satisfied?

15. Suppose that the plurality method is used on the following preference table. If candidate C drops out, is the irrelevant alternatives criterion satisfied? Explain your answer.

Number of Votes	90	75	45
First Choice	B	C	A
Second Choice	C	A	C
Third Choice	A	B	B

In Exercises 16–24, an HMO has 10 doctors to be apportioned among three clinics. The HMO decides to apportion the doctors based on the average weekly patient load for each clinic, given in the following table.

Clinic	A	B	C
Average Weekly Patient Load	119	165	216

16. Find the standard divisor.
17. Find each clinic's standard quota.
18. Find each clinic's lower quota and upper quota.
19. Use Hamilton's method to apportion the doctors to the clinics.
20. Use Jefferson's method to apportion the doctors to the clinics.
21. Use Adams's method to apportion the doctors to the clinics.
22. Use Webster's method with $d = 47.7$ to apportion the doctors to the clinics.
23. Suppose that the HMO hires one new doctor. Using Hamilton's method, does the Alabama paradox occur when the number of doctors is increased from 10 to 11?
24. As given in the original description, assume that the HMO has 10 doctors. Suppose that a third clinic, clinic D, with the average weekly patient load shown in the table, is added to the HMO. The administration hires 2 new doctors for clinic D. Use Hamilton's method to determine if the new-states paradox occurs when the doctors are reapportioned.

Clinic	A	B	C	D
Average Weekly Patient Load	119	165	216	110

25. Write one sentence for a person not familiar with the mathematics of voting and apportionment that summarizes the two impossibility theorems discussed in this chapter.

15

Graph Theory

- A more user-friendly map for a city's subway system is needed.
- Public works administrators must find the most efficient routes for snowplows, garbage trucks, and street sweepers.
- A sales director traveling to branch offices needs to minimize the cost of the trip.
- You need to run a series of errands and return home using the shortest route.
- After a heavy snow, campus services must clear a minimum number of sidewalks and still ensure that students walking from building to building will be able to do so along cleared paths.
- You need to represent the parent-child relationships for five generations of your family.

These unrelated problems can be solved using special diagrams, called *graphs*. Graph theory was launched by the Swiss mathematician Leonhard Euler (1707–1783). Euler analyzed a puzzle involving a city with seven bridges. Would it be possible to walk through the city and cross each of its bridges exactly once? Although graph theory developed from this puzzle, you will see how graphs are used to solve a diverse series of realistic problems faced by businesses and individuals.

SECTION 15.1 • GRAPHS, PATHS, AND CIRCUITS

OBJECTIVES

1. Understand relationships in a graph.
2. Model relationships using graphs.
3. Understand and use the vocabulary of graph theory.

FIGURE 15.1
Source: Time, May 8, 2006

The "six degrees of separation" theory states that anyone in the world can be joined to any other person through a chain of no more than four intermediate connections. Figure 15.1 indicates that only two intermediate connections link Oprah Winfrey to Steve Jobs.

The diagram in Figure 15.1 is an example of a *graph*. A graph provides a structure for describing relationships. Relationships between people (friendship, love, connections, etc.) can be described by means of a graph. These graphs are different from the line, bar, circle, and rectangular coordinate graphs we have seen throughout the book. Instead they tell us how a group of objects are related to each other. Let's begin with the definition of a graph.

STUDY TIP

Graphs were briefly introduced in Section 10.7. However, it is not necessary to read that section before covering this chapter.

1 | Understand relationships in a graph.

DEFINITION OF A GRAPH

A **graph** consists of a finite set of points, called **vertices** (singular is *vertex*) and line segments or curves, called **edges**, that start and end at vertices. An edge that starts and ends at the same vertex is called a **loop**.

Figure 15.2 shows an example of a graph. This graph has four vertices, labeled $A, B, C,$ and D. (We will often use uppercase letters to refer to vertices.) If there is not more than one edge between two vertices, we can use the two vertices to refer to that edge. For example, the edge that connects vertex A to vertex D can be called edge AD or edge DA. The loop on the lower right can be referred to as edge CC or loop CC.

We will always indicate vertices by black dots. In Figure 15.2, the point where edges AC and DB cross has no black dot. Thus, this point is not a vertex. **Not every point where two edges cross is a vertex.** You might find it useful to think of one of the edges as passing above the other.

In a graph, the important information is which vertices are connected by edges. Two graphs are **equivalent** if they have the same number of vertices connected to each other in the same way. The placement of the vertices and the shapes of the edges are unimportant.

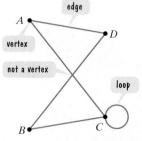

FIGURE 15.2 An example of a graph

EXAMPLE 1   UNDERSTANDING RELATIONSHIPS IN GRAPHS

Explain why Figures 15.3(a) and (b) show equivalent graphs.

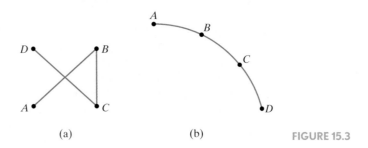

(a)   (b)   FIGURE 15.3

SOLUTION In both figures, the vertices are A, B, C, and D. Both graphs have an edge that connects vertex A to vertex B (edge AB or BA), an edge that connects vertex B to vertex C (edge BC or CB), and an edge that connects vertex C to vertex D (edge CD or DC). Because the two graphs have the same number of vertices connected to each other in the same way, they are equivalent.

 Explain why Figures 15.4(a) and (b) show equivalent graphs.

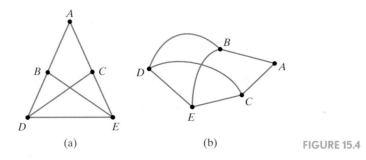

(a)   (b)   FIGURE 15.4

2 | Model relationships using graphs.

Modeling Relationships Using Graphs

Examples 2 through 5 illustrate a number of different situations that we can represent, or model, using graphs. We begin with a situation that was briefly discussed in Chapter 10. Our graph will tell how a group of land masses are related to each other.

EXAMPLE 2   MODELING KÖNIGSBERG WITH A GRAPH

In the early 1700s, the city of Königsberg, Germany, was located on both banks and two islands of the Pregel River. Figure 15.5 shows that the town's sections were connected by seven bridges. Draw a graph that models the layout of Königsberg. Use vertices to represent the land masses and edges to represent the bridges.

Left Bank   FIGURE 15.5 The layout of Königsberg

SOLUTION In drawing the graph, the only thing that matters is the relationship between land masses and bridges: which land masses are connected to each other and by how many bridges. We label each of the four land masses with an uppercase letter, shown in Figure 15.6(a).

Next, we use points to represent the land masses. Figure 15.6(b) shows vertices A, B, L, and R. The precise placement of these vertices is not important.

Now we are ready to draw the edges that represent the bridges. There are two bridges that connect island A to right bank R. Therefore, we draw two edges connecting vertex A to vertex R, shown in the graph in Figure 15.6(c). Can you see that there is only one bridge that connects island A to island B? Thus, we draw one edge connecting vertex A to vertex B in our graph. There are also two bridges connecting island A to left bank L, so we draw two edges connecting vertex A to vertex L. Continuing in this manner, we obtain the graph shown in Figure 15.6(c).

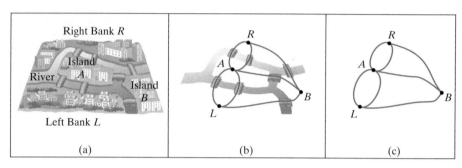

FIGURE 15.6 Creating a graph that models the layout of Königsberg

2 The city of Metroville is located on both banks and three islands of the Metro River. Figure 15.7 shows that the town's sections are connected by five bridges. Draw a graph that models the layout of Metroville.

FIGURE 15.7

In the next example, our graph will tell how a group of states are related to each other.

EXAMPLE 3 MODELING BORDERING RELATIONSHIPS FOR THE NEW ENGLAND STATES

The map in Figure 15.8 shows the New England states. Draw a graph that models which New England states share a common border. Use vertices to represent the states and edges to represent common borders.

SOLUTION Because the states are labeled with their abbreviations, we can use the abbreviations in Figure 15.9(a) to label each vertex. We use points to represent these vertices, shown in Figure 15.9(b). The precise placement of these vertices is not important.

FIGURE 15.8 The New England states

Now we are ready to draw the edges that represent common borders. Whenever two states share a common border, we connect the respective vertices with an edge. For example, Rhode Island shares a common border with Connecticut and with Massachusetts. Therefore, we draw an edge that connects vertex RI to vertex CT and one that connects vertex RI to vertex MA, shown in Figure 15.9(c). Can you see that Massachusetts shares a common border with four states, resulting in edges connecting MA to CT, MA to RI, MA to VT, and MA to NH? Continuing in this manner, we obtain the graph shown in Figure 15.9(c).

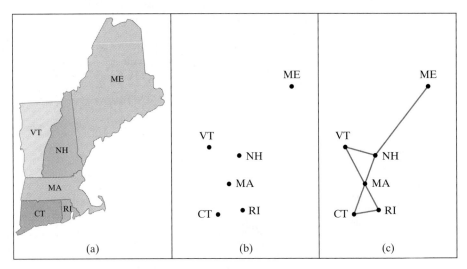

FIGURE 15.9 Creating a graph that models bordering relationships among New England states

 3 Create a graph that models the bordering relationships among the five states shown in Figure 15.10.

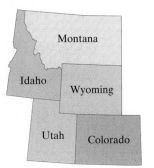

FIGURE 15.10

In the next example, our graph will tell how rooms in a floor plan are related to each other.

FIGURE 15.11

EXAMPLE 4   MODELING CONNECTING RELATIONSHIPS IN A FLOOR PLAN

The floor plan of a four-room house is shown in Figure 15.11. The rooms are labeled *A*, *B*, *C*, and *D*. The outside of the house is labeled *E*. The openings represent doors. Draw a graph that models the connecting relationships in the floor plan. Use vertices to represent the rooms and the outside, and edges to represent the connecting doors.

SOLUTION Because the rooms and outside are labeled, we can use the letters in Figure 15.12(a) to label each vertex. We use points to represent these vertices, shown in Figure 15.12(b).

Now we are ready to draw the edges that represent the doors. Two doors connect the outside, E, with room A, so we draw two edges that connect vertex E to vertex A, shown in Figure 15.12(c). Only one door connects the outside, E, with room B, so we draw one edge from vertex E to vertex B. Two doors connect the outside, E, to room C; we draw two edges from E to C. Counting doors from the outside to each room and doors between the rooms, the graph is completed as shown in Figure 15.12(c).

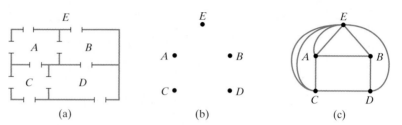

FIGURE 15.12 Creating a graph that models connecting relationships between rooms

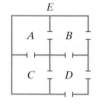

FIGURE 15.13

CHECK POINT 4 The floor plan of a four-room house is shown in Figure 15.13. The rooms are labeled A, B, C, and D. The outside of the house is labeled E. Draw a graph that models the connecting relationships in the floor plan.

In setting up routes for mail carriers, the post office is interested in delivering mail along the route that involves the least amount of walking or driving. Graphs play an important role in problems concerned with finding efficient ways to route services such as mail delivery, garbage collection, and police protection. The first step in the planning and design of delivery routes is creating graphs that model neighborhoods.

FIGURE 15.14

EXAMPLE 5   MODELING WALKING RELATIONSHIPS FOR A NEIGHBORHOOD'S STREETS

A mail carrier delivers mail to the four-block neighborhood shown in Figure 15.14. She parks her truck at the intersection shown in the figure and then walks to deliver mail to each of the houses. The streets on the outside of the neighborhood have houses on one side only. By contrast, the interior streets have houses on both sides of the street. On these streets, the mail carrier must walk down the street twice, covering each side separately. Draw a graph that models the streets of the neighborhood walked by the mail carrier. Use vertices to represent the street intersections and corners. Use one edge if streets must be covered only once and two edges for streets that must be covered twice.

SOLUTION We begin by labeling each of the corners and street intersections with an uppercase letter, shown in Figure 15.15(a).

Next, we use points to represent the corners and street intersections. Figure 15.15(b) shows vertices A through I.

Now we are ready to draw the edges that represent walking relationships between corners and street intersections. The street from B to A must be covered only once, so we draw an edge that connects vertex A to vertex B, shown in Figure 15.15(c). The same is true for the street from A to D. By contrast, the street from D to E has houses on both sides and must be walked twice. Therefore, we draw two edges that connect vertex D to vertex E. Continuing in this manner, the graph is completed as shown in Figure 15.15(c).

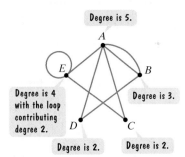

FIGURE 15.15

CHECK POINT **5**   A security guard needs to walk the streets of the neighborhood shown in Figure 15.14. Unlike the postal worker, the guard would like to walk down each street once, whether or not the street has houses on both sides. Draw a graph that models the streets of the neighborhood walked by the security guard.

3 | Understand and use the vocabulary of graph theory.

The Vocabulary of Graph Theory

Every branch of mathematics has its own unique vocabulary. We conclude this section by introducing some of the terms used in graph theory.

The **degree of a vertex** is the number of edges at that vertex. If a loop connects a vertex to itself, that loop contributes 2 to the degree of the vertex. On a graph, the degree of each vertex is found by counting the number of line segments or curves attached to the vertex. Figure 15.16 illustrates a graph and the degree of each vertex.

FIGURE 15.16 The degrees of a graph's vertices

A vertex with an even number of edges attached to it is an **even vertex**. For example, in Figure 15.16, vertices E, D, and C are even. A vertex with an odd number of edges attached to it is an **odd vertex**. In Figure 15.16, vertices A and B are odd.

Two vertices in a graph are said to be **adjacent vertices** if there is at least one edge connecting them. It is helpful to think of adjacent vertices as *connected* vertices.

STUDY TIP

Vertices that are near each other are not necessarily adjacent. In Figure 15.16, vertices C and D are not adjacent because there is no edge connecting them.

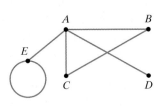

FIGURE 15.17

EXAMPLE 6   IDENTIFYING ADJACENT VERTICES

List the pairs of adjacent vertices for the graph in Figure 15.16.

SOLUTION A systematic way to approach this problem is to first list all the pairs of adjacent vertices involving vertex A, then all those involving B but not A, then all those involving C but neither A nor B, then those involving D but not A, B, or C. Finally, check to see if E is adjacent to itself. (It is.) Thus, the adjacent vertices are A and B, A and C, A and D, A and E, B and D, C and E, and E and E.

CHECK POINT **6**   List the pairs of adjacent vertices for the graph in Figure 15.17.

We can use adjacent vertices to describe movement along a graph. A **path** in a graph is a sequence of adjacent vertices and the edges connecting them. Although a vertex can appear on the path more than once, **an edge can be part of a path only once**. For example, a path along a graph, shown in red, is illustrated in Figure 15.18.

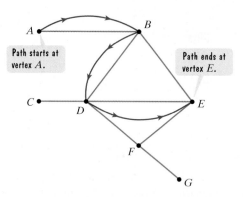

FIGURE 15.18 A path along a graph

You can think of this path as movement from vertex A to vertex B to vertex D to vertex E. We can refer to this path using a sequence of vertices separated by commas. Thus, the path shown in Figure 15.18 is described by A, B, D, E.

The graph in Figure 15.18 has many paths. Can you see that a path does not have to include every vertex and every edge of a graph?

A **circuit** is a path that begins and ends at the same vertex. In Figure 15.19, the path given by B, D, F, E, B, is a circuit. Observe that every circuit is a path. However, because not every path ends at the same vertex where it starts, not every path is a circuit.

The words *connected* and *disconnected* are used to describe graphs. A graph is **connected** if for any two of its vertices there is at least one path connecting them. Thus, a graph is connected if it consists of one piece. If a graph is not connected, it is said to be **disconnected**. A disconnected graph is made up of pieces that are by themselves connected. Such pieces are called the **components** of the graph. Figure 15.20 illustrates connected and disconnected graphs.

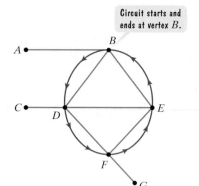

FIGURE 15.19 A circuit along a graph

Connected Graphs

(a)   (b)

Disconnected Graphs

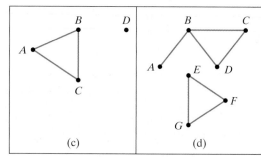

(c)   (d)

FIGURE 15.20 Examples of two connected graphs and two disconnected graphs

STUDY TIP

Do not confuse the definition of *bridge* in graph theory with the *bridges* connecting sections of a city such as Königsberg. In our graph for the layout of Königsberg [Figure 15.6(c) on page 826], none of the edges that model the city's bridges are bridges as defined in graph theory.

A cliché says that if you burn a bridge behind you, you'll never get back to where you were. This cliché tells us something about the word *bridge* in graph theory. A **bridge** is an edge that if removed from a connected graph would leave behind a disconnected graph. For example, compare Figures 15.20(a) and (c). If edge BD were removed from Figure 15.20(a), vertex D would be isolated from the rest of the graph, leaving behind the disconnected graph in Figure 15.20(c). Thus, BD is a bridge for the graph in Figure 15.20(a).

Next, compare Figures 15.20(b) and (d). If edge BE were removed from Figure 15.20(b), the graph would become disconnected, shown by the two components in Figure 15.20(d). Thus, BE is a bridge for the graph in Figure 15.20(b).

Subway Simplification

London's subway system is as sprawling as the city it serves. Drawing the system on a map made it difficult for users to follow. Planning a trip with it was about as easy as finding one's way into and out of a maze—and more difficult if the trip involved changing trains.

In 1931, draftsman Henry C. Beck found a solution, which led to the London underground map so widely used today. Beck's proposal for a user-friendly subway map was to abandon the idea that it should be a literal representation of how the lines ran underground. Instead, it should show which vertices (subway stations) are connected by edges (underground routes). Beck knew that two graphs are equivalent if they have the same number of vertices connected to each other in the same way. The important information was the relationship between the stations. The shapes of the edges were unimportant. For simplicity, Beck used horizontal, vertical, and diagonal lines to represent edges. He also enlarged the central, most complex, part of the system in relation to the simple parts at the outskirts. In 1933, a few experimental copies of the simplified graph that modeled the underground system were printed. They were an immediate success.

Tangled Lines London's subway system is difficult to use on a conventional map. However, a simple graph that models the system (inset) helps travelers find their way.

E X E R C I S E   S E T   1 5 . 1 ●●●●●●

• Practice and Application Exercises

The graph models the baseball schedule for a week. The vertices represent the teams. Each game played during that week is represented as an edge between two teams. Use the information in the graph to solve Exercises 1–4.

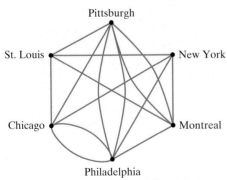

1. How many games are scheduled for Pittsburgh during the week? List the teams that they are playing. How many times are they playing each of these teams?

2. How many games are scheduled for Montreal during the week? List the teams that they are playing. How many times are they playing each of these teams?

3. Do the positions of New York and Montreal correspond to their geographic locations on a map? If not, is the graph drawn incorrectly? Explain your answer.

4. Do the positions of New York and Chicago correspond to their geographic locations on a map? If not, is the graph drawn incorrectly? Explain your answer.

In Exercises 5–6, draw two equivalent graphs for each description.

5. The vertices are $A, B, C,$ and $D.$ The edges are $AB, BC, BD, CD,$ and $CC.$

6. The vertices are $A, B, C,$ and $D.$ The edges are $AD, BC, DC, BB,$ and $DB.$

In Exercises 7–8, explain why the two figures show equivalent graphs. Then draw a third equivalent graph.

7.

8.
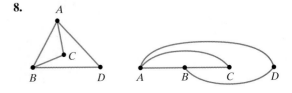

9. Eight students form a math homework group. The students in the group are Zeb, Stryder, Amy, Jed, Evito, Moray, Carrie, and Oryan. Prior to forming the group, Stryder was friends with everyone but Moray. Moray was friends with Zeb, Amy, Carrie, and Evito. Jed was friends with Stryder, Evito, Oryan, and Zeb. Draw a graph that models pairs of friendships among the eight students prior to forming the math homework group.

10. An environmental action group has six members, A, B, C, D, E, and F. The group has three committees: The Preserving Open Space Committee (B, D, and F), the Fund Raising Committee (B, C, and D), and the Wetlands Protection Committee (A, C, D, and E). Draw a graph that models the common members among committees. Use vertices to represent committees and edges to represent common members.

In Exercises 11–12, draw a graph that models the layout of the city shown in each map. Use vertices to represent the land masses and edges to represent the bridges.

11. The City of Gothamville

12. The City of Wisdomville

In Exercises 13–14, create a graph that models the bordering relationships among the states shown in each map. Use vertices to represent the states and edges to represent common borders.

13.

14.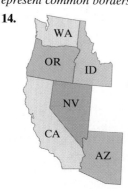

In Exercises 15–18, draw a graph that models the connecting relationships in each floor plan. Use vertices to represent the rooms and the outside, and edges to represent the connecting doors.

15.

16.

17.

18.

In Exercises 19–20, a security guard needs to walk the streets of the neighborhood shown in each figure. The guard is to walk down each street once, whether or not the street has houses on both sides. Draw a graph that models the neighborhood. Use vertices to represent the street intersections and corners. Use edges to represent the streets the security guard needs to walk.

19.

20.

In Exercises 21–22, a mail carrier is to walk the streets of the neighborhood shown in Exercises 19 and 20, respectively. Unlike the security guard, the mail carrier must walk down each street with houses on both sides twice, covering each side separately. Draw a graph that models the neighborhood for the mail carrier. Use vertices to represent the street intersections and corners. Use edges to represent the streets the mail carrier needs to walk, with one edge for streets covered once and two edges for streets covered twice.

21. See the figure for Exercise 19.

22. See the figure for Exercise 20.

In Exercises 23–33, use the following graph.

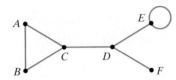

23. Find the degree of each vertex in the graph.

24. Identify the even vertices and identify the odd vertices.

25. Which vertices are adjacent to vertex A?

26. Which vertices are adjacent to vertex D?

27. Use vertices to describe two paths that start at vertex A and end at vertex D.

28. Use vertices to describe two paths that start at vertex B and end at vertex D.

29. Which edges shown on the graph are not included in the following path: E, E, D, C, B, A?

30. Which edges shown on the graph are not included in the following path: E, E, D, C, A, B?

31. Explain why edge CD is a bridge.

32. Explain why edge DE is a bridge.

33. Identify an edge on the graph other than those in Exercises 31 and 32 that is a bridge.

In Exercises 34–48, use the following graph.

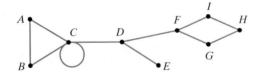

34. Find the degree of each vertex in the graph.

35. Identify the even vertices and identify the odd vertices.

36. Which vertices (or vertex) are adjacent to vertex E?

37. Which vertices are adjacent to vertex F?

38. Use vertices to describe two paths that start at vertex A and end at vertex F.

39. Use vertices to describe two paths that start at vertex B and end at vertex F.

40. Use vertices to describe a circuit that begins and ends at vertex F.

41. Use vertices to describe a circuit that begins and ends at vertex G.

42. Use vertices to describe a path from vertex H to vertex E, passing through vertex I, but not through vertex G.

43. Use vertices to describe a path from vertex A to vertex I, passing through vertices B and G, as well as through the loop.

44. Explain why A, C, D, E, D is not a path.

45. Explain why G, F, D, E, D is not a path.

46. Explain why A, C, D, G is not a path.

47. Explain why H, I, F, E is not a path.

48. Identify three edges that are bridges. Then show the components of the resulting graph once each bridge is removed.

In Exercises 49–52, draw a graph with the given characteristics.

49. The graph has four even vertices.

50. The graph has six odd vertices.

51. The graph has four odd vertices and at least one loop.

52. The graph has eight vertices and exactly one bridge.

• Writing in Mathematics

53. What is a graph? Define vertices and edges as part of your description.

54. Describe how to use a graph to determine whether or not a point where two edges cross is a vertex.

55. What are equivalent graphs?

56. Because a graph can be drawn in many equivalent ways, describe the important part in drawing a graph.

57. What is meant by the degree of a graph's vertex and how is it determined?

58. Describe how to determine if a vertex is even or odd.

59. What are adjacent vertices? If two vertices are near each other in a graph, are they necessarily adjacent? Explain your answer.

60. What is a path in a graph?

61. What is a circuit? Describe the difference between a path and a circuit.

62. What is a connected graph?

63. What is a bridge?

64. Describe a situation involving relationships that can be modeled with a graph.

65. Describe one advantage and one disadvantage of using the graph for the baseball schedule in Exercises 1–4 rather than consulting a newspaper or television guide.

• Critical Thinking Exercises

66. Draw a graph with six vertices and two bridges.

67. Use the information in Exercise 10 to draw a graph that models which pairs of members are on the same committee. (The number of edges should match the number of committees on which two members serve together.)

68. Use inductive reasoning to make a conjecture that compares the sum of the degrees of the vertices of a graph and the number of edges in that graph.

• Group Exercises

69. Group members should determine a relationship that exists among some, but not all, members. Did some of you know one another before the course began? Do some of you have the same academic major? Be as creative as possible in determining this relationship. Then create a graph that serves as a model for describing this relationship.

70. Each group member should select a favorite television series, movie, or novel with an extensive and interesting cast of characters. Determine a relationship that exists among some, but not all, of the characters. Represent the characters as vertices and use edges to show these relationships. Each person should share his or her model with the group, including aspects of the model that give rise to good comedy or drama.

SECTION 15.2 • EULER PATHS AND EULER CIRCUITS

Since the 1970s, municipal services in New York City, including garbage collection, curb sweeping, and snow removal, have been scheduled and organized using graph models. By determining efficient routes for snowplows, garbage trucks, and street sweepers, New York is able to save tens of millions of dollars per year. Such routes must ensure that each street is serviced exactly once without having service vehicles retrace portions of their route.

In the previous section, you learned how to model physical settings with graphs. Now you will see how paths and circuits can solve problems such as constructing efficient routes along city streets for garbage pickup or mail delivery. To solve such problems, we begin by defining special kinds of paths and circuits.

① Understand the definition of an Euler path.

Euler Paths and Euler Circuits

We have seen that a path in a graph is a sequence of adjacent vertices and the edges connecting them. Recall that an edge can be part of a path only once. If a path passes through each edge of a graph exactly one time, it is called an *Euler path*.

> **DEFINITION OF AN EULER PATH**
> An **Euler path** is a path that travels through *every edge* of a graph once and only once. Each edge must be traveled and no edge can be retraced.

We know that vertices separated by commas can be used to designate paths. As we discuss Euler paths, you can use a pencil to trace these paths. We can also indicate a starting vertex and numbered edges to illustrate Euler paths. For example, examine the graph in Figure 15.21.

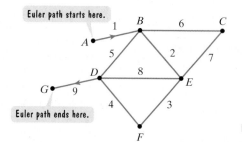

FIGURE 15.21 An Euler path: $A, B, E, F, D, B, C, E, D, G$

The path $A, B, E, F, D, B, C, E, D, G$ is an Euler path because each edge is traveled once. Trace this path with your pencil. Now try using the numbers along the edges.

The voice balloon indicates a starting vertex, A, and the arrow shows which way to trace first. When you arrive at the next vertex, B, take the next numbered edge, 2. When you arrive at the next vertex, E, take the next numbered edge, 3. Continue in this manner until numbered edge 9 ends the path at vertex G.

We will use vertices as well as numbered edges to designate Euler paths. Do you see why the Euler path in Figure 15.21 is not a circuit? A circuit must begin and end at the same vertex. The Euler path in Figure 15.21 begins at vertex A and ends at vertex G.

If an Euler path begins and ends at the same vertex, it is called an *Euler circuit*.

2 | Understand the definition of an Euler circuit.

> ### DEFINITION OF AN EULER CIRCUIT
> An **Euler circuit** is a circuit that travels through every edge of a graph once and only once. Like all circuits, an Euler circuit must begin and end at the same vertex.

The graph in Figure 15.22 shows an Euler circuit.

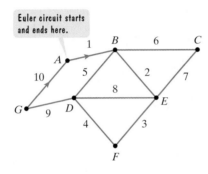

FIGURE 15.22 An Euler circuit: $A, B, E, F, D, B, C, E, D, G, A$

The path $A, B, E, F, D, B, C, E, D, G, A$, shown with numbered edges 1 through 10, is an Euler circuit. Do you see why? Each edge is traced only once. Furthermore, the path begins and ends at the same vertex, A. Notice that **every Euler circuit is an Euler path**. However, **not every Euler path is an Euler circuit**.

Some graphs have no Euler paths. Other graphs have several Euler paths. Furthermore, some graphs with Euler paths have no Euler circuits. **Euler's Theorem** is used to determine if a graph contains Euler paths or Euler circuits.

3 | Use Euler's Theorem.

> ### EULER'S THEOREM
> The following statements are true for connected graphs:
>
> **1.** If a graph has exactly two odd vertices, then it has at least one Euler path, but no Euler circuit. Each Euler path must start at one of the odd vertices and end at the other one.
>
> **2.** If a graph has no odd vertices (all even vertices), it has at least one Euler circuit (which, by definition, is also an Euler path). An Euler circuit can start and end at any vertex.
>
> **3.** If a graph has more than two odd vertices, then it has no Euler paths and no Euler circuits.

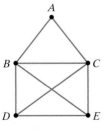

FIGURE 15.23

| EXAMPLE 1 | USING EULER'S THEOREM |

a. Explain why the graph in Figure 15.23 has at least one Euler path.

b. Use trial and error to find one such path.

SOLUTION

a. In Figure 15.24, we count the number of edges at each vertex to determine if the vertex is odd or even. We see that there are exactly two odd vertices, namely D and E. By the first statement in Euler's Theorem, the graph has at least one Euler path, but no Euler circuit.

b. Euler's Theorem tells us that a possible Euler path must start at one of the odd vertices and end at the other one. We will use trial and error to determine an Euler path, starting at vertex D and ending at vertex E. Figure 15.25 shows an Euler path: $D, C, B, E, C, A, B, D, E$. Trace this path and verify the numbers along the edges.

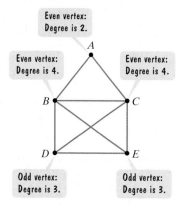

FIGURE 15.24 The graph has two odd vertices.

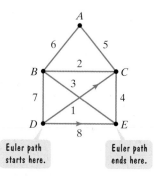

FIGURE 15.25 An Euler path: $D, C, B, E, C, A, B, D, E$

○

CHECK POINT 1 Refer to the graph in Figure 15.23 on page 835. Use trial and error to find an Euler path that starts at E and ends at D. Number the edges of the graph to indicate the path. Then use vertex letters separated by commas to name the path.

───●

EXAMPLE 2　USING EULER'S THEOREM

a. Explain why the graph in Figure 15.26 has at least one Euler circuit.
b. Use trial and error to find one such circuit.

SOLUTION

a. In Figure 15.27, we count the number of edges at each vertex to determine if the vertex is odd or even. We see that the graph has no odd vertices. By the second statement in Euler's Theorem, the graph has at least one Euler circuit.

FIGURE 15.26

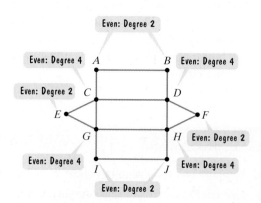

FIGURE 15.27 The graph has no odd vertices.

b. An Euler circuit can start and end at any vertex. We will use trial and error to determine an Euler circuit, starting and ending at vertex H. Remember that you must trace every edge exactly once and start and end at H. Figure 15.28 shows an Euler circuit. Trace this circuit using the vertices in the figure's caption and verify the numbers along the edges.

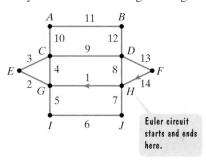

FIGURE 15.28 An Euler circuit: $H, G, E, C, G, I, J, H, D, C, A, B, D, F, H$

○

CHECK POINT 2 Refer to the graph in Figure 15.26 in the margin on the previous page. Use trial and error to find an Euler circuit that starts and ends at G. Number the edges of the graph to indicate the circuit. Then use vertex letters separated by commas to name the circuit.

Figure 15.29 shows a graph with one even vertex and four odd vertices. Because the graph has more than two odd vertices, by the third statement in Euler's Theorem, it has no Euler paths and no Euler circuits.

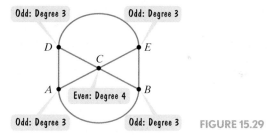

FIGURE 15.29

4 | Solve problems using Euler's Theorem.

Applications of Euler's Theorem

We can use Euler's Theorem to solve problems involving situations modeled by graphs. For example, we return to the graph that models the layout of Königsberg, shown in Figure 15.30(c). As we mentioned in Chapter 10, people in the city were interested in finding if it were possible to walk through the city so as to cross each bridge exactly once. Translated into the language of graph theory, we are interested in whether the graph in Figure 15.30(c) has an Euler path. Count the number of odd vertices. The graph has four odd vertices. Because it has more than two odd vertices, it has no Euler paths. Thus, there is no possible way anyone in Königsberg can walk across all of the bridges without having to recross some of the them.

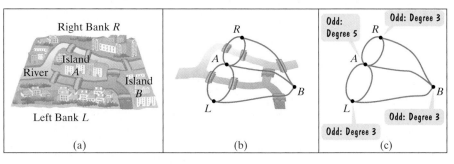

FIGURE 15.30 Revisiting the graph that models the layout of Königsberg

EXAMPLE 3 APPLYING EULER'S THEOREM

Figure 15.31(c) shows the graph we developed to model the connecting relationships in a floor plan. Recall from our work in Section 15.1 that A, B, C, and D represent the rooms and E represents the outside of the house. The edges represent the connecting doors.

a. Is it possible to find a path that uses each door exactly once?

b. If it is possible, use trial and error to show such a path on the graph in Figure 15.31(c) and on the floor plan in Figure 15.31(a).

(a)   (b)   (c)

FIGURE 15.31 Revisiting the graph that models the layout of a floor plan

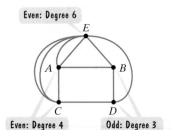

FIGURE 15.32 The graph has two odd vertices.

SOLUTION

a. A path that uses each door (or edge) exactly once means that we are looking for an Euler path or an Euler circuit on the graph in Figure 15.31(c). Figure 15.32 indicates that there are exactly two odd vertices, namely B and D. By Euler's Theorem, the graph has at least one Euler path, but no Euler circuit. It is possible to find a path that uses each door exactly once. It is not possible to begin and end the walk in the same place.

b. Euler's Theorem tells us that a possible Euler path must start at one of the odd vertices and end at the other one. We will use trial and error to determine an Euler path, starting at vertex B (room B in the floor plan) and ending at vertex D (room D in the floor plan). Figure 15.33(a) shows an Euler path on the graph. Figure 15.33(b) translates the path into a walk through the rooms.

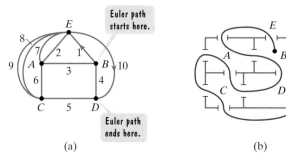

FIGURE 15.33 An Euler path: B, E, A, B, D, C, A, E, C, E, D shown on a graph and on a floor plan

(a)   (b)

CHECK POINT 3 The floor plan of a four-room house and a graph that models the connecting relationships in the floor plan are shown in Figure 15.34.

a. Is it possible to find a path that uses each door exactly once?

b. If it is possible, use trial and error to show such a path on the graph in Figure 15.34(b) and the floor plan in Figure 15.34(a).

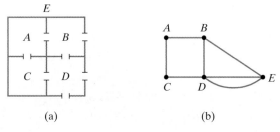

(a)   (b)

FIGURE 15.34 A floor plan and a graph that models its connecting relationships

5 | Use Fleury's Algorithm to find possible Euler paths and Euler circuits.

Finding Possible Euler Paths and Euler Circuits without Using Trial and Error

Euler's Theorem enables us to count a graph's odd vertices and determine if it has an Euler path or an Euler circuit. Unfortunately, the theorem provides almost no assistance in finding an actual Euler path or circuit. There is, however, an algorithm, or procedure, for finding such paths and circuits, called **Fleury's Algorithm**.

> **FLEURY'S ALGORITHM**
>
> If Euler's Theorem indicates the existence of an Euler path or Euler circuit, one can be found using the following procedure:
>
> **1.** If the graph has exactly two odd vertices (and therefore an Euler path), choose one of the two odd vertices as the starting point. If the graph has no odd vertices (and therefore an Euler circuit), choose any vertex as the starting point.
>
> **2.** Number edges as you trace through the graph according to the following rules:
> - After you have traveled over an edge, erase it. (This is because you must travel each edge exactly once.) Show the erased edges as dashed lines.
> - When faced with a choice of edges to trace, choose an edge that is not a bridge. Travel over an edge that is a bridge only if there is no alternative.

STUDY TIP

Don't cross a bridge unless you have to!

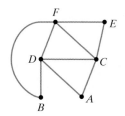

FIGURE 15.35

EXAMPLE 4 USING FLEURY'S ALGORITHM

The graph in Figure 15.35 has at least one Euler circuit. Find one by Fleury's Algorithm.

SOLUTION The graph has no odd vertices, so we can begin at any vertex. We choose vertex A as the starting point and proceed as follows.

Step 1

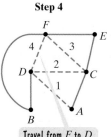

Travel from A to D and erase edge AD.

We can also travel from A to C.

Step 2

CA is a bridge. If it were removed, vertex A would be isolated from the rest of the graph.

Travel from D to C and erase edge DC.

We can also travel from D to F or B.

Step 3

FE is a bridge. If it were removed, the graph would have two disconnected components.

Travel from C to F and erase edge CF.

We can also travel from C to E, but not from C to A. Don't cross the bridge.

Step 4

Travel from F to D and erase edge FD.

We can also travel from F to B, but not from F to E. Don't cross the bridge.

Step 5

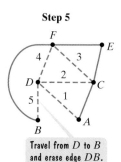

Travel from D to B and erase edge DB.

There are no other choices.

Steps 6, 7, 8, 9

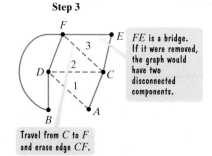

Travel from B to F, F to E, E to C, and C to A, and erase the respective edges.

There are no choices at each step.

The completed Euler circuit is shown in Figure 15.36.

Euler circuit starts and ends here.

FIGURE 15.36 An Euler circuit:
$A, D, C, F, D, B, F, E, C, A$

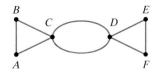

FIGURE 15.37

CHECK POINT 4 The graph in Figure 15.37 has at least one Euler circuit. Find one by Fleury's Algorithm.

In the exercise set, we will revisit many of the graph models from the previous section. In solving problems with these models, you can use trial and error or Fleury's Algorithm to find possible Euler paths and Euler circuits. The procedure of Fleury's Algorithm is useful as graphs become more complicated.

Here is a summary, in chart form, of Euler's Theorem that you might find helpful in the exercise set that follows:

SUMMARY OF EULER'S THEOREM

Number of Odd Vertices	Euler Paths	Euler Circuits
None (all even)	at least one	at least one
exactly two	at least one	none
more than two	none	none

EXERCISE SET 15.2 ●●●●●●

• Practice Exercises

In Exercises 1–6, use the graph shown. In each exercise, a path along the graph is described. Trace this path with a pencil and number the edges. Then determine if the path is an Euler path, an Euler circuit, or neither. Explain your answer.

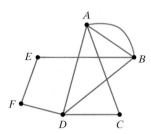

1. $F, E, B, A, C, D, A, B, D$
2. $F, E, B, A, B, D, C, A, D$
3. $F, E, B, A, C, D, A, B, D, F$
4. $F, E, B, A, B, D, C, A, D, F$
5. $A, B, A, C, D, B, E, F, D$
6. $A, B, A, C, D, F, E, B, D$

In Exercises 7–8, a graph is given.

   a. *Explain why the graph has at least one Euler path.*

   b. *Use trial and error or Fleury's Algorithm to find one such path.*

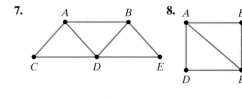

7.   8.

In Exercises 9–10, a graph is given.

   a. *Explain why the graph has at least one Euler circuit.*

   b. *Use trial and error or Fleury's Algorithm to find one such circuit.*

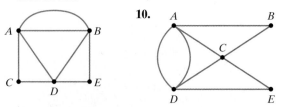

9.   10.

In Exercises 11–12, a graph is given. Explain why each graph has no Euler paths and no Euler circuits.

11.

12.

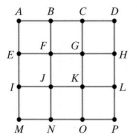

In Exercises 13–18, a connected graph is described. Determine whether the graph has an Euler path (but not an Euler circuit), an Euler circuit, or neither an Euler path nor an Euler circuit. Explain your answer.

13. The graph has 60 even vertices and no odd vertices.

14. The graph has 80 even vertices and no odd vertices.

15. The graph has 58 even vertices and two odd vertices.

16. The graph has 78 even vertices and two odd vertices.

17. The graph has 57 even vertices and four odd vertices.

18. The graph has 77 even vertices and four odd vertices.

In Exercises 19–32, a graph is given.

   a. Determine whether the graph has an Euler path, an Euler circuit, or neither.

   b. If the graph has an Euler path or circuit, use trial and error or Fleury's Algorithm to find one.

19.

20.

21.

22.

23.

24.

25.

26.

27.

28.

29.

30.

31.

32.

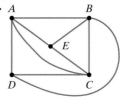

In Exercises 33–36, use Fleury's Algorithm to find an Euler path.

33.

34.

35.

36.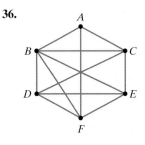

In Exercises 37–40, use Fleury's Algorithm to find an Euler circuit.

37.

38.

39.

40.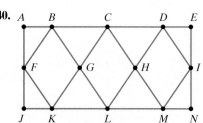

• Practice Plus

In Exercises 41–44, a graph is given.

   a. *Modify the graph by removing the least number of edges so that the resulting graph has an Euler circuit.*

   b. *Find an Euler circuit for the modified graph.*

41.

42.

43.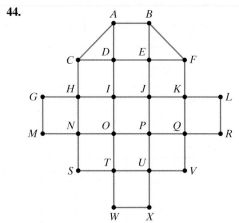

44.

• Application Exercises

In Exercises 45–48, we revisit the four-block neighborhood discussed in the previous section. Recall that a mail carrier parks her truck at the intersection shown in the figure and then walks to deliver mail to each of the houses. The streets on the outside of the neighborhood have houses on one side only. The interior streets have houses on both sides of the street. On these streets, the mail carrier must walk down the street twice, covering each side of the street separately. A graph that models the streets of the neighborhood walked by the mail carrier is shown.

Mail carrier starts here.

45. Use Euler's Theorem to explain why it is possible for the mail carrier to park at B, deliver mail to each house without retracing her route, and then return to B.

46. Use trial and error or Fleury's Algorithm to find an Euler circuit that starts and ends at vertex B on the graph that models the neighborhood.

47. Use your Euler circuit in Exercise 46 to show the mail carrier the route she should follow on the map of the neighborhood. Use the method of your choice, such as red lines with arrows, but be sure that the route is clearly designated.

48. A security guard needs to walk the streets of the neighborhood. Unlike the postal worker, the guard is to walk down each street once, whether or not the street has houses on both sides. Draw a graph that models the streets of the neighborhood walked by the security guard. Then determine whether the residents in the neighborhood will be able to establish a route for the security guard so that each street is walked exactly once. If this is possible, use your map to show where the guard should begin the walk.

49. A security guard needs to walk the streets of the neighborhood shown, walking each street once.

a. Draw a graph that models the streets of the neighborhood walked by the security guard.

b. Determine whether the residents in the neighborhood will be able to establish a route for the security guard so that each street is walked exactly once. If this is possible, use your map to show where the guard should begin the walk.

50. A mail carrier needs to deliver mail to each house in the three-block neighborhood shown. He plans to park at one of the street intersections and walk to deliver mail. All streets have houses on both sides. This means that the mail carrier must walk down every street twice, delivering mail to each side separately.

a. Draw a graph that models the streets of the neighborhood walked by the mail carrier.

b. Use the graph to determine if the carrier can park at an intersection, deliver mail to each house without retracing the side of any street, and return to the parked truck.

c. If such a walk is possible, show the path on your graph in part (a). Then trace this route on the neighborhood map in a manner that is clear to the mail carrier.

In Exercises 51–52, the layout of a city with land masses and bridges is shown.

a. *Draw a graph that models the layout of the city. Use vertices to represent the land masses and edges to represent the bridges.*

b. *Use the graph to determine if the city residents would be able to walk across all of the bridges without crossing the same bridge twice.*

c. *If such a walk is possible, show the path on your graph in part (a). Then trace this route on the city map in a manner that is clear to the city's residents.*

51.

52.

53. The figure shows a map of a portion of New York City with the bridge and tunnel connections. Use a graph to determine if it is possible to visit Manhattan, Long Island, Staten Island, and New Jersey using each bridge or tunnel only once.

In Exercises 54–55, a floor plan is shown.

   a. *Draw a graph that models the connecting relationships in each floor plan. Use vertices to represent the rooms and the outside, and edges to represent the connecting doors.*

   b. *Use your graph to determine if it is possible to find a path that uses each door only once.*

   c. *If such a path is possible, show it on your graph in part (a). Then trace this route on the floor plan in a manner that is clear to a person strolling through the house.*

54.

55.

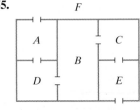

In Exercises 56–58, we revisit the map of the New England states discussed in the previous section. Shown in the figure are the map and the graph that models the bordering relationships among the six states.

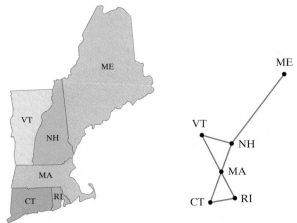

56. Use Euler's Theorem to explain why it is possible to find a path that crosses each common state border exactly once.

57. Use trial and error or Fleury's Algorithm to find an Euler path on the graph that models the map.

58. Use your Euler path in Exercise 57 to show the route on the map of the New England states.

In Exercises 59–60, a map is shown.

   a. *Draw a graph that models each map. Use vertices to represent the states and edges to represent common borders.*

   b. *Use your graph to determine if it is possible to find a path that crosses each common state border exactly once.*

   c. *If such a trip is possible, show the path on your graph in part (a). Then trace this route on the map in a manner that is clear to people driving through these states.*

   d. *Determine if it is possible to find a path that crosses each common state border exactly once, starting and ending the trip in the same state.*

59. **60.**

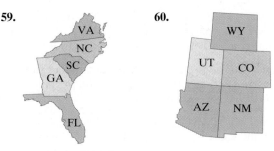

• Writing in Mathematics

61. What is an Euler path?

62. What is an Euler circuit?

63. How do you determine if a graph has at least one Euler path, but no Euler circuit?

64. How do you determine if a graph has at least one Euler circuit?

65. How do you determine if a graph has no Euler paths and no Euler circuits?

66. What is the purpose of Fleury's Algorithm?

67. If a graph has at least one Euler path, but no Euler circuit, which vertex should be chosen as the starting point for a path?

68. Explain why it is important that the director of municipal services (police patrols, garbage collection, curb sweeping, snow removal) of a large city have a knowledge of graph theory.

• Critical Thinking Exercises

69. Refer to the layout of Königsberg in Figure 15.30 on page 837. Suppose that the citizens of the city decide to build a new bridge. Where should it be located to make it possible to walk through the city and cross each bridge exactly once? If such a location is not possible, so state and explain why.

70. A police car would like to patrol each street in the neighborhood shown on the map exactly once. Use a numbering system from 1 through 31, one number per street, to show the police how this can be done.

71. Use Fleury's Algorithm to find an Euler circuit.

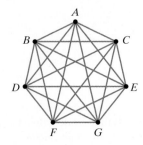

SECTION 15.3 • HAMILTON PATHS AND HAMILTON CIRCUITS

OBJECTIVES

1. Understand the definitions of Hamilton paths and Hamilton circuits.

2. Find the number of Hamilton circuits in a complete graph.

3. Understand and use weighted graphs.

4. Use the Brute Force Method to solve traveling salesperson problems.

5. Use the Nearest Neighbor Method to approximate solutions to traveling salesperson problems.

In the last section, we studied paths and circuits that covered every edge of a graph. Using every edge of a graph exactly once is helpful for garbage collection, curb sweeping, or snow removal. But what about a United Parcel Service (UPS) driver trying to find the best way to deliver packages around town? We can model the delivery locations as the vertices on a graph and the roads between the locations as the edges. The driver is only concerned with finding a path that passes through each vertex of the graph once. It is not important to use every road, or edge, between delivery locations. In this section, we focus on paths and circuits that contain each vertex of a graph exactly once.

1 | Understand the definitions of Hamilton paths and Hamilton circuits.

Hamilton Paths and Hamilton Circuits

Trying to find the best way to deliver packages around town or planning the best route by which to run a series of errands can be modeled and solved using paths and circuits that pass through each vertex of a graph exactly once. These kinds of paths and circuits are named after the Irish mathematician William Rowan Hamilton (1805–1865).

STUDY TIP

If you take the word *edge* in the definition of an Euler circuit and replace it by the word *vertex*, you obtain the definition of a Hamilton circuit. However, the two kinds of circuits are otherwise unrelated.

> **HAMILTON PATHS AND CIRCUITS**
> A path that passes through each vertex of a graph exactly once is called a **Hamilton path**. If a Hamilton path begins and ends at the same vertex and passes through all other vertices exactly once, it is called a **Hamilton circuit**.

FIGURE 15.38

EXAMPLE 1 | EXAMPLES OF HAMILTON PATHS AND HAMILTON CIRCUITS

a. Find a Hamilton path for the graph in Figure 15.38.

b. Find a Hamilton circuit for the graph in Figure 15.38.

SOLUTION

a. A Hamilton path must pass through each vertex exactly once. The graph has many Hamilton paths. An example of such a path is

$$A, B, C, D, E.$$

b. A Hamilton circuit must pass through every vertex exactly once and begin and end at the same vertex. The graph has many Hamilton circuits. An example of such a circuit is

$$A, B, C, D, E, A.$$

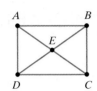

FIGURE 15.38 (repeated)

The graph in Figure 15.38 has many Hamilton paths and circuits. However, because it has four vertices of odd degree, it has no Euler paths and no Euler circuits. When it comes to Hamilton circuits and Euler circuits, a graph can have one or the other, or both, or neither.

a. Find a Hamilton path that begins at vertex E for the graph in Figure 15.39.

b. Find a Hamilton circuit that begins at vertex E for the graph in Figure 15.39.

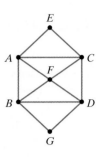

FIGURE 15.39

Consider the graph in Figure 15.40. It has many Hamilton paths, such as

$$A, B, E, C, D \quad \text{or} \quad C, D, E, A, B.$$

However, it has no Hamilton circuits. Regardless of the starting point, it is necessary to pass through vertex E more than once to return to the starting point.

A **complete graph** is a graph that has an edge between each pair of its vertices. Can you see that the graph in Figure 15.40 is not complete? There is no edge between vertex A and vertex D. Nor is there an edge between vertex B and vertex C. Complete graphs are significant because **every complete graph with three or more vertices has a Hamilton circuit**. The graph in Figure 15.40 is not complete and has no Hamilton circuits.

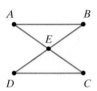

FIGURE 15.40

The Number of Hamilton Circuits in a Complete Graph

2 | Find the number of Hamilton circuits in a complete graph.

The graph in Figure 15.41 has an edge between each pair of its four vertices. Thus, the graph is complete and has a Hamilton circuit. Actually, it has a complete repertoire of Hamilton circuits. For example, one Hamilton circuit is

$$A, B, C, D, A.$$

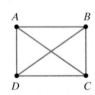

FIGURE 15.41

Any two circuits that pass through the same vertices in the same order will be considered to be the same. For example, here are four different sequences of letters that produce the same Hamilton circuit on the graph in Figure 15.41:

$$A, B, C, D, A \text{ and } B, C, D, A, B \text{ and } C, D, A, B, C \text{ and } D, A, B, C, D.$$

> The Hamilton circuit passing through A, B, C, and D clockwise along the four outside edges can be written in four ways.

In order to avoid this duplication, in forming a Hamilton circuit, we can always assume that it begins at A.

There are six different, or unique, Hamilton circuits for the graph with four vertices in Figure 15.41. They are given as follows:

How many different Hamilton circuits are there in a complete graph? For a complete graph with four vertices, the preceding list indicates that the number of circuits depends upon the number of permutations of the three letters B, C, and D. If a graph has n vertices, once we list vertex A, there are $n - 1$ remaining letters. The number of Hamilton circuits depends upon the number of permutations of the $n - 1$ letters.

Recall from our work in Chapter 11 that factorial notation is useful in determining the number of ordered arrangements, or permutations. If n is a positive integer, then $n!$ (n factorial) is the product of all positive integers from n down to 1. For example, $4! = 4 \cdot 3 \cdot 2 \cdot 1 = 24$ and $6! = 6 \cdot 5 \cdot 4 \cdot 3 \cdot 2 \cdot 1 = 720$.

We can find the number of ordered arrangements of $n - 1$ letters using the Fundamental Counting Principle, discussed in Section 11.1. With $n - 1$ letters to arrange, there are $n - 1$ choices for first position. Once you've chosen the first letter, you'll have $n - 2$ choices for second position. Continuing in this manner, there are $n - 3$ choices for third position, $n - 4$ choices for fourth position, down to only one choice (the one remaining letter) for last position. We multiply the number of choices to find the total number of ordered arrangements:

$$(n - 1)(n - 2)(n - 3) \cdot \cdots \cdot 1.$$

This product, by definition, is $(n - 1)!$. This expression therefore describes the number of Hamilton circuits in a complete graph with n vertices.

> **THE NUMBER OF HAMILTON CIRCUITS IN A COMPLETE GRAPH**
> The number of Hamilton circuits in a complete graph with n vertices is
> $$(n - 1)!.$$

EXAMPLE 2	DETERMINING THE NUMBER OF HAMILTON CIRCUITS

Determine the number of Hamilton circuits in a complete graph with

a. four vertices.   **b.** five vertices.   **c.** eight vertices.

SOLUTION In each case, we use the expression $(n - 1)!$. For four vertices, substitute 4 for n in the expression. For five and eight vertices, substitute 5 and 8, respectively, for n.

a. A complete graph with four vertices has $(4 - 1)! = 3! = 3 \cdot 2 \cdot 1 = 6$ Hamilton circuits. These are the six circuits that we listed at the bottom of page 846.

b. A complete graph with five vertices has

$$(5 - 1)! = 4! = 4 \cdot 3 \cdot 2 \cdot 1 = 24 \text{ Hamilton circuits.}$$

c. A complete graph with eight vertices has

$$(8 - 1)! = 7! = 7 \cdot 6 \cdot 5 \cdot 4 \cdot 3 \cdot 2 \cdot 1 = 5040 \text{ Hamilton circuits.}$$

As the number of vertices in a complete graph increases, notice how quickly the number of Hamilton circuits increases.

○

 CHECK POINT 2 Determine the number of Hamilton circuits in a complete graph with

a. three vertices.   **b.** six vertices.   **c.** ten vertices.

3 Understand and use weighted graphs.

Weighted Graphs and the Traveling Salesperson Problem

Sales directors for large companies are often required to visit regional offices in a number of different cities. How can these visits be scheduled in the cheapest possible way?

For example, a sales director who lives in city A is required to fly to regional offices in cities B, C, and D. Other than starting and ending the trip in city A, there are no restrictions as to the order in which the other three cities are visited.

The one-way fares between each of the four cities are given in Table 15.1. A graph that models this information is shown in Figure 15.42. The vertices represent the cities. The airfare between each pair of cities is shown as a number on the respective edge.

TABLE 15.1 ONE-WAY AIRFARES				
	A	**B**	**C**	**D**
A	*	$190	$124	$157
B	$190	*	$126	$155
C	$124	$126	*	$179
D	$157	$155	$179	*

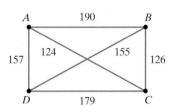

FIGURE 15.42 Modeling Table 15.1 with a graph

STUDY TIP

In a weighted graph, the lengths of the edges do not have to be proportional to the weights.

A complete graph whose edges have numbers attached to them is called a **weighted graph**. The numbers shown along the edges of a weighted graph are called the **weights** of the edges. Figure 15.42 is an example of a weighted graph. The weight of edge AB is 190, modeling a $190 airfare from city A to city B. The sales director needs to find the least expensive way to visit cities B, C, and D once, and return home to A. Our goal is to find the Hamilton circuit with the lowest associated cost.

EXAMPLE 3   UNDERSTANDING THE INFORMATION IN A WEIGHTED GRAPH

Use the weighted graph in Figure 15.42 to find the cost of the trip for the Hamilton circuit A, B, D, C, A.

SOLUTION The trip described by the Hamilton circuit A, B, D, C, A involves the sum of four costs:

$$\$190 + \$155 + \$179 + \$124 = \$648.$$

This is the cost from A to B in A, B, D, C, A.	This is the cost from B to D in A, B, D, C, A.	This is the cost from D to C in A, B, D, C, A.	This is the cost from C to A in A, B, D, C, A.

The cost of the trip is $648.

 Use the weighted graph in Figure 15.42 to find the cost of the trip for the Hamilton circuit A, C, B, D, A.

4 | Use the Brute Force Method to solve traveling salesperson problems.

The traveling salesperson problem can be stated as follows:

THE TRAVELING SALESPERSON PROBLEM

The **traveling salesperson problem** is the problem of finding a Hamilton circuit in a complete weighted graph for which the sum of the weights of the edges is a minimum. Such a Hamilton circuit is called the **optimal Hamilton circuit** or the **optimal solution**.

One method for finding an optimal Hamilton circuit is called the **Brute Force Method**.

> ### THE BRUTE FORCE METHOD OF SOLVING TRAVELING SALESPERSON PROBLEMS
>
> The optimal solution is found using the following steps:
>
> 1. Model the problem with a complete, weighted graph.
> 2. Make a list of all possible Hamilton circuits.
> 3. Determine the sum of the weights of the edges for each of these Hamilton circuits.
> 4. The Hamilton circuit with the minimum sum of weights is the optimal solution.

EXAMPLE 4   USING THE BRUTE FORCE METHOD

Use the weighted graph in Figure 15.42, repeated in the margin, to find the optimal solution. Describe what this means for the sales director who starts at A, flies once to each of B, C, and D, and returns home to A.

SOLUTION The graph has four vertices. Thus, using $(n - 1)!$, there are $(4 - 1)! = 3! = 6$ possible Hamilton circuits. The six possible Hamilton circuits and their total costs are shown in Table 15.2.

FIGURE 15.42 (repeated)

TABLE 15.2 POSSIBLE HAMILTON CIRCUITS AND THEIR TOTAL COSTS

Hamilton Circuit	Sum of the Weights of the Edges	=	Total Cost
A, B, C, D, A	$190 + 126 + 179 + 157$	=	$652
A, B, D, C, A	$190 + 155 + 179 + 124$	=	$648
A, C, B, D, A	$124 + 126 + 155 + 157$	=	$562
A, C, D, B, A	$124 + 179 + 155 + 190$	=	$648
A, D, B, C, A	$157 + 155 + 126 + 124$	=	$562
A, D, C, B, A	$157 + 179 + 126 + 190$	=	$652

Minimum sums

The voice balloon in the last column indicates that two Hamilton circuits have the minimum cost of $562. The optimal solution is either

$$A, C, B, D, A \quad \text{or} \quad A, D, B, C, A.$$

For the sales director, this means that either route shown in Figure 15.43 is the least expensive way to visit the regional offices in cities B, C, and D. Notice that the route in Figure 15.43(b) involves visiting the cities in the reverse order of the route in Figure 15.43(a). Although these are different Hamilton circuits, because the one-way airfares are the same in either direction, the cost is the same regardless of the direction flown.

(a) Fly from A to C to B to D and then back to A.

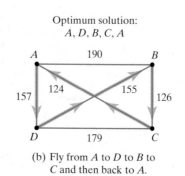

(b) Fly from A to D to B to C and then back to A.

FIGURE 15.43 Options for an optimal solution

A
70   30   20
D
50   10
C   B
15

FIGURE 15.44

Use the Brute Force Method to find the optimal solution for the complete, weighted graph in Figure 15.44. List Hamilton circuits as in Table 15.2 on page 849.

As the number of vertices increases, the rapidly increasing number of possible Hamilton circuits makes the Brute Force Method impractical. Unfortunately, mathematicians have not been able to establish another method for solving the traveling salesperson problem, and they do not know whether it is even possible to find such a method. There are, however, a number of methods for finding approximate solutions.

BLITZER BONUS

The Brute Force Method and Supercomputers

Suppose that a supercomputer can find the sum of the weights of one billion, or 10^9, Hamilton circuits per second. Because there are 31,536,000 seconds in a year, the computer can calculate the sums for approximately 3.2×10^{16} Hamilton circuits in one year. The table shows that as the number of vertices increases, the Brute Force Method is useless even with a powerful computer.

COMPUTER TIME NEEDED TO SOLVE
THE TRAVELING SALESPERSON PROBLEM

Number of Vertices	Number of Hamilton Circuits	Time Needed by a Supercomputer to Find Sums of All Hamilton Circuits
18	$17! \approx 3.6 \times 10^{14}$	≈ 0.01 year ≈ 3.7 days
19	$18! \approx 6.4 \times 10^{15}$	≈ 0.2 year ≈ 73 days
20	$19! \approx 1.2 \times 10^{17}$	≈ 3.8 years
21	$20! \approx 2.4 \times 10^{18}$	≈ 76 years
22	$21! \approx 5.1 \times 10^{19}$	≈ 1597 years
23	$22! \approx 1.1 \times 10^{21}$	$\approx 35,125$ years

5 | Use the Nearest Neighbor Method to approximate solutions to traveling salesperson problems.

Suppose a sales director who lives in city A is required to fly to regional offices in ten other cities and then return home to city A. With $(11 - 1)!$, or 3,628,800, possible Hamilton circuits, a list is out of the question. What do you think of this option? Start at city A. From there, fly to the city to which the airfare is cheapest. Then from there fly to the next city to which the airfare is cheapest, and so on. From the last of the ten cities, fly home to city A.

By continually taking an edge with the smallest weight, we can find approximate solutions to traveling salesperson problems. This method is called the **Nearest Neighbor Method**.

THE NEAREST NEIGHBOR METHOD OF FINDING APPROXIMATE
SOLUTIONS TO TRAVELING SALESPERSON PROBLEMS
The optimal solution can be approximated using the following steps:

1. Model the problem with a complete, weighted graph.
2. Identify the vertex that serves as the starting point.
3. From the starting point, choose the edge with the smallest weight. Move along this edge to the second vertex. (If there is more than one edge with the smallest weight, choose either one.)
4. From the second vertex, choose the edge with the smallest weight that does not lead to a vertex already visited. Move along this edge to the third vertex.
5. Continue building the circuit, one vertex at a time, by moving along the edge with the smallest weight until all vertices are visited.
6. From the last vertex, return to the starting point.

FIGURE 15.45

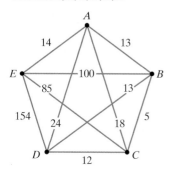

FIGURE 15.46 An approximate
solution: A, C, E, D, B, A

EXAMPLE 5   USING THE NEAREST NEIGHBOR METHOD

A sales director who lives in city A is required to fly to regional offices in cities $B, C,$ $D,$ and $E.$ The weighted graph showing the one-way airfares is given in Figure 15.45. Use the Nearest Neighbor Method to find an approximate solution. What is the total cost?

SOLUTION The Nearest Neighbor Method is carried out as follows:

- Start at $A.$
- Choose the edge with the smallest weight: 114. Move along this edge to $C.$ (cost: $114)
- From C choose the edge with the smallest weight that does not lead to A: 115. Move along this edge to $E.$ (cost: $115)
- From $E,$ choose the edge with the smallest weight that does not lead to a city already visited: 194. Move along this edge to $D.$ (cost: $194)
- From $D,$ there is little choice but to fly to $B,$ the only city not yet visited. (cost: $145)
- From $B,$ close the circuit and return home to $A.$ (cost: $180)

An approximate solution is the Hamilton circuit

$$A, C, E, D, B, A.$$

The circuit is shown in Figure 15.46. The total cost is

$$\$114 + \$115 + \$194 + \$145 + \$180 = \$748.$$

The Brute Force Method can be applied to the 24 possible Hamilton circuits in Example 5. How does the actual solution compare with the $748 total cost obtained by the Nearest Neighbor Method? The actual solution is A, D, B, C, E, A or the reverse order $A, E, C, B, D, A,$ and the cost is $651. This shows that the Nearest Neighbor Method does not always give the optimal solution. Of the 24 Hamilton circuits, eight result in a total cost that is less than the $748 we obtained in Example 5.

CHECK POINT 5   Use the Nearest Neighbor Method to approximate the optimal solution for the complete, weighted graph in Figure 15.47. Begin the circuit at vertex $A.$ What is the total weight of the resulting Hamilton circuit?

FIGURE 15.47

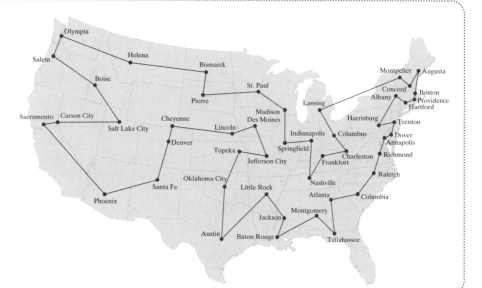

EXERCISE SET 15.3 ●●●●●○

• **Practice Exercises**

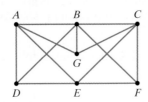

In Exercises 1–4, use the graph shown.

1. Find a Hamilton path that begins at *A* and ends at *B*.
2. Find a Hamilton path that begins at *G* and ends at *E*.
3. Find a Hamilton circuit that begins as *A, B,* ....
4. Find a Hamilton circuit that begins as *A, G,* ....

In Exercises 5–8, use the graph shown.

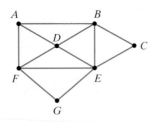

5. Find a Hamilton path that begins at *A* and ends at *D*.
6. Find a Hamilton path that begins at *A* and ends at *G*.
7. Find a Hamilton circuit that begins at *A* and ends with the pair of vertices *D, A*.
8. Find a Hamilton circuit that begins at *F* and ends with the pair of vertices *D, F*.

For each graph in Exercises 9–14,

    a. *Determine if the graph must have Hamilton circuits. Explain your answer.*

    b. *If the graph must have Hamilton circuits, determine the number of such circuits.*

9.

10.

11.

12.

13.

14.

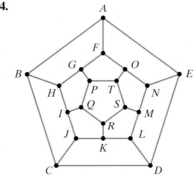

In Exercises 15–18, determine the number of Hamilton circuits in a complete graph with the given number of vertices.

15. 3   **16.** 4   **17.** 12   **18.** 13

In Exercises 19–24, use the complete, weighted graph shown.

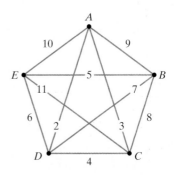

19. Find the weight of edge *CE*.

20. Find the weight of edge *BD*.

21. Find the total weight of the Hamilton circuit

$$A, B, C, E, D, A.$$

22. Find the total weight of the Hamilton circuit

$$A, B, D, C, E, A.$$

23. Find the total weight of the Hamilton circuit

$$A, B, D, E, C, A.$$

24. Find the total weight of the Hamilton circuit

$$A, B, E, C, D, A.$$

In Exercises 25–34, use the complete, weighted graph shown.

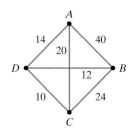

25. Find the total weight of the Hamilton circuit A, B, C, D, A.

26. Find the total weight of the Hamilton circuit A, B, D, C, A.

27. Find the total weight of the Hamilton circuit A, C, B, D, A.

28. Find the total weight of the Hamilton circuit A, C, D, B, A.

29. Find the total weight of the Hamilton circuit A, D, B, C, A.

30. Find the total weight of the Hamilton circuit A, D, C, B, A.

31. Use your answers from Exercises 25–30 and the Brute Force Method to find the optimal solution.

32. Use the Nearest Neighbor Method, with starting vertex A, to find an approximate solution. What is the total weight of the Hamilton circuit?

33. Use the Nearest Neighbor Method, with starting vertex B, to find an approximate solution. What is the total weight of the Hamilton circuit?

34. Use the Nearest Neighbor Method, with starting vertex C, to find an approximate solution. What is the total weight of the Hamilton circuit?

• Practice Plus

In Exercises 35–38, a graph is given.

    a. *Modify the graph by adding the least number of edges so that the resulting graph is complete. Determine the number of Hamilton circuits for the modified graph.*

    b. *Give two Hamilton circuits for the modified graph in part (a).*

    c. *Modify the given graph by removing the least number of edges so that the resulting graph has an Euler circuit.*

    d. *Find an Euler circuit for the modified graph in part (c).*

35.   **36.**

37.

38.

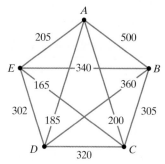

• Application Exercises

In Exercises 39–40, a sales director who lives in city A is required to fly to regional offices in cities B, C, D, and E. The weighted graph shows the one-way airfares between any two cities.

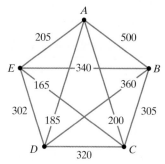

39. Use the Brute Force Method to find the optimal solution. Describe what this means for the sales director. (*Hint*: Because the airfares are the same in either direction, you need only compute the total cost for 12 Hamilton circuits:

    A, B, C, D, E, A; A, B, C, E, D, A;

    A, B, D, C, E, A; A, B, D, E, C, A;

    A, B, E, C, D, A; A, B, E, D, C, A;

    A, C, B, D, E, A; A, C, B, E, D, A;

    A, C, D, B, E, A; A, C, E, B, D, A;

    A, D, B, C, E, A; A, D, C, B, E, A.)

40. Use the Nearest Neighbor Method, with starting vertex A, to find an approximate solution. What is the total cost for this Hamilton circuit?

You have five errands to run around town, in no particular order. You plan to start and end at home. You must go to the post office, deposit a check at the bank, drop off dry cleaning, visit a friend at the hospital, and get a flu shot. The map shows your home and the locations of your five errands. Each block represents one mile. Also shown is a weighted graph with distances on the appropriate edges. In Exercises 41–44, your goal is to run the errands and return home using the shortest route.

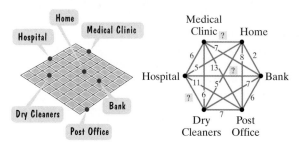

41. Use the map to fill in the three missing weights in the graph.

42. If each Hamilton circuit represents a route to run your errands, how many different routes are possible?

(In Exercises 43–44, continue to refer to the map and weighted graph at the bottom of the previous page.)

43. Using the Brute Force Method, the optimal solution is Home, Bank, Post Office, Dry Cleaners, Hospital, Medical Clinic, Home. What is the total length of the shortest route?

44. Use the Nearest Neighbor Method to find an approximate solution. What is the total length of the shortest route using this solution? How does this compare with your answer to Exercise 43?

In Exercises 45–47, you have three errands to run around town, although in no particular order. You plan to start and end at home. You must go to the bank, the post office, and the market. Distances, in miles, between any two of these locations are given in the table.

DISTANCES (IN MILES) BETWEEN LOCATIONS

	Home	Bank	Post Office	Market
Home	*	3	5.5	3.5
Bank	3	*	4	5
Post Office	5.5	4	*	4.5
Market	3.5	5	4.5	*

45. Create a complete, weighted graph that models the information in the table.

46. Use the Brute Force Method to find the shortest route to run your errands and return home. What is the minimum distance you can travel?

47. Use the Nearest Neighbor Method to approximate the shortest route to run your errands and return home. What is the minimum distance given by the Hamilton circuit? How does this compare with your answer to Exercise 46?

• Writing in Mathematics

48. What is a Hamilton path? How does this differ from an Euler path?

49. What is a Hamilton circuit? How does this differ from an Euler circuit?

50. What is a complete graph?

51. How can you look at a graph and determine if it has a Hamilton circuit?

52. Describe how to determine the number of Hamilton circuits in a complete graph.

53. What is a weighted graph and what are the weights?

54. What is the traveling salesperson problem? What is the optimal solution?

55. Describe the Brute Force Method of solving traveling salesperson problems.

56. Why is the Brute Force Method impractical for large numbers of vertices?

57. Describe the Nearest Neighbor Method for approximating the optimal solution to traveling salesperson problems.

58. Describe a practical example of a traveling salesperson problem other than those involving one-way airfares or distances between errand locations.

59. An efficient solution for solving traveling salesperson problems has eluded mathematicians for more than 50 years. What explanations can you offer for this?

• Critical Thinking Exercises

60. A complete graph has 120 distinct Hamilton circuits. How many vertices does the graph have?

61. The answer section in a math textbook states that the number of Hamilton circuits in a particular complete graph is 25. How do you know that there is an error in the answer section?

62. Ambassadors from countries $A, B, C, D, E,$ and F are to be seated around a circular conference table. Friendly relations among the various countries are described as follows: A has friendly relations with B and F. B has friendly relations with $A, C,$ and E. C has friendly relations with $B, D, E,$ and F. E has friendly relations with $B, C, D,$ and F. All friendly relations are mutual. Using vertices to represent countries and edges to represent friendly relations, draw a graph that models the information given. Then use a Hamilton circuit to devise a seating arrangement around the table so that the ambassadors from B and E are seated next to each other, and each ambassador represents a country that has friendly relations with the countries represented by the ambassadors next to him or her.

• Group Exercise

63. In this group exercise, you will create and solve a traveling salesperson problem similar to Exercises 39 and 40. Consult the graph given for these exercises as you work on this activity.

  a. Group members should agree on four cities to be visited.

  b. As shown in the graph for Exercises 39 and 40, assume that you are located at A. Let $B, C, D,$ and E represent each of the four cities you have agreed upon. Consult the Internet and use one-way airfares between cities to create a weighted graph.

  c. As you did in Exercise 39, use the Brute Force Method to find the optimal solution to visiting each of your chosen cities and returning home.

  d. As you did in Exercise 40, use the Nearest Neighbor Method to approximate the optimal solution. How much money does the group save using the optimal solution instead of the approximation?

SECTION 15.4 • TREES

I need to call the Weather Channel to let them know I just shoveled three feet of "partly cloudy" off my driveway. This late spring storm caught all of us by surprise. I was amazed that classes were not cancelled. Somehow the campus groundskeeper managed to shovel the minimum total length of walkways while ensuring that students could walk from building to building.

The general theme of this section is finding an efficient network linking a set of points. Think about the cleared campus sidewalks. Because of the unexpected storm, there is not enough time to shovel every sidewalk. Instead, campus services must clear a select number of sidewalks so that by moving from building to building, students can reach any location without having to trudge through mountains of snow. Finding efficient networks is accomplished using special kinds of graphs, called *trees*.

1 Understand the definition and properties of a tree.

Trees

The campus groundskeeper is interested in a path that passes though each vertex (campus building) of a graph exactly once with the smallest possible number of edges (cleared sidewalks). A graph with the smallest number of edges that allows all vertices to be reached from all other vertices is called a *tree*.

Figure 15.48 shows examples of graphs that are trees.

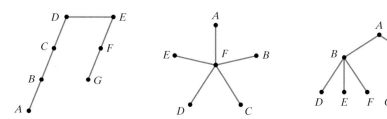

FIGURE 15.48 Examples of graphs that are trees

Notice that each graph is connected. This is a requirement because we must be able to reach any vertex from any other vertex. Furthermore, no graph contains any circuits. This is because vertices must be reached with the smallest number of edges.

Thus, the graphs in Figure 15.49 are not trees. The circuits create redundant connections—take away each redundant connection and all vertices can still be reached from all other vertices.

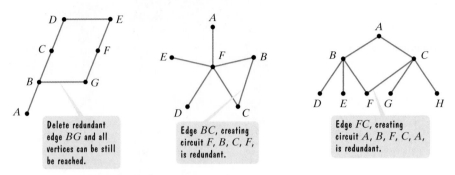

FIGURE 15.49 Examples of graphs that are not trees

Using these ideas, we are now ready to define a tree and list some of its properties.

STUDY TIP

Do not confuse a *connected* graph with a *complete* graph. A connected graph has at least one path between each pair of its vertices. Because a tree has exactly one path joining any two vertices, it is connected. By contrast, a complete graph has an edge between each pair of its vertices. A tree is not a complete graph. In clearing campus sidewalks, there is not enough time to create an edge (a cleared path) between each pair of buildings (vertices).

> **DEFINITION AND PROPERTIES OF A TREE**
>
> A **tree** is a graph that is connected and has no circuits. All trees have the following properties:
>
> 1. There is one and only one path joining any two vertices.
> 2. Every edge is a bridge.
> 3. A tree with n vertices must have $n - 1$ edges.

Property 3 is a numerical property of trees that relates the number of vertices and the number of edges. The total number of edges is always one less than the number of vertices. For example, a tree with 5 vertices must have $5 - 1$, or 4, edges.

EXAMPLE 1   IDENTIFYING TREES

Which graph in Figure 15.50 is a tree? Explain why the other two graphs shown are not trees.

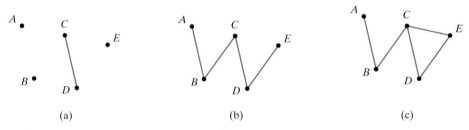

FIGURE 15.50 Identifying a tree

SOLUTION The graph in Figure 15.50(b) is a tree. It is connected and has no circuits. There is only one path joining any two vertices. Every edge is a bridge; if removed, each edge would create a disconnected graph. Finally, the graph has 5 vertices and $5 - 1$, or 4, edges.

The graph in Figure 15.50(a) is not a tree because it is disconnected. There are five vertices and only one edge; a tree with five vertices must have four edges.

The graph in Figure 15.50(c) is not a tree because it has a circuit, namely C, D, E, C. There are five vertices and five edges; a tree with five vertices must have four edges.   ○

Which graph in Figure 15.51 is a tree? Explain why the other two graphs shown are not trees.

FIGURE 15.51

(a)   **(b)**   **(c)**

Find a spanning tree for a connected graph.

Spanning Trees

One way to increase the efficiency of a network is to remove redundant connections. We are interested in a **subgraph**, meaning a set of vertices and edges chosen from among those of the original graph. Figure 15.52 illustrates a graph and two possible subgraphs.

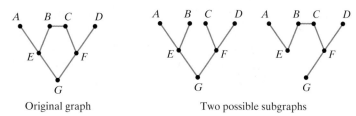

Original graph   Two possible subgraphs

FIGURE 15.52 A graph and two possible subgraphs

The original graph is a connected graph with seven vertices and seven edges. Each subgraph has all seven of the vertices of the connected graph and six of its edges. Although the original graph is not a tree, each subgraph is a tree—that is, each is connected and contains no circuits.

A subgraph that contains all of a connected graph's vertices, is connected, and contains no circuits is called a **spanning tree**. The two subgraphs in Figure 15.52 are spanning trees for the original graph. By removing redundant connections, the spanning trees increase the efficiency of the network modeled by the original graph.

It is possible to start with a connected graph, retain all of its vertices, and remove edges until a spanning tree remains. Being a tree, the spanning tree must have one less edge than it has vertices.

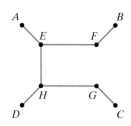

FIGURE 15.53

EXAMPLE 2   FINDING A SPANNING TREE

Find a spanning tree for the graph in Figure 15.53.

SOLUTION A possible spanning tree must contain all eight vertices shown in the connected graph in Figure 15.53. The spanning tree must have one less edge than it has vertices, so it must have seven edges. The graph in Figure 15.53 has 12 edges, so we need to remove five edges. We break the inner rectangular circuit by removing edge FG. We break the outer rectangular circuit by removing all four of its edges while retaining the edges leading to vertices $A, B, C,$ and D. This leaves us the spanning tree in Figure 15.54. Notice that each edge is a bridge and no circuits are present.

 Find a spanning tree for the graph in Figure 15.55.

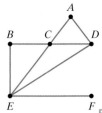

FIGURE 15.54 A spanning tree for the graph in Figure 15.53

FIGURE 15.55

3 | Find the minimum spanning tree for a weighted graph.

Minimum Spanning Trees and Kruskal's Algorithm

Many applied problems involve creating the most efficient network for a weighted graph. The weights often model distances, costs, or time, which we want to minimize. We do this by finding a *minimum spanning tree*.

> **MINIMUM SPANNING TREES**
>
> The **minimum spanning tree** for a weighted graph is a spanning tree with the smallest possible total weight.

Figures 15.56(b) and (c) show two spanning trees for the weighted graph in Figure 15.56(a). The total weight for the spanning tree in Figure 15.56(c), 107, is less than that in Figure 15.56(b), 119. Is this the minimum spanning tree, or should we continue to explore other possible spanning trees whose total weight might be less than 107?

(a) Original
    weighted graph

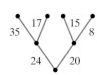

(b) A spanning tree
    with weight
    35 + 24 + 20 + 8 + 17 + 15
    = 119

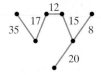

(c) A spanning tree
    with weight
    35 + 17 + 12 + 15 + 20 + 8
    = 107

FIGURE 15.56 A weighted graph and two spanning trees with their weights

A very simple graph can have many spanning trees. Finding the minimum spanning tree by finding all possible spanning trees and comparing their weights would be too time-consuming. In 1956, the American mathematician Joseph Kruskal discovered a procedure that will always yield a minimum spanning tree for a weighted graph. The basic idea in **Kruskal's Algorithm** is to always pick the smallest available edge but avoid creating any circuits.

> **KRUSKAL'S ALGORITHM**
>
> Here is a procedure for finding the minimum spanning tree from a weighted graph:
>
> **1.** Find the edge with the smallest weight in the graph. If there is more than one, pick one at random. Mark it in red (or using any other designation).
>
> **2.** Find the next-smallest edge in the graph. If there is more than one, pick one at random. Mark it in red.
>
> **3.** Find the next-smallest unmarked edge in the graph that does not create a red circuit. If there is more than one, pick one at random. Mark it in red.
>
> **4.** Repeat step 3 until all vertices have been included. The red edges are the desired minimum spanning tree.

EXAMPLE 3   USING KRUSKAL'S ALGORITHM

Seven buildings on a college campus are connected by the sidewalks shown in Figure 15.57. The weighted graph in Figure 15.58 represents buildings as vertices,

FIGURE 15.57 A campus with seven buildings and connecting sidewalks

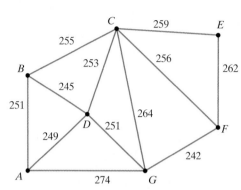

FIGURE 15.58 A weighted graph modeling the campus in Figure 15.57

sidewalks as edges, and sidewalk lengths as weights. A heavy snow has fallen and the sidewalks need to be cleared quickly. Campus services decides to clear as little as possible and still ensure that students walking from building to building will be able to do so along cleared paths. Determine the shortest series of sidewalks to clear. What is the total length of the sidewalks that need to be cleared?

SOLUTION Campus services wants to keep the total length of cleared sidewalks to a minimum and still have a cleared path connecting any two buildings. Thus, they are seeking a minimum spanning tree for the weighted graph in Figure 15.58. We find this minimum spanning tree using Kruskal's Algorithm. Refer to Figure 15.59 as you read the steps in the algorithm.

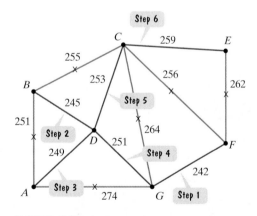

FIGURE 15.59 Finding a minimum spanning tree

Step 1. Find the edge with the smallest weight. Select edge *GF* (length: 242 feet) by marking it in red.

Step 2. Find the next-smallest edge in the graph. Select edge *BD* (length: 245 feet) by marking it in red.

Step 3. Find the next-smallest edge in the graph. Select edge *AD* (length: 249 feet) by marking it in red.

Step 4. Find the next-smallest edge in the graph that does not create a circuit. The next-smallest edges are *AB* and *DG* (length of each: 251 feet). Do not select *AB*—it creates a circuit. Select edge *DG* by marking it in red.

FIGURE 15.59 (repeated)

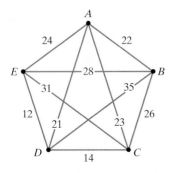

FIGURE 15.60

Step 5. Find the next-smallest edge in the graph that does not create a circuit. Select edge *CD* (length: 253 feet) by marking it in red. Notice that this does not create a circuit.

Step 6. Find the next-smallest edge in the graph that does not create a circuit. The next-smallest edge is *BC* (length: 255 feet), but this creates a circuit. Discard *BC*. The next-smallest edge is *CF* (length: 256 feet), but this also creates a circuit. Discard *CF*. The next-smallest edge is *CE* (length: 259 feet). This does not create a circuit, so select edge *CE* by marking it in red.

Can you see that the minimum spanning tree in Figure 15.59 is completed? The red subgraph contains all of the graph's seven vertices, is connected, contains no circuits, and has 7 − 1, or 6, edges. Therefore, the red subgraph in Figure 15.59 shows the shortest series of sidewalks to clear. From the figure, we see that there are

$$242 + 245 + 249 + 251 + 253 + 259,$$

or 1499 feet of sidewalks that need to be cleared.

CHECK POINT 3 Use Kruskal's Algorithm to find the minimum spanning tree for the graph in Figure 15.60. Give the total weight of the minimum spanning tree.

BLITZER BONUS

A Family Tree: The Sopranos

The Sopranos: Only on cable could they have gotten away with this violent and satiric profile of an angst-ridden mafia family man and his dysfunctional domestic clan. Figure 15.61 shows three generations of HBO's Soprano family. Figure 15.62 models this information with a tree. The vertices represent some of the pictured people. The edges represent parent-child relationships. Genealogists use trees like the one in Figure 15.62 to show the relationship between members of different generations of a family.

FIGURE 15.61 Three generations of the Soprano family

FIGURE 15.62 A tree modeling Soprano parent-child relationships

Corrado "Junior" Soprano, Jr.

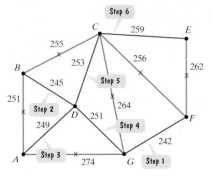

Giovanni "Johnny Boy" Soprano

Livia Pollio

Barbara Soprano

Janice "Parvati" Soprano

Anthony "Tony" Soprano

Carmella DeAngelis Soprano

Anthony "A.J." Soprano, Jr.

Meadow Soprano

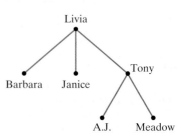

Livia

Barbara Janice Tony

A.J. Meadow

E X E R C I S E   S E T   1 5 . 4   ●●●●●●

• Practice Exercises

In Exercises 1–10, determine whether each graph is a tree. If the graph is not a tree, give a reason why.

1.
A   B   C   D

2.

3.

4.

5.

6.

7.

8.

9.

10.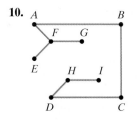

In Exercises 11–18, a graph with no loops or multiple edges is described. Which one of the following applies to the description?

  i *The described graph is a tree.*

  ii *The described graph is not a tree.*

  iii *The described graph may or may not be a tree.*

11. The graph has five vertices, and there is exactly one path from any vertex to any other vertex.

12. The graph has five vertices, is connected, and every edge is a bridge.

13. The graph has eight vertices and five edges.

14. The graph has nine vertices and six edges.

15. The graph has eight vertices, seven edges, and a Hamilton circuit.

16. The graph has nine vertices, eight edges, and a Hamilton circuit.

17. The graph has five vertices and four edges.

18. The graph has four vertices and three edges.

In Exercises 19–24, find a spanning tree for each connected graph. Because many spanning trees are possible, answers will vary. Do not be concerned if your spanning tree is not the same as the sample given in the answer section. Be sure that your spanning tree is connected, contains no circuits, and that each edge is a bridge, with one less edge than vertices.

19.

20.

21.

22.

23.

24.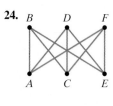

In Exercises 25–32, use Kruskal's Algorithm to find the minimum spanning tree for each weighted graph. Give the total weight of the minimum spanning tree.

25.

26.

27.

28.

29.

30.

31.

32.

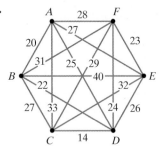

• **Practice Plus**

In Exercises 33–34, find four spanning trees for each connected graph.

33. A   B   **34.**   A

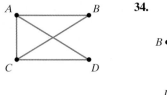

      C   D   B   C

                                         D   E

In Exercises 35–38, use a modification of Kruskal's Algorithm to find the maximum spanning tree for each weighted graph. Give the total weight of the maximum spanning tree.

35. Use the graph in Exercise 27.

36. Use the graph in Exercise 28.

37. Use the graph in Exercise 29.

38. Use the graph in Exercise 30.

• **Application Exercises**

39. Use a tree to model the parent-child relationships in the following family:

> Peter has three children: Zoila, Keanu, and Sandra. Zoila has two children: Sean and Helen. Keanu has no children. Sandra has one child: Martin.

Use vertices to model the people and edges to represent the parent-child relationships.

40. Use a tree to model the employee relationships among the chief administrators of a large community college system:

> Three campus vice presidents report directly to the college president. On two campuses, the academic dean, the dean for administration, and the dean of student services report directly to the vice president. On the third campus, only the academic dean and the dean for administration report directly to the vice president.

41. A college campus plans to provide awnings above its sidewalks to shelter students from the rain as they walk from the parking lot and between buildings. To save money, awnings will not be placed over all of the sidewalks shown in the figure. Just enough awnings will be placed over a select number of sidewalks to ensure that students walking from building to building will be able to do so without getting wet.

a. Use a weighted graph to model the given map. Represent buildings as vertices, sidewalks as edges, and sidewalk lengths as weights.

b. Use Kruskal's Algorithm to find a minimum spanning tree that allows students to move between the parking lot and any buildings shown without getting wet. What is the total length of the sidewalks that need to be sheltered by awnings?

42. A fiber-optic cable system is to be installed along highways connecting six cities. The cities include Boston, Cincinnati, Cleveland, Detroit, New York, and Philadelphia. The highway distances, in miles, between the cities are given in the table at the top of the next page.

a. Model this information with a weighted, complete graph.

b. Use Kruskal's Algorithm to find a minimum spanning tree that would connect each city using the smallest amount of cable. Determine the total length of cable needed.

	Boston	Cincinnati	Cleveland	Detroit	New York	Philadelphia
Boston	*	840	628	734	222	296
Cincinnati	840	*	244	269	647	567
Cleveland	628	244	*	170	473	413
Detroit	734	269	170	*	641	573
New York	222	647	473	641	*	101
Philadelphia	296	567	413	573	101	*

43. The graph shows a proposed layout of an irrigation system. The main water source is located at vertex C. The other vertices represent the proposed sprinkler head locations. The edges indicate all possible choices for installing underground pipes. The weights show the distances, in feet, between proposed sprinkler head locations. The sprinkler system will work if each sprinkler head is connected to the main water source through one or more underground pipes. Use Kruskal's Algorithm to determine the layout of the irrigation system and the smallest number of feet of underground pipes.

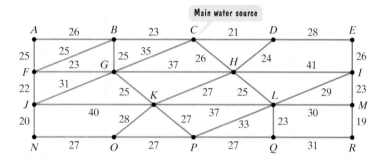

44. The graph shows a proposed layout of a bike trail system to be installed between the towns shown. The vertices represent the ten towns, designated A through J. The edges indicate all possible choices for building the trail. The weights show the distances, in miles, between bike trailheads connecting the towns. Use Kruskal's Algorithm to determine the minimum mileage for the bike trail and the layout of the trail system.

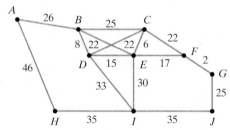

• Writing in Mathematics

45. What is a tree?

46. If a graph is given, how do you determine whether or not it is a tree?

47. Describe the relationship between the number of vertices and the number of edges in a tree.

48. What is a subgraph?

49. What is a spanning tree?

50. Describe how to obtain a spanning tree for a connected graph.

51. What is the minimum spanning tree for a weighted graph?

52. In your own words, briefly describe how to find the minimum spanning tree using Kruskal's Algorithm.

53. Describe a practical problem that can be solved using Kruskal's Algorithm.

• Critical Thinking Exercises

54. Find all the possible spanning trees for the given graph.

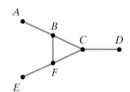

55. Give an example of a tree with 6 vertices whose degrees are 1, 1, 2, 2, 2, and 2.

• Group Exercise

56. Group members should determine a project whose installation would enhance the quality of life on campus or in your community. For example, the project might involve installing awnings over campus sidewalks, building a community bike path, creating a community hiking trail, or installing a metrorail system providing easy access to your community's most desirable locations. The project that you determine should be one that can be carried out most efficiently using a minimum spanning tree. Begin by defining the project and its locations (vertices). Group members should then research the distances between the various locations in the project. Once these distances have been determined, the group should reassemble and create a graph that models the project. Then find a minimum spanning tree that serves as the most efficient way to carry out your project.

●●●●●● CHAPTER SUMMARY, REVIEW, AND TEST

● S U M M A R Y   DEFINITIONS AND CONCEPTS   EXAMPLES

15.1 Graphs, Paths, and Circuits

a. A graph consists of a finite set of points, called vertices, and line segments or curves, called edges, that start and end at vertices. A loop is an edge that starts and ends at the same vertex. Equivalent graphs have the same number of vertices connected to each other in the same way.

Ex. 1, p. 825;
Ex. 2, p. 825;
Ex. 3, p. 826;
Ex. 4, p. 827;
Ex. 5, p. 828

b. The Vocabulary of Graph Theory

   1. The degree of a vertex is the number of edges at that vertex. A loop connecting a vertex to itself contributes 2 to the degree of that vertex.

   2. A vertex with an even number of edges attached is an even vertex; one with an odd number of edges attached is an odd vertex.

   3. Two vertices are adjacent if there is at least one edge connecting them.

Ex. 6, p. 829

   4. A path in a graph is a sequence of adjacent vertices and the edges connecting them. An edge can be part of a path only once.

Figure 15.18, p. 830

   5. A circuit is a path that begins and ends at the same vertex.

Figure 15.19, p. 830

   6. A graph is connected if for any two of its vertices there is at least one path connecting them. A connected graph consists of one piece. A graph that is not connected, made up of components, is called disconnected.

Figure 15.20, p. 830

   7. A bridge is an edge that if removed from a connected graph would leave behind a disconnected graph.

15.2 Euler Paths and Euler Circuits

a. An Euler path is a path that travels through every edge of a graph once and only once.

Figure 15.21, p. 834

b. An Euler circuit is a circuit that travels through every edge of a graph once and only once.

Figure 15.22, p. 835

c. Euler's Theorem determines if a graph contains Euler paths or Euler circuits.

Ex. 1, p. 835;
Ex. 2, p. 836;
Ex. 3, p. 838

   • A graph with exactly two odd vertices has at least one Euler path, but no Euler circuit. Each Euler path starts at an odd vertex and ends at the other odd vertex.

   • A graph with no odd vertices has at least one Euler circuit that can start and end at any vertex.

   • A graph with more than two odd vertices has no Euler paths and no Euler circuits.

d. If Euler's Theorem indicates the existence of Euler paths or Euler circuits, trial and error or Fleury's Algorithm can be used to find such paths or circuits. Fleury's Algorithm is explained in the box on page 839.

Ex. 4, p. 839

15.3 Hamilton Paths and Hamilton Circuits

a. A path that passes through each vertex of a graph exactly once is called a Hamilton path. If a Hamilton path begins and ends at the same vertex and passes through all other vertices exactly once, it is called a Hamilton circuit.

Ex. 1, p. 845

b. A complete graph is a graph that has an edge between each pair of its vertices. A complete graph with n vertices has $(n - 1)!$ Hamilton circuits.

Ex. 2, p. 847

c. A complete graph whose edges have numbers, called weights, attached to them is called a weighted graph.   Ex. 3, p. 848

d. The traveling salesperson problem is the problem of finding a Hamilton circuit in a complete, weighted graph for which the sum of the weights of the edges is a minimum. Such a Hamilton circuit is called the optimal Hamilton circuit or the optimal solution.

e. The Brute Force Method can be used to solve the traveling salesperson problem. The method, given in the box on page 849, involves determining the sum of the weights of the edges for all possible Hamilton circuits.   Ex. 4, p. 849

f. The Nearest Neighbor Method can be used to approximate the optimal solution to traveling salesperson problems. The method, given in the box on page 850, involves continually taking an edge with the smallest weight.   Ex. 5, p. 851

15.4 Trees

a. A tree is a graph that is connected and has no circuits.   Ex. 1, p. 856

b. Properties of Trees

    1. There is one and only one path joining any two vertices.

    2. Every edge is a bridge.

    3. A tree with n vertices has $n - 1$ edges.

c. A subgraph is a set of vertices and edges chosen from among those of the original graph.

d. A spanning tree is a subgraph that contains all of a connected graph's vertices, is connected, and contains no circuits.   Ex. 2, p. 857

e. The minimum spanning tree for a weighted graph is a spanning tree with the smallest possible total weight.

f. Kruskal's Algorithm, described in the box on page 858, gives a procedure for finding the minimum spanning tree from a weighted graph. The basic idea is to always pick the smallest available edge, but avoid creating any circuits.   Ex. 3, p. 859

REVIEW EXERCISES

15.1

1. Explain why the two figures show equivalent graphs. Then draw a third equivalent graph.

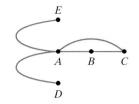

In Exercises 2–8, use the following graph.

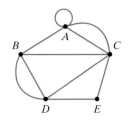

2. Find the degree of each vertex in the graph.

3. Identify the even vertices and identify the odd vertices.

4. Which vertices are adjacent to vertex D?

5. Use vertices to describe two paths that start at vertex E and end at vertex A.

6. Use vertices to describe a circuit that begins and ends at vertex E.

7. Is the graph connected? Explain your answer.

8. Is any edge in the graph a bridge? Explain your answer.

9. List all edges that are bridges in the graph shown.

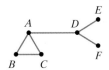

10. Draw a graph that models the layout of the city shown in the map. Use vertices to represent the land masses and edges to represent the bridges.

11. Draw a graph that models the bordering relationships among the states shown in the map. Use vertices to represent the states and edges to represent common borders.

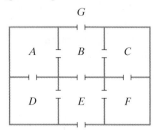

12. Draw a graph that models the connecting relationships in the floor plan. Use vertices to represent the rooms and the outside, and edges to represent the connecting doors.

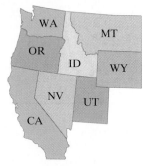

15.2

In Exercises 13–15, a graph is given.

    a. *Determine whether the graph has an Euler path, an Euler circuit, or neither.*

    b. *If the graph has an Euler path or circuit, use trial and error or Fleury's Algorithm to find one.*

13.

14.

15.

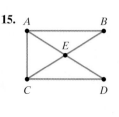

16. Use Fleury's Algorithm to find an Euler path.

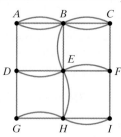

17. Use Fleury's Algorithm to find an Euler circuit.

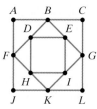

18. Refer to Exercise 10.

    a. Use your graph to determine if the city residents would be able to walk across all of the bridges without crossing the same bridge twice.

    b. If such a walk is possible, show the path on your graph. Then trace this route on the city map in a manner that is clear to the city's residents.

    c. Use your graph to determine if there is a path that crosses each bridge exactly once and begins and ends on the same island. Explain your answer.

19. Refer to Exercise 11. Use your graph to determine if it is possible to find a path that crosses each common state border exactly once. Explain your answer.

20. Refer to Exercise 12.

    a. Use your graph to determine if it is possible to find a path that uses each door exactly once.

    b. If such a path is possible, show it on your graph. Then trace this route on the floor plan in a manner that is clear to a person strolling through the house.

21. A security guard needs to walk the streets of the neighborhood in the figure shown. The guard is to walk down each street once, whether or not the street has houses on both sides.

    a. Draw a graph that models the streets of the neighborhood walked by the security guard.

    b. Use your graph to determine if the security guard can walk each street exactly once. Explain your answer.

    c. If so, use the map to show where the guard should begin and where the guard should end the walk.

15.3

In Exercises 22–23, use the graph shown.

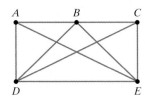

22. Find a Hamilton circuit that begins as $A, E, \ldots$.

23. Find a Hamilton circuit that begins as $D, B, \ldots$.

For each graph in Exercises 24–27,

  a. *Determine if the graph must have Hamilton circuits. Explain your answer.*

  b. *If the graph must have Hamilton circuits, determine the number of such circuits.*

24.

25.

26.

27.

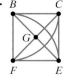

In Exercises 28–30, use the complete, weighted graph shown.

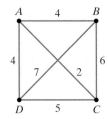

28. Find the total weight of each of the six possible Hamilton circuits:

A, B, C, D, A A, B, D, C, A A, C, B, D, A

A, C, D, B, A A, D, B, C, A A, D, C, B, A.

29. Use your answers from Exercise 28 and the Brute Force Method to find the optimal solution.

30. Use the Nearest Neighbor Method, with starting vertex A, to find an approximate solution. What is the total weight of the Hamilton circuit?

31. Use the Nearest Neighbor Method to find a Hamilton circuit that begins at vertex A in the given graph. What is the total weight of the Hamilton circuit?

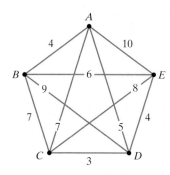

The table shows the one-way airfares between cities. Use this information to solve Exercises 32–33.

	A	B	C	D	E
A	*	$220	$240	$290	$430
B	$220	*	$260	$320	$360
C	$240	$260	*	$180	$300
D	$290	$320	$180	*	$250
E	$430	$360	$300	$250	*

32. Draw a graph that models the information in the table. Use vertices to represent the cities and weights on appropriate edges to show airfares.

33. A sales director who lives in city A is required to fly to regional offices in cities $B, C, D,$ and E, and then return to city A. Use the Nearest Neighbor Method to approximate the optimal route. What is the total cost for this Hamilton circuit?

15.4

In Exercises 34–36, determine whether each graph is a tree. If the graph is not a tree, give a reason why.

34.

35.

36.

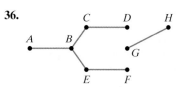

In Exercises 37–38, find a spanning tree for each connected graph.

37.

38.

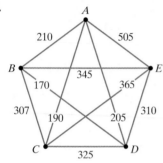

In Exercises 39–40, use Kruskal's Algorithm to find the minimum spanning tree for each weighted graph. Give the total weight of the minimum spanning tree.

39.

40.

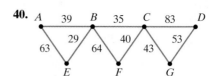

41. A fiber-optic cable system is to be installed along highways connecting nine cities. The weighted graph shows the highway distances, in miles, between the cities, designated *A* through *I*. Use Kruskal's Algorithm to determine the layout of the cable system and the smallest length of cable needed.

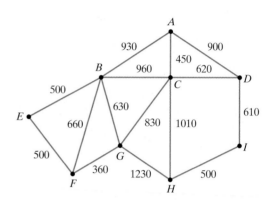

● ● ● ● ● ●   CHAPTER 15 TEST

In Exercises 1–4, use the following graph.

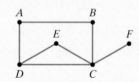

1. Find the degree of each vertex.

2. Use vertices to describe two paths that start at vertex *A* and end at vertex *E*.

3. Use vertices to describe a circuit that starts at vertex *B* and passes through vertex *E*.

4. List all edges that are bridges.

5. Draw a graph that models the bordering relationships among the countries shown in the map. Use vertices to represent the countries and edges to represent common borders.

In Exercises 6–8, a graph is given.

a. *Determine whether the graph has an Euler path, an Euler circuit, or neither.*

b. *If the graph has an Euler path or circuit, use trial and error or Fleury's Algorithm to find one.*

6.

7.

8.
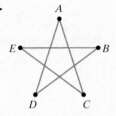

9. Use Fleury's Algorithm to find an Euler circuit.

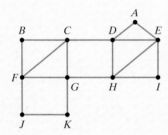

10. a. Draw a graph that models the layout of the city shown in the map.

b. Use your graph to determine if the city residents would be able to walk across all of the bridges without crossing the same bridge twice. Explain your answer.

c. If such a walk is possible, where should it begin?

11. a. Draw a graph that models the connecting relationships in the floor plan shown at the top of the next column.

b. Use your graph to determine if it is possible to find a path that uses each door exactly once. Explain your answer.

c. If such a path is possible, where should it begin?

12. a. Draw a graph that models the streets of the neighborhood for a police officer who is to walk each street once.

b. Use your map to determine if the officer can walk each street exactly once. Explain your answer.

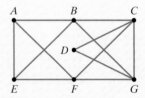

13. Find two Hamilton circuits in the graph shown. One circuit should begin as $A, B, \dots$. The second circuit should begin as $A, F, \dots$.

14. How many Hamilton circuits are there in a complete graph with five vertices?

The table shows the one-way airfares between cities. Use this information to solve Exercises 15–16.

	A	*B*	*C*	*D*
A	*	$460	$200	$210
B	$460	*	$720	$680
C	$200	$720	*	$105
D	$210	$680	$105	*

15. Draw a graph that models the information in the table. Use vertices to represent the cities and weights on appropriate edges to show airfares.

16. A sales director who lives in city A is required to fly to regional offices in cities B, C, and D, and then return to city A. Use the Brute Force Method to approximate the optimal route. What is the total cost for this Hamilton circuit? (*Hint*: The six possible Hamilton circuits are

A, B, C, D, A; A, B, D, C, A;

A, C, B, D, A; A, C, D, B, A;

A, D, B, C, A; A, D, C, B, A.)

17. Use the Nearest Neighbor Method to find a Hamilton circuit that begins at vertex A in the given graph. What is the total weight of the Hamilton circuit?

18. Is the graph shown a tree? Explain your answer.

19. Find a spanning tree for the graph shown.

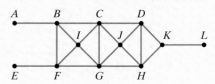

20. Use Kruskal's Algorithm to find the minimum spanning tree for the weighted graph shown. Give the total weight of the minimum spanning tree.

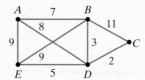

Answers to Selected Exercises

CHAPTER 1

Section 1.1

Check Point Exercises

1. a. Each number in the list is obtained by adding 6 to the previous number.; 33   **b.** Each number in the list is obtained by multiplying the previous number by 5.; 1250   **c.** To get the second number, multiply the previous number by 2. Then multiply by 3 and then by 4. Then multiply by 2, then by 3, and then by 4, repeatedly.; 3456   **d.** To get the second number, add 8 to the previous number. Then add 8 and then subtract 14. Then add 8, then add 8, and then subtract 14, repeatedly.; 7   **2. a.** Starting with the third number, each number is the sum of the previous two numbers.; 76   **b.** Starting with the second number, each number is one less than twice the previous number.; 257
3. The figures alternate between rectangles and triangles, and the number of appendages follows the pattern: one, two, three, one, two, three, etc.;
4. a. The result of the process is two times the original number selected.
   b. Representing the original number as n, we have

Select a number:	n
Multiply the number by 4:	$4n$
Add 6 to the product:	$4n + 6$
Divide this sum by 2:	$\dfrac{4n + 6}{2} = 2n + 3$
Subtract 3 from the quotient:	$2n + 3 - 3 = 2n.$

Exercise Set 1.1

1. Each number in the list is obtained by adding 4 to the previous number.; 28

3. Each number in the list is obtained by subtracting 5 from the previous number.; 12

5. Each number in the list is obtained by multiplying the previous number by 3.; 729

7. Each number in the list is obtained by multiplying the previous number by 2.; 32

9. The numbers in the list alternate between 1 and numbers obtained by multiplying the number prior to the previous number by 2.; 32

11. Each number in the list is obtained by subtracting 2 from the previous number.; -6

13. Each number in the list is obtained by adding 4 to the denominator of the previous fraction.; $\dfrac{1}{22}$

15. Each number in the list is obtained by multiplying the previous number by $\dfrac{1}{3}$.; $\dfrac{1}{81}$

17. The second number is obtained by adding 4 to the first number. The third number is obtained by adding 5 to the second number. The number being added to the previous number increases by 1 each time.; 42   **19.** The second number is obtained by adding 3 to the first number. The third number is obtained by adding 5 to the second number. The number being added to the previous number increases by 2 each time.; 51

21. Starting with the third number, each number is the sum of the previous two numbers.; 71   **23.** To get the second number, add 5 to the previous number. Then add 5 and then subtract 7. Then add 5, then add 5, and then subtract 7, repeatedly.; 18   **25.** The second number is obtained by multiplying the first number by 2. The third number is obtained by subtracting 1 from the second number. Then multiply by 2 and then subtract 1, repeatedly.; 33   **27.** Each number in the list is obtained by multiplying the previous number by $-\dfrac{1}{4}$.; $\dfrac{1}{4}$ **29.** For each pair in the list, the second number is obtained by subtracting 4 from the first number.; -1

31. The pattern is: square, triangle, circle, square, triangle, circle, etc.;

33. Each figure contains the letter of the alphabet following the letter in the previous figure with one more occurrence than in the previous figure.;

d	d	d
d	d	

35. a. The result of the process is two times the original number selected.
   b. Representing the original number as n, we have

Select a number:	n
Multiply the number by 4:	$4n$
Add 8 to the product:	$4n + 8$
Divide this sum by 2:	$\dfrac{4n + 8}{2} = 2n + 4$
Subtract 4 from the quotient:	$2n + 4 - 4 = 2n.$

37. a. The result of the process is 3.
   b. Representing the original number as n, we have

Select a number:	n
Add 5:	$n + 5$
Double the result:	$2(n + 5) = 2n + 10$
Subtract 4:	$2n + 10 - 4 = 2n + 6$
Divide by 2:	$\dfrac{2n + 6}{2} = n + 3$
Subtract n:	$n + 3 - n = 3.$

39. $1 + 2 + 3 + 4 + 5 + 6 = \dfrac{6 \times 7}{2}$; $21 = 21$ **41.** $1 + 3 + 5 + 7 + 9 + 11 = 6 \times 6$; $36 = 36$ **43.** $98{,}765 \times 9 + 3 = 888{,}888$; correct
45. $165 \times 3367 = 555{,}555$; correct   **47.** b   **49.** c   **51.** deductive reasoning; Answers will vary.   **53.** inductive reasoning; Answers will vary.
55. a. $28, 36, 45, 55, 66$ **b.** $36, 49, 64, 81, 100$ **c.** $35, 51, 70, 92, 117$ **d.** square   **61.** $(11 - 7)^2 = 121 - 154 + 49$ **63.** Answers will vary;
an example is: $1, 5, 1, 10, 1, \ldots$.   **65. a.** 36; 4356; $443{,}556$; $44{,}435{,}556$ **b.** In each multiplication, a number is multiplied by itself; this number has
one more digit than the number in the previous multiplication; all such digits are 6.; Each product has one more digit of 4 than the previous product,
followed by a digit of 3, followed by one more digit of 5 than the previous product, ending in a digit of 6; the first product has zero digits of 4 and zero
digits of 5.   **c.** $66{,}666 \times 66{,}666 = 4{,}444{,}355{,}556$; $666{,}666 \times 666{,}666 = 444{,}443{,}555{,}556$ **d.** inductive reasoning; Answers will vary.

Section 1.2

Check Point Exercises

1. a. $300{,}000{,}000$ **b.** $295{,}700{,}000$ **2. a.** 3.1 **b.** 3.1416 **3. a.** $\$2, \$1, \$5, \$4, \$1, \$2$, and $\$3$; $\approx \$18$ **b.** no   **4. a.** $\approx \$2000$ per wk
b. $\approx \$100{,}000$ per yr   **5. a.** $0.63 \times 178{,}586{,}613$ **b.** $0.6 \times 200{,}000{,}000 = 120{,}000{,}000$; $\approx 120{,}000{,}000$ (120 million) non-owners
6. a. ≈ 0.17 yr for each subsequent birth year   **b.** ≈ 88.1 yr   **7. a.** ≈ 118 democracies   **b.** 1981–1985   **c.** 1977   **8. a.** ≈ 0.12 million
motorcycles per yr   **b.** $M = 0.4 + 0.12x$ **c.** ≈ 2.2 million motorcycles

Exercise Set 1.2

1. a. $47{,}451{,}900$ **b.** $47{,}452{,}000$ **c.** $47{,}450{,}000$ **d.** $47{,}500{,}000$ **e.** $47{,}000{,}000$ **f.** $50{,}000{,}000$ **3.** 2.718 **5.** 2.71828
7. 2.718281828 **9.** $350 + 600 = 950$; 955; reasonably well   **11.** $9 + 1 + 19 = 29$; 29.23; quite well   **13.** $32 - 11 = 21$; 20.911; quite well
15. $40 \times 6 = 240$; 218.185; not so well   **17.** $0.8 \times 400 = 320$; 327.06; reasonably well   **19.** $48 \div 3 = 16$; ≈ 16.49; quite well
21. 30% of 200,000 is 60,000.; $59{,}920.96$; quite well   **23.** $\approx \$43$ **25.** $\approx \$40{,}000$ per yr   **27.** $\approx \$24{,}000$ **29.** $\approx \$1000$ **31.** $\approx \$30$ per hr
33. $\approx 700{,}800$ hr   **35.** ≈ 40; ≈ 42.03; quite reasonable   **37.** b   **39.** c   **41.** ≈ 3 hr   **43.** $\approx 100{,}000{,}000$ American adults
45. a. ≈ 85 people per 100   **b.** ≈ 5400 people   **47. a.** $\approx \$13$ per yr   **b.** $\approx \$326$ **49. a.** 1960; ≈ 4100 cigarettes per adult
b. 1940–1950   **c.** 1930   **51. a.** $\approx \$857$ per yr   **b.** $C = 14{,}000 + 857x$ **c.** $\approx \$25{,}998$ **67.** a   **69.** b   **71.** ≈ 667 days; ≈ 1.8 yr

Section 1.3

Check Point Exercises

1. the amount of money given to the cashier   **2.** The 128-ounce bottle at approximately 4¢ an ounce is the better value.   **3.** 14 months
4. 5 combinations   **5.** 6 outfits   **6.** A route that will cost less than $1460 is A, D, E, C, B, A.

Trick Questions

1. 12   **2.** 12   **3.** sister and brother   **4.** match

Exercise Set 1.3

1. the price of the computer   **3.** the number of words on the page   **5.** unnecessary information: weekly salary of $350; extra pay: $180
7. unnecessary information: $20 given to the parking attendant; charge: $4.50   **9. a.** 24-ounce box for $4.59   **b.** 22¢ per ounce for the 15.3-ounce
box and $3.06 per pound for the 24-ounce box   **c.** no; Answers will vary.   **11.** $3000   **13.** $50   **15.** $90   **17.** $4525   **19.** $565
21. 4 mi   **23.** $104   **25.** $14,300   **27.** 5 ways   **29.** 6 ways   **31.** 9 ways   **33.** 10 different total scores   **35.** B owes $18 and C owes $2.;
A is owed $14, D is owed $4, and E is owed $2.; B should give A $14 and D $4, while C should give E $2.   **37.** 4 ways   **39.** Andy, Darnell, Caleb,
Beth, Ella   **41.** Home, Bank, Post Office, Dry Cleaners, Home
43. Sample answer: **45.** Bob's major is psychology.
    CO, WY, UT, AZ, NM, CO, UT

47. a.

5	22	18
28	15	2
12	8	25

b.

4	9	8
11	7	3
6	5	10

49.

9	6	7
8	1	4
3	2	5

51.

```
        156
   28)4368
        28
       156
       140
       168
       168
         0
```

57. the dentist with poor dental work   **59.** Friday

61. Sample answer:

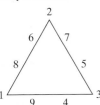

63. There is no missing dollar; in the end, the customers paid a total of $27 of which $25 went to the restaurant and $2 was stolen by the waiter.

65. Answers will vary; an example is

State	A	B	C	D
Congressional Seats	4	6	8	12

Chapter 1 Review Exercises

1. deductive reasoning: Answers will vary.   **2.** inductive reasoning; Answers will vary.   **3.** Each number in the list is obtained by adding 5 to the previous number.; 24   **4.** Each number in the list is obtained by multiplying the previous number by 2.; 112   **5.** The successive differences are consecutive counting numbers beginning with 2.; 21   **6.** Each number in the list is obtained by writing a fraction with a denominator that is one more than the denominator of the previous fraction before it is reduced to lowest terms.; $\frac{3}{8}$ **7.** Each number in the list is obtained by multiplying the previous number by $-\frac{1}{2}$.; $\frac{5}{2}$ **8.** Each number in the list is obtained by subtracting 60 from the previous number; -200.
9. Each number beginning with the third number is the sum of the two previous numbers.; 42   **10.** To get the second number, multiply the first number by 3. Then multiply the second number by 2 to get the third number. Then multiply by 3 and then by 2, repeatedly.; 432   **11.** The figures alternate between squares and circles, and in each figure the tick mark has been rotated 90° clockwise from its position in the previous figure.;
12. $2 + 4 + 8 + 16 + 32 = 64 - 2$; correct   **13.** $444 \div 12 = 37$; correct
14. a. The result is the original number.
   b. Representing the original number as n, we have
      Select a number: n
      Double the number: $2n$
      Add 4 to the product: $2n + 4$
      Divide the sum by 2: $\frac{2n + 4}{2} = n + 2$
      Subtract 2 from the quotient: $n + 2 - 2 = n$.
15. a. 4,115,600   **b.** 4,116,000   **c.** 4,100,000   **d.** 4,000,000   **16. a.** 1.5   **b.** 1.51   **c.** 1.507   **d.** 1.5065917
17. ≈ 16; 15.71; quite reasonable   **18.** ≈ 450; 432.67; somewhat reasonable   **19.** ≈ 5; ≈ 4.76; quite reasonable
20. ≈ 2400; 2397.0548; quite reasonable   **21.** $\approx \$18.00$ **22.** $\approx \$560$ **23.** $\approx \$60$ **24.** $\approx 1,600,000$ liberals   **25.** b   **26.** c
27. a. called gay, lesbian, or a homophobic name; women: 13%; men: 37%   **b.** $\approx 3,600,000$ women   **28. a.** ≈ 1.5 million Americans per yr
b. ≈ 57.8 million Americans   **29. a.** 1900; 400,000 dropouts   **b.** 1985–1990   **c.** 1985   **30. a.** ≈ 0.26 billion dollars per yr
b. $L = 1.7 + 0.26x$ **c.** $\approx \$5.34$ billion   **31.** the weight of the child   **32.** unnecessary information: $20 given to driver; cost of trip: $8.00
33. 8 lb   **34.** $885   **35.** Plan A; $90   **36.** 5.75 hr or 5 hr 45 min   **37.** $15,500   **38.** 6 combinations

Chapter 1 Test

1. deductive   **2.** inductive   **3.** Each number in the list is obtained by adding 5 to the previous number.; 20   **4.** Each number in the list is obtained by multiplying the previous number by $\frac{1}{2}$.; $\frac{1}{96}$ **5.** $3367 \times 15 = 50,505$ **6.** The outer figure is always a square; the inner figure follows the pattern: triangle, circle, square, triangle, circle, square, etc.; the number of appendages on the outer square alternates between 1 and 2.;
7. a. The original number is doubled.
   b. Representing the original number as n, we have
      Select a number: n
      Multiply the number by 4: $4n$
      Add 8 to the product: $4n + 8$
      Divide the sum by 2: $\frac{4n + 8}{2} = 2n + 4$
      Subtract 4 from the quotient: $2n + 4 - 4 = 2n$.
8. 3,300,000   **9.** 706.38   **10.** $\approx \$90$ **11.** $\approx \$25,000$ per person   **12.** ≈ 60 **13.** $\approx 28,000,000$ cases   **14.** a   **15. a.** 2001; ≈ 1220
discharges   **b.** 1996   **c.** ≈ 9500 discharges   **16. a.** $\approx 0.5\%$ per yr decrease   **b.** $S = 37.4 - 0.5x$ **c.** $\approx 17.4\%$ **17.** Estes Rental; $12
18. $14,080   **19.** 26 weeks   **20.** Belgium; 160,000 people

CHAPTER 2

Section 2.1

Check Point Exercises

1. L is the set of the first six letters of the alphabet.   **2.** $M = \{$April, August$\}$ **3.** $O = \{1, 3, 5, 7, 9\}$ **4. a.** not the empty set
b. empty set   **c.** not the empty set   **d.** not the empty set   **5. a.** true   **b.** true   **c.** false   **6. a.** $A = \{1, 2, 3\}$

b. $B = \{15, 16, 17, 18, \ldots\}$ **c.** $O = \{1, 3, 5, 7, \ldots\}$ **7. a.** $\{1, 2, 3, 4, \ldots, 199\}$ **b.** $\{51, 52, 53, 54, \ldots, 200\}$ **8. a.** $n(A) = 5$
b. $n(B) = 1$ **c.** $n(C) = 8$ **d.** $n(D) = 0$ **9.** Yes; each language in the table is paired with a distinct number of 15–24-year olds.
10. a. true   **b.** false

Exercise Set 2.1

1. well defined; set   **3.** not well defined; not a set   **5.** well defined; set   **7.** the set of planets in our solar system   **9.** the set of months
that begin with J   **11.** the set of natural numbers greater than 5   **13.** the set of natural numbers between 6 and 20, inclusive
15. {winter, spring, summer, fall}   **17.** {September, October, November, December}   **19.** $\{1, 2, 3\}$ **21.** $\{1, 3, 5, 7, 9, 11\}$ **23.** $\{1, 2, 3, 4, 5\}$
25. $\{6, 7, 8, 9, \ldots\}$ **27.** $\{7, 8, 9, 10\}$ **29.** $\{10, 11, 12, 13, \ldots, 79\}$ **31.** $\{2\}$ **33.** not the empty set   **35.** empty set   **37.** not the empty set
39. empty set   **41.** empty set   **43.** not the empty set   **45.** not the empty set   **47.** true   **49.** true   **51.** false   **53.** true   **55.** false
57. false   **59.** true   **61.** false   **63.** false   **65.** true   **67.** 5   **69.** 15   **71.** 0   **73.** 1   **75.** 4   **77.** 5   **79.** 0
81. a. not equivalent; Answers will vary.   **b.** not equal; Answers will vary.   **83. a.** equivalent; Answers will vary.   **b.** not equal; Answers
will vary.   **85. a.** equivalent; Answers will vary.   **b.** equal; Answers will vary.   **87. a.** equivalent; Answers will vary.   **b.** not equal;
Answers will vary.   **89. a.** equivalent; Answers will vary.   **b.** equal; Answers will vary.   **91.** infinite   **93.** finite   **95.** finite
97. $\{x \mid x \in \mathbf{N} \text{ and } x \geq 61\}$ **99.** $\{x \mid x \in \mathbf{N} \text{ and } 61 \leq x \leq 89\}$ **101.** Answers will vary; an example is: $\{0, 1, 2, 3\}$ and $\{1, 2, 3, 4\}$.
103. impossible; Answers will vary.   **105.** {New Zealand, Australia, United States}   **107.** {Australia, United States, United Kingdom,
Switzerland, Ireland}   **109.** {United Kingdom, Switzerland, Ireland}   **111.** $\varnothing$ or { }   **113.** $\{12, 19\}$ **115.** $\{20, 21\}$
117. no one-to-one correspondence; not equivalent   **125.** a

Section 2.2

Check Point Exercises

1. a. $\not\subseteq$ **b.** $\subseteq$ **c.** $\subseteq$ **2. a.** $\subseteq$, $\subset$ **b.** $\subseteq$, $\subset$ **3.** yes   **4. a.** 16; 15   **b.** 64; 63   **5. a.** 8; the number of different combi-
nations of the books that you can take on vacation   **b.** $\varnothing$, {*The Da Vinci Code*}, {*The Lord of the Rings*}, {*America (The Book)*},
{*The Da Vinci Code, The Lord of the Rings*}, {*The Da Vinci Code, America (The Book)*}, {*The Lord of the Rings, America (The Book)*},
{*The Da Vinci Code, The Lord of the Rings, America (The Book)*}   **c.** 7

Exercise Set 2.2

1. $\subseteq$ **3.** $\not\subseteq$ **5.** $\not\subseteq$ **7.** $\not\subseteq$ **9.** $\subseteq$ **11.** $\not\subseteq$ **13.** both   **15.** $\subseteq$ **17.** both   **19.** $\subseteq$ **21.** neither   **23.** true
25. false; Answers will vary.   **27.** true   **29.** false; Answers will vary.   **31.** true   **33.** false; Answers will vary.   **35.** true
37. $\varnothing$, {border collie}, {poodle}, {border collie, poodle}   **39.** $\varnothing$, {t}, {a}, {b}, {t, a}, {t, b}, {a, b}, {t, a, b}   **41.** $\varnothing$ and {0}   **43.** 16; 15
45. 64; 63   **47.** 128; 127   **49.** 8; 7   **51.** false; The set $\{1, 2, 3, \ldots, 1000\}$ has $2^{1000} - 1$ proper subsets.   **53.** true   **55.** false; $\varnothing \subseteq \{\varnothing, \{\varnothing\}\}$
57. true   **59.** true   **61.** true   **63.** false; The set of subsets of {a, e, i, o, u} contains 32 elements.   **65.** false; $D \subseteq T$ **67.** true
69. false; If $x \in W$, then $x \in D$.   **71.** true   **73.** true   **75.** 32   **77.** 64   **79.** 256   **87.** b   **89.** 7

Section 2.3

Check Point Exercises

1. a. $\{1, 5, 6, 7, 9\}$ **b.** $\{1, 5, 6\}$ **c.** $\{7, 9\}$ **2. a.** {a, b, c, d}   **b.** {e}   **c.** {e, f, g}   **d.** {f, g}   **3.** {b, c, e}   **4. a.** $\{7, 10\}$
b. $\varnothing$ **c.** $\varnothing$ **5. a.** $\{1, 3, 5, 6, 7, 10, 11\}$ **b.** $\{1, 2, 3, 4, 5, 6, 7\}$ **c.** $\{1, 2, 3\}$ **6. a.** {a, d}   **b.** {a, d}   **7. a.** {5}
b. $\{2, 3, 7, 11, 13, 17, 19\}$ **c.** $\{2, 3, 5, 7, 11, 13\}$ **d.** $\{17, 19\}$ **e.** $\{5, 7, 11, 13, 17, 19\}$ **f.** $\{2, 3\}$ **8.** 385 students

Exercise Set 2.3

1. the set of all composers   **3.** the set of all brands of soft drinks   **5.** {c, d, e}   **7.** {b, c, d, e, f}   **9.** $\{6, 7, 8, 9, \ldots, 20\}$
11. $\{2, 4, 6, 8, \ldots, 20\}$ **13.** $\{21, 22, 23, 24, \ldots\}$ **15.** $\{1, 3, 5, 7, \ldots\}$ **17.** $\{1, 3\}$ **19.** $\{1, 2, 3, 5, 7\}$ **21.** $\{2, 4, 6\}$ **23.** $\{4, 6\}$
25. $\{1, 3, 5, 7\}$ or A **27.** $\{1, 2, 4, 6, 7\}$ **29.** $\{1, 2, 4, 6, 7\}$ **31.** $\{4, 6\}$ **33.** $\{1, 3, 5, 7\}$ or A **35.** $\varnothing$ **37.** $\{1, 2, 3, 4, 5, 6, 7\}$ or U
39. $\{1, 3, 5, 7\}$ or A **41.** {g, h}   **43.** {a, b, g, h}   **45.** {b, c, d, e, f} or C **47.** {c, d, e, f}   **49.** {a, g, h} or A **51.** {a, b, c, d, e, f, g, h}
or U **53.** {a, b, c, d, e, f, g, h} or U **55.** {c, d, e, f}   **57.** {a, g, h} or A **59.** $\varnothing$ **61.** {a, b, c, d, e, f, g, h} or U **63.** {a, g, h} or A
65. {a, c, d, e, f, g, h}   **67.** $\{1, 3, 4, 7\}$ **69.** $\{1, 2, 3, 4, 5, 6, 7, 8, 9\}$ **71.** $\{3, 7\}$ **73.** $\{1, 4, 8, 9\}$ **75.** $\{8, 9\}$ **77.** $\{1, 4\}$
79. {△, two, four, six}   **81.** {△, #, $, two, four, six}   **83.** 6   **85.** 5   **87.** {#, $, two, four, six, 10, 01}   **89.** {two, four, six}   **91.** 4
93. 31   **95.** 27   **97.** $\{1, 2, 3, 4, 5, 6, 7, 8\}$ or U **99.** $\{1, 3, 5, 7\}$ or A **101.** $\{1, 7\}$ **103.** $\{1, 3, 5, 6, 7, 8\}$
105. $\{23, 29, 31, 37, 41, 43, 53, 59, 61, 67, 71\}$ **107.** 60   **109.** {Ashley, Mike, Josh}   **111.** {Ashley, Mike, Josh, Emily, Hanna, Ethan}
113. {Ashley}   **115.** {Jacob}   **117.** I   **119.** I   **121.** IV   **123.** I   **125.** IV   **127.** II   **129.** III   **131.** I
133. {spacial-temporal toys, sports equipment, toy cars and trucks}   **135.** {dollhouses, spacial-temporal toys, sports equipment, toy cars and trucks}
137. $\varnothing$ **139.** 283 people   **153.** d
155.

157.

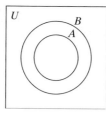

Section 2.4

Check Point Exercises

1. a. {a, b, c, d, f}　　**b.** {a, b, c, d, f}　　**c.** {a, b, d}
2. a. {5, 6, 7, 8, 9}　　**b.** {1, 2, 5, 6, 7, 8, 9, 10, 12}　　**c.** {5, 6, 7}　　**d.** {3, 4, 6, 8, 11}　　**e.** {1, 2, 3, 5, 6, 7, 8, 9, 10, 11, 12}
3.

4. a. IV　　**b.** IV　　**c.** $(A \cup B)' = A' \cap B'$　　**5. a.** II, IV, and V　　**b.** II, IV, and V　　**c.** $A \cap (B \cup C) = (A \cap B) \cup (A \cap C)$

Exercise Set 2.4

1. {1, 2, 3, 5, 7}　　**3.** {1, 2, 3, 5, 7}　　**5.** {2}　　**7.** {2}　　**9.** ∅　　**11.** {4, 6}　　**13.** {a, b, g, h}　　**15.** {a, b, g, h}　　**17.** {b}　　**19.** {b}
21. ∅　　**23.** {c, d, e, f}　　**25.** II, III, V, and VI　　**27.** I, II, IV, V, VI, and VII　　**29.** II and V　　**31.** I, IV, VII, and VIII　　**33.** {1, 2, 3, 4, 5, 6, 7, 8}
35. {1, 2, 3, 4, 5, 6, 7, 8, 9, 10, 11}　　**37.** {12, 13}　　**39.** {4, 5, 6}　　**41.** {6}　　**43.** {1, 2, 3, 4, 5, 7, 8, 9, 10, 11, 12, 13}
45.　　　　　　　　　　　　　　　　**47.**

49. a. II　　**b.** II　　**c.** $A \cap B = B \cap A$　　**51. a.** I, III, and IV　　**b.** IV　　**c.** no; Answers will vary.　　**53.** not equal　　**55.** not equal
57. equal　　**59. a.** II, IV, V, VI, and VII　　**b.** II, IV, V, VI, and VII　　**c.** $(A \cap B) \cup C = (A \cup C) \cap (B \cup C)$　　**61. a.** II, IV, and V
b. I, II, IV, V, and VI　　**c.** no; Answers will vary.　　**63.** not true　　**65.** true; theorem　　**67.** true; theorem　　**69. a.** {c, e, f}; {c, e, f}
b. {1, 3, 5, 7, 8}; {1, 3, 5, 7, 8}　　**c.** $A \cup (B' \cap C') = (A \cup B') \cap (A \cup C')$　　**d.** theorem　　**71.** $(A \cap B)' \cap (A \cup B)$　　**73.** $A' \cup B$
75. $(A \cap B) \cup C$　　**77.** $A' \cap (B \cup C)$　　**79.** {Ann, Jose, Al, Gavin, Amy, Ron, Grace}　　**81.** {Jose}　　**83.** {Lily, Emma}
85. {Lily, Emma, Ann, Jose, Lee, Maria, Fred, Ben, Sheila, Ellen, Gary}　　**87.** {Lily, Emma, Al, Gavin, Amy, Lee, Maria}　　**89.** {Al, Gavin, Amy}
91. The set of students who scored 90% or above on exam 1 and exam 3 but not on exam 2　　**93.** II　　**95.** V　　**97.** I　　**99.** III　　**101.** V
103. VII　　**105.**　　　　　　　　　　　　　　　**109.** AB^+　　**111.** no

Section 2.5

Check Point Exercises

1. a. 75　　**b.** 90　　**c.** 20　　**d.** 145　　**e.** 55　　**f.** 70　　**g.** 30　　**h.** 175　　**2. a.** 490 men　　**b.** 510 men
3.　　　　　　　　　　　　　　**4. a.** 63　　**b.** 3　　**c.** 136　　**d.** 30　　**e.** 228　　**f.** 22

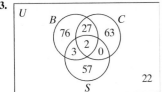

Exercise Set 2.5

1. 26　　**3.** 17　　**5.** 37　　**7.** 7　　**9.** I: 14; III: 22; IV: 5　　**11.** 17　　**13.** 6　　**15.** 28　　**17.** 9　　**19.** 3　　**21.** 19　　**23.** 21　　**25.** 34

27. I: 5; II: 1; III: 4; IV: 3; VI: 1; VII: 8; VIII: 6   **29.** I: 5; II: 10; III: 3; IV: 4; V: 7; VI: 1; VII: 6; VIII: 2   **31.** impossible; There are only 10 elements in set A but there are 13 elements in set A that are also in sets B or C. A similar problem exists for set C.   **33.** 18   **35.** 9   **37.** 9

39. a–d.

41. a–d.

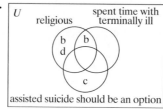

e. Answers will vary.

43.

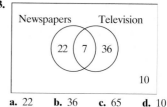

a. 22   **b.** 36   **c.** 65   **d.** 10

45.

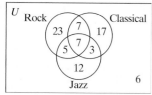

a. 23   **b.** 3   **c.** 32   **d.** 52
e. 22   **f.** 6

47. a. 1500   **b.** 1135   **c.** 56   **d.** 327   **e.** 526   **f.** 366   **g.** 1191   **51.** b   **53.** Under the conditions given concerning enrollment in math, chemistry, and psychology courses, the total number of students is 100, not 90.

Chapter 2 Review Exercises

1. the set of days of the week beginning with the letter T   **2.** the set of natural numbers between 1 and 10, inclusive   **3.** $\{m, i, s\}$
4. $\{8, 9, 10, 11, 12\}$ **5.** $\{1, 2, 3, \ldots, 30\}$ **6.** not empty   **7.** empty set   **8.** $\in$ **9.** $\notin$ **10.** 12   **11.** 15   **12.** $\neq$ **13.** $\neq$
14. equivalent   **15.** both   **16.** finite   **17.** infinite   **18.** $\subseteq$ **19.** $\not\subseteq$ **20.** $\subseteq$ **21.** $\subseteq$ **22.** both   **23.** false; Answers will vary.
24. false; Answers will vary.   **25.** true   **26.** false; Answers will vary.   **27.** true   **28.** false; It has $2^1 = 2$ subsets.   **29.** true
30. $\varnothing, \{1\}, \{5\}, \{1, 5\}; \{1, 5\}$ **31.** 32; 31   **32.** 8; 7   **33.** $\{1, 2, 4\}$ **34.** $\{1, 2, 3, 4, 6, 7, 8\}$ **35.** $\{5\}$ **36.** $\{6, 7, 8\}$ **37.** $\{6, 7, 8\}$
38. $\{4, 5, 6\}$ **39.** $\{2, 3, 6, 7\}$ **40.** $\{1, 4, 5, 6, 8, 9\}$ **41.** $\{4, 5\}$ **42.** $\{1, 2, 3, 6, 7, 8, 9\}$ **43.** $\{2, 3, 7\}$ **44.** $\{6\}$ **45.** $\{1, 2, 3, 4, 5, 6, 7, 8, 9\}$
46. 33   **47.** $\{1, 2, 3, 4, 5\}$ **48.** $\{1, 2, 3, 4, 5, 6, 7, 8\}$ or U **49.** $\{c, d, e, f, k, p, r\}$ **50.** $\{f, p\}$ **51.** $\{c, d, f, k, p, r\}$ **52.** $\{c, d, e\}$
53. $\{a, b, c, d, e, g, h, p, r\}$ **54.** $\{f\}$ **55.**

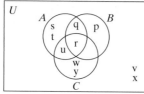

56. Use Figure 2.21 on page 84.

Set	Regions in the Venn Diagram
A	I, II
B	II, III
$A \cup B$	I, II, III
$(A \cup B)'$	IV

Set	Regions in the Venn Diagram
A'	III, IV
B'	I, IV
$A' \cap B'$	IV

Since $(A \cup B)'$ and $A' \cap B'$ represent the same region, $(A \cup B)' = A' \cap B'$.

57. Use Figure 2.22 on page 85.

Set	Regions in the Venn Diagram
A	I, II, IV, V
B	II, III, V, VI
C	IV, V, VI, VII
$B \cup C$	II, III, IV, V, VI, VII
$A \cap (B \cup C)$	II, IV, V

Set	Regions in the Venn Diagram
A	I, II, IV, V
B	II, III, V, VI
C	IV, V, VI, VII
$B \cap C$	V, VI
$A \cup (B \cap C)$	I, II, IV, V, VI

Since $A \cap (B \cup C)$ and $A \cup (B \cap C)$ do not represent the same regions, $A \cap (B \cup C) = A \cup (B \cap C)$ is false.

58. a. I   **b.** III   **c.** VIII   **d.** II   **e.** V

59. a–c.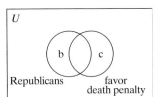

60. a. 250 **b.** 800 **c.** 200 **61. a.** 50 **b.** 26 **c.** 130 **d.** 46 **e.** 0

Chapter 2 Test

1. {18, 19, 20, 21, 22, 23, 24} **2.** false; Answers will vary. **3.** true **4.** true **5.** false; Answers will vary. **6.** true
7. false; Answers will vary. **8.** false; Answers will vary. **9.** false; Answers will vary. **10.** ∅, {6}, {9}, {6, 9}; {6, 9} **11.** {a, b, c, d, e, f}
12. {a, b, c, d, f, g} **13.** {b, c, d} **14.** {a, e} **15.** 5 **16.** {b, c, d, i, j, k} **17.** {a} **18.** {a, f, h}
19. **20.** theorem **21. a.** V **b.** VII **c.** IV **d.** I **e.** VI
22. a. **b.** 263 **c.** 25 **d.** 62 **e.** 0 **f.** 147 **g.** 116

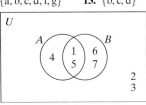

CHAPTER 3

Section 3.1

Check Point Exercises

1. a. Paris is not the capital of Spain. **b.** July is a month. **2. a.** $\sim p$ **b.** $\sim q$ **3.** Chicago O'Hare is not the world's busiest airport.
4. Some new tax dollars will not be used to improve education.; At least one new tax dollar will not be used to improve education.

Exercise Set 3.1

1. statement **3.** statement **5.** not a statement **7.** statement **9.** not a statement **11.** statement **13.** statement
15. It is not raining. **17.** The Dallas Cowboys are the team with the most Super Bowl wins. **19.** Chocolate in moderation is good for the heart.
21. $\sim p$ **23.** $\sim r$ **25.** Listening to classical music does not make infants smarter. **27.** Sigmund Freud's father was 20 years older than
his mother **29. a.** There are no whales that are not mammals. **b.** Some whales are not mammals. **31. a.** At least one student is a
business major. **b.** No students are business majors. **33. a.** At least one thief is not a criminal. **b.** All thieves are criminals.
35. a. All Democratic presidents have not been impeached. **b.** Some Democratic presidents have been impeached. **37.** Some Africans
have Jewish ancestry. **39.** Some rap is not hip-hop. **41. a.** All birds are parrots. **b.** false; Some birds are not parrots.
43. a. No college students are business majors. **b.** false; Some college students are business majors. **45. a.** All people like Sara Lee.
b. Some people don't like Sara Lee. **47. a.** No safe thing is exciting. **b.** Some safe things are exciting. **49. a.** Some great actors are
not Tom Hanks **b.** All great actors are Tom Hanks. **51.** b **53.** true **55.** false; Some college students in the United States
are willing to marry without romantic love. **57.** true **59.** false; The sentence "5% of college students in Australia are willing to marry without
romantic love" is a statement. **69.** Answers will vary.

Section 3.2

Check Point Exercises

1. a. $q \wedge p$ **b.** $\sim p \wedge q$ **2. a.** $p \vee q$ **b.** $q \vee \sim p$ **3. a.** $\sim p \rightarrow \sim q$ **b.** $q \rightarrow \sim p$ **4.** $\sim q \rightarrow p$ **5. a.** $q \leftrightarrow p$
b. $\sim p \leftrightarrow \sim q$ **6. a.** It is not true that he earns \$105,000 yearly and that he is often happy. **b.** He is not often happy and he earns
\$105,000 yearly. **c.** It is not true that if he is often happy then he earns \$105,000 yearly. **7. a.** If the plant is fertilized and watered, then it
will not wilt. **b.** The plant is fertilized, and if it is watered then it will not wilt. **8.** p: There is too much homework.; q: A teacher is boring.;
r: I take the class. **a.** $(p \vee q) \rightarrow \sim r$ **b.** $p \vee (q \rightarrow \sim r)$

Exercise Set 3.2

1. $p \wedge q$ **3.** $q \wedge \sim p$ **5.** $\sim q \wedge p$ **7.** $p \vee q$ **9.** $p \vee \sim q$ **11.** $p \rightarrow q$ **13.** $\sim p \rightarrow \sim q$ **15.** $\sim q \rightarrow \sim p$ **17.** $p \rightarrow q$
19. $p \rightarrow \sim q$ **21.** $q \rightarrow \sim p$ **23.** $p \rightarrow \sim q$ **25.** $q \rightarrow \sim p$ **27.** $p \leftrightarrow q$ **29.** $\sim q \leftrightarrow \sim p$ **31.** $q \leftrightarrow p$ **33.** The heater is not
working and the house is cold. **35.** The heater is working or the house is not cold. **37.** If the heater is working, then the house is not cold.
39. The heater is working if and only if the house is not cold. **41.** It is July 4th and we are not having a barbecue. **43.** It is not July 4th or we
are having a barbecue. **45.** If we are having a barbecue, then it is not July 4th. **47.** It is not July 4th if and only if we are having a barbecue.
49. It is not true that Romeo loves Juliet and Juliet loves Romeo. **51.** Romeo does not love Juliet and Juliet loves Romeo. **53.** Neither Juliet
loves Romeo nor Romeo loves Juliet. **55.** Juliet does not love Romeo or Romeo loves Juliet. **57.** Romeo does not love Juliet and Juliet does
not love Romeo. **59.** $(p \vee q) \vee r$ **61.** $(p \vee \sim q) \rightarrow r$ **63.** $r \leftrightarrow (p \wedge \sim q)$ **65.** $(p \wedge \sim q) \rightarrow r$ **67.** If the temperature is above
85° and we have finished studying, then we will go to the beach. **69.** The temperature is above 85°, and if we have finished studying then we will
go to the beach. **71.** $\sim r \rightarrow (\sim p \vee \sim q)$; If we do not go to the beach, then the temperature is not above 85° or we have not finished studying.
73. If we do not go to the beach then we have not finished studying, or the temperature is above 85°. **75.** $r \leftrightarrow (p \wedge q)$; We will go to the beach if
and only if the temperature is above 85° and we have finished studying. **77.** The temperature is above 85° if and only if we have finished studying,
and we go to the beach. **79.** If we do not go to the beach, then it is not true that both the temperature is above 85° and we have finished studying.

81. p: I like the teacher.; q: The course is interesting.; r: I miss class.; $(p \lor q) \to \sim r$ **83.** p: I like the teacher.; q: The course is interesting.; r: I miss class.; $p \lor (q \to \sim r)$ **85.** p: I like the teacher.; q: The course is interesting.; r: I miss class.; $r \leftrightarrow \sim (p \land q)$ **87.** p: I like the teacher.; q: The course is interesting.; r: I miss class.; $p \to (\sim r \leftrightarrow q)$ **89.** p: I like the teacher.; q: The course is interesting.; r: I miss class.; s: I spend extra time reading the book.; $(\sim p \land r) \to (\sim q \lor s)$ **91.** p: Being French is necessary for being a Parisian.; q: Being German is necessary for being a Berliner.; $\sim p \to \sim q$ **93.** p: You file an income tax report.; q: You file a complete statement of earnings.; r: You are a taxpayer.; s: You are an authorized tax preparer.; $(r \lor s) \to (p \land q)$ **95.** p: You are wealthy.; q: You are happy.; r: You live contentedly.; $\sim (p \to (q \land r))$ **97.** $[p \to (q \lor r)] \leftrightarrow (p \land r)$ **99.** $(p \to p) \leftrightarrow [(p \land p) \to \sim p]$ **101.** $\sim p \to q$ **103.** $(p \to q) \land \sim q$ **105.** $((p \to q) \land \sim p) \to \sim q$ **115.** p: Shooting unarmed citizens is morally justifiable.; q: Bombing unarmed citizens is morally justifiable.; $((p \leftrightarrow q) \land \sim p) \to \sim q$

Section 3.3

Check Point Exercises

1. a. false   **b.** true   **c.** false   **d.** true

2.

p	q	$p \lor q$	$\sim (p \lor q)$
T	T	T	F
T	F	T	F
F	T	T	F
F	F	F	T

$\sim (p \lor q)$ is true when both p and q are false; otherwise, $\sim (p \lor q)$ is false.

3.

p	q	$\sim p$	$\sim q$	$\sim p \land \sim q$
T	T	F	F	F
T	F	F	T	F
F	T	T	F	F
F	F	T	T	T

$\sim p \land \sim q$ is true when both p and q are false; otherwise, $\sim p \land \sim q$ is false.

4.

p	q	$\sim q$	$p \land \sim q$	$\sim p$	$(p \land \sim q) \lor \sim p$
T	T	F	F	F	F
T	F	T	T	F	T
F	T	F	F	T	T
F	F	T	F	T	T

$(p \land \sim q) \lor \sim p$ is false when both p and q are true; otherwise, $(p \land \sim q) \lor \sim p$ is true.

5.

p	$\sim p$	$p \land \sim p$
T	F	F
F	T	F

$p \land \sim p$ is false in all cases.

6. p: I study hard.; q: I ace the final.; r: I fail the course.

a.

p	q	r	$q \lor r$	$p \land (q \lor r)$
T	T	T	T	T
T	T	F	T	T
T	F	T	T	T
T	F	F	F	F
F	T	T	T	F
F	T	F	T	F
F	F	T	T	F
F	F	F	F	F

b. false

7. true

Exercise Set 3.3

1. true   **3.** false   **5.** false   **7.** false   **9.** true   **11.** true   **13.** true   **15.** true

17.

p	$\sim p$	$\sim p \land p$
T	F	F
F	T	F

19.

p	q	$\sim p$	$\sim p \land q$
T	T	F	F
T	F	F	F
F	T	T	T
F	F	T	F

21.

p	q	$p \vee q$	$\sim(p \vee q)$
T	T	T	F
T	F	T	F
F	T	T	F
F	F	F	T

23.

p	q	$\sim p$	$\sim q$	$\sim p \wedge \sim q$
T	T	F	F	F
T	F	F	T	F
F	T	T	F	F
F	F	T	T	T

25.

p	q	$\sim q$	$p \vee \sim q$
T	T	F	T
T	F	T	T
F	T	F	F
F	F	T	T

27.

p	q	$\sim p$	$\sim p \vee q$	$\sim(\sim p \vee q)$
T	T	F	T	F
T	F	F	F	T
F	T	T	T	F
F	F	T	T	F

29.

p	q	$\sim p$	$p \vee q$	$(p \vee q) \wedge \sim p$
T	T	F	T	F
T	F	F	T	F
F	T	T	T	T
F	F	T	F	F

31.

p	q	$\sim p$	$\sim q$	$p \wedge \sim q$	$\sim p \vee (p \wedge \sim q)$
T	T	F	F	F	F
T	F	F	T	T	T
F	T	T	F	F	T
F	F	T	T	F	T

33.

p	q	$\sim p$	$\sim q$	$p \vee q$	$\sim p \vee \sim q$	$(p \vee q) \wedge (\sim p \vee \sim q)$
T	T	F	F	T	F	F
T	F	F	T	T	T	T
F	T	T	F	T	T	T
F	F	T	T	F	T	F

35.

p	q	$\sim q$	$p \wedge \sim q$	$p \wedge q$	$(p \wedge \sim q) \vee (p \wedge q)$
T	T	F	F	T	T
T	F	T	T	F	T
F	T	F	F	F	F
F	F	T	F	F	F

37.

p	q	r	$\sim q$	$\sim q \vee r$	$p \wedge (\sim q \vee r)$
T	T	T	F	T	T
T	T	F	F	F	F
T	F	T	T	T	T
T	F	F	T	T	T
F	T	T	F	T	F
F	T	F	F	F	F
F	F	T	T	T	F
F	F	F	T	T	F

39.

p	q	r	$\sim p$	$\sim q$	$r \wedge \sim p$	$(r \wedge \sim p) \vee \sim q$
T	T	T	F	F	F	F
T	T	F	F	F	F	F
T	F	T	F	T	F	T
T	F	F	F	T	F	T
F	T	T	T	F	T	T
F	T	F	T	F	F	F
F	F	T	T	T	T	T
F	F	F	T	T	F	T

41.

p	q	r	$p \vee q$	$\sim(p \vee q)$	$\sim r$	$\sim(p \vee q) \wedge \sim r$
T	T	T	T	F	F	F
T	T	F	T	F	T	F
T	F	T	T	F	F	F
T	F	F	T	F	T	F
F	T	T	T	F	F	F
F	T	F	T	F	T	F
F	F	T	F	T	F	F
F	F	F	F	T	T	T

43. a. p: You did the dishes.; q: You left the room a mess.; $\sim p \wedge q$ **b.** See truth table for Exercise 19.   **c.** The statement is true when p is false and q is true.

45. a. p: I bought a meal ticket.; q: I used it.; $\sim (p \wedge \sim q)$

b.

p	q	$\sim q$	$p \wedge \sim q$	$\sim (p \wedge \sim q)$
T	T	F	F	T
T	F	T	T	F
F	T	F	F	T
F	F	T	F	T

c. Answers will vary; an example is: The statement is true when p and q are true.

47. a. p: The student is intelligent.; q: The student is an overachiever.; $(p \vee q) \wedge \sim q$

b.

p	q	$\sim q$	$p \vee q$	$(p \vee q) \wedge \sim q$
T	T	F	T	F
T	F	T	T	T
F	T	F	T	F
F	F	T	F	F

c. The statement is true when p is true and q is false.

49. a. p: Married people are healthier than single people.; q: Married people are more economically stable than single people.; r: Children of married people do better on a variety of indicators.; $(p \wedge q) \wedge r$

b.

p	q	r	$p \wedge q$	$(p \wedge q) \wedge r$
T	T	T	T	T
T	T	F	T	F
T	F	T	F	F
T	F	F	F	F
F	T	T	F	F
F	T	F	F	F
F	F	T	F	F
F	F	F	F	F

c. The statement is true when p, q, and r are all true.

51. a. p: I go to office hours.; q: I ask questions.; r: My professor remembers me.; $(p \wedge q) \vee \sim r$

b.

p	q	r	$\sim r$	$p \wedge q$	$(p \wedge q) \vee \sim r$
T	T	T	F	T	T
T	T	F	T	T	T
T	F	T	F	F	F
T	F	F	T	F	T
F	T	T	F	F	F
F	T	F	T	F	T
F	F	T	F	F	F
F	F	F	T	F	T

c. Answers will vary; an example is: The statement is true when p, q, and r are all true.

53. false   **55.** true   **57.** true   **59.** false   **61.** true

63.

p	q	$\sim [\sim (p \wedge \sim q) \vee \sim (\sim p \vee q)]$
T	T	F
T	F	F
F	T	F
F	F	F

65.

p	q	r	$[(p \wedge \sim r) \vee (q \wedge \sim r)] \wedge \sim (\sim p \vee r)$
T	T	T	F
T	T	F	T
T	F	T	F
T	F	F	T
F	T	T	F
F	T	F	F
F	F	T	F
F	F	F	F

67. *p*: You notice this notice.; *q*: You notice this notice is not worth noticing.; $(p \vee \sim p) \wedge q$

p	*q*	$\sim p$	$p \vee \sim p$	$(p \vee \sim p) \wedge q$
T	T	F	T	T
T	F	F	T	F
F	T	T	T	T
F	F	T	T	F

The statement is true when *q* is true.

69. *p*: $x \leq 3$; *q*: $x \geq 7$; $\sim (p \vee q) \wedge (\sim p \wedge \sim q)$

p	*q*	$\sim p$	$\sim q$	$p \vee q$	$\sim (p \vee q)$	$\sim p \wedge \sim q$	$\sim (p \vee q) \wedge (\sim p \wedge \sim q)$
T	T	F	F	T	F	F	F
T	F	F	T	T	F	F	F
F	T	T	F	T	F	F	F
F	F	T	T	F	T	T	T

The statement is true when both *p* and *q* are false.

71. The chance of divorce peaks during the fourth year of marriage and the chance of divorce does not decrease after four years of marriage.; false
73. The chance of divorce does not peak during the fourth year of marriage and more than 2% of all divorces occur during the 25th year of marriage.; false **75.** The chance of divorce peaks during the fourth year of marriage or the chance of divorce does not decrease after four years of marriage.; true **77.** The chance of divorce does not peak during the fourth year of marriage or more than 2% of all divorces occur during the 25th year of marriage.; false **79.** The chance of divorce peaks during the fourth year of marriage and the chance of divorce decreases after four years of marriage, or more than 2% of all divorces occur during the 25th year of marriage.; true **81.** *p*: In 2004, 29.5% of college freshman were liberal.; *q*: In 2004, 25.1% of college freshman were conservative.; $\sim (p \wedge q)$; true **83.** *p*: From 1984 through 2004, the percentage of liberal college freshman increased.; *q*: From 1984 through 2004, the percentage of conservative college freshman decreased.; *r*: From 1984 through 2004, the percentage of moderate college freshman increased.; $(p \vee q) \wedge \sim r$; true **85. a.** Hora Gershwin **b.** Bolera Mozart does not have a master's degree in music. Cha-Cha Bach does not either play three instruments or have five years experience playing with a symphony orchestra.

97.

p	*q*	$p \veebar q$
T	T	F
T	F	T
F	T	T
F	F	F

Section 3.4

Check Point Exercises

1.

p	*q*	$\sim p$	$\sim q$	$\sim p \rightarrow \sim q$
T	T	F	F	T
T	F	F	T	T
F	T	T	F	F
F	F	T	T	T

2. The table shows that $[(p \rightarrow q) \wedge \sim q] \rightarrow \sim p$ is always true; therefore, it is a tautology.

p	*q*	$\sim p$	$\sim q$	$p \rightarrow q$	$(p \rightarrow q) \wedge \sim q$	$[(p \rightarrow q) \wedge \sim q] \rightarrow \sim p$
T	T	F	F	T	F	T
T	F	F	T	F	F	T
F	T	T	F	T	F	T
F	F	T	T	T	T	T

3. a. *p*: You use Hair Grow.; *q*: You apply it daily.; *r*: You go bald.

p	*q*	*r*	$\sim r$	$p \wedge q$	$(p \wedge q) \rightarrow \sim r$
T	T	T	F	T	F
T	T	F	T	T	T
T	F	T	F	F	T
T	F	F	T	F	T
F	T	T	F	F	T
F	T	F	T	F	T
F	F	T	F	F	T
F	F	F	T	F	T

4.

p	*q*	$p \vee q$	$\sim p$	$\sim p \rightarrow q$	$(p \vee q) \leftrightarrow (\sim p \rightarrow q)$
T	T	T	F	T	T
T	F	T	F	T	T
F	T	T	T	T	T
F	F	F	T	F	T

Because all cases are true, the statement is a tautology.

b. no

5. true

Exercise Set 3.4

1.

p	q	$\sim q$	$p \to \sim q$
T	T	F	F
T	F	T	T
F	T	F	T
F	F	T	T

3.

p	q	$q \to p$	$\sim(q \to p)$
T	T	T	F
T	F	T	F
F	T	F	T
F	F	T	F

5.

p	q	$p \wedge q$	$p \vee q$	$(p \wedge q) \to (p \vee q)$
T	T	T	T	T
T	F	F	T	T
F	T	F	T	T
F	F	F	F	T

7.

p	q	$p \to q$	$\sim q$	$(p \to q) \wedge \sim q$
T	T	T	F	F
T	F	F	T	F
F	T	T	F	F
F	F	T	T	T

9.

p	q	r	$p \vee q$	$(p \vee q) \to r$
T	T	T	T	T
T	T	F	T	F
T	F	T	T	T
T	F	F	T	F
F	T	T	T	T
F	T	F	T	F
F	F	T	F	T
F	F	F	F	T

11.

p	q	r	$p \wedge q$	$r \to (p \wedge q)$
T	T	T	T	T
T	T	F	T	T
T	F	T	F	F
T	F	F	F	T
F	T	T	F	F
F	T	F	F	T
F	F	T	F	F
F	F	F	F	T

13.

p	q	r	$\sim q$	$\sim r$	$\sim q \to p$	$\sim r \wedge (\sim q \to p)$
T	T	T	F	F	T	F
T	T	F	F	T	T	T
T	F	T	T	F	T	F
T	F	F	T	T	T	T
F	T	T	F	F	T	F
F	T	F	F	T	T	T
F	F	T	T	F	F	F
F	F	F	T	T	F	T

15.

p	q	r	$\sim q$	$p \wedge r$	$\sim(p \wedge r)$	$\sim q \vee r$	$\sim(p \wedge r) \to (\sim q \vee r)$
T	T	T	F	T	F	T	T
T	T	F	F	F	T	F	F
T	F	T	T	T	F	T	T
T	F	F	T	F	T	T	T
F	T	T	F	F	T	T	T
F	T	F	F	F	T	F	F
F	F	T	T	F	T	T	T
F	F	F	T	F	T	T	T

17.

p	q	$\sim q$	$p \leftrightarrow \sim q$
T	T	F	F
T	F	T	T
F	T	F	T
F	F	T	F

19.

p	q	$p \leftrightarrow q$	$\sim(p \leftrightarrow q)$
T	T	T	F
T	F	F	T
F	T	F	T
F	F	T	F

21.

p	q	$p \leftrightarrow q$	$(p \leftrightarrow q) \to p$
T	T	T	T
T	F	F	T
F	T	F	T
F	F	T	F

23.

p	q	$\sim p$	$\sim p \leftrightarrow q$	$\sim p \to q$	$(\sim p \leftrightarrow q) \to (\sim p \to q)$
T	T	F	F	T	T
T	F	F	T	T	T
F	T	T	T	T	T
F	F	T	F	F	T

25.

p	q	$p \wedge q$	$q \to p$	$(p \wedge q) \wedge (q \to p)$	$[(p \wedge q) \wedge (q \to p)] \leftrightarrow (p \wedge q)$
T	T	T	T	T	T
T	F	F	T	F	T
F	T	F	F	F	T
F	F	F	T	F	T

27.

p	q	r	$\sim r$	$p \leftrightarrow q$	$(p \leftrightarrow q) \to \sim r$
T	T	T	F	T	F
T	T	F	T	T	T
T	F	T	F	F	T
T	F	F	T	F	T
F	T	T	F	F	T
F	T	F	T	F	T
F	F	T	F	T	F
F	F	F	T	T	T

29.

p	q	r	$p \wedge r$	$q \vee r$	$\sim (q \vee r)$	$(p \wedge r) \leftrightarrow \sim (q \vee r)$
T	T	T	T	T	F	F
T	T	F	F	T	F	T
T	F	T	T	T	F	F
T	F	F	F	F	T	F
F	T	T	F	T	F	T
F	T	F	F	T	F	T
F	F	T	F	T	F	T
F	F	F	F	F	T	F

31.

p	q	r	$\sim q$	$\sim q \wedge p$	$r \vee (\sim q \wedge p)$	$\sim p$	$[r \vee (\sim q \wedge p)] \leftrightarrow \sim p$
T	T	T	F	F	T	F	F
T	T	F	F	F	F	F	T
T	F	T	T	T	T	F	F
T	F	F	T	T	T	F	F
F	T	T	F	F	T	T	T
F	T	F	F	F	F	T	F
F	F	T	T	F	T	T	T
F	F	F	T	F	F	T	F

33. neither

p	q	$p \to q$	$(p \to q) \wedge q$	$[(p \to q) \wedge q] \to p$
T	T	T	T	T
T	F	F	F	T
F	T	T	T	F
F	F	T	F	T

35. tautology

p	q	$\sim p$	$\sim q$	$p \to q$	$(p \to q) \wedge \sim q$	$[(p \to q) \wedge \sim q] \to \sim p$
T	T	F	F	T	F	T
T	F	F	T	F	F	T
F	T	T	F	T	F	T
F	F	T	T	T	T	T

37. neither

p	q	$\sim q$	$p \vee q$	$(p \vee q) \wedge p$	$[(p \vee q) \wedge p] \to \sim q$
T	T	F	T	T	F
T	F	T	T	T	T
F	T	F	T	F	T
F	F	T	F	F	T

39. tautology

p	q	$\sim p$	$p \to q$	$\sim p \lor q$	$(p \to q) \to (\sim p \lor q)$
T	T	F	T	T	T
T	F	F	F	F	T
F	T	T	T	T	T
F	F	T	T	T	T

41. self-contradiction

p	q	$\sim p$	$\sim q$	$p \land q$	$\sim p \lor \sim q$	$(p \land q) \land (\sim p \lor \sim q)$
T	T	F	F	T	F	F
T	F	F	T	F	T	F
F	T	T	F	F	T	F
F	F	T	T	F	T	F

43. neither

p	q	$\sim p$	$\sim q$	$p \land q$	$\sim (p \land q)$	$\sim p \land \sim q$	$\sim (p \land q) \leftrightarrow (\sim p \land \sim q)$
T	T	F	F	T	F	F	T
T	F	F	T	F	T	F	F
F	T	T	F	F	T	F	F
F	F	T	T	F	T	T	T

45. neither

p	q	$p \to q$	$q \to p$	$(p \to q) \leftrightarrow (q \to p)$
T	T	T	T	T
T	F	F	T	F
F	T	T	F	F
F	F	T	T	T

47. tautology

p	q	$\sim p$	$p \to q$	$\sim p \lor q$	$(p \to q) \leftrightarrow (\sim p \lor q)$
T	T	F	T	T	T
T	F	F	F	F	T
F	T	T	T	T	T
F	F	T	T	T	T

49. tautology

p	q	$p \leftrightarrow q$	$p \to q$	$q \to p$	$(q \to p) \land (p \to q)$	$(p \leftrightarrow q) \leftrightarrow [(q \to p) \land (p \to q)]$
T	T	T	T	T	T	T
T	F	F	F	T	F	T
F	T	F	T	F	F	T
F	F	T	T	T	T	T

51. neither

p	q	r	$\sim p$	$p \land q$	$\sim p \lor r$	$(p \land q) \leftrightarrow (\sim p \lor r)$
T	T	T	F	T	T	T
T	T	F	F	T	F	F
T	F	T	F	F	T	F
T	F	F	F	F	F	T
F	T	T	T	F	T	F
F	T	F	T	F	T	F
F	F	T	T	F	T	F
F	F	F	T	F	T	F

53. tautology

p	q	r	$p \to q$	$q \to r$	$(p \to q) \wedge (q \to r)$	$p \to r$	$[(p \to q) \wedge (q \to r)] \to (p \to r)$
T	T	T	T	T	T	T	T
T	T	F	T	F	F	F	T
T	F	T	F	T	F	T	T
T	F	F	F	T	F	F	T
F	T	T	T	T	T	T	T
F	T	F	T	F	F	T	T
F	F	T	T	T	T	T	T
F	F	F	T	T	T	T	T

55. neither

p	q	r	$[(q \to r) \wedge (r \to \sim p)] \leftrightarrow (q \wedge p)$
T	T	T	F
T	T	F	F
T	F	T	T
T	F	F	F
F	T	T	F
F	T	F	T
F	F	T	F
F	F	F	F

57. a. p: You do homework right after class.; q: You fall behind.; $(p \to \sim q) \wedge (\sim p \to q)$

b.

p	q	$\sim p$	$\sim q$	$p \to \sim q$	$\sim p \to q$	$(p \to \sim q) \wedge (\sim p \to q)$
T	T	F	F	F	T	F
T	F	F	T	T	T	T
F	T	T	F	T	T	T
F	F	T	T	T	F	F

c. Answers will vary; an example is: The statement is true when p and q have opposite truth values.

59. a. p: You cut and paste from the Internet.; q: You cite the source.; r: You are charged with plagiarism.; $(p \wedge \sim q) \to r$

b.

p	q	r	$\sim q$	$p \wedge \sim q$	$(p \wedge \sim q) \to r$
T	T	T	F	F	T
T	T	F	F	F	T
T	F	T	T	T	T
T	F	F	T	T	F
F	T	T	F	F	T
F	T	F	F	F	T
F	F	T	T	F	T
F	F	F	T	F	T

c. Answers will vary; an example is: The statement is true when p, q, and r are all true.

61. a. p: You are comfortable in your room.; q: You are honest with your roommate.; r: You enjoy the college experience.; $(p \leftrightarrow q) \vee \sim r$

b.

p	q	r	$\sim r$	$p \leftrightarrow q$	$(p \leftrightarrow q) \vee \sim r$
T	T	T	F	T	T
T	T	F	T	T	T
T	F	T	F	F	F
T	F	F	T	F	T
F	T	T	F	F	F
F	T	F	T	F	T
F	F	T	F	T	T
F	F	F	T	T	T

c. Answers will vary; an example is: The statement is true when p, q, and r are all true.

63. a. p: I enjoy the course.; q: I choose the class based on the professor.; r: I choose the class based on the course description.; $p \leftrightarrow (q \wedge \sim r)$

b.

p	q	r	$\sim r$	$q \wedge \sim r$	$p \leftrightarrow (q \wedge \sim r)$
T	T	T	F	F	F
T	T	F	T	T	T
T	F	T	F	F	F
T	F	F	T	F	F
F	T	T	F	F	T
F	T	F	T	T	F
F	F	T	F	F	T
F	F	F	T	F	T

c. Answers will vary; an example is: The statement is true when $p, q,$ and r are all false.

65. false   **67.** true   **69.** false   **71.** true   **73.** true

75. $(p \rightarrow q) \leftrightarrow [(p \wedge q) \rightarrow \sim p]$

p	q	$(p \rightarrow q) \leftrightarrow [(p \wedge q) \rightarrow \sim p]$
T	T	F
T	F	F
F	T	T
F	F	T

77. $[p \rightarrow (\sim q \vee r)] \leftrightarrow (p \wedge r)$

p	q	r	$[p \rightarrow (\sim q \vee r)] \leftrightarrow (p \wedge r)$
T	T	T	T
T	T	F	T
T	F	T	T
T	F	F	F
F	T	T	F
F	T	F	F
F	F	T	F
F	F	F	F

79. p: You love a person.; q: You marry that person.; $(q \rightarrow p) \wedge (\sim p \rightarrow \sim q)$

p	q	$\sim p$	$\sim q$	$q \rightarrow p$	$\sim p \rightarrow \sim q$	$(q \rightarrow p) \wedge (\sim p \rightarrow \sim q)$
T	T	F	F	T	T	T
T	F	F	T	T	T	T
F	T	T	F	F	F	F
F	F	T	T	T	T	T

Answers will vary; an example is: The statement is true when both p and q are true.

81. p: You are happy.; q: You live contentedly.; r: You are wealthy.; $\sim [r \rightarrow (p \wedge q)]$

p	q	r	$p \wedge q$	$r \rightarrow (p \wedge q)$	$\sim [r \rightarrow (p \wedge q)]$
T	T	T	T	T	F
T	T	F	T	T	F
T	F	T	F	F	T
T	F	F	F	T	F
F	T	T	F	F	T
F	T	F	F	T	F
F	F	T	F	F	T
F	F	F	F	T	F

Answers will vary; an example is: The statement is true when p is false and both q and r are true.

83. p: Men averaged more hours than women for every year shown.; q: Men averaged more hours than women in 2002 through 2005.; r: Women averaged more hours than men in 2001.; $(\sim p \wedge q) \rightarrow r$; true   **85.** p: Men averaged 2.4 hours more than women in 2005.; q: Men averaged 1.2 hours more than women in 2004.; r: Men averaged fewer hours in 2005 than in 2002.; $(p \leftrightarrow q) \vee r$; true   **87.** false   **89.** false
97. no; Answers will vary.   **99.** Answers will vary; examples are: $p \vee q, p \wedge q, \sim(p \wedge q),$ and $(p \vee q) \rightarrow \sim(p \wedge q)$.

Section 3.5

Check Point Exercises

1. a.

p	q	$\sim q$	$p \vee q$	$\sim q \rightarrow p$
T	T	F	T	T
T	F	T	T	T
F	T	F	T	T
F	F	T	F	F

The statements are equivalent since their truth values are the same.

b. If I don't lose my scholarship, then I attend classes.

2.

p	$\sim p$	$\sim (\sim p)$	$\sim [\sim (\sim p)]$
T	F	T	F
F	T	F	T

Since the truth values are the same,
$\sim [\sim (\sim p)] \equiv \sim p$.

3. c   **4. a.** If you're not driving too closely, then you can't read this.   **b.** If it's not time to do the laundry, then you have underwear.
c. If supervision during exams is required, then some students are not honest.   **d.** $q \to (p \lor r)$ **5.** Converse: If you don't see a Club Med, then you are in Iran.; Inverse: If you are not in Iran, then you see a Club Med.; Contrapositive: If you see a Club Med, then you are not in Iran.
6. You do not have a fever and you have the flu.   **7.** Bart Simpson is not a cartoon character or Tony Soprano is not a cartoon character.
8. You do not leave by 5 P.M. and you arrive home on time.   **9. a.** Some horror movies are not scary or none are funny.   **b.** Your workouts are not strenuous and you get stronger.   **10.** If we cannot swim or we can sail, it is windy.

Exercise Set 3.5

1. a.

p	q	$\sim p$	$p \lor q$	$\sim p \to q$
T	T	F	T	T
T	F	F	T	T
F	T	T	T	T
F	F	T	F	F

   b. The United States supports the development of solar-powered cars or it will suffer increasing atmospheric pollution.
3. not equivalent   **5.** equivalent   **7.** equivalent   **9.** not equivalent   **11.** not equivalent   **13.** equivalent   **15.** a   **17.** c
19. Converse: If I am in Illinois, then I am in Chicago.; Inverse: If I am not in Chicago, then I am not in Illinois.; Contrapositive: If I am not in Illinois, then I am not in Chicago.   **21.** Converse: If I cannot hear you, then the stereo is playing.; Inverse: If the stereo is not playing, then I can hear you.; Contrapositive: If I can hear you, then the stereo is not playing.   **23.** Converse: If you die, you don't laugh.; Inverse: If you laugh, you don't die.; Contrapositive: If you don't die, you laugh.   **25.** Converse: If all troops were withdrawn, then the president is telling the truth.; Inverse: If the president is not telling the truth, then some troops were not withdrawn.; Contrapositive: If some troops were not withdrawn, then the president was not telling the truth.   **27.** Converse: If some people suffer, then all institutions place profit above human need.; Inverse: If some institutions do not place profit above human need, then no people suffer.; Contrapositive: If no people suffer, then some institutions do not place profit above human need.
29. Converse: $\sim r \to \sim q$; Inverse: $q \to r$; Contrapositive: $r \to q$ **31.** I am in Los Angeles and not in California.   **33.** It is purple and it is a carrot.
35. He doesn't and I won't.   **37.** There is a blizzard and some schools are not closed.   **39.** $\sim q \land r$ **41.** Australia is not an island or China is not an island.   **43.** My high school did not encourage creativity or it did not encourage diversity.   **45.** Jewish scripture does not give a clear indication of a heaven and it does not give a clear indication of an afterlife.   **47.** The United States has eradicated neither poverty nor racism.
49. $p \lor \sim q$ **51.** If you do not succeed, you did not attend lecture or did not study.   **53.** If his wife does not cook and his child does not cook, then he does.   **55.** $(\sim q \land r) \to \sim p$ **57.** I'm going to neither Seattle nor San Francisco.   **59.** I do not study and I pass.   **61.** I am going or he is not going.   **63.** A bill does not become law or it receives majority approval.   **65.** $\sim p \land q$ **67.** $\sim p \lor (\sim q \land \sim r)$
69. none   **71.** none   **73.** none   **75.** a and b   **77.** If there is no pain, there is no gain.; Converse: If there is no gain, then there is no pain.; Inverse: If there is pain, then there is gain.; Contrapositive: If there is gain, then there is pain.; Negation: There is no pain and there is gain.
79. If you follow Buddha's "Middle Way," then you are neither hedonistic nor ascetic.; Converse: If you are neither hedonistic nor ascetic, then you follow Buddha's "Middle Way."; Inverse: If you do not follow Buddha's "Middle Way," then you are either hedonistic or ascetic.; Contrapositive: If you are either hedonistic or ascetic, then you do not follow Buddha's "Middle Way."; Negation: You follow Buddha's "Middle Way" and you are either hedonistic or ascetic.   **81.** $p \land (\sim r \lor s)$ **83.** $\sim p \lor (r \land s)$ **85. a.** false   **b.** Smith does not comprise 1.006% or Johnson does not comprise 0.699%.   **c.** true   **87. a.** true   **b.** Brown does not comprise 0.699% and Williams comprises 0.621%.   **c.** false   **89. a.** true
b. Brown does not comprise 0.621% and Jones comprises 0.621%.   **c.** false   **91. a.** true   **b.** Smith is not the top name or does not comprise 1.006%, and Johnson comprises 0.810%.   **c.** false   **103.** We will replace or repair the roof, or we will not sell the house.

Section 3.6

Check Point Exercises

1. valid   **2.** valid   **3.** invalid   **4. a.** valid   **b.** invalid   **c.** valid   **5.** valid   **6.** Some schools across the country are not reexamining their educational objectives.

Exercise Set 3.6

1. invalid   **3.** valid   **5.** valid   **7.** invalid   **9.** invalid   **11.** valid   **13.** valid

15. $\dfrac{\begin{array}{l}p \to \sim q\\ q\end{array}}{\therefore \sim p}$ valid   **17.** $\dfrac{\begin{array}{l}p \lor q\\ q\end{array}}{\therefore \sim p}$ invalid   **19.** $\dfrac{\begin{array}{l}p \to q\\ q\end{array}}{\therefore p}$ invalid   **21.** $\dfrac{\begin{array}{l}p \to q\\ \sim p \to q\end{array}}{\therefore q}$ valid   **23.** $\dfrac{\begin{array}{l}p \lor q\\ \sim q\end{array}}{\therefore p}$ valid   **25.** $\dfrac{\begin{array}{l}p \to q\\ \sim p\end{array}}{\therefore \sim q}$ invalid   **27.** $\dfrac{\begin{array}{l}p \to q\\ q \to r\end{array}}{\therefore p \to r}$ valid   **29.** $\dfrac{\begin{array}{l}p \to q\\ q \to r\end{array}}{\therefore r \to p}$ invalid

31. $\dfrac{\begin{array}{l}(p \land q) \to r\\ p \land \sim r\end{array}}{\therefore \sim q}$ valid   **33.** $\dfrac{\begin{array}{l}(p \lor q) \to r\\ \sim r\end{array}}{\therefore \sim p \land \sim q}$ valid   **35.** $\dfrac{\begin{array}{l}(p \lor q) \to r\\ r\end{array}}{\therefore p \lor q}$ invalid   **37.** $\dfrac{\begin{array}{l}(p \land q) \to r\\ \sim p \lor \sim q\end{array}}{\therefore \sim r}$ invalid   **39.** $\dfrac{\begin{array}{l}p \to q\\ \sim p \to r\end{array}}{\therefore q \lor r}$ valid   **41.** $\dfrac{\begin{array}{l}p \to q\\ q \to \sim r\\ r\end{array}}{\therefore \sim p}$ valid

43. My best friend is not a chemist.   **45.** They were dropped from prime time.   **47.** Some electricity is not off.
49. If I vacation in Paris, I gain weight.

51. $\dfrac{\begin{array}{l}p \to q\\ \sim p\end{array}}{\therefore \sim q}$ invalid   **53.** $\dfrac{\begin{array}{l}p \lor q\\ \sim p\end{array}}{\therefore q}$ valid   **55.** $\dfrac{\begin{array}{l}p \to q\\ q\end{array}}{\therefore p}$ invalid   **57.** $\dfrac{\begin{array}{l}p \to q\\ \sim q\end{array}}{\therefore \sim p}$ valid   **59.** $\dfrac{\begin{array}{l}p \to q\\ q \to r\end{array}}{\therefore p \to r}$ valid   **61.** $\dfrac{\begin{array}{l}p \to q\\ \sim q\end{array}}{\therefore \sim p}$ valid   **63.** h   **65.** i   **67.** c   **69.** a   **71.** j   **73.** d

83. People sometimes speak without being spoken to.   **85.** The doctor either destroys the base on which the placebo rests or jeopardizes a relationship built on trust.

Section 3.7

Check Point Exercises

1. valid   **2.** invalid   **3.** valid   **4.** invalid   **5.** invalid   **6.** invalid

Exercise Set 3.7

1. valid   **3.** invalid   **5.** valid   **7.** invalid   **9.** invalid   **11.** valid   **13.** valid   **15.** invalid   **17.** invalid   **19.** valid   **21.** valid
23. valid   **25.** invalid   **27.** invalid   **29.** valid   **31.** invalid   **33.** invalid   **35.** invalid   **37.** valid   **39.** valid
43. b   **45.** Some teachers are amusing people.

Chapter 3 Review Exercises

1. $(p \wedge q) \rightarrow r$; If the temperature is below 32° and we have finished studying, we will go to the movies.   **2.** $\sim r \rightarrow (\sim p \vee \sim q)$; If we do not go to the movies, then the temperature is not below 32° or we have not finished studying.   **3.** The temperature is below 32°, and if we finish studying, we will go to the movies.   **4.** We will go to the movies if and only if the temperature is below 32° and we have finished studying.
5. It is not true that both the temperature is below 32° and we have finished studying.   **6.** We will not go to the movies if and only if the temperature is not below 32° or we have not finished studying.   **7.** $(p \wedge q) \vee r$ **8.** $(p \vee \sim q) \rightarrow r$ **9.** $q \rightarrow (p \leftrightarrow r)$ **10.** $r \leftrightarrow (p \wedge \sim q)$
11. $p \rightarrow r$ **12.** $q \rightarrow \sim r$ **13.** Some houses are not made with wood.   **14.** Some students major in business.   **15.** No crimes are motivated by passion.   **16.** All Democrats are registered voters.   **17.** Some new taxes will not be used for education.

18. neither

p	q	$\sim p$	$\sim p \wedge q$	$p \vee (\sim p \wedge q)$
T	T	F	F	T
T	F	F	F	T
F	T	T	T	T
F	F	T	F	F

19. neither

p	q	$\sim p$	$\sim q$	$\sim p \vee \sim q$
T	T	F	F	F
T	F	F	T	T
F	T	T	F	T
F	F	T	T	T

20. neither

p	q	$\sim p$	$\sim p \vee q$	$p \rightarrow (\sim p \vee q)$
T	T	F	T	T
T	F	F	F	F
F	T	T	T	T
F	F	T	T	T

21. neither

p	q	$\sim q$	$p \leftrightarrow \sim q$
T	T	F	F
T	F	T	T
F	T	F	T
F	F	T	F

22. tautology

p	q	$\sim p$	$\sim q$	$p \vee q$	$\sim (p \vee q)$	$\sim p \wedge \sim q$	$\sim (p \vee q) \rightarrow (\sim p \wedge \sim q)$
T	T	F	F	T	F	F	T
T	F	F	T	T	F	F	T
F	T	T	F	T	F	F	T
F	F	T	T	F	T	T	T

23. neither

p	q	r	$\sim r$	$p \vee q$	$(p \vee q) \rightarrow \sim r$
T	T	T	F	T	F
T	T	F	T	T	T
T	F	T	F	T	F
T	F	F	T	T	T
F	T	T	F	T	F
F	T	F	T	T	T
F	F	T	F	F	T
F	F	F	T	F	T

24. neither

p	q	r	$p \wedge q$	$p \wedge r$	$(p \wedge q) \leftrightarrow (p \wedge r)$
T	T	T	T	T	T
T	T	F	T	F	F
T	F	T	F	T	F
T	F	F	F	F	T
F	T	T	F	F	T
F	T	F	F	F	T
F	F	T	F	F	T
F	F	F	F	F	T

25. neither

p	q	r	$r \rightarrow p$	$q \vee (r \rightarrow p)$	$p \wedge [q \vee (r \rightarrow p)]$
T	T	T	T	T	T
T	T	F	T	T	T
T	F	T	T	T	T
T	F	F	T	T	T
F	T	T	F	T	F
F	T	F	T	T	F
F	F	T	F	F	F
F	F	F	T	T	F

26. a. p: I'm in class.; q: I'm studying.; $(p \vee q) \wedge \sim p$

b.

p	q	$\sim p$	$p \vee q$	$(p \vee q) \wedge \sim p$
T	T	F	T	F
T	F	F	T	F
F	T	T	T	T
F	F	T	F	F

c. The statement is true when p is false and q is true.

27. a. p: You spit from a truck.; q: It's legal.; r: You spit from a car.; $(p \rightarrow q) \wedge (r \rightarrow \sim q)$

b.

p	q	r	$\sim q$	$p \rightarrow q$	$r \rightarrow \sim q$	$(p \rightarrow q) \wedge (r \rightarrow \sim q)$
T	T	T	F	T	F	F
T	T	F	F	T	T	T
T	F	T	T	F	T	F
T	F	F	T	F	T	F
F	T	T	F	T	F	F
F	T	F	F	T	T	T
F	F	T	T	T	T	T
F	F	F	T	T	T	T

c. The statement is true when p and q are both false.

28. false **29.** true **30.** true **31.** false **32.** p: \$60.0 million was spent in 2002.; q: Spending decreased from 2002 to 2003.; $p \wedge \sim q$; false
33. p: More money was spent in 2003 than 2004.; q: \$67.9 million was spent in 2003.; r: \$53.6 million was spent in 2004.; $p \rightarrow (q \vee r)$; true
34. p: \$55.8 million was spent in 2001.; q: \$60.0 million was spent in 2002.; r: \$67.9 million was spent in 2004.; $(p \leftrightarrow q) \vee \sim r$; true

35. a.

p	q	$\sim p$	$\sim p \vee q$	$p \rightarrow q$
T	T	F	T	T
T	F	F	F	F
F	T	T	T	T
F	F	T	T	T

b. If the triangle is isosceles, then it has two equal sides.
36. c **37.** not equivalent **38.** equivalent **39.** Converse: If I am in the South, then I am in Atlanta.; Inverse: If I am not in Atlanta, then I am not in the South.; Contrapositive: If I am not in the South, then I am not in Atlanta. **40.** Converse: If today is not a holiday, then I am in class.; Inverse: If I am not in class, then today is a holiday.; Contrapositive: If today is a holiday, then I am not in class. **41.** Converse: If I pass all courses, then I worked hard.; Inverse: If I don't work hard, then I don't pass some courses.; Contrapositive: If I do not pass some course, then I did not work hard.
42. Converse: $\sim q \rightarrow \sim p$; Inverse: $p \rightarrow q$.; Contrapositive: $q \rightarrow p$ **43.** An argument is sound and it is not valid. **44.** I do not work hard and I succeed. **45.** $\sim r \wedge \sim p$ **46.** Chicago is not a city or Maine is not a city. **47.** Ernest Hemingway was neither a musician nor an actor.
48. If a number is not 0, the number is positive or negative. **49.** I do not work hard and I succeed. **50.** She is using her car or she is not taking a bus. **51.** $p \wedge \sim q$ **52.** a and c **53.** a and b **54.** a and c **55.** none **56.** invalid **57.** valid

58. $\dfrac{\begin{array}{c} p \rightarrow q \\ q \end{array}}{\therefore p}$ invalid **59.** $\dfrac{\begin{array}{c} p \vee q \\ q \end{array}}{\therefore \sim p}$ invalid **60.** $\dfrac{\begin{array}{c} p \vee q \\ \sim p \end{array}}{\therefore q}$ valid **61.** $\dfrac{\begin{array}{c} p \rightarrow q \\ \sim q \end{array}}{\therefore \sim p}$ valid **62.** $\dfrac{\begin{array}{c} p \rightarrow \sim q \\ \sim p \rightarrow q \end{array}}{\therefore p \leftrightarrow \sim q}$ valid **63.** $\dfrac{\begin{array}{c} p \rightarrow \sim q \\ r \rightarrow q \end{array}}{\therefore \sim r \rightarrow p}$ invalid

64. invalid **65.** valid **66.** valid **67.** invalid **68.** invalid **69.** valid

Chapter 3 Test

1. If I'm registered and I'm a citizen, then I vote. **2.** I don't vote if and only if I'm not registered or I'm not a citizen. **3.** I'm neither registered nor a citizen. **4.** $(p \wedge q) \vee \sim r$ **5.** $(\sim p \vee \sim q) \rightarrow \sim r$ **6.** $r \rightarrow q$ **7.** Some numbers are not divisible by 5. **8.** No people wear glasses.

9.

p	q	$\sim p$	$\sim p \vee q$	$p \wedge (\sim p \vee q)$
T	T	F	T	T
T	F	F	F	F
F	T	T	T	F
F	F	T	T	F

10.

p	q	$\sim p$	$\sim q$	$p \wedge q$	$\sim (p \wedge q)$	$(\sim p \vee \sim q)$	$\sim (p \wedge q) \leftrightarrow (\sim p \vee \sim q)$
T	T	F	F	T	F	F	T
T	F	F	T	F	T	T	T
F	T	T	F	F	T	T	T
F	F	T	T	F	T	T	T

11.

p	q	r	$q \vee r$	$p \leftrightarrow (q \vee r)$
T	T	T	T	T
T	T	F	T	T
T	F	T	T	T
T	F	F	F	F
F	T	T	T	F
F	T	F	T	F
F	F	T	T	F
F	F	F	F	T

12. p: You break the law.; q: You change the law.; $(p \wedge q) \to \sim p$

p	q	$\sim p$	$p \wedge q$	$(p \wedge q) \to \sim p$
T	T	F	T	F
T	F	F	F	T
F	T	T	F	T
F	F	T	F	T

Answers will vary; an example is: The statement is true when p is false.
13. true   **14.** true   **15. a.** p: There was a decrease in the percentage of students who considered "being very well off financially" essential.; q: There was a decrease in the percentage of students who considered "developing a meaningful philosophy of life" essential.; r: There was a decrease in the percentage of students who considered "raising a family" essential.; $\sim p \vee (q \wedge r)$ **b.** true   **16.** b   **17.** If it snows, then it is not August.
18. Converse: If I cannot concentrate, then the radio is playing.; Inverse: If the radio is not playing, then I can concentrate.   **19.** It is cold and we use the pool.   **20.** The test is not today and the party is not tonight.   **21.** The banana is not green or it is ready to eat.   **22.** a and b
23. a and c   **24.** invalid   **25.** valid   **26.** invalid   **27.** invalid   **28.** valid   **29.** invalid

CHAPTER 4

Section 4.1

Check Point Exercises

1. a. 49   **b.** 125   **c.** 1   **d.** 100,000   **e.** 1,000,000   **f.** 18   **2. a.** $(4 \times 10^3) + (0 \times 10^2) + (2 \times 10^1) + (6 \times 1)$ or $(4 \times 1000) + (0 \times 100) + (2 \times 10) + (6 \times 1)$ **b.** $(2 \times 10^4) + (4 \times 10^3) + (2 \times 10^2) + (3 \times 10^1) + (2 \times 1)$ or $(2 \times 10,000) + (4 \times 1000) + (2 \times 100) + (3 \times 10) + (2 \times 1)$ **3. a.** 6073   **b.** 80,900   **4.** 12,031   **5.** 80,293

Exercise Set 4.1

1. 25   **3.** 8   **5.** 81   **7.** 100,000   **9.** $(3 \times 10^1) + (6 \times 1)$ **11.** $(2 \times 10^2) + (4 \times 10^1) + (9 \times 1)$ **13.** $(7 \times 10^2) + (0 \times 10^1) + (3 \times 1)$
15. $(4 \times 10^3) + (8 \times 10^2) + (5 \times 10^1) + (6 \times 1)$ **17.** $(3 \times 10^3) + (0 \times 10^2) + (7 \times 10^1) + (0 \times 1)$
19. $(3 \times 10^4) + (4 \times 10^3) + (5 \times 10^2) + (6 \times 10^1) + (9 \times 1)$
21. $(2 \times 10^8) + (3 \times 10^7) + (0 \times 10^6) + (0 \times 10^5) + (0 \times 10^4) + (7 \times 10^3) + (0 \times 10^2) + (0 \times 10^1) + (4 \times 1)$
23. 73   **25.** 385   **27.** 528,743   **29.** 7002   **31.** 600,002,007   **33.** 23   **35.** 1262   **37.** 11,523   **39.** 2,416,271   **41.** 14   **43.** 6846
45. 3048   **47.** 14,411   **49.** 75,610   **51.** $(4 \times 10^4) + (6 \times 10^3) + (2 \times 10^2) + (2 \times 10^1) + (5 \times 1)$
53. $(2 \times 10^3) + (2 \times 10^2) + (9 \times 10^1) + (9 \times 1)$ **55.** 0.4759   **57.** 0.700203   **59.** 5000.03   **61.** 30,700.05809   **63.** 9734   **65.** 8097
67. 365 is the number of days in a non-leap year.   **77.** $<<<<\vee\vee\vee\vee$ $<<\vee\vee\vee\vee\vee\vee$

Section 4.2

Check Point Exercises

1. 487   **2.** 51   **3.** 2772   **4.** 11_{five} **5.** 1031_{seven} **6.** 42023_{five}

Exercise Set 4.2

1. 23 **3.** 42 **5.** 30 **7.** 11 **9.** 455 **11.** 28,909 **13.** 8342 **15.** 53 **17.** 44,261 **19.** 12_{five} **21.** 14_{seven} **23.** 10_{two}
25. 31_{four} **27.** 101_{six} **29.** 322_{five} **31.** 1230_{four} **33.** 10011_{two} **35.** 12010_{three} **37.** 1442_{six} **39.** 4443_{seven}
41. $<\,<\,<\,<\,<$ $<\,<\,<\,<\,<\,\vee\,\vee$ **43.** $\vee\,\vee\,\vee\,\vee\,\vee\,\vee$ $<\,<\,<\,\vee\,\vee$ $<\,<\,\vee\,\vee\,\vee\,\vee\,\vee$
45. [Mayan numeral] **47.** [Mayan numeral]

49. 25_{seven} **51.** 623_{eight} **53.** 1000110 **55.** 1101101 **57.** PAL **59.** 100110111011111101101 **65.** $\text{EC4}_{\text{sixteen}}$; $\text{EC6}_{\text{sixteen}}$

Section 4.3

Check Point Exercises

1. 131_{five} **2.** 1110_{two} **3.** 13_{five} **4.** 1605_{seven} **5.** 201_{seven} **6.** 23_{four}

Exercise Set 4.3

1. 102_{four} **3.** 110_{two} **5.** 1310_{five} **7.** 1302_{seven} **9.** 15760_{nine} **11.** 23536_{seven} **13.** 13_{four} **15.** 4_{five} **17.** 206_{eight} **19.** 366_{seven}
21. 10_{two} **23.** 111_{three} **25.** 152_{six} **27.** 11_{two} **29.** 4011_{seven} **31.** 3114_{eight} **33.** 312_{four} **35.** 20_{four} **37.** 41_{five} remainder of 1_{five}
39. 1000110_{two} **41.** 110000_{two} **43.** 110111_{two} **45.** $71\text{BE}_{\text{sixteen}}$ **47.** 01100; 11101 **49.** 10001; 11001 **51.** 01100; 00110; 00100; 11011
53. The circuit in Exercise 47 **57.** 56_{seven}

Section 4.4

Check Point Exercises

1. 300,222 **2.** [Egyptian hieroglyphic numeral] **3.** 1361 **4.** 1447 **5.** CCCXCIX **6.** [Chinese numeral] **7.** 885

Exercise Set 4.4

1. 322 **3.** 300,423 **5.** 132 **7.** [Egyptian hieroglyphic numeral] **9.** [Egyptian hieroglyphic numeral]
11. [Egyptian hieroglyphic numeral] **13.** 11 **15.** 16 **17.** 40 **19.** 59 **21.** 146 **23.** 1621 **25.** 2677
27. 9466 **29.** XLIII **31.** CXXIX **33.** MDCCCXCVI **35.** $\overline{\text{VI}}$DCCCXCII **37.** 88 **39.** 527 **41.** 2776
43. [Chinese numeral] **45.** [Chinese numeral] **47.** [Chinese numeral] **49.** 12 **51.** 234 **53.** $\mu\gamma$ **55.** $\upsilon\pi\gamma$

57. MMCCCXXIV; [Chinese numeral] **59. a.** [Egyptian hieroglyphic numeral] **b.** [Chinese numeral]

61. 3104_{five} **63.** 1232_{five} **65.** [Egyptian hieroglyphic numeral] **67.** 1776; Declaration of Independence

69. 4,640,224; MMMMDCXLCCXXIV   **77.** Preceding: ⑨⑨∩∩∩∩∩∩∩∩∩∩IIIIIII

Following: ⑨⑨⑨

Chapter 4 Review Exercises

1. 121   **2.** 343   **3.** $(4 \times 10^2) + (7 \times 10^1) + (2 \times 1)$ **4.** $(8 \times 10^3) + (0 \times 10^2) + (7 \times 10^1) + (6 \times 1)$
5. $(7 \times 10^4) + (0 \times 10^3) + (3 \times 10^2) + (2 \times 10^1) + (9 \times 1)$ **6.** 706,953   **7.** 740,000,306   **8.** 673   **9.** 8430   **10.** 2331
11. 65,536   **12.** Each position represents a particular value. The symbol in each position tells how many of that value are represented.
13. 19   **14.** 6   **15.** 325   **16.** 805   **17.** 4051   **18.** 560   **19.** 324_{five} **20.** 10101_{two} **21.** 122112_{three} **22.** 26452_{seven}
23. 111140_{six} **24.** $3A2_{twelve}$ **25.** 132_{seven} **26.** 1401_{eight} **27.** 110000_{two} **28.** $AD0_{sixteen}$ **29.** 5_{six} **30.** 345_{seven} **31.** 11_{two}
32. 2304_{five} **33.** 222_{four} **34.** 354_{seven} **35.** 1102_{five} **36.** 133_{four} **37.** 12_{five} **38.** 1246   **39.** 12,432
40. ⑥⑥⑨⑨⑨⑨⑨∩∩∩∩∩∩∩∩∩∩IIIIII   **41.** ⦅⦅⦅⑥⑥⑥⑥⑨⑨⑨⑨⑨⑨∩∩∩∩∩∩∩III   **42.** 2314
43. DDDDDCCCCBBBBBBBBBBAA   **44.** Answers will vary.   **45.** 163   **46.** 1034   **47.** 1990   **48.** XLIX   **49.** MMCMLXV
50. If symbols increase in value from left to right, subtract the value of the symbol on the left from the value of the symbol on the right. Answers will vary.
51. 554   **52.** 8253   **53.** 二   **54.** 二   **55.** 365   **56.** 4520   **57.** G   **58.** F   **59.** Answers will vary.

舌	千
七	五
十	百
囚	八
	十
	七

57.	58.
G	F
Y	Z
I	H
X	Y
C	E
	X
	D

60. 653   **61.** 678   **62.** ν*νγ*   **63.** ∏*β*   **64.** 357   **65.** 37,894   **66.** 80,618   **67.** WRG   **68.** IfVQC   **69.** Answers will vary.

Chapter 4 Test

1. 729   **2.** $(5 \times 10^2) + (6 \times 10^1) + (7 \times 1)$ **3.** $(6 \times 10^4) + (3 \times 10^3) + (0 \times 10^2) + (2 \times 10^1) + (8 \times 1)$ **4.** 7493   **5.** 400,206
6. A number represents "How many?" whereas a numeral is a symbol used to write a number.   **7.** A symbol for zero is needed for a place holder when there are no values for a position.   **8.** 72,731   **9.** 1560   **10.** 113   **11.** 223   **12.** 53   **13.** 2212_{three} **14.** 111000_{two}
15. 24334_{five} **16.** 1212_{five} **17.** 414_{seven} **18.** 250_{six} **19.** 221_{five} **20.** 20,303   **21.** ⦅⦅⦅⑥⑥⑨⑨⑨⑨⑨⑨⑨∩∩∩IIIII
22. 1994   **23.** CDLIX   **24.** Answers will vary.

CHAPTER 5

Section 5.1

Check Point Exercises

1. b   **2.** $2^3 \cdot 3 \cdot 5$ **3.** 75   **4.** 96   **5.** 90   **6.** 5:00 P.M.

Exercise Set 5.1

1. a. yes   **b.** no   **c.** yes   **d.** no   **e.** no   **f.** yes   **g.** no   **h.** no   **i.** no   **3. a.** yes   **b.** yes   **c.** yes   **d.** no   **e.** yes
f. yes   **g.** no   **h.** no   **i.** yes   **5. a.** yes   **b.** no   **c.** yes   **d.** no   **e.** no   **f.** no   **g.** no   **h.** no   **i.** no   **7. a.** yes
b. yes   **c.** yes   **d.** no   **e.** yes   **f.** yes   **g.** yes   **h.** no   **i.** yes   **9. a.** yes   **b.** yes   **c.** yes   **d.** yes   **e.** yes   **f.** yes
g. yes   **h.** yes   **i.** yes   **11.** true; $5 + 9 + 5 + 8 = 27$ which is divisible by 3.   **13.** true; the last two digits of 10,612 form the number 12 and
12 is divisible by 4.   **15.** false   **17.** true; 104,538 is an even number so it is divisible by 2. $1 + 0 + 4 + 5 + 3 + 8 = 21$ which is divisible by 3 so it
is divisible by 3. Any number divisible by 2 and 3 is divisible by 6.   **19.** true; the last three digits of 20,104 form the number 104 and 104 is divisible
by 8.   **21.** false   **23.** true; $5 + 1 + 7 + 8 + 7 + 2 = 30$ which is divisible by 3 so it is divisible by 3. The last two digits of 517,872 form the
number 72 and 72 is divisible by 4 so it is divisible by 4. Any number divisible by 3 and 4 is divisible by 12.   **25.** $3 \cdot 5^2$ **27.** $2^3 \cdot 7$
29. $3 \cdot 5 \cdot 7$ **31.** $2^2 \cdot 5^3$ **33.** $3 \cdot 13 \cdot 17$ **35.** $3 \cdot 5 \cdot 59$ **37.** $2^5 \cdot 3^2 \cdot 5$ **39.** $2^2 \cdot 499$ **41.** $3 \cdot 5^2 \cdot 7^2$ **43.** $2^3 \cdot 3 \cdot 5^2 \cdot 11 \cdot 13$
45. 14   **47.** 2   **49.** 12   **51.** 24   **53.** 38   **55.** 15   **57.** 168   **59.** 336   **61.** 540   **63.** 360   **65.** 3420   **67.** 4560   **69.** 8
71. 6   **73.** 2, 6   **75.** perfect   **77.** not perfect   **79.** not an emirp   **81.** emirp   **83.** not a Germain prime   **85.** not a Germain prime
87. 648; 648; Answers will vary. An example is: The product of the greatest common divisor and least common multiple of two numbers equals the
product of the two numbers.   **89.** The numbers are the prime numbers between 1 and 97.   **91.** 12   **93.** 10   **95.** July 1   **97.** 90 min or $1\frac{1}{2}$ hr
111. GCD: $2^{14} \cdot 3^{25} \cdot 5^{30}$; LCM: $2^{17} \cdot 3^{37} \cdot 5^{31}$ **113.** 2:20 A.M. on the third day   **115.** yes   **117.** yes

Section 5.2

Check Point Exercises

1.

(a)	(b)	(c)

$$\begin{array}{ccccccccccc} \leftarrow & + & \bullet & + & + & \bullet & + & + & \bullet & + & \rightarrow \\ -5 & -4 & -3 & -2 & -1 & 0 & 1 & 2 & 3 & 4 & 5 \end{array}$$

2. a. >   **b.** <   **c.** <   **d.** <   **3. a.** 8   **b.** 6   **4. a.** 37   **b.** −4   **c.** −24

5. $15 billion   **6. a.** 25   **b.** −25   **c.** −64   **d.** 81   **7.** 36   **8.** 82

Exercise Set 5.2

1.   number line with point at 3 (−5 to 5)   **3.** number line with point at −3 (−5 to 5)   **5.** <   **7.** <   **9.** >   **11.** <   **13.** 14
15. 14   **17.** 300,000   **19.** −12   **21.** 4   **23.** −3   **25.** −5   **27.** −18   **29.** 0   **31.** 5   **33.** −7   **35.** 14   **37.** 11   **39.** −9
41. −28   **43.** −54   **45.** 21   **47.** −12   **49.** 13   **51.** 0   **53.** 25   **55.** 25   **57.** 64   **59.** −125   **61.** 625   **63.** −81
65. 81   **67.** −3   **69.** −7   **71.** 30   **73.** 0   **75.** undefined   **77.** −20   **79.** −31   **81.** 25   **83.** 13   **85.** 13   **87.** 33
89. 32   **91.** −24   **93.** 0   **95.** −32   **97.** 45   **99.** 14   **101.** −36   **103.** 88   **105.** $-10 - (-2)^3; -2$ **107.** $[2(7-10)]^2; 36$
109. \$389 billion   **111.** \$25 billion   **113.** 19,757 ft   **115.** −\$158 billion; deficit   **117.** \$554 billion   **119.** 7°F   **121.** −2°F
133. $(8-2) \cdot 3 - 4 = 14$ **135.** −36

Section 5.3

Check Point Exercises

1. $\frac{4}{5}$ **2.** $\frac{21}{8}$ **3.** $1\frac{2}{3}$ **4. a.** 0.375   **b.** $0.\overline{45}$ **5. a.** $\frac{9}{10}$ **b.** $\frac{43}{50}$ **c.** $\frac{53}{1000}$ **6.** $\frac{2}{9}$ **7.** $\frac{79}{99}$ **8. a.** $\frac{8}{33}$ **b.** $\frac{3}{2}$ or $1\frac{1}{2}$
c. $\frac{51}{10}$ or $5\frac{1}{10}$ **9. a.** $\frac{36}{55}$ **b.** $-\frac{4}{3}$ or $-1\frac{1}{3}$ **c.** $\frac{3}{2}$ or $1\frac{1}{2}$ **10. a.** $\frac{2}{3}$ **b.** $\frac{3}{2}$ or $1\frac{1}{2}$ **c.** $-\frac{9}{4}$ or $-2\frac{1}{4}$ **11.** $\frac{19}{20}$ **12.** $-\frac{17}{60}$ **13.** $\frac{5}{12}$
14. $2\frac{4}{5}$ eggs; 3 eggs

Exercise Set 5.3

1. $\frac{2}{3}$ **3.** $\frac{5}{6}$ **5.** $\frac{4}{7}$ **7.** $\frac{5}{9}$ **9.** $\frac{9}{10}$ **11.** $\frac{14}{19}$ **13.** $\frac{19}{8}$ **15.** $-\frac{38}{5}$ **17.** $\frac{199}{16}$ **19.** $4\frac{3}{5}$ **21.** $-8\frac{4}{9}$ **23.** $35\frac{11}{20}$ **25.** 0.75
27. 0.35   **29.** 0.875   **31.** $0.\overline{81}$ **33.** $3.\overline{142857}$ **35.** $0.\overline{285714}$ **37.** $\frac{3}{10}$ **39.** $\frac{2}{5}$ **41.** $\frac{39}{100}$ **43.** $\frac{41}{50}$ **45.** $\frac{29}{40}$ **47.** $\frac{5399}{10,000}$
49. $\frac{7}{9}$ **51.** 1   **53.** $\frac{4}{11}$ **55.** $\frac{257}{999}$ **57.** $\frac{21}{88}$ **59.** $-\frac{7}{120}$ **61.** $\frac{3}{2}$ **63.** 6   **65.** $\frac{10}{3}$ **67.** $-\frac{14}{15}$ **69.** 6   **71.** $\frac{5}{11}$ **73.** $\frac{2}{3}$
75. $\frac{2}{3}$ **77.** $\frac{7}{10}$ **79.** $\frac{9}{10}$ **81.** $\frac{53}{120}$ **83.** $\frac{1}{2}$ **85.** $\frac{7}{12}$ **87.** $-\frac{71}{150}$ **89.** $1\frac{5}{12}$ **91.** $\frac{4}{15}$ **93.** $\frac{7}{24}$ **95.** $\frac{7}{12}$ **97.** $-\frac{3}{4}$
99. Both are equal to $\frac{169}{36}$.   **101.** $-\frac{9}{40}$ **103.** $-1\frac{1}{36}$ **105.** $-19\frac{3}{4}$ **107.** $\frac{1}{2^2 \cdot 3}$ **109.** $-\frac{289}{2^4 \cdot 5^4 \cdot 7}$ **111.** $0.5\overline{4}; 0.58\overline{3}$; <
113. $-0.8\overline{3}; -0.\overline{8}$; >   **115.** $\frac{86}{192}; \frac{43}{96}$ **117.** $\frac{1}{3}$ cup butter, $\frac{5}{2} = 2.5$ ounces unsweetened chocolate, $\frac{3}{4}$ cup sugar, 1 teaspoon vanilla, 1 egg,
$\frac{1}{2}$ cup flour   **119.** $\frac{5}{6}$ cup butter, $\frac{25}{4} = 6.25$ ounces unsweetened chocolate, $\frac{15}{8} = 1\frac{7}{8}$ cups sugar, $\frac{5}{2} = 2\frac{1}{2}$ teaspoons vanilla, $\frac{5}{2} = 2\frac{1}{2}$ eggs,
$\frac{5}{4} = 1\frac{1}{4}$ cups flour   **121.** 24 brownies   **123.** $3\frac{2}{3}$ c   **125.** $\frac{4}{5}$ yr   **127.** $-\frac{9}{10}$ yr   **129.** $\frac{1}{3}$ of the business   **131.** $1\frac{3}{20}$ mi; $\frac{7}{20}$ mi   **133.** $\frac{1}{10}$
147.

sheet music staff

say does   that   Star-span-gled Ban-ner   yet   wave O'er the

149. a. 0.24625   **b.** 1.45248   **c.** 0.00112

Section 5.4

Check Point Exercises

1. a. $2\sqrt{3}$ **b.** $2\sqrt{15}$ **c.** cannot be simplified   **2. a.** $\sqrt{30}$ **b.** 10   **c.** $2\sqrt{3}$ **3. a.** 4   **b.** $2\sqrt{2}$ **4. a.** $18\sqrt{3}$ **b.** $-5\sqrt{13}$
c. $8\sqrt{10}$ **5. a.** $3\sqrt{3}$ **b.** $-13\sqrt{2}$ **6. a.** $\frac{5\sqrt{10}}{2}$ **b.** $\frac{\sqrt{14}}{7}$ **c.** $\frac{5\sqrt{2}}{6}$

Exercise Set 5.4

1. 3   **3.** 5   **5.** 8   **7.** 11   **9.** 13   **11. a.** 13.2   **b.** 13.15   **c.** 13.153   **13. a.** 133.3   **b.** 133.27 **c.** 133.270   **15. a.** 1.8
b. 1.77   **c.** 1.772   **17.** $2\sqrt{5}$ **19.** $4\sqrt{5}$ **21.** $5\sqrt{10}$ **23.** $14\sqrt{7}$ **25.** $\sqrt{42}$ **27.** 6   **29.** $3\sqrt{2}$ **31.** $2\sqrt{13}$ **33.** 3
35. $3\sqrt{5}$ **37.** $-4\sqrt{3}$ **39.** $13\sqrt{3}$ **41.** $-2\sqrt{13}$ **43.** $2\sqrt{5}$ **45.** $7\sqrt{2}$ **47.** $3\sqrt{5}$ **49.** $2\sqrt{2}$ **51.** $34\sqrt{2}$ **53.** $-\frac{3}{2}\sqrt{3}$
55. $11\sqrt{3}$ **57.** $\frac{5\sqrt{3}}{3}$ **59.** $3\sqrt{7}$ **61.** $\frac{2\sqrt{30}}{5}$ **63.** $\frac{5\sqrt{3}}{2}$ **65.** $\frac{\sqrt{10}}{5}$ **67.** $20\sqrt{2} - 5\sqrt{3}$ **69.** $-7\sqrt{7}$ **71.** $\frac{43\sqrt{2}}{35}$ **73.** $\frac{5\sqrt{6}}{6}$
75. $6\sqrt{3}$ miles; 10.4 miles   **77.** 70 mph; He was speeding.   **79. a.** 41 in.   **b.** 40.6 in.; quite well   **81. a.** 36 cm   **b.** 44.7 cm
c. 46.9 cm   **d.** The model describes healthy children.   **83.** $0.6R_f$; 60 weeks   **93.** <   **95.** >   **97.** −7 and −6
99. Answers will vary.; An example is $(3 + \sqrt{2}) - (1 + \sqrt{2}) = 2$.

Section 5.5

Check Point Exercises

1. a. $\sqrt{9}$ **b.** $0, \sqrt{9}$ **c.** $-9, 0, \sqrt{9}$ **d.** $-9, -1.3, 0, 0.\overline{3}, \sqrt{9}$ **e.** $\frac{\pi}{2}, \sqrt{10}$ **f.** $-9, -1.3, 0, 0.\overline{3}, \frac{\pi}{2}, \sqrt{9}, \sqrt{10}$

2. a. associative property of multiplication   **b.** commutative property of addition   **c.** distributive property of multiplication over addition
d. commutative property of multiplication   **3. a.** yes   **b.** no

Exercise Set 5.5

1. a. $\sqrt{100}$ **b.** $0, \sqrt{100}$ **c.** $-9, 0, \sqrt{100}$ **d.** $-9, -\frac{4}{5}, 0, 0.25, 9.2, \sqrt{100}$ **e.** $\sqrt{3}$ **f.** $-9, -\frac{4}{5}, 0, 0.25, \sqrt{3}, 9.2, \sqrt{100}$

3. a. $\sqrt{64}$ **b.** $0, \sqrt{64}$ **c.** $-11, 0, \sqrt{64}$ **d.** $-11, -\frac{5}{6}, 0, 0.75, \sqrt{64}$ **e.** $\sqrt{5}, \pi$ **f.** $-11, -\frac{5}{6}, 0, 0.75, \sqrt{5}, \pi, \sqrt{64}$

5. 0 **7.** Answers will vary; an example is: $\frac{1}{2}$.   **9.** Answers will vary; an example is: 1.   **11.** Answers will vary; an example is: $\sqrt{2}$.

13. 4   **15.** 6   **17.** 4; 3   **19.** 7   **21.** $30 + 5\sqrt{2}$ **23.** $3\sqrt{7} + \sqrt{14}$ **25.** $5\sqrt{3} + 3$ **27.** $2\sqrt{3} + 6$

29. commutative property of addition   **31.** associative property of addition   **33.** commutative property of addition

35. distributive property of multiplication over addition   **37.** associative property of multiplication   **39.** Answers will vary; an example is:
$1 - 2 = -1$.   **41.** Answers will vary; an example is: $4 \div 8 = \frac{1}{2}$.   **43.** Answers will vary; an example is: $\sqrt{2} \cdot \sqrt{2} = 2$.   **45.** true   **47.** false
49. distributive property; commutative property of addition; associative property of addition; distributive property; commutative property of addition
51. vampire   **53.** vampire   **55.** narcissistic   **57.** narcissistic   **59. a.** distributive property   **b.** approximately 108 mg; Answers will vary.
69. c

Section 5.6

Check Point Exercises

1. a. 1   **b.** 1   **c.** 1   **d.** -1 **2. a.** $\frac{1}{81}$ **b.** $\frac{1}{216}$ **c.** $\frac{1}{12}$ **3. a.** 7,400,000,000   **b.** 0.000003017   **4. a.** 7.41×10^9
b. 9.2×10^{-8} **5.** $\$5.19 \times 10^{11}$ **6.** 520,000   **7.** 0.0000023   **8. a.** 1.872×10^4 **b.** 18,720   **9.** $\$2500$

Exercise Set 5.6

1. $2^5 = 32$ **3.** $4^3 = 64$ **5.** $2^6 = 64$ **7.** $1^{20} = 1$ **9.** $4^2 = 16$ **11.** $2^4 = 16$ **13.** 1   **15.** 1   **17.** -1 **19.** $\frac{1}{4}$ **21.** $\frac{1}{64}$

23. $\frac{1}{32}$ **25.** $3^2 = 9$ **27.** $3^{-2} = \frac{1}{9}$ **29.** $2^{-4} = \frac{1}{16}$ **31.** 270   **33.** 912,000   **35.** 80,000,000   **37.** 100,000   **39.** 0.79
41. 0.0215   **43.** 0.000786   **45.** 0.00000318   **47.** 3.7×10^2 **49.** 3.6×10^3 **51.** 3.2×10^4 **53.** 2.2×10^8 **55.** 2.7×10^{-2}
57. 3.7×10^{-3} **59.** 2.93×10^{-6} **61.** 8.2×10^7 **63.** 4.1×10^5 **65.** 2.1×10^{-6} **67.** 600,000   **69.** 60,000   **71.** 0.123
73. 30,000   **75.** 3,000,000   **77.** 0.03   **79.** 0.0021   **81.** $(8.2 \times 10^7)(3.0 \times 10^9) = 2.46 \times 10^{17}$ **83.** $(5.0 \times 10^{-4})(6.0 \times 10^6) = 3 \times 10^3$
85. $\frac{9.5 \times 10^6}{5 \times 10^2} = 1.9 \times 10^4$ **87.** $\frac{8 \times 10^{-5}}{2 \times 10^2} = 4 \times 10^{-7}$ **89.** $\frac{4.8 \times 10^{11}}{1.2 \times 10^{-4}} = 4 \times 10^{15}$ **91.** $\frac{11}{18}$ **93.** $\frac{99}{25} = 3\frac{24}{25}$ **95.** 2.5×10^{-3}
97. 8×10^{-5} **99.** $\$4.65 \times 10^{10}$ **101.** $\$1 \times 10^8$ **103.** approximately 67 hot dogs per person   **105.** $2.5 \times 10^2 = 250$ chickens
107. a. $\$1.0813 \times 10^4$; $\$10,813$ **b.** $\$901$ **109.** Medicare; $\$3242$ **111.** 1.06×10^{-18} gram   **113.** 3.1536×10^7 **125.** d   **127.** $\frac{1}{4}$

Section 5.7

Check Point Exercises

1. 100, 120, 140, 160, 180, and 200   **2.** 8, 5, 2, -1, -4, and -7 **3.** -34 **4. a.** $a_n = 1.16n + 10.84$ **b.** 68.8 million
5. $12, -6, 3, -\frac{3}{2}, \frac{3}{4}$, and $-\frac{3}{8}$ **6.** 3645   **7.** $a_n = 3(2)^{n-1}$; 384

Exercise Set 5.7

1. 8, 10, 12, 14, 16, and 18   **3.** 200, 220, 240, 260, 280, and 300   **5.** $-7, -3, 1, 5, 9$, and 13   **7.** $-400, -100, 200, 500, 800$, and 1100
9. 7, 4, 1, $-2, -5$, and -8 **11.** 200, 140, 80, 20, -40, and -100 **13.** $\frac{5}{2}, 3, \frac{7}{2}, 4, \frac{9}{2}$, and 5   **15.** $\frac{3}{2}, \frac{7}{4}, 2, \frac{9}{4}, \frac{5}{2}$, and $\frac{11}{4}$
17. 4.25, 4.55, 4.85, 5.15, 5.45, and 5.75   **19.** 4.5, 3.75, 3, 2.25, 1.5, and 0.75   **21.** 33   **23.** 252   **25.** 67   **27.** 955   **29.** 82   **31.** -142
33. -43 **35.** -248 **37.** $\frac{23}{2}$ **39.** 1.75   **41.** $a_n = 1 + (n-1)4$; 77   **43.** $a_n = 7 + (n-1)(-4)$; -69 **45.** $a_n = 9 + (n-1)2$; 47
47. $a_n = -20 + (n-1)(-4)$; -96 **49.** 4, 8, 16, 32, 64, and 128   **51.** 1000, 1000, 1000, 1000, 1000, and 1000   **53.** $3, -6, 12, -24, 48$, and -96
55. $10, -40, 160, -640, 2560$, and $-10,240$ **57.** $2000, -2000, 2000, -2000, 2000$, and -2000 **59.** $-2, 6, -18, 54, -162$, and 486
61. $-6, 30, -150, 750, -3750$, and 18,750   **63.** $\frac{1}{4}, \frac{1}{2}, 1, 2, 4$, and 8   **65.** $\frac{1}{4}, \frac{1}{8}, \frac{1}{16}, \frac{1}{32}, \frac{1}{64}$, and $\frac{1}{128}$ **67.** $-\frac{1}{16}, \frac{1}{4}, -1, 4, -16$, and 64

69. $2, 0.2, 0.02, 0.002, 0.0002,$ and 0.00002 **71.** 256 **73.** $2{,}324{,}522{,}934 \approx 2.32 \times 10^9$ **75.** 50 **77.** 320 **79.** -2 **81.** 486

83. $\dfrac{3}{64}$ **85.** $-\dfrac{2}{27}$ **87.** $\approx -1.82 \times 10^{-9}$ **89.** 0.1 **91.** $a_n = 3(4)^{n-1}; 12{,}288$ **93.** $a_n = 18\left(\dfrac{1}{3}\right)^{n-1}; \dfrac{2}{81}$ **95.** $a_n = 1.5(-2)^{n-1}; 96$

97. $a_n = 0.0004(-10)^{n-1}; 400$ **99.** arithmetic; 18 and 22 **101.** geometric; 405 and 1215 **103.** arithmetic; 13 and 18

105. geometric; $\dfrac{3}{16}$ and $\dfrac{3}{32}$ **107.** arithmetic; $\dfrac{5}{2}$ and 3 **109.** geometric; 7 and -7 **111.** arithmetic; -49 and -63

113. geometric; $25\sqrt{5}$ and 125 **115.** arithmetic; 310 **117.** geometric; $59{,}048$ **119.** geometric; -1023 **121.** arithmetic; 80 **123.** 5050

125. a. $a_n = 23.08 + 0.12n$ **b.** 27.88 years old **127.** Company A; $\$1400$ **129.** $\$16{,}384$ **131.** $\$3{,}795{,}957$

133. a. $1.013, 1.013, 1.013, 1.013, 1.013, 1.013, 1.013$; the population is increasing geometrically with $r \approx 1.013$. **b.** $a_n = 29.76(1.013)^{n-1}$

c. ≈ 33.86; very well **143.** d

Chapter 5 Review Exercises

1. 2: yes; 3: yes; 4: yes; 5: no; 6: yes; 8: yes; 9: no; 10: no; 12: yes **2.** 2: yes; 3: yes; 4: no; 5: yes; 6: yes; 8: no; 9: yes; 10: yes; 12: no **3.** $3 \cdot 5 \cdot 47$
4. $2^6 \cdot 3 \cdot 5$ **5.** $3 \cdot 5^2 \cdot 7 \cdot 13$ **6.** GCD: 6; LCM: 240 **7.** GCD: 6; LCM: 900 **8.** GCD: 2; LCM: 27,432 **9.** 12 **10.** 11:48 A.M.
11. $<$ **12.** $>$ **13.** 860 **14.** 53 **15.** 0 **16.** -3 **17.** -11 **18.** -15 **19.** 1 **20.** 99 **21.** -15 **22.** 9 **23.** -4
24. -16 **25.** -16 **26.** 10 **27.** -2 **28.** 17 **29.** $\$658$ billion **30.** $\dfrac{8}{15}$ **31.** $\dfrac{6}{25}$ **32.** $\dfrac{11}{12}$ **33.** $\dfrac{64}{11}$ **34.** $-\dfrac{23}{7}$ **35.** $5\dfrac{2}{5}$

36. $-1\dfrac{8}{9}$ **37.** 0.8 **38.** $0.\overline{428571}$ **39.** 0.625 **40.** 0.5625 **41.** $\dfrac{3}{5}$ **42.** $\dfrac{17}{25}$ **43.** $\dfrac{147}{250}$ **44.** $\dfrac{21}{2500}$ **45.** $\dfrac{5}{9}$ **46.** $\dfrac{34}{99}$

47. $\dfrac{113}{999}$ **48.** $\dfrac{21}{50}$ **49.** $\dfrac{35}{6}$ **50.** $\dfrac{8}{3}$ **51.** $-\dfrac{1}{4}$ **52.** $\dfrac{2}{3}$ **53.** $\dfrac{43}{36}$ **54.** $\dfrac{37}{60}$ **55.** $\dfrac{11}{15}$ **56.** $\dfrac{5}{16}$ **57.** $\dfrac{15}{112}$ **58.** $\dfrac{27}{40}$

59. $11\dfrac{1}{4}$ or about 11 pounds **60.** $\dfrac{5}{12}$ of the tank **61.** $2\sqrt{7}$ **62.** $6\sqrt{2}$ **63.** $5\sqrt{6}$ **64.** $10\sqrt{3}$ **65.** $4\sqrt{3}$ **66.** $5\sqrt{2}$

67. $2\sqrt{3}$ **68.** 3 **69.** $5\sqrt{5}$ **70.** $-6\sqrt{11}$ **71.** $7\sqrt{2}$ **72.** $-17\sqrt{3}$ **73.** $12\sqrt{2}$ **74.** $6\sqrt{5}$ **75.** $\dfrac{\sqrt{6}}{3}$

76. $8\sqrt{3} \approx 13.9$ feet per second **77. a.** $\sqrt{81}$ **b.** $0, \sqrt{81}$ **c.** $-17, 0, \sqrt{81}$ **d.** $-17, -\dfrac{9}{13}, 0, 0.75, \sqrt{81}$ **e.** $\sqrt{2}, \pi$

f. $-17, -\dfrac{9}{13}, 0, 0.75, \sqrt{2}, \pi, \sqrt{81}$ **78.** Answers will vary; an example is: 0. **79.** Answers will vary; an example is: $\dfrac{1}{2}$.

80. Answers will vary; an example is: $\sqrt{2}$. **81.** commutative property of addition **82.** associative property of multiplication
83. distributive property of multiplication over addition **84.** commutative property of multiplication **85.** commutative property of multiplication
86. commutative property of addition **87.** Answers will vary; an example is: $2 \div 6 = \dfrac{1}{3}$. **88.** Answers will vary; an example is: $0 - 2 = -2$.

89. 216 **90.** 64 **91.** 16 **92.** 729 **93.** 25 **94.** 1 **95.** 1 **96.** $\dfrac{1}{216}$ **97.** $\dfrac{1}{16}$ **98.** $\dfrac{1}{49}$ **99.** 27 **100.** 460
101. $37{,}400$ **102.** 0.00255 **103.** 0.0000745 **104.** 7.52×10^3 **105.** 3.59×10^6 **106.** 7.25×10^{-3} **107.** 4.09×10^{-7}
108. 4.2×10^{13} **109.** 9.7×10^{-5} **110.** 390 **111.** $1{,}150{,}000$ **112.** 0.023 **113.** 40 **114.** $(6.0 \times 10^4)(5.4 \times 10^5) = 3.24 \times 10^{10}$

115. $(9.1 \times 10^4)(4 \times 10^{-4}) = 3.64 \times 10^1$ **116.** $\dfrac{8.4 \times 10^6}{4 \times 10^3} = 2.1 \times 10^3$ **117.** $\dfrac{3 \times 10^{-6}}{6 \times 10^{-8}} = 5 \times 10^1$ **118.** 1000 yr **119.** $\$4.5 \times 10^{10}$

120. 1.3×10^{10} people **121.** $7, 11, 15, 19, 23,$ and 27 **122.** $-4, -9, -14, -19, -24,$ and -29 **123.** $\dfrac{3}{2}, 1, \dfrac{1}{2}, 0, -\dfrac{1}{2},$ and -1 **124.** 20

125. -30 **126.** -38 **127.** $a_n = -7 + (n-1)4; 69$ **128.** $a_n = 200 + (n-1)(-20); -180$ **129.** $3, 6, 12, 24, 48,$ and 96

130. $\dfrac{1}{2}, \dfrac{1}{4}, \dfrac{1}{8}, \dfrac{1}{16}, \dfrac{1}{32},$ and $\dfrac{1}{64}$ **131.** $16, -8, 4, -2, 1,$ and $-\dfrac{1}{2}$ **132.** 54 **133.** $\dfrac{1}{2}$ **134.** -48 **135.** $a_n = 1(2)^{n-1}; 128$

136. $a_n = 100\left(\dfrac{1}{10}\right)^{n-1}; \dfrac{1}{100{,}000}$ **137.** arithmetic; 24 and 29 **138.** geometric; 162 and 486 **139.** geometric; $\dfrac{1}{256}$ and $\dfrac{1}{1024}$

140. arithmetic; -28 and -35 **141. a.** $a_n = 32.04 - 0.54n$ **b.** 22.32% **c.** potatoes: $a_n = 19.27 - 0.27n; 14.41\%$; salads: $a_n = 13.99 - 0.29n$;

8.77%; bread: $a_n = 10.06 - 0.26n; 5.38\%$ **142. a.** $\dfrac{5.9}{4.2} \approx 1.4; \dfrac{8.3}{5.9} \approx 1.4; \dfrac{11.6}{8.3} \approx 1.4; \dfrac{16.2}{11.6} \approx 1.4; \dfrac{22.7}{16.2} \approx 1.4$ **b.** $4.2(1.4)^{n-1}$ **c.** 62.0 million

Chapter 5 Test

1. $2, 3, 4, 6, 8, 9,$ and 12 **2.** $2^2 \cdot 3^2 \cdot 7$ **3.** GCD: 24; LCM: 144 **4.** 1 **5.** -4 **6.** -32 **7.** $0.58\overline{3}$ **8.** $\dfrac{64}{99}$ **9.** $\dfrac{1}{5}$ **10.** $\dfrac{37}{60}$

11. $-\dfrac{19}{2}$ **12.** $\dfrac{7}{12}$ **13.** $5\sqrt{2}$ **14.** $9\sqrt{2}$ **15.** $3\sqrt{2}$ **16.** $-7, -\dfrac{4}{5}, 0, 0.25, \sqrt{4},$ and $\dfrac{22}{7}$ **17.** commutative property of addition

18. distributive property of multiplication over addition **19.** 243 **20.** 64 **21.** $\dfrac{1}{64}$ **22.** 7500 **23.** $\dfrac{4.9 \times 10^4}{7 \times 10^{-3}} = 7 \times 10^6$

24. $\$7267$ **25.** $1, -4, -9, -14, -19,$ and -24 **26.** 22 **27.** $16, 8, 4, 2, 1,$ and $\dfrac{1}{2}$ **28.** 320

CHAPTER 6

Section 6.1

Check Point Exercises

1. 608 **2.** -2 **3.** -94 **4.** Model 3 **5.** $3x - 21$ **6.** $38x^2 + 23x$ **7.** $2x + 36$

Exercise Set 6.1

1. 27 **3.** 23 **5.** 29 **7.** -2 **9.** 140 **11.** 217 **13.** 176 **15.** 30 **17.** 44 **19.** 22 **21.** 27 **23.** -12 **25.** 69
27. -33 **29.** -8 **31.** 10°C **33.** 60 ft **35.** $17x$ **37.** $-3x^2$ **39.** $3x + 15$ **41.** $8x - 12$ **43.** $15x + 16$ **45.** $27x - 10$
47. $29y - 29$ **49.** $8y - 12$ **51.** $16y - 25$ **53.** $12x^2 + 11$ **55.** $-2x^2 - 9$ **57.** $x - (x + 4); -4$ **59.** $6(-5x); -30x$
61. $5x - 2x; 3x$ **63.** $8x - (3x + 6); 5x - 6$ **65.** 313; very well **67.** 1348 **69.** Model 1 **71.** very well **73. a.** \$32,000
b. \$32,616; reasonably well **c.** \$32,597; reasonably well **75.** Model 1 **83.** d **85. a.** \$50.50, \$5.50, and \$1.00 per clock, respectively
b. no; Answers will vary.

Section 6.2

Check Point Exercises

1. $\{6\}$ **2.** $\{-2\}$ **3.** $\{2\}$ **4.** $\{5\}$ **5.** $\{-2\}$ **6.** 3.7; shown as the point (3.7, 10) **7.** $w = \dfrac{P - 2l}{2}$ **8.** $m = \dfrac{T - D}{p}$ **9.** $\varnothing$
10. $\{x \mid x \text{ is a real number}\}$

Exercise Set 6.2

1. $\{10\}$ **3.** $\{-17\}$ **5.** $\{12\}$ **7.** $\{9\}$ **9.** $\{-3\}$ **11.** $\left\{-\dfrac{1}{4}\right\}$ **13.** $\{3\}$ **15.** $\{11\}$ **17.** $\{-17\}$ **19.** $\{11\}$ **21.** $\left\{\dfrac{7}{5}\right\}$
23. $\left\{\dfrac{25}{3}\right\}$ **25.** $\{8\}$ **27.** $\{-3\}$ **29.** $\{2\}$ **31.** $\{-4\}$ **33.** $\left\{-\dfrac{1}{5}\right\}$ **35.** $\{-4\}$ **37.** $\{5\}$ **39.** $\{6\}$ **41.** $\left\{-\dfrac{7}{2}\right\}$ **43.** $\{1\}$
45. $\{24\}$ **47.** $\{20\}$ **49.** $\{5\}$ **51.** $L = \dfrac{A}{W}$ **53.** $b = \dfrac{2A}{h}$ **55.** $P = \dfrac{I}{rt}$ **57.** $m = \dfrac{E}{c^2}$ **59.** $m = \dfrac{y - b}{x}$ **61.** $a = 2A - b$
63. $r = \dfrac{S - P}{Pt}$ **65.** $x = \dfrac{C - By}{A}$ **67.** $n = \dfrac{a_n - a_1}{d} + 1$ or $n = \dfrac{a_n - a_1 + d}{d}$ **69.** $\varnothing$ **71.** $\{x \mid x \text{ is a real number}\}$ **73.** $\left\{\dfrac{2}{3}\right\}$
75. $\{x \mid x \text{ is a real number}\}$ **77.** $\varnothing$ **79.** $\{0\}$ **81.** $\varnothing$ **83.** $\{0\}$ **85.** 2 **87.** 161 **89.** $\{-2\}$ **91.** $\varnothing$ **93.** $\{10\}$ **95.** $\{-2\}$
97. 2013 **99.** 120 chirps per minute **101.** 409.2 ft **103.** 2011 **105.** 2014 **107.** 2022 **117.** c

Section 6.3

Check Point Exercises

1. 12 **2.** 2011 **3.** basketball: 1.6 million; bicycle riding: 1.3 million; football: 1 million **4.** 300 min

Exercise Set 6.3

1. 6 **3.** 19 and 45 **5.** 2050 **7.** 2008 **9.** 2025; 9,900,000 **11.** births: 375 thousand; deaths: 146 thousand **13.** race: 3844; sexual
orientation: 1239 **15.** after 5 months; \$165 **17.** 30 times **19.** \$600 of merchandise; \$580 **21.** 11 hr **23.** \$1350 **29.** 5 ft 7 in.
31. uncle: 60 yr old; woman: 20 yr old **33.** \$4000 for the mother; \$8000 for the boy; \$2000 for the girl

Section 6.4

Check Point Exercises

1. a. $\{15\}$ **b.** $\{140\}$ **2.** \$1500 **3.** 720 deer **4.** 66 gal **5.** 556 ft **6.** ≈ 4.36 lb per in^2

Exercise Set 6.4

1. $\{14\}$ **3.** $\{27\}$ **5.** $\left\{-\dfrac{9}{4}\right\}$ **7.** $\{-15\}$ **9.** $\left\{\dfrac{7}{2}\right\}$ **11.** $\{10\}$ **13.** 156 **15.** 30 **17.** $x = \dfrac{ab}{c}$ **19.** $x = \dfrac{(a + b)d}{c}$ **21.** $x = \dfrac{ab}{c}$
23. \$1115.38 **25.** $\approx 20{,}489$ fur seal pups **27.** \$950 **29.** 31 lb **31.** 154.1 in. or ≈ 12.8 ft **33.** ≈ 607 lb **35.** 120 ft **37.** 0.88°C
39. 6.4 lb **41.** 112 decibels **49.** The front sprocket can be replaced by a 100-tooth sprocket, or the rear sprocket can be replaced with a
12-tooth sprocket. **51.** The destructive power is 4 times as strong.

Section 6.5

Check Point Exercises

1. a.
b.
c.
2. $\{x \mid x \le 4\}$;

3. a. $\{x|x < 8\}$;

b. $\{x|x > -3\}$;

4. $\{x|x < -6\}$;

5. $\{x|x \geq 1\}$;

6. $\{x|-1 \leq x < 4\}$;

7. at least 83%

Exercise Set 6.5

1.

3.

5.

7.

9.

11.

13. $\{x|x > 5\}$;

15. $\{x|x \leq 5\}$;

17. $\{x|x < 3\}$;

19. $\{x|x < 5\}$;

21. $\{x|x \geq -5\}$;

23. $\{x|x > 5\}$;

25. $\{x|x < 5\}$;

27. $\{x|x < 8\}$;

29. $\{x|x > -6\}$;

31. $\{x|x > -5\}$;

33. $\{x|x \leq 5\}$;

35. $\{x|x \leq 3\}$;

37. $\{x|x < 16\}$;

39. $\{x|x > -3\}$;

41. $\{x|x \geq -2\}$;

43. $\{x|x > -4\}$;

45. $\{x|x \geq 4\}$;

47. $\left\{x\middle|x > \dfrac{11}{3}\right\}$;

$\frac{11}{3}$

49. $\{x|x > 2\}$;

51. $\{x|x < 3\}$;

53. $\left\{x\middle|x > \dfrac{5}{3}\right\}$;

$\frac{5}{3}$

55. $\{x|x \geq -10\}$;

57. $\{x|x < -6\}$;

59. $\{x|3 < x < 5\}$;

61. $\{x|-1 \leq x < 3\}$;

63. $\{x|-5 < x \leq -2\}$;

65. $\{x|3 \leq x < 6\}$;

67. $x > \dfrac{C - By}{A}$ **69.** $x < \dfrac{C - By}{A}$ **71.** $\{x|x + 5 \geq 2x\}$ **73.** $\{x|2(4 + x) \leq 36\}$ **75.** $\left\{x\middle|\dfrac{3x}{5} + 4 \leq 34\right\}$ **77.** $\{x|0 < x < 4\}$

79. intimacy $\geq$ passion or passion $\leq$ intimacy   **81.** commitment $>$ passion or passion $<$ commitment   **83.** 9; after 3 years
85. more than 28 years; years after 2012   **87. a.** 88; no   **b.** at least 68   **89.** at most 1280 mi   **91.** at most 29 bags   **93.** between 80 and
110 minutes, inclusive   **99.** more than 1200 packages

Section 6.6

Check Point Exercises

1. $x^2 + 11x + 30$ **2.** $28x^2 - x - 15$ **3.** $(x + 2)(x + 3)$ **4.** $(x + 5)(x - 2)$ **5.** $(5x - 4)(x - 2)$ **6.** $(3y - 1)(2y + 7)$

7. $\{-6, 3\}$ **8.** $\{-2, 8\}$ **9.** $\left\{-4, \frac{1}{2}\right\}$ **10.** $\left\{-\frac{1}{2}, \frac{1}{4}\right\}$ **11.** $\left\{\frac{3 + \sqrt{7}}{2}, \frac{3 - \sqrt{7}}{2}\right\}$ **12.** approximately 26 years old

Exercise Set 6.6

1. $x^2 + 8x + 15$ **3.** $x^2 - 2x - 15$ **5.** $2x^2 + 3x - 2$ **7.** $12x^2 - 43x + 35$ **9.** $(x + 2)(x + 3)$ **11.** $(x - 5)(x + 3)$

13. $(x - 5)(x - 3)$ **15.** $(x - 12)(x + 3)$ **17.** prime   **19.** $(x + 1)(x + 16)$ **21.** $(2x + 1)(x + 3)$ **23.** $(2x - 5)(x - 6)$

25. $(3x + 2)(x - 1)$ **27.** $(3x - 28)(x + 1)$ **29.** $(3x - 4)(2x - 1)$ **31.** $(2x + 3)(2x + 5)$ **33.** $\{-3, 8\}$ **35.** $\left\{-\frac{5}{4}, 2\right\}$

37. $\{-5, -3\}$ **39.** $\{-3, 5\}$ **41.** $\{-3, 7\}$ **43.** $\{-8, -1\}$ **45.** $\{6\}$ **47.** $\left\{-\frac{1}{2}, 4\right\}$ **49.** $\left\{-2, \frac{9}{5}\right\}$ **51.** $\left\{-\frac{7}{2}, -\frac{1}{3}\right\}$ **53.** $\{-5, -3\}$

55. $\left\{\frac{-5 + \sqrt{13}}{2}, \frac{-5 - \sqrt{13}}{2}\right\}$ **57.** $\{-2 + \sqrt{10}, -2 - \sqrt{10}\}$ **59.** $\{-2 + \sqrt{11}, -2 - \sqrt{11}\}$ **61.** $\{-3, 6\}$ **63.** $\left\{-\frac{2}{3}, \frac{3}{2}\right\}$

65. $\{1 + \sqrt{11}, 1 - \sqrt{11}\}$ **67.** $\left\{\frac{1 + \sqrt{57}}{2}, \frac{1 - \sqrt{57}}{2}\right\}$ **69.** $\left\{\frac{-3 + \sqrt{3}}{6}, \frac{-3 - \sqrt{3}}{6}\right\}$ **71.** $\left\{\frac{3}{2}\right\}$ **73.** $\left\{-\frac{2}{3}, 4\right\}$ **75.** $\{-3, 1\}$

77. $\left\{1, -\frac{5}{2}\right\}$ **79.** $\{\pm \sqrt{6}\}$ **81.** $1 + \sqrt{7}$ **83.** 9 teams   **85.** exactly   **87.** 2014   **89.** 33-yr-olds and 58-yr-olds; The formula models the trend in the data quite well.   **97.** 8 and 16   **99.** $(x^n + 9)(x^n + 11)$

Chapter 6 Review Exercises

1. 33   **2.** 15   **3.** -48 **4.** 805 million; fairly well, but slight overestimation   **5.** $17x - 15$ **6.** $5y - 13$ **7.** $14x^2 + x$ **8.** $\{6\}$

9. $\{2\}$ **10.** $\{12\}$ **11.** $\left\{-\frac{13}{3}\right\}$ **12.** $\{2\}$ **13.** $\varnothing$ **14.** $\{x \mid x \text{ is a real number}\}$ **15.** $x = \frac{By + C}{A}$ **16.** $h = \frac{2A}{b}$ **17.** $B = 2A - C$

18. $g = \frac{s - vt}{t^2}$ **19.** 2012   **20.** $7x - 1 = 5x + 9; 5$ **21.** Chicken Caesar: 495; Express Taco: 620; Mandarin Chicken: 590   **22.** 2013

23. 500 min   **24.** United States: 20.5 million barrels per day; China: 6.5 million barrels per day   **25.** $\{5\}$ **26.** $\{-65\}$ **27.** $\left\{\frac{2}{5}\right\}$ **28.** $\{3\}$

29. 324 teachers   **30.** 287 trout   **31.** $154   **32.** 1600 ft   **33.** 5 hr

34. $\{x \mid x < 4\}$;

35. $\{x \mid x > -8\}$;

36. $\{x \mid x \geq -3\}$;

37. $\{x \mid x > 6\}$;

38. $\{x \mid x \geq 4\}$;

39. $\{x \mid x \leq 2\}$;

40. $\left\{x \mid -\frac{3}{4} < x \leq 1\right\}$;

41. at least 64   **42.** $x^2 + 4x - 45$ **43.** $12x^2 - 13x - 14$ **44.** $(x - 4)(x + 3)$

45. $(x - 5)(x - 3)$ **46.** prime   **47.** $(3x - 2)(x - 5)$ **48.** $(2x - 5)(3x + 2)$ **49.** prime

50. $\{-7, 2\}$ **51.** $\{-4, 8\}$ **52.** $\left\{-8, \frac{1}{2}\right\}$ **53.** $\{-5, -2\}$ **54.** $\{1, 3\}$

55. $\left\{\frac{5 + \sqrt{41}}{2}, \frac{5 - \sqrt{41}}{2}\right\}$ **56.** $\left\{-3, \frac{1}{2}\right\}$ **57.** $\left\{\frac{3 + 2\sqrt{6}}{3}, \frac{3 - 2\sqrt{6}}{3}\right\}$ **58.** 2012

Chapter 6 Test

1. -44 **2.** $14x - 4$ **3.** 616 convictions   **4.** $\{-5\}$ **5.** $\{2\}$ **6.** $\varnothing$ **7.** $\{-15\}$ **8.** $y = \frac{Ax + A}{B}$ **9.** 2008   **10.** 63.8

11. fitness trainer: $50,950; teacher: $28,080   **12.** 5 years   **13.** 20 prints; $3.80   **14.** $\left\{\frac{15}{2}\right\}$ **15.** $\{3\}$ **16.** 6000 tule elk

17. 137.5 lb per in^2 **18.** 4 hours

19. $\{x \mid x \leq -3\}$;

20. $\{x \mid x > 7\}$;

21. $\left\{x \mid -2 \leq x < \frac{5}{2}\right\}$;

22. at least 92   **23.** $6x^2 - 7x - 20$ **24.** $(2x - 5)(x - 2)$ **25.** $\{-9, 4\}$ **26.** $\left\{\frac{-2 + \sqrt{2}}{2}, \frac{-2 - \sqrt{2}}{2}\right\}$ **27.** 2018   **28.** 2018

29. quite well

CHAPTER 7

Section 7.1

Check Point Exercises

1.

2.

3. a. $y = 2x$ $y = 10 + x$

x	(x, y)
0	$(0, 0)$
2	$(2, 4)$
4	$(4, 8)$
6	$(6, 12)$
8	$(8, 16)$
10	$(10, 20)$
12	$(12, 24)$

x	(x, y)
0	$(0, 10)$
2	$(2, 12)$
4	$(4, 14)$
6	$(6, 16)$
8	$(8, 18)$
10	$(10, 20)$
12	$(12, 22)$

b.

c. $(10, 20)$; When the bridge is used 10 times during a month, the cost is $20 with or without the coupon book.

4. a. 73%   **b.** 72.8%

5. ; The graph of g is the graph of f shifted down 3 units.

6. a. function   **b.** function   **c.** not a function   **7. a.** 0 to 3 hours   **b.** 3 to 13 hours   **c.** 0.05 mg per 100 ml; after 3 hours
d. None of the drug is left in the body.   **e.** No vertical line intersects the graph in more than one point.

Exercise Set 7.1

1.

3.

5.

7.

9.

11.

13.

15.

17.

19.

21.

23.

25.

27.

29.

31.

33. a. 4   **b.** -3 **35. a.** 19   **b.** -2 **37. a.** 5   **b.** 5   **39. a.** 53   **b.** 8   **41. a.** 26   **b.** 19

43.

x	$f(x) = x^2 - 1$
-2	3
-1	0
0	-1
1	0
2	3

45.

x	$f(x) = x - 1$
-2	-3
-1	-2
0	-1
1	0
2	1

47.

x	$f(x) = (x - 2)^2$
0	4
1	1
2	0
3	1
4	4

49.

x	$f(x) = x^3 + 1$
-3	-26
-2	-7
-1	0
0	1
1	2

51. function **53.** function **55.** not a function **57.** function **59.** $-2; 10$ **61.** -38

63. $y = 2x + 4$

65. $y = 3 - x^2$

67. $(91, 125)$; In 1991, 125 thousand acres were used for cultivation. **69.** 2000 and 2003 **71.** 2001; 25 thousand acres **73.** 1991 and 1992
75. a. 707; Approximately 707,000 bachelor's degrees were awarded to women in 2000.; $(20, 707)$ **b.** a slight overestimation
77. a. 68; Approximately 68,000 more bachelor's degrees were awarded to women than to men in 1990.; The points on the graphs with first coordinate
10 are 68 units apart. **b.** not very well **79. a.** 2001; 9200 hate crimes **b.** 9191 hate crimes **81.** 8123; $(2, 8123)$ **89.** -2 **91.** 1

Section 7.2

Check Point Exercises

1.

2. a. $m = 6$ **b.** $m = -\dfrac{7}{5}$ **3.**

4.

5.

6.

7. $\dfrac{3.5}{13} = \dfrac{7}{26} \approx 0.27$; The slope indicates that the number of men living alone is projected to increase by 0.27 million each year. **8.** $S(x) = 0.22x + 1$

Exercise Set 7.2

1.

3.

5.

7.

9. -1; falls **11.** $\dfrac{1}{4}$; rises **13.** -5; falls **15.** undefined; vertical **17.** -4; falls **19.** 0; horizontal

21.

23.

25.

27.

29.

31.

33. a. $y = -3x$ or $y = -3x + 0$

35. a. $y = \frac{4}{3}x$ or $y = \frac{4}{3}x + 0$

37. a. $y = -2x + 3$

b. slope $= -3$; y-intercept $= 0$

b. slope $= \frac{4}{3}$; y-intercept $= 0$

b. slope $= -2$; y-intercept $= 3$

c.

c.

c.

39. a. $y = -\frac{7}{2}x + 7$

b. slope $= -\frac{7}{2}$; y-intercept $= 7$

c.

41.

43.

45.

47.

49. $m = -\frac{a}{b}$; falls   **51.** undefined slope; vertical   **53.** $m = -\frac{A}{B}$; $b = \frac{C}{B}$ **55.** -2 **57.** m_1, m_3, m_2, m_4 **59. a.** -0.075; Between 2000

and 2002, the average price decreased 7.5 cents per year.   **b.** 0.24; Between 2002 and 2005, the average price increased 24 cents per year.

61. a. 33; In 1999 (0 years after 1999), there were 33 million HIV/AIDS cases.   **b.** 2; The number of HIV/AIDS cases increased by 2 million each year.

c. $y = 2x + 33$ **d.** 55 million HIV/AIDS cases   **73.** $F = \frac{9}{5}C + 32$

Section 7.3

Check Point Exercises

1. not a solution   **2.**

; $\{(-3, 4)\}$ **3.** $\{(6, 11)\}$ **4.** $\{(1, -2)\}$ **5.** $\{(2, -1)\}$ **6.** $\{(2, -1)\}$ **7.** $\varnothing$

8. $\{(x,y) \mid y = 4x - 4\}$ or $\{(x,y) \mid 8x - 2y = 8\}$ **9. a.** $C(x) = 300{,}000 + 30x$ **b.** $R(x) = 80x$ **c.** $(6000, 480{,}000)$; The company will break

even if it produces and sells 6000 pairs of shoes.

Exercise Set 7.3

1. solution   **3.** not a solution

5.

7.

9.

11.

$\{(4, 2)\}$

$\{(3, 0)\}$

$\{(-1, 4)\}$

$\{(3, -4)\}$

13. $\{(1, 3)\}$ **15.** $\{(5, 1)\}$ **17.** $\{(2, 1)\}$ **19.** $\{(-1, 3)\}$ **21.** $\{(4, 5)\}$ **23.** $\left\{\left(-4, \frac{5}{4}\right)\right\}$ **25.** $\{(2, -1)\}$ **27.** $\{(3, 0)\}$ **29.** $\{(-4, 3)\}$

31. $\{(3, 1)\}$ **33.** $\{(1, -2)\}$ **35.** $\{(-5, -2)\}$ **37.** $\varnothing$ **39.** $\{(x,y) \mid y = 3x - 5\}$ or $\{(x,y) \mid 21x - 35 = 7y\}$ **41.** $\{(1, 4)\}$

43. $\{(x,y) \mid x + 3y = 2\}$ or $\{(x,y) \mid 3x + 9y = 6\}$ **45.** $y = x - 4$; $y = -\frac{1}{3}x + 4$ **47.** $\left\{ \left(\frac{1}{a}, 3 \right) \right\}$ **49.** $m = -4, b = 3$ **51.** 500 radios

53. -6000; When the company produces and sells 200 radios, the loss is $6000.   **55. a.** $P(x) = 20x - 10,000$ **b.** $190,000

57. a. $C(x) = 18,000 + 20x$ **b.** $R(x) = 80x$ **c.** $(300, 24,000)$; When 300 canoes are produced and sold, both revenue and cost are $24,000.

59. a. $C(x) = 30,000 + 2500x$ **b.** $R(x) = 3125x$ **c.** $(48, 150,000)$; For 48 sold-out performances, both cost and revenue are $150,000.

61. a. $y = -0.75x + 38$ **b.** $y = -x + 40$ **c.** 1993; 32%   **63.** Pan pizza: 1120 calories; beef burrito: 430 calories   **65.** Scrambled eggs: 366 mg cholesterol; Double Beef Whopper: 175 mg cholesterol   **67.** 50 rooms with kitchen facilities, 150 rooms without kitchen facilities

79. downstairs: 3 people; upstairs: 5 people

Section 7.4

Check Point Exercises

1.

2. $y > -\frac{3}{4}x$

3. a. $y > 1$ **b.** $x \le -2$

4. $B = (60, 20)$; Using $T = 60$ and $P = 20$, each of the three inequalities for grasslands is true: $60 \ge 35$, true; $5(60) - 7(20) \ge 70$, true; $3(60) - 35(20) \le -140$, true.

5. $x + 2y > 4$
$2x - 3y \le -6$

6.

Exercise Set 7.4

1. $x + y \ge 2$

3.

5.

7.

9.

11. $y > \frac{1}{3}x$

13. $y \le 3x + 2$

15. $y < -\frac{1}{4}x$

17. $x \le 2$

19. $y > -4$

21. $y \ge 0$

23. $3x + 6y \le 6$
$2x + y \le 8$

25.

27.

29.

31.

33.

35. $y > 2x - 3$
$y < -x + 6$

37. $x + 2y \le 4$
$y \ge x - 3$

39. $y \ge -2x + 4$

41. $x + y \le 4$
$3x + y \le 6$

43. $y > \frac{3}{2}x - 2$ or $y < 4$

45. a. $A = (20, 150)$; A 20-year-old with a heart rate of 150 beats per minute is within the target range. **b.** $10 \le 20 \le 70$, true; $150 \ge 0.7(220 - 20)$, true; $150 \le 0.8(220 - 20)$, true **47.** $10 \le a \le 70$; $H \ge 0.6(220 - a)$; $H \le 0.7(220 - a)$
49. a. $50x + 150y > 2000$

b.

50x + 150y > 2000

51. a. 27.1 **b.** overweight **59.** $y > x - 3$; $y \le x$ **61.** no solution **63.** infinitely many solutions

Section 7.5

Check Point Exercises

1. $z = 25x + 55y$ **2.** $x + y \le 80$ **3.** $30 \le x \le 80$; $10 \le y \le 30$; objective function: $z = 25x + 55y$; constraints: $x + y \le 80$; $30 \le x \le 80$; $10 \le y \le 30$ **4.** 50 bookshelves and 30 desks; $2900

Exercise Set 7.5

1. $(1, 2): 17$; $(2, 10): 70$; $(7, 5): 65$; $(8, 3): 58$; maximum: $z = 70$; minimum: $z = 17$
3. $(0, 0): 0$; $(0, 8): 400$; $(4, 9): 610$; $(8, 0): 320$; maximum: $z = 610$; minimum: $z = 0$

5. a.

7. a.

9. a.

b. $(0, 1): 1$; $(6, 13): 19$; $(6, 1): 7$
c. maximum of 19 at $x = 6$ and $y = 13$; minimum of 1 at $x = 0$ and $y = 1$

b. $(0, 10): 100$; $(4, 8): 104$; $(12, 0): 72$; $(0, 0): 0$
c. maximum of 104 at $x = 4$ and $y = 8$; minimum of 0 at $x = 0$ and $y = 0$

b. $(0, 3): -6$; $(0, 2): -4$; $(2, 0): 10$; $(5, 0): 25$; $(5, 3): 19$
c. maximum value: 25 at $x = 5$ and $y = 0$

11. a.

13. a. $z = 10x + 7y$
b. $x + y \le 20$; $x \ge 3$; $x \le 8$
c.

b. $(0, 6): 72$; $(0, 0): 0$; $(5, 0): 50$; $(3, 4): 78$

c. maximum value: 78 at $x = 3$ and $y = 4$

d. $(3, 0): 30$; $(8, 0): 80$; $(3, 17): 149$; $(8, 12): 164$
e. 8; 12; $164

15. 300 cartons of food and 200 cartons of clothing **17.** 50 students and 100 parents

Section 7.6

Check Point Exercises

1.

$f(x) = 3^x$

2. a. the exponential function g **b.** f: fairly well; g: not very well **3.** 6.8%

4. $x = 3^y$;

5. 34°; extremely well **6.**

7. 45 years old; 190 accidents per 50 million miles driven

Exercise Set 7.6

1.   **3.**   **5.**   **7.** $x = 4^y$;

9. a. upward
  b. $(-4, -9)$
  c. $(-7, 0)$ and $(-1, 0)$
  d. $(0, 7)$
  e.

11. a. upward
  b. $(1, -9)$
  c. $(-2, 0)$ and $(4, 0)$
  d. $(0, -8)$
  e.

13. a. downward
  b. $(2, 1)$
  c. $(1, 0)$ and $(3, 0)$
  d. $(0, -3)$
  e.

15. a.
  b. logarithmic

17. a.
  b. linear

19. a.
  b. quadratic

21. a.
  b. exponential

23.
  decreasing, although rate of decrease is slowing down

25.
  decreasing, although rate of decrease is slowing down

27. a. downward
  b. $(1, 7)$
  c. $(-0.9, 0)$ and $(2.9, 0)$
  d. $(0, 5)$
  e.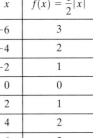

29. $(3, 2)$ **31. a.** increasing more and more rapidly   **b.** $f(x) = 1.402(1.078)^x$ **c.** 22.6%; fairly well, small overestimation   **33.** linear
35. 64%; slight overestimation   **37. a.** 95.3%   **b.** Height increases rapidly at first and then more slowly.   **39. a.** The data decrease
then increase.   **b.** $f(x) = 0.22x^2 - 0.49x + 7.68$ **c.** 2000; 7.4 million; extremely well   **47.** c   **49.** 1

Chapter 7 Review Exercises

1.   **2.**   **3.**   **4.** **5.**

6. **7.** **8.** 3   **9.** 26   **10.** 30   **11.** −64   **12.**

x	$f(x) = \frac{1}{2}\|x\|$
-6	3
-4	2
-2	1
0	0
2	1
4	2
6	3

13.

x	$f(x) = x^2 - 2$
-2	2
-1	-1
0	-2
1	-1
2	2

14. y is a function of x.   **15.** y is not a function of x.   **16. a.** 3.1; In 1960, Jewish Americans comprised about 3.1% of the U.S. population.
b. 1940; 3.7%   **c.** 1900; 1.4%   **d.** No vertical line intersects the graph in more than one point.   **e.** The percentage of Jewish Americans in the U.S. population was increasing until 1940 and has been decreasing ever since.

17.

18.

19.

20. $-\dfrac{1}{2}$; falls   **21.** 3; rises   **22.** 0; horizontal   **23.** undefined; vertical

24.

25.

26.

27.

28. a. $y = -2x$

b. slope: -2; y-intercept: 0

c.

29. a. $y = \dfrac{5}{3}x$

b. slope: $\dfrac{5}{3}$; y-intercept: 0

c.

30. a. $y = -\dfrac{3}{2}x + 2$

b. slope: $-\dfrac{3}{2}$; y-intecept: 2

c.

31.

32.

33.

34. a. 2970; In 1990 (0 years after 1990), the average credit card debt was $2970.   **b.** 453; The average credit card debt increased $453 per year.
c. $y = 453x + 2970$ **d.** $12,030   **35.** $\{(2, 3)\}$ **36.** $\{(-2, -3)\}$ **37.** $\{(3, 2)\}$ **38.** $\{(4. -2)\}$ **39.** $\{(1, 5)\}$ **40.** $\{(2, 3)\}$
41. $\{(-9, 3)\}$ **42.** $\{(3, 4)\}$ **43.** $\{(2, -3)\}$ **44.** $\varnothing$ **45.** $\{(3, -1)\}$ **46.** $\{(x,y)\,|\,3x - 2y = 6\}$ or $\{(x,y)\,|\,6x - 4y = 12\}$
47. a. $C(x) = 60,000 + 200x$ **b.** $R(x) = 450x$ **c.** $(240, 108,000)$; This means the company will break even if it produces and sells 240 desks.
48. Japan: 73.6 yr; Switzerland: 72.8 yr

49.

50.

51.

52.

53.

54.

55.

56.

57.

58.

59.

60.

61.

62. $(1, 0)$: 2; $\left(\dfrac{1}{2}, \dfrac{1}{2}\right)$: $\dfrac{5}{2}$;
$(2, 2)$: 10; $(4, 0)$: 8;
maximum: 10; minimum: 2

63. a.

b. $(0, 2)$: 6; $(0, 5)$: 15; $(6, 5)$: 27; $(6, 0)$: 12; $(2, 0)$: 4
c. maximum of 27 at $x = 6$ and $y = 5$;
minimum of 4 at $x = 2$ and $y = 0$

64. a. $z = 500x + 350y$
b. $x + y \le 200$; $x \ge 10$; $y \ge 80$
c.

$x + y \le 200$
$x \ge 10, y \ge 80$

d. $(10, 80)$: 33,000; $(10, 190)$: 71,500; $(120, 80)$: 88,000
e. 120; 80; 88,000

65.

66.

67. $x = 2^y$;

68. a. upward
b. $(3, -16)$
c. $(-1, 0)$ and $(7, 0)$
d. $(0, -7)$
e.

69. a. downward
b. $(-1, 4)$
c. $(-3, 0)$ and $(1, 0)$
d. $(0, 3)$
e.

70. a.

Percentage of U.S. High School Seniors Taking Steroids

b. quadratic

71. a.

Hybrid Car Sales in U.S.

b. exponential

72. a.

Percentage of U.S. Households with TVs with Cable Television

b. logarithmic

73. a.

Average Monthly Cellphone Bills

b. linear

74. 559 ppm; nearly double **75.** 210.6 million; slightly more than twice the 2003 population **76. a.** -1.7; The percentage of companies performing drug tests is decreasing by 1.7 each year. **b.** logarithmic model

Chapter 7 Test

1.

2. 21
3. y is not a function of x. **4.** y is a function of x.
5. a. Yes; no vertical line intersects the graph in more than one point. **b.** 0; The eagle was on the ground after 15 seconds.
c. 45 meters **d.** between 3 and 12 seconds

6.

7. $m = 3$

8. (img_4)

9.

8.

9.

8. img placeholder

10. a. 180; In 2000 (0 years after 2000), an American adult read a newspaper an average of 180 hours per year. **b.** -2; The average number of hours decreased 2 hours per year. **c.** $y = -2x + 180$ **d.** 156 hours **11.** $\{(2, 4)\}$ **12.** $\{(1, -3)\}$ **13.** $\{(6, -5)\}$
14. a. $C(x) = 360,000 + 850x$ **b.** $R(x) = 1150x$ **c.** $(1200, 1,380,000)$; The company will break even if it produces and sells 1200 computers.

15.

16.

17.

18.

19. $(2, 0)$: 6; $(2, 6)$: 18; $(6, 3)$: 24; $(8, 0)$: 24; maximum: 24; minimum: 6 **20.** 26 **21.** 50 regular skis, 100 deluxe skis; $35,000

22.

23. $x = 3^y$;

24.

25. linear **26.** logarithmic **27.** exponential **28.** quadratic **29. a.** 159 million; extremely well. **b.** 375 million **30. a.** 15.3;
The number of Internet users is increasing by 15.3 million each year. **b.** logarithmic model **c.** f: 137.3 million; g: 141.3 million; logarithmic model; yes

CHAPTER 8

Section 8.1

Check Point Exercises

1. 12.5%   **2.** 2.3%   **3. a.** 0.67   **b.** 2.5   **4. a.** $75.60   **b.** $1335.60   **5. a.** $133   **b.** $247   **6.** $4365   **7. a.** $66\frac{2}{3}$%   **b.** 40%
8. 35%   **9.** 20%   **10. a.** $1152   **b.** 4% decrease

Exercise Set 8.1

1. 40%   **3.** 25%   **5.** 37.5%   **7.** 2.5%   **9.** 11.25%   **11.** 59%   **13.** 38.44%   **15.** 287%   **17.** 1487%   **19.** 10,000%
21. 0.72   **23.** 0.436   **25.** 1.3   **27.** 0.02   **29.** 0.005   **31.** 0.00625   **33.** 0.625   **35.** 6   **37.** 7.2   **39.** 5   **41.** 170   **43.** 20%
45. 12%   **47. a.** $1008   **b.** $17,808   **49. a.** $103.20   **b.** $756.80   **51.** $4815   **53.** $2442.50   **55.** $7030   **57.** $15,220
59. a. $1530   **b.** $1405   **c.** 14.7%   **61.** 56.1%   **63.** 50%   **65.** 15%   **67.** no; 2% decrease   **77.** $2588.93

Section 8.2

Check Point Exercises

1. $150   **2.** $336   **3.** $2091   **4.** 18%   **5.** $3846.16   **6. a.** $1200   **b.** $3800   **c.** 15.8%

Exercise Set 8.2

1. $240   **3.** $10.80   **5.** $318.75   **7.** $426.25   **9.** $3420   **11.** $38,350   **13.** $9390   **15.** 7.5%   **17.** 9%   **19.** 31.3%
21. $5172.42   **23.** $8917.20   **25.** $4509.59   **27. a.** $93.33   **b.** $1906.67   **c.** 7.3%   **29. a.** $1560   **b.** $10,440   **c.** 7.5%
31. $r = \dfrac{A - P}{Pt}$ **33.** $P = \dfrac{A}{1 + rt}$ **35. a.** $247.50   **b.** $4247.50   **37.** 21.4%   **39.** $2654.87   **45. a.** $A = 275t + 5000$
b. Answers will vary; an example is: The rate of change of the future value per year is $275.

Section 8.3

Check Point Exercises

1. a. $1216.65   **b.** $216.65   **2. a.** $6253.23   **b.** $2053.23   **3. a.** $14,859.47   **b.** $14,918.25   **4.** $6189.55   **5. a.** $6628.28
b. 10.5%   **6.** ≈ 8.24%

Exercise Set 8.3

1. a. $10,816   **b.** $816   **3. a.** $3655.21   **b.** $655.21   **5. a.** $12,795.12   **b.** $3295.12   **7. a.** $5149.12   **b.** $649.12
9. a. $1855.10   **b.** $355.10   **11. a.** $49,189.33   **b.** $29,189.33   **13. a.** $13,116.51   **b.** $13,140.67   **c.** $13,157.04   **d.** $13,165.31
15. 7% compounded monthly   **17.** $8374.84   **19.** $7528.59   **21. a.** $10,457.65   **b.** 4.6%   **23.** 6.1%   **25.** 6.2%   **27.** 6.2%
29. 8.3%; 8.25%; 8% compounded monthly   **31.** 5.6%; 5.5%; 5.5% compounded semiannually   **33.** 22.5 yr   **35.** 4.3 yr   **37.** 8.3 yr
39. a. ≈ $4,117,800,000   **b.** ≈ $4,277,900,000   **41.** $65,728.51   **43.** $21,679.39   **51.** $8544.49

Section 8.4

Check Point Exercises

1. a. $6620   **b.** $620   **2. a.** $777,170   **b.** $657,170   **3. a.** $333,946   **b.** $291,946   **4. a.** $187   **b.** deposits: $40,392; interest:
$59,608   **5. a.** high: $63.38; low: $42.37   **b.** $2160   **c.** 1.5%; This is much lower than a bank account paying 3.5%.   **d.** 7,203,200 shares
e. high: $49.94; low: $48.33   **f.** $49.50   **g.** The closing price is up $0.03 from the previous day's closing price.   **h.** ≈ $1.34

Exercise Set 8.4

1. a. $66,132   **b.** $26,132   **3. a.** $702,528   **b.** $542,528   **5. a.** $50,226   **b.** $32,226   **7. a.** $9076   **b.** $4076   **9. a.** $28,850
b. $4850   **11. a.** $4530   **b.** deposits: $81,540; interest: $58,460   **13. a.** $1323   **b.** deposits: $158,760; interest: $41,240   **15. a.** $356
b. deposits: $170,880; interest: $829,120   **17. a.** $920   **b.** deposits: $18,400; interest: $1600   **19. a.** high: $73.25; low: $45.44   **b.** $840
c. 2.2%; Answers will vary.   **d.** 591,500 shares   **e.** high: $56.38; low: $54.38   **f.** $55.50   **g.** $1.25 increase   **h.** ≈ $3.26   **21. a.** $30,000
b. $30,000   **23. a.** $287   **b.** with: $6254; without: $7115   **c.** with: 12.5%; without: 14.2%   **25.** $P = \dfrac{Ar}{(1 + r)^t - 1}$; the deposit at the end of
each year that yields A dollars after t years with interest rate r compounded annually   **27. a.** $11,617   **b.** $1617   **29. a.** $87,052
b. $63,052   **31. a.** $693,031   **b.** $293,031   **33. a.** $401   **b.** deposits: $3208; interest: $292   **35.** $641; $3,653,860

Section 8.5

Check Point Exercises

1. a. $13,720   **b.** $19,180   **c.** $5180   **2.** ≈ 13.5%   **3. a.** ≈ $2057.85   **b.** $9597.15   **4. a.** ≈ $1885.18   **b.** $9769.82
5. a. $59.52   **b.** $4849.52   **c.** $135   **6.** unpaid balance method: $113.40; previous balance method: $122.40; average daily balance
method: $115.43

Exercise Set 8.5

1. a. $22,000   **b.** $29,600   **c.** $2600   **3. a.** $1000   **b.** $1420   **c.** $320   **5.** 12.5%   **7.** 14.5%   **9.** 13.0%   **11. a.** $17,000

b. $22,133   **c.** $4633   **d.** 10.0%   **13. a.** $1805.73   **b.** $11,534.62   **c.** $1686.11   **d.** $11,654.24   **15. a.** $11.05   **b.** $1013.05
c. $\approx$ $28   **17. a.** $4.96   **b.** $618.61   **c.** $61.86   **19. a.** $7.50   **b.** $45   **c.** $13.75   **31.** b   **33.** Answers will vary.
35. a. 31 days; $376.26   **b.** $4.89   **c.** $471.04

Section 8.6

Check Point Exercises

1. a. $1627   **b.** $117,360   **c.** $148,860
2.

Payment Number	Interest Payment	Principal Payment	Balance of Loan
1	$1166.67	$383.33	$199,616.67
2	$1164.43	$385.57	$199,231.10

3. a. payment: $367; interest: $2616   **b.** payment: $278; interest: $5016   **c.** Monthly payments are less with the longer-term loan, but there is more interest with this loan.

Exercise Set 8.6

1. a. $44,000   **b.** $176,000   **c.** $5280   **d.** $1171   **e.** $245,560   **3.** $60,120   **5.** 20-year at 7.5%; $106,440   **7.** Mortgage A; $11,300
9. a. $210   **b.** $840   **11. a.** $137; lower monthly payment   **b.** $732; less interest   **13.** monthly payment: $386; total interest: $432;
$176 more each month; $408 less interest

15. a. monthly payment: $244.13; total interest: $1718.24
b.

Payment Number	Interest	Principal	Loan Balance
1	$66.67	$177.46	$9822.54
2	$65.48	$178.65	$9643.89
3	$64.29	$179.84	$9464.05

17. a. monthly payment: $347.13; total interest: $43,311.20
b.

Payment Number	Interest	Principal	Loan Balance
1	$283.33	$63.80	$39,936.20
2	$282.88	$64.25	$39,871.95
3	$282.43	$64.70	$39,807.25

c. $148.81 more each month; $23,798.40 less interest

27.

$$P\left(1 + \frac{r}{n}\right)^{nt} = \frac{\text{PMT}\left[\left(1 + \frac{r}{n}\right)^{nt} - 1\right]}{\frac{r}{n}}$$

$$P\left(\frac{r}{n}\right)\left(1 + \frac{r}{n}\right)^{nt} = \text{PMT}\left[\left(1 + \frac{r}{n}\right)^{nt} - 1\right]$$

$$\frac{P\left(\frac{r}{n}\right)\left(1 + \frac{r}{n}\right)^{nt}}{\left(1 + \frac{r}{n}\right)^{nt} - 1} = \text{PMT}$$

$$\frac{P\left(\frac{r}{n}\right)}{1 - \left(1 + \frac{r}{n}\right)^{-nt}} = \text{PMT}$$

Chapter 8 Review Exercises

1. 80%   **2.** 12.5%   **3.** 75%   **4.** 72%   **5.** 0.35%   **6.** 475.6%   **7.** 0.65   **8.** 0.997   **9.** 1.50   **10.** 0.03   **11.** 0.0065
12. 0.0025   **13.** 9.6   **14. a.** $1.44   **b.** $25.44   **15. a.** $297.50   **b.** $552.50   **16.** $3535   **17.** 12.5% increase   **18.** 35% decrease
19. no; $9900; 1% decrease   **20.** $180   **21.** $2520   **22.** $1200   **23.** $900   **24. a.** $122.50   **b.** $3622.50   **25.** $12,738   **26.** 7.5%
27. $13,389.12   **28.** $9287.93   **29.** 40%   **30. a.** $94.50   **b.** $1705.50   **c.** 7.4%   **31. a.** $8114.92   **b.** $1114.92   **32. a.** $38,490.80
b. $8490.80   **33. a.** $5556.46   **b.** $3056.46   **34.** 7% compounded monthly; $362   **35.** $16,653.64   **36.** $13,175.19   **37. a.** $2122.73
b. 6.1%   **38.** 5.6%; Answers will vary; an example is: The same amount of money would earn 5.6% in a simple interest account for a year.
39. 6.25% compounded monthly   **40. a.** $19,129   **b.** $8729   **41. a.** $91,361   **b.** $55,361   **42. a.** $1049   **b.** $20,980; $4020
43. high: $64.06; low: $26.13   **44.** $144   **45.** 0.3%   **46.** 545,800 shares   **47.** high: $61.25; low: $59.25   **48.** $61.00   **49.** $1.75 increase
50. $1.49   **52. a.** $16,000   **b.** $21,500   **c.** $5000   **d.** 11.5%   **53. a.** $250.40   **b.** $4229.60   **54. a.** $213.11   **b.** $4336.89

55. Answers will vary.   **56. a.** $16.50   **b.** $1756.50   **c.** $49   **57. a.** $28.80   **b.** $64.80   **c.** $34.61   **58. a.** $48,000   **b.** $192,000
c. $3840   **d.** $1277   **e.** $267,720   **59.** 20-year at 8%; $53,040; Answers will vary.   **60. a.** option A: $769; option B: $699; Answers will vary.
b. Mortgage A: $20,900   **61. a.** monthly payment: $465; total interest: $1740   **b.** monthly payment: $305; total interest: $3300   **c.** Longer term
has lower monthly payment but greater total interest.

62. a. $464.89
   b. $1845.36
   c.

Payment Number	Interest	Principal	Loan Balance
1	$139.68	$325.21	$8986.79
2	$134.80	$330.09	$8656.70
3	$129.85	$335.04	$8321.66

Chapter 8 Test

1. a. $18   **b.** $102   **2.** $3430   **3.** 75%   **4.** $72; $2472   **5.** 25%   **6.** $6698.57   **7.** 4.58%; Answers will vary; an example is:
The same amount of money would earn 4.58% in a simple interest account for a year.   **8. a.** $8297   **b.** $2297   **9. a.** $7067   **b.** $1067
c. Only part of the $6000 is invested for the entire five years.; Answers will vary.   **10.** $2070   **11.** $704 per month; $1,162,080 interest
12. high: $25.75; low: $25.50   **13.** $2030   **14.** $386.25   **15.** $13,000   **16.** $21,000   **17.** $5000   **18.** 13.5%   **19.** $819.67
20. $6680.33   **21.** $15.60   **22.** $1335.60   **23.** $37   **24.** $16.80   **25.** $12,000   **26.** $108,000   **27.** $2160   **28.** $830.52
29. $190,987.20

30. a. monthly payment: $230; total interest: $7600
   b.

Payment Number	Interest	Principal	Loan Balance
1	$113.33	$116.67	$19,883.33
2	$112.67	$117.33	$19,766.00

CHAPTER 9

Section 9.1

Check Point Exercises

1. a. 6.5 ft   **b.** 3.25 mi   **c.** $\frac{1}{12}$ yd   **2. a.** 8 km   **b.** 53,000 mm   **c.** 0.0604 hm   **d.** 6720 cm   **3. a.** 243.84 cm   **b.** ≈ 22.22 yd
c. ≈ 1181.1 in.   **4.** 37.5 mi/hr

Exercise Set 9.1

1. 2.5 ft   **3.** 360 in.   **5.** $\frac{1}{6}$ yd ≈ 0.17 yd   **7.** 216 in.   **9.** 18 ft   **11.** 2 yd   **13.** 4.5 mi   **15.** 3960 ft   **17.** 500 cm   **19.** 1630 m
21. 0.03178 hm   **23.** 0.000023 m   **25.** 21.96 dm   **27.** 35.56 cm   **29.** ≈ 5.51 in.   **31.** 424 km   **33.** 165.625 mi   **35.** ≈ 13.33 yd
37. ≈ 55.12 in.   **39.** 0.4064 dam   **41.** 1.524 m   **43.** ≈ 16.40 ft   **45.** 60 mi/hr   **47.** 72 km/hr   **49.** 457.2 cm   **51.** $8\frac{1}{3}$ yd
53. 48.28032 km   **55.** 176 ft/sec   **57.** meter   **59.** millimeter   **61.** meter   **63.** millimeter   **65.** millimeter   **67.** b   **69.** a
71. c   **73.** a   **75.** 0.216 km   **77.** 148.8 million km   **87.** 9 hm   **89.** 11 m or 1.1 dam

Section 9.2

Check Point Exercises

1. 8 square units   **2.** 219.3 people per square mile   **3. a.** 0.72 ha   **b.** ≈ $576,389 per hectare   **4.** 9 cubic units   **5.** 74,800 gal
6. 220 L

Exercise Set 9.2

1. 16 square units   **3.** 8 square units   **5.** ≈ 2.15 in.²   **7.** 37.5 yd²   **9.** 25.5 acres   **11.** 91 cm²   **13.** 24 cubic units
15. 74,800 gal   **17.** 1600 gal   **19.** 9 gal   **21.** 13.5 yd³   **23.** 45 L   **25.** 17 mL   **27.** 1500 cm³   **29.** 150 cm³   **31.** 12,000 dm³
33. a. 1900: 25.6 people per square mile; 2000: 79.6 people per square mile   **b.** 210.9%   **35.** 17.0 people per square kilometer
37. a. 20 acres   **b.** $12,500 per acre   **39.** square centimeters   **41.** square kilometers   **43.** b   **45.** b   **47.** 336,600 gal   **49.** 4 L
57. 12,139.4 people per square mile   **59.** Answers will vary.   **61.** 6.5 liters; Answers will vary.

Section 9.3

Check Point Exercises

1. a. 420 mg   **b.** 6.2 g   **2.** 145 kg   **3. a.** 83.7 kg   **b.** 100.44 mg   **4.** 122°F   **5.** 15°C

Exercise Set 9.3

1. 740 mg   **3.** 0.87 g   **5.** 800 cg   **7.** 18,600 g   **9.** 0.000018 g   **11.** 50 kg   **13.** 4200 cm³   **15.** 1100 t   **17.** 40,000 g   **19.** 2.25 lb
21. 1008 g   **23.** 243 kg   **25.** 36,000 g   **27.** 1200 lb   **29.** ≈ 222.22 T   **31.** 50°F   **33.** 95°F   **35.** 134.6°F   **37.** 23°F

39. 20°C **41.** 5°C **43.** 22.2°C **45.** −5°C **47.** 176.7°C **49.** −30°C **51. a.** $\frac{9}{5}$; Fahrenheit temperature increases by $\frac{9}{5}$° for each 1° change in Celsius temperature. **b.** $F = \frac{9}{5}C + 32$ **53.** true **55.** false **57.** false **59.** milligram **61.** gram **63.** kilogram **65.** kilogram **67.** b **69.** a **71.** c **73.** 13.28 kg **75.** $1.06 **77.** Purchasing the regular size is more economical. **79.** 90 mg **81. a.** 43 mg **b.** 516 mg **83.** a **85.** c **87.** 19.4°F **95.** b

Chapter 9 Review Exercises

1. 5.75 ft **2.** 0.25 yd **3.** 7 yd **4.** 2.5 mi **5.** 2280 cm **6.** 70 m **7.** 1920 m **8.** 0.0144 hm **9.** 0.0005 m **10.** 180 mm **11.** 58.42 cm **12.** ≈ 7.48 in. **13.** 528 km **14.** 375 mi **15.** ≈ 15.56 yd **16.** ≈ 39.37 ft **17.** ≈ 28.13 mi/hr **18.** 96 km/hr **19.** 0.024 km, 24,000 cm, 2400 m **20.** 4.8 km **21.** 24 square units **22.** 84.5 people per square mile; In the United States, there is an average of 84.5 people for each square mile. **23.** 18 acres **24.** ≈ 333.33 ft² **25.** 31.2 km² **26.** a **27.** 24 cubic units **28.** 251,328 gal **29.** 76 L **30.** c **31–32.** Answers will vary. **33.** 1240 mg **34.** 1200 cg **35.** 0.000012 g **36.** 0.00045 kg **37.** 50,000 cm³ **38.** 4000 dm³, 4,000,000 g **39.** 94.5 kg **40.** 14 oz **41.** kilograms; Answers will vary. **42.** 2.25 lb **43.** a **44.** c **45.** 59°F **46.** 212°F **47.** 41°F **48.** 32°F **49.** −13°F **50.** 15°C **51.** 5°C **52.** 100°C **53.** 37°C **54.** ≈ −17.8°C **55.** −10°C **56.** more; Answers will vary.

Chapter 9 Test

1. 0.00807 hm **2.** 250 in. **3.** 4.8 km **4.** mm **5.** cm **6.** km **7.** 128 km/hr **8.** 9 times **9.** 200.8 people per square mile; In Spain, there is an average of 200.8 people for each square mile. **10.** 45 acres **11.** b **12.** Answers will vary.; 1000 times **13.** 74,800 gal **14.** b **15.** 0.137 kg **16.** 40.5 kg **17.** kg **18.** mg **19.** 86°F **20.** 80°C **21.** d

CHAPTER 10

Section 10.1

Check Point Exercises

1. 30° **2.** 71° **3.** 46°, 134° **4.** $m\angle 1 = 57°, m\angle 2 = 123°$, and $m\angle 3 = 123°$ **5.** $m\angle 1 = 29°, m\angle 2 = 29°, m\angle 3 = 151°, m\angle 4 = 151°, m\angle 5 = 29°, m\angle 6 = 151°$, and $m\angle 7 = 151°$

Exercise Set 10.1

1. 150° **3.** 90° **5.** 20°; acute **7.** 160°; obtuse **9.** 180°; straight **11.** 65° **13.** 146° **15.** 42°; 132° **17.** 1°; 91° **19.** 52.6°; 142.6° **21.** $x + x + 12° = 90°; 39°, 51°$ **23.** $x + 3x = 180°; 45°, 135°$ **25.** $m\angle 1 = 108°; m\angle 2 = 72°; m\angle 3 = 108°$ **27.** $m\angle 1 = 50°; m\angle 2 = 90°; m\angle 3 = 50°$ **29.** $m\angle 1 = 68°; m\angle 2 = 68°; m\angle 3 = 112°; m\angle 4 = 112°; m\angle 5 = 68°; m\angle 6 = 68°; m\angle 7 = 112°$ **31.** $m\angle 1 = 38°; m\angle 2 = 52°; m\angle 3 = 142°$ **33.** 60°, 30° **35.** 112°, 112° **37.** $\overline{BC}$ **39.** $\overline{AD}$ **41.** $\overleftrightarrow{AD}$ **43.** $\overline{AD}$ **45.** 45° **47.** When two parallel lines are intersected by a transversal, corresponding angles have the same measure. **57.** d

Section 10.2

Check Point Exercises

1. 49° **2.** $m\angle 1 = 90°; m\angle 2 = 54°; m\angle 3 = 54°; m\angle 4 = 68°; m\angle 5 = 112°$ **3.** 32 in. **4.** 32 yd **5.** 25 ft **6.** 120 yd

Exercise Set 10.2

1. 67° **3.** 32° **5.** $m\angle 1 = 50°; m\angle 2 = 130°; m\angle 3 = 50°; m\angle 4 = 130°; m\angle 5 = 50°$ **7.** $m\angle 1 = 50°; m\angle 2 = 50°; m\angle 3 = 80°; m\angle 4 = 130°; m\angle 5 = 130°$ **9.** $m\angle 1 = 55°; m\angle 2 = 65°; m\angle 3 = 60°; m\angle 4 = 65°; m\angle 5 = 60°; m\angle 6 = 120°; m\angle 7 = 60°; m\angle 8 = 60°; m\angle 9 = 55°; m\angle 10 = 55°$ **11.** 5 in. **13.** 6 m **15.** 16 in. **17.** 5 **19.** 9 **21.** 17 m **23.** 39 m **25.** 12 cm **27.** 50°, 50°, 80° **29.** 40°, 80°, 60° **31.** If $a^2 + b^2 = c^2$, then the triangle is a right triangle. **33.** not a right triangle **35.** 71.7 ft **37.** $4\sqrt{5} \approx 8.9$ ft **39.** $5\sqrt{7}$ ft ≈ 13.2 ft **41.** $70\sqrt{2} \approx 99.0$ ft **43.** $2\sqrt{5} \approx 4.5$ mi **45. a.** 3.3 m; 10.8 ft; no **b.** 3.32 m; 2 cm; 1 in.; no **c.** 19.7 ft; Answers will vary. **55.** 70° **57.** 5 ft by 12 ft

Section 10.3

Check Point Exercises

1. $3120 **2. a.** 1800° **b.** 150° **3.** Each angle of a regular octagon measures 135°. 360° is not a multiple of 135°.

Exercise Set 10.3

1. quadrilateral **3.** pentagon **5.** a: square; b: rhombus; d: rectangle; e: parallelogram **7.** a: square; d: rectangle **9.** c: trapezoid **11.** 30 cm **13.** 28 yd **15.** 1000 in. **17.** 27 ft **19.** 18 yd **21.** 84 yd **23.** 32 ft **25.** 540° **27.** 360° **29.** 108°; 72° **31. a.** 540° **b.** $m\angle A = 140°; m\angle B = 40°$ **33. a.** squares, hexagons, dodecagons (12-sided polygons) **b.** 3 angles; 90°, 120°, 150° **c.** The sum of the measures is 360°. **35. a.** triangles, hexagons **b.** 4 angles; 60°, 60°, 120°, 120° **c.** The sum of the measures is 360°. **37.** no; Each angle of the polygon measures 140°. 360° is not a multiple of 140°. **39.** 50 yd by 200 yd **41.** 160 ft by 360 ft **43.** 115°, 115°, 120°, 120° **45.** If the polygons were all regular polygons, the sum would be 363°. The sum is not 360°. **47.** $5600 **49.** 48 **59.** 6a

Section 10.4

Check Point Exercises

1. 66 ft^2; yes **2.** \$672 **3.** 60 in.^{2} **4.** 30 ft^2 **5.** 105 ft^2 **6.** 10π in.; 31.4 in. **7.** 49.7 ft **8.** large pizza

Exercise Set 10.4

1. 18 m^2 **3.** 16 in.^{2} **5.** 2100 cm^2 **7.** 56 in.^{2} **9.** 20.58 yd^2 **11.** 30 in.^{2} **13.** 91 m^2 **15.** C: 8π cm, $\approx$ 25.1 cm; A: 16π cm^2, $\approx$ 50.3 cm^2 **17.** C: 12π yd, $\approx$ 37.7 yd; A: 36π yd^2, $\approx$ 113.1 yd^2 **19.** 72 m^2 **21.** 300 m^2 **23.** $100 + 50\pi$; 257.1 cm^2 **25.** 192 cm^2 **27.** perimeter: 54 ft; area: 168 ft^2 **29.** length: 20 ft; width: 15 ft **31.** base: 5 cm; height: 6 cm **33.** \$556.50 **35.** 148 ft^2 **37. a.** 23 bags **b.** \$575 **39. a.** 3680 ft^2 **b.** 15 cans of paint **c.** \$404.25 **41.** \$933.40 **43.** 40π m; 125.7 m **45.** 377 plants **47.** large pizza **55.** by a factor of $\frac{9}{4}$ **57.** \$13,032.73

Section 10.5

Check Point Exercises

1. 105 ft^3 **2.** 8 yd^3 **3.** 48 ft^3 **4.** 302 in.^{3} **5.** 101 in.^{3} **6.** no **7.** 632 yd^2

Exercise Set 10.5

1. 36 in.^{3} **3.** 64 cm^3 **5.** 175 yd^3 **7.** 56 in.^{3} **9.** 150π cm^3, 471 cm^3 **11.** 3024π in.^{3}, 9500 in.^{3} **13.** 48π m^3, 151 m^3 **15.** 15π yd^3, 47 yd^3 **17.** 288π m^3, 905 m^3 **19.** 972π cm^3, 3054 cm^3 **21.** 62 m^2 **23.** 96 ft^2 **25.** 324π cm^3, 1018 cm^3 **27.** surface area: 186 yd^2; volume: 148 yd^3 **29.** 666 yd^2 **31.** $\frac{1}{8}$ **33.** 9 times **35.** \$40 **37.** no **39. a.** 3,386,880 yd^3 **b.** 2,257,920 blocks **41.** yes **43.** \$27 **47.** The volume is multiplied by 8. **49.** 168 cm^3 **51.** 84 cm^2

Section 10.6

Check Point Exercises

1. $\sin A = \frac{3}{5}$; $\cos A = \frac{4}{5}$; $\tan A = \frac{3}{4}$ **2.** 263 cm **3.** 298 cm **4.** 994 ft **5.** 54°

Exercise Set 10.6

1. $\sin A = \frac{3}{5}$; $\cos A = \frac{4}{5}$; $\tan A = \frac{3}{4}$ **3.** $\sin A = \frac{20}{29}$; $\cos A = \frac{21}{29}$; $\tan A = \frac{20}{21}$ **5.** $\sin A = \frac{5}{13}$; $\cos A = \frac{12}{13}$; $\tan A = \frac{5}{12}$ **7.** $\sin A = \frac{4}{5}$; $\cos A = \frac{3}{5}$; $\tan A = \frac{4}{3}$ **9.** 188 cm **11.** 182 in. **13.** 7 m **15.** 22 yd **17.** 40 m **19.** $m\angle B = 50°$, $a = 18$ yd, $c = 29$ yd **21.** $m\angle B = 38°$, $a = 43$ cm, $b = 33$ cm **23.** 37° **25.** 28° **27.** 653 units **29.** 39 units **31.** 298 units **33.** 257 units **35.** 529 yd **37.** 2879 ft **39.** 2059 ft **41.** 695 ft **43.** 36° **45.** 1376 ft **47.** 15.1° **59. a.** 357 ft **b.** 394 ft

Section 10.7

Check Point Exercises

1. Answers will vary.

Exercise Set 10.7

1. a. traversable **b.** sample path: D, A, B, D, C, B **3. a.** traversable **b.** sample path: A, D, C, B, D, E, A, B **5.** not traversable
7.

9. no

11. 2 **13.** sample path: $B, E, A, B, D, C, A, E, C, E, D$ **15.** 2 **17.** 4 **19.** Answers will vary. **21.** The sum of the angles of such a quadrilateral is greater than 360°. **23.** yes

Chapter 10 Review Exercises

1. $\angle 3$ **2.** $\angle 5$ **3.** $\angle 4$ and $\angle 6$ **4.** $\angle 1$ and $\angle 6$ **5.** $\angle 4$ and $\angle 1$ **6.** $\angle 2$ **7.** $\angle 5$ **8.** 65° **9.** 49° **10.** 17° **11.** 134° **12.** $m\angle 1 = 110°$; $m\angle 2 = 70°$; $m\angle 3 = 110°$ **13.** $m\angle 1 = 138°$; $m\angle 2 = 42°$; $m\angle 3 = 138°$; $m\angle 4 = 138°$; $m\angle 5 = 42°$; $m\angle 6 = 42°$; $m\angle 7 = 138°$ **14.** 72° **15.** 51° **16.** $m\angle 1 = 90°$; $m\angle 2 = 90°$; $m\angle 3 = 140°$; $m\angle 4 = 40°$; $m\angle 5 = 140°$ **17.** $m\angle 1 = 80°$; $m\angle 2 = 65°$; $m\angle 3 = 115°$; $m\angle 4 = 80°$; $m\angle 5 = 100°$; $m\angle 6 = 80°$ **18.** 5 ft **19.** 3.75 ft **20.** 10 ft **21.** 7.2 in. **22.** 10.2 cm **23.** 12.5 ft **24.** 15 ft **25.** 12 yd **26.** rectangle, square **27.** rhombus, square **28.** parallelogram, rhombus, trapezoid **29.** 30 cm **30.** 4480 yd **31.** 44 m **32.** 1800° **33.** 1080° **34.** $m\angle 1 = 135°$; $m\angle 2 = 45°$ **35.** \$132 **36. a.** triangles, hexagons **b.** 5 angles; 60°, 60°, 60°, 60°, 120° **c.** The sum of the measures is 360°. **37.** yes; Each angle of a regular hexagon measures 120°, and 360° is a multiple of 120°. **38.** 32.5 ft^2 **39.** 20 m^2 **40.** 50 cm^2 **41.** 135 yd^2 **42.** $C = 20\pi$ m $\approx$ 62.8 m; $A = 100\pi$ m^2 $\approx$ 314.2 m^2

43. 192 in.^{2} **44.** 28 m^2 **45.** \$787.50   **46.** \$650   **47.** 31 yd   **48.** 60 cm^3 **49.** 960 m^3 **50.** 128π yd^3, 402 yd^3

51. $\frac{44,800\pi}{3}$ in.^{3}, 46,914 in.^{3} **52.** 288π m^3, 905 m^3 **53.** 126 m^2 **54.** 4800 m^3 **55.** 651,775 m^3 **56.** \$80

57. sin $A = \frac{3}{5}$; cos $A = \frac{4}{5}$; tan $A = \frac{3}{4}$ **58.** 42 mm   **59.** 23 cm   **60.** 37 in.   **61.** 58°   **62.** 772 ft   **63.** 31 m   **64.** 56°
65. not traversable   **66.** traversable; sample path: $A, B, C, D, A, B, C, D, A$ **67.** 0   **68.** 2   **69.** 1   **70.** 2   **71.** Answers will vary.
72. Answers will vary.

Chapter 10 Test

1. 36°; 126°   **2.** 133°   **3.** 70°   **4.** 35°   **5.** 3.2 in.   **6.** 10 ft   **7.** 1440°   **8.** 40 cm   **9.** d   **10. a.** triangles, squares
b. 5 angles; 60°, 60°, 60°, 90°, 90°   **c.** The sum of the measures is 360°.   **11.** 517 m^2 **12.** 525 in.^{2} **13. a.** 12 cm   **b.** 30 cm   **c.** 30 cm^2
14. $C: = 40\pi$ m, 125.7 m; $A: 400\pi$ m^2, 1256.6 m^2 **15.** 108 tiles   **16.** 18 ft^3 **17.** 16 m^3 **18.** 175π cm^3, 550 cm^3 **19.** 85 cm   **20.** 70 ft
21. traversable; sample path: B, C, A, E, C, D, E **22.** Answers will vary.

CHAPTER 11

Section 11.1

Check Point Exercises

1. 150   **2.** 40   **3.** 30   **4.** 160   **5.** 729   **6.** 90,000

Exercise Set 11.1

1. 80   **3.** 12   **5.** 6   **7.** 40   **9.** 144; Answers will vary.   **11.** 8   **13.** 96   **15.** 243   **17.** 144   **19.** 676,000   **21.** 2187   **27.** 720 hr

Section 11.2

Check Point Exercises

1. 2   **2.** 120   **3. a.** 504   **b.** 524,160   **c.** 100   **4.** 840   **5.** 15,120   **6.** 420

Exercise Set 11.2

1. 720   **3.** 120   **5.** 120   **7.** 362,880   **9.** 6   **11.** 4   **13.** 504   **15.** 570,024   **17.** 3,047,466,240   **19.** 600   **21.** 10,712   **23.** 5034
25. 24   **27.** 6   **29.** 42   **31.** 1716   **33.** 3024   **35.** 6720   **37.** 720   **39.** 1   **41.** 720   **43.** 8,648,640   **45.** 120   **47.** 15,120
49. 180   **51.** 831,600   **53.** 105   **55.** 280   **65.** 360   **67.** 14,400   **69.** $\frac{n(n-1)\cdots3\cdot2\cdot1}{2} = n(n-1)\cdots3$

Section 11.3

Check Point Exercises

1. a. combinations   **b.** permutations   **2.** 35   **3.** 1820   **4.** 23,049,600

Exercise Set 11.3

1. combinations   **3.** permutations   **5.** 6   **7.** 126   **9.** 330   **11.** 8   **13.** 1   **15.** 4060   **17.** 1   **19.** 7   **21.** 0   **23.** $\frac{3}{4}$
25. −9499   **27.** $\frac{3}{68}$ **29.** 20   **31.** 495   **33.** 24,310   **35.** 22,957,480   **37.** 360 ways   **39.** 1716 ways   **41.** 1140 ways
43. 840 passwords   **45.** 2730 cones   **47.** 735   **49.** 4,516,932,420   **51.** 720   **53.** 20   **55.** 24   **57.** 12   **63.** The 5/36 lottery is
easier to win.; Answers will vary.   **65.** 570 sec or 9.5 min; 2340 sec or 39 min

Section 11.4

Check Point Exercises

1. a. $\frac{1}{6}$ **b.** $\frac{1}{2}$ **c.** 0   **d.** 1   **2. a.** $\frac{1}{13}$ **b.** $\frac{1}{2}$ **c.** $\frac{1}{26}$ **3.** $\frac{1}{2}$ **4. a.** 0.24   **b.** 0.48

Exercise Set 11.4

1. $\frac{1}{6}$ **3.** $\frac{1}{2}$ **5.** $\frac{1}{3}$ **7.** 1   **9.** 0   **11.** $\frac{1}{13}$ **13.** $\frac{1}{4}$ **15.** $\frac{3}{13}$ **17.** $\frac{1}{52}$ **19.** 0   **21.** $\frac{1}{4}$ **23.** $\frac{1}{2}$ **25.** $\frac{1}{2}$ **27.** $\frac{3}{8}$ **29.** $\frac{3}{8}$
31. $\frac{7}{8}$ **33.** 0   **35.** $\frac{1}{4}$ **37.** $\frac{1}{9}$ **39.** 0   **41.** $\frac{3}{10}$ **43.** $\frac{1}{5}$ **45.** $\frac{1}{2}$ **47.** 0   **49.** $\frac{1}{4}$ **51.** $\frac{1}{4}$ **53.** $\frac{1}{2}$ **55.** 0.43   **57.** 0.13
59. 0.03   **61.** 0.38   **63.** 0.78   **65.** 0.12   **75.** $\frac{3}{8} = 0.375$

Section 11.5

Check Point Exercises

1. $\frac{1}{60}$ **2.** $\frac{1}{13,983,816} \approx 0.0000000715$ **3. a.** $\frac{1}{6}$ **b.** $\frac{1}{2}$

Exercise Set 11.5

1. a. 120 **b.** 6 **c.** $\frac{1}{20}$ **3. a.** $\frac{1}{6}$ **b.** $\frac{1}{30}$ **c.** $\frac{1}{720}$ **d.** $\frac{1}{3}$ **5. a.** 84 **b.** 10 **c.** $\frac{5}{42}$ **7.** $\frac{1}{18,009,460} \approx 0.0000000555;$

$\frac{100}{18,009,460} \approx 0.00000555$ **9. a.** $\frac{1}{177,100} \approx 0.00000565$ **b.** $\frac{27,132}{177,100} \approx 0.153$ **11.** $\frac{3}{10} = 0.3$ **13. a.** 2,598,960 **b.** 1287

c. $\frac{1287}{2,598,960} \approx 0.000495$ **15.** $\frac{11}{1105} \approx 0.00995$ **17.** $\frac{36}{270,725} \approx 0.000133$ **23.** \$9,004,730 **25.** $\frac{1}{10}$

Section 11.6

Check Point Exercises

1. $\frac{3}{4}$ **2. a.** $\frac{160}{191}$ **b.** $\frac{182}{191}$ **3.** $\frac{1}{3}$ **4.** $\frac{27}{50}$ **5.** $\frac{3}{4}$ **6. a.** 0.99 **b.** 0.65 **7. a.** 2:50 or 1:25 **b.** 50:2 or 25:1 **8.** 199:1
9. $1:15; \frac{1}{16}$

Exercise Set 11.6

1. $\frac{12}{13}$ **3.** $\frac{3}{4}$ **5.** $\frac{10}{13}$ **7.** $\frac{2,598,924}{2,598,960} \approx 0.999986$ **9.** $\frac{2,595,216}{2,598,960} \approx 0.998559$ **11. a.** 0.10 **b.** 0.90 **13.** $\frac{23}{28}$ **15.** $\frac{95}{112}$ **17.** $\frac{2}{13}$

19. $\frac{1}{13}$ **21.** $\frac{1}{26}$ **23.** $\frac{9}{22}$ **25.** $\frac{5}{6}$ **27.** $\frac{7}{13}$ **29.** $\frac{11}{26}$ **31.** $\frac{3}{4}$ **33.** $\frac{5}{8}$ **35.** $\frac{33}{40}$ **37.** $\frac{4}{5}$ **39.** $\frac{7}{10}$ **41.** $\frac{8}{11}$ **43.** $\frac{108}{187}$

45. $\frac{122}{187}$ **47.** 3:8; 8:3 **49.** $\frac{93}{143}$ **51.** $\frac{127}{143}$ **53.** $\frac{5}{13}$ **55.** 38:105; 105:38 **57.** 1:142; 142:1 **59.** 11:2; 2:11 **61.** 2:1 **63.** 1:2

65. a. 9:91 **b.** 91:9 **67.** 1:3 **69.** 1:1 **71.** 12:1 **73.** 25:1 **75.** 47:5 **77.** 49:1 **79.** 9:10 **81.** 14:5 **83.** 14:5 **85.** 9:10

87. $\frac{3}{7}$ **89.** $\frac{4}{25}; 84$ **91.** $\frac{1}{1000}$ **101.** 0.06

Section 11.7

Check Point Exercises

1. $\frac{1}{361} \approx 0.00277$ **2.** $\frac{1}{16}$ **3. a.** $\frac{625}{130,321} \approx 0.005$ **b.** $\frac{38,416}{130,321} \approx 0.295$ **c.** $\frac{91,905}{130,321} \approx 0.705$ **4.** $\frac{1}{221} \approx 0.00452$ **5.** $\frac{11}{850} \approx 0.0129$
6. $\frac{1}{2}$ **7. a.** $\frac{9}{10} = 0.9$ **b.** $\frac{45}{479} \approx 0.094$

Exercise Set 11.7

1. $\frac{1}{6}$ **3.** $\frac{1}{36}$ **5.** $\frac{1}{4}$ **7.** $\frac{1}{36}$ **9.** $\frac{1}{8}$ **11.** $\frac{1}{36}$ **13.** $\frac{1}{3}$ **15.** $\frac{3}{52}$ **17.** $\frac{1}{169}$ **19.** $\frac{1}{4}$ **21.** $\frac{1}{64}$ **23.** $\frac{1}{6}$ **25. a.** $\frac{1}{256} \approx 0.00391$

b. $\frac{1}{4096} \approx 0.000244$ **c.** ≈ 0.524 **d.** ≈ 0.476 **27.** 0.0144 **29.** 0.008 **31.** 0.4686 **33.** $\frac{7}{29}$ **35.** $\frac{5}{87}$ **37.** $\frac{2}{21}$ **39.** $\frac{4}{35}$

41. $\frac{11}{21}$ **43.** $\frac{1}{57}$ **45.** $\frac{8}{855}$ **47.** $\frac{11}{57}$ **49.** $\frac{1}{5}$ **51.** $\frac{2}{3}$ **53.** $\frac{3}{4}$ **55.** $\frac{3}{4}$ **57.** $\frac{412,368}{412,878} \approx 0.999$ **59.** $\frac{412,368}{574,895} \approx 0.717$ **61.** 0.898

63. 0.168 **65.** 0.542 **67.** 0.415 **69.** 0.103 **71.** 0.886 **81.** 0.59049 **83. a.** Answers will vary. **b.** $\frac{365}{365} \cdot \frac{364}{365} \cdot \frac{363}{365} \approx 0.992$

c. ≈ 0.008 **d.** 0.411 **e.** 23 people

Section 11.8

Check Point Exercises

1. 2.5 **2.** 2 **3. a.** \$8000; In the long run, the average cost of a claim is \$8000. **b.** \$8000 **4.** 0; no; Answers will vary.
5. table entries: \$998, \$48, and −\$2; expected value: −\$0.90; In the long run, a person can expect to lose an average of \$0.90 for each ticket purchased.;
Answers will vary. **6.** −\$0.20; In the long run, a person can expect to lose an average of \$0.20 for each card purchased.

Exercise Set 11.8

1. 1.75 **3. a.** \$29,000; In the long run, the average cost of a claim is \$29,000. **b.** \$29,000 **c.** \$29,050 **5.** \$0; Answers will vary. **7.** \$0.73
9. $\frac{1}{16} = 0.0625$; yes **11.** the second mall **13. a.** \$140,000 **b.** no **15.** $\approx -\$0.17$; In the long run, a person can expect to lose an average
of about \$0.17 for each game played. **17.** $\approx -\$0.05$; In the long run, a person can expect to lose an average of about \$0.05 for each game played.
19. −\$0.50; In the long run, a person can expect to lose an average of \$0.50 for each game played. **27.** \$160

Chapter 11 Review Exercises

1. 800 **2.** 20 **3.** 9900 **4.** 125 **5.** 243 **6.** 60 **7.** 720 **8.** 120 **9.** 120 **10.** 240 **11.** 800 **12.** 114 **13.** 990
14. 151,200 **15.** 9900 **16.** 32,760 **17.** 1,860,480 **18.** 420 **19.** 60 **20.** combinations **21.** permutations **22.** combinations

23. 330 **24.** 2002 **25.** 210 **26.** 1287 **27.** 1140 **28.** 55,440 **29.** $\frac{1}{6}$ **30.** $\frac{2}{3}$ **31.** 1 **32.** 0 **33.** $\frac{1}{13}$ **34.** $\frac{3}{13}$ **35.** $\frac{3}{13}$

36. $\frac{1}{52}$ **37.** $\frac{1}{26}$ **38.** $\frac{1}{2}$ **39.** $\frac{1}{3}$ **40.** $\frac{1}{6}$ **41. a.** $\frac{1}{2}$ **b.** 0 **42.** 0.623 **43.** 0.518 **44.** 0.149 **45.** $\frac{1}{24}$ **46.** $\frac{1}{6}$ **47.** $\frac{1}{30}$

48. $\frac{1}{720}$ **49.** $\frac{1}{3}$ **50. a.** $\frac{1}{15,504} \approx 0.0000645$ **b.** $\frac{100}{15,504} \approx 0.00645$ **51. a.** $\frac{1}{14}$ **b.** $\frac{3}{7}$ **52.** $\frac{3}{26}$ **53.** $\frac{5}{6}$ **54.** $\frac{1}{2}$ **55.** $\frac{1}{3}$

56. $\frac{2}{3}$ **57.** 1 **58.** $\frac{10}{13}$ **59.** $\frac{3}{4}$ **60.** $\frac{2}{13}$ **61.** $\frac{1}{13}$ **62.** $\frac{7}{13}$ **63.** $\frac{11}{26}$ **64.** $\frac{5}{6}$ **65.** $\frac{5}{6}$ **66.** $\frac{1}{2}$ **67.** $\frac{2}{3}$ **68.** 1 **69.** $\frac{5}{6}$

70. $\frac{4}{5}$ **71.** $\frac{3}{4}$ **72.** $\frac{18}{25}$ **73.** $\frac{6}{7}$ **74.** $\frac{3}{5}$ **75.** $\frac{12}{35}$ **76.** in favor: 1:12; against: 12:1 **77.** 99:1 **78.** $\frac{3}{4}$ **79.** $\frac{2}{9}$ **80.** $\frac{1}{36}$ **81.** $\frac{1}{9}$

82. $\frac{1}{36}$ **83.** $\frac{8}{27}$ **84.** $\frac{1}{32}$ **85. a.** 0.04 **b.** 0.008 **c.** 0.4096 **d.** 0.5904 **86.** $\frac{1}{9}$ **87.** $\frac{1}{12}$ **88.** $\frac{1}{196}$ **89.** $\frac{1}{3}$ **90.** $\frac{3}{10}$

91. a. $\frac{1}{2}$ **b.** $\frac{2}{7}$ **92.** $\frac{27}{29}$ **93.** $\frac{4}{29}$ **94.** $\frac{144}{145}$ **95.** $\frac{11}{20}$ **96.** $\frac{11}{135}$ **97.** $\frac{1}{125}$ **98.** $\frac{1}{232}$ **99.** $\frac{19}{1044}$ **100.** $\frac{26,098}{30,242} \approx 0.863$

101. $\frac{11,586}{30,242} \approx 0.383$ **102.** $\frac{27,818}{30,242} \approx 0.920$ **103.** $\frac{15,892}{30,242} \approx 0.525$ **104.** $\frac{4186}{30,242} \approx 0.138$ **105.** $\frac{3887}{26,098} \approx 0.149$ **106.** $\frac{2225}{2424} \approx 0.918$

107. 3.125 **108. a.** \$0.50; In the long run, the average cost of a claim is \$0.50. **b.** \$10.00 **109.** \$4500; Answers will vary.
110. $-$\$0.25; In the long run, a person can expect to lose an average of \$0.25 for each game played.

Chapter 11 Test

1. 240 **2.** 24 **3.** 720 **4.** 990 **5.** 210 **6.** 420 **7.** $\frac{6}{25}$ **8.** $\frac{17}{25}$ **9.** $\frac{11}{25}$ **10.** $\frac{5}{13}$ **11.** $\frac{1}{210}$ **12.** $\frac{10}{1001} \approx 0.00999$ **13.** $\frac{1}{2}$

14. $\frac{1}{16}$ **15.** $\frac{1}{8000} = 0.000125$ **16.** $\frac{8}{13}$ **17.** $\frac{3}{5}$ **18.** $\frac{1}{19}$ **19.** $\frac{1}{256}$ **20.** 3:4 **21. a.** 4:1 **b.** $\frac{4}{5}$ **22.** $\frac{3}{5}$ **23.** $\frac{39}{50}$ **24.** $\frac{3}{5}$

25. $\frac{9}{19}$ **26.** $\frac{7}{150}$ **27.** \$1000; Answers will vary. **28.** $-$\$12.75; In the long run, a person can expect to lose an average of \$12.75 for each
game played.

CHAPTER 12

Section 12.1

Check Point Exercises

1. a. the set containing all the city's homeless **b.** no: People already in the shelters are probably less likely to be against mandatory residence in
the shelters. **2.** By selecting people from a shelter, homeless people who do not go to the shelters have no chance of being selected. An appropriate
method would be to randomly select neighborhoods of the city and then randomly survey homeless people within the selected neighborhood.

3.

Grade	Frequency
A	3
B	5
C	9
D	2
F	1
	20

4.

Class	Frequency
40–49	1
50–59	5
60–69	4
70–79	15
80–89	5
90–99	7
	37

5.

Stem	Leaves
4	1
5	8 2 8 0 7
6	8 2 9 9
7	3 5 9 9 7 5 5 3 3 6 7 1 7 1 5
8	7 3 9 9 1
9	4 6 9 7 5 8 0

Exercise Set 12.1

1. a. population: all American men aged 18 or older; sample: those men actually polled **b.** each man's impression of his own health; qualitative
3. c **5.** 7; 31 **7.** 151

9.

Time Spent on Homework (in hours)	Number of Students
15	4
16	5
17	6
18	5
19	4
20	2
21	2
22	0
23	0
24	2
	30

11. 0, 5, 10, … , 40, 45 **13.** 5 **15.** 13 **17.** the 5–9 class

19.

Age at Inauguration	Number of Presidents
41–45	2
46–50	8
51–55	15
56–60	9
61–65	7
66–70	2
	43

21. a. **b.**

23.

25. b

27.

Stem	Leaves
2	8 8 9 5
3	8 7 0 1 2 7 6 4 0 5
4	8 2 2 1 4 5 4 6 2 0 8 2 7 9
5	9 4 1 9 1 0
6	3 2 3 6 6 3

The greatest number of college professors are in their 40s.

29. Time intervals on the horizontal axis do not represent equal amounts of time.   **31.** Percentages do not add up to 100%.
33. It is not clear whether the lengths of the bars represent the percentage or the loan amount.

45.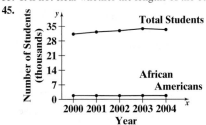

Section 12.2

Check Point Exercises

1. a. 30   **b.** 30   **2.** 36   **3. a.** 35   **b.** 82   **4.** 5   **5.** 162.5   **6.** 54.5   **7. a.** $66.94 billion   **b.** $30 billion
c. One data items is much greater than the other items.   **8.** 8   **9.** $124,500   **10.** mean: 158.6 cal; median: 153 cal; mode: 138 cal; midrange: 151 cal

Exercise Set 12.2

1. 4.125   **3.** 95   **5.** 62   **7.** ≈ 3.45 **9.** ≈ 4.71 **11.** ≈ 6.26 **13.** 3.5   **15.** 95   **17.** 60   **19.** 3.6   **21.** 5   **23.** 6   **25.** 3
27. 95   **29.** 40   **31.** 2.5, 4.2 (bimodal)   **33.** 5   **35.** 6   **37.** 4.5   **39.** 95   **41.** 70   **43.** 3.3   **45.** 4.5   **47.** 5.5
49. mean: 30; median: 30; mode: 30; midrange: 30   **51.** mean: approximately 12.4; median: 12.5; mode: 13; midrange: 12.5
53. mean: approximately 31.3; median: 31; mode: 31; midrange: 33   **55. a.** 67.4   **b.** 69   **c.** 71   **d.** 69.5   **57. a.** approximately 19.2
b. 18   **c.** 19   **d.** 24   **59. a.** ≈ 17.27 **b.** 17   **c.** 7, 12, 17   **d.** 24.5   **61.** 175 lb   **63.** 177.5 lb   **65.** ≈ 2.76
77. All 30 students had the same grade.

Section 12.3

Check Point Exercises

1. 9   **2.** mean: 6;   **3.** ≈ 3.92   **4.** sample A: 3.74; sample B: 28.06   **5. a.** stocks   **b.** stocks; Answers will vary.

Data item	Deviation
2	−4
4	−2
7	1
11	5

Exercise Set 12.3

1. 4   **3.** 8   **5.** 2

7. a.

Data item	Deviation
3	−9
5	−7
7	−5
12	0
18	6
27	15

b. 0

9. a.

Data item	Deviation
29	−20
38	−11
48	−1
49	0
53	4
77	28

b. 0

11. a. 91
b.

Data item	Deviation
85	−6
95	4
90	−1
85	−6
100	9

c. 0

13. a. 155
b.

Data item	Deviation
146	−9
153	−2
155	0
160	5
161	6

c. 0

15. a. 2.70
b.

Data item	Deviation
2.25	−0.45
3.50	0.80
2.75	0.05
3.10	0.40
1.90	−0.80

c. 0

17. ≈ 1.58   **19.** ≈ 3.46   **21.** ≈ 0.89   **23.** 3   **25.** ≈ 2.14
27. *Sample A*: mean: 12; range: 12; standard deviation: ≈ 4.32
  Sample B: mean: 12; range: 12; standard deviation: ≈ 5.07
  Sample C: mean: 12; range: 12; standard deviation: 6
  The samples have the same mean and range, but different standard deviations.
29. 0   **31.** 1   **33.** 7.91   **35.** 1.55   **37. a.** Best Actor; Most of the ages for Best Actor are in the upper 30s and lower 40s while all of the ages for Best Actress are in the upper 20s and lower 30s.   **b.** Best Actor: 38.57; Best Actress: 30.71   **c.** Best Actor; There is greater spread in the ages for Best Actor, since one age, 29, is much lower than the other ages.   **d.** Best Actor: 5.68; Best Actress: 3.77   **47.** a   **51.** The mean is increased by 2.; The standard deviation is unaffected.

Section 12.4

Check Point Exercises

1. a. 75.5 in.   **b.** 58 in.   **2. a.** 95%   **b.** 47.5%   **c.** 16%   **3. a.** 2   **b.** 0   **c.** −1   **4.** ACT   **5. a.** 64   **b.** 128
6. 75% of the scores on the SAT are less than this student's score.   **7.** 88.49%   **8.** 8.08%   **9.** 83.01%   **10. a.** ±4.5%
b. We can be 95% confident that between 49.5% and 58.5% of American adults support physician-assisted suicide.   **c.** The percentage of American adults who support physician-assisted suicide may be less than 50%.

Exercise Set 12.4

1. 120   **3.** 160   **5.** 150   **7.** 60   **9.** 90   **11.** 68%   **13.** 34%   **15.** 47.5%   **17.** 49.85%   **19.** 16%   **21.** 2.5%   **23.** 95%
25. 47.5%   **27.** 16%   **29.** 2.5%   **31.** 0.15%   **33.** 1   **35.** 3   **37.** 0.5   **39.** 1.75   **41.** 0   **43.** −1   **45.** −1.5   **47.** −3.25
49. 1.5   **51.** 2.25   **53.** −1.25   **55.** −1.5   **57.** The person who scores 127 on the Wechsler has the higher IQ.   **59.** 500   **61.** 475
63. 250   **65.** 275   **67. a.** 72.57%   **b.** 27.43%   **69. a.** 88.49%   **b.** 11.51%   **71. a.** 24.2%   **b.** 75.8%   **73. a.** 11.51%
b. 88.49%   **75.** 33.99%   **77.** 15.74%   **79.** 86.64%   **81.** 28.57%   **83.** 91.92%   **85.** 27.43%   **87.** 88.49%   **89.** 6.69%
91. 45.14%   **93.** 6.68%   **95.** 24.17%   **97. a.** ±2.1%   **b.** We can be 95% confident that between 15.9% and 20.1% of parents in the population consider a doctor as the dream job for their child.   **99. a.** ±1.6%   **b.** We can be 95% confident that between 58.6% and 61.8% of all TV households watched the final episode of "M*A*S*H".   **101.** 0.2%   **103. a.** skewed to the right   **b.** 5.6 murders per 100,000 residents
c. 5 murders per 100,000 residents   **d.** yes; The mean is greater than the median which is consistent with a distribution skewed to the right.
e. 6.3; yes; For a normal distribution, almost 100% of the z-scores are between −3 and 3.   **119.** 630

Section 12.5

Check Point Exercises

1. This indicates a moderate relationship. **2.** -0.84 **3.** $y = -22.97x + 260.56$; 30.86 deaths per 100,000 people **4.** yes

Exercise Set 12.5

1.

There appears to be a positive correlation.

3.

There appears to be a negative correlation.

5.

There appears to be a positive correlation.

7.

There appears to be a positive correlation.

9. false **11.** true **13.** true **15.** false **17.** true **19.** false **21.** true **23.** false **25.** false **27.** a **29.** d **31.** 0.855
33. -0.954 **35. a.** 0.75 **b.** $y = 1.52x - 3.38$ **c.** 21 years **37. a.** 0.885 **b.** $y = 0.85x + 4.05$ **c.** 16 murders per 100,000 people
39. A correlation does exist. **41.** A correlation does not exist. **43.** A correlation does exist. **45.** A correlation does not exist.

Chapter 12 Review Exercises

1. population: American women ages 25 through 60; sample: 1511 women randomly selected from the population **2.** how often she entertains guests for dinner **3.** a

4.

Time Spent on Homework (in hours)	Number of Students
6	1
7	3
8	3
9	2
10	1
	10

5.

6.

7.

Grades	Number of Students
0–39	19
40–49	8
50–59	6
60–69	6
70–79	5
80–89	3
90–100	3
	50

8.

Stem	Leaves
1	8 4 3 3 7 1
2	4 6 9 9 2 7
3	4 9 6 1 5 1 1
4	4 7 9 1 2 2 0 5
5	4 7 9 0 6 1
6	3 7 0 8 3 9
7	2 5 4 0 3
8	1 7 6
9	1 0 5

9. Sizes of barrels are not scaled proportionally in terms of the data they represent. **10.** 91.2 **11.** 17 **12.** 2.3 **13.** 11 **14.** 28
15. 2 **16.** 27 **17.** 585, 587 (bimodal) **18.** 2 **19.** 91 **20.** 19.5 **21.** 2.5

24. a.

Age at First Inauguration	Number of Presidents
42	1
43	1
44	0
45	0
46	2
47	1
48	1
49	2
50	1
51	5
52	2
53	0
54	5
55	4
56	3
57	4
58	1
59	0
60	1
61	3
62	1
63	0
64	2
65	1
66	0
67	0
68	1
69	1
	43

b. mean: ≈ 54.84 yr; median: 55 yr; mode: 51 yr, 54 yr (bimodal); midrange: 55.5 yr

27. a.

Data item	Deviation
29	−6
9	−26
8	−27
22	−13
46	11
51	16
48	13
42	7
53	18
42	7

b. 0

28. a. 50

b.

Data item	Deviation
36	−14
26	−24
24	−26
90	40
74	24

c. 0

25. 18   **26.** 564

29. ≈ 4.05 **30.** ≈ 5.13 **31.** mean: 49; range: 76; standard deviation: ≈ 24.32 **32.** Set A: mean: 80; standard deviation: 0; Set B: mean: 80; standard deviation: ≈ 11.55; Answers will vary.   **33.** Answers will vary.   **34.** 86   **35.** 98   **36.** 60   **37.** 68%   **38.** 95%   **39.** 34%
40. 99.7%   **41.** 16%   **42.** 84%   **43.** 2.5%   **44.** 0   **45.** 2   **46.** 1.6   **47.** −3   **48.** −1.2   **49.** vocabulary test
50. 38,000 miles   **51.** 41,000 miles   **52.** 22,000 miles   **53.** 91.92%   **54.** 96.41%   **55.** 88.33%   **56.** 10.69%   **57.** 75%   **58.** 14%
59. 11%   **60. a.** $\pm 2.2\%$ **b.** We can be 95% confident that between 12.8% and 17.2% of executives of American companies have careers not related to their college degrees.   **61. a.** skewed to the right   **b.** mean: 2.1 syllables; median: 2 syllables; mode: 1 syllable   **c.** yes; The mean is greater than the median which is consistent with a distribution skewed to the right.

62.

There appears to be a positive correlation.

63.

There appears to be a negative correlation.

64. false   **65.** true   **66.** false   **67.** false   **68.** true   **69.** false   **70.** true   **71.** c   **72. a.** 0.972   **b.** $y = 0.509x + 0.537$
73. a. 0.99   **b.** There is a correlation.

Chapter 12 Test

1. d   **2.**

Score	Frequency
3	1
4	2
5	3
6	2
7	2
8	3
9	2
10	1
	16

3.

4.

5.

Class	Frequency
40–49	3
50–59	6
60–69	6
70–79	7
80–89	6
90–99	2
	30

6.

Stem	Leaves
4	8 1 6
5	1 0 5 0 9 0
6	7 2 0 3 1 1
7	9 8 3 1 9 1 5
8	9 3 0 8 9 1
9	3 0

7. The roofline gives the impression that the percentage of home-schooled students grew at the same rate each year between the years shown which might not have happened.   **8.** ≈ 3.67 **9.** 3   **10.** 4   **11.** ≈ 2.34 **12.** 2.25   **13.** 2   **14.** 2   **15.** Answers will vary.
16. 34%   **17.** 2.5%   **18.** student   **19.** 8.08%   **20.** 41%
21. a. $\pm 10\%$ **b.** We can be 95% confident that between 50% and 70% of all students are very satisfied with their professors.
22. ; There appears to be a strong negative correlation.
23. false   **24.** false   **25.** true   **26.** Answers will vary.

CHAPTER 13

Section 13.1

Check Point Exercises

1. E; The sum of two odd numbers is an even number.   **2.** not closed   **3.** closed   **4.** not closed
5. $(1\oplus3)\oplus2 = 1\oplus(3\oplus2)$ **6.** g **7.** -12 **8.** $\dfrac{1}{12}$ **9. a.** k **b.** l is the inverse of j; k is its own inverse; j is the inverse of l; m is its own inverse.
$$0\oplus2 = 1\oplus1$$
$$2 = 2$$

Exercise Set 13.1

1. $\{e, a, b, c\}$ **3.** c **5.** a **7.** e **9.** b **11.** e **13.** a **15.** not closed; Answers will vary.   **17.** closed; The sum of any two natural numbers is a natural number.   **19.** not closed; Answers will vary.   **21.** not closed; $b * a = c$ is not an element of the set $\{a, b\}$.   **23.** Both sides of the equality equal 1.   **25.** Both sides of the equality equal 0.   **27.** commutative property; The entries in the table are mirror images about the diagonal line that extends from the upper left corner to the lower right corner.   **29.** Both sides of the equality equal 4.   **31.** Both sides of the equality equal 0.   **33. a.** b **b.** a **c.** not associative; When the grouping changes, the answer changes.   **35.** Answers will vary. Sample answer: $(5 - 2) - 1 = 3 - 1 = 2$ but $5 - (2 - 1) = 5 - 1 = 4$.   **37.** -29 **39.** $\dfrac{1}{29}$ **41.** a **43.** c **45.** e **47.** c **49.** e **51.** a
53. d **55.** b **57.** 0   **59.** 4   **61.** 2   **63. a.** d **b.** d is its own inverse.; $a, b,$ and c do not have inverses.
65. a. $e \triangle (c \square d) = e \triangle a = a$; $(e \triangle c) \square (e \triangle d) = d \square c = a$ **b.** distributive property
67. c **69.** b **71.** d
73. The mathematical system shows all possible starting and ending position for the four-way switch. The starting positions are shown in the left column. The number of clockwise turns are shown across the top. The 25 entries in the table represent the final position of the switch for each starting position and number of clockwise turns.
75.–79.

$\times$	E	O
E	E	E
O	E	O

75. closed; All entries in the body of the table are elements of the set $\{E, O\}$.
77. Answers will vary. Sample answer: $(O \times E) \times O = E \times O = E$ and $O \times (E \times O) = O \times E = E$.
79. E does not have an inverse.
89. a. $\begin{bmatrix} 15 & 20 \\ 35 & 46 \end{bmatrix}$ **b.** $\begin{bmatrix} 4 & 7 \\ 34 & 57 \end{bmatrix}$ **c.** This multiplication is not commutative.

Section 13.2

Check Point Exercises

1. a. 1. All entries in the table are elements of the set $\{E, O\}$; thus, the system is closed.
    2. Two examples of the associative property follow. Answers will vary.
    $(O \circ E) \circ O = O \circ O = E$ and $O \circ (E \circ O) = O \circ O = E$
    $(E \circ O) \circ E = O \circ E = O$ and $E \circ (O \circ E) = E \circ O = O$
    3. E is the identity element.
    4. E is its own inverse, and O is its own inverse. Each element has an inverse. Since the system meets the four requirements, the system is a group.
  b. Since $E \circ O = O$ and $O \circ E = O$, the order does not matter. Thus, the group is commutative.
2. a. $(8 + 5) + 11 = 1 + 11 = 0$ and $8 + (5 + 11) = 8 + 4 = 0$ **b.** Both sides of the equality equal 1.
3. a. true   **b.** true   **c.** false   **4. a.** 4 (mod 5)   **b.** 2 (mod 7)   **c.** 5 (mod 13)   **5.** Tuesday

Exercise Set 13.2

1. 8-fold rotational symmetry **3.** 18-fold rotational symmetry **5.** All entries in the body of the table are elements of the set $\{e, p, q, r, s, t\}$.
7. $(r \circ t) \circ q = p \circ q = e$ and $r \circ (t \circ q) = r \circ r = e$ **9.** e **11.** q **13.** r **15.** t **17.** t **19.** The operation is not commutative.
21. Answers will vary. Sample answer: The element 2 does not have an inverse.

23. a.

+	0	1	2	3	4	5
0	0	1	2	3	4	5
1	1	2	3	4	5	0
2	2	3	4	5	0	1
3	3	4	5	0	1	2
4	4	5	0	1	2	3
5	5	0	1	2	3	4

b. 1. Since all entries in the body of the table are elements of the set, the closure property is satisfied. **2.** Since the result of using clock addition to add 3 elements is the same regardless of whether the first two elements are grouped or the last two elements are grouped, the associative property is satisfied.
Example 1:
$(1 + 2) + 3 = 3 + 3 = 0$
$1 + (2 + 3) = 1 + 5 = 0$
Example 2:
$(2 + 4) + 5 = 0 + 5 = 5$
$2 + (4 + 5) = 2 + 3 = 5$
3. Since 0 is an element of the set and $0 + e = e$ and $e + 0 = e$ for all elements e in the set, the identity property is satisfied. **4.** Since each element has an inverse within the set, the inverse property is satisfied. **5.** Since the entries in the table are symmetric about the diagonal from the upper left corner to the lower right corner, we know that the order of clock addition does not matter. The commutative property is satisfied.
Since all 5 properties are satisfied, this mathematical system is a commutative group.

25. true **27.** true **29.** false; $84 \equiv 0 \pmod 7$ **31.** false; $23 \equiv 3 \pmod 4$ **33.** true **35.** 5 (mod 6) **37.** 3 (mod 6) **39.** 4 (mod 7)
41. 48 (mod 50) **43.** 11 (mod 12) **45. a.** 6 (mod 7) **b.** 6 (mod 7) **c.** distributive property **47.** 2 **49.** 1, 3, and 5 **51.** none
53. 1800 **55.** 0020 **57.** Sunday **59.** *beam me up* **61.** valid **63.** not valid **65.** valid **67.** valid **69.** not valid
79. Answers will vary. In general, $(a \cdot b) \cdot c = (a - b + ab) \cdot c$

$$= a - b + ab - c + (a - b + ab)c$$
$$= a - b + ab - c + ac - bc + abc$$
$$= a - b - c + ab + ac - bc + abc$$
$$a \cdot (b \cdot c) = a \cdot (b - c + bc)$$
$$= a - (b - c + bc) + a(b - c + bc)$$
$$= a - b + c - bc + ab - ac + abc$$

Since $(a \cdot b) \cdot c \neq a \cdot (b \cdot c)$, the associative property is not satisfied. Thus the mathematical system is not a group.

81. 8:00 A.M.

Chapter 13 Review Exercises

1. $\{e, c, f, r\}$ **2.** closed; All entries in the body of the table are elements of the set $\{e, c, f, r\}$. **3.** r **4.** f **5.** c **6.** Both expressions equal e. **7.** Both expressions equal c. **8.** Both expressions equal f. **9.** commutative property **10.** The entries in the table are mirror images about the diagonal from the upper left corner to the lower right corner. **11.** Both expressions equal f. **12.** Both expressions equal e.
13. associative property **14.** e **15.** e **16.** r **17.** f **18.** c **19.** not closed; $1 + 1 = 2$ which is not in the set. **20.** closed; All products result in either 0 or 1. **21.** not closed; $1 \div 2 = \dfrac{1}{2}$ which is not in the set. **22.** -123 **23.** $\dfrac{1}{123}$

24. a.

∘	0	1	2	3	4
0	0	1	2	3	4
1	1	1	2	3	4
2	2	2	2	3	4
3	3	3	3	3	4
4	4	4	4	4	4

b. 0 **c.** no inverse; No element combined with 2 results in 0.

25. 3-fold rotational symmetry **26.** 18-fold rotational symmetry

27. a.

+	0	1	2	3	4
0	0	1	2	3	4
1	1	2	3	4	0
2	2	3	4	0	1
3	3	4	0	1	2
4	4	0	1	2	3

b. 1. Since all entries in the body of the table are elements of the set, the closure property is satisfied. **2.** Since the result of using clock addition to add 3 elements is the same regardless of whether the first two elements are grouped or the last two elements are grouped, the associative property is satisfied.
Example:
$(1 + 2) + 3 = 3 + 3 = 1$
$1 + (2 + 3) = 1 + 0 = 1$
3. Since 0 is an element of the set and $0 + e = e$ and $e + 0 = e$ for all elements e in the set, the identity property is satisfied. **4.** Since each element has an inverse within the set, the inverse property is satisfied. **5.** Since the entries in the table are symmetric about the diagonal from the upper left corner to the lower right corner, we know that the order of clock addition does not matter. The commutative property is satisfied.
Since all 5 properties are satisfied, this mathematical system is a commutative group.

28. false; $17 \equiv 1 \pmod 8$ **29.** false; $37 \equiv 2 \pmod 5$ **30.** true **31.** 1 (mod 6) **32.** 6 (mod 8) **33.** 7 (mod 9) **34.** 1 (mod 20)

Chapter 13 Test

1. closed; All entries in the body of the table are elements of the set $\{x, y, z\}$.   **2.** Both expressions equal x.; commutative property
3. Both expressions equal y.; associative property   **4.** x **5.** x is its own inverse. z is the inverse of y. y is the inverse of z.

6. not closed; $1 + 1 = 2$ which is not in the set.   **7.** $\frac{1}{5}$; $5 \times \frac{1}{5} = 1$ **8.** 6-fold rotational symmetry; Since it takes 6 equal turns to restore the

design to its original position and each of these turns is a design that is identical to the original, the design has 6-fold rotational symmetry.

9.

+	0	1	2	3
0	0	1	2	3
1	1	2	3	0
2	2	3	0	1
3	3	0	1	2

10. Check that all properties are satisfied:
1. Since all entries in the body of the table are elements of the set, the closure property is satisfied.   **2.** Since the result of using clock addition to add 3 elements is the same regardless of whether the first two elements are grouped or the last two elements are grouped, the associative property is satisfied.
Example:
$(1 + 2) + 3 = 3 + 3 = 2$
$1 + (2 + 3) = 1 + 1 = 2$
3. Since 0 is an element of the set and $0 + e = e$ and $e + 0 = e$ for all elements e in the set, the identity property is satisfied.   **4.** Since each element has an inverse within the set, the inverse property is satisfied.   **5.** Since the entries in the table are symmetric about the diagonal from the upper left corner to the lower right corner, we know that the order of clock addition does not matter. The commutative property is satisfied.
Since all 5 properties are satisfied, this mathematical system is a commutative group.

11. true   **12.** false; $14 \equiv 0 \,(\text{mod } 7)$ **13.** $10 \,(\text{mod } 11)$ **14.** $5 \,(\text{mod } 10)$

CHAPTER 14

Section 14.1

Check Point Exercises

1. a. 4210   **b.** 40   **c.** 2865   **2.** Donna   **3.** Bob   **4.** Carmen   **5.** Bob

Exercise Set 14.1

1. 7; 5; 4   **3.**

Number of Votes	5	1	4	2
First Choice	A	B	C	C
Second Choice	B	D	B	B
Third Choice	C	C	D	A
Fourth Choice	D	A	A	D

5. a. 26   **b.** 8   **c.** 22   **d.** 3   **7.** musical   **9.** Darwin   **11.** Comedy   **13.** Freud   **15.** Comedy   **17.** Einstein   **19.** 10
21. 28   **23.** Comedy   **25.** Hawking   **27.** A   **29.** B   **31.** Rent   **33.** Rent   **35. a.** C   **b.** A   **37.** C   **49.** b

Section 14.2

Check Point Exercises

1. a. A   **b.** B   **2. a.** B   **b.** A   **3. a.** A   **b.** C   **c.** yes   **4. a.** A   **b.** D   **c.** yes

Exercise Set 14.2

1. a. D   **b.** A   **c.** no   **3. a.** A   **b.** V   **c.** no   **5. a.** A   **b.** C   **c.** no   **7. a.** C   **b.** B   **c.** no
9. a. S   **b.**

Number of Votes	15	8
First Choice	S	L
Second Choice	L	S

; S   **c.** yes

11. a. A   **b.** no   **13. a.** C   **b.** no   **15. a.** B   **b.** no   **c.** no   **d.** A; no   **17. a.** B   **b.** no   **c.** no
19. a. A   **b.** yes   **c.** yes   **d.**

Number of Votes	7	3	2
First Choice	A	B	A
Second Choice	B	C	C
Third Choice	C	A	B

; A   **e.** yes   **f.** no

Section 14.3

Check Point Exercises

1. a. 50   **b.** 22.24; 22.36; 26.4; 30.3; 98.7   **2.** 22; 22; 27; 30; 99   **3.** 22; 22; 26; 30; 100   **4.** 22; 23; 27; 30; 98   **5.** 22; 22; 27; 30; 99

Exercise Set 14.3

1. a. 20; 20,000   **b.** 6.9; 13.3; 26.7; 33.1   **c.**

State	Lower Quota	Upper Quota
A	6	7
B	13	14
C	26	27
D	33	34

3. 7; 13; 27; 33   **5.** 30; 41; 53; 73; 103   **7.** 3; 5; 12; 15; 22   **9.** 17; 55; 24; 54   **11.** 28; 33; 53; 15; 22; 29   **13.** 12; 10; 8   **15.** 4; 10; 6
17. 20; 24; 29; 29; 98   **19.** 57; 81; 68; 44   **21.** 57; 81; 68; 44   **23.** 7; 2; 2; 2; 8; 14; 4; 5; 10; 10; 13; 2; 6; 2; 18   **25.** 7; 2; 2; 2; 8; 14; 4; 5; 10; 10; 12; 2; 6; 3; 18

Section 14.4

Check Point Exercises

1. B's apportionment decreases from 11 to 10.   **2. a.** 10; 19; 71   **b.** State A: 1.005%; State B: 0.998%   **c.** State A loses a seat to State B, even though the population of State A is increasing at a faster rate.   **3. a.** 21; 79   **b.** With North High added to the district, West High loses a counselor to East High.

Exercise Set 14.4

1. a. 16; 8; 6   **b.** 17; 9; 5; Liberal Arts Math loses a teaching assistant when the total number of teaching assistants is raised from 30 to 31. This is an example of the Alabama paradox.   **3.** State A loses a seat when the total number of seats increases from 40 to 41.
5. a. 4; 6; 14   **b.** 28.3%; 26.3%; 14.7%   **c.** 3; 7; 14; A loses a seat while B gains, even though A has a faster increasing population. The population paradox does occur.   **7.** C loses a truck to B even though C increased in population faster than B.   **9. a.** 10; 90   **b.** Branch B loses a promotion when branch C is added. This means the new-states paradox has occurred.   **11. a.** 9; 91   **b.** State B loses a seat when state C is added.
13. a. 6; 13; 31   **b.** The new-states paradox does not occur. As long as the modified divisor, d, remains the same, adding a new state cannot change the number of seats held by existing states.

Chapter 14 Review Exercises

1.

Number of Votes	4	3	3	2
First Choice	A	B	C	C
Second Choice	B	D	B	B
Third Choice	C	C	D	A
Fourth Choice	D	A	A	D

2. 23   **3.** 4   **4.** 16   **5.** 14   **6.** Musical   **7.** Comedy   **8.** Musical
9. Musical   **10.** A   **11.** B   **12.** A   **13.** A   **14.** B   **15.** A; no
16. A; no   **17.** B   **18.** B; yes   **19.** A   **20.** B   **21.** A   **22.** A
23. A; Borda count method   **24.** B   **25.** A; no   **26.** A

27.

Number of Votes	400	450
First Choice	A	C
Second Choice	C	A

; C; no

28. B   **29.** B still wins. The irrelevant alternatives criterion is satisfied.   **30.** 50.05
31. 5.49; 7.83; 12.21; 14.47   **32.** A: 5, 6; B: 7, 8; C: 12, 13; D: 14, 15   **33.** 6; 8; 12; 14
34. 5; 8; 12; 15   **35.** 6; 8; 12; 14   **36.** 6; 8; 12; 14   **37.** 14; 42; 62; 82   **38.** 13; 42; 63; 82
39. 14; 42; 63; 81   **40.** 14; 42; 62; 82   **41. a.** 8; 67; 75   **b.** The Alabama paradox occurs.
42. a. 72; 20; 8   **b.** 0.8%; 1.3%   **c.** The population paradox occurs.
43. a. 7; 26   **b.** The new-states paradox does not occur.   **44.** False. Answers will vary.

Chapter 14 Test

1. 3600   **2.** 600   **3.** 1500   **4.** 1500   **5.** B   **6.** B   **7.** A   **8.** A   **9.** A   **10.** A; yes   **11.** A   **12.** B; no   **13.** C
14. B; no   **15.** no   **16.** 50   **17.** 2.38; 3.3; 4.32   **18.** A: 2, 3; B: 3, 4; C: 4, 5   **19.** 3; 3; 4   **20.** 2; 3; 5   **21.** 3; 3; 4   **22.** 2; 3; 5
23. yes   **24.** The new-states paradox does not occur.   **25.** Answers will vary.

CHAPTER 15

Section 15.1

Check Point Exercises

1. The two graphs have the same number of vertices connected to each other in the same way.

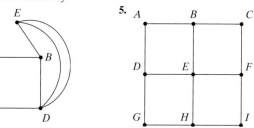

6. A and B, A and C, A and D, A and E, B and C, and E and E

Exercise Set 15.1

1. 6; St. Louis, Chicago, Philadelphia, Montreal; 1, 1, 2, 2   **3.** No; no; Answers will vary.

5. Possible answers:

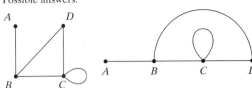

7. The two graphs have the same number of vertices connected in the same way, so they are the equivalent. Possible answer:

9.

11.

13.

15.

17.

19.

21.

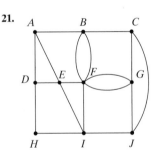

23. A: 2; B: 2; C: 3; D: 3; E: 3; F: 1   **25.** B and C **27.** A, C, D; A, B, C, D **29.** AC and DF **31.** While edge CD is included, the graph is connected. If we remove CD, the graph will be disconnected.   **33.** DF **35.** Even: A, B, G, H, I; odd: C, D, E, F **37.** D, G, and I
39. Possible answers: B, C, D, F; B, A, C, D, F **41.** G, F, I, H, G **43.** $A, B, C, C, D, F, G, H, I$ **45.** G, F, D, E, D requires that edge DE be traversed twice. This is not allowed within a path.   **47.** No edge connects F and E.

49. Possible answer:

51. Possible answer:

67.

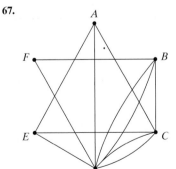

Section 15.2

Check Point Exercises

1. 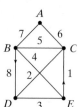 ; $E, C, D, E, B, C, A, B, D$ **2.** 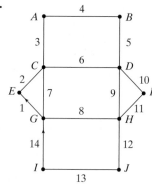 ; $G, E, C, A, B, D, C, G, H, D, F, H, J, I, G$

3. a. yes **b.**

4.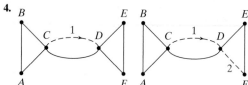

Exercise Set 15.2

1.

neither

3.

Euler circuit

5.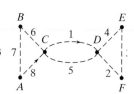

neither

7. a. There are two odd vertices.
  b. Possible answer:

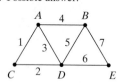

9. a. There are no odd vertices.
  b. Possible answer:

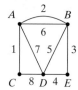

11. There are more than two odd vertices. **13.** Euler circuit **15.** Euler path, but no Euler circuit **17.** neither an Euler path nor an Euler circuit

19. a. Euler circuit
  b. Possible answer:

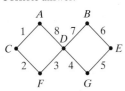

21. a. Euler path
  b. Possible answer:

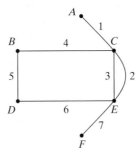

23. a. neither

25. a. Euler path
  b. Possible answer:

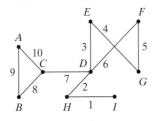

27. a. Euler circuit
  b. Possible answer:

29. a. neither

31. a. Euler path
  b. Possible answer:

33. Possible answer:

35. Possible answer:

37. Possible answer:

39. Possible answer:

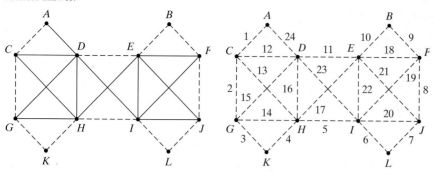

41. a. Remove FG.   **b.** Sample answer: $EC, CB, BD, DF, FA, AD, DG, GH, HC, CG, GB, BH, HE$

43. a. Remove BA and FJ.   **b.** Sample answer: $CA, AD, DI, IH, HG, GF, FC, CD, DE, EH, HJ, JG, GB, BC$

45. The graph has an Euler circuit.

47.

49. a.

b. Yes; begin at B or E.

51. a.

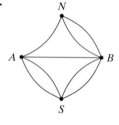

b. Yes, they can.
c. Possible answer:

53.

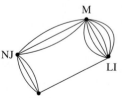

; It is possible.

55. a.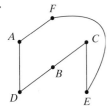

b. It is possible.
c. Possible answer:

57. Possible answer:

59. a.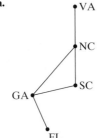

b. not possible
d. not possible

Section 15.3

Check Point Exercises

1. a. Possible answer: E, C, D, G, B, A, F **b.** Possible answer: E, C, D, G, B, F, A, E **2. a.** 2 **b.** 120 **c.** 362,880 **3.** $562
4.

Hamilton Circuit	Sum of the Weights of the Edges	=	Total Cost
A, B, C, D, A	$20 + 15 + 50 + 30$	=	$115
A, B, D, C, A	$20 + 10 + 50 + 70$	=	$150
A, C, B, D, A	$70 + 15 + 10 + 30$	=	$125
A, C, D, B, A	$70 + 50 + 10 + 20$	=	$150
A, D, B, C, A	$30 + 10 + 15 + 70$	=	$125
A, D, C, B, A	$30 + 50 + 15 + 20$	=	$115

5. A, B, C, D, E, A; 198

A, B, C, D, A; A, D, C, B, A

Exercise Set 15.3

1. Possible answer: A, G, C, F, E, D, B **3.** Possible answer: A, B, G, C, F, E, D, A **5.** Possible answer: A, F, G, E, C, B, D
7. Possible answer: A, B, C, E, G, F, D, A **9. a.** no **11. a.** yes **b.** 120 **13. a.** no **15.** 2 **17.** 39,916,800 **19.** 11 **21.** 36
23. 36 **25.** 88 **27.** 70 **29.** 70 **31.** A, C, B, D, A and A, D, B, C, A **33.** B, D, C, A, B; 82 **35. a.** Add AB.; 6
b. Sample answers: AD, DB, BC, CA; CA, AB, BD, DC **c.** Remove CD. **d.** Sample answer: AC, CB, BD, DA
37. a. Add AB, AC, BC, and DE.; 24 **b.** Sample answers: AB, BC, CE, ED, DA; AB, BC, CD, DE, EA **c.** Remove BD and BE.
d. Sample answer: AE, EC, CD, DA **39.** A, D, B, C, E, A

41.

43. 30 **45.**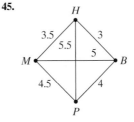

47. H, B, P, M, H; 15 mi; same

Section 15.4

Check Point Exercises

1. Figure 15.51(c)   **2.** Possible answer:

3.

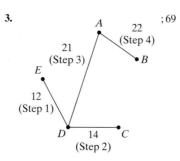

; 69

Exercise Set 15.4

1. yes   **3.** no   **5.** yes   **7.** no   **9.** yes   **11.** i.   **13.** ii.   **15.** ii.   **17.** iii.

19.

21.

23.

25.

; 120

27.

; 42

29.

; 85

31.

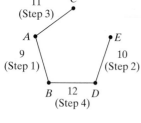

; 91

33. Sample answers: AB, AC, CD; AB, BC, CD; AB, AD, CD; AB, AD, BC **35.** AE, BC, CD, CE; 64

37. Sample answer: $AE, BC, BE, CF, DE, EH, FG, FJ, HI$; 141

39.

41. a.

b.

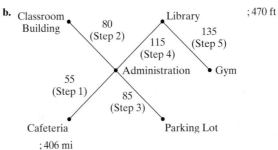

; 470 ft

; 406 mi

43.

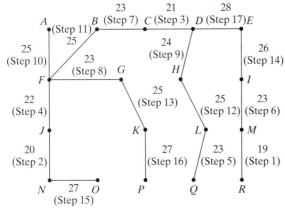

Chapter 15 Review Exercises

1. Both graphs have the same number of vertices, and these vertices are connected in the same ways. Possible answer:

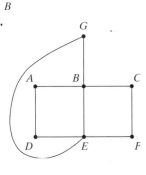

2. *A*: 5; *B*: 4; *C*: 5; *D*: 4; *E*: 2   **3.** Even: *B, D, E*; odd: *A, C*

4. *B, C,* and *E*   **5.** Possible answer: *E, D, B, A* and *E, C, A*

6. Possible answer: *E, D, C, E*   **7.** yes   **8.** no   **9.** *AD, DE,* and *DF*

10.

11.

12.

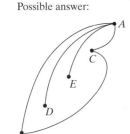

13. a. neither

14. a. Euler circuit
   b. Possible answer:

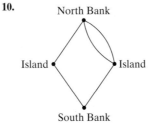

15. a. Euler path
   b. Possible answer:

16.

17.

18. a. yes   **b.**

c. no

19. It is possible.   **20. a.** yes   **b.** Possible answer:

21. a.

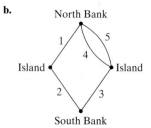

b. yes
c. The guard should begin at C and end at F, or vice versa.

22. Possible answer: A, E, C, B, D, A
23. Possible answer: D, B, A, E, C, D
24. a. no
25. a. yes   **b.** 6
26. a. no
27. a. yes   **b.** 24

28. A, B, C, D, A: 19; A, B, D, C, A: 18; A, C, B, D, A: 19; A, C, D, B, A: 18; A, D, B, C, A: 19; A, D, C, B, A: 19
29. A, B, D, C, A and A, C, D, B, A **30.** A, C, D, B, A; 18   **31.** A, B, E, D, C, A; 24

32.

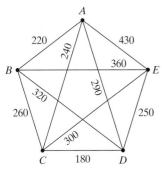

33. *A, B, C, D, E*; $1340   **34.** yes   **35.** No. It has a circuit.   **36.** No. It is disconnected.
37. Possible answer: **38.** Possible answer:

    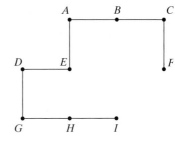

39.   ; 875   **40.**   ; 239

41.   ; 4370 mi

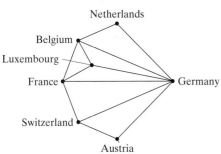

Chapter 15 Test
1. *A*: 2; *B*: 2; *C*: 4; *D*: 3; *E*: 2; *F*: 1   **2.** Possible answer: *A, D, E* and *A, B, C, E*   **3.** *B, A, D, E, C, B*   **4.** *CF*

5.   **6. a.** Euler path   **b.** Possible answer: **7. a.** neither

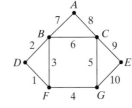

8. a. Euler circuit   **b.** Possible answer:

9.

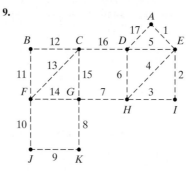

10. a.   **b.** yes   **c.** at one of the islands

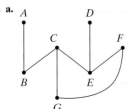

11. a.   **b.** no   **12. a.**   **b.** no

13. A, B, C, D, G, F, E, A and A, F, G, D, C, B, E, A **14.** 24

15.   **16.** A, B, D, C, A or A, C, D, B, A; \$1445
17. A, E, D, C, B, A; 33
18. no

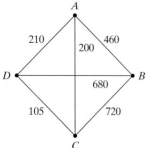

19. Possible answer: **20.**   ; 17

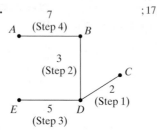

Photo Credits ●●●●●●

CHAPTER 10 **CO** Foreground: Darrell Gulin/Photodisc/Getty Images; Background: Jh Pete Carmichael/Riser/Getty Images **p. 538** San Francisco MOMA/Olivier Laude Photography **p. 545** Creators Syndicate, Inc. **p. 546** VAGA **p. 549** Robert Ginn/PhotoEdit, Inc. **p. 555** "That's Dancing!" from MGM/UA Entertainment Co. Courtesy The Kobal Collection **p. 556** Omni-Photo Communications, Inc. **p. 557** Tim Eagan/Woodfin Camp & Associates **p. 561** The M. C. Escher Company BV **p. 564** Bart Geerligs/Getty Images, Inc.-Taxi **p. 568** Benjamin Shearn/Getty Images, Inc.-Taxi **p. 570** J. Silver/SuperStock, Inc. **p. 574** Paramount TV/Everett Collection **p. 576** Doug Armand/Getty Images, Inc.-Stone Allstock **p. 582** Chris Noble/Getty Images, Inc.-Stone Allstock **p. 586** Janet Foster/Masterfile Corporation **p. 590** (top) Hugh Sitton/Getty Images, Inc.-Stone Allstock; (bottom left) J. A. Kraulis/Masterfile Corporation; (bottom right) Gregory Sams/Photo Researchers, Inc. **p. 594** Ari Lehtonen **p. 595** M. C. Escher's "Circle Limit III" © 2006 The M.C. Escher Company – Holland. All rights reserved. www.mcescher.com **p. 597** (top) Daryl Hepting, Ph.D.; (middle left and right) Gregory Sams/Science Photo Library/Photo Researchers, Inc. **p. 598** SuperStock, Inc.

CHAPTER 11 **CO** Abraham Lincoln: © Bettmann/CORBIS. All Rights Reserved. John F. Kennedy: © Bettmann/CORBIS. All Rights Reserved. **p. 608** AP Wide World Photos **p. 609** SuperStock, Inc. **p. 613** (left) ©2001 by Vaughn Youtz; (middle) AP Wide World Photos; (right) AP Wide World Photos **p. 614** Corbis/Sygma **p. 621** Marilyn Monroe: Picture Desk, Inc./Kobal Collection. James Dean: Imapress/Globe Photos, Inc. Jim Morrison: Michael Ochs Archives.com. Kurt Cobain: S.I.N./Corbis/Bettmann. Selena: AP Wide World Photos **p. 627** Larry Kolvoord/The Image Works **p. 630** Paul S. Howell/Getty Images, Inc.-Liaison **p. 632** Ron Avery/SuperStock, Inc. **p. 635** Greg Heins/Addison Gallery of American Art **p. 636** Sue Klemen/Stock Boston **p. 637** Corrado Giambalvo/AP Wide World Photos **p. 641** Grant V. Faint/Getty Images-Iconica **p. 645** Manoj Shah/Getty Images, Inc.-Stone Allstock **p. 649** Alec Pytlowany/Masterfile Corporation **p. 653** Jerry Driendl/Getty Images, Inc.-Taxi **p. 654** UPI/Corbis/Bettmann **p. 663** Tom Le Goff/Getty Images/Digital Vision **p. 667** Miro Vintoniv/Stock Boston **p. 668** Bob Daemmrich/Stock Boston

CHAPTER 12 **CO** Foreground left: Rob Goldman/Getty Images, Inc. Foreground right: Tim Macpherson/Getty Images, Inc.-Stone Allstock. Background: Ingram Publishing/Getty Images **p. 680** CBS-TV/Picture Desk, Inc./Kobal Collection **p. 681** Art Resource/The New York Public Library **p. 692** King Features Syndicate **p. 705** Getty Images, Inc.-Photodisc **p. 712** Robert Brenner/PhotoEdit, Inc. **p. 714** Simon Warner, Photographer **p. 717** Michael Newman/PhotoEdit, Inc. **p. 721** Norbert Schafer/Corbis/Stock Market **p. 730** Culver Pictures, Inc. **p. 733** Stuart Westmorland/Getty Images, Inc.-Stone Allstock

CHAPTER 13 **CO** Foreground: Gail Shumway; Background: joSon/Getty Images, Inc.-Stone Allstock **p. 757** Gerben Oppermans/Getty Images, Inc.-Stone Allstock **p. 758** (top) Ben Davidson; (bottom) Dr. Gerald D. Carr, PhD. **p. 759** (top) Joyce Photographics/Photo Researchers, Inc.; (bottom) Golt/Rapho/Photo Researchers, Inc. **p. 760** U.S. Postal Service

CHAPTER 14 **CO** Foreground: Jupiter Images-PictureArts Corporation; Background: Jupiter Images Picturerequest-Royalty Free **p. 772** Photofest **p. 777** Archive Photos/Jupiter Images-FoodPix-Creatas-Brand X-Banana Stock-PictureQuest **p. 779** AP Wide World Photos **p. 784** AFP Photo/Adrian Dennis/Getty Images, Inc.-Agence France Presse **p. 787** The Granger Collection, New York **p. 791** AFP Photo/Rhona Wise/Getty Images, Inc.-Agence France Presse **p. 792** Michael Schuman/Corbis/SABA Press Photos, Inc. **p. 796** The Granger Collection **p. 799** The Granger Collection, New York **p. 801** The Granger Collection, New York **p. 802** The Granger Collection, New York **p. 804** The Granger Collection, New York **p. 809** (left) Ohio Historical Society; (right) The Granger Collection, New York **p. 811** Benelux Press, b.v./eStock Photography/Jupiter Images-FoodPix-Creatas-Brand X-Banana Stock-PictureQuest **p. 813** The Granger Collection, New York

CHAPTER 15 **CO** Foreground: Businessman running: Emmanuel Faure/Taxi/Getty Images; Train station: Will & Deni McIntyre/Photodisc/Getty Images; Family: Baerbel Schmidt/Getty Images, Inc.-Stone Allstock; Background: Alan & Sandy Carey/Photodisc/Getty Images **p. 824** Oprah Winfrey: Stephane Cardinale/CORBIS-NY; George W. Bush: Folio/Omni-Photo Communications, Inc.; Bono: Chris Wattie/Corbis/Reuters America LLC; Steve Jobs: James Leynse/Corbis/Bettmann **p. 834** Bernard Boutrit/Woodfin Camp & Associates **p. 845** AP Wide World Photos **p. 855** Gary Harwood/Corbis/Reuters America LLC **p. 859** Japan Society

Subject Index ●●●●●●

Index of Applications●●●●●●